Chemistry for Today

CHM124
University of Rhode Island

8e

Spencer L. Seager | Michael R. Slabaugh

CENGAGE
Learning·

Australia • Brazil • Japan • Korea • Mexico • Singapore • Spain • United Kingdom • United States

Chemistry for Today: CHM124: University of Rhode Island, 8e

Sources:

Chemistry for Today: General, Organic, and Biochemistry, 8th Edition
Spencer L. Seager | Michael R. Slabaugh
© 2014, 2011 Cengage Learning. All rights reserved.

Introduction to General, Organic and Biochemistry, 10th Edition
Frederick A. Bettelheim | William H. Brown | Mary K. Campbell | Shawn O. Farrell | Omar Torres
© 2013, 2010, 2007 Cengage Learning. All rights reserved.

Senior Manager, Student Engagement:

Linda deStefano

Janey Moeller

Manager, Student Engagement:

Julie Dierig

Marketing Manager:

Rachael Kloos

Manager, Production Editorial:

Kim Fry

Manager, Intellectual Property Project Manager:

Brian Methe

Senior Manager, Production and Manufacturing:

Donna M. Brown

Manager, Production:

Terri Daley

For product information and technology assistance, contact us at
Cengage Learning Customer & Sales Support, 1-800-354-9706
For permission to use material from this text or product,
submit all requests online at **cengage.com/permissions**
Further permissions questions can be emailed to
permissionrequest@cengage.com

This book contains select works from existing Cengage Learning resources and was produced by Cengage Learning Custom Solutions for collegiate use. As such, those adopting and/or contributing to this work are responsible for editorial content accuracy, continuity and completeness.

Compilation © 2014 Cengage Learning

ISBN-13: 978-1-305-30412-3

ISBN-10: 1-305-30412-8

WCN: 01-100-101

Cengage Learning

5191 Natorp Boulevard
Mason, Ohio 45040
USA

Cengage Learning is a leading provider of customized learning solutions with office locations around the globe, including Singapore, the United Kingdom, Australia, Mexico, Brazil, and Japan. Locate your local office at:
international.cengage.com/region.

Cengage Learning products are represented in Canada by Nelson Education, Ltd.
For your lifelong learning solutions, visit **www.cengage.com/custom.**
Visit our corporate website at **www.cengage.com.**

Printed in the United States of America

Brief Contents

From:
Chemistry for Today: General, Organic, and Biochemistry
8th Edition
Spencer L. Seager | Michael R. Slabaugh

From:
Introduction to General, Organic and Biochemistry
10th Edition
Frederick A. Bettelheim | William H. Brown | Mary K. Campbell | Shawn O.
Farrell | Omar Torres

From:
Chemistry for Today: General, Organic, and Biochemistry
8th Edition
Spencer L. Seager | Michael R. Slabaugh

GETTING STARTED

Welcome to OWLv2, a newly improved version of the OWLv1 chemistry learning system. OWL stands for **Online Web-based Learning** and is an integrated, online course system for teaching and learning chemistry disciplines. OWLv2 provides you with the tools you need for studying class materials, taking assignments, and tracking your grades from wherever you have Internet access.

While working at your own pace, or within a schedule set up by your instructor, you can work on step-by-step tutorials, interactive simulations, homework questions, read an interactive eBook, take exams, and track your overall course progress. OWLv2 gives you an easy-to-use, personalized online environment that you can manage to best suit your needs.

In this upgraded version of OWL, you will find many of the same features as in version 1, but there are a few key differences. If you are taking more than one course, you only need to perform a single sign-on at one site to access all of your Cengage Learning online courses. Also OWLv2 has a reorganized user interface with clearly labeled tabs for each feature of your course.

OWLv2 - Tabbed Navigation

Note: As a live, web-based program, OWLv2 is updated regularly with new features and improvements. Please refer to OWLv2's online **Help** for the most current information.

Registering for Your OWLv2 Course

When getting started with OWLv2, you first direct your browser to https://login.cengage.com/. From this page you can either log in as a returning user or create a new account. Once logged in, you can purchase course materials, register for a new course, or open any of your registered course content from your CengageBrain **My Home** page.

There are two codes you need to use when registering for your new online course and course materials.

- The first code is the **Course Key**, which is provided by your instructor. This key is usually sent to you in an email or is provided as part of the information supplied in a class handout.

 If you initially register with a Course Key, you are provided with a "try before you buy" trial period. The trial period allows access to your course for a limited amount of time before you are required to make a purchase.

- The second code is the **Access Code**, which is proof of purchase for your course materials. You can buy an Access Code on the CengageBrain website, or it can also come bundled with your textbook. When submitted, this code provides you with continuous access to your online course materials.

Note: If your trial period should expire before you have a chance to submit an Access Code, any work on assignments or grades you have acquired are saved. However, you will be unable to log in until the Access Code that corresponds to your course title is submitted.

➢ To register as a new user

1. Direct your web browser to https://login.cengage.com/.

 Note: You may want to bookmark this page for easy access when logging in again.

2. Under **Students CengageBrain** click the **New Student User?** button.

 The **Enter Your Code or Course Key** page opens.

Entering a Course Key or Access Code

3. Enter your **Course Key** (or **Access Code**) exactly as it appears.

If you are registering with a **Course Key**, you will have a "try before you buy" trial period. The trial period gives you access to your course for a limited time, before you are required to purchase and submit an **Access Code**.

4. If required, confirm your course information.

5. Click the **Continue** button and the **Account Information** page opens.

6. Enter your name, a valid email address, a password, select a time zone, and select a security question/answer.

 Make a note of the email address and password you use when creating your account. You will need this information later, when signing in again.

 Note: Your instructor may use the email address you provide for course communications, be sure to check it periodically.

7. Select **I Agree** for the **License Agreement**, confirm your age, and indicate your preference for receiving promotional messages.

8. Click the **Continue** button when you have completed the form.

9. If required, use the institution selector to find your school.

 - Enter the search parameters such as institution type and location and click **Search**.

 - Select your school from the list and click **Continue**.

 Note: If you are unable to find your school, you can click the **Contact Tech Support** link at the bottom of the page for assistance.

 Once your account is created the **CengageBrain My Home** page opens.

CengageBrain My Home Page

> **Note:** You can see the **days remaining** on your trial period listed just below the **Open** button. Buttons for the options to either **Buy** or **Rent** your textbook are also available from your **CengageBrain My Home** page.

10. Click the **Open** button for your course, under the **My Courses & Materials** heading. (When available, you will see additional **Open** buttons that provide access to your eBook and any supplemental resources.)

 The OWLv2 **New Account** confirmation will open in a new browser window.

11. Confirm that you are registered with the correct institution, and then click **Continue** to launch OWLv2 and access your new course.

> **Note:** If you initially registered with an **Access Code**, you will be prompted to enter the **Course Key** now.

Signing In as a Returning User

Once you have successfully created an account with OWLv2, you can sign in as a returning user or register for additional courses from wherever you have Internet access.

➤ **To sign in to OWLv2 as a returning user**

1. Sign in to **CengageBrain** by going to https://login.cengage.com/.

2. Enter your email address and password in the fields provided exactly as you entered them when you created your account.

3. Click the **Sign In** button and the **CengageBrain My Home** page opens.

4. Click the **Open** button for your course, under the **My Courses & Materials** heading, and OWLv2 will open in a new browser window.

CengageBrain My Home Page

You may see additional **Open** buttons that provide access to your eBook and any supplemental resources.

Note: You can see the **days remaining** on your trial period listed just below the **Open** button.

➢ **To register for additional courses**

1. Sign in to **CengageBrain** by logging in to https://login.cengage.com/. Your CengageBrain **My Home** page opens.

2. Enter your **Course Key** (or **Access Code**) exactly as it appears in the **Have Another Product to Register?** text box.

Have Another Product to Register?
Register another Access Code. For Aplia, CengageNOW, or MindTap enter your Course Key.

Register

Your Access Code should be similar to PP8XLP3XD528HC

Course Key example: ABCD-23M4-EFGH

What's this?

Registering for Additional Products

3. If required, confirm your course information and click **Continue**.

4. Click the **Register** button.

If successful, you will see a confirmation message just below the Register text box, and your new course listed under the **My Courses & Materials** heading.

5. Click the **Open** button for your new course to launch OWLv2 in a new browser window.

6. If you registered with an **Access Code**, you will be prompted to enter the **Course Key**, which is provided by your instructor.

System Setup for OWLv2

Once signed in, you can use the **Run System Check** option to evaluate your browser and plug-in settings in detail. The link is located in the **Tools** menu at the top of most pages in OWLv2.

If any issues are discovered with your system's configuration, they are listed under the **Plug-in Check Results** heading. You can click the help icon ⊚ to see detailed instructions for downloading the required browser plug-ins.

The OWLv2 System Check

Note: You can also refer to the instructions in "OWLv2 System Requirements" on page iv for additional information on configuring your computer, or contact tech support at http://cengage.com/support.

Using the Header Links and Page Tabs

The header links and page tabs appear at the top of nearly every page in OWLv2.

Tools

Use this drop-down menu to access links to the **System Check**, the **Basic Calculator**, the **Math/Graphing Tool**, and the **Student ID** editor.

The **Basic Calculator** link provides quick access to a simplified calculator that does not include specialized features for scientific notation, logarithmic functions, and trigonometric functions. For advanced calculations, you can use the scientific **Calculator** located in **Tools > Math/Graphing Tools**.

The **Math/Graphing Tool** link opens a window containing several helpful utilities you can use, including a scientific calculator, a math glossary, a shapes library, and graphing tools.

The **Run System Check** link opens a utility you can use to verify that your system and browser settings conform to the OWLv2 system requirements. See "System Setup for OWLv2" on page 8 for more details.

The **Student ID** link opens a page where you can enter and submit an identification number provided by your instructor. This ID is used to help track and identify your progress in the instructor's **Gradebook** and gradebook reports.

Help

Use this link to open the OWLv2 online Help with the table of contents, index, and search functions enabled.

Sign Out

Use this link to sign out of your current OWLv2 session.

Click the page tabs which are located beneath the header links to navigate to the following pages:

Courses

The **Courses** page displays the names of your instructor(s) and your overall grade for all of your OWLv2 courses. The **Go To** column supplies buttons to open pages for viewing your assignments, grades, and the syllabus specific to each course (when a syllabus is available). From this page you can also register for additional courses by using the **Course Key** provided by your instructor.

Grades

The **Grades** page allows you easily track your grades, with grade details and sorting options for organizing the display of your assignments, courses, and self-study. By providing multiple views, OWLv2 helps you monitor your progress in both your self-study materials or graded assignments, and find specific grades quickly.

Assignments

The **Assignments** page provides an overview of your assignment details. It shows you your assignment's **Date Due**, **Grading Category**, **Actions** you can perform, **# of Submissions**, **# of Submissions Allowed**, **Time Allowed**, **Notes**, and your **Score** for completed and partially completed assignments such as tests and homework.

The Assignments page also allows you to **Take** an assignment for the first time, or **Retake** or **Resume** an assignment (if your instructor permits it).

You can organize your assignment list in several ways, including looking at assignments in a particular course, at all your assignments at once, or just those available for you to take right now.

Study Tools

The **Study Tools** page provides access to your registered materials in OWLv2 such as eBooks, Tutorials, and Personalized Study titles on a self-study basis. However, your instructor has the ability to hide any content that is assigned for a grade.

Work that you access and complete on the **Study Tools** page is for ungraded self-study only. Your progress is tracked in both your **Grades** page and your instructor's **Gradebook**. Any work you do on the Study Tools page does not count toward your graded course assignments.

PowerSearch

You may see a **PowerSearch** tab if your school library subscribes to the PowerSearch service. **PowerSearch** allows students and instructors to access a wide range of periodical, reference, and source information over multiple databases.

Note: For technical support, please use either the **Cengage Technical Support** or **Nelson Technical Support** links in the page footer. See "Contacting Cengage Technical Support" on page 51 for additional details.

Signing Out

When you are done accessing your personal OWLv2 pages and assignments, click the **Sign Out** link in the page header. Using this link closes the current session properly. Also, whenever you need to make changes to your account or course materials on the CengageBrain site, it is recommended that you sign out from OWLv2.

Note: Always use the provided OWLv2 buttons and links to close assignments or go to another page. Do not use your browser's **Close** button or **Back/Forward** buttons; this could cause you to lose unsaved work.

PREFACE

The Image of Chemistry

We, as authors, are pleased that the acceptance of the previous seven editions of this textbook by students and their teachers has made it possible to publish this eighth edition. In the earlier editions, we expressed our concern about the negative image of chemistry held by many of our students, and their genuine fear of working with chemicals in the laboratory. Unfortunately, this negative image not only persists, but seems to be intensifying. Reports in the media related to chemicals or to chemistry continue to be primarily negative, and in many cases seem to be designed to increase the fear and concern of the general public. With this edition, we continue to hope that those who use this book will gain a more positive understanding and appreciation of the important contributions that chemistry makes in their lives.

Theme and Organization

This edition continues the theme of the positive and useful contributions made by chemistry in our world.

This text is designed to be used in either a two-semester or three-quarter course of study that provides an introduction to general chemistry, organic chemistry, and biochemistry. Most students who take such courses are majoring in nursing, other health professions, or the life sciences, and consider biochemistry to be the most relevant part of the course of study. However, an understanding of biochemistry depends upon a sound background in organic chemistry, which in turn depends upon a good foundation in general chemistry. We have attempted to present the general and organic chemistry in sufficient depth and breadth to make the biochemistry understandable.

As with previous editions, this textbook is published in a complete hardcover form and a two-volume paperback edition. One volume of the paperback edition contains all the general chemistry and the first two chapters of organic chemistry from the hardcover text. The second volume of the paperback edition contains all the organic chemistry and biochemistry of the hardcover edition. The availability of the textbook in these various forms has been a very popular feature among those who use the text because of the flexibility it affords them.

The decisions about what to include and what to omit from the text were based on our combined 75-plus years of teaching, input from numerous reviewers and adopters, and our philosophy that a textbook functions as a personal tutor to each student. In the role of a personal tutor, a text must be more than just a collection of facts, data, and exercises. It should also help students relate to the material they are studying, carefully guide them through more difficult material, provide them with interesting and relevant examples of chemistry in their lives, and become a reference and a resource that they can use in other courses or their professions.

New to This Edition

In this eighth edition of the text, we have some exciting new features, including Case Studies, which begin each chapter, and Ask an Expert boxes written by CNN health expert Dr. Melina B. Jampolis. We have also retained features that received a positive reception from our own students, the students of other adopters, other teachers, and reviewers. The retained features are 23 *Study Skills* boxes that include 5 reaction maps; 4 *How Reactions Occur* boxes; 45 *Chemistry Around Us* boxes, including 14 new to this edition. The 13 *At The Counter* boxes reflect coverage of both prescription and non-prescription health-related products. There are 25 *Chemistry and Your Health* boxes, with 5 new to this edition. A greatly expanded feature of this eighth edition is the *Allied Health Exam Connection* that follows the exercises at the end of each chapter. This feature consists of examples of chemistry questions found on typical entrance examinations used to screen applicants to allied health professional programs. In addition, approximately 20% of the end-of-chapter exercises have been changed.

Allied Health Exam Connection

The following questions are from these sources:

1. *Nursing School Entrance Exam* © 2005, Learning Express, LLC.
2. *McGraw-Hill's Nursing School Entrance Exams* by Thomas A. Evangelist, Tamara B. Orr and Judy Unrein © 2009, The McGraw-Hill Companies, Inc.
3. *NSEE Nursing School Entrance Exams*, 3rd Edition © 2009, Kaplan Publishing.
4. *Cliffs Test Prep: Nursing School Entrance Exams* by Fred N. Grayson © 2004, Wiley Publishing, Inc.
5. *Peterson's Master the Nursing School and Allied Health Entrance Exams*, 18th Edition by Marion F. Gooding © 2008, Peterson's, a Nelnet Company.

9.126 An acid is a substance that dissociates in water into one or more _____ ions and one or more _____.

 a. hydrogen . . . anions

 b. hydrogen . . . cations

 c. hydroxide . . . anions

 d. hydroxide . . . cations

 a. sulfate ions

 b. water ions

 c. hydrogen ions

 d. oxygen ions

9.133 When a solution has a pH of 7, it is:

 a. a strong base

 b. a strong acid

 c. a weak base

 d. neutral

9.134 A common detergent has a pH of 11.0, so the detergent is:

 a. neutral

 b. acidic

 c. alkaline

 d. none of the above

9.135 In a 0.001 M solution of HCl, the pH is:

 a. 2

 b. −3

 c. 1

Also new to this edition are many new photographs and updated art to further enhance student comprehension of key concepts, processes, and preparation.

1. *Step 1.* Put 0.125 mol of solute into a 250-mL flask.

2. *Step 2.* Add some water and dissolve the solute.

3. *Step 3.* Fill the flask to the mark with water. Mix thoroughly.

Figure 7.8 Preparation of a 0.500 M solution. Use the data given in the figure and show by a calculation that the resulting solution is 0.500 M.

Revision Summary of Eighth Edition:

Chapter 1:
- New Case Study
- New Case Study Follow-up
- Several revised figures
- New photography
- New Ask an Expert: *Does Food Density Matter When You're Trying to Lose Weight?*
- New Chemistry Around Us: *Effects of Temperature on Body Function*
- 20% new Exercises

Chapter 2:
- New Case Study
- New Case Study Follow-up
- Several revised figures
- New photography
- Updated element table
- New Chemistry Around Us: *Looking at Atoms*
- New At the Counter: *Nonprescription Medicines*
- 20% new Exercises

Chapter 3:
- New Case Study
- New Case Study Follow-up
- Several revised figures
- New photography
- New Chemistry and Your Health: Iron: *Too Much of a Good Thing?*
- New Ask an Expert: *Are Calcium Supplements Necessary?*
- 20% new Exercises

Chapter 4:
- New Case Study
- New Case Study Follow-up
- Several revised figures
- New photography
- New Chemistry Around Us: *Rare Earths Are All Around You*
- 20% new Exercises

Chapter 5:
- New Case Study
- New Case Study Follow-up
- Several revised figures
- New photography
- New Chemistry Around Us: *Redox Reactions and Energy for Life*
- 20% new Exercises

Chapter 6:
- New Case Study
- New Case Study Follow-up
- Several revised figures
- New photography
- New Chemistry Around Us: *Blood Pressure: A Barometer of Health*
- 20% new Exercises

Chapter 7:
- New Case Study
- New Case Study Follow-up
- Several revised figures

- New photography
- New Chemistry and Your Health: *The Risk of Dehydration During Vigorous Youth Activities*
- 20% new Exercises

Chapter 8:

- New Case Study
- New Case Study Follow-up
- Several revised figures
- New photography
- 20% new Exercises

Chapter 9:

- New Case Study
- New Case Study Follow-up
- Several revised figures
- New photography
- New Ask an Expert: *Does Diet Play a Role in Peptic Ulcer Disease?*
- New Chemistry Around Us: *Carbon Dioxide in the Oceans*
- 20% new Exercises

Chapter 10:

- New Case Study
- New Case Study Follow-up
- Several revised figures
- New photography
- New Chemistry Around Us: *Radiation Exposure in Modern Life*
- 20% new Exercises

Chapter 11:

- New Case Study
- New Case Study Follow-up
- Several revised figures
- New photography
- New Ask an Expert: *Is Organic Food Worth the Price?*
- New Chemistry Around Us: *Oil Production from Wells and Sands*
- 20% new Exercises

Chapter 12:

- New Case Study
- New Case Study Follow-up
- Several revised figures
- New photography
- 20% new Exercises

Chapter 13:

- New Case Study
- New Case Study Follow-up
- Several revised figures
- New photography
- New Chemistry Around Us: *Alcohol and Antidepressants Don't Mix*
- New Chemistry And Your Health: *Why Do Teens Drink?*
- New Ask an Expert: *What Are Polyphenols?*
- 20% new Exercises

Chapter 14:

- New Case Study
- New Case Study Follow-up

- Several revised figures
- New photography
- 20% new Exercises

Chapter 15:

- New Case Study
- New Case Study Follow-up
- Several revised figures
- New photography
- 20% new Exercises

Chapter 16:

- New Case Study
- New Case Study Follow-up
- Several revised figures
- New photography
- New Ask an Expert: *Does Caffeine Help with Weight Loss?*
- 20% new Exercises

Chapter 17:

- New Case Study
- New Case Study Follow-up
- Several revised figures
- New photography
- New Ask an Expert: *Is High-Fructose Corn Syrup Worse for Your Health than Table Sugar?*
- 20% new Exercises

Chapter 18:

- New Case Study
- New Case Study Follow-up
- Several revised figures
- New photography
- New Ask an Expert: *How Significantly Can Diet Really Lower Cholesterol?*
- New Chemistry and Your Health: *Performance Enhancing Steroids*
- New Chemistry Around Us: *Algae in Your Fuel Tank*
- New Chemistry Around Us: *Olive Oil: A Heart-Healthy Lipid*
- 20% new Exercises

Chapter 19:

- New Case Study
- New Case Study Follow-up
- Several revised figures
- New photography
- New Ask an Expert: *Can a Higher Protein Diet Help Me Lose Weight?*
- 20% new Exercises

Chapter 20:

- New Case Study
- New Case Study Follow-up
- Several revised figures
- New photography
- 20% new Exercises

Chapter 21:

- New Case Study
- New Case Study Follow-up
- Several revised figures

- New photography
- New Chemistry Around Us: *Is There a DNA Checkup in Your Future?*
- 20% new Exercises

Chapter 22:
- New Case Study
- New Case Study Follow-up
- Several revised figures
- New photography
- New Choose My Plate Nutrition Guide
- New Chemistry and Your Health: *Vitamin Water: Beneficial or Not?*
- New Ask an Expert: *Is It Better to Take a Fiber Supplement or to Eat Fiber-Fortified Foods?*
- 20% new Exercises

Chapter 23:
- New Case Study
- New Case Study Follow-up
- Several revised figures
- New photography
- New Ask an Expert: *How can we Avoid Energy Crashes?*
- New Chemistry Around Us: *What Is the Best Weight-Loss Strategy?*
- 20% new Exercises

Chapter 24:
- New Case Study
- New Case Study Follow-up
- New photography
- New Chemistry Around Us: *Phenylalanine and Diet Foods*
- New Ask an Expert: *Are Certain Foods Better for the Brain?*
- 20% new Exercises

Chapter 25:
- New Case Study
- New Case Study Follow-up
- New photography
- 20% new Exercises

Case Study

Raju, a 15-year-old high-school student, was small for his age. Perhaps he took after his mother, who was quite petite. In the middle of his school year, Raju began having severe headaches, feeling them mostly behind his eyes. Over-the-counter remedies didn't seem to help much. Raju's mother had suffered from migraine headaches for some time. His doctor was inclined to diagnose migraine disorder, but Raju's symptoms didn't seem to completely support that diagnosis. Motivated by intuition, the doctor ordered an MRI scan. An MRI scan produces clear images of soft tissues such as the brain. Raju's scan revealed a golf ball–sized tumor impinging on the pituitary gland, located close to the hypothalamus, at the base of the brain. The tumor was likely the cause of Raju's growth issues as well as the headaches, because the pituitary gland regulates hormones related to growth. Fortunately, Raju's tumor was operable. He is now leading a normal life and annual MRI tests have shown no recurrence of the tumor.

How does an MRI scan work? What element in the body does an MRI scan detect? How important is it for health professionals to consider unlikely explanations for seemingly straightforward symptoms?

Features

Each chapter has features especially designed to help students study effectively, as well as organize, understand, and enjoy the material in the course.

Case Studies. These scenarios introduce you the students, to diverse situations a health-care professional might encounter. The purpose of the case studies is to stimulate inquiry; for that reason, we've placed them at the beginning of each chapter of the book. Vocabulary and scenarios may be unfamiliar to you who are studying these course materials, but our intent is to raise questions, and pique your curiosity. Medicine has long been described as an art. The questions raised by these case studies rarely have a single correct answer. With the knowledge that you gain from this text and your future training, acceptable answers to the questions raised in our scenarios will become apparent. A Case Study Follow-up to each Case Study can be found at the end of each chapter before the Concept Summary.

Chapter Outlines and Learning Objectives. At the beginning of each chapter, a list of learning objectives provides students with a convenient overview of what they should gain by studying the chapter. In order to help students navigate through each chapter and focus on key concepts, these objectives are repeated at the beginning of the section in which the applicable information is discussed. The objectives are referred to again in the concept summary at the end of each chapter along with one or two suggested end-of-chapter exercises. By working the suggested exercises, students get a quick indication of how well they have met the stated learning objectives. Thus, students begin each chapter with a set of objectives and end with an indication of how well they satisfied the objectives.

Key Terms. Identified within the text by the use of bold type, key terms are defined in the margin near the place where they are introduced. Students reviewing a chapter can quickly identify the important concepts on each page with this marginal glossary. A full glossary of key terms and concepts appears at the end of the text.

At the Counter. These boxed features contain useful information about health-related products that are readily available to consumers with or without a prescription. The information in each box provides a connection between the chemical behavior of the product and its effect on the body.

AT THE COUNTER 12.1

Smoking: It's Quitting Time

Smoking is a difficult habit to break, especially if the attempt is made by stopping abruptly—going "cold turkey." Mark Twain described the more reasonable gradual approach when he said, "Habit is habit, and not to be flung out of the window by any man, but coaxed downstairs a step at a time." Smokers do not have to go "cold turkey" because there are several OTC aids available, as well as some new prescription products to help them gradually overcome the strong urge to smoke—and eventually quit.

The transdermal (absorbed through the skin) nicotine patch is available over the counter in doses of 7–22 mg. When used as

The Nicotrol nicotine inhalation system has also received FDA approval. This inhaler, available only by prescription, consists of a plastic cylinder about the size of a cigarette that encloses a cartridge containing nicotine. When a smoker "puffs" on the device, nicotine vapors are absorbed through the lining of the mouth and throat. It takes about 80 puffs to deliver the amount of nicotine obtained from a single cigarette. An advantage of using the system is that a smoker still mimics the hand-to-mouth behavior of smoking, a part of the smoking habit that will be easier to break once nicotine withdrawal symptoms subside.

One of the newest prescription products designed to help break the smoking habit does not contain any nicotine. It is an antidepressant called bupropion that has been shown to be ef-

Chemistry Around Us. These boxed features present everyday applications of chemistry that emphasize in a real way the important role of chemistry in our lives. Forty percent of these are new to this edition and emphasize health-related applications of chemistry.

Chemistry and Your Health. These boxed features contain current chemistry-related health issues such as "The Importance of Color in Your Diet," and questions about topics such as safety concerns surrounding genetically modified foods and the relationship between C-reactive protein and heart disease.

CHEMISTRY AND YOUR HEALTH 10.1

Is Irradiated Food Safe?

In 1993, four deaths and hundreds of illnesses were linked to the eating of undercooked ground beef that was contaminated with *E. coli* bacteria. In 1997 the largest recall of meat products in U.S. history up to that time took place when a producer voluntarily recalled 25 million pounds of ground beef suspected of being contaminated with the same type of bacteria. In 2002, a new meat product recall record was established when 27.4 million pounds of poultry products was recalled because of possible contamination by *Listeria*, a potentially deadly type of bacteria.

purchase and use them. Some irradiated foods are used unintentionally as a result of the labeling rules. For example, irradiated spices or fresh strawberries sold in a grocery store must have labels that indicate they have been irradiated. However, when such irradiated foods are used as ingredients in other foods, the other foods are not required to have irradiation labels. Also, irradiation labeling does not apply to foods served in restaurants.

Two factors that currently contribute to low consumer acceptance of irradiated food are continuing misconceptions about the effects of radiation on food and the low availability of irradiated foods for sale. Some misconceptions that are difficult to eliminate despite reassuring results from

Ask an Expert. Boxes written by Dr. Melina B. Jampolis engage students by presenting questions and answers about nutrition and health, as related to chemistry, that are relevant and important in today's world.

Ask an Expert 1.1

Q: Does food density matter when you're trying to lose weight?

A: When it comes to losing weight, it seems like there is a new fad diet out every month. Low fat, low carb, high protein, vegan, vegetarian low carb—the choices are endless. What really works for weight loss? The answer varies among individuals and likely depends on a combination of genes, food preferences, and lifestyle. But one of the most important concepts for achieving permanent weight loss is the energy density of the food you consume. Energy density refers to the number of calories per gram in a given type of food. Eating foods that have a lower energy density allows you to eat larger, more satisfying, portions while consuming fewer calories. Research has shown that this is important both mentally and physically when it comes to weight

DR. MELINA B. JAMPOLIS, M.D.

Dr. Melina B. Jampolis, M.D. is a Los Angeles, California, Physician Nutrition Specialist—a specialty

Examples. To reinforce students in their problem-solving skill development, complete step-by-step solutions for numerous examples are included in each chapter.

Learning Checks. Short self-check exercises follow examples and discussions of key or difficult concepts. A complete set of solutions is included in Appendix C. These allow students to measure immediately their understanding and progress.

Study Skills. Most chapters contain a *Study Skills* feature in which a challenging topic, skill, or concept of the chapter is addressed. Study suggestions, analogies, and approaches are provided to help students master these ideas.

How Reactions Occur. The mechanisms of representative organic reactions are presented in four boxed inserts to help students dispel the mystery of how these reactions take place.

Concept Summary. Located at the end of each chapter, this feature provides a concise review of the concepts and includes suggested exercises to check achievement of the learning objectives related to the concepts.

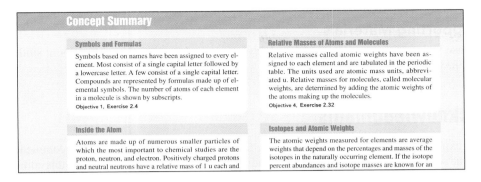

Key Terms and Concepts. These are listed at the end of the chapter for easy review, with a reference to the chapter section in which they are presented.

Key Equations. This feature provides a useful summary of general equations and reactions from the chapter. This feature is particularly helpful to students in the organic chemistry chapters.

Exercises. Nearly 1,700 end-of-chapter exercises are arranged by section. Approximately half of the exercises are answered in the back of the text. Complete solutions to these answered exercises are included in the Student Study Guide. Solutions and answers to the remaining exercises are provided in the Instructor's Manual. We have included a significant number of clinical and other familiar applications of chemistry in the exercises.

Allied Health Exam Connection. These examples of chemistry questions from typical entrance exams used to screen applicants to allied health professional programs help students focus their attention on the type of chemical concepts considered important in such programs.

Chemistry for Thought. Included at the end of each chapter are special questions designed to encourage students to expand their reasoning skills. Some of these exercises are based on photographs found in the chapter, while others emphasize clinical or other useful applications of chemistry.

Possible Course Outlines

This text may be used effectively in either a two-semester or three-quarter course of study:

First semester: Chapters 1–13 (general chemistry and three chapters of organic chemistry)

Second semester: Chapters 14–25 (organic chemistry and biochemistry)

First semester: Chapters 1–10 (general chemistry)

Second semester: Chapters 11–21 (organic chemistry and some biochemistry)

First quarter: Chapters 1–10 (general chemistry)

Second quarter: Chapters 11–18 (organic chemistry)

Third quarter: Chapters 19–25 (biochemistry)

Supporting Materials

Please visit **www.cengage.com/chemistry/seager/gob8e** for information about student and instructor resources for this text.

Acknowledgments

We express our sincere appreciation to the following reviewers, who read and commented on the seventh edition and offered helpful advice and suggestions for improving this edition:

Judith Ciottone
Fitchburg State University

Caroline Clower
Clayton State University

Meldath Govindan
Fitchburg State University

Jeff Owens
Highline Community College

Dwight Patterson
Middle Tennessee State University

James Petrich
San Antonio College

John Vincent
University of Alabama

Scott White
Southern Arkansas University

We also express appreciation to the following reviewers, who helped us revise the first seven editions:

Hugh Akers
Lamar University–Beaumont

Johanne I. Artman
Del Mar College

Gabriele Backes
Portland Community College

Bruce Banks
University of North Carolina–Greensboro

Deb Breiter
Rockford College

Lorraine C. Brewer
University of Arkansas

Martin Brock
Eastern Kentucky University

Jonathan T. Brockman
College of DuPage

Kathleen Brunke
Christopher Newport University

Christine Brzezowski
University of Utah

David Boykin
Georgia State University

Sybil K. Burgess
University of North Carolina–Wilmington

Sharmaine S. Cady
East Stroudsburg University

Linda J. Chandler
Salt Lake Community College

Tom Chang
Utah State University

Ngee Sing Chong
Middle Tennessee State University

Sharon Cruse
Northern Louisiana University

Thomas D. Crute
Augusta College

Jack L. Dalton
Boise State University

Lorraine Deck
University of New Mexico

Kathleen A. Donnelly
Russell Sage College

Jan Fausset
Front Range Community College

Patricia Fish
The College of St. Catherine

Harold Fisher
University of Rhode Island

John W. Francis
Columbus State Community

Wes Fritz
College of DuPage

Jean Gade
Northern Kentucky University

Jane D. Grant
Florida Community College

Galen George
Santa Rosa Junior College

Anita Gnezda
Ball State University

James K. Hardy
University of Akron

Leland Harris
University of Arizona

Robert H. Harris
University of Nebraska–Lincoln

David C. Hawkinson
University of South Dakota

Jack Hefley
Blinn College

Claudia Hein
Diablo Valley College

John Henderson
Jackson Community College

Mary Herrmann
University of Cincinnati

Arthur R. Hubscher
Brigham Young University–Idaho

Kenneth Hughes
University of Wisconsin–Oshkosh

Jeffrey A. Hurlbut
Metropolitan State College of Denver

Jim Johnson
Sinclair Community College

Richard. F. Jones
Sinclair Community College

Frederick Jury
Collin County Community College

Lidija Kampa
Kean College of New Jersey

Laura Kibler-Herzog
Georgia State University

Margaret G. Kimble
*Indiana University–Purdue University
 Fort Wayne*

James F. Kirby
Quinnipiac University

Peter J. Krieger
Palm Beach Community College

Terrie L. Lampe

De Kalb College–Central Campus

Carol Larocque
Cambrian College

Richard Lavallee
Santa Monica College

Donald Linn
*Indiana University—Purdue University
 Fort Wayne*

Leslie J. Lovett
Fairmont State College

James Luba
University of Arkansas at Little Rock

Regan Luken
University of South Dakota

Gregory Marks
Carroll University

Armin Mayr
El Paso Community College

James McConaghy
Wayne College

Evan McHugh
Pikes Peak Community College

Trudy McKee
Thomas Jefferson University

Melvin Merken
Worcester State College

W. Robert Midden
Bowling Green State University

Pamela S. Mork
Concordia College

Phillip E. Morris, Jr.
University of Alabama–Birmingham

Robert N. Nelson
Georgia Southern University

Marie Nguyen
Highline Community College

Elva Mae Nicholson
Eastern Michigan University

H. Clyde Odom
Charleston Southern University

Howard K. Ono
California State University–Fresno

James A. Petrich
San Antonio College

Thomas G. Richmond
University of Utah

James Schreck
University of Northern Colorado

William Scovell
Bowling Green State University

Jean M. Shankweiler
El Camino Community College

Francis X. Smith
King's College

J. Donald Smith
University of Massachusetts–Dartmouth

Malcolm P. Stevens
University of Hartford

Eric R. Taylor
University of Southwestern Louisiana

Krista Thomas
Johnson County Community College

Linda Thomas-Glover
Guilford Technical Community College

Mary Lee Trawick
Baylor University

James A. Thomson
University of Waterloo

Katherin Vafeades
University of Texas–San Antonio

Cary Willard
Grossmont College

Don Williams
Hope College

Les Wynston
California State University–Long Beach

Jean Yockey
University of South Dakota

We also give special thanks to Mary Finch, Publisher, and Alyssa White, Development Editor for Cengage Learning, who guided and encouraged us in the preparation of this eighth edition. We would also like to thank: Teresa Trego, Senior Content Project Manager; Lisa Weber, Senior Media Editor; Nicole Hamm, Senior Marketing Manager; and Krista Mastroianni, Assistant Editor. All were essential to the team and contributed greatly to the success of the project. We are very grateful for the superb work of Greg Johnson of PreMediaGlobal for his outstanding coordination of production, and the excellent photos obtained by Tim McDonough of Bill Smith Studio Group. We are especially pleased with the new feature Ask an Expert and wish to thank Dr. Melina B. Jampolis for her excellent work. We appreciate the significant help of four associates, Monica Linford, who did an excellent job writing a case study for each chapter, Mary Ann Francis, who helped with submitting manuscript, Audrey Stokes, who checked exercise answers, and Vince McGrath, who proofread everything.

Finally, we extend our love and heartfelt thanks to our families for their patience, support, encouragement, and understanding during a project that occupied much of our time and energy.

Spencer L. Seager

Michael R. Slabaugh

Case Study

Isabelle was a perfectionist and a straight-A student. She kept her room clean, followed the rules, and never gave her parents any trouble. Isabelle was a pretty girl; but having gone through puberty early, by sixth grade she was larger than her peers. Isabelle was not emotionally prepared to accept the weight gain that accompanies puberty. By the beginning of seventh grade she began counting calories. By eighth grade she started to binge and purge. She was 5'6" tall and felt that it was unacceptable to be over 100 lbs. Her parents weren't concerned. They saw Isabelle sometimes consuming large amounts of food—but they just thought she had a high metabolic rate. Isabelle moved on to college, and her parents saw her infrequently. They were shocked to receive a call one day from a hospital informing them that Isabelle had collapsed during a choir rehearsal. Her heart rate was elevated, her blood pressure was low, and her eyes appeared sunken. Isabelle was dehydrated and had an electrolyte imbalance. She was given an IV and referred to the Behavioral Health Unit to receive treatment for her eating disorder.

How do anorexia and bulimia differ? Can a patient have both at the same time? How does family involvement influence patient outcomes?

Follow-up to this Case Study appears at the end the chapter before the Concept Summary.

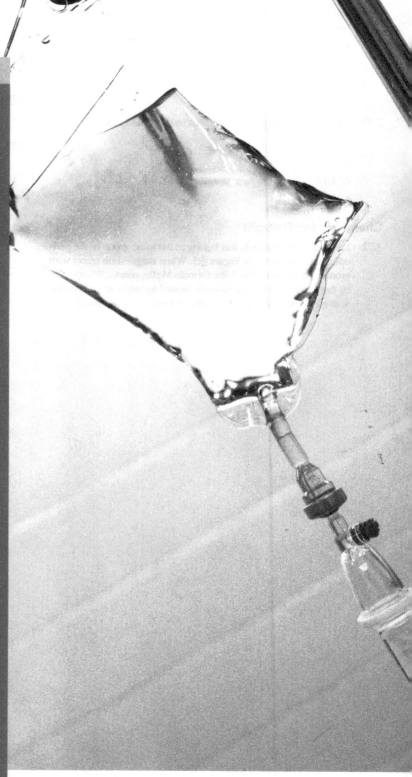

Learning Objectives

When you have completed your study of this chapter, you should be able to:

1 Draw correct Lewis structures for atoms of representative elements. **(Section 4.1)**

2 Use electronic configurations to determine the number of electrons gained or lost by atoms as they achieve noble gas electronic configurations. **(Section 4.2)**

3 Use the octet rule to correctly predict the ions formed during the formation of ionic compounds, and write correct formulas for binary ionic compounds containing a representative metal and a representative nonmetal. **(Section 4.3)**

4 Correctly name binary ionic compounds. **(Section 4.4)**

5 Determine formula weights for ionic compounds. **(Section 4.5)**

6 Draw correct Lewis structures for covalent molecules. **(Section 4.6)**

7 Draw correct Lewis structures for polyatomic ions. **(Section 4.7)**

8 Use VSEPR theory to predict the shapes of molecules and polyatomic ions. **(Section 4.8)**

9 Use electronegativities to classify covalent bonds of molecules, and determine whether covalent molecules are polar or nonpolar. **(Section 4.9)**

10 Write correct formulas for ionic compounds containing representative metals and polyatomic ions, and correctly name binary covalent compounds and compounds containing polyatomic ions. **(Section 4.10)**

11 Relate melting and boiling points of pure substances to the strength and type of interparticle forces present in the substances. **(Section 4.11)**

n the discussion to this point, we have emphasized that matter is composed of tiny particles. However, we have not yet discussed the forces that hold these particles together to form the matter familiar to us. It is these forces that produce many of the properties associated with various types of matter—properties such as the electrical conductivity of copper wire, the melting point of butter, and the boiling point of water.

4.1 Noble Gas Configurations

Learning Objective

1. Draw correct Lewis structures for atoms of representative elements.

The octet rule, proposed in 1916 by G. N. Lewis (an American) and Walter Kossel (a German), was the first widely accepted theory to describe bonding between atoms. The basis for the rule was the observed chemical stability of the noble gases. Because the noble gases did not react readily with other substances and because chemical reactivity depends on electronic structure, chemists concluded that the electronic structure of the noble gases represented a stable (low-energy) configuration. This noble gas configuration (see Section 3.4) is characterized by two electrons in the valence shell of helium and eight valence-shell electrons for the other members of the group (Ne, Ar, Kr, Xe, and Rn).

▶ Example 4.1

Use the techniques described in Section 3.4 to write the electronic configurations for the noble gases. Identify the valence-shell electrons, and verify the noble gas configurations just mentioned.

Solution

The subshell-filling order in Figure 3.7 gives the electronic configurations shown below. Valence-shell electrons are in darker type, and the noble gas configurations are verified.

		Number of Valence-shell Electrons
He:	$1s^2$	2
Ne:	$1s^2 2s^2 2p^6$	8
Ar:	$1s^2 2s^2 2p^6 3s^2 3p^6$	8
Kr:	$1s^2 2s^2 2p^6 3s^2 3p^6 4s^2 3d^{10} 4p^6$	8
Xe:	$1s^2 2s^2 2p^6 3s^2 3p^6 4s^2 3d^{10} 4p^6 5s^2 4d^{10} 5p^6$	8
Rn:	$1s^2 2s^2 2p^6 3s^2 3p^6 4s^2 3d^{10} 4p^6 5s^2 4d^{10} 5p^6 6s^2 4f^{14} 5d^{10} 6p^6$	8

▶ **LEARNING CHECK 4.1** Write the electronic configurations for F and K. What would have to be done to change these configurations to noble gas configurations (how many electrons would have to be added or removed)?

Lewis structure A representation of an atom or ion in which the elemental symbol represents the atomic nucleus and all but the valence-shell electrons. The valence-shell electrons are represented by dots arranged around the elemental symbol.

A simplified way to represent the valence-shell electrons of atoms was invented by G. N. Lewis. In these representations, called electron-dot formulas or **Lewis structures,** the symbol for an element represents the nucleus and all electrons around the nucleus except those in the valence shell. Valence-shell electrons are shown as dots around the symbol. Thus, rubidium is represented as Rb·.

When a Lewis structure is to be written for an element, it is necessary to determine the number of valence-shell electrons in the element. This can be done by writing the electronic configuration using the methods described in Chapter 3 and identifying the valence-shell electrons as those with the highest n value. A simpler alternative for representative elements is to refer to the periodic table and note that the number of valence-shell electrons in the atoms of an element is the same as the number of the group in the periodic table to which the element belongs. The group number used must be the one that precedes the letter A, not the one in parentheses as given in the periodic table inside the front cover of this book. Using this method, we see that rubidium belongs to group IA(1) and therefore has one valence-shell electron.

▶ Example 4.2

Draw Lewis structures for atoms of the following:

a. element number 4
b. cesium (Cs)
c. aluminum (Al)
d. selenium (Se)

The accepted procedure is to write the element's symbol and put a dot for each valence electron in one of four equally spaced locations around the symbol. Imagine a square around the symbol. Each side of the square represents one of the four locations. An element with four valence electrons would have one dot in each of the four locations. A fifth electron would be represented by one additional dot in one of the locations. Each location can have a maximum of two dots.

Solution

a. Element number 4 is beryllium; it belongs to group IIA(2) and thus has two valence-shell electrons. The Lewis structure is Be$\cdot$.

b. Cesium is in group IA(1), has one valence-shell electron, and has the Lewis structure Cs$\cdot$.

c. Aluminum is in group IIIA(13). It has three valence-shell electrons and is represented by the following Lewis structure: Al$\cdot$.

d. Selenium is in group VIA(16) and thus has six valence-shell electrons. The Lewis structure is $:\overset{\cdot\cdot}{Se}\cdot$.

▶ **LEARNING CHECK 4.2** Draw Lewis structures for atoms of the following:

a. element number 9
b. magnesium (Mg)
c. sulfur (S)
d. krypton (Kr)

It is important to clearly understand the relationship between Lewis structures and electronic configurations for atoms. The following example and learning check will help you review this relationship.

▶ Example 4.3

Represent the following using abbreviated electronic configurations and Lewis structures:

a. F　　　　**b.** K　　　　**c.** Mg　　　　**d.** Si

Solution

a. Fluorine (F) contains 9 electrons, with 7 of them classified as valence electrons (those in the $2s$ and $2p$ subshells). The configuration and Lewis structure are

$$[\text{He}]2s^2 2p^5 \qquad \text{and} \qquad :\overset{\cdot\cdot}{F}\cdot$$

b. Potassium (K) contains 19 electrons, with 1 of them classified as a valence electron (the 1 in the $4s$ subshell). The configuration and Lewis structure are

$$[\text{Ar}]4s^1 \qquad \text{and} \qquad \text{K}\cdot$$

c. Magnesium (Mg) contains 12 electrons, with 2 of them classified as valence electrons (the 2 in the $3s$ subshell). The configuration and Lewis structure are

$$[\text{Ne}]3s^2 \qquad \text{and} \qquad \overset{\cdot}{\text{Mg}}\cdot$$

d. Silicon (Si) contains 14 electrons, with 4 of them classified as valence electrons (those in the $3s$ and $3p$ subshells). The configuration and Lewis structure are

$$[\text{Ne}]3s^2 3p^2 \qquad \text{and} \qquad \cdot\overset{\cdot}{\text{Si}}\cdot$$

▶ **LEARNING CHECK 4.3** Using the two methods illustrated in Example 4.3, write electronic configurations and Lewis structures for the following atoms:

a. Li　　　　**b.** Br　　　　**c.** Sr　　　　**d.** S

4.2 Ionic Bonding

Learning Objective

2. Use electronic configurations to determine the number of electrons gained or lost by atoms as they achieve noble gas electronic configurations.

octet rule A rule for predicting electron behavior in reacting atoms. It says that atoms will gain or lose sufficient electrons to achieve an outer electron arrangement identical to that of a noble gas. This arrangement usually consists of eight electrons in the valence shell.

simple ion An atom that has acquired a net positive or negative charge by losing or gaining electrons.

ionic bond The attractive force that holds together ions of opposite charge.

According to the **octet rule** of Lewis and Kossel, atoms tend to interact through electronic rearrangements that produce a noble gas electronic configuration for each atom involved in the interaction. Except for the lowest-energy shell, this means that each atom ends up with eight electrons in the valence shell. There are exceptions to this octet rule, but it is still used because of the amount of information it provides. It is especially effective in describing reactions between the representative elements of the periodic table (see Figure 3.10).

During some chemical interactions, the octet rule is satisfied when electrons are transferred from one atom to another. As a result of the transfers, neutral atoms acquire net positive or negative electrical charges and become attracted to one another. These charged atoms are called **simple ions,** and the attractive force between oppositely charged atoms constitutes an **ionic bond.** A second type of interaction that also satisfies the octet rule is discussed in Section 4.6.

▶ Example 4.4

Show how the following atoms can achieve a noble gas configuration and become ions by gaining or losing electrons:

a. Na **b.** Cl

Solution

a. The electronic structure of sodium (Na) is represented below using an abbreviated configuration and a Lewis structure:

$$[Ne]3s^1 \qquad \text{and} \qquad Na\cdot$$

The first representation makes it obvious that the Ne configuration with 8 electrons in the valence shell would result if the Na atom lost the single electron located in the $3s$ subshell. The loss is represented by the following equation:

$$Na \rightarrow Na^+ + 1e^-$$

Notice that the removal of a single negative electron from a neutral Na atom leaves the atom with 11 positive protons in the nucleus and 10 negative electrons. This gives the atom a net positive charge. The atom has become a positive ion.

b. The electronic structure for chlorine (Cl) is shown below using an abbreviated configuration and a Lewis structure:

$$[Ne]3s^23p^5 \qquad \text{and} \qquad :\overset{..}{\underset{..}{Cl}}\cdot$$

The Cl atom can achieve an Ne configuration by losing the 7 valence electrons. However, it is energetically much more favorable to achieve the configuration of argon (Ar) by adding 1 electron to the valence shell. This electron would complete an octet and change a Cl atom into a negative chloride ion as represented by the following equation, where Cl^- represents a Cl atom with 17 protons and 18 electrons, giving the atom a net negative charge:

$$Cl + 1e^- \rightarrow Cl^-$$

▶ LEARNING CHECK 4.4
In Learning Check 4.1, you described what had to be done to change the electronic configurations of F and K to noble gas configurations. Write equations to illustrate these changes.

As a general rule, metals lose electrons and nonmetals gain electrons during ionic bond formation. The number of electrons lost or gained by a single atom rarely exceeds three, and this number can be predicted accurately for representative elements by using the periodic table. The number of electrons easily lost by a representative metal atom is the same as the group number (represented by roman numerals preceding the A in the periodic table). The number of electrons that tend to be gained by a representative nonmetal atom is equal to eight minus the group number. However, the nonmetal hydrogen is an exception. In most reactions, it loses one electron, consistent with its placement in group IA(1). In other, less common, reactions it gains one electron just as group VIIA(17) elements do.

▶ Example 4.5

Use the periodic table to predict the number of electrons lost or gained by atoms of the following elements during ionic bond formation. Write an equation to represent the process in each case.

a. Li
b. Any group IIA(2) element, represented by the symbol M
c. element number 15
d. carbon

Solution

a. Lithium (Li), a metal, is in group IA(1); therefore it will lose 1 electron per atom:

$$Li \rightarrow Li^+ + 1e^-$$

b. Any group IIA(2) metal will lose 2 electrons; therefore,

$$M \rightarrow M^{2+} + 2e^-$$

c. Element number 15 is phosphorus (P), a nonmetal of group VA(15). It will gain $8 - 5 = 3$ electrons. The equation is

$$P + 3e^- \rightarrow P^{3-}$$

d. Carbon (C) is in group IVA(14) and is a nonmetal. It should, therefore, gain $8 - 4 = 4$ electrons. However, no more than 3 electrons generally become involved in ionic bond formation, so we conclude that carbon will not react readily to form ionic bonds.

▶ **LEARNING CHECK 4.5** Predict the number of electrons that would be gained or lost during ionic bond formation for each of the following elements. Write an equation to represent each predicted change.

a. element number 34 **b.** Rb **c.** element number 18 **d.** In

While your attention is focused on noble gas configurations, it is appropriate to emphasize the following point: The attainment of a noble gas electronic configuration by an atom does not mean that the atom is converted into a noble gas. Instead, as seen above, the atoms are converted into simple ions (charged atoms). This point is emphasized by the comparison given in ▶ Table 4.1. Notice that the electronic configuration of Mg^{2+} is the same as that of Ne, but the number of protons (the atomic number) of Mg^{2+} is still the same as that of Mg. Atoms and simple ions that have identical electronic configurations are said to be **isoelectronic.**

isoelectronic A term that literally means "same electronic," used to describe atoms or ions that have identical electronic configurations.

TABLE 4.1 A Metal Atom, a Metal Ion, and a Noble Gas Atom Compared

Particle	Symbol	Number of Protons in Nucleus	Number of Electrons Around Nucleus	Net Charge on Particle
Magnesium atom	Mg	12	12	0
Magnesium ion	Mg^{2+}	12	10	+2
Neon atom	Ne	10	10	0

4.3 Ionic Compounds

Learning Objective

3. Use the octet rule to correctly predict the ions formed during the formation of ionic compounds, and write correct formulas for binary ionic compounds containing a representative metal and a representative nonmetal.

So far the discussion has focused on the electron-transfer process as it occurs for isolated atoms. In reality, the electrons lost by a metal are the same ones gained by the nonmetal with which it is reacting. Substances formed from such reactions are called *ionic compounds*. No atom can lose electrons unless another atom is available to accept them, as shown in the formulas used to represent ionic compounds. These formulas represent the combining ratio of the positive and negative ions found in the compounds. This ratio is determined by the charges on the ions, which are determined by the number of electrons transferred.

▶ Example 4.6

Represent the electron-transfer process that takes place when the following pairs of elements react ionically. Determine the formula for each resulting ionic compound.

a. Na and Cl **b.** Mg and F

Solution

a. Sodium (Na) is in group IA(1), and we can write

$$Na \rightarrow Na^+ + 1e^-$$

Chlorine (Cl), in group VIIA(17), reacts as follows:

$$Cl + 1e^- \rightarrow Cl^-$$

The resulting ions, Na^+ and Cl^-, will combine in a 1:1 ratio because the total positive and total negative charges in the final formula must add up to zero. The formula then is NaCl. Note that the metal is written first in the formula, a generally followed practice. Also, the formula is written using the smallest number of each ion possible—in this case, one of each.

The actual electron-transfer process and the achievement of octets can more easily be visualized as follows:

$$\underset{\text{Na}}{[Ne]3s^1} + \underset{\text{Cl}}{[Ne]3s^23p^5} \rightarrow [Ne] + \underset{\text{Cl}^-}{[Ne]3s^23p^6}$$
$$\underset{Na^+}{}$$

In this representation, it must be remembered that the $[Ne]3s^23p^6$ electronic configuration of Cl^- is the same configuration as argon, the noble gas that follows chlorine in the periodic table.

Fight Hypertension with Potassium

In the United States, hypertension (high blood pressure) is the primary reason people visit doctor's offices, and more prescriptions are written for its treatment than any other health problem. In addition to the use of prescription drugs, hypertension is also usually treated by reducing or eliminating the dietary intake of sodium in the form of table salt (sodium chloride). Recently released research results indicate that combining an increase in dietary potassium intake with a reduction in sodium intake is probably the most important dietary decision (after excess weight loss) people can make to reduce cardiovascular diseases, including hypertension.

Studies reveal that in societies with diets rich in fruits and vegetables, only 1% of the population suffers from hypertension. By contrast, 33% of adults have hypertension in industrialized societies where the diet contains larger amounts of processed foods, which often contain added salt. The typical diet in the United States contains about twice the sodium and only half the 4700 milligrams per day of potassium currently recommended by the American Heart Association.

It might seem that taking a daily supplement is the only way to ensure a daily potassium intake as high as 4.7 grams, but that is not the case. Nature provides many potassium-rich foods such as squash, potatoes, tomatoes, carrots, spinach, beans, bananas, apricots, prunes, melons, peaches, halibut, tuna, trout, and low-fat dairy products. Specific examples of the potassium content of a few dietary potassium sources are given in the following table:

banana, 1 medium—422 mg
© iStockphoto.com/ZoneCreative

sweet potato, 1 baked—694 mg
© iStockphoto.com/EddWestmacott

white potato, 1 baked—610 mg
© iStockphoto.com/Viktor Kitaykin

white beans, canned, ½ cup—595 mg
© iStockphoto.com/Stephan Hoerold

yogurt, plain, nonfat, 8 oz—595 mg © Foodcollection/PhotoLibrary

halibut, cooked, 3 oz—490 mg © iStockphoto.com/Stacie Peterson

tuna, yellowfin, cooked, 3 oz—484 mg © iStockphoto.com/Eugene Bochkarev

lima beans, cooked, ½ cup—484 mg © iStockphoto.com/Joan Kimball

winter squash, cooked, ½ cup—448 mg © iStockphoto.com/velvetsnow

In addition to potassium, some studies have shown that the minerals magnesium and calcium may also have a positive influence in maintaining healthy blood pressure. The fruits and vegetables that provide potassium in the diet are also good sources of these two minerals. So, the parental directions traditionally given to children to "eat your fruits and vegetables and drink your milk" have been given scientific validity for all of us as a way to help maintain healthy levels of blood pressure.

b. Magnesium (Mg) of group IIA(2) will lose two electrons per atom, whereas fluorine (F) of group VIIA(17) will gain one electron per atom. Therefore, we can write

$$Mg \rightarrow Mg^{2+} + 2e^-$$
$$F + 1e^- \rightarrow F^-$$

It is apparent that two fluorine atoms will be required to accept the electrons from one magnesium atom. From another point of view, two F^- ions will be needed to balance the charge of a single Mg^{2+} ion. Both observations lead to the formula MgF_2 for the compound. Note the use of subscripts to indicate the number of ions involved in the formula. The subscript 1, on Mg, is understood and never written.

▶ **LEARNING CHECK 4.6** Write equations to represent the formation of ions for each of the following pairs of elements. Write a formula for the ionic compound that would form in each case.

a. Mg and O **b.** K and S **c.** Ca and Br

binary compound A compound made up of two different elements.

Ionic compounds of the types used in Example 4.6 and Learning Check 4.6 are called **binary compounds** because each contains only two different kinds of atoms, Na and Cl in one case (see ▶ Figure 4.1) and Mg and F in the other.

Figure 4.1 The reaction of sodium metal and chlorine gas. The vigorous reaction releases energy that heats the flask contents to a high temperature. Would you expect a similar reaction to occur between potassium metal and fluorine gas?

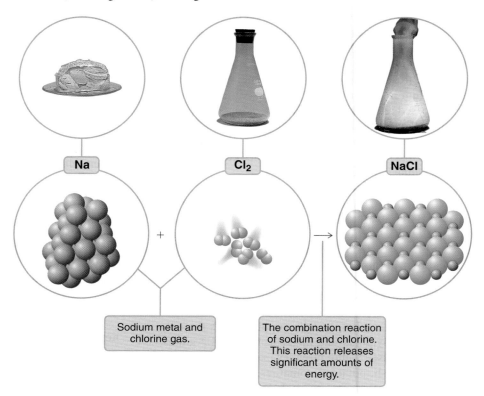

Sodium metal and chlorine gas.

The combination reaction of sodium and chlorine. This reaction releases significant amounts of energy.

4.4 Naming Binary Ionic Compounds

Learning Objective

4. Correctly name binary ionic compounds.

Names for binary ionic compounds are easily assigned when the names of the two elements involved are known. The name of the metallic element is given first, followed by the stem of the nonmetallic elemental name to which the suffix *-ide* has been added.

$$\text{name} = \text{metal} + \text{nonmetal stem} + \text{-ide}$$

The stem of the name of a nonmetal is the name of the nonmetal with the ending dropped. ▶ Table 4.2 gives the stem of the names of some common nonmetallic elements.

TABLE 4.2 Stem Names and Ion Formulas of Common Nonmetallic Elements

Element	Stem	Formula of Ion
Bromine	brom-	Br^-
Chlorine	chlor-	Cl^-
Fluorine	fluor-	F^-
Iodine	iod-	I^-
Nitrogen	nitr-	N^{3-}
Oxygen	ox-	O^{2-}
Phosphorus	phosph-	P^{3-}
Sulfur	sulf-	S^{2-}

▶ Example 4.7

Name the following binary ionic compounds:

a. KCl **b.** SrO **c.** Ca_3N_2

Solution

a. The metal is potassium (K), and the nonmetal is chlorine (Cl). Thus, the compound name is potassium <u>chlor</u>ide (the stem of the nonmetallic name is underlined).
b. Similarly, strontium (Sr) and oxygen (O) give the compound name strontium <u>ox</u>ide.
c. The elements are calcium (Ca) and nitrogen (N), hence the name calcium <u>nitr</u>ide.

▶ **LEARNING CHECK 4.7** Assign names to the binary compounds whose formulas you wrote in Learning Check 4.6.

Names for the constituent ions of a binary compound are obtained in the same way as the compound name. Thus, K^+ is a potassium ion, whereas Cl^- is a chloride ion.

Some metal atoms, especially those of transition and inner-transition elements, form more than one type of charged ion. Copper, for example, forms both Cu^+ and Cu^{2+}, and iron forms Fe^{2+} and Fe^{3+}. The names of ionic compounds containing such elements must indicate which ion is present in the compound. A nomenclature system that does this well indicates the ionic charge of the metal ion by a roman numeral in parentheses following the name of the metal. Thus, CuCl is copper(I) chloride and $CuCl_2$ is copper(II) chloride. These names are expressed verbally as "copper one chloride" and "copper two chloride."

An older system is still in use but works only for naming compounds of metals that can form only two different charged ions. In this method, the endings *-ous* and *-ic* are attached to the stem of the metal name. For metals with elemental symbols derived from non-English names, the stem of the non-English name is used. The *-ous* ending is always used with the ion of lower charge and the *-ic* ending with the ion of higher charge. Thus, CuCl is cuprous chloride, and $CuCl_2$ is cupric chloride. In the case of iron, $FeCl_2$ is ferrous chloride, and $FeCl_3$ is ferric chloride (see ▶ Figure 4.2). Notice that the Cu^{2+} ion was called cupric, whereas the Fe^{2+} was called ferrous. The designations do not tell the actual ionic charge, but only which of the two is higher (Cu^{2+} and Fe^{3+}) or lower (Cu^+ and Fe^{2+}) for the metal in question.

Cuprous Cupric chloride

A B

C D

Ferrous Ferric chloride

© Jeffrey M. Seager

Figure 4.2 Chloride compounds of copper and iron. Top: Cuprous and cupric chloride. Bottom: Ferrous and ferric chloride.

4.5 The Smallest Unit of Ionic Compounds

Learning Objective

5. Determine formula weights for ionic compounds.

In Section 1.3, a molecule was defined as the smallest unit of a pure substance capable of a stable, independent existence. As you will see later, some compound formulas are used to represent single molecules. True molecular formulas represent the precise numbers of atoms of each element that are found in a molecule. However, as we have seen, formulas for ionic compounds represent only the simplest combining ratio of the ions in the compounds.

The stable form of an ionic compound is not a molecule, but a crystal in which many ions of opposite charge occupy **lattice sites** in a rigid three-dimensional arrangement called a **crystal lattice**. For example, the lattice of sodium chloride (ordinary table salt) represented in ▶ Figure 4.3 is the stable form of pure sodium chloride.

lattice site The individual location occupied by a particle in a crystal lattice.

crystal lattice A rigid three-dimensional arrangement of particles.

Figure 4.3 Crystal lattice for sodium chloride (table salt).

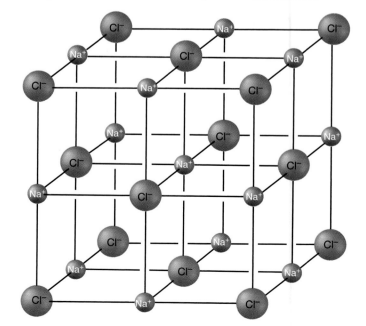

Unless otherwise noted all art on this page © Cengage Learning 2014

Even though the formulas of ionic compounds do not represent true molecular formulas, they are often used as if they did. This is especially true when equations representing chemical reactions are written, or when the mole concept is applied to chemical formulas (see Section 2.7). When the atomic weights of the atoms making up a true molecular formula are added together, the result is called the molecular weight of the compound (Section 2.4). A similar quantity obtained by adding up the atomic weights of the atoms shown in the formula of an ionic compound is called a **formula weight.** The mole concept is applied to formula weights in a manner similar to the way it is applied to molecular weights.

formula weight The sum of the atomic weights of the atoms shown in the formula of an ionic compound.

▶ Example 4.9

Carbon dioxide, CO_2, is a molecular compound, whereas magnesium chloride, $MgCl_2$, is an ionic compound.

a. Determine the molecular weight for CO_2 and the formula weight for $MgCl_2$ in atomic mass units.
b. Determine the mass in grams of 1.00 mol of each compound.
c. Determine the number of CO_2 molecules in 1.00 mol and the number of Mg^{2+} and Cl^- ions in 1.00 mol of $MgCl_2$.

Solution

a. For CO_2, the molecular weight is the sum of the atomic weights of the atoms in the formula:

$$MW = (1)(\text{at. wt. C}) + (2)(\text{at. wt. O}) = (1)(12.0 \text{ u}) + (2)(16.0 \text{ u})$$
$$MW = 44.0 \text{ u}$$

For $MgCl_2$, the formula weight is also equal to the sum of the atomic weights of the atoms in the formula:

$$FW = (1)(\text{at. wt. Mg}) + (2)(\text{at. wt. Cl}) = (1)(24.3 \text{ u}) + (2)(35.5 \text{ u})$$
$$FW = 95.3 \text{ u}$$

b. According to Section 2.6, 1.00 mol of a molecular compound has a mass in grams equal to the molecular weight of the compound. Thus, 1.00 mol CO_2 = 44.0 g CO_2.
 For ionic compounds, 1.00 mol of compound has a mass in grams equal to the formula weight of the compound. Thus, 1.00 mol $MgCl_2$ = 95.3 g $MgCl_2$.

c. In Section 2.6 we learned that 1.00 mol of a molecular compound contains Avogadro's number of molecules. Thus, 1.00 mol CO_2 = 6.02×10^{23} molecules of CO_2.
 In the case of ionic compounds, 1.00 mol of compound contains Avogadro's number of formula units. That is, 1.00 mol of magnesium chloride contains Avogadro's number of $MgCl_2$ units, where each unit represents one Mg^{2+} ion and two Cl^- ions. Thus,

$$1.00 \text{ mol } MgCl_2 = 6.02 \times 10^{23} \text{ } MgCl_2 \text{ units}$$

or

$$1.00 \text{ mol } MgCl_2 = 6.02 \times 10^{23} \text{ } Mg^{2+} \text{ ions} + 1.20 \times 10^{24} \text{ } Cl^- \text{ ions}$$

Note that the number of Cl^- ions is simply twice Avogadro's number.

▶ LEARNING CHECK 4.9 Determine the same quantities that were determined in Example 4.9, but use the molecular compound hydrogen sulfide, H_2S, and the ionic compound calcium oxide, CaO.

4.6 Covalent Bonding

Learning Objective

6. Draw correct Lewis structures for covalent molecules.

In Example 4.5, we found that carbon, a nonmetal, would have to gain four electrons in order to form ionic bonds. We concluded that carbon does not generally form ionic bonds. Yet carbon is known to form many compounds with other elements. Also, electron transfers would not be expected to take place between two atoms of the same element because such an exchange would not change the electronic configuration of the atoms involved. Yet molecules of elements containing two atoms, such as chlorine (Cl_2), oxygen (O_2), and nitrogen (N_2), are known to exist and, in fact, represent the stable form in which these elements occur in nature. What is the nature of the bonding in these molecules?

Again, G. N. Lewis provided an answer by suggesting that the valence-shell electrons of the atoms in such molecules are shared in a way that satisfies the octet rule for each of the atoms. This process is symbolized below for fluorine, (F_2), using Lewis structures:

$$:\ddot{F}\cdot + \cdot\ddot{F}: \longrightarrow :\ddot{F}:\ddot{F}:$$

shared pair (counted in octet of each atom)

Sometimes the shared electron pairs are shown as straight lines, and sometimes the nonshared pairs are not shown, as illustrated in Example 4.10.

▶ Example 4.10

Represent the following reactions using Lewis structures:

a. $Cl + Cl \rightarrow Cl_2$ **b.** $H + H \rightarrow H_2$

Solution

a. Each chlorine (Cl) atom has seven valence-shell electrons. Because one electron from each atom is shared, the octet rule is satisfied for each atom

$$:\ddot{C}l\cdot + \cdot\ddot{C}l: \longrightarrow :\ddot{C}l:\ddot{C}l:$$

shared pair

The structure of Cl_2 can also be represented as

$$:\ddot{C}l-\ddot{C}l: \quad \text{or} \quad Cl-Cl$$

b. Each hydrogen (H) atom has one valence-shell electron. By sharing the two electrons, each H atom achieves the helium (He) structure:

$$H\cdot + \cdot H \rightarrow H:H \quad \text{or} \quad H-H$$

▶ **LEARNING CHECK 4.10** Represent the following reactions using Lewis structures:

a. $N + N \rightarrow N_2$ (more than two electrons will be shared) **b.** $Br + Br \rightarrow Br_2$

To understand the origin of the attractive force between atoms that results from electron sharing, consider the H_2 molecule and the concept of atomic orbital overlap. Suppose two H atoms are moving toward each other. Each atom has a single electron in a spherical $1s$ orbital. While the atoms are separated, the orbitals are independent of each other; but as the atoms get closer together, the orbitals overlap and blend to create an orbital common to both atoms called a *molecular orbital*. The two shared electrons then move throughout the overlap region but have a high probability of being found somewhere between the two

Water: One of Earth's Special Compounds

An adequate supply of clean water is essential to our health and well-being. We can live without food for many days, but life would end in only a few days without water. Our circulatory system is an aqueous stream that distributes an amazing variety of substances throughout the body. Our cells are filled with water solutions in which the chemical reactions of life take place. Without water and its unique properties, life would not be possible on Earth.

Three-fourths of Earth's surface is covered with water, which gives the planet a blue color when it is viewed from space. The oceans represent the world's largest liquid solution. Water participates in most of the chemical reactions that occur in nature.

Most water used for human consumption comes from reservoirs, lakes, rivers, and wells. Much of this water is used and reused by numerous cities as it travels downstream. Such reused water may become seriously polluted with waste from previous users and with pathogenic microorganisms. As a safety precaution, most of the water we use undergoes chemical and physical treatment to purify it. This treatment process includes settling, whereby specific materials are added to bring down suspended solids. This is followed by filtration through sand and gravel to remove still more suspended matter. The filtered water may then be aerated by spraying it into the air. This part of the treatment process removes some odors and improves the taste of the water. Charcoal filtration, a treatment process that is gaining in use, also removes odors along with colored materials. In a final step, chlorine or another disinfectant is added to kill any remaining bacteria.

© Andrey Kekyalyaynen/Shutterstock.com

The treatment of water before use is an important safety precaution.

nuclei. As a result, both of the positive nuclei are attracted toward the negative pair of electrons and hence toward each other. This process, represented in ❯ Figure 4.4, produces a net attractive force between the nuclei. This attractive force is the **covalent bond** that holds the atoms together. Because forces cannot be seen, we represent only the presence of the shared electron pair between the atoms (by a pair of dots or a line) and remember that an attractive force is also there.

covalent bond The attractive force that results between two atoms that are both attracted to a shared pair of electrons.

Figure 4.4 Orbital overlap during covalent bond formation.

A: Separated atoms
B: Orbitals touch
C: Orbitals overlap; a covalent bond is formed

Covalent bonding between like atoms has been described, but it also occurs between unlike atoms. Examples of both types are given in ❯ Table 4.3. Lewis structures, like those in Table 4.3, are most easily drawn by using a systematic approach such as the one represented by the following steps:

1. Use the molecular formula to determine how many atoms of each kind are in the molecule.
2. Use the given connecting pattern of the atoms to draw an initial structure for the molecule, with the atoms arranged properly.
3. Determine the total number of valence-shell electrons contained in the atoms of the molecule.

TABLE 4.3 Examples of Covalent Bonding

Molecule	Atomic Lewis structure	Sharing pattern	Molecular Lewis structure
Nitrogen gas (N_2)	$\cdot\ddot{N}\cdot$ $(1s^2 2s^2 2p^3)$	:N⇌N:	:N ::: N:
Carbon dioxide (CO_2) (each O is bonded to the C)	$\cdot\dot{C}\cdot$ $(1s^2 2s^2 2p^2)$ $:\ddot{O}\cdot$ $(1s^2 2s^2 2p^4)$	:O C O:	:O :: C :: O:
Formaldehyde (H_2CO) (each H and the O are bonded to the C)	$\cdot\dot{C}\cdot$ $(1s^2 2s^2 2p^2)$ $:\ddot{O}\cdot$ $(1s^2 2s^2 2p^4)$ $H\cdot$ $(1s^1)$	H· C O: H·	H C :: O: H
Methane (CH_4) (each H is bonded to the C)	$\cdot\dot{C}\cdot$ $(1s^2 2s^2 2p^2)$ $H\cdot$ $(1s^1)$	H C H H H	H:C:H H H
Ammonia (NH_3) (each H is bonded to the N)	$\cdot\ddot{N}\cdot$ $(1s^2 2s^2 2p^3)$ $H\cdot$ $(1s^1)$	H N H H	H:N:H H
Water (H_2O) (each H is bonded to the O)	$:\ddot{O}\cdot$ $(1s^2 2s^2 2p^4)$ $H\cdot$ $(1s^1)$	:O H H	:O:H H
Oxygen diflouride (OF_2) (each F is bonded to the O)	$:\ddot{O}\cdot$ $(1s^2 2s^2 2p^4)$ $:\dot{F}:$ $(1s^2 2s^2 2p^5)$	:O F: :F:	:O:F: :F:

4. Put one pair of electrons between each bonded pair of atoms in the initial structure drawn in Step 2. Subtract the number of electrons used in this step from the total number determined in Step 3. Use the remaining electrons to complete the octets of all atoms in the structure, beginning with the atoms that are present in greatest number in the molecule. Remember, hydrogen atoms require only one pair to achieve the electronic configuration of helium.

5. If all octets cannot be satisfied with the available electrons, move nonbonding pairs (those that are not between bonded atoms) to positions between bonded atoms to complete octets. This will create **double** or **triple bonds** between some atoms.

double and triple bonds The bonds resulting from the sharing of two and three pairs of electrons, respectively.

▶ Example 4.11

Draw Lewis structures for the following molecules:

a. NH_3 **b.** SO_3 **c.** C_2H_2

Solution

a. Step 1. The formula indicates that the molecule contains 1 nitrogen (N) atom and 3 hydrogen (H) atoms.

Step 2. The connecting pattern will have to be given to you in some form. Table 4.3 shows that each H atom is connected to the N atom; thus, we draw

$$\text{H N H}$$
$$\text{H}$$

Step 3. Nitrogen is in group VA(15) of the periodic table and so has 5 valence electrons; hydrogen is in group IA(1) and has 1 valence electron. The total is 8 (5 from one N atom and 3 from the three H atoms).

Step 4. We put one pair of electrons between each H atom and the N atom in the initial structure drawn in Step 2:

$$\text{H:N:H}$$
$$\ddot{\text{H}}$$

This required 6 of the 8 available electrons. The remaining pair is used to complete the octet of nitrogen. Remember, hydrogen achieves the noble gas configuration of helium with only 2 electrons:

$$\text{H:}\ddot{\text{N}}\text{:H} \qquad \text{or} \qquad \text{H} - \ddot{\text{N}} - \text{H}$$
$$\ddot{\text{H}} \qquad\qquad\qquad\qquad\quad |$$
$$\qquad\qquad\qquad\qquad\qquad\quad \text{H}$$

Step 5. All octets are satisfied by Step 4, so nothing more needs to be done.

b. Step 1. The formula indicates that 1 sulfur (S) and 3 oxygen (O) atoms are present in a molecule.

Step 2. Each O atom is bonded only to the S atom; thus, we draw

$$\text{O S O}$$
$$\text{O}$$

Step 3. Sulfur and oxygen are both in group VIA(16), and so each atom has 6 valence electrons. The total is 24 (6 from the one S atom and 18 from the three O atoms).

Step 4. We put one pair of electrons between each O atom and the S atom:

$$\text{O:S:O}$$
$$\ddot{\text{O}}$$

This required 6 of the 24 available electrons. The remaining 18 are used to complete the octets, beginning with the O atoms:

$$:\ddot{\text{O}}:\text{S}:\ddot{\text{O}}:$$
$$:\ddot{\text{O}}:$$

Step 5. We see that the octet of sulfur is not completed, even though all available electrons have been used. If one nonbonding pair of any one of the three O atoms is moved to a bonding position between the oxygen and sulfur, it will help satisfy the octet of both atoms. The final Lewis structure is given below. Note that it contains a double bond between one of the oxygens and the sulfur:

$$:\ddot{\text{O}}:\text{S}::\ddot{\text{O}}: \qquad \text{or} \qquad :\ddot{\text{O}} - \text{S} = \ddot{\text{O}}:$$
$$:\ddot{\text{O}}: \qquad\qquad\qquad\qquad\quad | $$
$$\qquad\qquad\qquad\qquad\qquad\quad :\ddot{\text{O}}:$$

If a nonbonding pair of electrons from either of the other two oxygens is used, the following structures result. These are just as acceptable as the preceding structures:

$$:\text{O} = \text{S} - \ddot{\text{O}}: \qquad\qquad :\ddot{\text{O}} - \text{S} - \ddot{\text{O}}:$$
$$| \qquad\qquad\qquad\qquad\qquad ||$$
$$:\ddot{\text{O}}: \qquad\qquad\qquad\qquad \text{O}:$$

c. Step 1. The formula indicates 2 carbon (C) atoms and 2 hydrogen (H) atoms per C_2H_2 molecule.

Step 2. The C atoms are bonded to each other, and 1 H atom is bonded to each C atom.

$$H\ C\ C\ H$$

Step 3. Carbon is in group IVA(14) and has 4 valence electrons; hydrogen is in group IA(1) and has 1 valence electron. The total electrons available is 10 (8 from the two C atoms and 2 from the two H atoms).

Step 4. We put one pair of electrons between the two C atoms and between each C atom and H atom.

$$H:C:C:H$$

This required 6 of the available 10 electrons. The remaining 4 electrons are used to complete the C octets (remember, hydrogen needs only 2 electrons):

$$H:C:\overset{..}{\underset{..}{C}}:H$$

Step 5. All electrons are used in Step 4, but the octet of 1 C atom is still incomplete. It needs two more pairs. If both nonbonding pairs on the second C atom were shared with the first C atom, both carbons would have complete octets. The result is

$$H:C:::C:H \qquad \text{or} \qquad H-C\equiv C-H$$

This molecule contains a triple bond (three shared pairs) between the C atoms.

▶ **LEARNING CHECK 4.11** Draw Lewis structures for the following molecules:

a. CH_4 (each H atom is bonded to the C atom)
b. H_2CO (the O atom and two H atoms are each bonded to the C atom)
c. HNO_3 (the O atoms are each bonded to the N atom, and the H atom is bonded to one of the O atoms)

4.7 Polyatomic Ions

Learning Objective

7. Draw correct Lewis structures for polyatomic ions.

polyatomic ions Covalently bonded groups of atoms that carry a net electrical charge.

An interesting combination of ionic and covalent bonding is found in compounds that contain **polyatomic ions.** These ions are covalently bonded groups of atoms that carry a net electrical charge. With the exception of the ammonium ion, NH_4^+, the common poly-atomic ions are negatively charged.

Lewis structures can be drawn for polyatomic ions with just a slight modification in the steps given earlier for covalently bonded molecules. In Step 3, the total number of electrons available is obtained by first determining the total number of valence-shell electrons contained in the atoms of the ion. To this number are added electrons representing the number required to give the negative charge to the ion.

For example, in the SO_4^{2-} ion, the total number of valence-shell electrons is 30, with 6 coming from the sulfur atom and 6 from each of the four oxygen atoms. To this number we add 2 because two additional electrons are required to give the group of neutral atoms the charge of 2− found on the ion. This gives 32 total available electrons.

The only exception to this procedure for the common polyatomic ions is for the positively charged ammonium ion, NH_4^+. In this case, the number of electrons available is the total number of valence electrons minus 1, because one electron would have to be removed from the neutral group of atoms to produce the + charge on the ion.

► Example 4.12

Draw Lewis structures for the following polyatomic ions. The connecting patterns of the atoms to each other are indicated.

a. SO_4^{2-} (each O atom is bonded to the S atom)
b. NO_3^- (each O atom is bonded to the N atom)
c. $H_2PO_4^-$ (each O atom is bonded to the P atom, and each H atom is bonded to an O atom)

Solution

a. The only difference between drawing Lewis structures for molecules and polyatomic ions comes in Step 3, where the total number of valence-shell electrons is determined.

Step 1. The formula indicates the ion contains one sulfur (S) atom and four oxygen (O) atoms.

Step 2. The given bonding relationships lead to the following initial structure:

$$\begin{matrix} & O & \\ O & S & O \\ & O & \end{matrix}$$

Step 3. Both the S and O atoms are in group VIA(16), so each atom contributes 6 valence electrons. The total number of valence-shell electrons from the atoms is therefore $5 \times 6 = 30$. However, the ion has a 2− charge. This charge comes from the presence of 2 electrons in the ion in addition to the electrons from the constituent atoms. These two additional electrons must be included in the total valence-shell electrons. Thus, the total number of electrons is $30 + 2 = 32$.

Step 4. The following is obtained when the 32 electrons are distributed among the atoms of the initial structure of Step 2:

$$\begin{matrix} & :\overset{..}{O}: & \\ :\overset{..}{O}:\overset{..}{\underset{..}{S}}:\overset{..}{O}: \\ & :\overset{..}{O}: & \end{matrix}$$

Step 5. All octets are satisfied by Step 4. However, it is conventional to enclose Lewis structures of polyatomic ions in brackets and to indicate the net charge on the ion. Thus, the Lewis structures are

$$\left[\begin{matrix} & :\overset{..}{O}: & \\ :\overset{..}{O}:\overset{..}{\underset{..}{S}}:\overset{..}{O}: \\ & :\overset{..}{O}: & \end{matrix}\right]^{2-} \quad \text{or} \quad \left[\begin{matrix} & O & \\ & | & \\ O & -S- & O \\ & | & \\ & O & \end{matrix}\right]^{2-}$$

where the second structure does not show nonbonding (unshared) electron pairs, and the bonding pairs are represented by lines.

b. Step 1. Three oxygen (O) atoms and one nitrogen (N) atom are found in the ion.

Step 2.

$$\begin{matrix} & O & \\ O & N & O \end{matrix}$$

Step 3. Electrons from oxygen = $3 \times 6 = 18$.
Electrons from nitrogen = $1 \times 5 = 5$.
One electron comes from the ionic charge = 1.
Total electrons = $18 + 5 + 1 = 24$.

Step 4.

$$\begin{matrix} & :\overset{..}{O}: & \\ :\overset{..}{O}:\overset{..}{\underset{..}{N}}:\overset{..}{O}: \end{matrix}$$

Step 5. The octet of nitrogen is not satisfied by Step 4, so an unshared pair of electrons on an O atom must be shared with the N atom. This will form a double bond in the ion. The resulting Lewis structures are

$$\left[\begin{array}{c} :\ddot{O}: \\ :\ddot{O}:N::\ddot{O}: \end{array} \right]^{-} \qquad \text{or} \qquad \left[\begin{array}{c} O \\ | \\ O-N=O \end{array} \right]^{-}$$

c. Step 1. Two hydrogen (H) atoms, one phosphorus (P) atom, and four oxygen (O) atoms are found in the ion.

Step 2.

$$\begin{array}{c} O \\ O\ P\ O\ H \\ O \\ H \end{array}$$

Step 3. Electrons from hydrogen = $2 \times 1 = 2$.
Electrons from oxygen = $4 \times 6 = 24$.
Electrons from phosphorus = $1 \times 5 = 5$.
Electron from ionic charge = 1.
Total electrons = $2 + 24 + 5 + 1 = 32$.

Step 4.

$$\begin{array}{c} :\ddot{O}: \\ :\ddot{O}:\ddot{P}:\ddot{O}:H \\ :\ddot{O}: \\ H \end{array}$$

Step 5. All octets are satisfied by Step 4 (remember, H atoms are satisfied by a single pair of electrons). The resulting Lewis structures are

$$\left[\begin{array}{c} :\ddot{O}: \\ :\ddot{O}:\ddot{P}:\ddot{O}:H \\ :\ddot{O}: \\ H \end{array} \right]^{-} \qquad \text{or} \qquad \left[\begin{array}{c} O \\ | \\ O-P-O-H \\ | \\ O \\ | \\ H \end{array} \right]^{-}$$

▶ **LEARNING CHECK 4.12** Draw Lewis structures for the following polyatomic ions:

a. PO_4^{3-} (each O atom is bonded to the P atom)
b. SO_3^{2-} (each O atom is bonded to the S atom)
c. NH_4^+ (each H atom is bonded to the N atom)

4.8 Shapes of Molecules and Polyatomic Ions

Learning Objective

8. Use VSEPR theory to predict the shapes of molecules and polyatomic ions.

Most molecules and polyatomic ions do not have flat, two-dimensional shapes like those implied by the molecular Lewis structures of Table 4.3. In fact, the atoms of most molecules and polyatomic ions form distinct three-dimensional shapes. Being able to predict the shape is important because the shape contributes to the properties of the molecule or ion. This can be done quite readily for molecules composed of representative elements.

To predict molecular or ionic shapes, first draw Lewis structures for the molecules or ions using the methods discussed in Sections 4.6 and 4.7. Once you have drawn the Lewis structure

for a molecule or ion, you can predict its shape by applying a simple theory to the structure. The theory is called the *valence-shell electron-pair repulsion theory*, or **VSEPR theory** (sometimes pronounced "vesper" theory). According to VSEPR theory, electron pairs in the valence shell of an atom are repelled by other electron pairs and get as far away from one another as possible. Any atom in a molecule or ion that is bonded to two or more other atoms is called a *central atom*. When the VSEPR theory is applied to the valence-shell electrons of central atoms, the shape of the molecule or ion containing the atoms can be predicted. Two rules are followed:

VSEPR theory A theory based on the mutual repulsion of electron pairs. It is used to predict molecular shapes.

1. All valence-shell electron pairs around the central atom are counted equally, regardless of whether they are bonding or nonbonding pairs.
2. Double or triple bonds between atoms are treated like a single pair of electrons when predicting shapes.

The electron pairs around a central atom will become oriented in space to get as far away from one another as possible. Thus, two pairs will be oriented with one pair on each opposite side of the central atom. Three pairs will form a triangle around the central atom, and four pairs will be located at the corners of a regular tetrahedron with the central atom in the center (see ▶ Figure 4.5 and ▶ Figure 4.6). The VSEPR theory can be used to predict shapes of molecules and ions with five or more pairs on the central atom, but we will not go beyond four pairs in this book.

$$\colon E \colon \qquad E \qquad E$$

Two electron pairs Three electron pairs Four electron pairs

Figure 4.5 Arrangements of electron pairs around a central atom (E).

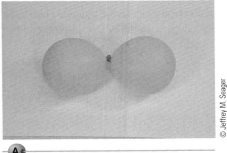

A ⟨ Two balloons: linear

B ⟨ Three balloons; triangular

C ⟨ Four balloons; tetrahedral

© Jeffrey M. Seager

Figure 4.6 When balloons of the same size and shape are tied together, they will assume positions like those taken by pairs of valence electrons around a central atom. Where would the central atom be located in these balloon models?

▶ Example 4.13

Draw Lewis structures for the following molecules, apply the VSEPR theory, and predict the shape of each molecule:

a. CO_2 (each O atom is bonded to the C atom)
b. C_2Cl_4 (the C atoms are bonded together, and two Cl atoms are bonded to each C atom)
c. NH_3 (each H atom is bonded to the N atom)
d. H_2O (each H atom is bonded to the O atom)

Solution

a. The Lewis structure is $:\ddot{O}=C=\ddot{O}:$. The central atom is carbon (C) and it has two pairs of electrons in the valence shell surrounding it (remember, each double bond is treated like a single pair of electrons in the VSEPR theory). The two pairs will be located on opposite sides of the C atom, so the molecule has the shape drawn above with the O, C, and O atoms in a line; it is a linear molecule.

b. The Lewis structure is

Both C atoms are central atoms in this molecule, and each one has three electron pairs in the valence shell (again, the double bond is treated as only one pair). The three pairs around each C atom will be arranged in the shape of a triangle:

Thus, the molecule has the shape of two flat triangles in the same plane connected together at one point:

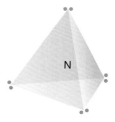

c. The Lewis structure is

$$H - \ddot{N} - H$$
$$\underset{H}{|}$$

The central atom is nitrogen (N), and it has four electron pairs in the valence shell. The four pairs will be located at the corners of a tetrahedron with the N atom in the middle:

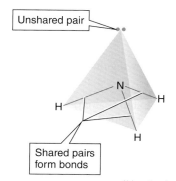

The shape of the molecule is determined only by the positions of the atoms, not by the position of the unshared pair of electrons. Thus, the NH_3 molecule has the shape of a pyramid with a triangular base. The N atom is at the peak of the pyramid, and an H atom is at each corner of the base:

d. The Lewis structure is H $:\overset{..}{O}:$ H. The central atom is oxygen (O), and it is seen to have four pairs of electrons in its valence shell. The four pairs will be located at the corners of a tetrahedron with the O atom in the middle:

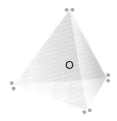

Once again, the shape of the molecule is determined by the locations of the atoms. Thus, H_2O is seen as having a bent or angular shape:

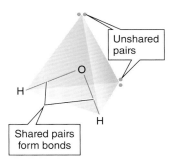

▶ **LEARNING CHECK 4.13** Predict the shapes of the following molecules by applying the VSEPR theory:

a. BF_3 (the Lewis structure is

$$:\overset{..}{\underset{..}{F}}:$$
$$B:\overset{..}{\underset{..}{F}}:$$
$$:\overset{..}{\underset{..}{F}}:$$

for this molecule, which does not obey the octet rule).

b. CCl_4 (each Cl atom is bonded to the C atom)
c. SO_2 (each O atom is bonded to the S atom)
d. CS_2 (each S atom is bonded to the C atom)

▶ **Example 4.14**

Use the VSEPR theory to predict the shapes of the following polyatomic ions. The Lewis structures were drawn in Example 4.12.

a. SO_4^{2-}
b. NO_3^-

Solution

a. The Lewis structure from Example 4.12 is

$$\left[\begin{array}{c} :\overset{..}{\underset{..}{O}}: \\ :\overset{..}{\underset{..}{O}}:\overset{..}{\underset{..}{S}}:\overset{..}{\underset{..}{O}}: \\ :\overset{..}{\underset{..}{O}}: \end{array} \right]^{2-}$$

We see that sulfur is the central atom, and it has four electron pairs around it. The four pairs will be located at the corners of a tetrahedron with the S in the middle.

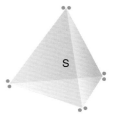

The shape of the ion is determined by the location of the oxygen atoms. Thus, the ion has a tetrahedral shape:

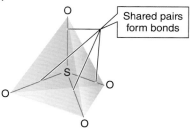

Shared pairs form bonds

b. The Lewis structure from Example 4.12 is

$$\left[\begin{array}{c} :\ddot{O}: \\ :\ddot{O}:\ddot{N}::\ddot{O}: \end{array} \right]^{-}$$

We see that nitrogen is the central atom, and it has three electron pairs around it. Remember, the double bond formed by the two shared electron pairs between the nitrogen and one of the oxygens counts as only one pair in the VSEPR theory. The three pairs will form a triangle around the N.

An oxygen is located at each corner of the triangle, so the ion has a flat triangular shape:

Shared pairs form bonds

▶ **LEARNING CHECK 4.14** Use the VSEPR theory to predict the shapes of the following polyatomic ions. The Lewis structures were drawn in Learning Check 4.12.

a. PO_4^{3-} **b.** SO_3^{2-} **c.** NH_4^{+}

4.9 The Polarity of Covalent Molecules

Learning Objective

9. Use electronegativities to classify covalent bonds of molecules, and determine whether covalent molecules are polar or nonpolar.

Molecules of chlorine (Cl—Cl) and hydrogen chloride (H—Cl) have a number of similarities. For example, they contain two atoms each and are therefore diatomic

Versatile Zinc Oxide

While the jury is still out on the usefulness of zinc compounds in treating the symptoms of the common cold, the usefulness of zinc oxide as a topical astringent, antiseptic, and skin protectant is well established. Zinc oxide, with the simple formula ZnO, is a coarse white or grayish powder that is insoluble in water or in alcohol. Because of this insolubility, it is often blended with other ingredients to produce a suspension of the solid in such forms as lotions, creams, or salves. The solid compound in a finely divided form is sometimes added to products such as baby powders.

In these forms, zinc oxide is used topically on the skin as a sunscreen to block harmful ultraviolet rays, and as a shield from various chemical irritants. In addition, products containing the compound are used to relieve a number of common skin conditions, including diaper rash; poison ivy, oak, and sumac rashes; eczema; external hemorrhoids; and insect bites. In these applications its antiseptic property helps prevent infections, and it is thought to promote healing by attracting protein to the affected areas of the skin, thereby encouraging new tissue growth. In these topical applications, the insolubility and consistency of zinc oxide prevent it from being absorbed into the skin. As a result, side effects or allergic reactions to the compound are rare, even with long-term use.

In addition to its valuable medical uses, this versatile compound is also found in a wide variety of commercial applications. It functions as a pigment and reinforcing agent in some rubber products; as a pigment and mold-growth inhibitor in paints; as a pigment in ceramics, floor tile, and glass; as a thickener in cosmetics; as a feed additive for cattle; and as a dietary supplement for humans.

Zinc oxide in the form of an ointment is convenient and easy to use.

© Michael C. Slabaugh

molecules, and the atoms are held together by a single covalent bond. Some differences also exist, the most obvious being the homoatomic nature of the chlorine molecule (an element) and the heteroatomic nature of the hydrogen chloride molecule (a compound). This difference influences the distribution of the shared electrons in the two molecules.

An electron pair shared by two identical atoms is attracted equally to each of the atoms, and the probability of finding the electrons close to an atom is equal for the two atoms. Thus, on average, the electrons spend exactly the same amount of time associated with each atom. Covalent bonds of this type are called **nonpolar covalent bonds.**

Different atoms generally have different tendencies to attract the shared electrons of a covalent bond. A measurement of this tendency is called **electronegativity.** The electronegativity of the elements is a property that follows trends in the periodic table. It increases from left to right across a period and decreases from top to bottom of a group. These trends are shown in ▶ Table 4.4, which contains electronegativity values for the common representative elements. As a result of electronegativity differences, the bonding electrons shared by two different atoms are shared unequally. The electrons spend more of their time near the atom with the higher electronegativity. The resulting shift in average location of bonding electrons is called **bond polarization** and produces a **polar covalent bond.**

As a result of the unequal electron sharing, the more electronegative atom acquires a partial negative charge ($\delta-$), and the less electronegative atom has a partial positive charge ($\delta+$). The molecule as a whole has no net charge, just an uneven charge distribution.

nonpolar covalent bond A covalent bond in which the bonding pair of electrons is shared equally by the bonded atoms.

electronegativity The tendency of an atom to attract shared electrons of a covalent bond.

bond polarization A result of shared electrons being attracted to the more electronegative atom of a bonded pair of atoms.

polar covalent bond A covalent bond that shows bond polarization; that is, the bonding electrons are shared unequally.

TABLE 4.4 Electronegativities for the Common Representative Elements

Increasing electronegativity →

		H 2.1				
Li 1.0	Be 1.5	B 2.0	C 2.5	N 3.0	O 3.5	F 4.0
Na 0.9	Mg 1.2	Al 1.5	Si 1.8	P 2.1	S 2.5	Cl 3.0
K 0.8	Ca 1.0	Ga 1.6	Ge 1.8	As 2.0	Se 2.4	Br 2.8
Rb 0.8	Sr 1.0	In 1.7	Sn 1.8	Sb 1.9	Te 2.1	I 2.5
Cs 0.7	Ba 0.9					

Decreasing electronegativity ↓

▶ Example 4.15

Use only the periodic table to determine the following for the diatomic covalent molecules listed below: (1) the more electronegative element, (2) the direction of bond polarization, and (3) the charge distribution resulting from the polarization.

a. I—Cl **b.** Br—Br **c.** C≡O

Solution

a. Both chlorine (Cl) and iodine (I) belong to group VIIA(17); chlorine is higher in the group and therefore is the more electronegative. The bond polarization (shift in average bonding-electron location) will be toward chlorine, as indicated by the arrow shown below the bond. The result is a partial negative charge on Cl and a partial positive charge on I:

$$\overset{\delta+}{I}\underset{\rightarrow}{—}\overset{\delta-}{Cl}$$

b. Since both bromine (Br) atoms have the same electronegativity, no bond polarization or unequal charge distribution results. The molecule is nonpolar covalent and is represented as Br—Br.

c. Oxygen (O) and carbon (C) both belong to the second period. Oxygen, being located farther to the right in the period, is the more electronegative. Thus, the molecule is represented as

$$\overset{\delta+}{C}\underset{\rightarrow}{≡}\overset{\delta-}{O}$$

▶ **LEARNING CHECK 4.15** Use only the periodic table and show the direction of any bond polarization and resulting charge distribution in the following molecules:

a. N≡N **b.** I—Br **c.** H—Br

The extent of bond polarization depends on electronegativity differences between the bonded atoms and forms one basis for a classification of bonds. When the electronegativity difference (ΔEN) between the bonded atoms is 0.0, the bond is classified as nonpolar

covalent (the electrons are shared equally). When ΔEN is 2.1 or greater, the bond is classified as ionic (the electrons are transferred). When ΔEN is between 0.0 and 2.1, the bond is classified as polar covalent (the electrons are unequally shared, and the bond is polarized). Note, however, that the change from purely covalent to completely ionic compounds is gradual and continuous as ΔEN values change. Thus, a bond between hydrogen (H) and boron (B) ($\Delta EN = 0.1$) is classified as polar, but the electron sharing is only slightly unequal and the bond is only slightly polar (see ▶ Figure 4.7). As the values in Table 4.4 indicate, compounds formed by a reaction of a metal with a nonmetal are generally ionic, while those between nonmetals are either nonpolar or polar covalent.

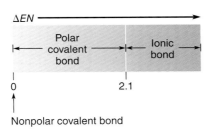

Figure 4.7 The darker the shading, the larger ΔEN is for the bonded atoms. Larger ΔEN values correspond to greater inequality in the sharing of the bonding electrons.

▶ Example 4.16

Using Table 4.4, classify the bonds in the following compounds as nonpolar covalent, ionic, or polar covalent:

a. ClF **b.** MgO **c.** PI$_3$

Solution

a. The electronegativities of chlorine (Cl) and fluorine (F) are 3.0 and 4.0, respectively. Obtain the ΔEN value by subtracting the smaller from the larger, regardless of the order of the elements in the formula. Thus,

$$\Delta EN = 4.0 - 3.0 = 1.0$$

and the bond is polar covalent.

b. Similarly,

$$\Delta EN = 3.5 - 1.2 = 2.3$$

and the bond is ionic.

c. The ΔEN is determined for each phosphorus–iodine bond:

$$\Delta EN = 2.5 - 2.1 = 0.4$$

Thus, each bond is classified as polar covalent.

▶ **LEARNING CHECK 4.16** Using Table 4.4, classify the bonds in the following compounds as nonpolar covalent, ionic, or polar covalent:

a. KF **b.** NO **c.** AlN **d.** K$_2$O

You can now predict the polarity of bonds within molecules, but it is also important to be able to predict the polar nature of the molecules themselves. The terms *polar* and *nonpolar*, when used to describe molecules, indicate their electrical charge symmetry (see ▶ Figure 4.8). In **polar molecules** (often called dipoles), the charge distribution resulting from bond polarizations is nonsymmetric. In **nonpolar molecules,** any charges caused by bond polarization are symmetrically distributed through the molecule. ▶ Table 4.5 illustrates polar and nonpolar molecules. The molecular shapes were determined by using the VSEPR theory.

polar molecule A molecule that contains polarized bonds and in which the resulting charges are distributed nonsymmetrically throughout the molecule.

nonpolar molecule A molecule that contains no polarized bonds, or a molecule containing polarized bonds in which the resulting charges are distributed symmetrically throughout the molecule.

Figure 4.8 Polar and nonpolar molecules are affected differently by electrical charges. The ΔEN between C and Cl is 0.5. Propose a reason why CCl_4 molecules are nonpolar.

A A stream of polar water molecules is attracted by a charged balloon.

© Spencer L. Seager

B A stream of nonpolar carbon tetrachloride (CCl_4) molecules is not affected by a charged balloon.

© Spencer L. Seager

TABLE 4.5 The Polarity of Molecules

Molecular formula	Geometric structure	Bond polarization and molecular charge distribution	Geometry of charge distribution	Classification of charge distribution	Classification of molecule
H_2	H — H	H — H	No charges	No charges	Nonpolar
HCl	H — Cl	$\overset{\delta+}{H} \Rightarrow \overset{\delta-}{Cl}$	+ −	Nonsymmetric	Polar
CO_2	O = C = O	$\overset{\delta-}{O} \Leftleftarrows \overset{\delta2+}{C} \Rrightarrow \overset{\delta-}{O}$	− 2+ −	Symmetric	Nonpolar
BF_3	F, B, F, F	$\overset{\delta-}{F}$... $\overset{\delta3+}{B}$... $\overset{\delta-}{F}$, $\overset{\delta-}{F}$	−, 3+, − −	Symmetric	Nonpolar
N_2O	N ≡ N — O	$N \equiv \overset{\delta+}{N} \Rightarrow \overset{\delta-}{O}$	+ −	Nonsymmetric	Polar
H_2O	H — O, H	$\overset{\delta+}{H} \Rightarrow \overset{\delta2-}{O}$, $\overset{\delta+}{H}$	+ 2− +	Nonsymmetric	Polar

4.10 More about Naming Compounds

Learning Objective

10. Write correct formulas for ionic compounds containing representative metals and polyatomic ions, and correctly name binary covalent compounds and compounds containing polyatomic ions.

In Section 4.4, we discussed the rules for naming binary ionic compounds. In this section, we expand the rules to include the naming of binary covalent compounds and ionic compounds that contain polyatomic ions.

It is apparent from Table 4.4 that covalent bonds (including polar covalent) form most often between representative elements classified as nonmetals. It is not possible to predict formulas for these compounds in a simple way, as was done for ionic compounds in Section 4.4. However, simple rules do exist for naming binary covalent compounds on the basis of their formulas. The rules are similar to those used to name binary ionic compounds: (1) Give the name of the less electronegative element first (the element given first in the formula), (2) give the stem of the name of the more electronegative element next and add the suffix -*ide*, and (3) indicate the number of each type of atom in the molecule by means of the Greek prefixes listed in ▶ Table 4.6.

▶ Example 4.17

Name the following binary covalent compounds:

a. CO_2 **b.** CO **c.** NO_2 **d.** N_2O_5 **e.** CS_2

Solution

a. The elements are carbon (C) and oxygen (O), and carbon is the less electronegative. Because the stem of oxygen is *ox-*, the two portions of the name will be carbon and oxide. Only one C atom is found in the molecule, but the prefix *mono-* is not used when it appears at the beginning of a name. The two O atoms in the molecule are indicated by the prefix *di-*. The name therefore is carbon dioxide.

b. Similarly, we arrive at the name carbon monoxide for CO.

c. NO_2 is assigned the name nitrogen dioxide.

d. N_2O_5 is assigned the name dinitrogen pentoxide. Note: The a is dropped from the *penta-* prefix for oxygen. This is done to avoid the pronunciation problem created by having two vowels next to each other in a name (dinitrogen pentaoxide).

e. CS_2 is named carbon disulfide.

▶ LEARNING CHECK 4.17 Name the following binary covalent compounds:

a. SO_3 b. BF_3 c. S_2O_7 d. CCl_4

The formulas and names of some common polyatomic ions are given in ▶ Table 4.7. From this information, the formulas and names for compounds containing polyatomic ions can be written. The rules are essentially the same as those used earlier for binary ionic compounds. In the formulas, the metal (or ammonium ion) is written first, the positive and

TABLE 4.6 Greek Numerical Prefixes

Number	Prefix
1	*mono-*
2	*di-*
3	*tri-*
4	*tetra-*
5	*penta-*
6	*hexa-*
7	*hepta-*
8	*octa-*
9	*nona-*
10	*deca-*

TABLE 4.7 Some Common Polyatomic Ions

Very Common		Common	
NH_4^+	ammonium	CrO_4^{2-}	chromate
$C_2H_3O_2^-$	acetate	$Cr_2O_7^{2-}$	dichromate
CO_3^{2-}	carbonate	NO_2^-	nitrite
ClO_3^-	chlorate	MnO_4^-	permanganate
CN^-	cyanide	SO_3^{2-}	sulfite
HCO_3^-	hydrogen carbonate (bicarbonate)	ClO^-	hypochlorite
OH^-	hydroxide	HPO_4^{2-}	hydrogen phosphate
NO_3^-	nitrate	$H_2PO_4^-$	dihydrogen phosphate
PO_4^{3-}	phosphate	HSO_4^-	hydrogen sulfate (bisulfate)
SO_4^{2-}	sulfate	HSO_3^-	hydrogen sulfite (bisulfite)

Help with Polar and Nonpolar Molecules

When concepts are closely related, it is very easy to become confused. In this chapter, the terms *polar* and *nonpolar* are used to describe both bonds and molecules. What is the correct way to apply the terms?

It may be helpful to remember the numbers 3 and 2: three types of bonds, but only two types of molecules. The bonds are nonpolar covalent ($\Delta EN = 0$), polar covalent ($\Delta EN = 0.1$–2.0), and ionic ($\Delta EN = 2.1$ or greater). Remember that compounds bonded by ionic bonds do not form molecules, so there are only two types of molecules: nonpolar and polar.

The polarity of a molecule depends on two factors: (1) the polarity of the bonds between the atoms of the molecule, and (2) the geometric arrangement of the atoms in space. First, determine whether any of the bonds between atoms are polar. If only nonpolar bonds are present, the molecule will be non-polar regardless of the geometric arrangement of the atoms. However, if one or more polar bonds are found, the arrangement of the atoms must be considered as a second step.

For diatomic (two-atom) molecules, a polar bond between the atoms results in a polar molecule:

A—A $\Delta EN = 0$ because atoms are identical; nonpolar
A—B If $\Delta EN = 0$; nonpolar
A—B If $\Delta EN = 0.1$–2.0; polar

Thus, we see that for diatomic molecules, the type of bond between atoms and the resulting type of molecule is the same.

For a molecule that contains polar bonds and three or more atoms, the molecular geometry must be known and taken into account before the polar nature of the molecule can be determined. Remember, the unequal sharing of electrons between two atoms bonded by a polar bond will cause one of the bonded atoms to have a partial positive charge and one a partial negative charge. If these atoms with their charges are symmetrically arranged in space to form the molecule, the molecule will be nonpolar. Thus, each of the following planar (flat) molecules will be nonpolar even if the bonds between the atoms are polar:

On the other hand, each of the following molecules will be polar if they contain polar bonds because the resulting charges on the atoms are not distributed symmetrically in space:

negative charges must add up to zero, and parentheses are used around the polyatomic ions if more than one is used. In names, the positive metal (or ammonium) ion is given first, followed by the name of the negative polyatomic ion (see ▶ Figure 4.9). No numerical

Figure 4.9 Examples of compounds that contain polyatomic ions. The samples are shown as solids and as solids dissolved in water. Referring to Table 4.7, write formulas for these compounds (clockwise from top): potassium carbonate, potassium chromate, potassium phosphate, and potassium permanganate.

prefixes are used except where they are a part of the polyatomic ion name. Names and formulas of acids (compounds in which hydrogen is bound to polyatomic ions) will be given in Chapter 9.

▶ Example 4.18

Write formulas and names for compounds composed of ions of the following metals and the polyatomic ions indicated:

a. Na and NO_3^- **c.** K and HPO_4^{2-}
b. Ca and ClO_3^- **d.** NH_4^+ and NO_3^-

Solution

a. Sodium (Na) is a group IA(1) metal and forms Na^+ ions. Electrical neutrality requires a combining ratio of one Na^+ for one NO_3^-. The formula is $NaNO_3$. The name is given by the metal name plus the polyatomic ion name: sodium nitrate.

b. Calcium (Ca), a group IIA(2) metal, forms Ca^{2+} ions. Electrical neutrality therefore requires a combining ratio of one Ca^{2+} for two ClO_3^- ions. The formula is $Ca(ClO_3)_2$. (NOTE: The use of parentheses around the polyatomic ion prevents the confusion resulting from writing $CaClO_{32}$, which implies that there are 32 oxygen atoms in the formula. Parentheses are always used when multiples of a specific polyatomic ion are used in a formula and are indicated by a subscript.) The name is calcium chlorate.

c. Potassium (K), a group IA(1) metal, forms K^+ ions. The required combining ratio of 2:1 gives the formula K_2HPO_4. The name is potassium hydrogen phosphate.

d. The NH_4^+ is not a metallic ion, but it behaves like one in numerous compounds. The 1:1 combining ratio gives the formula NH_4NO_3. (NOTE: The polyatomic ions are written separately, and the nitrogen atoms are not grouped to give a formula such as $N_2H_4O_3$.) The name is ammonium nitrate.

▶ LEARNING CHECK 4.18

Write formulas and names for compounds containing ions of the following metals and the polyatomic ions indicated:

a. Ca and HPO_4^{2-} **c.** K and MnO_4^-
b. Mg and PO_4^{3-} **d.** NH_4^+ and $Cr_2O_7^{2-}$

4.11 Other Interparticle Forces

Learning Objective

11. Relate melting and boiling points of pure substances to the strength and type of interparticle forces present in the substances.

Ionic and covalent bonding can account for certain properties of many substances. However, some experimental observations can be explained only by proposing the existence of other types of forces between particles.

Earlier in this chapter, a crystal lattice was described in connection with ionic bonding (see Figure 4.3). Most pure substances (elements or compounds) in the solid state also exist in the form of a crystal lattice. However, in some of these solids, neutral atoms or molecules occupy the lattice sites instead of ions. When solids are melted, the forces holding the lattice particles in place are overcome, and the particles move about more freely in what is called the liquid state. The addition of more heat overcomes the attractive interparticle forces to a still greater extent, and the liquid is converted into a gas or vapor; the liquid boils. Particles in the vapor state move about very freely and are influenced only slightly by interparticle attractions. Thus, the temperatures at which melting and boiling take place give an indication of the strength of the interparticle forces that are being

overcome. (These states of matter—solid, liquid, and gas—are discussed in more detail in Chapter 6.)

Suppose an experiment is carried out with several pure substances. Some are familiar to you, but others you probably have never seen in the solid state. The substances are listed in ❱ Table 4.8, together with some pertinent information.

TABLE 4.8 Some Characteristics of Selected Pure Substances

Substance	Formula or Symbol	Classification	Particles Occupying Lattice Sites
Sodium chloride	NaCl	Compound	Na^+ and Cl^- ions
Water	H_2O	Compound	H_2O molecules
Carbon monoxide	CO	Compound	CO molecules
Quartz (pure sand)	SiO_2	Compound	Si and O atoms
Copper metal	Cu	Element	Cu atoms
Oxygen	O_2	Element	O_2 molecules

The experiment is started at the very low temperature of –220°C to have all substances in the solid state. The temperature is then increased slowly and uniformly to 2600°C, at which point all the substances will be in the gaseous state. See ❱ Table 4.9, which gives only those temperatures corresponding to a specific change in one of the substances.

TABLE 4.9 The Behavior of Selected Pure Substances in Response to Heating

Temperature (°C)	Oxygen (O_2)	Carbon Monoxide (CO)	Water (H_2O)	Salt (NaCl)	Copper (Cu)	Quartz (SiO_2)
–220	Solid	Solid	Solid	Solid	Solid	Solid
–218	**Melts**	Solid	Solid	Solid	Solid	Solid
–199	Liquid	**Melts**	Solid	Solid	Solid	Solid
–192	Liquid	**Boils**	Solid	Solid	Solid	Solid
–183	**Boils**	Gas	Solid	Solid	Solid	Solid
0	Gas	Gas	**Melts**	Solid	Solid	Solid
100	Gas	Gas	**Boils**	Solid	Solid	Solid
801	Gas	Gas	Gas	**Melts**	Solid	Solid
1083	Gas	Gas	Gas	Liquid	**Melts**	Solid
1413	Gas	Gas	Gas	**Boils**	Liquid	Solid
1610	Gas	Gas	Gas	Gas	Liquid	**Melts**
2230	Gas	Gas	Gas	Gas	Liquid	**Boils**
2595	Gas	Gas	Gas	Gas	**Boils**	Gas
2600	Gas	Gas	Gas	Gas	Gas	Gas

The melting points of the substances used in this experiment show that the weakest interparticle forces are found in solid oxygen. The forces then increase in the order CO, H_2O, NaCl, Cu, and SiO_2. With two exceptions, the boiling points follow the same order. How do these melting and boiling points relate to the lattice particles of these substances?

Rare Earths Are All Around You

The label "rare earth" is almost always used when referring to the metals yttrium, lanthanum, and the metallic elements found in the first row of the inner transition elements of the periodic table (elements number 58 through 71). The discovery of these metals began in the late eighteenth century. In nature, they are found in the form of metal oxides, or "earths." The word "rare" in the name would seem to indicate that these metals occur naturally in very small amounts. In fact, the rarest of these rare earths is nearly 200 times more abundant in nature than gold! The name actually refers to the rarity of natural deposits large enough and concentrated enough to be mined profitably.

Most people would probably find it difficult to name even one product or use of rare earth elements that significantly influence their lives. However, the list of such products is extensive. One significant example is permanent magnets. The inclusion of rare earth metals in their formulation makes it possible to manufacture tiny magnets that are much more powerful than conventional magnets of similar size. The availability of these small but powerful magnets makes possible the production of familiar electronic devices such as smart phones and MP3 players. Very large rare earth magnets also prove to be important in such applications as massive electricity-producing wind turbines. Some large turbines are made using magnets containing 500 pounds or more of the rare earth neodymium. The use of rare earth magnets has also made possible the availability of small electrically powered portable tools such as drills, grinders, and saws used in the construction trades.

Hybrid automobiles could not function well without the use of rare earth metals. Lanthanum is used in their very efficient energy-storing batteries, and powerful neodymium-containing magnets are used in their electric motors.

Military uses of rare earth metals are numerous. Night-vision goggles contain lanthanum, gadolinium, and yttrium. Heat-resistant magnets that contain samarium are found in the control systems of drone aircraft and some cruise missiles.

Rare earth metals are also found in numerous commonly used everyday items. Some sunglasses are tinted by the addition of praseodymium, erbium, and neodymium to the glass mixture. The presence of the rare earths in the glass provides color to reduce glare from visible light, and it also protects the eyes from invisible but potentially damaging ultraviolet radiation. Fluorescent light bulbs contain small amounts of yttrium and terbium. The red and green screen colors of the liquid crystal displays (LCDs) used on many small visual devices such as smart phones and DVD players are produced by europium and terbium.

In recent years, the characteristics of the rare earth market place have become a concern. The United States currently has 13 percent of the world's rare earth reserves and was the largest supplier of rare earth metals from about 1965 until 1985, when China, which owns 48 percent of the world reserves, entered the world market. China now supplies 97 percent of the rare earth needs worldwide. In 2010, China shook up global rare earth markets when it cut off rare earth shipments to Japan for a month because of a diplomatic dispute. The power of one nation to essentially control rare earth availability to all other nations is seen by many as a serious issue.

In addition to the supply issue, the steady increase in the use of rare earth elements in the manufacturing of high-tech goods has sent prices soaring. Dysprosium, which sold for $6.77 a pound in 2002, sold for $212.00 a pound in 2011. During just two months in the summer of 2010, the price of cerium increased by 450%. Some experts predicted that world demand would probably exceed supply in the near future. With such serious supply, demand, and pricing issues before us, the rare earths might, indeed, live up to their name and become rare.

A young woman using an iPad.

The lattice particles in solid silicon dioxide are individual atoms of silicon and oxygen. They are held together in the lattice by covalent bonds. Solids of this type are called **network solids,** and when such solids are melted or vaporized, strong covalent bonds must be broken.

The individual atoms that are the lattice particles of copper metal are held together in the lattice by what is called a **metallic bond.** As described in Section 4.2, the atoms of metals lose valence-shell electrons readily. Imagine a large number of metal atoms occupying lattice sites. Now imagine that the valence-shell electrons of each of the atoms move readily throughout the lattice. The attraction of the positive kernels (the metal atom nuclei

network solid A solid in which the lattice sites are occupied by atoms that are covalently bonded to each other.

metallic bond An attractive force responsible for holding solid metals together. It originates from the attraction between positively charged atomic kernels that occupy the lattice sites and mobile electrons that move freely through the lattice.

plus low-level electrons) to the mobile electrons, and hence to one another, constitutes a metallic bond. The mobile electrons of the metallic bond are responsible for a number of the observed properties of metals, including high thermal conductivity, high electrical conductivity, and the characteristic metallic luster.

The bonds broken when sodium chloride (NaCl) melts or boils are ionic bonds resulting from attractions between positive (Na^+) and negative (Cl^-) ions, the lattice particles in Figure 4.3. As shown by Table 4.9, these bonds are generally quite strong.

The lattice particles of solid carbon monoxide (CO) are the nonsymmetric CO molecules. These molecules are polar because of the nonsymmetric distribution of charges between the carbon and oxygen atoms. They are held in the solid lattice by **dipolar forces** resulting from the attraction of the positive end of one polar molecule to the negative end of another polar molecule. These forces are usually weak, and melting and vaporization take place at very low temperatures. Such substances are usually thought of as gases because that is their normal state at room temperature.

Water molecules, the lattice particles of ice, are also held in place by dipolar forces. However, these forces are stronger than those of the dipoles for CO. In water molecules, the hydrogens carry a partial positive charge, and the oxygen has a partial negative charge (see Table 4.5). Thus, the hydrogens of one molecule are attracted to the oxygens of other molecules. This attraction, called **hydrogen bonding,** is stronger than most other dipolar attractions because of the small size of the hydrogen atom and the high electronegativity of oxygen (see ▶ Figure 4.10). Hydrogen bonding occurs in gases, liquids, and solids composed of polar molecules in which hydrogen atoms are covalently bonded to highly electronegative elements (generally O, N, or F).

dipolar force The attractive force that exists between the positive end of one polar molecule and the negative end of another.

hydrogen bonding The result of attractive dipolar forces between molecules in which hydrogen atoms are covalently bonded to very electronegative elements (O, N, or F).

A Polar water molecule **B** Hydrogen bonding in liquid water **C** Hydrogen bonding in solid water

Figure 4.10 Hydrogen bonding in water. Hydrogen bonds are dotted, and covalent bonds are solid.

Water is the most well-known substance in which hydrogen bonding dramatically influences the properties. These properties make water useful in many processes, including those characteristic of living organisms. Because of this widespread use, water is not often thought of as being a peculiar substance. However, it is often the peculiarities that make it so useful.

As we saw in Example 4.13d, water molecules are angular. Because of this shape and the large difference in electronegativity between hydrogen and oxygen, water molecules are polar, with partial positive charges on the hydrogens and a partial negative charge on the oxygen, as shown in Figure 4.10a. The attractions between these oppositely charged parts of the molecules result in hydrogen bonding. This is represented for the liquid and solid states of water in Figures 4.10b and c.

Let's look at some of the peculiar properties of water. As shown in Table 4.9, water has a normal boiling point of 100°C. This is much higher than would be predicted from the measured boiling points of compounds containing hydrogen and the other members of group VIA(16) of the periodic table. The boiling point of H_2Te is –2.2°C, of H_2Se is –41.3°C, and of H_2S is –60.3°C. Thus, it appears that the boiling point decreases with decreasing compound molecular weight. On the basis of this trend, water should boil at approximately –64°C. The 164-degree difference between predicted and measured boiling points is caused by strong hydrogen bonds between water molecules in the liquid. The other three compounds do not have strong hydrogen bonds between molecules because the electronegativites of the elements to which hydrogen is covalently bonded are too low. This deviation from prediction makes water a liquid at normal temperatures and allows it to be used in many of the ways familiar to us.

It is also common knowledge that solid water (ice) floats on liquid water (see ▶ Figure 4.11). Nothing peculiar here—or is there? In fact, there is. Water, like most other liquids, increases in density as it is cooled. This means that a specific mass of liquid decreases in volume as its temperature is lowered. Unlike most liquids, water behaves this way only until it reaches a temperature of about 4°C, as shown by the data in ▶ Table 4.10. Then, its density decreases as it is cooled further. When its temperature reaches 0°C, water freezes and, in the process, undergoes a dramatic decrease in density. Put another way, a quantity of liquid water at 0°C expands significantly when it freezes to solid at 0°C. Thus, a specific volume of ice has a lower mass than the same volume of liquid water, so the ice floats on the water. Hydrogen bonds between water molecules are, once again, responsible. The strong hydrogen bonds orient water molecules into a very open three-dimensional crystal lattice when it freezes (see Figure 4.10c). This open lattice of the solid occupies more space than is occupied by the molecules in the liquid state.

Even though containers or engines might be ruptured or cracked if water is allowed to freeze in them, the overall effect of this characteristic of water is beneficial. If ice did not float, it would form on natural waters in the winter and sink to the bottom. Gradually, ponds, lakes, and other bodies of water would fill with ice. In the spring, the ice would melt from the top down because the heavier solid ice would stay under the water. As a result, most natural waters in areas that experience freezing winters would contain significant amounts of ice year-round. It would be a strange (and possibly hostile) environment for us and for wildlife.

The amount of heat required to melt a quantity of solid and the amount of heat required to vaporize a quantity of liquid also depend on the attractive forces between molecules. As expected, these are high for water, compared with the hydrogen compounds of the three other elements in group VIA(16). The beneficial results of these high values for water will be discussed in Chapter 6.

The forces between O_2 molecules, the lattice particles of solid oxygen, do not fit into any of the classifications we have discussed to this point. The O_2 molecule is not polar and contains no ionic or metallic bonds, and solid oxygen melts at much too low a temperature to fit into the category of a network solid. The forces between O_2 molecules are called **dispersion forces** and result from momentary nonsymmetric electron distributions in the molecules.

The nonbonding electrons in an O_2 molecule can be visualized as being uniformly distributed. However, there is a small statistical chance that, during their normal movement, more of the electrons will momentarily be on one side of a molecule than on the other. This condition causes the molecule to become dipolar for an instant. The resulting negative side of the dipole will tend to repel electrons of adjoining molecules and induce them also to become dipolar (they become induced dipoles). The original (statistical) dipole and all induced dipoles are then attracted to one another. This happens many times per second throughout the solid or liquid oxygen. The net effect is a weak dispersion force of attraction between the molecules. The net force is weak because it represents the average result of many weak, short-lived attractions per second between molecules.

© Volodymyr Goinyk/Shutterstock.com

Figure 4.11 Icebergs move as a result of wind and ocean currents. They can be very dangerous to ships, so their positions are reported and their probable courses estimated by an International Ice Patrol. The patrol was established in 1914 following the sinking of the *Titanic*.

TABLE 4.10 Water Density as a Function of Temperature

Temperature (°C)	Water Density (g/mL)
100	0.9586
80	0.9719
60	0.9833
40	0.9923
20	0.9982
10	0.9997
5	0.9999
4 (actually 3.98)	1.0000
2	0.9999
0 (liquid H_2O)	0.9998
0 (solid H_2O)	0.9170

dispersion forces Very weak attractive forces acting between the particles of all matter. They result from momentary nonsymmetric electron distributions in molecules or atoms.

Dispersion forces exist in all matter, but because they are very weak, their contribution is negligible when other, stronger forces are also present. Thus, solid water is held together by dispersion forces and hydrogen bonds, but the properties are almost entirely the result of the hydrogen bonds. The ease with which a dipole can be induced increases with the size of the particle (atoms or molecules). The larger the particle, the stronger the resulting dipolar attraction (dispersion force), and the harder to separate the particles by melting or boiling. Thus, we expect to find the melting and boiling points of the elements increase as we move down a group of the periodic table.

TABLE 4.11 The Normal Melting and Boiling Points of Group VIIA(17) Elements

Substance	Melting Point (°C)	Boiling Point (°C)
F_2	−223	−188
Cl_2	−103	−34.6
Br_2	−7.2	58.8
I_2	113.9	184.3

▶ **Example 4.19**

Illustrate the behavior of dispersion forces by using the information in ▶ Table 4.11.

Solution
The molecules increase in size in the order F_2, Cl_2, Br_2, I_2. The strength of dispersion forces increases in the same order, as shown in Table 4.11 by the increases in melting and boiling points.

▶ **LEARNING CHECK 4.19** Using only the periodic table, predict which member of each of the following pairs of elements would have the higher melting and boiling points:

a. O and Se **b.** Sb and P **c.** He and Ne

The melting and boiling points in Example 4.19 indicate the variation in magnitude of dispersion forces. Similar variations are found for the other forces described in this section; sometimes their strengths overlap. For example, some metallic bonds are weaker than ionic bonds, whereas others are stronger. This is illustrated in ▶ Figure 4.12, which summarizes the relative strengths of interparticle forces.

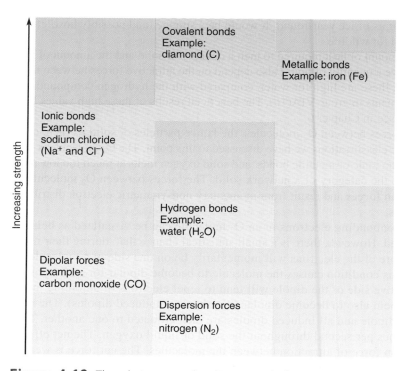

Figure 4.12 The relative strengths of interparticle forces.

Case Study Follow-up

Anorexia is characterized by failure to maintain a body weight of at least 85% of normal, whereas bulimia involves the intake of large quantities of food and then eliminating it by one or more of the following methods: forced vomiting, excessive use of laxatives, fasting, and exercise. Bulimic behaviors can result in electrolyte imbalances (Section 25.5). Many people with bulimia maintain a normal or slightly elevated weight. A patient who may "binge and purge" but also fasts and exercises to the point of failing to maintain 85% of recommended body weight would be considered anorexic, whereas a person who mainly binges and purges but maintains a normal weight would be considered bulimic. A 5' 6" tall woman who weighs below 102 lbs, with no other explanation for her low weight, would be considered anorexic. Both eating disorders occur more prevalently in females who come from highly controlling families where nurturance is lacking. When there is a family-environment component in the etiology of the eating disorder, it is helpful for the entire family to receive counseling in order to improve the functioning of family relationships and to create an environment where healthy thinking and behavior can thrive. If the person with the eating disorder receives treatment and subsequently returns to an unchanged family environment, chances of maintaining recovery are reduced.

Concept Summary

Noble Gas Configurations

The lack of reactivity for noble gases led to the proposal that the electronic configurations of the noble gases represented stable configurations. These configurations, usually consisting of eight electrons in the valence shell, can be represented in several useful ways.

Objective 1, Exercise 4.2

Ionic Bonding

Ionic compounds are formed when reacting atoms gain or lose electrons to achieve a noble gas configuration of eight electrons in the valence shell. This octet rule predicts that atoms will be changed into charged particles called simple ions. Ions of opposite charge are attracted to each other; the attractive force is called an ionic bond.

Objective 2, Exercise 4.12

Ionic Compounds

Oppositely charged ions group together to form compounds in ratios determined by the positive and negative charges of the ions. The formulas representing these ratios contain the lowest number of each ion possible in a proportion such that the total positive charges and total negative charges used are equal.

Objective 3, Exercises 4.20 and 4.22

Naming Binary Ionic Compounds

Binary ionic compounds contain a metal and a nonmetal. They are named by naming the metal, then adding the suffix *-ide* to the stem of the nonmetal.

Objective 4, Exercise 4.30

The Smallest Unit of Ionic Compounds

Ionic compounds do not exist in the form of molecules but as three-dimensional arrangements of oppositely charged ions. The sum of the atomic weights of the elements in the formula of ionic compounds is called the formula weight and is used in calculations somewhat like the molecular weight of molecular compounds.

Objective 5, Exercise 4.38

Covalent Bonding

Elements with little or no tendency to gain or lose electrons often react and achieve noble gas electronic configurations by sharing electrons. Lewis structures are useful in representing electron sharing. Shared pairs of electrons exert an attractive force on both atoms that share them. The atoms are held together by this attraction to form a covalent bond.

Objective 6, Exercise 4.48

Polyatomic Ions

Polyatomic ions are groups of two or more covalently bonded atoms that carry a net electrical charge. They are conveniently represented using Lewis structures.

Objective 7, Exercise 4.50

Shapes of Molecules and Polyatomic Ions

The shapes of many molecules and polyatomic ions can be predicted by using the valence-shell electron-pair repulsion theory (VSEPR). According to the VSEPR theory, electron pairs in the valence shell of the central atom of a molecule or ion repel one another and become arranged so as to maximize their separation distances. The resulting arrangement determines the molecular or ionic shape when one or all of the electron pairs involved form bonds between the central atom and other atoms.

Objective 8, Exercises 4.52 and 4.54

The Polarity of Covalent Molecules

Shared electrons may be shared equally, or they may be attracted more strongly to one of the atoms they bond together. The tendency of a covalently bonded atom to attract shared electrons is called the electronegativity of the atom. Unequally shared bonding-electron pairs form polar covalent bonds. The extent of bond polarization can be estimated from the electronegativity differences between the bonded atoms. The higher the electronegativity difference, the more polar (or ionic) is the bond. Polar covalent bonds cause partial positive and negative charges to form within molecules. When these charges are symmetrically distributed in the molecule, it is said to be nonpolar. An unsymmetric distribution gives rise to a polar molecule.

Objective 9, Exercises 4.58 and 4.64

More about Naming Compounds

Binary covalent compounds are named using the name of the less electronegative element first, followed by the stem plus *-ide* of the more electronegative element. Greek prefixes are used to represent the number of each type of atom in molecules of the compounds. Ionic compounds that contain a metal ion (or ammonium ion) plus a polyatomic ion are named by first naming the metal (or ammonium ion) followed by the name of the polyatomic ion.

Objective 10, Assessment Exercises 4.66, 4.70, and 4.72

Other Interparticle Forces

Forces other than ionic and covalent bonds are also known to hold the particles of some pure substances together in the solid and liquid states. These forces include metallic bonds, dipolar attractions, hydrogen bonds, and dispersion forces. The strength of the predominant force acting in a substance is indicated by the melting and boiling points of the substance.

Objective 11, Exercises 4.78 and 4.80

Key Terms and Concepts

Binary compound (4.3)
Bond polarization (4.9)
Covalent bond (4.6)
Crystal lattice (4.5)
Dipolar force (4.11)
Dispersion force (4.11)
Double bond (4.6)
Electronegativity (4.9)
Formula weight (4.5)

Hydrogen bonding (4.11)
Ionic bond (4.2)
Isoelectronic (4.2)
Lattice site (4.5)
Lewis structure (4.1)
Metallic bond (4.11)
Network solid (4.11)
Nonpolar covalent bond (4.9)
Nonpolar molecule (4.9)

Octet rule (4.2)
Polar covalent bond (4.9)
Polar molecule (4.9)
Polyatomic ion (4.7)
Simple ion (4.2)
Triple bond (4.6)
VSEPR theory (4.8)

Exercises

Even-numbered exercises are answered in Appendix B.

Blue-numbered exercises are more challenging.

Noble Gas Configurations (Section 4.1)

4.1 Refer to the group numbers of the periodic table and draw Lewis structures for atoms of the following:

 a. lithium

 b. sodium

 c. chlorine

 d. boron

4.2 Refer to the group numbers of the periodic table and draw Lewis structures for atoms of the following:

 a. iodine

 b. strontium

 c. tin

 d. sulfur

4.3 Write abbreviated electronic configurations for the following:

 a. iodine

 b. element number 38

 c. As

 d. phosphorus

4.4 Write abbreviated electronic configurations for the following:

 a. tin

 b. Cs

 c. element number 49

 d. strontium

4.5 Draw Lewis structures for the elements given in Exercise 4.3.

4.6 Draw Lewis structures for the elements given in Exercise 4.4.

4.7 Use the symbol E to represent an element in a general way and draw Lewis structures for atoms of the following:

 a. Any group IA(1)element

 b. Any group IVA(14)element

4.8 Use the symbol E to represent an element in a general way and draw Lewis structures for atoms of the following:

 a. Any group IIA(2) element

 b. Any group VA(15) element

Ionic Bonding (Section 4.2)

4.9 Indicate both the minimum number of electrons that would have to be added and the minimum number that would have to be removed to change the electronic configuration of each element listed in Exercise 4.3 to a noble gas configuration.

4.10 Indicate both the minimum number of electrons that would have to be added and the minimum number that would have to be removed to change the electronic configuration of each element listed in Exercise 4.4 to a noble gas configuration.

4.11 Use the periodic table and predict the number of electrons that will be lost or gained by the following elements as they change into simple ions. Write an equation using elemental symbols, ionic symbols, and electrons to represent each change.

 a. Ca

 b. aluminum

 c. fluorine

 d. element number 34

4.12 Use the periodic table and predict the number of electrons that will be lost or gained by the following elements as they change into simple ions. Write an equation using elemental symbols, ionic symbols, and electrons to represent each change.

 a. Cs

 b. oxygen

 c. element number 7

 d. iodine

4.13 Write a symbol for each of the following ions:

 a. A bromine atom that has gained one electron

 b. A sodium atom that has lost one electron

 c. A sulfur atom that has gained two electrons

4.14 Write a symbol for each of the following ions:

 a. A phosphorus atom that has gained three electrons

 b. A strontium atom that has lost two electrons

 c. An iodine atom that has gained one electron

4.15 Identify the element in period 2 that would form each of the following ions. E is used as a general symbol for an element.

 a. E^-

 b. E^{2+}

 c. E^{3-}

 d. E^+

4.16 Identify the element in period 3 that would form each of the following ions. E is used as a general symbol for an element.

 a. E^{2-}

 b. E^{3+}

 c. E^+

 d. E^-

4.17 Identify the noble gas that is isoelectronic with each of the following ions:

 a. Mg^{2+}

 b. Te^{2-}

 c. N^{3-}

 d. Be^{2+}

4.18 Identify the noble gas that is isoelectronic with each of the following ions:

 a. Ca^{2+}

 b. S^{2-}

c. As^{3-}

d. Cs^+

Ionic Compounds (Section 4.3)

4.19 Write equations to represent positive and negative ion formation for the following pairs of elements. Then write a formula for the ionic compound that results when the ions combine.

a. Mg and S

b. strontium and nitrogen

c. elements number 3 and 34

4.20 Write equations to represent positive and negative ion formation for the following pairs of elements. Then write a formula for the ionic compound that results when the ions combine.

a. Ca and Cl

b. lithium and bromine

c. elements number 12 and 16

4.21 Write the formula for the ionic compound formed from Sr^{2+} and each of the following ions:

a. S^{2-}

b. Br^-

c. N^{3-}

d. Cl^-

4.22 Write the formula for the ionic compound formed from Ba^{2+} and each of the following ions:

a. Se^{2-}

b. P^{3-}

c. I^-

d. As^{3-}

4.23 Classify each of the following as a binary compound or not a binary compound:

a. HF

b. OF_2

c. H_2SO_4

d. H_2S

e. $MgBr_2$

4.24 Classify each of the following as a binary compound or not a binary compound:

a. CaS

b. Na_3P

c. $MgSO_4$

d. $NaHCO_3$

e. P_2O_5

Naming Binary Ionic Compounds (Section 4.4)

4.25 Name the following metal ions:

a. Ca^{2+}

b. K^+

c. Al^{3+}

d. Rb^+

4.26 Name the following metal ions:

a. Li^+

b. Mg^{2+}

c. Ba^{2+}

d. Cs^+

4.27 Name the following nonmetal ions:

a. Cl^-

b. N^{3-}

c. S^{2-}

d. Se^{2-}

4.28 Name the following nonmetal ions:

a. Br^-

b. O^{2-}

c. P^{3-}

d. Te^{2-}

4.29 Name the following binary ionic compounds:

a. K_2O

b. $SrCl_2$

c. Al_2O_3

d. LiBr

e. CaS

4.30 Name the following binary ionic compounds:

a. SrS

b. CaF_2

c. $BaCl_2$

d. Li_2O

e. MgO

4.31 Name the following binary ionic compounds, using a Roman numeral to indicate the charge on the metal ion:

a. $CrCl_2$ and $CrCl_3$

b. CoS and Co_2S_3

c. FeO and Fe_2O_3

d. $PbCl_2$ and $PbCl_4$

4.32 Name the following binary ionic compounds, using a Roman numeral to indicate the charge on the metal ion:

a. PbO and PbO_2

b. CuCl and $CuCl_2$

c. Au_2S and Au_2S_3

d. CoO and Co_2O_3

4.33 Name the binary compounds of Exercise 4.31 by adding the endings -*ous* and -*ic* to indicate the lower and higher ionic charges of the metal ion in each pair of compounds. The non-English root for lead (Pb) is *plumb-*.

4.34 Name the binary compounds of Exercise 4.32 by adding the endings -*ous* and -*ic* to indicate the lower and higher ionic charges of the metal ion in each pair of compounds. The non-English root for gold (Au) is *aur-*, and that of lead (Pb) is *plumb-*.

Even-numbered exercises answered in Appendix B.

Blue-numbered exercises are more challenging.

4.35 Write formulas for the following binary ionic compounds:

 a. manganese(II) chloride

 b. iron(III) sulfide

 c. chromium(II) oxide

 d. iron(II) bromide

 e. tin(II) chloride

4.36 Write formulas for the following binary ionic compounds:

 a. lead(IV) oxide

 b. cobalt(II) chloride

 c. copper(II) sulfide

 d. nickel(III) nitride

 e. platinum(II) phosphide

The Smallest Unit of Ionic Compounds (Section 4.5)

4.37 Determine the formula weight in atomic mass units for each of the following binary ionic compounds:

 a. Na_2O

 b. FeO

 c. PbS_2

 d. $AlCl_3$

4.38 Determine the formula weight in atomic mass units for each of the following binary ionic compounds:

 a. $NaBr$

 b. CaF_2

 c. Cu_2S

 d. Li_3N

4.39 Identify the ions that would occupy lattice sites in a solid sample of each compound given in Exercise 4.37.

4.40 Identify the ions that would occupy lattice sites in a solid sample of each compound given in Exercise 4.38.

4.41 Calculate the mass in grams of positive ions and negative ions contained in 1 mol of each compound given in Exercise 4.37.

4.42 Calculate the mass in grams of positive ions and negative ions contained in 1 mol of each compound given in Exercise 4.38.

4.43 Calculate the number of positive ions and negative ions contained in 1.00 mol of each compound given in Exercise 4.37.

4.44 Calculate the number of positive ions and negative ions contained in 1.00 mol of each compound given in Exercise 4.38.

Covalent Bonding (Section 4.6)

4.45 Represent the following reaction using Lewis structures:

$$I + I \rightarrow I_2$$

4.46 Represent the following reaction using Lewis structures:

$$8S \rightarrow S_8 \text{ (the atoms form a ring)}$$

4.47 Represent the following molecules by Lewis structures:

 a. HF

 b. IBr

 c. PH_3 (each H atom is bonded to the P atom)

 d. $HClO_2$ (the O atoms are each bonded to the Cl, and the H is bonded to one of the O atoms)

4.48 Represent the following molecules by Lewis structures:

 a. CH_4 (each H atom is bonded to the C atom)

 b. CO_2 (each O atom is bonded to the C atom)

 c. H_2Se (each H atom is bonded to the Se atom)

 d. NH_3 (each H atom is bonded to the N atom)

Polyatomic Ions (Section 4.7)

4.49 Draw Lewis structures for the following polyatomic ions:

 a. ClO_3^- (each O atom is bonded to the Cl atom)

 b. CN^-

 c. CO_3^{2-} (each O atom is bonded to the C atom)

4.50 Draw Lewis structures for the following polyatomic ions:

 a. NH_4^+ (each H atom is bonded to the N atom)

 b. PO_4^{3-} (each O atom is bonded to the P atom)

 c. SO_3^{2-} (each O atom is bonded to the S atom)

Shapes of Molecules and Polyatomic Ions (Section 4.8)

4.51 Draw Lewis structures for the following molecules:

 a. O_3 (the O atoms are bonded together, like beads on a string)

 b. CS_2 (each S atom is bonded to the C atom)

 c. SeO_2 (each O atom is bonded to the Se atom)

 d. H_2SO_3 (each O atom is bonded to the S atom, and one H atom is bonded to each of the two O atoms)

4.52 Predict the shape of each of the following molecules by first drawing a Lewis structure, then applying the VSEPR theory:

 a. H_2S (each H atom is bonded to the S atom)

 b. PCl_3 (each Cl atom is bonded to the P atom)

 c. OF_2 (each F atom is bonded to the O atom)

 d. SnF_4 (each F atom is bonded to the Sn atom)

4.53 Predict the shape of each of the following molecules by first drawing a Lewis structure, then applying the VSEPR theory:

 a. O_3 (see Exercise 4.51 for Lewis structure)

 b. SeO_2 (see Exercise 4.51 for Lewis structure)

 c. PH_3 (each H atom is bonded to the P atom)

 d. SO_3 (each O atom is bonded to the S atom)

4.54 Predict the shape of each of the following polyatomic ions by first drawing a Lewis structure, then applying the VSEPR theory:

 a. NO_2^- (each O is bonded to N)

 b. ClO_3^- (each O is bonded to Cl)

 c. CO_3^{2-} (each O is bonded to C)

 d. H_3O^+ (each H is bonded to O)

 Note the positive charge; compare with NH_4^+.

4.55 Predict the shape of each of the following polyatomic ions by first drawing a Lewis structure, then applying the VSEPR theory:

a. NH_2^- (each H is bonded to N)

b. PO_3^{3-} (each O is bonded to P)

c. $BeCl_4^{2-}$ (each Cl is bonded to Be)

d. ClO_4^- (each O is bonded to Cl)

The Polarity of Covalent Molecules (Section 4.9)

4.56 Use the periodic table and Table 4.4 to determine which of the following bonds will be polarized. Show the resulting charge distribution in those molecules that contain polarized bonds.

a. H—I

b.

c. O — O
$\diagdown$
O

4.57 Use the periodic table and Table 4.4 to determine which of the following bonds will be polarized. Show the resulting charge distribution in those molecules that contain polarized bonds.

a. Cl—F

b. H — Se
$\diagdown$
H

c. H $\diagdown$ H
$\quad$ B — B
H $\diagup$ $\diagdown$ H

4.58 Use Table 4.4 and classify the bonds in the following compounds as nonpolar covalent, polar covalent, or ionic:

a. LiBr

b. HCl

c. PH_3 (each H is bonded to P)

d. SO_2 (each O is bonded to S)

e. CsF

4.59 Use Table 4.4 and classify the bonds in the following compounds as nonpolar covalent, polar covalent, or ionic:

a. MgI_2 (each I is bonded to Mg)

b. NCl_3 (each Cl is bonded to N)

c. H_2S (each H is bonded to S)

d. RbF

e. SrO

4.60 On the basis of the charge distributions you drew for the molecules of Exercise 4.56, classify each of the molecules as polar or nonpolar.

4.61 On the basis of the charge distributions you drew for the molecules of Exercise 4.57, classify each of the molecules as polar or nonpolar.

4.62 Use Table 4.4 and predict the type of bond you would expect to find in compounds formed from the following elements:

a. magnesium and chlorine

b. carbon and hydrogen

c. phosphorus and hydrogen

4.63 Use Table 4.4 and predict the type of bond you would expect to find in compounds formed from the following elements:

a. sulfur and oxygen

b. aluminum and bromine

c. C and Cl

4.64 Show the charge distribution in the following molecules, and predict which are polar molecules:

a. C≡O

b. H — Se
$\quad$ |
$\quad$ H

c. $\quad$ I
$\quad$ |
$\quad$ Al
$\quad \diagup \quad \diagdown$
I $\qquad$ I

4.65 Show the charge distribution in the following molecules, and predict which are polar molecules:

a. S=C=S

b. H—C≡N

c. F — O
$\diagdown$
F

More about Naming Compounds (Section 4.10)

4.66 Name the following binary covalent compounds:

a. PCl_3

b. N_2O_5

c. CCl_4

d. BF_3

e. CS_2

4.67 Name the following binary covalent compounds:

a. SiO_2

b. SiF_4

c. P_2O_5

d. $AlBr_3$

e. CBr_4

4.68 Write formulas for the following binary covalent compounds:

a. chlorine dioxide

b. dinitrogen monoxide

c. sulfur dioxide

d. carbon tetrachloride

4.69 Write formulas for the following binary covalent compounds:

a. disulfur monoxide

b. sulfur hexafluoride

c. silicon tetrachloride

d. carbon diselenide

4.70 Write the formulas and names for compounds composed of ions of the following metals and the indicated polyatomic ions:

 a. calcium and the nitrite ion

 b. magnesium and the hypochlorite ion

 c. Cs and $Cr_2O_7^{2-}$

 d. K and SO_3^{2-}

4.71 Write the formulas and names for compounds composed of ions of the following metals and the indicated polyatomic ions:

 a. calcium and the phosphate ion

 b. sodium and the dichromate ion

 c. Li and CO_3^{2-}

 d. Na and PO_4^{3-}

4.72 Write formulas for the following compounds:

 a. barium hydroxide

 b. magnesium sulfite

 c. calcium carbonate

 d. ammonium sulfate

 e. lithium hydrogen carbonate

4.73 Write formulas for the following compounds:

 a. potassium permanganate

 b. calcium hydroxide

 c. calcium phosphate

 d. ammonium dihydrogen phosphate

 e. calcium hypochlorite

4.74 Write a formula for the following compounds, using M with appropriate charges to represent the metal ion:

 a. Any group IA(1) element and SO_3^{2-}

 b. Any group IA(1) element and $C_2H_3O_2^{-}$

 c. Any metal that forms M^{2+} ions and $Cr_2O_7^{2-}$

 d. Any metal that forms M^{3+} ions and PO_4^{3-}

 e. Any metal that forms M^{3+} ions and NO_3^{-}

4.75 Write a formula for the following compounds, using M with appropriate charges to represent the metal ion:

 a. Any group IIA(2) element and HSO_3^{-}

 b. Any group IIA(2) element and HPO_4^{2-}

 c. Any metal that forms M^{+} ions and NO_2^{-}

 d. Any metal that forms M^{3+} ions and CO_3^{2-}

 e. Any metal that forms M^{2+} ions and HPO_4^{2-}

Other Interparticle Forces (Section 4.11)

4.76 The covalent compounds ethyl alcohol and dimethyl ether both have the formula C_2H_6O. However, the alcohol melts at $-117.3°C$ and boils at $78.5°C$, whereas the ether melts at $-138.5°C$ and boils at $-23.7°C$. How could differences in forces between molecules be used to explain these observations?

4.77 The following structural formulas represent molecules of ethyl alcohol and dimethyl ether. Assign the correct name to each

formula and explain how your choice is consistent with your answer to Exercise 4.76.

4.78 Describe the predominant forces that exist between molecules of the noble gases. Arrange the noble gases in a predicted order of increasing boiling point (lowest first) and explain the reason for the order.

4.79 Use the concept of interparticle forces to propose an explanation for the fact that CO_2 is a soft, low-melting solid (dry ice), whereas SiO_2 is a hard solid (sand). Focus on the nature of the particles that occupy lattice sites in the solid.

4.80 Table sugar, sucrose, melts at about $185°C$. Which interparticle forces do you think are unlikely to be the predominant ones in the lattice of solid sucrose?

4.81 The formula for sucrose is $C_{12}H_{22}O_{11}$, where many of the hydrogens and oxygens are combined to form OH groups that are bonded to carbon atoms. What type of predominant interparticle bonding would you now propose for solid sucrose (see Exercise 4.80)?

Additional Exercises

4.82 Three atoms with an electronic configuration of $1s^1$ are covalently bonded to one atom with an electronic configuration of $1s^2\ 2s^2\ 2p^3$ to form a molecule. What is the formula of this molecule? Make a drawing to show how two of these molecules would hydrogen bond with each other.

4.83 Suppose an element from group IIA(2), and period 3 of the periodic table forms an ionic compound with the element that has an electronic configuration of $1s^2\ 2s^2\ 2p^5$. What would be the formula of the compound, and what would be the name of the compound?

4.84 What would be the mass in grams of 0.200 moles of the ionic compound formed when magnesium metal reacts with oxygen?

4.85 The ampere unit is used to describe the flow of electricity in an electrical circuit. One ampere is an amount of electricity corresponding to the flow of 6.2×10^{18} electrons past a point in a circuit in 1 second. In a hydrogen fuel cell, hydrogen atoms are dissociated into H^+ ions and electrons ($H \rightarrow H^+ + 1e^-$). How many grams of hydrogen must be dissociated each second in a fuel cell to produce 1 ampere of electricity?

4.86 If one atom of oxygen reacted with two atoms of nitrogen to form a molecule, what would be the formula of the molecule? Use Table 4.4 and Figure 4.7 to determine if the bond between the atoms is ionic or covalent. Also, name the compound that is formed.

Allied Health Exam Connection

The following questions are from these sources:

1. *Nursing School Entrance Exam* © 2005, Learning Express, LLC.

2. *McGraw-Hill's Nursing School Entrance Exams* by Thomas A. Evangelist, Tamara B. Orr and Judy Unrein © 2009, The McGraw-Hill Companies, Inc.

Even-numbered exercises answered in Appendix B.

3. *NSEE Nursing School Entrance Exams,* 3rd Edition © 2009, Kaplan Publishing.

4. *Cliffs Test Prep: Nursing School Entrance Exams* by Fred N. Grayson © 2004, Wiley Publishing, Inc.

5. *Peterson's Master the Nursing School and Allied Health Entrance Exams,* 18th Edition by Marion F. Gooding © 2008, Peterson's, a Nelnet Company.

4.87 Noble gases:
 a. have low boiling points
 b. are all gases at room temperature
 c. are also called inert gases
 d. all of the above

4.88 The elements in group Zero of the periodic table are considered inert gases because each has how many electrons in its outermost energy level?
 a. 8
 b. 7
 c. 4
 d. 2

4.89 Name the type of bond that is formed when *electrons are shared* between two atoms.
 a. shared bond
 b. ionic bond
 c. covalent bond
 d. multiple bond

4.90 Which of the following is the correct name for Li_2SO_3?
 a. lithium sulfite
 b. lithium sulfide
 c. lithium sulfate
 d. lithium disulfate

4.91 An atom becomes an ion that possesses a negative charge. The atom must have:
 a. gained protons
 b. lost protons
 b. lost electrons
 d. gained electrons

4.92 When calcium reacts with chlorine to form calcium chloride, it:
 a. shares two electrons
 b. gains two electrons
 c. loses two electrons
 d. gains one electron

4.93 Which of the following is the probable charge for an ion formed from Ca?
 a. +1
 b. +2
 c. −1
 d. −2

4.94 A covalent bond is believed to be caused by a:
 a. transfer of electrons
 b. sharing of electrons
 c. release of energy
 d. none of the above

4.95 Which molecule below has a nonpolar bond in which the electrons are being shared equally?
 a. H_2O
 b. NH_3
 c. Cl_2
 d. CH_4

4.96 What is the formula for bismuth (III) hydroxide?
 a. Bi_3OH
 b. $Bi(OH)_3$
 c. $Bi(OH)_2$
 d. $BiOH$

4.97 Which of the following species will combine with a chloride ion to produce ammonium chloride?
 a. NH_3
 b. K^+
 c. NH_4^+
 d. Al^{+++}

4.98 What type of bond is created when bromine and magnesium are reacted to form $MgBr_2$?
 a. polar covalent
 b. metallic
 c. ionic
 d. nonpolar covalent

4.99 The parts of an atom directly involved in ionic bonding are the:
 a. protons in the nucleus
 b. neutrons in the nucleus
 c. electrons in the outer energy shell
 d. electrons in the innermost energy shell

4.100 In forming an ionic bond with an atom of chlorine, a sodium atom will:
 a. receive 1 electron from the chlorine atom
 b. receive 2 electrons from the chlorine atom
 c. give up 1 electron to the chlorine atom
 d. give up 2 electrons to the chlorine atom

4.101 In bonding, what would happen between the electrons of K and Br?
 a. they would be transferred
 b. they would be shared
 c. none of the above
 d. they would be both transferred and shared

4.102 Which compound contains a bond with **no** ionic character?

 a. CO

 b. CaO

 c. K_2O

 d. Na_2O

4.103 Which of the following molecules is nonpolar?

 a. NH_3

 b. H_2O, NO_2

 c. PCl_3

 d. N_2

4.104 Which molecule is nonpolar and contains a nonpolar covalent bond?

 a. F_2

 b. HI

 c. KCl

 d. NH_3

4.105 Which of the following is a nonpolar covalent bond?

 a. the bond between two carbons

 b. the bond between sodium and chloride

 c. the bond between two water molecules

 d. the bond between nitrogen and hydrogen

4.106 The type of bond that forms between two molecules of water is a:

 a. polar covalent bond

 b. hydrogen bond

 c. nonpolar covalent bond

 d. peptide bond

4.107 Which of the following is an example of hydrogen bonding?

 a. The bond between O and H in a single molecule of water

 b. The bond between the O of one water molecule and the H of a second water molecule

 c. The bond between the O of one water molecule and the O of a second water molecule

 d. The bond between the H of one water molecule and the H of a second water molecule

Chemistry for Thought

4.108 Refer to Figure 4.1, and answer the question in the caption. What other metals and nonmetals would you predict might react in a similar way?

4.109 The colors of some compounds, such as those shown in Figure 4.2, result from the presence of water in the compounds. Propose an experiment you could perform to see if this was true for the compounds shown in Figure 4.2.

4.110 Refer to Figure 4.6, and answer the question in the caption. Propose the shapes that would be assumed by a group of five balloons and by a group of six balloons.

4.111 Refer to Figure 4.9. Two of the compounds are highly colored (other than white). All the compounds consist of potassium and a polyatomic ion. If you have not yet done so, write formulas for the compounds and see if you can find a characteristic of the polyatomic ions of the colored compounds that is not found in the white compounds. Then refer to Table 4.7 and predict which of the other polyatomic anions would form colored compounds of potassium.

4.112 Recall how a metal atom changes to form a positively charged metal ion. How do you think the sizes of a metal atom and a positive ion of the same metal will compare?

4.113 Recall how a nonmetal atom such as chlorine changes to form a negatively charged ion. How do you think the size of a nonmetal atom and a negatively charged ion of the same nonmetal will compare?

4.114 Neon atoms do *not* combine to form Ne_2 molecules. Explain.

4.115 Refer to Figure 4.8, and answer the question in the caption. The balloon carries a negative charge. What would happen if a positively charged object was used in place of the balloon?

4.116 It has been found that NO is a vital biological molecule. Explain how NO forms when a fuel such as natural gas, CH_4, is burned in air at a high temperature.

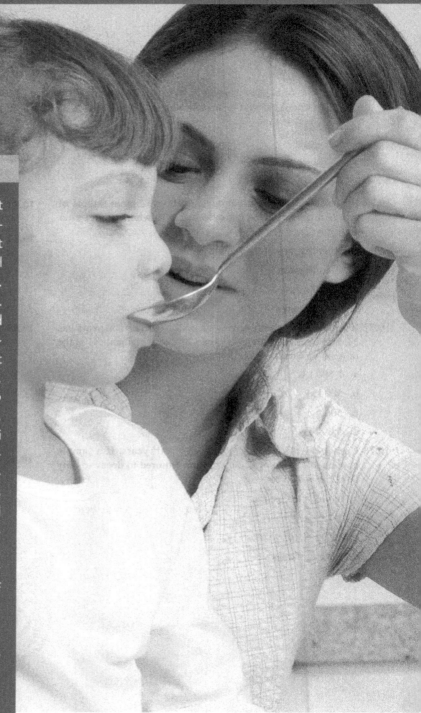

Case Study

Christi was at the end of her rope—she felt as if she had tried everything. Her daughter Mellissa was 4 years old, would start kindergarten in less than a year, and still wasn't able to control bowel movements. Nearly every day, Mellissa soiled her pants. Christi tried rewarding her with candy and even resorted to spanking, and the condescending advice of her mother-in-law didn't help. Mellissa would urinate in the toilet, but she seemed too busy playing or too stubborn to use it for anything else. Finally, in desperation and embarrassment, Christi consulted a pediatrician. He quickly diagnosed Mellissa with encopresis due to constipation. The doctor assured Christi it was neither poor parenting on her part nor bad behavior from her daughter that was causing the problem, but a medical condition. In addition to dietary changes, the doctor prescribed laxatives and 3 tablespoons of mineral oil daily. Mellissa disliked the mineral oil.

What behavioral techniques could Christi use to encourage her daughter to cooperate with the treatment? Should she punish Mellissa if she has an "accident"?

Follow-up to this Case Study appears at the end the chapter before the Concept Summary.

© Medioimages/Photodisc/Getty Images

Learning Objectives

When you have completed your study of this chapter, you should be able to:

1 Show that you understand the general importance of organic chemical compounds. **(Section 11.1)**

2 Recognize the molecular formulas of organic and inorganic compounds. **(Section 11.1)**

3 Explain some general differences between inorganic and organic compounds. **(Section 11.2)**

4 Use structural formulas to identify compounds that are isomers of each other. **(Section 11.3)**

5 Write condensed or expanded structural formulas for compounds. **(Section 11.4)**

6 Classify alkanes as normal or branched. **(Section 11.5)**

7 Use structural formulas to determine whether compounds are structural isomers. **(Section 11.6)**

8 Assign IUPAC names and draw structural formulas for alkanes. **(Section 11.7)**

9 Assign IUPAC names and draw structural formulas for cycloalkanes. **(Section 11.8)**

10 Name and draw structural formulas for geometric isomers of cycloalkanes. **(Section 11.9)**

11 Describe the key physical properties of alkanes. **(Section 11.10)**

12 Write alkane combustion reactions. **(Section 11.11)**

The word *organic* is used in several different contexts. Scientists of the 18th and 19th centuries studied compounds extracted from plants and animals and labeled them "organic" because they had been obtained from organized (living) systems. Organic fertilizer is organic in the original sense that it comes from a living organism. There is no universal definition of organic foods, but the term is generally taken to mean foods grown without the application of pesticides or synthetic fertilizers. When referring to organic chemistry, however, we mean the chemistry of carbon-containing compounds.

11.1 Carbon: The Element of Organic Compounds

Learning Objectives

1. Show that you understand the general importance of organic chemical compounds.

2. Be able to recognize the molecular formulas of organic and inorganic compounds.

Early chemists thought organic compounds could be produced only through the action of a "vital force," a special force active only in living organisms. This idea was central to the study of organic chemistry until 1828, because up to that time, no one had been able to synthesize an organic compound from its elements or from naturally occurring

minerals. In that year, Friedrich Wöhler, a German chemist, heated an inorganic salt called ammonium cyanate and produced urea. This compound, normally found in blood and urine, was unquestionably organic, and it had come from an inorganic source. The reaction is

$$NH_4NCO \xrightarrow{Heat} \underset{\text{urea}}{H-\underset{\underset{H}{|}}{N}-\underset{\overset{\parallel}{O}}{C}-\underset{\underset{H}{|}}{N}-H} \tag{11.1}$$

NH₄NCO
ammonium cyanate

Wöhler's urea synthesis discredited the "vital force" theory, and his success prompted other chemists to attempt to synthesize organic compounds. Today, organic compounds are being synthesized in thousands of laboratories, and most of the synthetics have never been isolated from natural sources.

Organic compounds share one unique feature: They all contain carbon. Therefore, **organic chemistry** is defined as the study of carbon-containing compounds. There are a few exceptions to this definition; a small number of carbon compounds—such as CO, CO_2, carbonates, and cyanides—were studied before Wöhler's urea synthesis. These were classified as inorganic because they were obtained from nonliving systems, and even though they contain carbon, we still consider them to be a part of **inorganic chemistry.**

The importance of carbon compounds to life on Earth cannot be overemphasized. If all carbon compounds were removed from Earth, its surface would be somewhat like the barren surface of the moon (see ❯ Figure 11.1). There would be no animals, plants, or any other form of life. If carbon-containing compounds were removed from the human body, all that would remain would be water, a very brittle skeleton, and a small residue of minerals. Many of the essential constituents of living matter—such as carbohydrates, fats, proteins, nucleic acids, enzymes, and hormones—are organic chemicals.

organic compound A compound that contains the element carbon.

organic chemistry The study of carbon-containing compounds.

inorganic chemistry The study of the elements and all noncarbon compounds.

Figure 11.1 Organic chemistry makes a tremendous difference when comparing the physical makeup of the Earth and the moon.

The essential needs of daily human life are food, fuel, shelter, and clothing. The principal components of food (with the exception of water) are organic. The fuels we use (e.g., wood, coal, petroleum, and natural gas) are mixtures of organic compounds. Our homes typically incorporate wood construction, and our clothing, whether made of natural or synthetic fibers, is organic.

Besides the major essentials, many of the smaller everyday things often taken for granted are also derived from carbon and its compounds. Consider an ordinary pencil. The "lead" (actually graphite), the wood, the rubber eraser, and the paint on the surface are all either carbon or carbon compounds. The paper in this book, the ink on its pages, and the glue holding it all together are also made of carbon compounds.

11.2 Organic and Inorganic Compounds Compared

Learning Objective

3. Explain some general differences between inorganic and organic compounds.

It is interesting that the subdivision of chemistry into its organic and inorganic branches results in one branch that deals with compounds composed mainly of one element and another branch that deals with compounds formed by the more than 100 remaining elements. However, this classification seems more reasonable when we recognize that known organic compounds are much more numerous than inorganic compounds. An estimated 500,000 inorganic compounds have been identified, but more than 9 million organic compounds are known, and thousands of new ones are synthesized or isolated each year.

One of the reasons for the large number of organic compounds is the unique ability of carbon atoms to form stable covalent bonds with other carbon atoms and with atoms of other elements. The resulting covalently bonded molecules may contain as few as one or more than a million carbon atoms.

In contrast, inorganic compounds are often characterized by the presence of ionic bonding. Covalent bonding also may be present, but it is less common. These differences generally cause organic and inorganic compounds to differ physically (see ❱ Figure 11.2) and chemically, as shown in ❱ Table 11.1.

Figure 11.2 Many organic compounds, such as ski wax, have relatively low melting points. What does this fact reveal about the forces between organic molecules?

© Adam Crowley/Stockbyte/Getty Images

TABLE 11.1 Properties of Typical Organic and Inorganic Compounds

Property	Organic Compounds	Inorganic Compounds
Bonding within molecules	Covalent	Often ionic
Forces between molecules	Generally weak	Quite strong
Normal physical state	Gases, liquids, or low-melting-point solids	Usually high-melting-point solids
Flammability	Often flammable	Usually nonflammable
Solubility in water	Often low	Often high
Conductivity of water solutions	Nonconductor	Conductor
Rate of chemical reactions	Usually slow	Usually fast

You will find that organic chemistry is very different from general or inorganic chemistry. By quickly picking up on the changes, you will help yourself prepare for quizzes and exams.

There is almost no math in these next five chapters or in the biochemistry section. Very few mathematical formulas need to be memorized. The problems you will encounter fall mainly into four categories: naming compounds and drawing structures, describing physical properties of substances, writing reactions, and identifying typical uses of compounds. This pattern holds true for all six of the organic chemistry chapters.

The naming of compounds is introduced in this chapter, and the rules developed here will serve as a starting point in the next five chapters. Therefore, it is important to master naming in this chapter. A well-developed skill in naming will help you do well on exams covering the coming chapters.

Only a few reactions are introduced in this chapter, but many more will be in future chapters. Writing organic reactions is just as important (and challenging) as naming structures, and Study Skills 12.1 will help you learn this skill. Identifying the uses of compounds can best be handled by making a list as you read the chapter or by highlighting compounds and their uses so that they are easy to review. All four categories of problems are covered by numerous end-of-chapter exercises to give you practice.

▶ **LEARNING CHECK 11.1** Classify each of the following compounds as organic or inorganic:

a. NaCl d. NaOH
b. CH_4 e. CH_3OH
c. C_6H_6 f. $Mg(NO_3)_2$

▶ **LEARNING CHECK 11.2** Decide whether each of the following characteristics most likely describes an organic or inorganic compound:

a. Flammable b. Low boiling point c. Soluble in water

11.3 Bonding Characteristics and Isomerism

Learning Objective

4. Be able to use structural formulas to identify compounds that are isomers of each other.

There are two major reasons for the astonishing number of organic compounds: the bonding characteristics of carbon atoms, and the isomerism of carbon-containing molecules. As a group IVA(14) element, a carbon atom has four valence electrons. Two of these outermost-shell electrons are in an *s* orbital, and two are in *p* orbitals (see Section 3.4):

$$\overset{\text{\large$\updownarrow$}}{\underset{2s}{\bigcirc}} \qquad \overset{\text{\large$\uparrow$}\ \text{\large$\uparrow$}}{\underset{2p}{\bigcirc\ \bigcirc\ \bigcirc}}$$

With only two unpaired electrons, we might predict that carbon would form just two covalent bonds with other atoms. Yet, we know from the formula of methane (CH_4) that carbon forms four bonds.

Linus Pauling (1901–1994), winner of the Nobel Prize in chemistry (1954) and Nobel Peace Prize (1963), developed a useful model to explain the bonding characteristics of carbon. Pauling found that a mathematical mixing of the 2*s* and three 2*p* orbitals could produce four new, equivalent orbitals (see ▶ Figure 11.3). Each of these **hybrid orbitals** has the same energy and is designated sp^3. An sp^3 orbital has a two-lobed shape, similar to

hybrid orbital An orbital produced from the combination of two or more nonequivalent orbitals of an atom.

the shape of a *p* orbital but with different-sized lobes (see ▶ Figure 11.4). Each of the four *sp*³ hybrid orbitals contains a single unpaired electron available for covalent bond formation. Thus, carbon forms four bonds.

Figure 11.3 The mixing of 2*s* and three 2*p* orbitals of a carbon atom to generate four *sp*³ carbon orbitals, each with energy intermediate between 2*s* and 2*p* orbitals.

Each carbon–hydrogen bond in methane arises from an overlap of a C (*sp*³) and an H (1*s*) orbital. The sharing of two electrons in this overlap region creates a sigma (σ) bond. The four equivalent *sp*³ orbitals point toward the corners of a regular tetrahedron (see ▶ Figure 11.5).

Carbon atoms also have the ability to bond covalently to other carbon atoms to form chains and networks. This means that two carbon atoms can join by sharing two electrons to form a single covalent bond:

$$\cdot\overset{\cdot}{\underset{\cdot}{C}}\cdot \;+\; \cdot\overset{\cdot}{\underset{\cdot}{C}}\cdot \;\longrightarrow\; \cdot\overset{\cdot}{\underset{\cdot}{C}}\!:\!\overset{\cdot}{\underset{\cdot}{C}}\cdot \qquad \text{or} \qquad \cdot\overset{\cdot}{\underset{\cdot}{C}}\!-\!\overset{\cdot}{\underset{\cdot}{C}}\cdot \qquad (11.2)$$

A third carbon atom can join the end of this chain:

$$\cdot\overset{\cdot}{\underset{\cdot}{C}}\!-\!\overset{\cdot}{\underset{\cdot}{C}}\cdot \;+\; \cdot\overset{\cdot}{\underset{\cdot}{C}}\cdot \;\longrightarrow\; \cdot\overset{\cdot}{\underset{\cdot}{C}}\!-\!\overset{\cdot}{\underset{\cdot}{C}}\!-\!\overset{\cdot}{\underset{\cdot}{C}}\cdot \qquad (11.3)$$

This process can continue and form carbon chains of almost any length, such as

$$\cdot\overset{\cdot}{\underset{\cdot}{C}}\!-\!\overset{\cdot}{\underset{\cdot}{C}}\!-\!\overset{\cdot}{\underset{\cdot}{C}}\!-\!\overset{\cdot}{\underset{\cdot}{C}}\!-\!\overset{\cdot}{\underset{\cdot}{C}}\!-\!\overset{\cdot}{\underset{\cdot}{C}}\!-\!\overset{\cdot}{\underset{\cdot}{C}}\!-\!\overset{\cdot}{\underset{\cdot}{C}}\!-\!\overset{\cdot}{\underset{\cdot}{C}}\cdot$$

The electrons not involved in forming the chain can be shared with electrons of other carbon atoms (to form chain branches) or with electrons of other elements such as hydrogen, oxygen, or nitrogen. Carbon atoms may also share more than one pair of electrons to form multiple bonds:

$$\cdot\overset{\cdot}{\underset{\cdot}{C}}\!-\!\overset{\cdot}{C}\!=\!\overset{\cdot}{C}\!-\!\overset{\cdot}{\underset{\cdot}{C}}\cdot \qquad\qquad \cdot\overset{\cdot}{\underset{\cdot}{C}}\!-\!C\!\equiv\!C\!-\!\overset{\cdot}{\underset{\cdot}{C}}\cdot$$

| Chain with double bond | Chain with triple bond |

In principle, there is no limit to the number of carbon atoms that can bond covalently. Thus, organic molecules range from the simple molecules such as methane (CH₄) to very complicated molecules containing over a million carbon atoms.

The variety of possible carbon atom arrangements is even more important than the size range of the resulting molecules. The carbon atoms in all but the very simplest organic molecules can bond in more than one arrangement, giving rise to different compounds with different structures and properties. This property, called **isomerism,** is characterized by compounds that have identical molecular formulas but different arrangements of atoms. One type of isomerism is characterized by compounds called **structural isomers.** Another type of isomerism is introduced in Section 11.9.

▶ Example 11.1

Use the usual rules for covalent bonding to show that a compound with the molecular formula C₂H₆O demonstrates the property of isomerism. Draw formulas for the isomers, showing all covalent bonds.

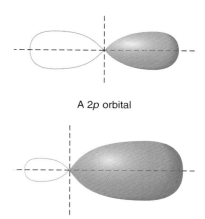

A 2*p* orbital

An *sp*³ hybrid orbital

Figure 11.4 A comparison of unhybridized *p* and *sp*³ hybridized orbital shapes. The atomic nucleus is at the junction of the lobes in each case.

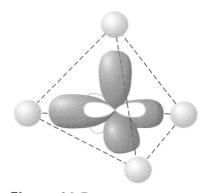

Figure 11.5 Directional characteristics of *sp*³ hybrid orbitals of carbon and the formation of C—H bonds in methane (CH₄). The hybrid orbitals point toward the corners of a regular tetrahedron. Hydrogen 1*s* orbitals are illustrated in position to form bonds by overlap with the major lobes of the hybrid orbitals.

isomerism A property in which two or more compounds have the same molecular formula but different arrangements of atoms.

structural isomers Compounds that have the same molecular formula but in which the atoms bond in different patterns.

Solution

Carbon forms four covalent bonds by sharing its four valence-shell electrons. Similarly, oxygen should form two covalent bonds, and hydrogen a single bond. On the basis of these bonding relationships, two structural isomers are possible:

$$\begin{array}{cccc} & H & H & \\ & | & | & \\ H - & C - & C & - O - H \\ & | & | & \\ & H & H & \end{array} \qquad \begin{array}{cccc} & H & & H \\ & | & & | \\ H - & C - & O - & C - H \\ & | & & | \\ & H & & H \end{array}$$

ethyl alcohol dimethyl ether

▶ **LEARNING CHECK 11.3** Which one of the structures below represents a structural isomer of

$$\begin{array}{ccc} H & O & H \\ | & \| & | \\ H - C - C - C - H \\ | & & | \\ H & & H \end{array} \quad ?$$

a.
$$\begin{array}{ccc} H & H & O - H \\ | & | & | \\ H - C = C - C - H \\ & & | \\ & & H \end{array}$$

c.
$$\begin{array}{ccc} H & H & O \\ | & | & \| \\ H - C - C - C - O - H \\ | & | \\ H & H \end{array}$$

b.
$$\begin{array}{ccc} H & H & O \\ | & | & \| \\ H - C = C - C - H \end{array}$$

The two isomers of Example 11.1 are quite different. Ethyl alcohol (grain alcohol) is a liquid at room temperature, whereas dimethyl ether is a gas. As we've seen before, the structural differences exert a significant influence on properties. From this example, we can see that molecular formulas such as C_2H_6O provide much less information about a compound than do structural formulas. ▶ Figure 11.6 shows ball-and-stick models of these two molecules.

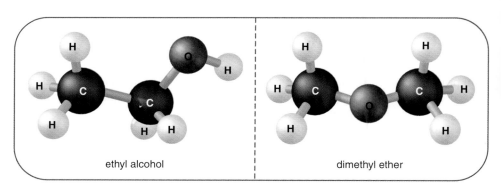

ethyl alcohol dimethyl ether

Figure 11.6 Ball-and-stick models of the isomers of C_2H_6O. Ethyl alcohol is a liquid at room temperature and completely soluble in water, whereas dimethyl ether is a gas at room temperature and only partially soluble in water.

As the number of carbon atoms in the molecular formula increases, the number of possible isomers increases dramatically. For example, 366,319 different isomers are possible for a molecular formula of $C_{20}H_{42}$. No one has prepared all these isomers or even drawn their structural formulas, but the number helps us understand why so many organic compounds have been either isolated from natural sources or synthesized.

11.4 Functional Groups: The Organization of Organic Chemistry

Learning Objective

5. Write condensed or expanded structural formulas for compounds.

Because of the enormous number of possible compounds, the study of organic chemistry might appear to be hopelessly difficult. However, the arrangement of organic compounds into a relatively small number of classes can simplify the study a great deal. This organization is done on the basis of characteristic structural features called **functional groups.** For example, compounds with a carbon–carbon double bond

$$\overset{\backslash}{\underset{/}{}} C = C \overset{/}{\underset{\backslash}{}}$$

are classified as alkenes. The major classes and functional groups are given in ▶ Table 11.2. Notice that each functional group in Table 11.2 (except for alkanes) contains a multiple bond or at least one oxygen or nitrogen atom.

In Table 11.2, we have used both expanded and condensed structural formulas for the compounds. **Expanded structural formulas** show all covalent bonds, whereas **condensed structural formulas** show only specific bonds. You should become familiar with both types, but especially with condensed formulas because they will be used often.

functional group A unique reactive combination of atoms that differentiates molecules of organic compounds of one class from those of another.

expanded structural formula A structural molecular formula showing all the covalent bonds.

condensed structural formula A structural molecular formula showing the general arrangement of atoms but without showing all the covalent bonds.

▶ Example 11.2

Write a condensed structural formula for each of the following compounds:

Solution

a. Usually the hydrogens belonging to a carbon are grouped to the right. Thus, the group

condenses to CH_3-, and

condenses to $-CH_2-$. Thus, the formula condenses to

$$CH_3-CH_2-CH_2-CH_3$$

Other acceptable condensations are

$$CH_3CH_2CH_2CH_3 \quad \text{and} \quad CH_3(CH_2)_2CH_3$$

Parentheses are used here to denote a series of two $-CH_2-$ groups.

TABLE 11.2 Classes and Functional Groups of Organic Compounds

Class	Functional Group	Example of Expanded Structural Formula	Example of Condensed Structural Formula	Common Name
Alkane	None	H—C—C—H (with H's)	CH_3CH_3	ethane
Alkene	$C=C$	$C=C$ (with H's)	$H_2C = CH_2$	ethylene
Alkyne	$-C \equiv C-$	$H-C \equiv C-H$	$HC \equiv CH$	acetylene
Aromatic	ring	ring structure	benzene ring	benzene
Alcohol	$-C-O-H$	$H-C-C-O-H$	$CH_3CH_2 - OH$	ethyl alcohol
Ether	$-C-O-C-$	$H-C-O-C-H$	$CH_3 - O - CH_3$	dimethyl ether
Amine	$-N-H$	$H-C-N-H$	$CH_3 - NH_2$	methylamine
Aldehyde	$-\overset{O}{\overset{\|}{C}}-H$	$H-C-\overset{O}{\overset{\|}{C}}-H$	$CH_3 - \overset{O}{\overset{\|}{C}} - H$	acetaldehyde
Ketone	$-C-\overset{O}{\overset{\|}{C}}-C-$	$H-C-\overset{O}{\overset{\|}{C}}-C-H$	$CH_3 - \overset{O}{\overset{\|}{C}} - CH_3$	acetone
Carboxylic acid	$-\overset{O}{\overset{\|}{C}}-O-H$	$H-C-\overset{O}{\overset{\|}{C}}-O-H$	$CH_3 - \overset{O}{\overset{\|}{C}} - OH$	acetic acid
Ester	$-\overset{O}{\overset{\|}{C}}-O-C-$	$H-C-\overset{O}{\overset{\|}{C}}-O-C-H$	$CH_3 - \overset{O}{\overset{\|}{C}} - O - CH_3$	methyl acetate
Amide	$-\overset{O}{\overset{\|}{C}}-N-H$	$H-C-\overset{O}{\overset{\|}{C}}-N-H$	$CH_3 - \overset{O}{\overset{\|}{C}} - NH_2$	acetamide

b. The group

$$-\overset{\displaystyle |}{\underset{\displaystyle H}{C}}-$$

condenses to $-\text{CH}-$. The condensed formula is therefore

$$\overset{\displaystyle CH_3}{\underset{}{CH_3-\overset{|}{CH}-CH_2-CH_2-CH_3}} \qquad \text{or} \qquad \overset{\displaystyle CH_3}{\underset{}{CH_3\overset{|}{CH}CH_2CH_2CH_3}}$$

or

$$(CH_3)_2CH(CH_2)_2CH_3$$

In the last form, the first set of parentheses indicates two identical CH_3 groups attached to the same carbon atom, and the second set of parentheses denotes two CH_2 groups.

> **LEARNING CHECK 11.4** Write a condensed structural formula for each of the following compounds. Retain the bonds to and within the functional groups.
>
> **a.**
> $$\underset{\displaystyle \overset{\displaystyle |}{H}\ \overset{\displaystyle |}{H}\quad \overset{\displaystyle |}{H}\ \overset{\displaystyle |}{H}\ \overset{\displaystyle |}{H}}{\overset{\displaystyle \overset{\displaystyle H}{|}\ \overset{\displaystyle OH}{|}\ \ \overset{\displaystyle H}{|}\ \overset{\displaystyle H}{|}\ \overset{\displaystyle H}{|}}{H-C-C\underline{}C-C-C-H}}$$
>
> **b.**
> $$\overset{\displaystyle H\qquad\quad H\qquad\quad H\ \ O}{\underset{\displaystyle H\quad H-\overset{|}{\underset{|}{C}}-H\quad H}{H-\overset{|}{\underset{|}{C}}\underline{}\overset{|}{\underset{|}{C}}\underline{}\overset{|}{C}-\overset{\|}{C}-OH}}$$

11.5 Alkane Structures

Learning Objective

6. Classify alkanes as normal or branched.

Hydrocarbons, the simplest of all organic compounds, contain only two elements, carbon and hydrogen. **Saturated hydrocarbons** or **alkanes** are organic compounds in which carbon is bonded to four other atoms by single bonds; there are no double or triple bonds in the molecule. Unsaturated hydrocarbons, studied later, are called alkenes, alkynes, and aromatics and contain double bonds, triple bonds, or six-carbon rings, as shown in
> Figure 11.7.

hydrocarbon An organic compound that contains only carbon and hydrogen.

saturated hydrocarbon Another name for an alkane.

alkane A hydrocarbon that contains only single bonds.

Figure 11.7 Classification of hydrocarbons.

DR. MELINA B. JAMPOLIS, M.D.

Dr. Melina B. Jampolis, M.D. is a Los Angeles, California, Physician Nutrition Specialist—a specialty practiced by only a few hundred physicians in the United States. She focuses exclusively on nutrition for weight loss and disease prevention and treatment.

Ask an Expert 11.1

Q: Is organic food worth the price?

A: "Organic" is a designation used by the United States Department of Agriculture (USDA) to certify food that is produced without the use of antibiotics, hormones, synthetic chemicals or fertilizers, most pesticides, bioengineering, ionizing radiation, or sewage sludge. Organic agriculture is "an ecological production management system that promotes and enhances biodiversity, biological cycles and soil biological activity" according to the USDA. During the past decade, organic foods, including produce, meat, dairy, and even packaged foods, have undergone a huge growth in use. This growth has been tempered by the fact that they are still generally more expensive than conventionally produced food. Does the extra expense justify the higher price? Many believe that organic products are higher in nutrients, but a recent systematic review of studies performed over the past 50 years did not find a difference in nutrient quality between organic and conventionally grown produce. When it comes to pesticide and chemical exposure, the reality is that we are exposed to potentially harmful chemicals in many things, ranging from consumer products, air, drinking water, pollution, food, and even our homes. In fact, the levels of pesticides allowed in agricultural products in the United States are much more strictly regulated than what people can spray in their homes.

What is the clinical relevance of the exposure to pesticides from agricultural products? We do not know. The ability to detect very small amounts of pesticides has improved over the past several decades with advances in analytical chemistry, which now allow some labs to detect levels as low as 10 parts per trillion. However, improved detection methods do not necessarily reflect the potential health risk. Most pesticides are neurotoxicants, meaning that they damage the brain. For this reason, two of the most potentially vulnerable populations include pregnant women and children from birth to 6 years old. Preliminary studies suggest that the offspring of pregnant women subjected to above-average pesticide exposure from living in farmworking communities do show effects on several indicators of brain development. In addition, adult farm workers with very high exposure show an increased risk of neurodegenerative disease.

Until convincing evidence to the contrary becomes available, the benefits of eating fruits and vegetables—which are low in calories and loaded with vitamins, minerals, and disease-fighting phytonutrients—even if they are not organically grown, likely far outweigh the risk for most people. If you are pregnant or have children under the age of 6 and want to limit their pesticide exposure without limiting their intake of produce, the environmental working group publishes an annual list of the top 12 foods that have been found to contain the most pesticides and the 15 that contain the least. Choose organic when you can from the top 12, but the most important thing you can do is make sure to get plenty of variety when it comes to produce. This will minimize your exposure and maximize your nutrition and health. The least-contaminated produce are often those protected by an outer coating (such as a corn husk) or thick skin (pineapple, watermelon, kiwi, cantaloupe, avocado, grapefruit, mango), so you can use that as a rough guide to direct you to produce with lower levels of pesticides.

Outer coatings on produce help minimize the exposure to pestic

Most life processes are based on the reactions of functional groups. Since alkanes have no functional group, they are not abundant in the human body. However, most compounds in human cells contain parts consisting solely of carbon and hydrogen that behave very much like hydrocarbons. Thus, to understand the chemical properties of the more complex biomolecules, it is useful to have some understanding of the structure, physical properties, and chemical behavior of hydrocarbons.

Another important reason for becoming familiar with the characteristics of hydrocarbons is the crucial role they play in modern industrial society. We use naturally occurring hydrocarbons as primary sources of energy and as important sources of raw materials for the manufacture of plastics, synthetic fibers, drugs, and hundreds of other compounds used daily (see ❱ Figure 11.8).

Alkanes can be represented by the general formula C_nH_{2n+2}, where n is the number of carbon atoms in the molecule. The simplest alkane, methane, contains one carbon atom and therefore has the molecular formula CH_4. The carbon atom is at the center, and the four bonds of the carbon atom are directed toward the hydrogen atoms at the corners of a regular tetrahedron; each hydrogen atom is geometrically equivalent to the other three in the molecule (see ❱ Figure 11.9). A tetrahedral orientation of bonds with bond angles of 109.5° is typical for carbon atoms that form four single bonds. Methane is the primary compound in natural gas. Tremendous quantities of natural gas are consumed worldwide because methane is an efficient, clean-burning fuel. It is used to heat homes, cook food, and power factories.

Figure 11.8 This golf club has the strength and light weight of aluminum yet is made from graphite (carbon) fibers reinforced with plastic. What other sports equipment is made from graphite fibers?

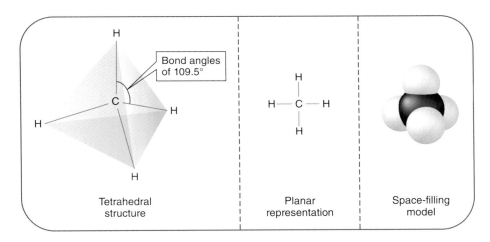

Tetrahedral structure — Planar representation — Space-filling model

Bond angles of 109.5°

Figure 11.9 Structural representations of methane, CH_4.

The next alkane is ethane, which has the molecular formula C_2H_6 and the structural formula CH_3—CH_3. This molecule may be thought of as a methane molecule with one hydrogen removed and a —CH_3 put in its place. Again, the carbon bonds have a tetrahedral geometry as shown in ❱ Figure 11.10. Ethane is a minor component of natural gas.

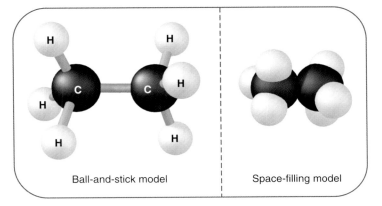

Ball-and-stick model — Space-filling model

Figure 11.10 Perspective models of the ethane molecule, CH_3CH_3.

Propane, the third alkane, has the molecular formula of C_3H_8 and the structural formula CH_3—CH_2—CH_3. Again, we can produce this molecule by removing a hydrogen

atom from the preceding compound (ethane) and substituting a —CH₃ in its place (see ▶ Figure 11.11). Since all six hydrogen atoms of ethane are equivalent, it makes no difference which one is replaced. Propane is used extensively as an industrial fuel, as well as for home heating and cooking (see Figure 11.11c).

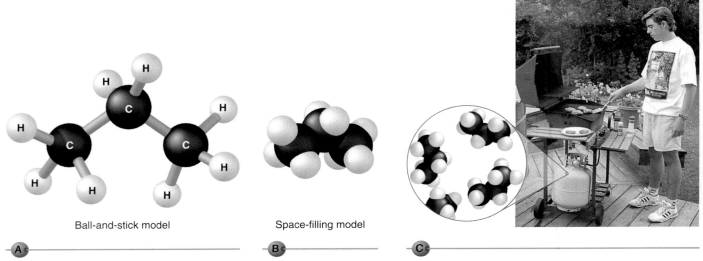

Ball-and-stick model Space-filling model

A ——————————————— B ————————— C

Figure 11.11 Perspective models **A** and **B** of the propane molecule $CH_3CH_2CH_3$. Propane is a common fuel for gas grills **C**.

The fourth member of the series, butane, with molecular formula C_4H_{10}, can also be produced by removing a hydrogen atom (this time from propane) and adding a —CH₃. However, all the hydrogen atoms of propane are not geometrically equivalent, and more than one position is available for substitution. Replacing a hydrogen atom on one of the end carbons of propane with —CH₃ produces a butane molecule that has the structural formula CH_3—CH_2—CH_2—CH_3. If, however, substitution is made on the central carbon atom of propane, the butane produced is

$$CH_3 - CH - CH_3$$
$$|$$
$$CH_3$$

normal alkane Any alkane in which all the carbon atoms are aligned in a continuous chain.

branched alkane An alkane in which at least one carbon atom is not part of a continuous chain.

Figure 11.12 Space-filling models of the isomeric butanes.

Notice that both butanes have the same molecular formula, C_4H_{10}. These two possible butanes are structural isomers because they have the same molecular formulas, but they have different atom-to-atom bonding sequences. The straight-chain isomer is called a **normal alkane** and the other is a **branched alkane** (▶ Figure 11.12).

The number of possible structural isomers increases dramatically with the number of carbon atoms in an alkane, as shown in ▶ Table 11.3.

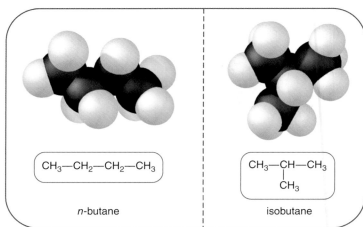

CH_3—CH_2—CH_2—CH_3

n-butane

CH_3—CH—CH_3
$|$
CH_3

isobutane

a. Determine the molecular formula of the alkane containing eight carbon atoms.
b. Draw the condensed structural formula of the normal isomer of the compound in part a.

11.6 Conformations of Alkanes

Learning Objective

7. Use structural formulas to determine whether compounds are structural isomers.

Remember that planar representations such as $CH_3—CH_2—CH_3$ or

$$
\begin{array}{ccc}
H & H & H \\
| & | & | \\
H—C—C—C—H \\
| & | & | \\
H & H & H
\end{array}
$$

are given with no attempt to accurately portray correct bond angles or molecular geometries. Structural formulas are usually written horizontally simply because it is convenient. It is also important to know that actual organic molecules are in constant motion—twisting, turning, vibrating, and bending. Groups connected by a single bond are capable of rotating about that bond much like a wheel rotates around an axle (see ▶ Figure 11.13). As a result of such rotation about single bonds, a molecule can exist in many different orientations, called **conformations.** In a sample of butane containing billions of identical molecules, there are countless conformations present at any instant, and each conformation is rapidly changing into another. Two of the possible conformations of butane are shown in ▶ Figure 11.14. We must be sure to recognize that these different conformations do not represent different structural isomers. In each case, the four carbon atoms are bonded in a

TABLE 11.3 Molecular Formulas and Possible Structural Isomers of Alkanes

Molecular Formula	Number of Possible Structural Isomers
C_4H_{10}	2
C_5H_{12}	3
C_6H_{14}	5
$C_{10}H_{22}$	75
$C_{20}H_{42}$	366,319
$C_{30}H_{62}$	4,111,846,763

conformations The different arrangements of atoms in space achieved by rotation about single bonds.

Figure 11.13 Rotation about single bonds (n-butane molecule).

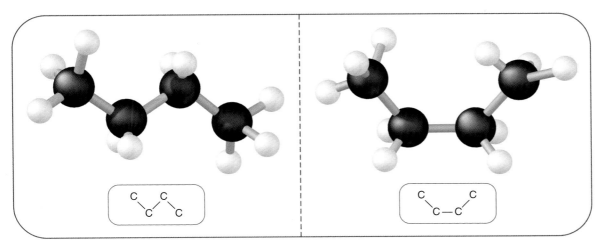

Figure 11.14 Perspective models and carbon skeletons of two conformations of *n*-butane.

continuous (unbranched) chain. Since the order of bonding is not changed, the conformations correspond to the same molecule. Two structures would be structural isomers only if bonds had to be broken and remade to convert one into the other.

▶ Example 11.3

Which of the following pairs are structural isomers, and which are simply different representations of the same molecule?

$$CH_3-CH_2-CH_2-CH_3 \qquad \begin{array}{c} CH_3 \\ | \\ CH_2-CH_2 \\ | \\ CH_3 \end{array}$$

$$\begin{array}{c} CH_3 \\ | \\ CH_3-CH-CH_2-CH_3 \end{array} \qquad \begin{array}{c} CH_3 \\ | \\ CH_3-CH_2-CH-CH_3 \end{array}$$

$$\begin{array}{c} CH_3 \\ | \\ CH_3-CH-CH_2-CH_2-CH_3 \end{array} \qquad \begin{array}{c} CH_3 \\ | \\ CH_3-CH_2-CH-CH_2-CH_3 \end{array}$$

Solution

a. Same molecule: In both molecules, the four carbons are bonded in a continuous chain.

$$\overset{1}{C}H_3-\overset{2}{C}H_2-\overset{3}{C}H_2-\overset{4}{C}H_3 \qquad \begin{array}{c} \overset{4}{C}H_3 \\ | \\ \overset{2}{C}H_2-\overset{3}{C}H_2 \\ | \\ \overset{1}{C}H_3 \end{array}$$

b. Same molecule: In both molecules, there is a continuous chain of four carbons with a branch at position 2. The molecule has simply been turned around.

$$\begin{array}{c} CH_3 \\ | \\ CH_3-CH-CH_2-CH_3 \\ {\scriptstyle 1 \quad\; 2 \quad\;\; 3 \quad\;\; 4} \end{array} \qquad \begin{array}{c} CH_3 \\ | \\ CH_3-CH_2-CH-CH_3 \\ {\scriptstyle 4 \quad\;\; 3 \quad\;\; 2 \quad\; 1} \end{array}$$

c. Structural isomers: Both molecules have a continuous chain of five carbons, but the branch is located at different positions.

$$\begin{array}{c} CH_3 \\ | \\ CH_3-CH-CH_2-CH_2-CH_3 \\ {\scriptstyle 1 \quad\; 2 \quad\;\; 3 \quad\;\; 4 \quad\;\; 5} \end{array} \qquad \begin{array}{c} CH_3 \\ | \\ CH_3-CH_2-CH-CH_2-CH_3 \\ {\scriptstyle 1 \quad\;\; 2 \quad\;\; 3 \quad\;\; 4 \quad\;\; 5} \end{array}$$

▶ LEARNING CHECK 11.6 Which of the following pairs represent structural isomers, and which are simply the same compound?

a. $\begin{array}{c} CH_3-CH_2-CH_2 \\ | \\ CH_2-CH_3 \end{array}$ $\qquad \begin{array}{c} CH_3-CH_2 \\ | \\ CH_2-CH_2 \\ | \\ CH_3 \end{array}$

b. $\begin{array}{c} CH_3 \\ | \\ CH_3-CH-CH_2-CH_3 \end{array}$ $\qquad \begin{array}{c} CH_2-CH_3 \\ | \\ CH_3-CH-CH_3 \end{array}$

c. $\begin{array}{c} CH_3 \\ | \\ CH_3-CH_2-CH-CH_2-CH_3 \end{array}$ $\qquad \begin{array}{c} CH_3 \\ | \\ CH_3-CH_2-CH_2-CH-CH_3 \end{array}$

11.7 Alkane Nomenclature

Learning Objective

8. Assign IUPAC names and draw structural formulas for alkanes.

When only a relatively few organic compounds were known, chemists gave them what are today called trivial or common names, such as methane, ethane, propane, and butane. The names for the larger alkanes were derived from the Greek prefixes that indicate the number of carbon atoms in the molecule. Thus, *pent*ane contains five carbons, *hex*ane has six, *hept*ane has seven, and so forth, as shown in ▶ Table 11.4.

TABLE 11.4 Names of Alkanes

Number of Carbon Atoms	Name	Molecular Formula	Structure of Normal Isomer
1	methane	CH_4	CH_4
2	ethane	C_2H_6	CH_3CH_3
3	propane	C_3H_8	$CH_3CH_2CH_3$
4	butane	C_4H_{10}	$CH_3CH_2CH_2CH_3$
5	pentane	C_5H_{12}	$CH_3CH_2CH_2CH_2CH_3$
6	hexane	C_6H_{14}	$CH_3CH_2CH_2CH_2CH_2CH_3$
7	heptane	C_7H_{16}	$CH_3CH_2CH_2CH_2CH_2CH_2CH_3$
8	octane	C_8H_{18}	$CH_3CH_2CH_2CH_2CH_2CH_2CH_2CH_3$
9	nonane	C_9H_{20}	$CH_3CH_2CH_2CH_2CH_2CH_2CH_2CH_2CH_3$
10	decane	$C_{10}H_{22}$	$CH_3CH_2CH_2CH_2CH_2CH_2CH_2CH_2CH_2CH_3$

As more compounds and isomers were discovered, however, it became increasingly difficult to devise unique names and much more difficult to commit them to memory. Obviously, a systematic method was needed. Such a method is now in use, but so are several common methods.

The names for the two isomeric butanes (*n*-butane and isobutane) illustrate the important features of the common nomenclature system used for alkanes. The stem *but-* indicates that four carbons are present in the molecule. The *-ane* ending signifies the alkane family. The prefix *n-* indicates that all carbons form an unbranched chain. The prefix *iso-* refers to compounds in which all carbons except one are in a continuous chain and in which that one carbon is branched from a next-to-the-end carbon, as shown:

$$CH_3CH_2CH_2CH_3$$
n-butane

$$CH_3\overset{\overset{\displaystyle CH_3}{|}}{C}HCH_3$$
isobutane

$$CH_3CH_2CH_2CH_2CH_3$$
n-pentane

$$CH_3\overset{\overset{\displaystyle CH_3}{|}}{C}HCH_2CH_3$$
isopentane

$$CH_3CH_2CH_2CH_2CH_2CH_3$$
n-hexane

$$CH_3\overset{\overset{\displaystyle CH_3}{|}}{C}HCH_2CH_2CH_3$$
isohexane

This common naming system has limitations. Pentane has three isomers, and hexane has five. The more complicated the compound, the greater the number of isomers, and the greater the number of special prefixes needed to name all the isomers. It would be extremely difficult and time-consuming to try to identify each of the 75 isomeric alkanes containing 10 carbon atoms by a unique prefix or name.

To devise a system of nomenclature that could be used for even the most complicated compounds, committees of chemists have met periodically since 1892. The system resulting from these meetings is called the IUPAC (International Union of Pure and Applied Chemistry) system. This system is much the same for all classes of organic compounds. The IUPAC name for an organic compound consists of three component parts:

| Prefix | Root | Ending |
| Denotes number and identity of attached groups | Denotes longest carbon chain | Denotes functional class |

The *root* of the IUPAC name specifies the longest continuous chain of carbon atoms in the compound. The roots for the first 10 normal hydrocarbons are based on the names given in Table 11.4: C_1 *meth-*, C_2 *eth-*, C_3 *prop-*, C_4 *but-*, C_5 *pent-*, C_6 *hex-*, C_7 *hept-*, C_8 *oct-*, C_9 *non-*, C_{10} *dec-*.

The *ending* of an IUPAC name specifies the functional class or the major functional group of the compound. The ending *-ane* specifies an alkane. Each of the other functional classes has a characteristic ending; for example, *-ene* is the ending for alkenes, and the *-ol* ending designates alcohols.

Prefixes are used to specify the identity, number, and location of atoms or groups of atoms that are attached to the longest carbon chain. ▶ Table 11.5 lists several common carbon-containing groups referred to as **alkyl groups.** Each alkyl group is a collection of atoms that can be thought of as an alkane minus one hydrogen atom. Alkyl groups are

alkyl group A group differing by one hydrogen from an alkane.

TABLE 11.5 Common Alkyl Groups

Parent Alkane	Structure of Parent Alkane	Structure of Alkyl Group	Name of Alkyl Group
methane	CH_4	CH_3-	methyl
ethane	CH_3CH_3	CH_3CH_2-	ethyl
propane	$CH_3CH_2CH_3$	$CH_3CH_2CH_2-$	propyl
		CH_3CHCH_3	isopropyl
n-butane	$CH_3CH_2CH_2CH_3$	$CH_3CH_2CH_2CH_2-$	butyl
		$CH_3CH_2CHCH_3$	*sec*-butyl (secondary-butyl)[a]
isobutane	CH_3CHCH_3 with CH_3 branch	CH_3CHCH_2- with CH_3 branch	isobutyl
		CH_3CCH_3 with CH_3 branch	*t*-butyl (tertiary-butyl)[a]

[a]For an explanation of *secondary* and *tertiary*, see Section 13.2.

named simply by dropping -*ane* from the name of the corresponding alkane and replacing it with -*yl*. For example, CH_3— is called a methyl group and CH_3—CH_2— an ethyl group:

CH_4	CH_3—CH_3	CH_3—	CH_3—CH_2—
methane	ethane	methyl group	ethyl group

Two different alkyl groups can be derived from propane, depending on which hydrogen is removed. Removal of a hydrogen from an end carbon results in a propyl group:

CH_3—CH_2—CH_3	CH_3—CH_2—CH_2—
propane	propyl group

Removal of a hydrogen from the center carbon results in an isopropyl group:

$$CH_3—CH_2—CH_3 \qquad CH_3—\overset{|}{CH}—CH_3$$
propane isopropyl group

An isopropyl group also can be represented by $(CH_3)_2CH$—. As shown in Table 11.5, four butyl groups can be derived from butane, two from the straight-chain, or normal, butane, and two from the branched-chain isobutane. A number of nonalkyl groups are also commonly used in naming organic compounds (see ▶ Table 11.6).

The following steps are useful when the IUPAC name of an alkane is written on the basis of its structural formula:

Step 1. Name the longest chain. The longest continuous carbon-atom chain is chosen as the basis for the name. The names are those given in Table 11.4.

TABLE 11.6 Common Nonalkyl Groups

Group	Name
—F	fluoro
—Cl	chloro
—Br	bromo
—I	iodo
—NO_2	nitro
—NH_2	amino

Example	Longest Chain	Comments
	C — C — C — C with C branch	This compound is a butane.
	C — C — C chain with C below	This compound is a pentane.
	two depictions of longest chain	Often there is more than one way to designate the longest chain. Either way, in this case, the compound is a hexane.

▶ **LEARNING CHECK 11.7** Identify the longest carbon chain in the following:

a.
$$CH_3$$
$$|$$
$$CH_2—CH_2—CH_3$$

b.
$$CH_3 \qquad\qquad CH_3$$
$$| \qquad\qquad\qquad |$$
$$CH_2—CH—CH_2$$
$$|$$
$$CH_3$$

c.
$$CH_3—CH—CH_3$$
$$|$$
$$CH_3—CH—CH_3$$

Step 2. Number the longest chain. The carbon atoms in the longest chain are numbered consecutively from the end that will give the lowest possible number to any carbon to which a group is attached.

$$\overset{4}{C}H_3 - \overset{3}{C}H_2 - \overset{2}{C}H - \overset{1}{C}H_3 \qquad \text{and not} \qquad \overset{1}{C}H_3 - \overset{2}{C}H_2 - \overset{3}{C}H - \overset{4}{C}H_3$$
$$\underset{CH_3}{|} \qquad\qquad\qquad\qquad\qquad\qquad \underset{CH_3}{|}$$

$$\overset{2}{C}H_2 - \overset{1}{C}H_3 \qquad\qquad\qquad \overset{4}{C}H_2 - \overset{5}{C}H_3$$
$$\overset{3}{|}\qquad\qquad\qquad\qquad\qquad\qquad \overset{2}{|}$$
$$CH_3 - \overset{}{C}H - \overset{4}{C}H_2 \qquad\qquad CH_3 - \overset{}{C}H - \overset{}{C}H_2$$
$$\overset{5}{|} \qquad\qquad\qquad \text{the chain may also} \qquad \overset{3}{} \overset{1}{|}$$
$$CH_3 \qquad\qquad\qquad \text{be numbered} \qquad\qquad CH_3$$

If two or more alkyl groups are attached to the longest chain and more than one numbering sequence is possible, the chain is numbered to get the lowest series of numbers. An easy way to follow this rule is to number from the end of the chain nearest a branch:

$$\overset{1}{C}H_3 - \overset{2}{C}H - \overset{3}{C}H_2 - \overset{4}{C}H - \overset{5}{C}H_2\overset{6}{C}H_3 \qquad \text{and not} \qquad \overset{6}{C}H_3 - \overset{5}{C}H - \overset{4}{C}H_2 - \overset{3}{C}H - \overset{2}{C}H_2 - \overset{1}{C}H_3$$
$$\underset{CH_3}{|} \qquad\quad \underset{CH_2-CH_3}{|} \qquad\qquad\qquad \underset{CH_3}{|} \qquad\quad \underset{CH_2-CH_3}{|}$$

Groups are located at positions 2 and 4 \qquad\qquad\qquad Groups are located at positions 3 and 5

$$\qquad\qquad\qquad\qquad \overset{CH_3}{|}$$
$$\overset{5}{C}H_3 - \overset{4}{C}H - \overset{3}{C}H_2 - \overset{2}{C} - \overset{1}{C}H_3 \qquad \text{and not} \qquad \overset{1}{C}H_3 - \overset{2}{C}H - \overset{3}{C}H_2 - \overset{4}{C} - \overset{5}{C}H_3$$
$$\underset{CH_3}{|} \qquad\quad \underset{CH_3}{|} \qquad\qquad\qquad\qquad \underset{CH_3}{|} \qquad\quad \underset{CH_3}{|}$$

Groups are located at \qquad\qquad\qquad\qquad Groups are located at
positions 2,2,4 \qquad\qquad\qquad\qquad\qquad\qquad positions 2,4,4

Here, a difference occurs with the second number in the sequence, so positions 2,2,4 is the lowest series and is used rather than positions 2,4,4.

▶ **LEARNING CHECK 11.8** Decide how to correctly number the longest chain in the following according to IUPAC rules:

a. $CH_3 - CH - CH_2 - CH_2 - CH_3$
$$\qquad\quad \underset{CH_2}{|}$$
$$\qquad\quad \underset{CH_3}{|}$$

b. $CH_3 - CH_2 - CH_2 - CH_2 - \overset{\overset{CH_3}{|}}{C} - CH_2 - CH - CH_3$
$$\qquad\qquad\qquad\qquad\qquad \underset{CH_3}{|} \qquad\quad \underset{CH_3}{|}$$

Step 3. Locate and name the attached alkyl groups. Each group is located by the number of the carbon atom to which it is attached on the chain.

$$\overset{4}{C}H_3 - \overset{3}{C}H_2 - \overset{2}{C}H - \overset{1}{C}H_3 \qquad$$ The attached group is located on carbon 2 of the chain, and it is a methyl group.
$$\qquad\qquad\qquad \underset{CH_3}{|}$$

$$\overset{1}{C}H_3 - \overset{2}{C}H - \overset{3}{C}H_2 - \overset{4}{C}H - \overset{5}{C}H_2 - \overset{6}{C}H_3 \qquad$$ The one-carbon group at position 2 is a methyl group. The two-carbon group at position 4 is an ethyl group.
$$\qquad\qquad \underset{CH_3}{|} \qquad\qquad \underset{CH_2-CH_3}{|}$$

▶ **LEARNING CHECK 11.9** Identify the alkyl groups attached to the horizontal line, which symbolizes a long carbon chain. Refer to Table 11.5 if necessary.

$$CH_3$$
$$|$$
$$CH - CH_3$$
$$|$$

CH_3	CH_2	$CH - CH_3$	$CH_2 - CH_3$
	CH_2	CH_2	
	CH_3	CH_3	

Step 4. Combine the longest chain and the branches into the name. The position and the name of the attached alkyl group are added to the name of the longest chain and written as one word:

$$\overset{4}{C}H_3 - \overset{3}{C}H_2 - \overset{2}{C}H - \overset{1}{C}H_3$$
$$|$$
$$CH_3$$

2-methylbutane

Additional steps are needed when more than one alkyl group is attached to the longest chain.

Step 5. Indicate the number and position of attached alkyl groups. If two or more of the same alkyl group occur as branches, the number of them is indicated by the prefixes *di-*, *tri-*, *tetra-*, *penta-*, etc., and the location of each is again indicated by a number. These position numbers, separated by commas, are put just before the name of the group, with hyphens before and after the numbers when necessary:

$$\overset{1}{C}H_3 - \overset{2}{C}H - \overset{3}{C}H_2 - \overset{4}{C}H - \overset{5}{C}H_3$$
$$\qquad |\qquad\qquad\quad |$$
$$\qquad CH_3\qquad\quad CH_3$$

2,4-dimethylpentane

$$\overset{1}{C}H_3 - \overset{2}{C}H_2 - \overset{3}{C} - \overset{4}{C}H_2 - \overset{5}{C}H_3$$
$$\qquad\qquad\qquad |$$
$$\qquad\qquad\quad CH_3$$
with CH_3 above C3

3,3-dimethylpentane

If two or more *different* alkyl groups are present, their names are alphabetized and added to the name of the basic alkane, again as one word. For purposes of alphabetizing, the prefixes *di-*, *tri-*, and so on are ignored, as are the italicized prefixes secondary *(sec)* and tertiary *(t)*. The prefix *iso-* is an exception and is used for alphabetizing:

$$\overset{1}{C}H_3 - \overset{2}{C}H - \overset{3}{C}H - \overset{4}{C}H_2 - \overset{5}{C}H - \overset{6}{C}H_2 - \overset{7}{C}H_2 - \overset{8}{C}H_3$$
$$\qquad\quad |\quad\ |\qquad\qquad\quad |$$
$$\qquad CH_3\ CH_3\qquad\quad CH - CH_3$$
$$\qquad\qquad\qquad\qquad\qquad\quad |$$
$$\qquad\qquad\qquad\qquad\qquad CH_3$$

5-isopropyl-2,3-dimethyloctane

a.
$$CH_3-CH_2-CH_2-CH_2-\underset{\underset{\displaystyle CH_3}{|}}{CH}-CH_3$$

b.
$$CH_3-CH_2-CH_2-\underset{\underset{\displaystyle CH_2-CH_3}{|}}{CH}-CH_2-\underset{\underset{\displaystyle CH_2-CH_3}{|}}{CH}-CH_3$$

c.
$$CH_3-CH_2-CH_2-\underset{\underset{\underset{\displaystyle CH_3}{|}}{\underset{\displaystyle CH-CH_3}{|}}}{CH}-\underset{\underset{\displaystyle CH_3}{|}}{CH}-\underset{\underset{\displaystyle CH_3}{|}}{CH}-CH_3$$

Naming compounds is a very important skill, as is the reverse process of using IUPAC nomenclature to specify a structural formula. The two processes are very similar. To obtain a formula from a name, determine the longest chain, number the chain, and add any attached groups.

► Example 11.4

Draw a condensed structural formula for 3-ethyl-2-methylhexane.

Solution
Use the last part of the name to determine the longest chain. Draw a chain of six carbons. Then, number the carbon atoms.

$$\underset{1}{C}-\underset{2}{C}-\underset{3}{C}-\underset{4}{C}-\underset{5}{C}-\underset{6}{C}$$

Attach a methyl group at position 2 and an ethyl group at position 3.

$$\underset{1}{C}-\underset{2}{C}-\underset{\underset{\displaystyle CH_2CH_3}{|3}}{C}-\underset{4}{C}-\underset{5}{C}-\underset{6}{C}$$
(with CH_3 attached above C-2)

Complete the structure by adding enough hydrogen atoms so that each carbon has four bonds.

$$CH_3-\underset{2}{CH}-\underset{\underset{\displaystyle CH_2CH_3}{|3}}{\underset{1}{CH}}-\underset{4}{CH_2}-\underset{5}{CH_2}-\underset{6}{CH_3}$$
(with CH_3 attached above C-2)

11.8 Cycloalkanes

Learning Objective

9. Assign IUPAC names and draw structural formulas for cycloalkanes.

From what we have said so far, the formula C_3H_6 cannot represent an alkane. Not enough hydrogens are present to allow each carbon to form four bonds, unless there are multiple bonds. For example, the structural formula $CH_3—CH{=}CH_2$ fits the molecular formula but cannot represent an alkane because of the double bond. The C_3H_6 formula does become acceptable for an alkane if the carbon atoms form a ring, or cyclic, structure rather than the open-chain structure shown:

$$C - C - C \qquad \begin{array}{c} C \\ / \quad \backslash \\ C - C \end{array}$$

Open chain Cyclic

The resulting saturated cyclic compound, called cyclopropane, has the structural formula

$$\begin{array}{c} CH_2 \\ / \quad \backslash \\ CH_2 - CH_2 \end{array}$$

Alkanes containing rings of carbon atoms are called **cycloalkanes.** Like the other alkanes, cycloalkanes are not found in human cells. However, several important molecules in human cells do contain rings of five or six atoms, and the study of cycloalkanes will help you better understand the chemical behavior of these complex molecules.

According to IUPAC rules, cycloalkanes are named by placing the prefix *cyclo-* before the name of the corresponding alkane with the same number of carbon atoms. Chemists often abbreviate the structural formulas for cycloalkanes and draw them as geometric figures (triangles, squares, etc.) in which each corner represents a carbon atom. The hydrogens are omitted (see ▶ Table 11.7). It is important to remember that each carbon atom still possesses four bonds, and that hydrogen is assumed to be bonded to the carbon atoms unless something else is indicated. When substituted cycloalkanes (those with attached groups) are named, the position of a single attached group does not need to be specified

cycloalkane An alkane in which carbon atoms form a ring.

TABLE 11.7 **Structural Formulas and Symbols for Common Cycloalkanes**

Name	Structural Formula	Condensed Formula
cyclopropane	$\begin{array}{c} CH_2 \\ / \quad \backslash \\ H_2C - CH_2 \end{array}$	△
cyclobutane	$\begin{array}{c} H_2C - CH_2 \\ \vert \qquad \vert \\ H_2C - CH_2 \end{array}$	□
cyclopentane	$\begin{array}{c} H_2 \\ C \\ / \quad \backslash \\ H_2C \quad\; CH_2 \\ \backslash \quad\; / \\ H_2C - CH_2 \end{array}$	⬠
cyclohexane	$\begin{array}{c} H_2 \\ C \\ / \quad \backslash \\ H_2C \quad\; CH_2 \\ \vert \qquad\quad \vert \\ H_2C \quad\; CH_2 \\ \backslash \;\, C \;\, / \\ H_2 \end{array}$	⬡

in the name because all positions in the ring are equivalent. However, when two or more groups are attached, their positions of attachment are indicated by numbers, just as they were for alkanes. The ring numbering begins with the carbon attached to the first group alphabetically and proceeds around the ring in the direction that will give the lowest numbers for the locations of the other attached groups.

methylcyclopentane

1,2-dimethylcyclopentane
not 1,5-dimethylcyclopentane

1-chloro-3-methylcyclopentane
not 1-chloro-4-methylcyclopentane
not 3-chloro-1-methylcyclopentane

▶ Example 11.5

Represent each of the following cycloalkanes by a geometric figure, and name each compound:

Solution

a. A pentagon represents a five-membered ring, which is called cyclopentane. This compound has a methyl group attached, so the name is methylcyclopentane. The position of a single alkyl group is not indicated by a number because the positions of all carbons in the ring are equivalent.

b. A hexagon represents a six-carbon ring, which is called cyclohexane. Two methyl groups are attached; thus we have a dimethylcyclohexane.

However, the positions of the two alkyl groups must be indicated. The ring is numbered beginning with a carbon to which a methyl group is attached, counting in the direction giving the lowest numbers. The correct name is 1,3-dimethylcyclohexane. Notice that a reverse numbering beginning at the same carbon would have given 1,5-dimethylcyclohexane. The number 3 in the correct name is lower than the 5 in the incorrect name.

a. CH_3

 CH_3

b. $CH_2 - CH_3$

c. CH_3

 $CH_2 - CH_3$

11.9 The Shape of Cycloalkanes

Learning Objective

10. Name and draw structural formulas for geometric isomers of cycloalkanes.

Recall from Section 11.5 that a tetrahedral orientation of bonds with bond angles of 109.5° is characteristic of carbon atoms that form four single bonds. A tetrahedral arrangement is the most stable because it results in the least crowding of the atoms. In certain cycloalkanes, however, a tetrahedral arrangement for all carbon-to-carbon bonds is not possible. For example, the bond angles between adjacent carbon–carbon bonds in planar cyclopropane molecules must be 60° (see ▶ Figure 11.15). In cyclobutane, they are close to 90°. As a result, cyclopropane and cyclobutane rings are much less stable than compounds with bond angles of about 109°. Both cyclobutane and cyclopentane bend slightly from a planar structure to reduce the crowding of hydrogen atoms (Figure 11.15). In larger cycloalkanes, the bonds to carbon atoms can be tetrahedrally arranged only when the carbon atoms do not lie in the same plane. For example, cyclohexane can assume several nonplanar shapes. The chair and boat forms, where all the bond angles are 109.5°, are shown in Figure 11.15.

cyclopropane

cyclobutane

cyclopentane

cyclohexane
(chair form)

cyclohexane
(boat form)

Figure 11.15 Ball-and-stick models for common cycloalkanes.

The free rotation that can take place around C—C single bonds in alkanes (Section 11.6) is not possible for the C—C bonds of cycloalkanes. The ring structure allows bending or puckering but prevents free rotation (see ▶ Figure 11.16). Any rotation of one carbon atom 180° relative to an adjacent carbon atom in a cycloalkane would require a single carbon–carbon bond to be broken somewhere in the ring. The breaking of such bonds would require a large amount of energy.

Free rotation

Free rotation not possible

Figure 11.16 Rotation about C—C single bonds occurs in open-chain compounds but not within rings.

Oil Production: From Wells and Sands

Petroleum, the most important fossil fuel used today, is sometimes called "black gold" in recognition of its importance worldwide. At times, the need for petroleum to keep modern societies fueled has seemed second only to the needs for food, shelter, and clothing.

It is generally believed that this complex mixture of hydrocarbons was formed over eons by the gradual decay of ocean-dwelling microscopic animals. The resulting crude oil, a viscous black liquid, collects in vast underground deposits in sedimentary rock. It is brought to the surface by drilling and pumping.

Useful products are obtained from crude oil by heating it to high temperatures at which various fractions boil off according to their boiling points. Most petroleum products are eventually burned as fuels such as gasoline, diesel fuel, heating oil, and kerosene. However, about 2% of the recovered petroleum is used to make organic compounds. This doesn't seem like much until the huge amount of crude oil produced and refined each year is taken into account. In fact, more than half of all industrial synthetic organic compounds produced annually come from petroleum. These industrial chemicals are converted into such familiar products as dyes, drugs, plastics, artificial fibers, detergents, and insecticides.

In addition to traditional deposits of petroleum, significant amounts of hydrocarbons are found in the form of oil sands. This material is a mixture of about 85% sand, clay, and water and 15% of a form of crude oil called *bitumen*. Oil sand deposits occur in many parts of the world, but the largest deposits are located in Alberta, Canada, and Venezuela. Only those located in Alberta have been developed for profit.

The deposits in Alberta are estimated to contain about 2.3 trillion barrels of oil—an amount roughly equal to all of the known conventional petroleum reserves in the rest of the world. With currently available technology only about 175 billion barrels, or about 8%, of the Alberta oil is recoverable. The percentage is quite small, but the amount of recoverable oil is still huge.

The province of Alberta currently produces about 1.5 million barrels of oil per day. Most of it is delivered to the United States and accounts for about 20% of the total oil imported into the country each year. It is estimated that this level of oil production will last for at least the next 100 years.

A very controversial aspect of production from these oil sands is the amount of water required and the treatment of the used water. On average, about four barrels of water are needed to recover each barrel of oil from the sands. Much of the used water is recycled, cleaned up, and reused. As a result, only about half a barrel of fresh water is needed to produce each barrel of oil. However, the recycling of used water involves the construction and use of retention ponds in which impurities in the used water settle out. The settling out process that takes place is very slow and often takes decades to be completed. At the present time, retention ponds holding 250 billion gallons of used water and covering more than 50 square miles dot the landscape in the mining region of Alberta. Many people worry about the possibility that ruptured retention ponds could allow toxic mining debris to spread over wide areas. Others object to trading valuable water for oil in the entire recovery process.

An aerial view of a tar sands mine in Alberta, Canada.

The lack of free rotation around C—C bonds in disubstituted cycloalkanes leads to an extremely important kind of isomerism called *stereoisomerism*. Two different compounds that have the same molecular formula and the same structural formula but different spatial arrangements of atoms are called **stereoisomers**. For example, consider a molecule of 1,2-dimethylcyclopentane. The cyclopentane ring is drawn in ◗ Figure 11.17 as a planar pentagon with the heavy lines indicating that two of the carbons are in front as one views

stereoisomers Compounds with the same structural formula but different spatial arrangements of atoms.

Figure 11.17 Two geometric isomers of 1,2-dimethylcyclopentane.

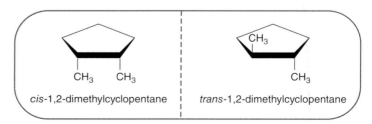

cis-1,2-dimethylcyclopentane | *trans*-1,2-dimethylcyclopentane

the structure. The groups attached to the ring project above or below the plane of the ring. Two stereoisomers are possible: Either both groups may project in the same direction from the plane, or they may project in opposite directions from the plane of the ring. Since the methyl groups cannot rotate from one side of the ring to the other, molecules of the two compounds represented in Figure 11.17 are distinct.

These two compounds have physical and chemical properties that are quite different and therefore can be separated from each other. Stereoisomers of this type, in which the spatial arrangement or geometry of their groups is maintained by rings, are called **geometric isomers** or cis-trans isomers. The prefix *cis-* denotes the isomer in which both groups are on the same side of the ring, and *trans-* denotes the isomer in which they are on opposite sides. To exist as geometric isomers, a disubstituted cycloalkane must be bound to groups at two different carbons of the ring. For example, there are no geometric isomers of 1,1-dimethylcyclohexane:

geometric isomers Molecules with restricted rotation around C—C bonds that differ in the three-dimensional arrangements of their atoms in space and not in the order of linkage of atoms.

cis- On the same side (as applied to geometric isomers).

trans- On opposite sides (as applied to geometric isomers).

Example 11.6

Name and draw structural formulas for all the isomers of dimethylcyclobutane. Indicate which ones are geometric isomers.

Solution

There are three possible locations for the two methyl groups: positions 1,1, positions 1,2, and positions 1,3.

Geometric isomerism is not possible in this case with the two groups bound to the same carbon of the ring

1,1-dimethylcyclobutane

Two groups on opposite sides of the planar ring

trans-1,2-dimethylcyclobutane

Two groups on the same side of the ring

cis-1,2-dimethylcyclobutane

trans-1,3-dimethylcyclobutane

cis-1,3-dimethylcyclobutane

▶ LEARNING CHECK 11.13

a. Identify each of the following cycloalkanes as a *cis-* or *trans-* compound:

(1)

(2)

(3)

b. Draw the structural formula for *cis*-1,2-dichlorocyclobutane.

Skin Moisturizers: Choosing One That Works

Healthy, normal human skin is kept moist by natural body oils contained in sebum, a secretion of the skin's sebaceous glands. The oily sebum helps the epidermis, or outer layer of the skin, retain the 10–30% of water it normally contains. However, some people suffer from skin that is naturally dry, or dry because of aging or contact with materials like paint thinner that dissolve and remove the sebum. Such individuals may find some relief by using OTC products called *moisturizers.*

Two types of skin moisturizers are commonly available. One type, which behaves like natural sebum, contains nonpolar oily substances that form a barrier and prevent water from passing through and evaporating from the skin. These barrier-forming products often contain combinations of materials from various sources, including mineral oil and petroleum jelly from petroleum; vegetable oils such as apricot oil; sesame seed oil, palm kernel oil, olive oil, and safflower oil; and lanolin, an animal fat from sheep oil glands and wool. While they effectively keep water from leaving the skin, these products are somewhat messy to use and leave the skin feeling greasy.

A second, more popular type of moisturizer works by attracting water from the air and skin. These products form a water-rich layer that adheres to the skin without giving it a greasy feel. The substances that attract water are called humectants, and are compounds capable of forming hydrogen bonds with water. Some examples of humectants used in

products of this type are glycerol, urea, lactic acid, and propylene glycol.

If you are shopping for a moisturizer, remember that the main characteristic you should look for in a product is the ability to form a barrier to prevent water evaporation, or the ability to act as a humectant. Some expensive products advertise that in addition to moisturizing, they also beautify the skin and even reverse aging because they contain proteins such as collagen and elastin, vitamins, hormones, or even DNA. It is unlikely that such substances can pass through the epidermis of the skin in sufficient amounts to provide the advertised benefits.

Alkane products marketed to soften and protect the skin.

11.10 Physical Properties of Alkanes

Learning Objective

11. Describe the key physical properties of alkanes.

Since alkanes are composed of nonpolar carbon–carbon and carbon–hydrogen bonds, alkanes are nonpolar molecules. Alkanes have lower melting and boiling points than other organic compounds of comparable molecular weight (see ▶ Table 11.8). This is because their nonpolar molecules exert very weak attractions for each other. Alkanes are odorless compounds.

The normal, or straight-chain, alkanes make up what is called a **homologous series.** This term describes any series of compounds in which each member differs from a previous member only by having an additional —CH₂— unit. The physical and chemical properties of compounds making up a homologous series are usually closely related and vary in a systematic and predictable way. For example, the boiling points of normal alkanes increase smoothly as the length of the carbon chain increases (see ▶ Figure 11.18). This pattern results from increasing dispersion forces as molecular weight increases. At ordinary temperatures and pressures, normal alkanes with 1 to 4 carbon atoms are gases, those with 5 to 20 carbon atoms are liquids, and those with more than 20 carbon atoms are waxy solids.

Because they are nonpolar, alkanes and other hydrocarbons are insoluble in water, which is a highly polar solvent. They are also less dense than water and thus float on it.

homologous series Compounds of the same functional class that differ by a —CH₂— group.

These two properties of hydrocarbons are partly responsible for the well-known serious effects of oil spills from ships (see ▶ Figure 11.19).

TABLE 11.8 Physical Properties of Some Normal Alkanes

Number of Carbon Atoms	IUPAC Name	Condensed Structural Formula	Melting Point (°C)	Boiling Point (°C)	Density (g/mL)
1	methane	CH_4	−182.5	−164.0	0.55
2	ethane	CH_3CH_3	−183.2	−88.6	0.57
3	propane	$CH_3CH_2CH_3$	−189.7	−42.1	0.58
4	butane	$CH_3CH_2CH_2CH_3$	−133.4	−0.5	0.60
5	pentane	$CH_3CH_2CH_2CH_2CH_3$	−129.7	36.1	0.63
6	hexane	$CH_3CH_2CH_2CH_2CH_2CH_3$	−95.3	68.9	0.66
7	heptane	$CH_3CH_2CH_2CH_2CH_2CH_2CH_3$	−90.6	98.4	0.68
8	octane	$CH_3CH_2CH_2CH_2CH_2CH_2CH_2CH_3$	−56.8	125.7	0.70
9	nonane	$CH_3CH_2CH_2CH_2CH_2CH_2CH_2CH_2CH_3$	−53.5	150.8	0.72
10	decane	$CH_3CH_2CH_2CH_2CH_2CH_2CH_2CH_2CH_2CH_3$	−29.7	174.1	0.73

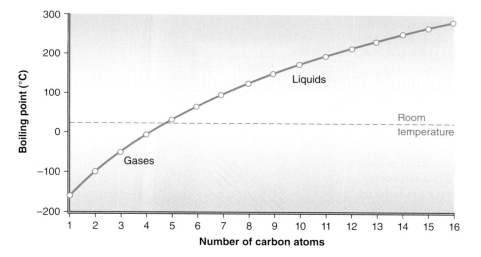

Figure 11.18 Normal alkane boiling points depend on chain length.

Figure 11.19 Oil spills can have serious and long-lasting effects on the environment because of the insolubility of hydrocarbons in water.

Liquid alkanes of higher molecular weight behave as emollients (skin softeners) when applied to the skin. An alkane mixture known as mineral oil is sometimes used to replace natural skin oils washed away by frequent bathing or swimming. Petroleum jelly (Vaseline is a well-known brand name) is a semisolid mixture of alkanes that is used as both an emollient and a protective film. Water and water solutions such as urine don't dissolve or penetrate the film, and the underlying skin is protected. Many cases of diaper rash have been prevented or treated this way.

The word **hydrophobic** (literally "water fearing") is often used to refer to molecules or parts of molecules that are insoluble in water. Many biomolecules, the large organic molecules associated with living organisms, contain nonpolar (hydrophobic) parts. Thus, such molecules are not water-soluble. Palmitic acid, for example, contains a large nonpolar hydrophobic portion and is insoluble in water.

hydrophobic Molecules or parts of molecules that repel (are insoluble in) water.

Nonpolar portion

$$CH_3-CH_2-CH_2-CH_2-CH_2-CH_2-CH_2-CH_2-CH_2-CH_2-CH_2-CH_2-CH_2-CH_2-CH_2-\overset{\displaystyle O}{\overset{\displaystyle \|}{C}}-OH$$

palmitic acid

Ice Storms and Deadly Carbon Monoxide

Every winter a killer waits to strike. The news headlines tell of a devastating winter storm as the country is pummeled with ice and snow. The storm is blamed for a number of deaths, many resulting from carbon monoxide poisoning after residents pulled power generators inside their homes to keep warm.

The incomplete combustion of alkanes and other carbon-containing fuels may produce carbon monoxide, CO. It is a common component of furnace, stove, and automobile exhaust. Normally, these fumes are emitted into the air and dispersed. However, whenever CO gas is released into closed spaces, lethal concentrations may develop. All of the following are known to have caused CO poisoning deaths: poor ventilation of a furnace or stove exhaust, running the engine of an automobile for a period of time in a closed garage, idling the engine of a snowbound car to keep the heater working, and using a barbecue grill as a source of heat in a house or camper (burning charcoal generates a large amount of carbon monoxide). Recently, the exhaust systems of snow-blocked vehicles have been identified as another cause of carbon monoxide poisoning. The problem is created when the end of a vehicle's exhaust pipe is obstructed or plugged by snow. CO-containing exhaust can leak through cracks in the exhaust system, penetrate the floorboard, and enter the passenger compartment of the vehicle. An estimated 1000 Americans die each year from unintentional CO poisoning, and as many as 10,000 require medical treatment.

Carbon monoxide is dangerous because of its ability to bind strongly with hemoglobin in red blood cells. When this occurs, the ability of the blood to transport oxygen (O_2) is reduced because the CO molecules occupy sites on hemoglobin molecules that are normally occupied by O_2 molecules.

Because it is colorless and odorless, carbon monoxide gas is a silent and stealthy potential killer. The following symptoms of CO poisoning are given in order of increasing severity and seriousness:

1. Slight headache, dizziness, drowsiness
2. Headache, throbbing temples
3. Weakness, mental confusion, nausea
4. Rapid pulse and respiration, fainting
5. Possibly fatal coma

All except the most severe cases of CO poisoning are reversible. The most important first aid treatment is to get the victim fresh air. Any person who feels ill and suspects CO poisoning might be the cause should immediately evacuate the building, get fresh air, and summon medical assistance. Victims are often treated with 100% oxygen delivered from a mask.

Consumer safety experts stress that combustion appliances should be inspected regularly for leaks or other malfunctions. Also, it is recommended that drivers should inspect exhaust pipes and clear any obstructions before starting vehicles that have been parked in snow. The Consumer Product Safety Commission recommends that CO detectors be installed near bedrooms in residences. These detectors sound an alarm before the gas reaches potentially lethal concentrations in the air.

Carbon monoxide detectors are relatively inexpensive and save lives.

11.11 Alkane Reactions

Learning Objective

12. Write alkane combustion reactions.

The alkanes are the least reactive of all organic compounds. In general, they do not react with strong acids (such as sulfuric acid), strong bases (such as sodium hydroxide), most oxidizing agents (such as potassium dichromate), and most reducing agents (such as sodium metal). This unreactive nature is reflected in the name *paraffins,* sometimes used to identify alkanes (from Latin words that mean "little affinity"). Paraffin wax, sometimes used to seal jars of homemade preserves, is a mixture of solid alkanes. Paraffin wax is also

used in the preparation of milk cartons and wax paper. The inertness of the compounds in the wax makes it ideal for these uses. Alkanes do undergo reactions with halogens such as chlorine and bromine, but these are not important for our purposes.

Perhaps the most significant reaction of alkanes is the rapid oxidation called combustion. In the presence of ample oxygen, alkanes burn to form carbon dioxide and water, liberating large quantities of heat:

$$CH_4 + 2O_2 \rightarrow CO_2 + 2H_2O + 212.8 \text{ kcal/mol} \tag{11.4}$$

It is this type of reaction that accounts for the wide use of hydrocarbons as fuels.

Natural gas contains methane (80–95%), some ethane, and small amounts of other hydrocarbons. Propane and butane are extracted from natural gas and sold in pressurized metal containers (bottled gas). In this form, they are used for heating and cooking in campers, trailers, boats, and rural homes.

Gasoline is a mixture of hydrocarbons (primarily alkanes) that contain 5 to 12 carbon atoms per molecule. Diesel fuel is a similar mixture, except the molecules contain 12 to 16 carbon atoms. The hot CO_2 and water vapor generated during combustion in an internal combustion engine have a much greater volume than the air and fuel mixture. It is this sudden increase in gaseous volume and pressure that pushes the pistons and delivers power to the crankshaft.

If there is not enough oxygen available, incomplete combustion of hydrocarbons occurs, and some carbon monoxide (CO) or even carbon (see ❯ Figure 11.20) may be produced (Reactions 11.5 and 11.6):

$$2CH_4 + 3O_2 \rightarrow 2CO + 4H_2O \tag{11.5}$$

$$CH_4 + O_2 \rightarrow C + 2H_2O \tag{11.6}$$

These reactions are usually undesirable because CO is toxic, and carbon deposits hinder engine performance. Occasionally, however, incomplete combustion is deliberately caused; specific carbon blacks (particularly lampblack, a pigment for ink) are produced by the incomplete combustion of natural gas.

Figure 11.20 A luminous yellow flame from a laboratory burner produces a deposit of carbon when insufficient air (O_2) is mixed with the gaseous fuel.

© Michael C. Slabaugh

Case Study Follow-up

Mineral oil is a mixture of light alkanes in the C-15 to C-40 range. Because mineral oil is hydrophobic it has a slippery quality that many people find unpleasant. Mineral oil is frequently used to treat encopresis (NLM, 2011). Behavioral techniques have been successful in increasing compliance with medication regimens in both children and adults (APA, 2004). It is important to set up a reliable routine so that a child knows what to expect. For example, medication should be given at the same time every day, in the same place, and in the same manner. Rewards should be immediate and of sufficient merit to encourage compliance. Some children need significant rewards in order to be persuaded to take an unpleasant medicine. Never underestimate the power of parental praise as part of the reward! Many parents object to behavioral programs that use rewards because they equate them with bribery. However, they do work. Eventually, once the desired behavior is established, the reward system can be phased out or the parent may choose a different behavior to reward. Punishing a child for soiling is counterproductive. Transferring responsibility to the child (e.g., having even a young child help clean up the mess) is more effective.

Concept Summary

Carbon: The Element of Organic Compounds

Organic compounds contain carbon, and organic chemistry is the study of those compounds. Inorganic chemistry is the study of the elements and all noncarbon compounds.
Objective 1 Exercise 11.2

Carbon compounds are of tremendous everyday importance to life on Earth and are the basis of all life processes.
Objective 2 Exercise 11.4

Organic and Inorganic Compounds Compared

The properties of organic and inorganic compounds often differ, largely as a result of bonding differences. Organic compounds contain primarily covalent bonds, whereas ionic bonding is more prevalent in inorganic compounds.
Objective 3 Exercise 11.8

Bonding Characteristics and Isomerism

Large numbers of organic compounds are possible because carbon atoms link to form chains and networks. An additional reason for the existence of so many organic compounds is the phenomenon of isomerism. Isomers are compounds that have the same molecular formula but different arrangements of atoms.
Objective 4, Exercise 11.20

Functional Groups: The Organization of Organic Chemistry

All organic compounds are grouped into classes based on characteristic features called functional groups. Compounds with their functional groups are represented by two types of structural formulas. Expanded structural formulas show all covalent bonds, whereas condensed structural formulas show no covalent bonds or only selected bonds.
Objective 5 Exercise 11.24

Alkane Structures

Alkanes are hydrocarbons that contain only single covalent bonds and can be represented by the formula C_nH_{2n12}. Alkanes possess a three-dimensional geometry in which each carbon is surrounded by four bonds directed to the corners of a tetrahedron. Methane, the simplest alkane, is an important fuel (natural gas) and a chemical feedstock for the preparation of other organic compounds. The number of structural isomers possible for an alkane increases dramatically with the number of carbon atoms present in the molecule. The straight-chain isomer is called a normal alkane; others are called branched isomers.
Objective 6 Exercise 11.28

Conformations of Alkanes

Rotation about the single bonds between carbon atoms allows alkanes to exist in many different conformations. When an alkane is drawn using only two dimensions, the structure can be represented in a variety of ways as long as the order of bonding is not changed.
Objective 7 Exercise 11.30

Alkane Nomenclature

Some simple alkanes are known by common names. More complex compounds are usually named using the IUPAC system. The characteristic IUPAC ending for alkanes is -*ane*.
Objective 8 Exercise 11.34

Cycloalkanes

These are alkanes in which the carbon atoms form a ring. The prefix *cyclo-* is used in the names of these compounds to indicate their cyclic nature.
Objective 9 Exercise 11.44

The Shape of Cycloalkanes

The carbon atom rings of cycloalkanes are usually shown as planar, although only cyclopropane is planar. Because rotation about the single bonds in the ring is restricted, certain disubstituted cycloalkanes can exist as geometric (*cis-trans*) isomers.
Objective 10 Exercise 11.54

Physical Properties of Alkanes

The physical properties of alkanes are typical of all hydrocarbons: nonpolar, insoluble in water, less dense than water, and increasing melting and boiling points with increasing molecular weight.
Objective 11 Exercise 11.56

Alkane Reactions

Alkanes are relatively unreactive and remain unchanged by most reagents. The reaction that is most significant is combustion.
Objective 12 Exercise 11.60

Key Terms and Concepts

Alkane (11.5)
Alkyl group (11.7)
Branched alkane (11.5)
cis- (11.9)
Condensed structural formula (11.4)
Conformations (11.6)
Cycloalkane (11.8)
Expanded structural formula (11.4)

Functional group (11.4)
Geometric isomers (11.9)
Homologous series (11.10)
Hybrid orbital (11.3)
Hydrocarbon (11.5)
Hydrophobic (11.10)
Inorganic chemistry (11.1)
Isomerism (11.3)

Normal alkane (11.5)
Organic chemistry (11.1)
Organic compound (11.1)
Saturated hydrocarbon (11.5)
Stereoisomers (11.9)
Structural isomers (11.3)
trans- (11.9)

Key Equations

| 1. | Complete combustion of alkanes (Section 11.11): | Alkane $+ O_2 \rightarrow CO_2 + H_2O$ |
| 2. | Incomplete combustion of alkanes (Section 11.11): | Alkane $+ O_2 \rightarrow$ CO (or C) $+ H_2O$ |

Exercises

Even-numbered exercises are answered in Appendix B.

Blue-numbered exercises are more challenging.

Carbon: The Element of Organic Compounds (Section 11.1)

11.1 Why were the compounds of carbon originally called organic compounds?

11.2 Name at least six items you recognize to be composed of organic compounds.

11.3 Describe what Wöhler did that made the vital force theory highly questionable.

11.4 What is the unique structural feature shared by all organic compounds?

11.5 Classify each of the following compounds as organic or inorganic:

 a. KBr **d.** LiOH

 b. H_2O **e.** $CH_3{-}NH_2$

 c. $H{-}C{\equiv}C{-}H$

Organic and Inorganic Compounds Compared (Section 11.2)

11.6 What kind of bond between atoms is most prevalent among organic compounds?

11.7 Are the majority of all compounds that are insoluble in water organic or inorganic? Why?

11.8 Indicate for each of the following characteristics whether it more likely describes an inorganic or an organic compound. Give one reason for your answer.

 a. This compound is a liquid that readily burns.

 b. A white solid upon heating is found to melt at 735°C.

 c. A liquid added to water floats on the surface and does not dissolve.

 d. This compound exists as a gas at room temperature and ignites easily.

 e. A solid substance melts at 65°C.

11.9 Devise a test, based on the general properties in Table 11.1, that you could use to quickly distinguish between the substances in each of the following pairs:

 a. Gasoline (liquid, organic) and water (liquid, inorganic)

 b. Naphthalene (solid, organic) and sodium chloride (solid, inorganic)

 c. Methane (gaseous, organic) and hydrogen chloride (gaseous, inorganic)

11.10 Explain why organic compounds are nonconductors of electricity.

11.11 Explain why the rate of chemical reactions is generally slow for organic compounds and usually fast for inorganic compounds.

Bonding Characteristics and Isomerism (Section 11.3)

11.12 Give two reasons for the existence of the tremendous number of organic compounds.

11.13 How many of carbon's electrons are unpaired and available for bonding according to an sp^3 hybridization model?

11.14 Describe what atomic orbitals overlap to produce a carbon–hydrogen bond in CH_4.

11.15 What molecular geometry exists when a central carbon atom bonds to four other atoms?

11.16 Compare the shapes of unhybridized p and hybridized sp^3 orbitals.

11.17 Use Example 11.1 and Tables 11.2 and 11.6 to determine the number of covalent bonds formed by atoms of the following elements: carbon, hydrogen, oxygen, nitrogen, and bromine.

11.18 Complete the following structures by adding hydrogen atoms where needed:

 a. C — C — C

 b. C — C = C

c.
$$\overset{\displaystyle O}{\underset{\displaystyle \|}{C-C}}$$

d. C — C — N

11.19 Complete the following structures by adding hydrogen atoms where needed.

a.
$$\overset{\displaystyle C}{\underset{\displaystyle |}{C-C-C-C}}$$

b. C — C ≡ C

c.
$$\overset{\displaystyle O}{\underset{\displaystyle \|}{C-C-N}}$$

d.
$$\overset{\displaystyle O}{\underset{\displaystyle \|}{O-C-C-C}}$$

11.20 Which of the following pairs of compounds are structural isomers?

a. $CH_3-CH=CH-CH_3$ and $CH_3-CH_2-CH_2-CH_3$

b. $CH_3-CH_2-CH_2-CH_2-CH_3$ and $CH_3-\underset{\underset{\displaystyle CH_3}{|}}{\overset{\overset{\displaystyle CH_3}{|}}{C}}-CH_3$

c. $CH_3-CH_2-\underset{\underset{\displaystyle CH_3}{|}}{CH}-OH$ and $CH_3-\overset{\overset{\displaystyle O}{\|}}{C}-CH_2-CH_3$

d. $CH_3-CH_2-\overset{\overset{\displaystyle O}{\|}}{C}-H$ and $CH_3-\overset{\overset{\displaystyle O}{\|}}{C}-CH_3$

e. $CH_3-CH_2-CH_2-NH_2$ and $CH_3-CH_2-NH-CH_3$

11.21 Group all the following compounds together that represent structural isomers of each other:

a. $CH_3-CH_2-\overset{\overset{\displaystyle O}{\|}}{C}-OH$

b. $CH_3-\overset{\overset{\displaystyle O}{\|}}{C}-CH_2-OH$

c. $CH_3-CH_2-CH_2-OH$

d. $CH_3-\overset{\overset{\displaystyle O}{\|}}{C}-CH_2-CH_3$

e. $CH_3-\underset{\underset{\displaystyle OH}{|}}{CH}-\overset{\overset{\displaystyle O}{\|}}{C}-H$

f. $CH_3-\overset{\overset{\displaystyle O}{\|}}{C}-O-CH_3$

g. $HO-CH_2-CH_2-CH_2-OH$

11.22 On the basis of the number of covalent bonds possible for each atom, determine which of the following structural formulas are correct. Explain what is wrong with the incorrect structures.

a. $H-\underset{\underset{\displaystyle H}{|}}{\overset{\overset{\displaystyle H}{|}}{C}}-H-\underset{\underset{\displaystyle H}{|}}{\overset{\overset{\displaystyle H}{|}}{C}}-H$

b. $H-\underset{\underset{\displaystyle H}{|}}{N}-\underset{\underset{\displaystyle H}{|}}{\overset{\overset{\displaystyle H}{|}}{C}}-\underset{\underset{\displaystyle H}{|}}{\overset{\overset{\displaystyle H}{|}}{C}}-H$

c. $H-\underset{\underset{\displaystyle H}{|}}{\overset{\overset{\displaystyle H}{|}}{C}}\rule{1cm}{0.4pt}\underset{\underset{\displaystyle H-\underset{\underset{\displaystyle H}{|}}{C}-H}{|}}{\overset{\overset{\displaystyle O}{\|}}{C}}\rule{1cm}{0.4pt}\underset{\underset{\displaystyle H}{|}}{\overset{\overset{\displaystyle H}{|}}{C}}-H$

d. $CH_3-C=C-CH_3$

e. $CH_3-\underset{\underset{\displaystyle CH_3}{|}}{\overset{\overset{\displaystyle OH}{|}}{CH}}-CH-\overset{\overset{\displaystyle O}{\|}}{C}-H$

Functional Groups: The Organization of Organic Chemistry (Section 11.4)

11.23 Identify each of the following as a condensed structural formula, expanded structural formula, or molecular formula:

a. $H-\underset{\underset{\displaystyle H}{|}}{\overset{\overset{\displaystyle H}{|}}{C}}-\underset{\underset{\displaystyle H}{|}}{\overset{\overset{\displaystyle H}{|}}{C}}=\overset{\overset{\displaystyle H}{|}}{C}$

b. $CH_3CH_2CH_2-OH$

c. $C_6H_{12}O_6$

d. $H_2N-\overset{\overset{\displaystyle O}{\|}}{C}-CH_2CH_3$

11.24 Write a condensed structural formula for the following compounds:

a. $H-\underset{\underset{\displaystyle H}{|}}{\overset{\overset{\displaystyle H}{|}}{C}}-\underset{\underset{\displaystyle H}{|}}{\overset{\overset{\displaystyle H}{|}}{C}}-\underset{\underset{\displaystyle H}{|}}{\overset{\overset{\displaystyle H}{|}}{C}}-C=C-\overset{\overset{\displaystyle O}{\|}}{C}-\underset{\underset{\displaystyle H}{|}}{\overset{\overset{\displaystyle H}{|}}{C}}-\underset{\underset{\displaystyle H}{|}}{\overset{\overset{\displaystyle H}{|}}{C}}-H$

b. $H-\underset{\underset{\displaystyle H}{|}}{\overset{\overset{\displaystyle H}{|}}{C}}-\underset{\underset{\displaystyle H}{|}}{\overset{\overset{\displaystyle H}{|}}{C}}-\overset{\overset{\displaystyle O}{\|}}{C}-\underset{\underset{\displaystyle H}{|}}{N}-H$

Unless otherwise noted all art on this page © Cengage Learning 2014

11.25 Write a condensed structural formula for the following compounds:

a.
```
        H   H
         \ /
  H       N    H   H
  |       |    |   |
H—C————————C — C = C — H
  |       |
  H     H—C—H
          |
          H
```

b.
```
      O   H        H   O
      ||  |        |   ||
b. H—O—C—C—O—C—C—H
          |        |
        H—C—H      H
          |
          H
```

11.26 Write an expanded structural formula for the following:

a.
```
      O
      ||
   H—C—CH₂—CH₂—NH₂
```

b.
```
   CH₃—CH—O—CH₃
         |
        CH₃
```

Alkane Structures (Section 11.5)

11.27 The name of the normal alkane containing 9 carbon atoms is nonane. What are the molecular and condensed structural formulas for nonane?

11.28 Classify each of the following compounds as a normal alkane or a branched alkane:

a.
```
   CH₃—CH—CH₃
        |
       CH₃
```

b.
```
   CH₃—CH₂—CH₂
            |
           CH₂—CH₃
```

c.
```
        CH₃
        |
   CH₂—CH₂
   |
   CH₃
```

d.
```
   CH₃—CH₂—CH₂
            |
           CH₃—CH₂
```

e.
```
   CH₃        CH₃
   |          |
   CH₂—CH₂—CH
              |
             CH₃
```

f.
```
             CH₃
             |
   CH₃—CH₂—C—CH₃
             |
             CH₃
```

Conformations of Alkanes (Section 11.6)

11.29 Why are different conformations of an alkane not considered structural isomers?

11.30 Which of the following pairs represent structural isomers, and which are simply the same compound?

a.
```
   H₃C   CH₂   and   CH₃CH₂CH₂CH₃
     \\ //\
     CH₂ CH₃
```

b.
```
   CH₃—CH₂—CH₂   and   CH₃CH₂CH₂CH₂CH₂CH₃
            |
   CH₃—CH₂—CH₂
```

c.
```
   CH₃—CH—CH₃   and   CH₃CH₂CH₂CH₃
        |
       CH₃
```

d.
```
   CH₃—CH—CH₂CH₃   and   CH₃—CH₂—CH—CH₃
        |                          |
       CH₃                        CH₃
```

Alkane Nomenclature (Section 11.7)

11.31 For each of the following carbon skeletons, give the number of carbon atoms in the longest continuous chain:

a.
```
        C—C
        |
   C—C—C—C
     |   |
     C   C—C
```

c.
```
      C—C—C
        |
   C—C—C—C
        |
        C—C
```

b.
```
   C—C—C—C—C
        |
        C—C—C—C
            |
            C—C—C
                |
                C—C
```

11.32 For each of the following carbon skeletons, give the number of carbon atoms in the longest continuous chain:

a.
```
        C—C
        |
   C—C—C—C—C
```

b.
```
        C
        |
   C—C—C—C
        |
        C—C—C
```

c.
```
      C—C
      |  |
      C  C—C
      |  |
   C—C  C—C
```

11.33 Identify the following alkyl groups:

a.
```
   CH₃—CH—
        |
       CH₃
```

b. CH₃—CH₂—CH₂—CH₂—

c. $CH_3-CH-CH_2-$
 |
 CH_3

d. CH_3-

11.34 Give the correct IUPAC name for each of the following alkanes:

a. $CH_3-CH-CH_2-CH_3$ with CH_3-CH_2 attached to the CH

b. CH_3-CH with CH_3 above and CH_3 below

c. $CH_3-CH_2-CH-CH-CH_2$ with CH_2-CH_3 on first CH, and CH_3 / $CH-CH_2-CH_2-CH_3$ on the second, with CH_2CH_3 below

d. $CH_3-CH_2-CH-CH_2-CH-CH_3$ with a $CH_3/CH_2/CH_2$ (CH_3) chain and $CH_3-CH_2-CH_2-CH$ with CH_2-CH_3

e. $CH_3-CH-CH_2-CH-CH_2CH_3$ with $CH_2-CH_2-CH_2-CH_3$ above and CH_2-CH_3 below

11.35 Give the correct IUPAC name for each of the following alkanes:

a. $CH_3-CH_2-CH-CH_3$ with CH_3 below the CH

b. CH_3-C-CH_3 with CH_3 above and CH_3 below the C

c. $CH_3-CH-CH-CH_3$ with CH_2-CH_3 above the first CH and CH_3 below the second CH

d. $CH_2-CH-C-CH_2-CH-CH_2-CH_3$ with substituents CH_3, CH_2(CH_3) on CH; CH_2(CH_3); $CH_2/CH-CH_3/CH_3$; and CH_3 / CH_2 above the C

e. $CH_3-CH_2-CH-CH-CH-CH_2-CH-CH$ with CH_3 above each of three CH groups and $CH_2-CH_2-CH_2-CH_3$ below

11.36 Draw a condensed structural formula for each of the following compounds:

 a. 3-ethylpentane

 b. 2,2-dimethylbutane

 c. 4-ethyl-3,3-dimethyl-5-propyldecane

 d. 5-*sec*-butyldecane

11.37 Draw a condensed structural formula for each of the following compounds:

 a. 2,3-dimethylbutane

 b. 3-isopropylheptane

 c. 5-*t*-butyl-2,3-dimethyloctane

 d. 4-ethyl-4-methyloctane

11.38 Draw the condensed structural formula for each of the three structural isomers of C_5H_{12}, and give the correct IUPAC names.

11.39 Isooctane is 2,2,4-trimethylpentane. Draw structural formulas for and name a branched heptane, hexane, pentane, and butane that are structural isomers of isooctane.

11.40 Draw structural formulas for the compounds and give correct IUPAC names for the five structural isomers of C_6H_{14}.

11.41 The following names are incorrect, according to IUPAC rules. Draw the structural formulas and tell why each name is incorrect. Write the correct name for each compound.

 a. 2,2-methylbutane

 b. 4-ethyl-5-methylheptane

 c. 2-ethyl-1,5-dimethylhexane

11.42 The following names are incorrect, according to IUPAC rules. Draw the structural formulas and tell why each name is incorrect. Write the correct name for each compound.

 a. 1,2-dimethylpropane

 b. 3,4-dimethylpentane

 c. 2-ethyl-4-methylpentane

 d. 2-bromo-3-ethylbutane

Cycloalkanes (Section 11.8)

11.43 The general formula for alkanes is C_nH_{2n+2}. Write a general formula for cycloalkanes.

11.44 Write the correct IUPAC name for each of the following:

a.

b.

c. (cyclohexane with two CH_3 groups on same carbon)

d. (cyclobutane with CH_3, CH_3 groups and CH_3, CH_3)

11.45 Write the correct IUPAC name for each of the following:

a. (cyclopropane triangle)

b. (cyclopentane with two CH_3 groups)

c. (cyclohexane with CH_3 and CH_2CH_3)

d. (cyclobutane with CH_3, $CHCH_3$, CH_3)

11.46 Draw the structural formulas corresponding to each of the following IUPAC names:

a. ethylcyclobutane

b. 1,1,2,5-tetramethylcyclohexane

c. 1-butyl-3-isopropylcyclopentane

11.47 Draw the structural formulas corresponding to each of the following IUPAC names:

a. 1,2-diethylcyclopentane

b. 1,2,4-trimethylcyclohexane

c. propylcyclobutane

11.48 Which of the following pairs of cycloalkanes represent structural isomers?

a. (cyclobutane with two CH_3 groups; cyclobutane with CH_3, CH_3)

b. (CH_2CH_3, CH_3 cyclopentane; cyclopentane with CH_2CH_3, CH_3)

c. CH_2CH_3 (cyclopropane); cyclopropane with CH_3

d. (cyclohexane with CH_3, CH_3) (cyclohexane with CH_3, CH_3)

11.49 Draw structural formulas for the five structural isomers of C_5H_{10} that are cycloalkanes.

The Shape of Cycloalkanes (Section 11.9)

11.50 Why does cyclohexane assume a chair form rather than a planar hexagon?

11.51 Explain the difference between geometric and structural isomers.

11.52 Which of the following cycloalkanes could show geometric isomerism? For each that could, draw structural formulas, and name both the *cis-* and the *trans-* isomers.

a. (cyclohexane with CH_3)

b. (cyclopentane with CH_3, CH_2CH_3)

c. (cyclobutane with CH_3, CH_3)

d. (cyclopropane with CH_3, $CHCH_3$, CH_3)

11.53 Draw structural formulas for *cis-* and *trans*-1,3-dibromocyclobutane.

11.54 Using the prefix *cis-* or *trans-*, name each of the following:

a. (cyclopropane with CH_2CH_3, CH_3)

b. (cyclopentane with Cl, Br)

c. (cyclobutane with $CH_2CH_2CH_3$, CH_3)

d. (cyclohexane with CH_3, CH_3)

11.55 For each of the following molecular formulas, give the structural formulas requested. In most cases, there are several possible structures.

a. C_6H_{14}, a normal alkane

b. C_6H_{14}, a branched alkane

c. C_5H_{12}, a pair of conformations

d. C_5H_{12}, a pair of structural isomers

e. C_5H_{10}, a cyclic hydrocarbon

f. C_6H_{12}, two cycloalkane geometric isomers

g. C_6H_{12}, a cycloalkane that has no geometric isomers

Physical Properties of Alkanes (Section 11.10)

11.56 The compound decane is a straight-chain alkane. Predict the following:

 a. Is decane a solid, liquid, or gas at room temperature?

 b. Is it soluble in water?

 c. Is it soluble in hexane?

 d. Is it more or less dense than water?

11.57 Explain why alkanes of low molecular weight have lower melting and boiling points than water.

11.58 Suppose you have a sample of 2-methylhexane and a sample of 2-methylheptane. Which sample would you expect to have the higher melting point? Boiling point?

11.59 Identify (circle) the alkanelike portions of the following molecules:

 a.

$$H_2N - CH - C - OH$$

(with $\overset{O}{\overset{\|}{}}$ above the C, and below CH: $CH-CH_3$, then CH_2, then CH_3)

 isoleucine (an amino acid)

 b.

$$CH_3-CH_2-CH_2-CH_2-CH_2-CH_2-CH_2-CH_2$$

$$Na^+{}^-O-C-CH_2-CH_2-CH_2-CH_2-CH_2-CH_2-CH_2$$

(with $\overset{O}{\overset{\|}{}}$ above the C)

 sodium palmitate (a soap)

 c.

$$CH-CH_2-CH_2-CH_2-CH_2-C-OH$$

(ring with $\overset{H_2}{C}$, H_2C, $S-S$; and $\overset{O}{\overset{\|}{}}$ above the C)

 lipoic acid (a component of a coenzyme)

 d.

(cyclohexane ring with CH_3 top, OH, and $CH-CH_3$ with CH_3 below)

 menthol (a flavoring)

Alkane Reactions (Section 11.11)

11.60 Write a balanced equation to represent the complete combustion of each of the following:

 a. Butane

 b.

$$CH_3-\underset{\underset{CH_3}{|}}{\overset{\overset{CH_3}{|}}{C}}-CH_3$$

 c.

(cyclopropane ring with CH_3)

11.61 Write a balanced equation to represent the complete combustion of each of the following:

 a. ethane

 b.

$$CH_3-\underset{\underset{CH_3}{|}}{CH}-CH_2-CH_3$$

 c.

(cyclopentane ring)

11.62 Write a balanced equation for the incomplete combustion of hexane, assuming the formation of carbon monoxide and water as the products.

11.63 Why is it dangerous to relight a furnace when a foul odor is present?

Additional Exercises

11.64 Using the concept of dispersion forces, explain why most cycloalkanes have higher boiling points than normal alkanes with the same number of carbon atoms.

11.65 Draw a Lewis electron dot formula for ethane (CH_3-CH_3). Explain why ethane molecules do not hydrogen-bond.

11.66 Your sometimes inept lab technician performed experiments to determine the vapor pressure of pentane, hexane, and heptane at 20°C. He gave you back the numbers of 113.9, 37.2, and 414.5 torr without identifying the compounds. Which vapor pressure value goes with which compound?

11.67 How many grams of water will be produced by the complete combustion of 10.0 g of methane (CH_4)?

11.68 How many liters of air at STP are needed to completely combust 1.00 g of methane (CH_4)? Air is composed of about 21% v/v oxygen (O_2).

Allied Health Exam Connection

The following questions are from these sources:

1. *Nursing School Entrance Exam* © 2005, Learning Express, LLC.

2. *McGraw-Hill's Nursing School Entrance Exams* by Thomas A. Evangelist, Tamara B. Orr and Judy Unrein © 2009, The McGraw-Hill Companies, Inc.

3. *NSEE Nursing School Entrance Exams,* 3rd Edition © 2009, Kaplan Publishing.

4. *Cliffs Test Prep: Nursing School Entrance Exams* by Fred N. Grayson © 2004, Wiley Publishing, Inc.

5. *Peterson's Master the Nursing School and Allied Health Entrance Exams,* 18th Edition by Marion F. Gooding © 2008, Peterson's, a Nelnet Company.

11.69 Which of the following are examples of organic compounds?

 a. $CaCO_3$

 b. NH_3

 c. NaCl

 d. $C_6H_{12}O_6$

11.70 Use the generic formula for alkanes (C_nH_{2n+2}) to derive molecular and condensed structural formulas for:

 a. Propane, 3 carbon atoms

 b. Octane, 8 carbon atoms

 c. Butane, 4 carbon atoms

11.71 Organic compounds are the basis for life as we know it because:

 a. Carbon-to-carbon bonds are strong

 b. Carbon can form long chains

 c. Carbon chains can include other elements to give rise to different functional groups

 d. All of the above are correct

11.72 Which of the following is an example of an alkane?

 a. C_2H_6

 b. C_2H_4

 c. CH_3OH

 d. $C_6H_{12}O_6$

11.73 The name of the compound CH_3—CH_2—CH_2—CH_3 is most likely:

 a. cyclobutane

 b. butane

 c. butene

 d. butyne

11.74 Which of the following are the general products of a combustion reaction?

 a. $C(s)$, O_2, and H_2

 b. $C(s)$, H_2O, and O_2

 c. CO_2 and H_2

 d. CO_2 and H_2O

11.75 Which is mostly methane?

 a. oil

 b. natural gas

 c. coal waste

 d. propane

11.76 The deadly property of carbon monoxide, if inhaled, is due to its:

 a. high affinity for O_2

 b. low affinity for hemoglobin

 c. high affinity for hemoglobin

 d. conversion to cyanide gas

Chemistry for Thought

11.77 Would you expect a molecule of urea produced in the body to have any different physical or chemical properties from a molecule of urea prepared in a laboratory?

11.78 Why might the study of organic compounds be important to someone interested in the health or life sciences?

11.79 Why do very few aqueous solutions of organic compounds conduct electricity?

11.80 The ski wax being examined in Figure 11.2 has a relatively low melting point. What does that fact reveal about the forces between molecules?

11.81 Charcoal briquettes sometimes burn with incomplete combustion when the air supply is limited. Why would it be hazardous to place a charcoal grill inside a home or a camper in an attempt to keep warm?

11.82 If carbon did not form hybridized orbitals, what would you expect to be the formula of the simplest compound of carbon and hydrogen?

11.83 What types of sports equipment are made from graphite fibers besides that shown in Figure 11.8?

11.84 A semi truck loaded with cyclohexane overturns during a rainstorm, spilling its contents over the road embankment. If the rain continues, what will be the fate of the cyclohexane?

11.85 On the way home from school, you drove through a construction zone, resulting in several tar deposits on the car's fender. What substances commonly found in the kitchen might help in removing the tar deposits?

11.86 Oil spills along coastal shores can be disastrous to the environment. What physical and chemical properties of alkanes contribute to the consequences of an oil spill?

11.87 Why might some farmers hesitate to grow and sell organic produce?

Case Study

Scott, a young man, worked as a subcontractor at a copper mine. In spite of extensive safety training provided by the mining company, one of his co-workers failed to properly secure a load of steel pipe on a truck. Scott knelt to place a chock under a wheel of the truck, and a pipe fell, crushing his leg. Scott's leg was amputated above the knee. The company accepted responsibility for his injury and covered his medical costs. Thanks to technological advances in plastics and computer design, Scott was offered a choice of colors and designs for his prosthetic leg. His company refused to pay the additional cost of personalizing his prosthesis. His physician recommended that the bill be covered, considering the psychological impact of a man losing a leg in his youth.

Is it a reasonable request for an insurance company to cover this additional cost? Is the ability of a patient to choose the design of the prosthesis important to self-esteem? How does self-esteem impact recovery?

Follow-up to this Case Study appears at the end the chapter before the Concept Summary.

© iStockphoto.com/MichaelSvoboda

Learning Objectives

When you have completed your study of this chapter, you should be able to:

1 Classify unsaturated hydrocarbons as alkenes, alkynes, or aromatics. **(Section 12.1)**

2 Write the IUPAC names of alkenes from their molecular structures. **(Section 12.1)**

3 Predict the existence of geometric (cis-trans) isomers from formulas of compounds. **(Section 12.2)**

4 Write the names and structural formulas for geometric isomers. **(Section 12.2)**

5 Write equations for addition reactions of alkenes, and use Markovnikov's rule

to predict the major products of certain reactions. **(Section 12.3)**

6 Write equations for addition polymerization, and list uses for addition polymers. **(Section 12.4)**

7 Write the IUPAC names of alkynes from their molecular structures. **(Section 12.5)**

8 Classify organic compounds as aliphatic or aromatic. **(Section 12.6)**

9 Name and draw structural formulas for aromatic compounds. **(Section 12.7)**

10 Recognize uses for specific aromatic compounds. **(Section 12.8)**

unsaturated hydrocarbons contain one or more double or triple bonds between carbon atoms and belong to one of three classes: alkenes, alkynes, or aromatic hydrocarbons. **Alkenes** contain one or more double bonds, **alkynes** contain one or more triple bonds, and **aromatic hydrocarbons** contain three double bonds alternating with three single bonds in a six-carbon ring. Ethylene (the simplest alkene), acetylene (the simplest alkyne), and benzene (the simplest aromatic) are represented by the following structural formulas:

unsaturated hydrocarbon A hydrocarbon containing one or more multiple bonds.

alkene A hydrocarbon containing one or more double bonds.

alkyne A hydrocarbon containing one or more triple bonds.

aromatic hydrocarbons Any organic compound that contains the characteristic benzene ring or similar feature.

ethylene
(an alkene)

acetylene
(an alkyne)

benzene
(an aromatic)

Alkenes and alkynes are called *unsaturated* because more hydrogen atoms can be added in somewhat the same sense that more solute can be added to an unsaturated solution. Benzene and other aromatic hydrocarbons also react to add hydrogen atoms; in general, however, they have chemical properties very different from those of alkenes and alkynes.

12.1 The Nomenclature of Alkenes

Learning Objectives

1. Classify unsaturated hydrocarbons as alkenes, alkynes, or aromatics.
2. Write the IUPAC names of alkenes from their molecular structure.

The general formula for alkenes is C_nH_{2n} (the same as that for cycloalkanes). The simplest members are well known by their common names, ethylene and propylene:

$$CH_2 = CH_2 \qquad CH_3 - CH = CH_2$$
$$\text{ethylene, } C_2H_4 \qquad \text{propylene, } C_3H_6$$

Three structural isomers have the formula C_4H_8:

$$CH_3 - CH_2 - CH = CH_2 \qquad CH_3 - CH = CH - CH_3 \qquad CH_3 - \underset{\underset{CH_3}{|}}{C} = CH_2$$

The number of structural isomers increases rapidly as the number of carbons increases because, besides variations in chain length and branching, variations occur in the position of the double bond. IUPAC nomenclature is extremely useful in differentiating among these many alkene compounds.

The IUPAC rules for naming alkenes are similar to those used for the alkanes, with a few additions to indicate the presence and location of double bonds.

Step 1. Name the longest chain that contains the double bond. The characteristic name ending is *-ene*.

Step 2. Number the longest chain of carbon atoms so that the carbon atoms joined by the double bond have numbers as low as possible.

Step 3. Locate the double bond by the lower-numbered carbon atom bound by the double bond.

Step 4. Locate and name attached groups.

Step 5. Combine the names for the attached groups and the longest chain into the name.

▶ Example 12.1

Name the following alkenes:

a. $CH_3 - CH = CH - CH_3$

c.
$$CH_3 - CH_2$$
$$|$$
$$C = CH_2$$
$$|$$
$$CH_3 - CH_2 - CH_2$$

b. $CH_3 - \underset{\underset{CH_3}{|}}{CH} - CH = CH_2$

d.
(cyclopentene ring)
$$CH_2$$
$$|$$
$$CH_3$$

Solution

a. The longest chain containing a double bond has four carbon atoms. The four-carbon alkane is butane. Thus, the compound is a butene:

$$\overset{1}{C}H_3 - \overset{2}{C}H = \overset{3}{C}H - \overset{4}{C}H_3$$

The chain can be numbered from either end because the double bond will be between carbons 2 and 3 either way. The position of the double bond is indicated by the lower-numbered carbon atom that is double-bonded, carbon 2 in this case. The name is 2-butene.

b. To give lower numbers to the carbons bound by the double bond, the chain is numbered from the right:

$$\overset{4}{C}H_3-\overset{3}{C}H-\overset{2}{C}H=\overset{1}{C}H_2 \qquad \text{not} \qquad \overset{1}{C}H_3-\overset{2}{C}H-\overset{3}{C}H=\overset{4}{C}H_2$$
$$\quad\quad\quad | \qquad\qquad\qquad\qquad\qquad\qquad\qquad | $$
$$\quad\quad\quad CH_3 \qquad\qquad\qquad\qquad\qquad\qquad CH_3$$

Thus, the compound is a 1-butene with an attached methyl group on carbon 3. Therefore, the name is 3-methyl-1-butene.

c. Care must be taken to select the longest chain containing the double bond. This compound is named as a pentene and not as a hexene because the double bond is not contained in the six-carbon chain:

$$CH_3-CH_2 \qquad\qquad\qquad\qquad \overset{1}{C}H_3-\overset{2}{C}H_2$$
$$\qquad | \qquad\qquad\qquad\qquad\qquad\qquad\qquad | $$
$$\quad\overset{2}{C}=\overset{1}{C}H_2 \qquad \text{not} \qquad\quad \overset{3}{C}=CH_2$$
$$\qquad | \qquad\qquad\qquad\qquad\qquad\qquad\qquad | $$
$$CH_3-CH_2-CH_2 \qquad\qquad CH_3-CH_2-CH_2$$
$$\;_5\qquad\;\;_4\qquad\;\;_3 \qquad\qquad\qquad\;\;_6\qquad\;\;_5\qquad\;\;_4$$

The compound is a 1-pentene with an ethyl group at position 2. Therefore, the name is 2-ethyl-1-pentene.

d. In cyclic alkenes, the ring is numbered so as to give the lowest possible numbers to the double-bonded carbons (they become carbons 1 and 2). The numbering direction around the ring is chosen so that attached groups are located on the lowest-numbered carbon atoms possible. Thus, the name is 3-ethylcyclopentene:

Notice that it is not called 3-ethyl-1-cyclopentene because the double bond is always between carbons 1 and 2, and therefore its position need not be indicated.

▶ **LEARNING CHECK 12.1** Give the IUPAC name for each of the following:

 Br
 |
a. $CH_2-CH=CH_2$

b. $CH_2=C-CH_2-CH_2-CH_3$
 |
 CH_2
 |
 CH_3

c. $CH_3 \quad CH_3$

Some compounds contain more than one double bond per molecule. Molecules of this type are important components of natural and synthetic rubber and other useful materials. The nomenclature of these compounds is the same as for the alkenes with one double bond, except that the endings *-diene, -triene,* and the like are used to denote the number of double bonds. Also, the locations of all the multiple bonds must be indicated in all molecules, including those with rings:

$$\overset{1}{C}H_2=\overset{2}{C}H-\overset{3}{C}H=\overset{4}{C}H_2$$
1,3-butadiene

1,3-cyclohexadiene

Watermelon: A Source of Lycopene

The thought of summer conjures up images of picnic tables and cool, fresh slices of watermelon. What most watermelon eaters don't realize is that in addition to enjoying a cool summer snack, they are also benefitting from a great source of lycopene, a red substance with the following highly unsaturated molecular structure:

Lycopene is known to help prevent certain types of cancer as well as heart disease, and watermelon is one of a small number of foods that contain this useful compound in large quantities. Other good food sources of lycopene are tomatoes, guava, and pink grapefruit.

The anti-cancer characteristics of lycopene are attributed to its antioxidant properties. It slows or prevents highly reactive oxygen-containing molecules from oxidizing cell components and causing the cells to malfunction. Research results indicate that tomatoes in the diet—especially cooked tomatoes, which contain concentrated amounts of lycopene—reduce the incidence of prostate cancer. In a study conducted at Harvard University, the incidence of prostate cancer was one-third lower in men who ate a lycopene-rich diet compared to a group who ate a low-lycopene diet.

It was long thought that heat-processed tomatoes represented the best source of lycopene in the diet. This was based on the large amounts of lycopene found in small servings of tomato juice. However, recent studies have found that red seedless watermelons contain as much lycopene as cooked tomatoes and in some cases more, depending on the variety of melon and the growing conditions.

Another factor to consider when looking for a good lycopene source is the ability of the body to digest and use the compound (bioavailability) when a lycopene-containing food is eaten. For example, the lycopene in cooked tomatoes is absorbed more readily during digestion than the lycopene in raw tomatoes. Also, it has been found that the absorption rate of lycopene goes up if the food containing it is eaten with food that contains fat. This characteristic is related to the nonpolar nature of lycopene molecules and their resulting significant solubility in fats. The level of lycopene in body fat is used as an indication of how much lycopene has been consumed in the diet. Increased lycopene levels in fat tissue have been linked to reduced risk of heart attack. The bioavailability of lycopene from raw watermelon has been found to be equal to that of lycopene obtained from cooked tomatoes. Studies are now being conducted to determine if the bioavailability of watermelon lycopene increases if the watermelon is eaten in a diet that also includes fat-containing foods.

In addition to its ability to satisfy a sweet tooth and serve as a good source of lycopene, watermelon is also an excellent source of the vitamins A, B_6, C, and thiamin. It is also fat free and low in calories, so why not include a big juicy slice of it as one of the five servings of fruits and vegetables recommended by the American Institute of Cancer Research that will reduce your risk of cancer? Enjoy yourself and try not to drip juice on your clothes.

Watermelon is an excellent source of lycopene.

© Ric Ergenbright/Corbis

▶ Example 12.2

Name the following compounds:

a. $CH_2{=}C{-}C{=}CH{-}CH{=}CH_2$, with a CH_3 group above the second C and a CH_3 group below the second C.

b. A cyclohexadiene ring with a CH_3 group and a CH_2CH_3 group.

Unless otherwise noted all art on this page © Cengage Learning 2014

Solution

a. This compound is a methyl-substituted hexatriene. The chain is numbered from the end nearest the branch because the direction of numbering, again, makes no difference in locating the double bonds correctly. The name is 2,3-dimethyl-1,3,5-hexatriene:

$$\underset{1}{CH_2}=\underset{2}{\overset{\overset{\displaystyle CH_3}{|}}{C}}-\underset{3}{\underset{\underset{\displaystyle CH_3}{|}}{C}}=\underset{4}{CH}-\underset{5}{CH}=\underset{6}{CH_2} \quad \text{and not} \quad \underset{6}{CH_2}=\underset{5}{\overset{\overset{\displaystyle CH_3}{|}}{C}}-\underset{4}{\underset{\underset{\displaystyle CH_3}{|}}{C}}=\underset{3}{CH}-\underset{2}{CH}=\underset{1}{CH_2}$$

2,3-dimethyl-1,3,5-hexatriene 4,5-dimethyl-1,3,5-hexatriene

b. This compound is a substituted cyclohexadiene. The ring is numbered as shown. The name is 5-ethyl-1-methyl-1,3-cyclohexadiene:

and not

5-ethyl-1-methyl-1,3-cyclohexadiene 6-ethyl-4-methyl-1,3-cyclohexadiene

▶ **LEARNING CHECK 12.2** Give the IUPAC name for each of the following:

a. $CH_2=CH-\overset{\overset{\displaystyle CH_3}{|}}{C}=CH_2$

b. $CH_2=\overset{\overset{\displaystyle CH_3}{|}}{C}-CH=CH-CH_2-CH=CH-CH_3$

c. Br

12.2 The Geometry of Alkenes

Learning Objectives

3. Predict the existence of geometric (cis-trans) isomers from the formulas of compounds.
4. Write the names and structural formulas for geometric isomers.

The hybridization of atomic orbitals discussed in Section 11.3 to explain the bonding characteristics of carbon atoms bonded to four other atoms can also be used to describe alkenes, compounds in which some carbon atoms are bonded to only three atoms. This hybridization involves mixing a 2*s* orbital and two 2*p* orbitals of a carbon atom to form three hybrid *sp*2 orbitals (see ▶ Figure 12.1).

Figure 12.1 A representation of *sp*2 hybridization of carbon. During hybridization, two of the 2*p* orbitals mix with the single 2*s* orbital to produce three *sp*2 hybrid orbitals. One 2*p* orbital is not hybridized and remains unchanged.

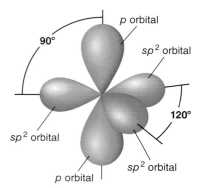

Figure 12.2 The unhybridized *p* orbital is perpendicular to the plane of the three *sp²* hybridized orbitals.

The three *sp²* hybrid orbitals lie in the same plane and are separated by angles of 120°. The unhybridized 2*p* orbital of the carbon atom is located perpendicular to the plane of the *sp²* hybrid orbitals (see ▶ Figure 12.2).

The bonding between the carbon atoms of ethylene results partially from the overlap of one *sp²* hybrid orbital of each carbon to form a sigma (σ) bond. The second carbon–carbon bond is formed when the unhybridized 2*p* orbitals of the carbons overlap sideways to form what is called a pi (π) bond. The remaining two *sp²* hybrid orbitals of each carbon overlap with the 1*s* orbitals of the hydrogen atoms to form sigma bonds. Thus, each ethylene molecule contains five sigma bonds (one carbon–carbon and four carbon–hydrogen) and one pi bond (carbon–carbon), as shown in ▶ Figure 12.3.

Experimental data support this hybridization model. Ethylene has been found to be a planar molecule with bond angles close to 120° between the atoms (see ▶ Figure 12.4).

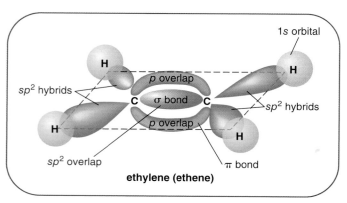

Figure 12.3 The bonding in ethylene is explained by combining two *sp²* hybridized carbon atoms. The C—H sigma bonds all lie in the same plane. The unhybridized *p* orbitals of the carbon atoms overlap above and below the molecular plane to form the pi bond.

Figure 12.4 All six atoms of ethylene lie in the same plane.

In addition to geometry, alkenes also differ from open-chain alkanes in that the double bonds prevent the relatively free rotation that is characteristic of carbon atoms bonded by single bonds. As a result, alkenes can exhibit geometric isomerism, the same type of stereoisomerism seen earlier for the cycloalkanes (Section 11.9). There are two geometric isomers of 2-butene:

$$
\begin{array}{ccc}
\text{H} & & \text{H} \\
\diagdown & & \diagup \\
& \text{C}=\text{C} & \\
\diagup & & \diagdown \\
\text{CH}_3 & & \text{CH}_3 \\
\end{array}
\qquad
\begin{array}{ccc}
\text{CH}_3 & & \text{H} \\
\diagdown & & \diagup \\
& \text{C}=\text{C} & \\
\diagup & & \diagdown \\
\text{H} & & \text{CH}_3 \\
\end{array}
$$

cis-2-butene *trans*-2-butene

Once again, the prefix *cis*- is used for the isomer in which the two similar or identical groups are on the same side of the double bond and *trans*- for the one in which they are on opposite sides. The two isomers *cis*- and *trans*-2-butene represent distinctly different compounds with different physical properties (see ▶ Table 12.1).

TABLE 12.1 Physical Properties of a Pair of Geometric Isomers

Isomer	Melting Point (°C)	Boiling Point (°C)	Density (g/mL)
cis-2-butene	−139.9	3.7	0.62
trans-2-butene	−105.6	0.9	0.60

Seeing the Light

Cis-trans isomerism is important in several biological processes, one of which is vision. When light strikes the retina, a cis double bond in the compound *retinal* (structurally related to vitamin A) is converted to a trans double bond. The conversion triggers a chain of events that finally results in our being able to see.

In a series of steps, *trans*-retinal is enzymatically converted back to *cis*-retinal so that the cycle can be repeated. Bright light temporarily destroys our ability to see in dim light because large quantities of *cis*-retinal are rapidly converted to the trans isomer by the bright light. It takes time for conversion of the *trans*-retinal back to *cis*-retinal. This difference in conversion rates between the *cis* and *trans* forms of retinal enables our eyes to adjust automatically to variations in light levels.

The vision process depends on a cis-trans reaction.

Not all double-bonded compounds show cis-trans stereoisomerism. Cis-trans stereoisomerism is found only in alkenes that have two different groups attached to each double-bonded carbon atom. In 2-butene, the two different groups are a methyl and a hydrogen for each double-bonded carbon:

two groups are different *two groups are different*

cis-2-butene

two groups are different *two groups are different*

trans-2-butene

If either double-bonded carbon is attached to identical groups, no cis-trans isomers are possible. Thus, there are no geometric isomers of ethene or propene:

two groups are the same

ethene

two groups are the same

propene

To see why this is so, let's try to draw geometric isomers of propene:

(A) is the same as (B)

Notice that structure (B) can be converted into (A) by just flipping it over. Thus, they are identical and not isomers.

▶ Example 12.3

Determine which of the following molecules can exhibit geometric isomerism, and draw structural formulas to illustrate your conclusions:

a. $Cl—CH=CH—Cl$
b. $CH_2=CH—Cl$
c. $Cl—CH=CH—CH_3$

Solution

a. Begin by drawing the carbon–carbon double bond with bond angles of 120° about each carbon atom:

Next, complete the structure and analyze each carbon of the double bond to see if it is attached to two different groups:

H and Cl are different groups *H and Cl are different groups*

In this case, each carbon is attached to two different groups and geometric isomers are possible:

cis trans

b. No geometric isomers are possible because one carbon contains two identical groups:

two identical groups

c. Geometric isomers are possible because there are two different groups on each carbon:

H and Cl are different *H and CH₃ are different*

cis-1-chloropropene *trans*-1-chloropropene

Unless otherwise noted all art on this page © Cengage Learning 2014

▶ LEARNING CHECK 12.3 Determine which of the following can exhibit geometric isomerism, and draw structural formulas for the *cis* and *trans* isomers of those that can:

a. $CH_2=C-CH_2-CH_3$
 |
 CH_3

c. $CH_3-C=CH-CH_3$
 |
 CH_3

b. $CH_3-CH-CH=CH-CH_3$
 |
 CH_3

12.3 Properties of Alkenes

Learning Objective

5. Write equations for addition reactions of alkenes, and use Markovnikov's rule to predict the major products of certain reactions.

Physical Properties

The alkenes are similar to the alkanes in physical properties—they are nonpolar compounds that are insoluble in water, soluble in nonpolar solvents, and less dense than water (see ▶ Table 12.2). Alkenes containing 4 carbon atoms or fewer are gases under ordinary conditions. Those containing 5 to 17 carbon atoms are liquids, and those with 18 or more carbon atoms are solids. Low molecular weight alkenes have somewhat unpleasant, gasoline-like odors.

TABLE 12.2 Physical Properties of Some Alkenes

IUPAC Name	Structural Formula	Boiling Point (°C)	Melting Point (°C)	Density (g/mL)
ethene	$CH_2=CH_2$	−104	−169	0.38
propene	$CH_2=CHCH_3$	−47	−185	0.52
1-butene	$CH_2=CHCH_2CH_3$	−6	−185	0.60
1-pentene	$CH_2=CHCH_2CH_2CH_3$	30	−138	0.64
1-hexene	$CH_2=CHCH_2CH_2CH_2CH_3$	63	−140	0.67
cyclohexene	⬡	83	−104	0.81

Chemical Properties

In contrast to alkanes, which are inert to almost all chemical reagents (Section 11.11), alkenes are quite reactive chemically. Since the only difference between an alkane and an alkene is the double bond, it is not surprising to learn that most of the reactions of alkenes take place at the double bond. These reactions follow the pattern:

$$\underset{/}{\overset{\backslash}{C}}=\underset{\backslash}{\overset{/}{C}} \quad + \quad A-B \quad \longrightarrow \quad \overset{A}{\underset{|}{\underset{|}{-C}}}-\overset{B}{\underset{|}{\underset{|}{C-}}} \qquad (12.1)$$

They are called **addition reactions** because a substance is added to the double bond. Addition reactions are characterized by two reactants that combine to form one product.

addition reaction A reaction in which a compound adds to a multiple bond.

Unsaturated Hydrocarbons **407**

Halogenation is one of the most common addition reactions. For example, when bromine, a halogen, is added to an alkene, the double bond reacts, and only a carbon–carbon single bond remains in the product. Without a double bond present, the product is referred to as a **haloalkane** or **alkyl halide.** Reaction 12.2 gives the general reaction, and Reaction 12.3 is a specific example, the bromination of 1-butene.

haloalkane or alkyl halide A derivative of an alkane in which one or more hydrogens are replaced by halogens.

General reaction:

$$\overset{\diagdown}{\diagup}C = C\overset{\diagup}{\diagdown} \; + \; Br - Br \; \longrightarrow \; -\underset{\underset{Br}{|}}{\overset{|}{C}} - \underset{\underset{Br}{|}}{\overset{|}{C}} - \qquad (12.2)$$

Specific example:

$$CH_3 - CH_2 - CH = CH_2 \; + \; Br - Br \; \longrightarrow \; CH_3 - CH_2 - \underset{\underset{Br}{|}}{CH} - \underset{\underset{Br}{|}}{CH_2} \qquad (12.3)$$

1-butene 1,2-dibromobutane

The addition of Br_2 to double bonds provides a simple laboratory test for unsaturation (see ▶ Figure 12.5). As the addition takes place, the characteristic red-brown color of the added bromine fades as it is used up, and the colorless dibromoalkane product forms.

Figure 12.5 The reaction of bromine with an unsaturated hydrocarbon.

© Joel Gordon

1 Dilute bromine solution added to 1-hexene loses its red-brown color immediately.

2 The remainder of the bromine solution is added. The last drops react as quickly as the first.

The addition of halogens is also used to quantitatively determine the degree of unsaturation in vegetable oils, margarines, and shortenings (Section 18.4). Chlorine reacts with alkenes to give dichloro products in an addition reaction similar to that of bromine. However, it is not used as a test for unsaturation because it is difficult to see the pale green color of chlorine in solution.

▶ **LEARNING CHECK 12.4** Write the structural formula for the product of each of the following reactions:

a. $CH_3 - \underset{\underset{CH_3}{|}}{C} = CH_2 + Br_2 \longrightarrow$

b. ⬠ $+ \; Cl_2 \longrightarrow$

hydrogenation A reaction in which the addition of hydrogen takes place.

In the presence of an appropriate catalyst (such as platinum, palladium, or nickel), hydrogen adds to alkenes and converts them into the corresponding alkanes. This reaction, which is called **hydrogenation,** is illustrated in Reactions 12.4 and 12.5.

General reaction:

$$\overset{\diagdown}{\diagup}C = C\overset{\diagup}{\diagdown} \; + \; H - H \; \overset{Pt}{\longrightarrow} \; -\underset{\underset{H}{|}}{\overset{|}{C}} - \underset{\underset{H}{|}}{\overset{|}{C}} - \qquad (12.4)$$

an alkane

Specific example: $CH_3CH = CHCH_3 + H-H \xrightarrow{Pt} CH_3CH - CHCH_3$ (12.5)

$$\underset{H \quad\; H}{\overset{|\qquad\;|}{}}$$

2-butene butane

The hydrogenation of vegetable oils is a very important commercial process. Vegetable oils, such as soybean and cottonseed oil, are composed of long-chain organic molecules that contain many alkene bonds. The high degree of unsaturation characteristic of these oils gave rise to the term **polyunsaturated.** Upon hydrogenation, the melting point of the oils is raised, and the oils become low-melting-point solids. These products are used in the form of margarine and shortening.

polyunsaturated A term usually applied to molecules with several double bonds.

▶ **LEARNING CHECK 12.5** Write the structural formula for the product of each of the following reactions:

a. $CH_3 - \underset{\underset{CH_3}{|}}{C} = CH - CH_3 + H_2 \xrightarrow{Pt}$

b. $+ \; H_2 \xrightarrow{Pt}$

A number of acidic compounds, such as the hydrogen halides—HF, HCl, HBr, and HI—also add to alkenes to give the corresponding alkyl halide. The reaction with HCl is illustrated as follows:

General reaction: $\overset{\diagdown}{\underset{\diagup}{}}C = C\overset{\diagup}{\underset{\diagdown}{}} \; + \; H - Cl \longrightarrow \; -\underset{\underset{H}{|}}{\overset{\overset{|}{}}{C}} - \underset{\underset{Cl}{|}}{\overset{\overset{|}{}}{C}} -$ (12.6)

Specific example: $CH_3CH = CHCH_3 \; + \; H - Cl \longrightarrow CH_3\underset{\underset{H \;\; Cl}{|\;\;\;|}}{CHCHCH_3}$ (12.7)

The addition reactions involving H_2, Cl_2, and Br_2 yield only one product because the same group (H and H or Br and Br) adds to each double-bonded carbon. However, with H—X, a different group adds to each carbon, and for certain alkenes, there are two possible products. For example, in the reaction of HBr with propene, two products might be expected: 1-bromopropane or 2-bromopropane,

$$CH_2 = CH - CH_3 + H - Br \longrightarrow \underset{\text{1-bromopropane}}{\underset{\underset{Br \;\; H}{|\;\;\;|}}{CH_2 - CH - CH_3}} \; \text{or} \; \underset{\text{2-bromopropane}}{\underset{\underset{H \;\; Br}{|\;\;\;|}}{CH_2 - CH - CH_3}} \quad (12.8)$$

It turns out that only one product, 2-bromopropane, is formed in significant amounts. This fact, first reported in 1869 by Russian chemist Vladimir Markovnikov, gave rise to a rule for predicting which product will be exclusively or predominantly formed. According to **Markovnikov's rule,** when a molecule of the form H—X adds to an alkene, the hydrogen becomes attached to a double-bonded carbon atom that is already bonded to the greatest number of hydrogens. A phrase to help you remember this rule is "the rich get richer." Applying this rule to propene, we find:

Markovnikov's rule In the addition of H—X to an alkene, the hydrogen becomes attached to the carbon atom that is already bonded to more hydrogens.

one hydrogen attached

$$CH_2 = CH - CH_3$$

two hydrogens attached *three hydrogens but they are not attached to the double-bonded carbons*

Therefore, H attaches to the end carbon of the double bond, Br attaches to the second carbon, and 2-bromopropane is the major product.

▶ Example 12.4

Use Markovnikov's rule to predict the major product in the following reactions:

a. $CH_3-\overset{\overset{\displaystyle CH_3}{|}}{C}=CH_2 + H-Cl$ b. [cyclopentene with CH_3] $+ H-Cl \longrightarrow$

Solution

a. Analyze the C=C to see which carbon atom has more hydrogens attached:

$CH_3-\overset{\overset{\displaystyle CH_3}{|}}{C}=CH_2$ *two hydrogens attached*

no hydrogens attached

The H of H—Cl will attach to the position that has more hydrogens. Thus, 2-chloro-2-methylpropane is the major product:

$CH_3-\overset{\overset{\displaystyle CH_3}{|}}{C}=CH_2$ *H attaches here to give* $CH_3-\overset{\overset{\displaystyle CH_3}{|}}{\underset{\underset{\displaystyle Cl}{|}}{C}}-\overset{}{\underset{\underset{\displaystyle H}{|}}{CH_2}}$

Cl attaches here

2-chloro-2-methylpropane

b. The challenge with a cyclic alkene is to remember that the hydrogens are not shown. Thus,

[cyclopentene with CH_3] is the same as [cyclopentene with CH_3 and H]

As before, the H of H—Cl will attach to the double-bonded carbon that has more hydrogens:

[cyclopentene with CH_3 and H] *Cl attaches here* *H attaches here* $\longrightarrow$ [cyclopentane with CH_3, Cl, H, H] or [cyclopentane with CH_3, Cl]

▶ LEARNING CHECK 12.6

Use Markovnikov's rule to predict the major product in the following reactions:

a. $CH_3-CH=\overset{\overset{\displaystyle CH_3}{|}}{C}-CH_2-CH_3 + HBr$

b. [cyclohexene with CH_3 and CH_2CH_3] $+$ $HBr \longrightarrow$

Remembering organic reactions for exams is challenging for most students. Because the number of reactions being studied increases rapidly over the semester, it is a good idea to develop a systematic way to organize them for easy and effective review.

One way to do this is to focus on the functional group concept. When an exam question asks you to complete a reaction by identifying the product, your first step should be to identify the functional group of the reactant. Usually, only the functional group portion of a molecule undergoes reaction. In addition, a particular functional group usually undergoes the same characteristic reactions regardless of the other features of the organic molecule to which it is bound. Thus, by remembering the behavior of a functional group under specific conditions, you can predict the reactions of many compounds, no matter how complex the structures look, as long as they contain the same functional group. For example, any structure containing a C=C will undergo reactions typical of alkenes. Other functional groups will be introduced in later chapters.

Keeping a reaction card file based on the functional group concept is a good way to organize reactions for review. Write the structures and names of the reactants on one side of an index card with an arrow showing any catalyst or special conditions. Write the product structure and name on the back of the card. We recommend that you do this for the general reaction (like those in the Key Reactions section at the end of most chapters) and for a specific example. Review your cards every day (this can even be done while waiting for a bus, etc.), and add to them as new reactions are studied. As an exam approaches, put aside the reactions you know well, and concentrate on the others in what should be a dwindling deck. This is an effective way to focus on learning what you don't know.

In the absence of a catalyst, water does not react with alkenes. But, if an acid catalyst such as sulfuric acid is added, water adds to carbon–carbon double bonds to give alcohols. In this reaction, which is called **hydration,** a water molecule is split in such a way that —H attaches to one carbon of the double bond, and —OH attaches to the other carbon. In Reactions 12.9–12.11, H_2O is written H—OH to emphasize the portions that add to the double bond. Notice that the addition follows Markovnikov's rule:

hydration The addition of water to a multiple bond.

$$\underset{/}{\overset{\backslash}{C}}=\underset{\backslash}{\overset{/}{C}} \quad + \quad H-OH \xrightarrow{\ H_2SO_4\ } \underset{\underset{H\ \ \ OH}{|\quad |}}{-C-C-} \qquad (12.9)$$

an alcohol

$$CH_3CH=CHCH_3 \quad + \quad H-OH \xrightarrow{\ H_2SO_4\ } \underset{\underset{H\quad OH}{|\quad \ |}}{CH_3CH-CHCH_3} \qquad (12.10)$$

2-butene · 2-butanol

$$CH_3CH=CH_2 \quad + \quad H-OH \xrightarrow{\ H_2SO_4\ } \underset{\underset{OH\quad H}{|\quad \ |}}{CH_3CH-CH_2} \qquad (12.11)$$

propene · 2-propanol

The hydration of alkenes provides a convenient method for preparing alcohols on a large scale. The reaction is also important in living organisms, but the catalyst is an enzyme rather than sulfuric acid. For example, one of the steps in the body's utilization of carbohydrates for energy involves the hydration of fumaric acid, which is catalyzed by the enzyme fumarase:

$$\underset{\text{fumaric acid}}{\overset{\overset{\textstyle O}{\|}}{HO-C}-CH=CH-\overset{\overset{\textstyle O}{\|}}{C}-OH} \ + \ H_2O \xrightarrow{\ \text{fumarase}\ } \underset{\text{malic acid}}{\overset{\overset{\textstyle O}{\|}}{HO-C}-\overset{\overset{\textstyle H}{|}}{CH}-\overset{\overset{\textstyle OH}{|}}{CH}-\overset{\overset{\textstyle O}{\|}}{C}-OH} \qquad (12.12)$$

▶ **LEARNING CHECK 12.7** Draw structural formulas for the major organic product of each of the following reactions:

a. $CH_3CH_2CH_2CH = CH_2 + H_2O \xrightarrow{H_2SO_4}$

b.

$$\text{(pentagon with double bond)} + H_2O \xrightarrow{H_2SO_4}$$

12.4 Addition Polymers

Learning Objective

6. Write equations for addition polymerization, and list uses for addition polymers.

Figure 12.6 Gore-Tex® is a thin, membranous material made by stretching Teflon fibers. Fabrics layered with Gore-Tex repel wind and rain but allow body perspiration to escape, making it an excellent fabric for sportswear.

polymerization A reaction that produces a polymer.

polymer A very large molecule made up of repeating units.

addition polymer A polymer formed by the linking together of many alkene molecules through addition reactions.

monomer The starting material that becomes the repeating units of polymers.

Certain alkenes undergo a very important reaction in the presence of specific catalysts. In this reaction, alkene molecules undergo an addition reaction with one another. The double bonds of the reacting alkenes are converted to single bonds as hundreds or thousands of molecules bond and form long chains. For example, several ethylene molecules react as follows:

$$CH_2 = CH_2 + CH_2 = CH_2 + CH_2 = CH_2 + CH_2 = CH_2 \xrightarrow[\text{catalysts}]{\text{Heat, pressure,}} \quad (12.13)$$

$$\text{ethylene molecules}$$

$$-CH_2 - CH_2 - CH_2 - CH_2 - CH_2 - CH_2 - CH_2 - CH_2 -$$

$$\text{polyethylene}$$

The product is commonly called polyethylene even though there are no longer any double bonds present. The newly formed bonds in this long chain are shown in color. This type of reaction is called a **polymerization,** and the long-chain product made up of repeating units is a **polymer** (*poly* = many, *mer* = parts). The trade names of many polymers such as Orlon®, Plexiglas®, Lucite®, and Teflon® are familiar (see ▶ Figure 12.6). These products are referred to as **addition polymers** because of the addition reaction between double-bonded compounds that is used to produce them. The starting materials that make up the repeating units of polymers are called **monomers** (*mono* = one, *mer* = part). Quite often, common names are used for both the polymer and the monomer.

It is not possible to give an exact formula for a polymer produced by a polymerization reaction because the individual polymer molecules vary in size. We could represent polymerization reactions as in Reaction 12.13. However, since this type of reaction is inconvenient, we adopt a commonly used approach: The polymer is represented by a simple repeating unit based on the monomer. For polyethylene, the unit is $-(CH_2-CH_2)-$. The large number of units making up the polymer is denoted by n, a whole number that varies from several hundred to several thousand. The polymerization reaction of ethylene is then written as:

$$n CH_2 = CH_2 \xrightarrow[\text{catalysts}]{\text{Heat, pressure,}} -(CH_2 - CH_2)_n \quad (12.14)$$

$$\text{ethylene} \qquad\qquad\qquad \text{polyethylene}$$

The lowercase n in Reaction 12.14 represents a large, unspecified number. From this reaction, we see that polyethylene is essentially a very long chain alkane. As a result, it has the chemical inertness of alkanes, a characteristic that makes polyethylene suitable for food storage containers, garbage bags, eating utensils, laboratory apparatus, and hospital equipment

A Reaction Map for Alkenes

A diagram may help you visualize and remember the four common addition reactions in this section. In each case, the alkene double bond reacts, and an alkane or alkane derivative is produced. The specific reagent determines the outcome of the reaction.

(see ▶ Figure 12.7). Polymer characteristics are modified by using alkenes with different groups attached to either or both of the double-bonded carbons. For example, the polymerization of vinyl chloride gives the polymer poly (vinyl chloride), PVC (Reaction 12.15):

$$n\text{CH}_2=\text{CH} \quad \xrightarrow[\text{catalysts}]{\text{Heat,}} \quad +\text{CH}_2-\text{CH}+_n \qquad (12.15)$$

vinyl chloride poly (vinyl chloride)

A — Packaging materials made from polyethylene

B — Polystyrene

C — Polyvinyl chloride

Figure 12.7 Common polymer-based consumer products.

The commercial product Saran Wrap is an example of a **copolymer,** which is a polymer made up of two different monomers (Reaction 12.16):

copolymer An addition polymer formed by the reaction of two different monomers.

$$n\text{CH}_2=\text{CH} + n\text{CH}_2=\text{C} \xrightarrow{\text{Catalyst}} +\text{CH}_2-\text{CH}-\text{CH}_2-\text{C}+_n \qquad (12.16)$$

vinyl chloride vinylidene chloride Saran Wrap

A number of the more important addition polymers are shown in ▶ Table 12.3. As you can tell by looking at some of the typical uses, addition polymers have become nearly indispensable in modern life (see ▶ Figure 12.8).

TABLE 12.3 Common Addition Polymers

Chemical Name and Trade Name(s)	Monomer	Polymer	Typical Uses				
polyethylene	$CH_2 = CH_2$	$+CH_2 - CH_2 +_n$	Bottles, plastic bags, film				
polypropylene	$CH_2 = CH$ $\quad\ \	$ $\quad\ CH_3$	$+CH_2 - CH +_n$ $\qquad\quad	$ $\qquad\ CH_3$	Carpet fiber, pipes, bottles, artificial turf		
poly (vinyl chloride) (PVC)	$CH_2 = CH$ $\quad\ \	$ $\quad\ Cl$	$+CH_2 - CH +_n$ $\qquad\quad	$ $\qquad\ Cl$	Synthetic leather, floor tiles, garden hoses, water pipe		
polytetrafluoroethylene (Teflon®)	$CF_2 = CF_2$	$+CF_2 - CF_2 +_n$	Pan coatings, plumbers' tape, heart valves, fabrics				
poly (methyl methacrylate) (Lucite®, Plexiglas®)	$\qquad\quad CH_3$ $\qquad\quad\	$ $CH_2 = C$ $\qquad\quad	$ $\qquad\ C - O - CH_3$ $\qquad\ \ \|$ $\qquad\ \ O$	$\qquad\quad CH_3$ $\qquad\quad\	$ $+CH_2 - C +_n$ $\qquad\quad	$ $\qquad\ C - O - CH_3$ $\qquad\ \ \|$ $\qquad\ \ O$	Airplane windows, paint, contact lenses, fiber optics
poly (vinyl acetate)	$CH_2 = CH$ $\qquad\quad	$ $\qquad\ O - C - CH_3$ $\qquad\qquad \|$ $\qquad\qquad O$	$+CH_2 - CH +_n$ $\qquad\qquad	$ $\qquad\quad O - C - CH_3$ $\qquad\qquad\quad \|$ $\qquad\qquad\quad O$	Adhesives, latex paint, chewing gum		
polyacrylonitrile (Orlon®, Acrilan®)	$CH_2 = CH$ $\quad\ \	$ $\quad\ CN$	$+CH_2 - CH +_n$ $\qquad\quad	$ $\qquad\ CN$	Carpets, fabrics		
polystyrene (Styrofoam®)	$CH_2 = CH$	$+CH_2 - CH +_n$	Food coolers, drinking cups, insulation				

© aceshot1/Shutterstock.com

1 Automobile safety glass contains a sheet of polyvinyl polymer layered between two sheets of glass to prevent the formation of sharp fragments.

© Ryan_Jorgensen/Jorgo/Shutterstock.com

2 The elasticity of bubble gum comes from a copolymer of styrene and 1,3-butadiene.

Figure 12.8 Two uses of addition polymers. What properties of addition polymers are exhibited in both of these products?

12.5 Alkynes

Learning Objective

7. Write the IUPAC names of alkynes from their molecular structures.

The characteristic feature of alkynes is the presence of a triple bond between carbon atoms. Thus, alkynes are also unsaturated hydrocarbons. Only a few compounds containing the carbon–carbon triple bond are found in nature. The simplest and most important compound of this series is ethyne, more commonly called acetylene (C_2H_2):

$$H - C \equiv C - H$$
acetylene

Acetylene is used in torches for welding steel and in making plastics and synthetic fibers.

Once again, orbital hybridization provides an explanation for the bonding of the carbon atoms. Structurally, the hydrogen and carbon atoms of acetylene molecules lie in a straight line. This same linearity of the triple bond and the two atoms attached to the triple-bonded carbons is found in all alkynes. These characteristics are explained by mixing a $2s$ and a single $2p$ orbital of each carbon to form a pair of sp hybrid orbitals. Two of the $2p$ orbitals of each carbon are unhybridized (see ▶ Figures 12.9 and 12.10).

Figure 12.9 sp hybridization occurs when one of the $2p$ orbitals of carbon mixes with the $2s$ orbital. Two $2p$ orbitals remain unhybridized.

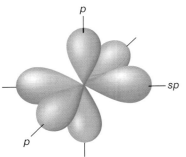

Figure 12.10 The unhybridized p orbitals are perpendicular to the two sp hybridized orbitals.

A carbon–carbon sigma bond in acetylene forms by the overlap of one sp hybrid orbital of each carbon. The other sp hybrid orbital of each carbon overlaps with a $1s$ orbital of a hydrogen to form a carbon–hydrogen sigma bond. The remaining pair of unhybridized p orbitals of each carbon overlap sideways to form a pair of pi bonds between the carbon atoms. Thus, each acetylene molecule contains three sigma bonds (two carbon–hydrogen and one carbon–carbon) and two pi bonds (both are carbon–carbon). This is shown in ▶ Figure 12.11.

Figure 12.11 The shape of acetylene is explained by sigma bonding between *sp* hybrid orbitals and pi bonding between unhybridized *p* orbitals.

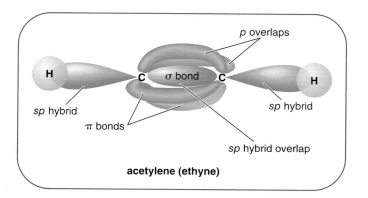

acetylene (ethyne)

Alkynes are named in exactly the same ways as alkenes, except the ending -*yne* is used:

$$\overset{4}{C}H_3\overset{3}{C}H_2-\overset{2}{C}\equiv\overset{1}{C}-H \qquad\qquad H-\overset{1}{C}\equiv\overset{2}{C}-\overset{3}{C}H-\overset{4}{C}H_3$$
$$\qquad\qquad\qquad\qquad\qquad\qquad\qquad\qquad | $$
$$\qquad\qquad\qquad\qquad\qquad\qquad\qquad\qquad CH_3$$

1-butyne 3-methyl-1-butyne

▶ **LEARNING CHECK 12.9** Give the IUPAC name for each of the following:

a. $CH_3-CH_2-C\equiv C-CH_3$

b. $CH_3-\overset{\displaystyle CH_3}{\overset{\displaystyle |}{CH}}-CH_2-C\equiv C-CH_3$

The physical properties of the alkynes are nearly the same as those of the corresponding alkenes and alkanes: They are insoluble in water, less dense than water, and have relatively low melting and boiling points. Alkynes also resemble alkenes in their addition reactions. The same substances (Br_2, H_2, HCl, etc.) that add to double bonds also add to triple bonds. The one significant difference is that alkynes consume twice as many moles of addition reagent as alkenes in addition reactions that go on to completion.

12.6 Aromatic Compounds and the Benzene Structure

Learning Objective

8. Classify organic compounds as aliphatic or aromatic.

Some of the early researchers in organic chemistry became intrigued by fragrant oils that could be extracted from certain plants. Oil of wintergreen and the flavor component of the vanilla bean are examples. The compounds responsible for the aromas had similar chemical properties. As a result, they were grouped together and called aromatic compounds.

As more and more aromatic compounds were isolated and studied, chemists gradually realized that aromatics contained at least six carbon atoms, had low hydrogen-to-carbon ratios (relative to other organic hydrocarbons), and were related to benzene (C_6H_6). For example, toluene, an aromatic compound from the bark of the South American tolu tree, has the formula C_7H_8.

Chemists also learned that the term *aromatic* was not always accurate. Many compounds that belong to the class because of chemical properties and structures are not at all fragrant. Conversely, there are many fragrant compounds that do not have aromatic compound properties or structures. Today, the old class name is used but with a different meaning. Aromatic compounds are those that contain the characteristic benzene ring or

The mechanism for the hydration of alkenes is believed to begin when H^+ from the acid catalyst is attracted to the electrons of the carbon–carbon double bond. The H^+ becomes bonded to one of the carbons by a sharing of electrons:

Step 1.

$$-C=C- + H^+ \longrightarrow \overset{\overset{\displaystyle H}{|}}{-C} - \overset{+}{C}-$$

a carbocation

This process leaves the second carbon with only three bonds about it and thus a positive charge. Such ions, referred to as **carbocations,** are extremely reactive.

As soon as it forms, the positive carbocation attracts any species that has readily available nonbonding electrons, whether it is an anion or a neutral molecule. In the case of water, the oxygen atom has two unshared pairs of electrons:

$$\overset{\ddot{O}}{\underset{H \quad\quad H}{\diagup \quad \diagdown}}$$

One pair of oxygen electrons forms a covalent bond with the carbocation:

Step 2.

$$\overset{\overset{\displaystyle H}{|}}{-C} - \overset{+}{C}- \ + \ \overset{\ddot{O}}{\underset{H \quad H}{\diagup \diagdown}} \ \longrightarrow \ -\overset{|}{C} - \overset{\overset{\displaystyle H \diagdown \quad \diagup H}{O^+}}{\underset{|}{C}}-$$

In the third step, H^+ is lost to produce the alcohol:

Step 3.

$$\overset{\overset{\displaystyle H \diagdown \quad \diagup H}{O^+}}{-\overset{|}{C} - \overset{|}{C}-} \longrightarrow -\overset{\overset{\displaystyle H}{|}}{C} - \overset{\overset{\displaystyle OH}{|}}{C} - \ + H^+$$

an alcohol

Notice that the acid catalyst, H^+, which initiated the reaction, is recovered unchanged in the final step of the mechanism.

By applying Step 2 of the mechanism for hydration, we can understand how HCl and HBr react with alkenes:

$$\overset{\overset{\displaystyle H}{|}}{-C} - \overset{+}{C}- \ + Br^- \longrightarrow -\overset{\overset{\displaystyle H}{|}}{C} - \overset{\overset{\displaystyle Br}{|}}{C}-$$

$$\overset{\overset{\displaystyle H}{|}}{-C} - \overset{+}{C}- \ + Cl^- \longrightarrow -\overset{\overset{\displaystyle H}{|}}{C} - \overset{\overset{\displaystyle Cl}{|}}{C}-$$

carbocation An ion of the form $-\overset{+}{\underset{|}{C}}-$

its structural relatives. Compounds that do not contain this structure (non-aromatic compounds) are referred to as **aliphatic compounds.** Alkanes, alkenes, and alkynes are, therefore, aliphatic compounds.

The molecular structure of benzene presented chemists with an intriguing puzzle after the compound was discovered in 1825 by Michael Faraday. The formula C_6H_6 indicated that the molecule was highly unsaturated. However, the compound did not show the typical reactivity of unsaturated hydrocarbons. Benzene underwent relatively few reactions, and these proceeded slowly and often required heat and catalysts. This was in marked contrast to alkenes, which reacted rapidly with many reagents, in some cases almost instantaneously. This apparent discrepancy between structure and reactivity plagued chemists until 1865, when Freidrich August Kekulé von Stradonitz (see ▶ Figure 12.12), a German chemist, suggested that the benzene molecule might be represented by a ring arrangement of carbon atoms with alternating single and double bonds between the carbon atoms:

aliphatic compound Any organic compound that is not aromatic.

Figure 12.12 Friedrich August Kekulé (1829–1896).

© Stock Montage

He later suggested that the double bonds alternate in their positions between carbon atoms to give two equivalent structures:

Kekulé structures

A modern interpretation of the benzene structure based on hybridization enables chemists to better understand and explain the chemical properties of benzene and other aromatic compounds. Each carbon atom in a benzene ring has three sp^2 hybrid orbitals and one unhybridized p orbital.

A single sigma bond between carbons of the benzene ring is formed by the overlap of two sp^2 orbitals, one from each of the double-bonded carbons. Because each carbon forms two single bonds, two of the sp^2 hybrid orbitals of each carbon are involved. The third sp^2 hybrid orbital of each carbon forms a single sigma bond with a hydrogen by overlapping with a $1s$ orbital of hydrogen. The unhybridized p orbitals of each carbon overlap sideways above and below the plane of the carbon ring to form two delocalized pi lobes that run completely around the ring in the shape of a double torus. The first torus represents the blended and overlapping orbital area of the six pi lobes that point up, and the torus underneath it represents the blending and overlapping orbital area of the six pi lobes that point down (see ▶ Figure 12.13).

Figure 12.13 A hybrid orbital view of the benzene structure.

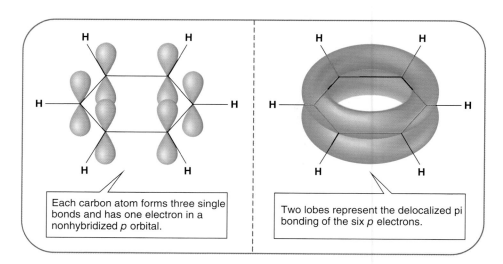

Each carbon atom forms three single bonds and has one electron in a nonhybridized p orbital.

Two lobes represent the delocalized pi bonding of the six p electrons.

This interpretation leads to the conclusion that six bonding electrons move freely around the double ring structure formed by the overlapping delocalized pi lobes. Because of this, the benzene structure is often represented by the symbol:

with the circle representing the evenly distributed electrons in the pi lobes. All six carbon and six hydrogen atoms in benzene molecules lie in the same plane (see Figure 12.13). Therefore, substituted aromatic compounds do not exhibit cis-trans isomerism.

As you draw the structure of aromatic compounds, remember that only one hydrogen atom or group can be attached to a particular position on the benzene ring. For example, compounds (A) and (B) below exist, but (C) does not. Examination of the Kekulé structure

of compound (C) shows that the carbon has five bonds attached to it in violation of the octet rule:

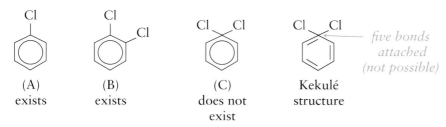

(A) (B) (C) Kekulé
exists exists does not structure
 exist

12.7 The Nomenclature of Benzene Derivatives

Learning Objective

9. Name and draw structural formulas for aromatic compounds.

The chemistry of the aromatic compounds developed somewhat haphazardly for many years before systematic nomenclature schemes were developed. Some of the common names used earlier have acquired historical respectability and are used today; some have even been incorporated into the modern systematic nomenclature system.

The following guidelines are all based on the IUPAC aromatic nomenclature system. They are not complete, and you will not be able to name all aromatic compounds by using them. However, you will be able to name and recognize those used in this book.

Guideline 1. When a single hydrogen of the benzene ring is replaced, the compound can be named as a derivative of benzene:

ethylbenzene nitrobenzene bromobenzene chlorobenzene

Guideline 2. A number of benzene derivatives are known by common names that are also IUPAC-accepted and are used preferentially over other possibilities. Thus, toluene is favored over methylbenzene, and aniline is used rather than aminobenzene:

toluene phenol aniline benzoic acid

Guideline 3. Compounds formed by replacing a hydrogen of benzene with a more complex hydrocarbon group can be named by designating the benzene ring as the group. This is shown as the benzene ring, C_6H_5—, which is also

called a **phenyl group**:

$$CH_3 - CH_2 - CH_2 - CH - CH_2 - CH_2 - CH_3$$

4-phenylheptane 1,1-diphenylcyclobutane

phenyl group A benzene ring with one hydrogen absent, C_6H_5—.

Beautiful, Brown ... and Overdone

For many people, a well-tanned skin is considered to be very attractive. However, the methods used to achieve this stylish appearance sometimes have some serious health drawbacks.

The body protects itself from ultraviolet (UV) radiation by producing a skin pigment called melanin. The accumulation of melanin in the skin leads to the characteristic tan color and protects the skin from burning and other damage caused by UV radiation. Melanin takes 3 to 5 days to form after initial exposure to the sun. Melanin then helps the skin to gradually tan if the exposed time is kept within reasonable bounds.

Teens are particularly susceptible to the risk of overexposure because they are still experiencing tremendous growth at the cellular level. However, people run the risk of developing skin cancer if they are exposed to the sun or to artificial sunlight in tanning salons too often or for long periods of time.

Anyone using the facilities of a tanning salon should find out the recommended exposure times for each bed. At the beginning of developing a tan, an individual should not tan more than every other day. As the tan develops, it is wise to cut back tanning sessions to no more than twice a week. Many salon owners allow individuals to tan for greater periods of time than is safely recommended. Every tanning bed has a chart indicating what frequency and duration are approved by safety standards. If the beds in a salon do not have such charts, the salon is not following safety guidelines, and it would be a good idea to leave.

Exposure to UV rays is known to stimulate addictive behavior that results in increasing tanning frequency and duration. Although a tan is commonly thought to be beautiful, skin cancer certainly is not. Be a conscientious and perceptive consumer.

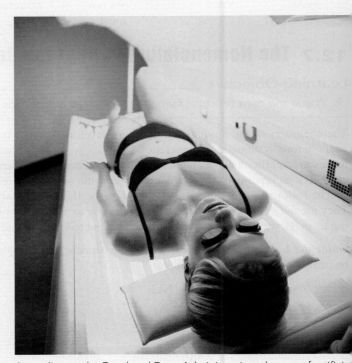

According to the Food and Drug Administration, the use of artificial tanning devices is not recommended for anyone.

It's easy to confuse the words *phenyl* and *phenol*. The key to keeping them straight is the ending: *-ol* means an alcohol (C_6H_5—OH), and *-yl* means a group (C_6H_5—).

Guideline 4. When two groups are attached to a benzene ring, three isomeric structures are possible. They can be designated by the prefixes *ortho (o), meta (m),* and *para (p):*

o-dibromobenzene *m*-dibromobenzene *p*-dibromobenzene

Guideline 5. When two or more groups are attached to a benzene ring, their positions can be indicated by numbering the carbon atoms of the ring so as to obtain the lowest

possible numbers for the attachment positions. Groups are arranged in alphabetical order. If there is a choice of identical sets of numbers, the group that comes first in alphabetical order is given the lower number. IUPAC-acceptable common names may be used:

m-bromochlorobenzene
or 1-bromo-3-chlorobenzene

1,2,4-trichlorobenzene

3,5-dichlorobenzoic acid

▶ Example 12.5

Name each of the following aromatic compounds:

a. b. c.

Solution

a. This compound is named as a substituted toluene. Both of the following are correct: 3-ethyltoluene and m-ethyltoluene. Note that in 3-ethyltoluene the methyl group, which is a part of the toluene structure, must be assigned to position number one.
b. This compound may be named as a substituted benzene or a substituted propane: propylbenzene, 1-phenylpropane.
c. When three groups are involved, the ring-numbering approach must be used: 3-chloro-5-ethylbenzoic acid.

▶ LEARNING CHECK 12.10 Name the following aromatic compounds:

a.

c.

b.

d.

Smoking: It's Quitting Time

Smoking is a difficult habit to break, especially if the attempt is made by stopping abruptly—going "cold turkey." Mark Twain described the more reasonable gradual approach when he said, "Habit is habit, and not to be flung out of the window by any man, but coaxed downstairs a step at a time." Smokers do not have to go "cold turkey" because there are several OTC aids available, as well as some new prescription products to help them gradually overcome the strong urge to smoke—and eventually quit.

The transdermal (absorbed through the skin) nicotine patch is available over the counter in doses of 7–22 mg. When used as directed, this method delivers a steady supply of nicotine to the bloodstream and helps minimize withdrawal symptoms. Nicotine gum also helps reduce withdrawal symptoms when used correctly. The gum should be chewed briefly and then held next to the cheek, allowing the lining of the mouth to absorb the nicotine.

With a prescription, smokers can also obtain a nasal spray that provides a small dose of nicotine each time it is used. This product, called Nicotrol NS®, was approved by the FDA even though inhaling the nicotine poses a small risk that smokers will become as dependent on the mist as they are on cigarettes. The nicotine from the nasal spray gets into the bloodstream faster than nicotine from the gum or patch, providing immediate relief from cigarette craving. A squirt into each nostril gives a smoker 1 mg of nicotine, but it is not supposed to be used more than five times per hour.

The Nicotrol nicotine inhalation system has also received FDA approval. This inhaler, available only by prescription, consists of a plastic cylinder about the size of a cigarette that encloses a cartridge containing nicotine. When a smoker "puffs" on the device, nicotine vapors are absorbed through the lining of the mouth and throat. It takes about 80 puffs to deliver the amount of nicotine obtained from a single cigarette. An advantage of using the system is that a smoker still mimics the hand-to-mouth behavior of smoking, a part of the smoking habit that will be easier to break once nicotine withdrawal symptoms subside.

One of the newest prescription products designed to help break the smoking habit does not contain any nicotine. It is an antidepressant called bupropion that has been shown to be effective in the treatment of nicotine addiction. It is believed that bupropion mimics some of the action of nicotine by releasing the brain chemicals norepinephrine and dopamine, but it is not completely understood how it works. During treatment, a bupropion tablet (marketed as Zyban®) is taken once a day for 3 days and then twice daily during the week before smoking is stopped. Usually, the treatment is continued for the next 6 or 12 weeks to help curb the craving for cigarettes.

If a smoker truly wants to quit, these aids alone will not do it. A smoker must have some kind of support from a formal program, or at least informal support from family and friends. A smoker should also get rid of all tobacco products and avoid smoking triggers, such as other smokers, stress, and alcohol. Exercise can also be a distraction from smoking and can minimize the weight gain that sometimes accompanies giving up smoking.

Nicotine replacement therapy is used to help stop smoking by delivering nicotine to the body in a low controlled dose.

Zyban is a nicotine-free anti-smoking pill.

12.8 Properties and Uses of Aromatic Compounds

Learning Objective

10. Recognize uses for specific aromatic compounds.

The physical properties of benzene and other aromatic hydrocarbons are similar to those of alkanes and alkenes. They are nonpolar and thus insoluble in water. This hydrophobic characteristic plays an important role in the chemistry of some proteins (Chapter 19).

Aromatic rings are relatively stable chemically. Because of this, benzene often reacts in such a way that the aromatic ring remains intact. Thus, benzene does not undergo the addition reactions that are characteristic of alkenes and alkynes. The predominant type of reaction of aromatic molecules is substitution, in which one of the ring hydrogens is replaced by some other group. Such aromatic reactions are of lesser importance for our purposes and are not shown here.

All aromatic compounds discussed to this point contain a single benzene ring. There are also substances called **polycyclic aromatic compounds,** which contain two or more benzene rings sharing a common side, or "fused" together. The simplest of these compounds, naphthalene, is the original active ingredient in mothballs:

polycyclic aromatic compound A derivative of benzene in which carbon atoms are shared between two or more benzene rings.

naphthalene

A number of more complex polycyclic aromatic compounds are known to be carcinogens—chemicals that cause cancer. Two of these compounds are:

a benzopyrene

a dibenzanthracene

These cancer-producing compounds are often formed as a result of heating organic materials to high temperatures. They are present in tobacco smoke (see ❱ Figure 12.14), automobile exhaust, and sometimes in burned or heavily browned food. Such compounds are believed to be at least partially responsible for the high incidence of lung and lip cancer among cigarette smokers. Those who smoke heavily face an increased risk of getting cancer. Chemists have identified more than 4000 compounds in cigarette smoke, including 43 known carcinogens. The Environmental Protection Agency (EPA) considers tobacco smoke a Class A carcinogen.

The major sources of aromatic compounds are petroleum and coal tar, a sticky, dark-colored material derived from coal. As with many classes of organic compounds, the simplest structures are the most important commercial materials.

Benzene and toluene are excellent laboratory and industrial solvents. In addition, they are the starting materials for the synthesis of hundreds of other valuable aromatic compounds that are intermediates in the manufacture of a wide variety of commercial products, including the important polymers Bakelite® and polystyrene (see ❱ Table 12.4).

A number of aromatic compounds are important in another respect: They must be present in our diet for proper nutrition. Unlike plants, which have the ability to synthesize the benzene ring from simpler materials, humans must obtain any necessary aromatic rings from their diet. This helps explain why certain amino acids, the building blocks of proteins, and some **vitamins** are dietary essentials (Table 12.4).

Figure 12.14 Cigarette smoke contains carcinogenic polycyclic aromatic compounds.

vitamin An organic nutrient that the body cannot produce in the small amounts needed for good health.

TABLE 12.4 Some Important Aromatic Compounds

Name	Structural Formula	Use
benzene		Industrial solvent and raw material
toluene	CH_3 attached to benzene ring	Industrial solvent and raw material
phenol	OH attached to benzene ring	Manufacture of Bakelite® and Formica®
aniline	NH_2 attached to benzene ring	Manufacture of drugs and dyes
styrene	$CH = CH_2$ attached to benzene ring	Preparation of polystyrene products
phenylalanine	$CH_2CH - C - OH$ with $=O$ above C and NH_2 below CH, attached to benzene ring	An essential amino acid
riboflavin	$CH_2 - CH - CH - CH - CH_2$ with OH groups; fused ring system with CH_3 groups, N, NH, O	Vitamin B$_2$

Case Study Follow-up

The Women's Health and Cancer Rights Act of 1998 requires insurance companies that cover mastectomies to cover all aspects of post-mastectomy reconstructive surgery (U.S.D.O.L., 1998). It could be argued that this surgery does nothing to prolong the cancer patient's life, but according to the act, it is considered a right for the woman to be restored to her former condition as much as possible. It is a matter of esthetic concern and self-esteem. In the same way, esthetic concerns are important to limb amputees. People who receive proper rehabilitation along with prosthetics are less likely to need expensive social welfare services. Prostheses help restore an amputee's dignity, productivity, and independence. The U.S. Armed Forces recognizes the value of prosthetics and allows service members with limb loss to choose a military or private prosthetist at no cost (Blough et al., 2010). There is a growing trend across the United States in which private insurance companies are significantly reducing prosthetic benefits or eliminating prosthetic coverage. Legislation is needed to increase parity between federal and private coverage (Turner, 2009). Self-assessment of physical appearance is important to self-esteem, which can influence levels of happiness, or, conversely, depression (Vohs et al., 2003). Allowing amputees to be involved in the design of their prosthetics can be important to their recovery.

The Nomenclature of Alkenes

Compounds containing double or triple bonds between carbon atoms are said to be unsaturated. The alkenes contain double bonds, alkynes contain triple bonds, and aromatics contain a six-membered ring with three double bonds. **Objective 1, Exercise 12.2.** In the IUPAC nomenclature system, alkene names end in -*ene*, and alkynes end in -*yne*. **Objective 2, Exercise 12.4**

The Geometry of Alkenes

In alkenes, the double-bonded carbons and the four groups attached to these carbons lie in the same plane. Because rotation about the double bond is restricted, alkenes may exist as geometric, or cis-trans, isomers. This type of stereoisomerism is possible when each double-bonded carbon is attached to two different groups. **Objective 3, Exercise 12.18** IUPAC names of stereoisomers contain the prefixes *cis*- or *trans*-. **Objective 4, Assessment Exercise 12.20**

Properties of Alkenes

The physical properties of alkenes are very similar to those of the alkanes. They are nonpolar, insoluble in water, less dense than water, and soluble in nonpolar solvents. Alkenes are quite reactive, and their characteristic reaction is addition to the double bond. Three important addition reactions are bromination (an example of halogenation) to give a dibrominated alkane, hydration to produce an alcohol, and the reaction with H—X to give an alkyl halide. The addition of H_2O and H—X are governed by Markovnikov's rule. **Objective 5, Exercise 12.26**

Addition Polymers

Addition polymers are formed from alkene monomers that undergo repeated addition reactions with each other. Many familiar and widely used materials, such as fibers and plastics, are addition polymers. **Objective 6, Exercise 12.36**

Alkynes

The alkynes contain triple bonds and possess a linear geometry of the two carbons and the two attached groups. Alkyne names end in -*yne*. **Objective 7, Exercise 12.44** The physical and chemical properties of alkynes are very similar to those of the alkenes.

Aromatic Compounds and the Benzene Structure

Benzene, the simplest aromatic compound, and other members of the aromatic class contain a six-membered ring with three double bonds. This aromatic ring is often drawn as a hexagon containing a circle, which represents the six electrons of the double bonds that move freely around the ring. All organic compounds that do not contain an aromatic ring are called aliphatic compounds. **Objective 8, Exercise 12.48**

The Nomenclature of Benzene Derivatives

Several acceptable IUPAC names are possible for many benzene compounds. Some IUPAC names are based on widely used common names such as toluene and aniline. Other compounds are named as derivatives of benzene or by designating the benzene ring as a phenyl group. **Objective 9, Exercises 12.52 and 12.54**

Properties and Uses of Aromatic Compounds

Aromatic hydrocarbons are nonpolar and have physical properties similar to those of the alkanes and alkenes. Benzene resists addition reactions typical of alkenes. Benzene and toluene are key industrial chemicals. Other important aromatics include phenol, aniline, and styrene. **Objective 10, Exercise 12.66**

Key Terms and Concepts

Addition polymer (12.4)
Addition reaction (12.3)
Aliphatic compound (12.6)
Alkene (Introduction)
Alkyne (Introduction)
Aromatic hydrocarbon (Introduction)
Carbocation (12.5)

Copolymer (12.4)
Haloalkane or alkyl halide (12.3)
Hydration (12.3)
Hydrogenation (12.3)
Markovnikov's rule (12.3)
Monomer (12.4)
Phenyl group (12.7)

Polycyclic aromatic compound (12.8)
Polymer (12.4)
Polymerization (12.4)
Polyunsaturated (12.3)
Unsaturated hydrocarbon (Introduction)
Vitamin (12.8)

Key Reactions

1.	Halogenation of an alkene (Section 12.3):	$\begin{array}{c}\diagdown \\ /\end{array} C = C \begin{array}{c}/ \\ \diagdown\end{array}$ + Br—Br $\longrightarrow$ —C—C— with Br, Br below	Reaction 12.2
2.	Hydrogenation of an alkene (Section 12.3):	$\begin{array}{c}\diagdown \\ /\end{array} C = C \begin{array}{c}/ \\ \diagdown\end{array}$ + H—H $\xrightarrow{\text{Pt}}$ —C—C— with H, H below	Reaction 12.4
3.	Addition of H—X to an alkene (Section 12.3):	$\begin{array}{c}\diagdown \\ /\end{array} C = C \begin{array}{c}/ \\ \diagdown\end{array}$ + H—Cl $\longrightarrow$ —C—C— with H, Cl below	Reaction 12.6
4.	Hydration of an alkene (Section 12.3):	$\begin{array}{c}\diagdown \\ /\end{array} C = C \begin{array}{c}/ \\ \diagdown\end{array}$ + H—OH $\xrightarrow{H_2SO_4}$ —C—C— with H, OH below	Reaction 12.9
5.	Addition polymerization of an alkene (Section 12.4):	$n CH_2 = CH_2 \xrightarrow[\text{catalysts}]{\text{Heat, pressure}} +CH_2 - CH_2 +_n$	Reaction 12.14

Exercises

Even-numbered exercises are answered in Appendix B.

Blue-numbered exercises are more challenging.

The Nomenclature of Alkenes (Section 12.1) and Alkynes (Section 12.5)

12.1 What is the definition of an unsaturated hydrocarbon?

12.2 Define the terms alkene, alkyne, and aromatic hydrocarbon.

12.3 Select those compounds that can be correctly called *unsaturated* and classify each one as an *alkene* or an *alkyne:*

a. $CH_3 — CH_2 — CH_3$

b. $CH_3CH = CHCH_3$

c. $H—C\equiv C—CH—CH_3$ with CH_3 below

d. (cyclopentene structure)

e. (cyclohexane with CH_3 structure)

f. (cyclopentane with $CH = CH_2$ structure)

g. $CH = CH$ / $CH_2 — CH_2$ (cyclobutene-like structure)

h. $CH_2 = CHCH_2CH_3$

i. CH_3CHCH_3 with CH_3 below

Unless otherwise noted all art on this page © Cengage Learning 2014

12.4 Give the IUPAC name for the following compounds:

a. $CH_3CH = CHCH_3$

b. $CH_3CH_2 - C = CHCH_3$
 with CH_2CH_3 below the C

c. $CH_3 - C \equiv C - C - CH_2CH_3$
 with CH_3 above and CH_3 below the fourth carbon

d. cyclopentene ring with CH_3

e. $CH_3CHCH_2 - C \equiv C - CH - CH_3$
 with Br above the second carbon and CH_3 below

f. cyclopropene ring with CH_3 at top, CH_3 and CH_2CH_3 at bottom

g. $CH_3CH - CH = CHCH_2CH = CH_2$
 with CH_3 above

12.5 Give the IUPAC name for the following compounds:

a. $CH_3CHCH = CHCH_2CH_3$
 with CH_3 below

b. $CH_3CH = CHCH = CHCHCH_3$
 with CH_3 below

c. cyclopentene ring

d. $CH_3 - C \equiv C - CH_2CH_3$

e. cyclohexene ring with CH_2CHCH_3 (CH_3) substituent and CH_3 substituent

f. cycloheptatriene ring with $CH_2CH_2CH_3$ substituent

g. $CH_2 = C - CH - CH = CHCH_2CH_3$
 with $CH_2CH_2CH_2CH_3$ above and CH_2CH_3 below

12.6 Draw structural formulas for the following compounds:

a. 3-ethyl-2-hexene

b. 3,4-dimethyl-1-pentene

c. 3-methyl-1,3-pentadiene

d. 2-isopropyl-4-methylcyclohexene

e. 1-butylcyclopropene

12.7 Draw structural formulas for the following compounds:

a. 4,4,5-trimethyl-2-heptyne

b. 1,3-cyclohexadiene

c. 2-t-butyl-4,4-dimethyl-1-pentene

d. 4-isopropyl-3,3-dimethyl-1,5-octadiene

e. 2-methyl-1,3-cyclopentadiene

f. 3-sec-butyl-3-t-butyl-1-heptyne

12.8 A compound has the molecular formula C_5H_8. Draw a structural formula for a compound with this formula that would be classified as (a) an alkyne, (b) a diene, and (c) a cyclic alkene. Give the IUPAC name for each compound.

12.9 Draw structural formulas and give IUPAC names for the 13 alkene isomers of C_6H_{12}. Ignore geometric isomers and cyclic structures.

12.10 a-Farnesene is a constituent of the natural wax found on apples. Given that a 12-carbon chain is named as a dodecane, what is the IUPAC name of a-farnesene?

$CH_3C = CHCH_2CH_2C = CHCH_2CH = CCH = CH_2$
 with CH_3 above each of the three branch carbons

α-farnesene

12.11 Each of the following names is wrong. Give the structure and correct name for each compound.

a. 3-pentene

b. 3-methyl-2-butene

c. 2-ethyl-3-pentyne

12.12 Each of the following names is wrong. Give the structure and correct name for each compound.

a. 2-methyl-4-hexene

b. 3,5-heptadiene

c. 4-methylcyclobutene

The Geometry of Alkenes (Section 12.2)

12.13 What type of hybridized orbital is present on carbon atoms bonded by a double bond? How many of these hybrid orbitals are on each carbon atom?

12.14 What type of orbital overlaps to form a pi bond in an alkene? What symbol is used to represent a pi bond? How many electrons are in a pi bond?

12.15 Describe the geometry of the carbon–carbon double bond and the two atoms attached to each of the double-bonded carbon atoms.

12.16 Explain the difference between geometric and structural isomers of alkenes.

12.17 Draw structural formulas and give IUPAC names for all the isomeric pentenes (C_5H_{10}) that are:

a. Alkenes that do not show geometric isomerism. There are four compounds.

b. Alkenes that do show geometric isomerism. There is one cis and one trans compound.

12.18 Which of the following alkenes can exist as cis-trans isomers? Draw structural formulas and name the cis and trans isomers.

a. $CH_3CH_2CH_2CH_2CH=CH_2$

b. $CH_3CH_2CH=CHCH_2CH_3$

c. $CH_3\overset{\displaystyle CH_3}{\underset{|}{C}}=CHCH_2CH_3$

12.19 Which of the following alkenes can exist as *cis-trans* isomers? Draw structural formulas and name the *cis* and *trans* isomers.

a. $CH_3CH_2CH_2CH=CHCH_2CH_2CH_3$

b. $CH_3CH=\overset{\displaystyle }{\underset{\displaystyle CH_2CH_3}{\underset{|}{C}}}-CH_2CH_3$

c. $BrCH_2CH=CHCH_2Br$

12.20 Draw structural formulas for the following:

a. *cis*-3-hexene

b. *trans*-3-heptene

12.21 Draw structural formulas for the following:

a. *trans*-3,4-dibromo-3-heptene

b. *cis*-1,4-dichloro-2-methyl-2-butene

Properties of Alkenes (Section 12.3)

12.22 In what ways are the physical properties of alkenes similar to those of alkanes?

12.23 Which of the following reactions is an addition reaction?

a. $A_2 + C_3H_6 \rightarrow C_3H_6A_2$

b. $A_2 + C_6H_6 \rightarrow C_6H_5A + HA$

c. $HA + C_4H_8 \rightarrow C_4H_9A$

d. $3O_2 + C_2H_4 \rightarrow 2CO_2 + 2H_2O$

e. $C_7H_{16} \rightarrow C_7H_8 + 4H_2$

12.24 State Markovnikov's rule, and write a reaction that illustrates its application.

12.25 Complete the following reactions. Where more than one product is possible, show only the one expected according to Markovnikov's rule.

a. $CH_2=CHCH_2CH_3 + H_2 \xrightarrow{Pt}$

b. $CH_2=CHCH_2CH_3 + Br_2 \longrightarrow$

c. $+ HCl \longrightarrow$

d. $CH_3CH_2\overset{\displaystyle CH_3}{\underset{|}{C}}=CH_2 + H_2O \xrightarrow{H_2SO_4}$

12.26 Complete the following reactions. Where more than one product is possible, show only the one expected according to Markovnikov's rule.

a. $+ Br_2 \longrightarrow$

b. $+ H_2O \xrightarrow{H_2SO_4}$

c. $CH_2=\overset{\displaystyle CH_3}{\underset{|}{C}}-CH=CH_2 + 2H_2 \xrightarrow{Pt}$

d. $+ HCl \longrightarrow$

12.27 Draw the structural formula for the alkenes with molecular formula C_5H_{10} that will react to give the following products. Show all correct structures if more than one starting material will react as shown.

a. $C_5H_{10} + Br_2 \longrightarrow CH_3CH_2\underset{\underset{\displaystyle Br}{|}}{C}H\underset{\underset{\displaystyle Br}{|}}{C}HCH_3$

b. $C_5H_{10} + H_2 \xrightarrow{Pt} CH_3CH_2CH_2CH_2CH_3$

c. $C_5H_{10} + H_2O \xrightarrow{H_2SO_4} CH_3\overset{\displaystyle CH_3}{\underset{\underset{\displaystyle OH}{|}}{C}}CH_2CH_3$

d. $C_5H_{10} + HBr \longrightarrow CH_3\underset{\underset{\displaystyle Br}{|}}{C}HCH_2CH_2CH_3$

12.28 What reagents would you use to prepare each of the following from 3-hexene?

a. $CH_3CH_2\underset{\underset{\displaystyle Br}{|}}{C}H\underset{\underset{\displaystyle Br}{|}}{C}HCH_2CH_3$

b. $CH_3CH_2CH_2CH_2CH_2CH_3$

c. $CH_3CH_2CH_2\underset{\underset{\displaystyle Cl}{|}}{C}HCH_2CH_3$

d. $CH_3CH_2CH_2\underset{\underset{\displaystyle OH}{|}}{C}HCH_2CH_3$

12.29 What is an important commercial application of hydrogenation?

12.30 Cyclohexane and 2-hexene both have the molecular formula C_6H_{12}. Describe a simple chemical test that would distinguish one from the other.

Unless otherwise noted all art on this page © Cengage Learning 2014

12.31 Terpin hydrate is used medicinally as an expectorant for coughs. It is prepared by the following addition reaction. What is the structure of terpin hydrate?

Addition Polymers (Section 12.4)

12.32 Explain what is meant by each of the following terms: *monomer, polymer, addition polymer,* and *copolymer.*

12.33 A section of polypropylene containing three units of monomer can be shown as:

Draw structural formulas for comparable three-unit sections of:

a. Teflon

b. Orlon

c. Lucite

12.34 Identify a structural feature characteristic of all monomers listed in Table 12.3.

12.35 Rubber cement contains a polymer of 2-methylpropene (isobutylene) called polyisobutylene. Write an equation for the polymerization reaction.

12.36 Much of today's plumbing in newly built homes is made from a plastic called poly (vinyl chloride), or PVC. Using Table 12.3, write a reaction for the formation of poly (vinyl chloride).

12.37 Identify a major use for each of the following addition polymers:

a. Styrofoam

b. Acrilan

c. Plexiglas

d. PVC

e. polypropylene

Alkynes (Section 12.5)

12.38 What type of hybridized orbital is present on carbon atoms bonded by a triple bond? How many of these hybrid orbitals are on each carbon atom?

12.39 How many sigma bonds and how many pi bonds make up the triple bond of an alkyne?

12.40 Describe the geometry in an alkyne of the carbon–carbon triple bond and the two attached atoms.

12.41 Explain why geometric isomerism is not possible in alkynes.

12.42 Give the common name and major uses of the simplest alkyne.

12.43 Describe the physical and chemical properties of alkynes.

12.44 Write the structural formulas and IUPAC names for all the isomeric alkynes with the formula C_5H_8.

Aromatic Compounds and the Benzene Structure (Section 12.6)

12.45 What type of hybridized orbital is present on the carbon atoms of a benzene ring? How many sigma bonds are formed by each carbon atom in a benzene ring?

12.46 What type of orbital overlaps to form the pi bonding in a benzene ring?

12.47 What does the circle within the hexagon represent in the structural formula for benzene?

12.48 Define the terms *aromatic* and *aliphatic.*

12.49 Limonene, which is present in citrus peelings, has a very pleasant lemonlike fragrance. However, it is not classified as an aromatic compound. Explain.

limonene

12.50 A disubstituted cycloalkane such as (a) exhibits *cis-trans* isomerism, whereas a disubstituted benzene (b) does not. Explain.

The Nomenclature of Benzene Derivatives (Section 12.7)

12.51 Give an IUPAC name for each of the following hydrocarbons as a derivative of benzene:

12.52 Give an IUPAC name for each of the following hydrocarbons as a derivative of benzene:

12.53 Give an IUPAC name for the following as hydrocarbons with the benzene ring as a substituent:

a. CH_2=C—CH_2CH_3

b.

12.54 Give an IUPAC name for the following as hydrocarbons with the benzene ring as a substituent:

a. CH_3CH_2CHCH=CH_2

b. $CH_3CHCH_2CH_2CHCH_3$

12.55 Name the following compounds, using the prefixed abbreviations for *ortho, meta,* and *para* and assigning IUPAC-acceptable common names:

a.

b.

12.56 Name the following compounds, using the prefixed abbreviations for *ortho, meta,* and *para* and assigning IUPAC-acceptable common names:

a.

b.

12.57 Name the following by numbering the benzene ring. IUPAC-acceptable common names may be used where appropriate:

a.

b.

12.58 Name the following by numbering the benzene ring. IUPAC-acceptable common names may be used where appropriate:

a.

b.

12.59 Draw structural formulas for the following:

a. 2,4-diethylaniline

b. 4-ethyltoluene

c. *p*-ethyltoluene

12.60 Write structural formulas for the following:

a. *o*-ethylphenol

b. *m*-chlorobenzoic acid

c. 3-methyl-3-phenylpentane

12.61 There are three bromonitrobenzene derivatives. Draw their structures and give an IUPAC name for each one.

Properties and Uses of Aromatic Compounds (Section 12.8)

12.62 Describe the chief physical properties of aromatic hydrocarbons.

12.63 Why does benzene not readily undergo addition reactions characteristic of other unsaturated compounds?

12.64 Compare the chemical behavior of benzene and cyclohexene.

12.65 For each of the following uses, list an appropriate aromatic compound:

a. A solvent

b. A vitamin

c. An essential amino acid

d. Starting material for dyes

12.66 For each of the following uses, list an appropriate aromatic compound:

 a. Used in the production of Formica

 b. A starting material for polystyrene

 c. Used to manufacture drugs

 d. A starting material for Bakelite

Additional Exercises

12.67 In general, alkynes have slightly higher boiling points and densities than structurally equivalent alkanes. What interparticle force would this be attributable to?

12.68 In Reaction 12.14, heat, pressure, and catalysts are needed to convert ethylene gas to polyethylene. Explain the effects of each of the three conditions (heat, pressure, catalysts) in terms of factors that affect reaction rates.

12.69 Propene reacts with a diatomic molecule whose atoms have the electronic configuration of $1s^2 2s^2 2p^6 3s^2 3p^5$. Draw the structure of the product formed and give its IUPAC name.

12.70 Draw a generalized energy diagram for the following reaction. Is the reaction endothermic or exothermic?

$$\text{alkene} + \text{water} \xrightarrow{H_2SO_4} \text{alcohol} + 10 \text{ kcal/mol}$$

12.71 What will be the limiting reactant when 25.0 g of 2-butene reacts with 25.0 g of iodine to produce 2,3-diiodobutane? How many moles of product could be produced?

$$CH_3CH{=}CHCH_3 + I_2 \longrightarrow CH_3\underset{\underset{I}{|}}{C}H\underset{\underset{I}{|}}{C}HCH_3$$

Allied Health Exam Connection

The following questions are from these sources:

1. *Nursing School Entrance Exam* © 2005, Learning Express, LLC.

2. *McGraw-Hill's Nursing School Entrance Exams* by Thomas A. Evangelist, Tamara B. Orr and Judy Unrein © 2009, The McGraw-Hill Companies, Inc.

3. *NSEE Nursing School Entrance Exams,* 3rd Edition © 2009, Kaplan Publishing.

4. *Cliffs Test Prep: Nursing School Entrance Exams* by Fred N. Grayson © 2004, Wiley Publishing, Inc.

5. *Peterson's Master the Nursing School and Allied Health Entrance Exams,* 18th Edition by Marion F. Gooding © 2008, Peterson's, a Nelnet Company.

12.72 Which of the following are aromatic compounds?

 a. benzene

 b. ethyl alcohol

 c. methane

 d. phenol

12.73 Identify which of the following general formulas would be used to characterize (1) an alkane, (2) an alkene with one C=C bond, and (3) an alkyne with one C≡C bond.

 a. C_nH_{2n}

 b. C_nH_{2n+2}

 c. C_nH_{2n-2}

12.74. The compound $CH_2{=}CH{-}CH_2{-}CH_2{-}CH_3$ is an example of:

 a. a pentane

 b. a hexene

 c. an alkene

 d. organic macromolecule

12.75 The correct structural formula for ethyne is:

 a. $H{-}C{\equiv}C{-}H$

 b. $H{-}C{\equiv}C{=}H$

 c. $H{-}C{\equiv}C{-}H$

 d. $H{=}C{=}C{=}H$

12.76 Protection of the skin from the harmful effects of ultraviolet light is provided by the pigment _____, which is produced by specialized cells within the stratum germinativum.

 a. carotene

 b. melanin

 c. keratin

 d. hemoglobin

Chemistry for Thought

12.77 Napthalene is the simplest polycyclic aromatic compound:

Draw a Kekulé structure for this compound like that shown for benzene in Section 12.6.

12.78 Why does propene not exhibit geometric isomerism?

12.79 Limonene is present in the rind of lemons and oranges. Based on its structure (see Exercise 12.49), would you consider it to be a solid, liquid, or gas at room temperature?

12.80 If the average molecular weight of polyethylene is 5.0×10^4 u, how many ethylene monomers ($CH_2{=}CH_2$) are contained in a molecule of the polymer?

12.81 Reactions to synthesize the benzene ring of aromatic compounds do not occur within the human body, and yet many essential body components involve the benzene structure. How does the human body get its supply of aromatic compounds?

12.82 Answer the question in the caption to Figure 12.8 pertaining to addition polymers.

12.83 Why can't alkanes undergo addition polymerization?

12.84 Some polymers produce toxic fumes when they are burning. Which polymer in Table 12.3 produces hydrogen cyanide, HCN? Which produces hydrogen chloride, HCl?

12.85 "Super glue" is an addition polymer of the following monomer. Draw a structural formula for a three-unit section of super glue.

$$CH_2{=}\underset{\underset{CN}{|}}{C}{-}O{-}\overset{\overset{O}{\|}}{C}{-}CH_3$$

12.86 One of the fragrant components in mint plants is menthene, a compound whose IUPAC name is 1-isopropyl-4-methylcyclohexene. Draw a structural formula for menthene.

Case Study

Ron was a 63-year-old retired Army sergeant. He went for a physical at his wife Sheila's urging. She was worried because Ron had become increasingly clumsy, including tripping and falling. He had difficulty hearing, and his memory seemed to be failing. Ron couldn't remember what day it was or what he had done two days ago, but he seemed to remember older memories just fine. Ron's father was in the last stages of Alzheimer's. Could Ron have the disease too? In addition to the routine exam and laboratory tests, the doctor asked some screening questions. She made it a habit to ask a particular question of all her adult patients: "On any one occasion during the past three months, have you had more than five alcoholic drinks?" Ron's affirmative reply caused the doctor to probe more deeply and to consider that alcoholism and the memory loss associated with Korsekoff's syndrome, a neurological disorder caused by the lack of vitamin B_1 in the brain, might be Ron's primary issue. By taking time to compassionately address his issues, the physician was able to convince Ron to check himself into treatment.

How important is addiction screening to the routine physical? How should a healthcare professional prioritize a patient's complex set of symptoms?

Follow-up to this Case Study appears at the end the chapter before the Concept Summary.

© haveseen/Shutterstock.com

Learning Objectives

When you have completed your study of this chapter, you should be able to:

1 Name and draw structural formulas for alcohols and phenols. (Section 13.1)

2 Classify alcohols as primary, secondary, or tertiary on the basis of their structural formulas. (Section 13.2)

3 Discuss how hydrogen bonding influences the physical properties of alcohols. (Section 13.3)

4 Write equations for alcohol dehydration and oxidation reactions. (Section 13.4)

5 Recognize uses for specific alcohols. (Section 13.5)

6 Recognize uses for specific phenols. (Section 13.6)

7 Name and draw structural formulas for ethers. (Section 13.7)

8 Describe the key physical and chemical properties of ethers. (Section 13.8)

9 Write equations for a thiol reaction with heavy metal ions and the production of disulfides that results when thiols are oxidized. (Section 13.9)

10 Identify functional groups in polyfunctional compounds. (Section 13.10)

Figure 13.1 A promising anti-cancer drug, taxol, is isolated from the bark of the Pacific yew tree. Though taxol is a complex compound, what does its name suggest about its structure?

© Tom and Pat Leeson/Photo Researchers, Inc.

A lcohols, phenols, and ethers are important organic compounds that occur naturally and are produced synthetically in significant amounts. They are used in numerous industrial and pharmaceutical applications (see ▶ Figure 13.1). Ethanol, for example, is one of the simplest and best known of all organic substances; the fermentation method for producing it was known and used by ancient civilizations. Menthol, a ten-carbon alcohol obtained from peppermint oil, is widely used as a flavoring agent. Cholesterol, with its complicated multiring molecular structure, has been implicated in some forms of heart disease. The chemistry of all of these substances is similar because the alcohol functional group behaves essentially the same, regardless of the complexity of the molecule in which it is found.

$CH_3—CH_2—OH$

ethanol

menthol

cholesterol

alcohol A compound in which an —OH group is connected to an aliphatic carbon atom.

hydroxy group The —OH functional group.

phenol A compound in which an —OH group is connected to a benzene ring. The parent compound is also called phenol.

Structurally, an **alcohol** is obtained from a hydrocarbon by replacing a hydrogen atom with a **hydroxy group** (—OH). A formula for an alcohol can be generalized as R—OH, where R— represents CH_3—, CH_3CH_2—, or any other singly bonded carbon–hydrogen group. Thus, R—OH can stand for CH_3—OH, CH_3CH_2—OH, and so on. If the replaced hydrogen was attached to an aromatic ring, the resulting compound is known as a **phenol:**

R— OH an alcohol

a phenol (benzene ring with —OH)

Alcohols and phenols may also be considered to be derived from water by the replacement of one of its hydrogen atoms with an alkyl group or an aromatic ring:

$$H — OH \xrightarrow{\text{Replace H with R}} R— OH$$
water an alcohol

$$H — OH \xrightarrow{\text{Replace H with}} \text{(benzene ring)} — OH$$
water a phenol

ether A compound that contains a

$$-\overset{|}{\underset{|}{C}}-O-\overset{|}{\underset{|}{C}}-$$

functional group.

For most people, the word *ether* generates images of surgeons and operating rooms. Chemists define an **ether** as an organic compound in which two carbon atoms are bonded to an oxygen atom. This structure results when both hydrogen atoms of water are replaced by alkyl groups:

$$H — O — H \xrightarrow[\text{H's with R}]{\text{Replace both}} R — O — R'$$
water an ether

R' indicates that the two R groups can be the same or different.

13.1 The Nomenclature of Alcohols and Phenols

Learning Objective

1. Name and draw structural formulas for alcohols and phenols.

The simpler alcohols are often known by common names, where the alkyl group name is followed by the word *alcohol:*

CH_3—OH CH_3CH_2—OH $CH_3CH_2CH_2$—OH
methyl alcohol ethyl alcohol propyl alcohol

CH_3CHCH_3
 |
 OH
isopropyl alcohol

The IUPAC rules for naming alcohols that contain a single hydroxy group are as follows:

Step 1. Name the longest chain to which the hydroxy group is attached. The chain name is obtained by dropping the final *-e* from the name of the hydrocarbon that contains the same number of carbon atoms and adding the ending *-ol.*

Step 2. Number the longest chain to give the lower number to the carbon with the attached hydroxy group.

Step 3. Locate the position of the hydroxy group by the number of the carbon atom to which it is attached.

Step 4. Locate and name any branches attached to the chain.

Step 5. Combine the name and location for other groups, the hydroxy group location, and the longest chain into the final name.

▶ Example 13.1

Name the following alcohols according to the IUPAC system:

a. CH_3—OH

b. $CH_3CH_2CH_2CHCH_2CH_3$
$\quad\quad\quad\quad\quad\quad |$
$\quad\quad\quad\quad\quad CH_2$—OH

c. (benzene ring)— CH_2CHCH_3
$\quad\quad\quad\quad\quad\quad\quad\quad |$
$\quad\quad\quad\quad\quad\quad\quad OH$

d.

HO CH_3

Solution

a. The longest chain has one carbon atom; thus, the alcohol will be called methanol (methane $- e + ol$). Since the —OH group can be attached only to the single carbon atom, no location number for —OH is needed.

b. The longest chain containing the —OH group is numbered as follows:

$$\overset{5}{C}H_3\overset{4}{C}H_2\overset{3}{C}H_2\overset{2}{C}HCH_2CH_3$$
$$|$$
$$\underset{1}{C}H_2—OH$$

Note that there is a longer chain (six carbon atoms), but the —OH group is not directly attached to it. The five-carbon chain makes the alcohol a pentanol. The —OH group is on carbon number 1; hence, the compound is a 1-pentanol. An ethyl group is attached to carbon number 2 of the chain, so the final name is 2-ethyl-1-pentanol.

c. The longest chain contains three carbon atoms, with the —OH group attached to carbon number 2. Hence, the compound is a 2-propanol. A benzene ring attached to carbon number 1 is named as a phenyl group. Therefore, the complete name is 1-phenyl-2-propanol. Note that the phenyl group is on carbon number 1 rather than number 3.

d. The —OH group is given preference, so the carbon to which it is attached is carbon number 1 of the ring. The —CH_3 group is located on carbon number 3 (since 3 is lower than 5, which would be obtained by counting the other way). The complete name is 3-methylcyclohexanol. Note that because the —OH group is always at the number-1 position in a ring, the position is not shown in the name.

▶ LEARNING CHECK 13.1 Provide IUPAC names for the following alcohols:

a.
$\quad CH_3$
$\quad |$
CH_3CHCH_2—OH

b.
$\quad\quad\quad OH$
$\quad\quad\quad |$
$CH_3CHCHCH_2CHCH_3$
$\quad\quad |\quad\quad\quad\quad |$
$\quad CH_2CH_3\quad CH_3$

c.
$\quad CH_3$
$\quad |$

OH

Compounds containing more than one hydroxy group are known. Alcohols containing two hydroxy groups are called *diols*. Those containing three —OH groups are called *triols*. The IUPAC nomenclature rules for these compounds are essentially the same as those for the single hydroxy alcohols, except that the ending *-diol* or *-triol* is attached to the name of the parent hydrocarbon.

▶ Example 13.2

Name the following alcohols according the IUPAC system:

a. CH$_2$—CH$_2$
 | |
 OH OH

b. CH$_3$
 |
 CH$_2$CHCH$_2$CH$_2$
 | |
 OH OH

c. CH$_2$—CH—CH$_2$
 | | |
 OH OH OH

Solution

a. The longest chain has two carbons, making this an ethanediol. The —OH groups attached to carbons 1 and 2 give the final name 1,2-ethanediol. This substance is also called ethylene glycol.

b. Because the longest chain has four carbons, the compound is a butanediol. The —OH groups are attached to carbons 1 and 4, and a methyl group is attached to carbon 2. The name is 2-methyl-1,4-butanediol.

c. The longest chain contains three carbons, so the compound is a propanetriol. The —OH groups are attached to carbons 1, 2, and 3, making the name 1,2,3-propanetriol. Common names for this substance are glycerin and glycerol.

▶ LEARNING CHECK 13.2 Give IUPAC names to the following diols:

a. OH OH
 | |
 CH$_2$CH$_2$CH$_2$CH$_2$

b. OH
 /\
 | |—OH

Substituted phenols are usually named as derivatives of the parent compound phenol:

phenol 4-bromophenol 2,4,6-tribromophenol

▶ LEARNING CHECK 13.3 Name this compound as a phenol:

CH$_2$CH$_3$
 |
 (ring)—OH

13.2 Classification of Alcohols

Learning Objective

2. Classify alcohols as primary, secondary, or tertiary on the basis of their structural formulas.

The characteristic chemistry of an alcohol sometimes depends on the groups bonded to the carbon atom that bears the hydroxy group. Alcohols are classified as primary, secondary, or tertiary on the basis of these attached groups (see ▶ Table 13.1). In **primary alcohols,** the hydroxy-bearing carbon atom is attached to one other carbon atom and two hydrogen atoms. The simplest alcohol, CH_3—OH, is also considered a primary alcohol. In **secondary alcohols,** the hydroxy-bearing carbon atom is attached to two other carbon atoms and one hydrogen atom. In **tertiary alcohols,** the hydroxy-bearing carbon atom is attached to three other carbon atoms. The use of R, R′, and R″ in Table 13.1 signifies that each of those alkyl groups may be different.

primary alcohol An alcohol in which the OH group is attached to CH_3 or to a carbon attached to one other carbon atom.

secondary alcohol An alcohol in which the carbon bearing the OH group is attached to two other carbon atoms.

tertiary alcohol An alcohol in which the carbon bearing the OH group is attached to three other carbon atoms.

TABLE 13.1 Primary, Secondary, and Tertiary Alcohols

	Primary	Secondary	Tertiary
General formula	R—CH_2—OH	R—CH—OH \| R′	R \| R′—C—OH \| R″
Specific example	$CH_3CH_2CH_2$—OH 1-propanol (propyl alcohol)	CH_3CH—OH \| CH_3 2-propanol (isopropyl alcohol)	CH_3 \| CH_3—C—OH \| CH_3 2-methyl-2-propanol (*t*-butyl alcohol)

▶ **LEARNING CHECK 13.4** Classify the following alcohols as primary, secondary, or tertiary:

a. $CH_3CH_2CH_2CH_2$—OH

b. ⬡—OH

c.
$$CH_3CH \begin{array}{c} OH \\ | \\ \\ | \\ CH_2CH_3 \end{array}$$

13.3 Physical Properties of Alcohols

Learning Objective

3. Discuss how hydrogen bonding influences the physical properties of alcohols.

The replacement of one hydrogen of water with an organic group does not cause all the waterlike properties to disappear. Thus, the lower molecular weight alcohols—methyl, ethyl, propyl, and isopropyl alcohols—are completely miscible with water. As the size of the alkyl group in an alcohol increases, the physical properties become less waterlike and more alkanelike. Long-chain alcohols are less soluble in water (see ▶ Figure 13.2) and more soluble in nonpolar solvents such as benzene, carbon tetrachloride, and ether. The solubility of alcohols in water depends on the number of carbon atoms per hydroxy group in the molecule. In general, one hydroxy group can solubilize three to four carbon atoms. The high solubility of the lower molecular weight alcohols in water can be attributed to hydrogen bonding between the alcohol and water molecules (see ▶ Figure 13.3).

Figure 13.2 The solubility of alcohols and linear alkanes in water.

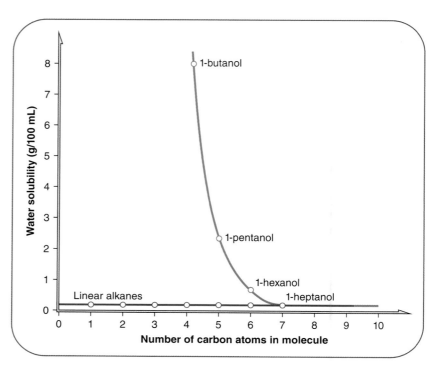

Figure 13.3 Hydrogen bonding in a water–methanol solution. A three-dimensional network of molecules and hydrogen bonds is formed.

In long-chain alcohols, the hydrophobic alkyl group does not form hydrogen bonds with water. Thus, in 1-heptanol, water molecules surround and form bonds with the —OH end but do not bond to the alkyl portion (see ▶ Figure 13.4). Because the alkyl portion is unsolvated, 1-heptanol is insoluble in water. Its solubility in water is comparable to that of heptane (seven carbon atoms), as shown in Figure 13.2.

Figure 13.4 Water interacts only with the —OH group of 1-heptanol.

▶ **LEARNING CHECK 13.5** Arrange the following compounds in order of increasing solubility in water (least soluble first, most soluble last):

a. $CH_3CH_2CH_2$—OH
b. $CH_3CH_2CH_3$
c. $CH_3(CH_2)_3CH_2$—OH

Hydrogen bonding also causes alcohols to have much higher boiling points than most other compounds of similar molecular weight. In this case, the hydrogen bonding is

between alcohol molecules (see ▶ Figure 13.5). Ethanol (CH_3CH_2OH) boils at 78°C, whereas methyl ether (CH_3—O—CH_3) (with the same molecular weight) boils at –24°C. Propane ($CH_3CH_2CH_3$) has nearly the same molecular weight but boils at –42°C (see ▶ Figure 13.6).

Figure 13.5 Hydrogen bonding in pure ethanol.

Figure 13.6 The boiling points of alcohols are higher than those of alkanes and ethers of similar molecular weights.

▶ **LEARNING CHECK 13.6** How can you explain the observation that methanol has a boiling point of 65°C, whereas propane, with a higher molecular weight, has a boiling point of –42°C?

13.4 Reactions of Alcohols

Learning Objective

4. Write equations for alcohol dehydration and oxidation reactions.

Alcohols undergo many reactions, but we will consider only two important ones at this time—alcohol dehydration and alcohol oxidation. In alcohol **dehydration,** water is chemically removed from an alcohol. This reaction can occur in two different ways, depending on the reaction temperature. At 140°C, the main product is an ether, whereas at higher temperatures (180°C), alkenes are the predominant products.

dehydration reaction A reaction in which water is chemically removed from a compound.

Dehydration to Produce an Alkene

When the elements of a water molecule are removed from a single alcohol molecule, an alkene is produced. A reaction of this type, in which two or more covalent bonds are broken and a new multiple bond is formed, is called an **elimination reaction.** In this case, a water molecule is eliminated from an alcohol. Reaction 13.1 gives a general reaction, and Reactions 13.2 and 13.3 are two specific examples:

elimination reaction A reaction in which two or more covalent bonds are broken and a new multiple bond is formed.

$$\text{General reaction:} \quad -\overset{|}{\underset{\underset{H}{|}}{C}} - \overset{|}{\underset{\underset{OH}{|}}{C}} - \xrightarrow[180°C]{H_2SO_4} \quad \diagdown C = C \diagup + H_2O \qquad (13.1)$$

alcohol alkene

$$\text{Specific example:} \quad CH_3CH - CH_2 \xrightarrow[180°C]{H_2SO_4} CH_3CH = CH_2 + H_2O \qquad (13.2)$$
$$\underset{OH \quad H}{}$$

2-propanol propene

$$\text{Specific example:} \quad CH_3CH_2CHCH_3 \xrightarrow[180°C]{H_2SO_4} CH_3CH = CHCH_3 + CH_3CH_2CH = CH_2 + H_2O$$
$$\underset{OH}{}$$

2-butene 1-butene
Principal product (90%) Minor product (10%)
(two carbon groups (one carbon group
on double bond) on double bond)

Notice that in Reaction 13.3 two alkenes can be produced, depending on which carbon next to the hydroxy-bearing carbon loses the hydrogen atom. The principal alkene produced in such cases will be the one in which the higher number of carbon groups is bonded to the double-bonded carbon atoms.

Alcohol dehydration is an important reaction in the human body, where enzymes (rather than sulfuric acid) function as catalysts. For example, the dehydration of citrate is part of the citric acid cycle discussed in Section 23.5. Note that the dehydration of citrate, 2-propanol (Reaction 13.2), and 2-butanol (Reaction 13.3) all involve exactly the same changes in bonding. In each reaction, an H and an —OH are removed from adjacent carbons, leaving a C=C double bond. The other molecular bonds in all three of those compounds do not change:

$$^-OOC - \overset{H}{\underset{\underset{H}{|}}{\overset{|}{C}}} - \overset{OH}{\underset{\underset{COO^-}{|}}{\overset{|}{C}}} - CH_2 - COO^- \xrightarrow{Enzyme} \quad \overset{H}{\diagdown} C = C \overset{CH_2 - COO^-}{\diagup} + H_2O \qquad (13.4)$$

citrate *cis*-aconitate

▶ **LEARNING CHECK 13.7** Predict the major products of the following reactions:

a.
$$\underset{OH}{CH_3CH_2CHCH_2CH_3} \xrightarrow[180°C]{H_2SO_4}$$

b.

The Dehydration of an Alcohol

A strong acid such as sulfuric acid initially reacts with an alcohol in much the same way that it reacts with water in solution. Ionization of the acid produces a proton (H^+) that is attracted to an oxygen atom of the alcohol:

$$CH_3CH_2-\overset{H}{\underset{H}{\overset{|}{O}}}: + H_2SO_4 \rightleftarrows CH_3CH_2-\overset{H}{\underset{H}{\overset{+}{O}}}: + HSO_4^-$$

protonated alcohol

The creation of a positive charge on the oxygen atom weakens the carbon–oxygen bond, which allows the following equilibrium reaction to take place:

$$CH_3CH_2-\overset{H}{\underset{H}{\overset{+}{O}}}: \rightleftarrows CH_3\overset{+}{C}H_2 + \overset{H}{\underset{H}{\overset{..}{O}}}$$

a carbocation water
(one product)

The ethyl carbocation is unstable because the carbon has only three bonds (six outer electrons) around it. To achieve an octet of electrons about this carbon, the carbocation donates an H^+ to a proton acceptor, such as HSO_4^-, and forms the double bond of the alkene product:

$$CH_2-\overset{+}{C}H_2 \longrightarrow CH_2=CH_2 + H_2SO_4$$
$$\underset{HSO_4^-}{\overset{|}{H}}$$

ethene regenerated catalyst

Dehydration to Produce an Ether

Alcohol dehydration can also occur when the elements of water are removed from two alcohol molecules. The residual molecular fragments of the alcohols bond and form an ether. This ether-forming reaction is useful mainly with primary alcohols. Reaction 13.5 gives the general reaction, and the formation of diethyl ether (the anesthetic ether) is a specific example (Reaction 13.6):

General
reaction: $R-O-H+H-O-R \xrightarrow[140°C]{H_2SO_4} R-O-R + H_2O$ (13.5)
 an alcohol an alcohol an ether

Specific
example: $CH_3CH_2-OH + HO-CH_2CH_3 \xrightarrow[140°C]{H_2SO_4} CH_3CH_2-O-CH_2CH_3 + H_2O$ (13.6)
 ethanol ethanol diethyl ether
 (ethyl alcohol) (ethyl alcohol)

Thus, an alcohol can be dehydrated to produce either an alkene or an ether. The type of dehydration that takes place is controlled by the temperature, with sulfuric acid serving as a catalyst. Although a mixture of alkene and ether products often results, we will use these temperatures to indicate that the major dehydration product is an alkene (at 180°C) or an ether (at 140°C).

The reaction that produces ethers is an example of a dehydration synthesis in which two molecules are joined and a new functional group is generated by the removal of a water molecule. Dehydration synthesis is important in living organisms because it is part of the formation of carbohydrates, fats, proteins, and many other essential substances.

▶ **LEARNING CHECK 13.8** What catalyst and reaction temperature would you use to accomplish each of the following reactions?

a. $2CH_3CH_2CH_2-OH \rightarrow CH_3CH_2CH_2-O-CH_2CH_2CH_3 + H_2O$

b. $CH_3\underset{\overset{|}{CH_3}}{CH}-OH \rightarrow CH_3CH=CH_2 + H_2O$

Oxidation

An oxidation reaction occurs when a molecule gains oxygen atoms or loses hydrogen atoms. Under appropriate conditions, alcohols can be oxidized in a controlled way (not combusted) by removing two hydrogen atoms per molecule. A number of oxidizing agents can be used, including potassium dichromate ($K_2Cr_2O_7$) and potassium permanganate ($KMnO_4$). The symbol (O) is used to represent an oxidizing agent. Reaction 13.7 gives the general reaction:

$$-\overset{\displaystyle |}{\underset{\displaystyle H}{C}}-O-H \ + \ (O) \longrightarrow -\overset{\displaystyle \overset{O}{\|}}{C}- \ + H_2O \qquad (13.7)$$

alcohol aldehyde
or ketone

The three classes of alcohols behave differently toward oxidizing agents.

Primary Alcohols. Reaction 13.8 gives the general reaction, and the formation of acetic acid is a specific example (Reaction 13.9):

General reaction:

$$R-\overset{\displaystyle \overset{OH}{|}}{\underset{\displaystyle H}{C}}-H + (O) \longrightarrow R-\overset{\displaystyle \overset{O}{\|}}{C}-H + H_2O \qquad (13.8)$$

aldehyde

primary alcohol

$$\xrightarrow[\text{(O)}]{\text{further oxidation}} R-\overset{\displaystyle \overset{O}{\|}}{C}-OH$$

carboxylic acid

Specific example:

$$CH_3CH_2-OH + (O) \longrightarrow CH_3-\overset{\displaystyle \overset{O}{\|}}{C}-H + H_2O \qquad (13.9)$$

ethanol acetaldehyde

$$\xrightarrow[\text{(O)}]{\text{further oxidation}} CH_3-\overset{\displaystyle \overset{O}{\|}}{C}-OH$$

acetic acid

The immediate product of the oxidation of a primary alcohol is an aldehyde. However, aldehydes are readily oxidized by the same oxidizing agents (Section 14.3) to give carboxylic acids. Therefore, the oxidation of a primary alcohol normally results in the corresponding carboxylic acid as the product. The oxidation of ethanol by $K_2Cr_2O_7$ is shown in ▶ Figure 13.7. Because aldehydes do not hydrogen bond (Section 14.2), they have lower boiling points than the corresponding alcohol or carboxylic acid. This makes it possible to isolate the aldehyde product before it is oxidized by maintaining the reaction temperature high enough to boil the aldehyde out of the reaction mixture before it can react.

▶ **LEARNING CHECK 13.9** Draw the structural formulas of the first and second products of the following reaction:

①

The tube on the left contains orange $K_2Cr_2O_7$ and is next to the colorless ethanol.

②

After mixing, the ethanol is oxidized, and chromium is reduced, forming a grayish-green precipitate.

Figure 13.7 Oxidation of ethanol by $K_2Cr_2O_7$. How might a color change like this one be used to measure alcohol concentration?

Secondary Alcohols. Reactions 13.10 and 13.11 give the general reaction and a specific example.

$$\underset{\substack{\text{secondary} \\ \text{alcohol}}}{R - \overset{\overset{\displaystyle OH}{|}}{\underset{\underset{\displaystyle H}{|}}{C}} - R'} + (O) \longrightarrow \underset{\text{ketone}}{R - \overset{\overset{\displaystyle O}{||}}{C} - R'} + H_2O \qquad (13.10)$$

General reaction:

$$\underset{\text{2-propanol}}{CH_3 - \overset{\overset{\displaystyle OH}{|}}{\underset{\underset{\displaystyle H}{|}}{C}} - CH_3} + (O) \longrightarrow \underset{\text{acetone}}{CH_3 - \overset{\overset{\displaystyle O}{||}}{C} - CH_3} + H_2O \qquad (13.11)$$

Specific example:

Secondary alcohols are oxidized to ketones in exactly the same way primary alcohols are oxidized to aldehydes, and by the same oxidizing agents. However, unlike aldehydes, ketones resist further oxidation, so this reaction provides an excellent way to prepare ketones.

▶ **LEARNING CHECK 13.10** Complete the following oxidation reaction:

$$+ \; (O) \longrightarrow$$

Tertiary Alcohols. A general reaction is given in Reaction 13.12:

General reaction:

$$R - \overset{\overset{\displaystyle OH}{|}}{\underset{\underset{\displaystyle R''}{|}}{C}} - R' + (O) \longrightarrow \text{no reaction} \qquad (13.12)$$

Tertiary alcohols do not have any hydrogen on the —OH-bearing carbon and thus do not react with oxidizing agents.

▶ **LEARNING CHECK 13.11** Which of the following alcohols will react with an oxidizing agent?

a.

b. CH_3 OH

c.
$CH_2 - OH$

Multistep Reactions

Alcohols are important organic compounds not only for their own commercial applications but because they can be converted by chemical reactions into a wide variety of other useful products. Most alcohols do not occur naturally in commercial quantities and therefore are prepared from alkenes.

It is very common in both laboratory and industrial processes for such preparations to involve a sequence of reactions. For example, the commercial production of vinyl plastic (PVC) begins with the alkene ethene:

$$CH_2=CH_2 \longrightarrow \overset{\overset{\displaystyle Cl}{|}}{CH_2=CH} \longrightarrow \overset{\overset{\displaystyle Cl}{|}}{+CH_2-CH+}$$

ethene vinyl chloride poly (vinyl chloride) (PVC)

Nature, too, employs multistep reactions to carry out processes essential to life. The glycolysis pathway used by the body to initiate the utilization of glucose for energy production involves a series of ten reactions (Section 23.3).

▶ **Example 13.3**

The following conversion requires more than one step. Show the reaction, reagents, and intermediate structures necessary to carry out the synthesis.

Solution

The best way to initially solve a multistep synthesis is to work backward from the final product. Identify the functional group present in the product—in this case, a ketone. Think how to prepare a ketone—by oxidizing an alcohol.

Now, working backward again, think how to prepare an alcohol—from an alkene through hydration.

Adding these two steps together gives

▶ **LEARNING CHECK 13.12** Show the reactions necessary to carry out the following conversion.

$$CH_2{=}CH_2 \longrightarrow CH_3CH_2-O-CH_2CH_3$$

13.5 Important Alcohols

Learning Objective

5. Recognize uses for specific alcohols.

The simplest alcohol, methanol or methyl alcohol, is a very important industrial chemical; more than 1 billion gallons are produced and used annually. It is sometimes known as wood alcohol because the principal source for many years was the distillation of wood.

Today, it is synthetically produced in large quantities by reacting hydrogen gas with carbon monoxide (Reaction 13.13):

$$CO + 2H_2 \xrightarrow[\text{heat, pressure}]{\text{Catalysts,}} CH_3-OH \qquad (13.13)$$

The industrial importance of methanol is due to its oxidation product, formaldehyde, which is a major starting material for the production of plastics. Methanol is used as a fuel in Indy-style racing cars (see ▶ Figure 13.8). It is also used as a fuel in products such as alcohol burners found in camping supplies.

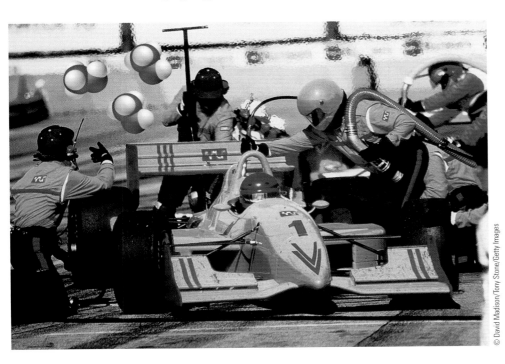

Figure 13.8 Racing cars are fueled by methanol. What would be the equation for the combustion of methanol?

© David Madison/Tony Stone/Getty Images

Methanol is highly toxic and causes permanent blindness if taken internally. Deaths and injuries have resulted as a consequence of mistakenly substituting methanol for ethyl alcohol in beverages.

Ethanol, or ethyl alcohol, CH_3CH_2-OH, is probably the most familiar alcohol because it is the active ingredient in alcoholic beverages. It is also used in pharmaceuticals as a solvent (tinctures are ethanol solutions) and in aftershave lotions as an antiseptic and skin softener. It is an important industrial solvent as well. The gasohol now marketed at many locations around the United States is a mixture of ethanol and gasoline.

Most ethanol used industrially is produced on a large scale by the direct hydration of ethylene obtained from petroleum (Reaction 13.14):

Ethanol

$$H_2C=CH_2+H-OH \xrightarrow[300°C]{70 \text{ atm}} \underset{\substack{| \quad |\\ H \quad OH}}{H_2C-CH_2} \qquad (13.14)$$
$$\text{ethylene} \qquad\qquad\qquad\qquad \text{ethanol}$$

Ethanol for beverages and increasingly for gasohol is produced by the yeast **fermentation** of carbohydrates such as sugars, starch, and cellulose. For example, a common method is the fermentation of glucose, grape sugar (Reaction 13.15):

fermentation A reaction of sugars, starch, or cellulose to produce ethanol and carbon dioxide.

$$C_6H_{12}O_6 \xrightarrow{\text{Yeast}} 2CH_3CH_2-OH+2CO_2 \qquad (13.15)$$
$$\text{glucose} \qquad\qquad \text{ethanol}$$

To solve a test question, using a stepwise approach is often helpful. First, decide what type of question is being asked. Is it a nomenclature, typical uses, physical properties, or a reaction question? Second, if you recognize it as, say, a reaction question, look for the functional group. Third, if there is an alcohol group in the starting material, identify the reagent and use the following diagram to predict the right products.

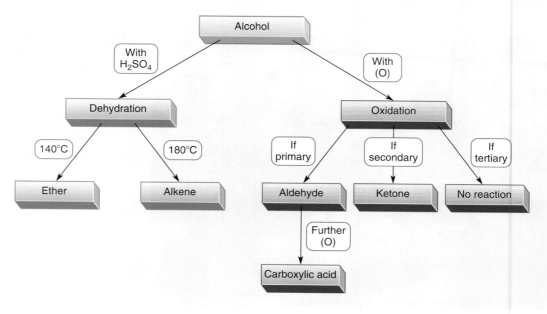

2-propanol (isopropyl alcohol), the main component of rubbing alcohol, acts as an astringent on the skin. It causes tissues to contract, hardens the skin, and limits secretions. Its rapid evaporation from the skin also lowers the skin temperature. It is used as an antiseptic in 70% solutions (see ▶ Figure 13.9). Isopropyl alcohol is toxic and should not be taken internally.

1,2,3-propanetriol is known more commonly as glycerol or glycerin:

$$\begin{array}{ccc} OH & OH & OH \\ | & | & | \\ CH_2 & -CH- & CH_2 \end{array}$$

1,2,3-propanetriol (glycerol)

Figure 13.9 Isopropyl alcohol is used as an antiseptic.

The hydrogen bonding resulting from the three hydroxy groups causes glycerol to be a syrupy, high-boiling liquid with an affinity for water. This property and its nontoxic nature make it valuable as a moistening agent in tobacco and many food products, such as candy and shredded coconut. Florists use glycerol to retain water that maintains the freshness of cut flowers. Glycerol is also used for its soothing qualities in shaving and toilet soaps and in many cosmetics. In Chapter 18 on lipids, we will see that glycerol forms part of the structure of body fats and oils.

Due to hydrogen bonding, 1,2-ethanediol (ethylene glycol) and 1,2-propanediol (propylene glycol) are both high-boiling liquids that are completely miscible with water.

$$\begin{array}{cc} OH & OH \\ | & | \\ CH_2 & -CH_2 \end{array} \qquad \begin{array}{ccc} OH & OH \\ | & | \\ CH_2 & -CH- CH_3 \end{array}$$

1,2-ethanediol 1,2-propanediol
(ethylene glycol) (propylene glycol)

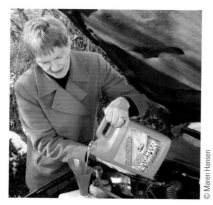

Figure 13.10 Ethylene glycol (HO—CH₂CH₂—OH) is used as an automotive antifreeze.

Their main uses are as automobile antifreeze (see ▶ Figure 13.10) and as a starting material for the manufacture of polyester fibers (Reaction 15.11).

Alcohols are very important biologically because the alcohol functional group occurs in a variety of compounds associated with biological systems. For example, sugars contain

Alcohol and Antidepressants Don't Mix

Individuals suffering from depression often demonstrate one or more of the following symptoms: extreme feelings of sadness or melancholy; feelings of inadequacy in facing life's challenges; inability to make decisions; physical inactivity; lack of appetite; inability to sleep; and frequent crying.

Antidepressant medications are designed to counteract these symptoms. However, when alcohol, itself a depressant, is combined with antidepressant medications, serious consequences can result. For example, some antidepressants cause sedation and drowsiness. Alcohol has similar effects, and the combination of the two could easily cause a person to fall asleep while driving. Initially, alcohol might seem to improve the mood of a depressed person, but its overall effect is often to increase the depression symptoms.

The combination of some types of antidepressants and alcohol influences coordination, judgment, and reaction time and other motor skills more than alcohol alone. When combined with certain types of alcoholic beverages and foods, antidepressants known as monoamine oxidase inhibitors (MAOIs) cause bodily reactions such as a dangerous increase in blood pressure. It has been found that people suffering from depression have an increased risk of becoming addicted to alcohol or other addictive substances.

Clearly, when these factors are all taken into consideration, it is not worth the risks for people being treated for depression to mix their antidepressant medications with alcohol.

When alcohol is combined with antidepressants, serious consequences can result.

several hydroxy groups, and starch and cellulose contain thousands of hydroxy groups (see Chapter 17). The structures and uses (see Figure 13.10) of some common alcohols are summarized in ▶ Table 13.2.

TABLE 13.2 Examples of Alcohols

Name	Structural Formula	Typical Uses
methanol (methyl alcohol)	CH_3—OH	Solvent, making formaldehyde
ethanol (ethyl alcohol)	CH_3CH_2—OH	Solvent, alcoholic beverages
2-propanol (isopropyl alcohol)	CH_3CHCH_3 \| OH	Rubbing alcohol, solvent
1-butanol (butanol)	$CH_3CH_2CH_2CH_2$—OH	Solvent, hydraulic fluid
1,2-ethanediol (ethylene glycol)	HO—CH_2CH_2—OH	Automobile antifreeze, polyester fibers
1,2-propanediol (propylene glycol)	CH_3CH—CH_2 \| \| OH OH	Moisturizer in lotions and foods, automobile antifreeze
1,2,3-propanetriol (glycerin, glycerol)	CH_2—CH—CH_2 \| \| \| OH OH OH	Moisturizer in foods, tobacco, and cosmetics
menthol	CH_3CHCH_3 OH CH_3	Cough drops, shaving lotion, mentholated tobacco

13.6 Characteristics and Uses of Phenols

Learning Objective

6. Recognize uses for specific phenols.

Phenol, C_6H_5OH, is a colorless, low-melting-point solid with a medicinal odor. The addition of a small amount of water causes the solid to liquefy at room temperature. This liquid mixture is sometimes called carbolic acid. Unlike alcohols, phenols are weak acids (Reactions 13.16 and 13.17), which can damage skin by denaturing the proteins in the skin, and they must be handled with care.

$$\text{phenol (a weak acid)} + H_2O \longrightarrow \text{phenoxide} + H_3O^+ \tag{13.16}$$

$$\text{phenol} + KOH \longrightarrow \text{potassium phenoxide} + H_2O \tag{13.17}$$

In dilute solutions, phenol is used as an antiseptic and disinfectant. Joseph Lister, an English surgeon, introduced the use of phenol as a hospital antiseptic in the late 1800s. Before that time, antiseptics had not been used, and very few patients survived even minor surgery because of postoperative infections. Today, there are effective derivatives used as antiseptics instead of phenol that are less irritating to the skin. Two such compounds, 4-chloro-3,5-dimethylphenol and 4-hexylresorcinol, are shown here.

phenol
(Lister's original disinfectant)

4-chloro-3,5-dimethylphenol
(nonirritating topical antiseptic)

4-hexylresorcinol
(used in mouthwashes and throat lozenges)

DR. MELINA B. JAMPOLIS, M.D.

Dr. Melina B. Jampolis, M.D. is a Los Angeles, California, Physician Nutrition Specialist—a specialty practiced by only a few hundred physicians in the United States. She focuses exclusively on nutrition for weight loss and disease prevention and treatment.

Ask an Expert 13.1

Q: What are polyphenols?

A: We often hear that we should be eating at least five servings a day of a variety of fruits and vegetables, but what is it about them that makes them so healthy? Most are loaded with important vitamins and minerals, but they are also excellent sources of phytonutrients (chemicals derived from plants that have nutritional value). One of the most-studied groups of phytonutrients are the polyphenols, which likely contribute considerably to the recognized disease-fighting properties of phytonutrients. Polyphenols are a group of molecules found in plants that protect them against UV radiation and pathogens. They are classified according to the number of phenol rings they possess and how the rings are bound. The four major classes include phenolic acids, flavonoids, stilbenes, and lignans. Epidemiological studies have shown an inverse association between intake of foods high in polyphenols and the incidence of diseases including heart disease, diabetes, and cancer. In animal and lab-based studies, polyphenols have been shown to decrease the growth of cancer cells, decrease cellular cholesterol uptake, modulate important enzymes and pathways involved in cellular activity, and act as potent antioxidants.

The most prevalent food sources of polyphenols are fruits and vegetables, green and black tea, red wine, coffee, dark chocolate, olives, and extra virgin olive oil. While some polyphenols are specific to a certain food, most foods contain a mixture, which is why eating a variety of these types of foods on a regular basis is advised. There are numerous factors that influence the quantity and bioavailability (the ability of the active form of a compound to reach the target tissue) of plant-based polyphenols. These include plant-growing conditions, cooking and storage, a person's genetic makeup and general health, and interaction with other nutrients and compounds. For example, the levels of resveratrol, a potent polyphenol found in red wine, vary considerably depending on the type of grape (pinot noir generally contains the most), the growing region and conditions, and the harvest year. When it comes to cooking, boiled carrots lose almost all of their polyphenols, while steamed carrots lose only 43%. The concentration of one of the polyphenols in extra virgin olive oil drops by up to 50% with frying, and in one study, when bottles where stored under diffused light, 45% of the polyphenols were lost in four months.

Dietary fat appears to enhance the absorption of polyphenol flavonoids, which may explain why the phenolic compounds in olive oil are especially bioavailable. Pectin, a type of fiber found in apples, appears to enhance the bioavailability of an abundant polyphenol known as quercetin. Finally, there appears to be significant individual genetic variability in the ability of individuals to produce the active metabolites of some phenols. Whether this can be overcome has yet to be established. Until more is known about the complex factors involved with the bioavailability of these powerful plant-based health-promoting compounds, your best bet is to consume them as food, not supplements, in as fresh a form as possible, and to limit the use of processing and cooking methods like boiling or frying.

Olive oil

Red wine

Coffee

Two other derivatives of phenol, *o*-phenylphenol and 2-benzyl-4-chlorophenol, are ingredients in Lysol®, a disinfectant for walls and furniture in hospitals and homes:

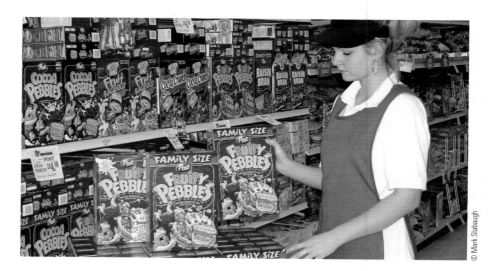

o-phenylphenol

2-benzyl-4-chlorophenol

antioxidant A substance that prevents another substance from being oxidized.

Other important phenols act as **antioxidants** by interfering with oxidizing reactions. These phenols are useful in protecting foods from spoilage and a variety of other materials from unwanted reactions. BHA and BHT are widely used as antioxidants in gasoline, lubricating oils, rubber, certain foods, and packaging materials for foods that might turn rancid (see ▶ Figure 13.11). In food or containers used to package food, the amount of

Figure 13.11 BHT is listed as a food ingredient that will "maintain freshness."

these antioxidants is limited to 200 ppm (parts per million) or 0.02%, based on the fat or oil content of the food. Notice that industrial nomenclature for these compounds does not follow IUPAC rules.

BHA (butylated hydroxy anisole)
2-*t*-butyl-4-methoxyphenol
(IUPAC name)

BHT (butylated hydroxy toluene)
2, 6-di-*t*-butyl-4-methylphenol
(IUPAC name)

▶ **LEARNING CHECK 13.14** What is an important use for each of the following phenols?

a. BHA **b.** 4-hexylresorcinol

Why Do Teens Drink?

Studies show that alcohol-related automobile accidents are a leading cause of teen deaths. Drownings, suicides, and murders involving teens have also been positively associated with alcohol use. Teens who use alcohol become sexually active at an earlier age than non-drinking teens. Unprotected sex, with its associated risks, is also more common among drinking teens. Poor academic performance and problems with social conduct have also been shown to correlate with alcohol use.

It is hard to imagine that this kind of information is not available to typical teens, with their many electronic communication devices and their tendency to interact with each other. Why, then, do teenagers drink?

It has been found that teens are particularly vulnerable to alcohol use. It has been suggested that physical changes accompanying puberty might make teens feel self-conscious and more likely to attempt to fit in and please their peers by going along with the group. Also, some teens have trouble understanding that their actions can have adverse consequences.

Some risk factors that contribute to the likelihood of a teen participating in underage drinking have been identified and include:

- Transitions such as a change in residence or schools or the obtaining of a drivers license.
- Increases in stress at home, work, or school.
- Family problems such as conflicts between family members or parental alcohol abuse.
- A history of behavior problems or mental health conditions.

Parents, teachers, and other mature adults should help teens to understand that the use of alcohol is accompanied by responsibilities that they might not yet be ready to accept.

Teens having a party with alcohol.

13.7 Ethers

Learning Objective

7. Name and draw structural formulas for ethers.

Ethers were introduced at the start of this chapter as compounds whose formula is R—O—R′. Common names for ethers are obtained by first naming the two groups attached to the oxygen and then adding the word *ether.* If the groups are the same, it is appropriate to use the prefix *di-,* as in diethyl ether, but many people omit the *di-* and simply say "ethyl ether."

Dimethyl ether

CH_3— O — CH_2CH_3
ethyl methyl ether

isopropyl phenyl ether

CH_3— O — CH_3
dimethyl ether
(methyl ether)

CH_3CH_2— O — CH_2CH_3
diethyl ether
(ethyl ether)

▶ **LEARNING CHECK 13.15** Assign a common name to the following:

a. CH_3CH_2—O—⬡

b. CH_3CH—O—$CHCH_3$ with CH_3 groups above each CH

alkoxy group The —O—R functional group.

In the IUPAC naming system for ethers, the —O—R group is called an **alkoxy group**. The *-yl* ending of the smaller R group is replaced by *-oxy*. For example, —O—CH_3 is called a methoxy group, —O—CH_2CH_3 is called ethoxy, and so on:

CH_3—O—CH_3
methoxymethane

$CH_3CH_2CHCH_3$ with O—CH_2CH_3 substituent
2-ethoxybenzene — 2-ethoxybutane

p-methoxybenzoic acid

▶ **LEARNING CHECK 13.16** Give IUPAC names for the following:

a. cyclopentane ring with O—CH_3 and O—CH_3 substituents

b. $CH_3CH_2CHCH_2CH_3$ with O—CH—CH_3 (CH bearing CH_3) substituent

heterocyclic ring A ring in which one or more atoms are an atom other than carbon.

The ether linkage is also found in cyclic structures. A ring that contains elements in addition to carbon is called a **heterocyclic ring.** Two common structures with oxygen-containing heterocyclic rings are:

furan pyran

Many carbohydrates contain the fundamental ring systems of furan and pyran (Chapter 17).

13.8 Properties of Ethers

Learning Objective

8. Describe the key physical and chemical properties of ethers.

The oxygen atom of ethers can form hydrogen bonds with water (see ▶ Figure 13.12A), so ethers are slightly more soluble in water than hydrocarbons but less soluble than alcohols of comparable molecular weight. Ethers, however, cannot form hydrogen bonds with other ether molecules in the pure state (Figure 13.12B), which results in low boiling points close to those of hydrocarbons with similar molecular weights.

The chief chemical property of ethers is that, like the alkanes, they are inert and do not react with most reagents. It is this property that makes diethyl ether such a useful solvent. Like hydrocarbons, ethers are flammable, and diethyl ether is especially flammable because of its high volatility. Diethyl ether was the first general anesthetic used in surgery. For many years, it was the most important compound used as an anesthetic, but it has now been largely replaced by other compounds.

▶ LEARNING CHECK 13.17

a. Explain why an ether boils at a lower temperature than an alcohol of similar molecular weight.
b. What is the most significant chemical property of ethers?

thiol A compound containing an —SH group.

sulfhydryl group The —SH functional group.

13.9 Thiols

Learning Objective

9. Write equations for a thiol reaction with heavy metal ions and the production of disulfides that results when thiols are oxidized.

Sulfur and oxygen belong to the same group of the periodic table, so it is not surprising that they form similar compounds. The sulfur counterparts (analogues) of alcohols contain an —SH group rather than an —OH group and are called **thiols** (an older name is mercaptans). The —SH is known as a **sulfhydryl group.**

<div align="center">

R — OH R — SH

an alcohol a thiol

</div>

Perhaps the most distinguishing feature of thiols is their strong and disagreeable odors. Two different thiols and a disulfide are responsible for the odor associated with skunks (see ▶ Figure 13.13).

Figure 13.13 Skunks use thiol chemistry as an effective defense mechanism. Thiols are more volatile than alcohols but less soluble in water. Why are these characteristics an advantage to skunks?

trans-2-butene-1-thiol 3-methyl-1-butanethiol methyl-1-(*trans*-2-butenyl)disulfide

Some less-offensive odors (and flavors) are also characteristic of thiols and disulfides. Freshly chopped onions emit propanethiol, and 1-propene-3-thiol and 3,3-di-(1-propenyl) disulfide are partially responsible for the odor and flavor of garlic. It is amazing that the

General Anesthetics

Anesthetics are compounds that induce a loss of sensation in a specific part (local anesthetic) or all (general anesthetic) of the body. A general anesthetic acts on the brain to produce unconsciousness as well as insensitivity to pain.

The word *ether* is often associated with general anesthetics because of the well-known use of ethyl ether for this purpose. Ethyl ether became generally used as an anesthetic for surgical operations in about 1850. Before that time, surgery was an agonizing procedure. The patient was strapped to a table and (if lucky) soon fainted from the pain. Divinyl ether (vinethene) is an anesthetic that acts more rapidly and is less nauseating than ethyl ether:

$$CH_2{=}CH{-}O{-}CH{=}CH_2$$
divinyl ether

Another common ether anesthetic is enflurane:

$$H{-}\overset{\underset{\displaystyle H}{\mid}}{\overset{\displaystyle F}{C}}{-}O{-}\overset{\underset{\displaystyle H}{\mid}}{\overset{\displaystyle F}{C}}{-}\overset{\underset{\displaystyle Cl}{\mid}}{\overset{\displaystyle F}{C}}{-}H$$
enflurane

Numerous inhalation anesthetics are not ethers at all. Nitrous oxide, for example, is a simple inorganic compound with the formula N_2O. Also known as "laughing gas," it is used as a general anesthetic by some dentists because its effects wear off quickly. Halothane, currently a popular general anesthetic, is a simple halogen derivative of ethane. It is nonflammable, does not cause nausea or similar upsets, and its effects wear off quickly:

$$H{-}\overset{\underset{\displaystyle Cl}{\mid}}{\overset{\displaystyle Br}{C}}{-}\overset{\underset{\displaystyle F}{\mid}}{\overset{\displaystyle F}{C}}{-}F$$
halothane

In modern surgical practice, the use of a single anesthetic has become quite rare. Usually, a patient is given an injection of a strong sedative that causes unconsciousness. A general anesthetic is then administered to provide insensitivity to pain and maintain the patient in an unconscious condition. A muscle relaxant may also be used to produce complete relaxation, while minimizing the need for, and hazards associated with, deep anesthesia.

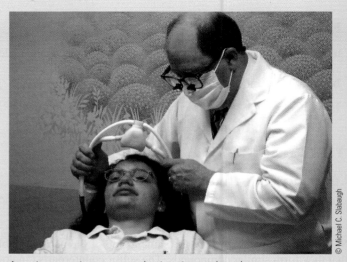

A patient receives an anesthetic prior to dental surgery.

© Michael C. Slabaugh

simple substitution of a sulfur atom for an oxygen atom can cause such a dramatic change in odor.

$$CH_3CH_2CH_2{-}SH \quad CH_2{=}CHCH_2 \quad CH_2{=}CHCH_2{-}S{-}S{-}CH_2CH{=}CH_2$$
$$\underset{\displaystyle SH}{\mid}$$

propanethiol 1-propene-3-thiol 3,3-di-(1-propenyl)disulfide

Gas companies make effective use of the odor of thiols. Natural gas (methane) has no odor, so the companies add a tiny amount of a thiol such as ethanethiol ($CH_3CH_2{-}SH$) to make it possible to detect leaking gas before a spark or match sets off an explosion.

Two reactions of the —SH group are important in the chemistry of proteins. When thiols are oxidized by agents such as O_2, a coupling reaction occurs (two molecules become one) to form a **disulfide**, a compound containing an —S—S— linkage:

disulfide A compound containing an —S—S— group.

General reaction:

$$2R{-}SH + (O) \rightarrow R{-}S{-}S{-}R + H_2O \qquad (13.18)$$
$$\text{a thiol} \qquad\qquad \text{a disulfide}$$

Specific example:

$$2CH_3{-}SH + (O) \rightarrow CH_3{-}S{-}S{-}CH_3 + H_2O \qquad (13.19)$$

Disulfide linkages are important structural features of some proteins, especially those of hair (see Section 19.6). The coupling reaction can be reversed by treating disulfides with a reducing agent (H) such as H_2, which regenerates the thiol:

General reaction:

$$R-S-S-R + 2(H) \rightarrow 2R-SH \tag{13.20}$$

Specific example:

$$CH_3-S-S-CH_3 + 2(H) \rightarrow 2CH_3-SH \tag{13.21}$$

The reaction of thiols with heavy metal ions, such as those of lead and mercury, to form insoluble compounds has adverse biological results. The metal ions (M^{2+}) react with sulfhydryl groups in the following way:

General reaction:

$$2R-SH + M^{2+} \rightarrow R-S-M-S-R + 2H^+ \tag{13.22}$$

Specific example:

$$2CH_3-SH + Hg^{2+} \rightarrow CH_3-S-Hg-S-CH_3 + 2H^+ \tag{13.23}$$

Many enzymes (catalysts for biological reactions—Section 20.7) contain —SH groups. Exposure to heavy metal ions ties up these groups, through Reaction 13.22, rendering the enzyme ineffective. The loss of enzymes in this manner can lead to serious biological consequences.

13.10 Polyfunctional Compounds

Learning Objective

10. Identify functional groups in polyfunctional compounds.

So far our study of organic molecules has included several compounds with more than one functional group. Compounds of this type, such as dienes and diols, are said to be **polyfunctional compounds**. Substances with different functional groups are also

polyfunctional compound
A compound with two or more functional groups.

referred to as polyfunctional. Compounds with multiple functional groups are very common in nature, and many play essential roles in life processes. For example, carbohydrate structures (Chapter 17) such as glucose typically involve a functional group at every carbon position.

$$\text{HO} - \text{CH}_2 - \underset{|}{\overset{OH}{CH}} - \underset{|}{\overset{OH}{CH}} - \underset{|}{\overset{OH}{CH}} - \underset{|}{\overset{OH}{CH}} - \overset{O}{\underset{||}{C}} - H$$

glucose

Even though some organic structures look quite complex, with multiple rings and long carbon chains, remember that it's the functional group or groups that determine the chemical properties of the compound. Thus, cholesterol, with two functional groups, should exhibit the reactions of both alkenes and alcohols.

cholesterol

cholesterol

▶ Example 13.4

Identify the functional groups in tetrahydrocannabinol, the active ingredient in marijuana.

tetrahydrocannabinol

Solution

To find functional groups, look for unique atoms or collections of atoms while ignoring ordinary rings, chains, and alkyl groups. Look for multiple bonds and atoms other than carbon. The tetrahydrocannabinol molecule has four functional groups: an ether, a phenolic —OH, the benzene ring, and a carbon–carbon double bond.

tetrahydrocannabinol

vitamin E

Case Study Follow-up

Alcohol abuse is the overconsumption of ethanol, usually in the form of alcoholic beverages but can include non-food substances such as mouthwash or nighttime cold medication. Alcohol abuse is the third leading preventable cause of death in the United States. Research has shown that screening of patients by healthcare providers for possible alcohol abuse can promote significant changes in the behavior of heavy drinkers that can positively influence their own and public health. Nearly 40% of traffic fatalities are alcohol related (NIAAA, 2011). Helping even a small percentage of alcoholics make a change can have a huge impact.

Palliative care focuses on relieving and preventing the suffering of patients. This approach can be useful in prioritizing symptoms. Focusing on a patient's most distressing symptoms based on patient self-assessment and self-report is often first priority. It is important to address the underlying causes—which might produce significant distress for the patient in the short term but will likely result in overall gains in the long run. Support for the patient in the form of alcohol and chemical abuse treatment centers is invaluable for successful recovery.

Concept Summary

The Nomenclature of Alcohols and Phenols

Alcohols are aliphatic compounds that contain the hydroxy functional group (—OH). Aromatic compounds with an —OH group attached to the ring are called phenols. Several alcohols are well-known by common names. In the IUPAC system, the characteristic ending -ol is used to designate alcohols. Phenols are named as derivatives of the parent compound phenol.
Objective 1, Exercises 13.4 and 13.10

Classification of Alcohols

Alcohols are classified on the basis of the number of carbon atoms bonded to the carbon that is attached to the —OH group. In primary alcohols, the OH-bonded carbon is bonded to one other carbon. In secondary alcohols, the OH-bonded carbon is bonded to two other carbons. In tertiary alcohols, the OH-bonded carbon is bonded to three other carbons.
Objective 2, Exercise 13.14

Concept Summary (continued)

Physical Properties of Alcohols

Hydrogen bonding can occur between alcohol molecules and between alcohol molecules and water. As a result, alcohols have higher boiling points than hydrocarbons of similar molecular weight, and low molecular weight alcohols are soluble in water.

Objective 3, Exercise 13.18

Reactions of Alcohols

Two important reactions of alcohols are dehydration and oxidation. Alcohols may be dehydrated in two different ways depending on the reaction temperature. With H_2SO_4 at 180°C, an alkene is produced, whereas at 140°C an ether is the product. The oxidation products obtained from the alcohols depend on the class of alcohol being oxidized. A primary alcohol produces an aldehyde that is further oxidized to a carboxylic acid. A secondary alcohol produces a ketone. A tertiary alcohol does not react with oxidizing agents.

Objective 4, Exercises 13.22 and 13.26

Important Alcohols

Some simple alcohols with commercial value are methanol (a solvent and fuel), ethanol (present in alcoholic beverages and gasohol), isopropyl alcohol (rubbing alcohol), ethylene glycol (antifreeze), and glycerol (a moistening agent).

Objective 5, Exercise 13.36

Characteristics and Uses of Phenols

Phenols are weak acids that are widely used for their antiseptic and disinfectant properties. Some phenols are used as antioxidants in foods and a variety of other materials.

Objective 6, Exercise 13.38

Ethers

Ethers contain an oxygen attached to two carbons as the characteristic functional group. In the IUPAC system, ethers are named as alkoxy derivatives of alkanes. The —O—R group is the alkoxy group that may have names such as methoxy (—O—CH_3) or ethoxy (—O—CH_2CH_3).

Objective 7, Exercise 13.42

Properties of Ethers

Like the alkanes, ethers are very unreactive substances. Pure ethers cannot form hydrogen bonds. As a result, their boiling points are comparable to those of hydrocarbons and lower than those of alcohols of similar molecular weight. Ethers are much less polar than alcohols but are still slightly soluble in water due to the limited formation of hydrogen bonds.

Objective 8, Exercise 13.46

Thiols

Thiols contain an —SH group, which often imparts a strong, disagreeable odor to the compound. Two reactions of thiols that are important in protein chemistry are their oxidation to produce a disulfide and their reaction with heavy metals such as mercury. Disulfides may be converted back to thiols by a reducing agent.

Objective 9, Exercise 13.52

Polyfunctional Compounds

It is common for organic compounds to contain more than one functional group. Many of the compounds that serve essential roles in life processes are polyfunctional.

Objective 10, Exercise 13.56

Key Terms and Concepts

Alcohol (Introduction)
Alkoxy group (13.7)
Antioxidant (13.6)
Dehydration reaction (13.4)
Disulfide (13.9)
Elimination reaction (13.4)

Ether (Introduction)
Fermentation (13.5)
Heterocyclic ring (13.7)
Hydroxy group (Introduction)
Phenol (Introduction)
Polyfunctional compound (13.10)

Primary alcohol (13.2)
Secondary alcohol (13.2)
Sulfhydryl group (13.9)
Tertiary alcohol (13.2)
Thiol (13.9)

Key Reactions

1.	Dehydration of alcohols to give alkenes (Section 13.4):	$$-\underset{\underset{\displaystyle H}{	}}{C}-\underset{\underset{\displaystyle OH}{	}}{C}- \xrightarrow[180°C]{H_2SO_4} \quad C=C \quad + \ H_2O$$	**Reaction 13.1**
2.	Dehydration of alcohols to give ethers (Section 13.4):	$$R-O-H+H-O-R \xrightarrow[140°C]{H_2SO_4} R-O-R+H_2O$$	**Reaction 13.5**		
3.	Oxidation of a primary alcohol to give an aldehyde and then a carboxylic acid (Section 13.4):	$$\underset{\text{primary alcohol}}{R-\underset{\underset{\displaystyle H}{	}}{\overset{\overset{\displaystyle OH}{	}}{C}}-H} + (O) \longrightarrow \underset{\text{aldehyde}}{R-\overset{\overset{\displaystyle O}{\|}}{C}-H} + H_2O$$ $$(O) \xrightarrow{\begin{array}{c}\text{further}\\\text{oxidation}\end{array}} \underset{\text{carboxylic acid}}{R-\overset{\overset{\displaystyle O}{\|}}{C}-OH}$$	**Reaction 13.8**
4.	Oxidation of a secondary alcohol to give a ketone (Section 13.4):	$$\underset{\substack{\text{secondary}\\\text{alcohol}}}{R-\underset{\underset{\displaystyle H}{	}}{\overset{\overset{\displaystyle OH}{	}}{C}}-R'} + (O) \longrightarrow \underset{\text{ketone}}{R-\overset{\overset{\displaystyle O}{\|}}{C}-R'} + H_2O$$	**Reaction 13.10**
5.	Attempted oxidation of a tertiary alcohol gives no reaction (Section 13.4):	$$R-\underset{\underset{\displaystyle R''}{	}}{\overset{\overset{\displaystyle OH}{	}}{C}}-R' + (O) \longrightarrow \text{ no reaction}$$	**Reaction 13.12**
6.	Oxidation of a thiol to give a disulfide (Section 13.9):	$$\underset{\text{a thiol}}{2R-SH} + (O) \longrightarrow \underset{\text{a disulfide}}{R-S-S-R} + H_2O$$	**Reaction 13.18**		
7.	Reduction of a disulfide to give thiols (Section 13.9):	$$R-S-S-R+2(H) \rightarrow 2R-SH$$	**Reaction 13.20**		
8.	Reaction of thiols with heavy metals (Section 13.9):	$$2R-SH+M^{2+} \rightarrow R-S-M-S-R+2H^+$$	**Reaction 13.22**		

Exercises

Even-numbered exercises are answered in Appendix B.

Blue-numbered exercises are more challenging.

The Nomenclature of Alcohols and Phenols (Section 13.1)

13.1 Draw general formulas for an alcohol and phenol, showing the functional group.

13.2 Draw a general formula for an ether, emphasizing the functional group.

13.3 Assign IUPAC names to the following alcohols:

a. $CH_3CH_2CH_2$ — OH

b.

$CH_2CH_2CH_2$ — OH

c.

$CH_3CHCHCH_2$ — OH with CH_3 above and Cl below

d.

$CH_2CH_2CH_2CH_2$ — OH with OH above

e.

Cyclopentane with Cl, OH, CH_2CH_3

f.

Cyclohexane with OH groups

13.4 Assign IUPAC names to the following alcohols:

a. $CH_3CH_2CH_2CH_2$ — OH

b. $CH_2CHCHCH_3$ with Br, Br, OH above

c. CH_3CH_2C — OH with CH_2CH_3 above and CH_2CH_3 below

d.

benzene with CH_2CH_2 — OH

e.

Cyclohexane with CH_3, OH, Br

f. $CH_3CHCH_2CHCH_3$ with OH, OH above

13.5 Several important alcohols are well-known by common names. Give a common name for each of the following:

a. CH_3 — OH

b. CH_3CHCH_3 with OH above

c. CH_3CH_2 — OH

d. CH_2 — CH_2 with OH, OH above

e. CH_2 — CH — CH_2 with OH, OH, OH above

13.6 Give each of the structures in Exercise 13.5 an IUPAC name.

13.7 Draw structural formulas for each of the following:

a. 2-methyl-1-butanol

b. 2-bromo-3-methyl-3-pentanol

c. 1-methylcyclopentanol

13.8 Draw structural formulas for each of the following:

a. 2-methyl-2-pentanol

b. 1,3-butanediol

c. 1-ethylcyclopentanol

13.9 Name each of the following as a derivative of phenol:

a.

benzene with $CHCH_3$ (CH_3 above) and OH

b.

benzene with OH, CH_3, CH_3

13.10 Name each of the following as a derivative of phenol:

a.

benzene with CH_2CH_3, OH

b.

benzene with OH, H_3C, CH_2CH_3, CH_3

13.11 Draw structural formulas for each of the following:

a. *m*-methylphenol b. 2,3-dichlorophenol

13.12 Draw structural formulas for each of the following:

 a. *o*-bromophenol **b.** 2,3,5-triethylphenol

Classification of Alcohols (Section 13.2)

13.13 What is the difference between a primary, secondary, and tertiary alcohol?

13.14 Classify the following alcohols as primary, secondary, or tertiary:

 a. CH_3CHCH_3
 |
 OH

 b. $CH_3CH_2—OH$

 CH_3
 |
 c. $CH_3CHCH_2—OH$

13.15 Classify the following alcohols as primary, secondary, or tertiary:

 CH_3
 |
 a. $CH_3CH_2C—OH$
 |
 CH_3

 b. $CH_3CH_2CH_2CH_2—OH$

 c.

13.16 Draw structural formulas for the four aliphatic alcohols with the molecular formula $C_4H_{10}O$. Name each compound using the IUPAC system and classify it as a primary, secondary, or tertiary alcohol.

Physical Properties of Alcohols (Section 13.3)

13.17 Why are the boiling points of alcohols much higher than the boiling points of alkanes with similar molecular weights?

13.18 Arrange the compounds of each group in order of increasing boiling point.

 a. ethanol, 1-propanol, methanol

 b. butane, ethylene glycol, 1-propanol

13.19 Which member of each of the following pairs would you expect to be more soluble in water? Briefly explain your choices.

 a. butane or 2-butanol

 b. 2-propanol or 2-pentanol

 c. 2-butanol or 2,3-butanediol

13.20 Draw structural formulas for the following molecules and use a dotted line to show the formation of hydrogen bonds:

 a. one molecule of 1-butanol and one molecule of ethanol

 b. cyclohexanol and water

13.21 Explain why the use of glycerol (1,2,3-propanetriol) in lotions helps retain water and keep the skin moist.

Reactions of Alcohols (Section 13.4)

13.22 Draw the structures of the chief product formed when the following alcohols are dehydrated to alkenes:

 a. $CH_3CHCH_2CH_3$
 |
 OH

 CH_3
 |
 b. $CH_3CHCHCH_3$
 |
 OH

13.23 Draw the structures of the chief product formed when the following alcohols are dehydrated to alkenes:

 a.

 b. OH
 |
 $CH_3CHCH—CH_3$
 |
 CH_2CH_3

13.24 Draw the structures of the ethers that can be produced from the following alcohols:

 a. $CH_3CH_2CH_2—OH$

 b.

 c.

13.25 Draw the structures of the two organic compounds that can be obtained by oxidizing $CH_3CH_2CH_2—OH$.

13.26 Give the structure of an alcohol that could be used to prepare each of the following compounds:

 a.

 O
 ||
 b. $CH_3CH_2CCH—CH_3$
 |
 CH_3

 O
 ||
 c. $CH_3CH_2CH_2—C—OH$

13.27 Give the structure of an alcohol that could be used to prepare each of the following compounds:

a.

b.

c. $CH_3CH-C-OH$ (with CH_3 and O labels)

13.28 What products would result from the following processes? Write an equation for each reaction.

a. 2-Methyl-2-butanol is subjected to controlled oxidation.

b. 1-Propanol is heated to 140°C in the presence of sulfuric acid.

c. 3-Pentanol is subjected to controlled oxidation.

d. 3-Pentanol is heated to 180°C in the presence of sulfuric acid.

e. 1-Hexanol is subjected to an *excess* of oxidizing agent.

13.29 What products would result from the following processes? Write an equation for each reaction.

a. 1-Butanol is heated to 140°C in the presence of sulfuric acid.

b. 1-Butanol is subjected to an *excess* of oxidizing agent.

c. 2-Pentanol is subjected to controlled oxidation.

d. 2-Pentanol is heated to 180°C in the presence of sulfuric acid.

e. 2-Methyl-2-pentanol is subjected to controlled oxidation.

13.30 Each of the following conversions requires more than one step, and some reactions studied in previous chapters may be needed. Show the reagents you would use and draw structural formulas for intermediate compounds formed in each conversion.

a. $CH_3CH_2CH=CH_2 \rightarrow CH_3CH_2CCH_3$ (with O)

b.

c. $CH_3CH_2CH_2CH_2 \rightarrow CH_3CH_2CCH_3$ (with OH and O)

13.31 Each of the following conversions requires more than one step, and some reactions studied in previous chapters may be needed. Show the reagents you would use and draw structural

formulas for intermediate compounds formed in each conversion.

a. $CH_2=CH_2 \rightarrow CH_3CH_2-O-CH_2CH_3$

b.

c. $CH_3CH_2CH_2 \rightarrow CH_3CHCH_3$ (with OH labels)

d. $CH_3CH_2CH_2CH_2 \rightarrow CH_3CH_2CHCH_3$ (with OH and Cl)

13.32 The three-carbon diol used in antifreeze is

$$CH_3 - CH - CH_2$$ (with OH OH)

It is nontoxic and is used as a moisturizing agent in foods. Oxidation of this substance within the liver produces pyruvic acid, which can be used by the body to supply energy. Give the structure of pyruvic acid.

Important Alcohols (Section 13.5)

13.33 Methanol is fairly volatile and evaporates quickly if spilled. Methanol is also absorbed quite readily through the skin. If, in the laboratory, methanol accidentally spilled on your clothing, why would it be a serious mistake to just let it evaporate?

13.34 Why is methanol such an important industrial chemical?

13.35 Suppose you are making some chocolate cordials (chocolate-coated candies with soft fruit filling). Why might you want to add a little glycerol to the filling?

13.36 Name an alcohol used in each of the following ways:

a. A moistening agent in many cosmetics

b. The solvent in solutions called tinctures

c. Automobile antifreeze

d. Rubbing alcohol

e. A flavoring in cough drops

f. Present in gasohol

Characteristics and Uses of Phenols (Section 13.6)

13.37 Name a phenol associated with each of the following:

a. A vitamin

b. A disinfectant cleaner

13.38 Name a phenol used in each of the following ways:

a. A disinfectant used for cleaning walls

b. An antiseptic found in some mouthwashes

c. An antioxidant used to prevent rancidity in foods

Unless otherwise noted all art on this page © Cengage Learning 2014

Ethers (Section 13.7)

13.39 Assign a common name to each of the following ethers:

a. $CH_3-O-CH_2CH_3$

b. $O-CH_2CH_2CH_3$ (attached to benzene ring)

c. $CH_3CH_2\overset{\overset{\displaystyle CH_3}{|}}{C}H-O-\overset{\overset{\displaystyle CH_3}{|}}{C}HCH_2CH_3$

13.40 Assign a common name to each of the following ethers:

a. $CH_3CH_2-O-\overset{\overset{\displaystyle }{}}{C}HCH_3$ with CH_3 branch c. (two benzene rings joined by O)

b. $CH_3-O-CH_2CH_2CH_2CH_3$

13.41 Assign the IUPAC name to each of the following ethers. Name the smaller alkyl group as the alkoxy group.

a. $CH_3-O-CH_2CH_2CH_3$

b. $CH_3\overset{\overset{\displaystyle }{}}{C}HCH_2CH_2-O-CH_3CH_3$ with CH_2CH_3 branch

c. (cyclopropane) $O-CH_2CH_2CH_3$

d. CH_3O — (benzene ring with) OCH_3 and OCH_3

13.42 Assign the IUPAC name to each of the following ethers. Name the smaller alkyl group as the alkoxy group.

a. $CH_3CH_2-O-CH_2CH_2CH_3$

b. $CH_3CH_2-O-\overset{\overset{\displaystyle }{}}{C}HCH_3$ with CH_3 branch

c. CH_3CH_2-O- (benzene ring) d. (cyclopentane with) OCH_3 and OCH_3

13.43 Draw structural formulas for the following:

a. butyl ethyl ether

b. methyl phenyl ether

c. diisopropyl ether

d. 3-ethoxyhexane

e. 1,2-dimethoxycyclobutane

13.44 Draw structural formulas for the following:

a. methyl propyl ether

b. isobutyl phenyl ether

c. 2-methoxybutane

d. 1,2,3-trimethoxycyclopropane

e. 2-*t*-butoxy-2-pentene

13.45 Give the IUPAC names and draw structural formulas for the six isomeric ethers of the molecular formula $C_5H_{12}O$.

Properties of Ethers (Section 13.8)

13.46 What is the chief chemical property of ethers?

13.47 Why is diethyl ether hazardous to use as an anesthetic or as a solvent in the laboratory?

13.48 Arrange the following compounds in order of decreasing solubility in water. Explain the basis for your decisions.

$CH_3CH_2CH_2-OH \quad CH_3CH_2CH_2CH_3 \quad CH_3CH_2-O-CH_3$

13.49 Arrange the compounds in Exercise 13.48 in order of decreasing boiling point. Explain your answer.

13.50 Draw structural formulas and use a dotted line to show hydrogen bonding between a molecule of diethyl ether and water.

Thiols (Section 13.9)

13.51 Complete the following reactions:

a. $2CH_3\overset{\overset{\displaystyle }{}}{C}H_2 + Hg^{2+} \longrightarrow$ with SH group

b. 2 (cyclopentane) $SH + (O) \longrightarrow$

c. $CH_3-S-S-CH_2CH_2CH_3 + 2(H) \rightarrow$

13.52 Complete the following reactions:

a. $2CH_3CH_2CH_2-SH + Hg^{2+} \rightarrow$

b. $2CH_3CH_2CH_2-SH + (O) \rightarrow$

c. (cyclopropane) $S-S-CH_3 + 2(H) \longrightarrow$

13.53 Lipoic acid is required by many microorganisms for proper growth. As a disulfide, it functions in the living system by catalyzing certain oxidation reactions and is reduced in the process. Write the structure of the reduction product.

(structure) $CH_2CH_2CH_2CH_2-\overset{\overset{\displaystyle O}{\|}}{C}-OH + 2(H) \longrightarrow$ with $S-S$ ring

lipoic acid

13.54 Alcohols and thiols can both be oxidized in a controlled way. What are the differences in the products?

Polyfunctional Compounds (Section 13.10)

13.55 Identify the functional groups in vanillin, the active ingredient in vanilla flavoring.

13.56 Identify the functional groups in cinnamaldehyde, present in cinnamon flavoring.

Additional Exercises

13.57
$$\text{alkene + water} \xrightleftharpoons{\text{H}_2\text{SO}_4} \text{alcohol + heat}$$

In simplistic terms, it can be thought that an equilibrium exists in the hydration-dehydration reactions above. Use LeChâtelier's principle to explain why the dehydration reaction is favored at $180°C$.

13.58 Thiols have lower boiling points and are less water soluble than the corresponding alcohol (e.g., CH_3CH_2-OH and CH_3CH_2-SH). Explain why.

13.59 Determine the oxidation numbers on the carbon atom in the following reaction.

methanol methanoic acid

13.60 Using the idea of aromaticity (the electronic structure of benzene), explain why phenol is a stronger acid than cyclohexanol.

13.61 Use general reactions to show how an alcohol ($R-O-H$) can behave as a weak Brønsted acid when it reacts with a strong Brønsted base (X^-). Next, show how an alcohol can behave as a weak Brønsted base in the presence of a strong Brønsted acid (HA).

Allied Health Exam Connection

The following questions are from these sources:

1. *Nursing School Entrance Exam* © 2005, Learning Express, LLC.

2. *McGraw-Hill's Nursing School Entrance Exams* by Thomas A. Evangelist, Tamara B. Orr and Judy Unrein © 2009, The McGraw-Hill Companies, Inc.

3. *NSEE Nursing School Entrance Exams,* 3rd Edition © 2009, Kaplan Publishing.

4. *Cliffs Test Prep: Nursing School Entrance Exams* by Fred N. Grayson © 2004, Wiley Publishing, Inc.

5. *Peterson's Master the Nursing School and Allied Health Entrance Exams,* 18th Edition by Marion F. Gooding © 2008, Peterson's, a Nelnet Company.

13.62 Which compound below contains the alcohol functional group?

 a. $C_2H_5OCH_3$

 b. C_3H_4

 c. CH_3CH_2CHO

 d. C_3H_7OH

13.63 The compound that has the greatest polarity is:

 a. $CH_3-CH_2-O-CH_2-CH_3$

 b. $CH_3-CH_2CH_2CH_2-CH_3$

 c. $CH_3-CH_2-CH_2-CH_2-CH_2-Cl$

 d. $CH_3-CH_2-CH_2-CH_2-CH_2-OH$

13.64 Alcoholic beverages contain:

 a. wood alcohol

 b. isopropyl alcohol

 c. glyceryl alcohol

 d. ethyl alcohol

13.65 Rubbing alcohol is:

 a. methyl alcohol

 b. ethyl alcohol

 c. phenol

 d. isopropyl alcohol

13.66 Which of the following compounds is an ether?

 a. CH_2CHO

 b. CH_3-O-CH_3

 c. CH_3-COOH

 d. CH_3-CH_2OH

Chemistry for Thought

13.67 Many aftershaves are 50% ethanol. What do you think is the purpose of the ethanol?

13.68 A mixture of ethanol and 1-propanol is heated to $140°C$ in the presence of sulfuric acid. Careful analysis reveals that three ethers are formed. Write formulas for these three products, name each, and explain why three form, rather than a single product.

13.69 The two-carbon alcohol in some antifreeze

is toxic if ingested. Reactions within the liver oxidize the diol to oxalic acid, which can form insoluble salts and damage the kidneys. Give the structure of oxalic acid.

13.70 Although ethanol is only mildly toxic to adults, it poses greater risks for fetuses. Why do you think this is the case?

13.71 The medicinal compound taxol is mentioned in Figure 13.1. What does the name indicate about its possible structure?

13.72 When diethyl ether is spilled on the skin, the skin takes on a dry appearance. Explain whether this effect is more likely due to a removal of water or a removal of natural skin oils.

13.73 Figure 13.8 points out that methanol is used as a fuel in racing cars. Write a balanced equation for the combustion of methanol.

13.74 Figure 13.13 focuses on the use of thiol chemistry by skunks. If thiols are more volatile than alcohols and less soluble in water, why do these properties represent an advantage to skunks?

13.75 Why do you think a dye is added to antifreeze before it is sold in stores?

13.76 Glycerol, or glycerin, is used as a moisturizer in foods such as candy and shredded coconut. What is the molecular explanation for its utility as a moisturizer?

Even-numbered exercises answered in Appendix B.
Blue-numbered exercises are more challenging. **465**

Case Study

Chris was a go-getter, always giving 110%. However, when the economy tanked, he lost his engineering job. Through a temporary service, he secured two jobs that together paid the bills. Unfortunately, one of the jobs was a graveyard shift and the other was a day shift on weekends. To say the least, this created havoc with his sleep schedule. Chris coped with his lack of energy by eating high-calorie junk food, and in just a few months he had gained 20 lbs. Disgusted with himself, he changed his diet; he almost completely cut out carbohydrates and consumed mainly meat products. His wife was annoyed by his overboard approach to weight loss and complained that he had "bad breath" since he started dieting. Chris explained that was a symptom of ketosis—a sign that his body was burning fat. Chris was happy with his progress until he found himself in the emergency room. Kidney stones had to be the worst pain he had ever experienced. Chris was told the stones were a result of ketosis.

How can Chris be encouraged to manage his health more gently and effectively? How do excess ketones affect the kidneys? What is a reasonable approach to weight loss?

Follow-up to this Case Study appears at the end the chapter before the Concept Summary.

Learning Objectives

When you have completed your study of this chapter, you should be able to:

1 Recognize the carbonyl group in compounds and classify the compounds as aldehydes or ketones. (**Section 14.1**)

2 Assign IUPAC names to aldehydes and ketones. (**Section 14.1**)

3 Compare the physical properties of aldehydes and ketones with those of compounds in other classes. (**Section 14.2**)

4 Write key reactions for aldehydes and ketones. (**Section 14.3**)

5 Give specific uses for aldehydes and ketones. (**Section 14.4**)

The carbonyl functional group is characteristic of both aldehydes and ketones. In a **carbonyl group,** a carbon is double bonded to an oxygen atom and single bonded to two other atoms:

$$\begin{array}{c} O \\ \parallel \\ - C - \end{array}$$
carbonyl group

carbonyl group

$$\begin{array}{c} O \\ \parallel \\ \text{The} \quad - C - \text{group.} \end{array}$$

Aldehydes and ketones occur widely in nature and play important roles in living organisms. For example, the carbonyl group is found in numerous carbohydrates, including glucose and fructose. Glucose, a major source of energy in living systems, is found combined with fructose in cane sugar:

glucose

fructose

In this chapter, we will study the naming of aldehydes and ketones, as well as some of their important reactions. These concepts will be very useful when we study the chemistry of carbohydrates in Chapter 17.

14.1 The Nomenclature of Aldehydes and Ketones

Learning Objectives

1. Recognize the carbonyl group in compounds and classify the compounds as aldehydes or ketones.
2. Assign IUPAC names to aldehydes and ketones.

When a carbonyl group is directly bonded to at least one hydrogen atom, the compound is an **aldehyde.** In **ketones,** two carbon atoms are directly bonded to the carbonyl group:

$$
\begin{array}{ccc}
\overset{O}{\overset{\|}{-C-}} & \overset{O}{\overset{\|}{-C-H}} & \overset{O}{\overset{|\;\;\|\;\;|}{-C-C-C-}} \\
\text{carbonyl group} & \text{aldehyde} & \text{ketone}
\end{array}
$$

Structural models of the simplest aldehyde (formaldehyde) and the simplest ketone (acetone) are shown in ▶ Figure 14.1.

Figure 14.1 Ball-and-stick models of formaldehyde and acetone.

Several aldehydes and ketones, in addition to formaldehyde and acetone, are well known by common names (see ▶ Table 14.1). Notice that aldehyde and ketone common names are easily recognized by the endings -*aldehyde* and -*one*, respectively.

In the IUPAC system, aldehydes are named by selecting the longest chain that includes the carbonyl carbon. The -*e* of the alkane that has the same number of carbons is replaced by -*al*. Because the carbonyl carbon in aldehydes is always at the end of the chain, it is always designated as carbon number 1.

aldehyde
A compound that contains the $-\overset{O}{\overset{\|}{C}}-H$ group; the general formula is $R-\overset{O}{\overset{\|}{C}}-H$.

ketone
A compound that contains the $-\overset{O}{\overset{|\;\;\|\;\;|}{C-C-C}}-$ group; the general formula is $R-\overset{O}{\overset{\|}{C}}-R'$.

TABLE 14.1 Some Common Aldehydes and Ketones

Structural Formula	IUPAC Name	Common Name	Boiling Point (°C)
Aldehydes			
$H-\overset{\overset{\displaystyle O}{\|\|}}{C}-H$	methanal	formaldehyde	−21
$CH_3-\overset{\overset{\displaystyle O}{\|\|}}{C}-H$	ethanal	acetaldehyde	21
$CH_3CH_2-\overset{\overset{\displaystyle O}{\|\|}}{C}-H$	propanal	propionaldehyde	49
$CH_3CH_2CH_2-\overset{\overset{\displaystyle O}{\|\|}}{C}-H$	butanal	butyraldehyde	76
$\text{C}_6\text{H}_5-\overset{\overset{\displaystyle O}{\|\|}}{C}-H$	benzaldehyde	benzaldehyde	178
Ketones			
$CH_3-\overset{\overset{\displaystyle O}{\|\|}}{C}-CH_3$	propanone	acetone	56
$CH_3-\overset{\overset{\displaystyle O}{\|\|}}{C}-CH_2CH_3$	butanone	methyl ethyl ketone (MEK)	80
cyclohexanone =O	cyclohexanone	cyclohexanone	156

Example 14.1

Name the following aldehydes according to the IUPAC system.

a. $CH_3CH_2CH_2-\overset{\overset{\displaystyle O}{\|\|}}{C}-H$

b. $CH_3\overset{\overset{\displaystyle Br}{\|}}{C}HCH_2-\overset{\overset{\displaystyle O}{\|\|}}{C}-H$

c. $CH_3CH_2\overset{\overset{\displaystyle \overset{\overset{\displaystyle O}{\|\|}}{C}-H}{\|}}{C}HCH_2CH_3$

Solution

a. This aldehyde contains four carbon atoms, and the name is butanal. The aldehyde group is always position number 1, so the number designating the aldehyde position is omitted from the name.

b. Carbon chain numbering begins with the carbonyl end of the molecule even though a lower number for the Br could be obtained by numbering from the left:

$$\underset{4}{CH_3}\underset{3}{CH}\underset{2}{CH_2}-\underset{1}{\overset{\overset{\displaystyle O}{||}}{C}}-H$$

with Br on carbon 3.

The compound is 3-bromobutanal.

c. The carbonyl group must be position number 1 in the chain even though a longer carbon chain (pentane) exists:

$$\overset{1}{C}-H$$ (carbonyl), attached to $\underset{4}{CH_3}\underset{3}{CH_2}\underset{2}{CH}CH_2CH_3$

The name is 2-ethylbutanal.

▶ **LEARNING CHECK 14.1** Give IUPAC names to the following aldehydes:

a. $CH_3CH_2CH_2CH_2-\overset{\overset{\displaystyle O}{||}}{C}-H$

b. $CH_3CHCHCH_2-\overset{\overset{\displaystyle O}{||}}{C}-H$ with CH_3 groups

In naming ketones by the IUPAC system, the longest chain that includes the carbonyl group is given the name of the corresponding alkane, with the *-e* replaced by *-one*. The chain is numbered from the end closest to the carbonyl group, and the carbonyl group position is indicated by a number.

▶ **Example 14.2**

Give IUPAC names to the following ketones:

a. $CH_3-\overset{\overset{\displaystyle O}{||}}{C}-CH_3$

b. $CH_3-\overset{\overset{\displaystyle O}{||}}{C}-CHCH_2CH_3$ with CH_3

c. cyclohexanone with CH_3

Solution

a. There are three carbons in the chain, and the correct name is propanone. The number 2 is not used in this case because the carbonyl group in a ketone cannot be on the end of a chain. Therefore, it must be in the number 2 position.

b. The chain is numbered from the left to give a lower number for the carbonyl carbon:

$$\underset{1}{CH_3}-\underset{2}{\overset{\overset{\displaystyle O}{||}}{C}}-\underset{3}{CH}\underset{4}{CH_2}\underset{5}{CH_3}$$ with CH_3

The complete name is 3-methyl-2-pentanone.

c. In cyclic ketones, the carbonyl carbon will always be at position 1, and so the number is omitted from the name:

The correct name is 2-methylcyclohexanone.

▶ **LEARNING CHECK 14.2** Give IUPAC names to the following ketones:

a.

$$\underset{|}{\overset{Br}{\underset{}{}}}\quad \underset{|}{\overset{Br}{\underset{}{}}}\quad \overset{O}{\overset{||}{}}$$

$CH_3CHCH_2CHCH_2 - C - CH_3$

b.

14.2 Physical Properties

Learning Objective

3. Compare the physical properties of aldehydes and ketones with those of compounds in other classes.

The physical properties of aldehydes and ketones can be explained by an examination of their structures. First, the lack of a hydrogen on the oxygen prevents the formation of hydrogen bonds between molecules:

Therefore, boiling points of pure aldehydes and ketones are expected to be lower than those of alcohols with similar molecular weights. Remember, alcohols can form hydrogen bonds with one another. ▶ Table 14.2 shows that the boiling points of propanal and acetone are 49°C and 56°C, respectively, whereas the alcohol of comparable molecular weight, 1-propanol, has a boiling point of 97°C.

TABLE 14.2 A Comparison of Physical Properties

Class	Example	Formula	Molecular weight	Boiling point (°C)	Water solubility		
Alkane	butane	$CH_3CH_2CH_2CH_3$	58	0	Insoluble		
Aldehyde	propanal	$CH_3CH_2 - \overset{O}{\overset{		}{C}} - H$	58	49	Soluble
Ketone	propanone (acetone)	$CH_3 - \overset{O}{\overset{		}{C}} - CH_3$	58	56	Soluble
Alcohol	1-propanol	$CH_3CH_2CH_2 - OH$	60	97	Soluble		

Faking a Tan

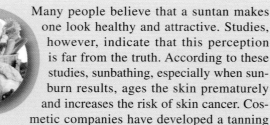

Many people believe that a suntan makes one look healthy and attractive. Studies, however, indicate that this perception is far from the truth. According to these studies, sunbathing, especially when sunburn results, ages the skin prematurely and increases the risk of skin cancer. Cosmetic companies have developed a tanning alternative for those not willing to risk using the sun but who want to be "fashionably" tan.

Tanning lotions and creams that chemically darken the skin are now available. The active ingredient in these "bronzers" is dihydroxyacetone (DHA), a colorless compound classified by the Food and Drug Administration as a safe skin dye.

$$HO-CH_2-\overset{\overset{\textstyle O}{\|}}{C}-CH_2-OH$$

dihydroxyacetone (DHA)

Within several hours of application, DHA produces a brown skin color by reacting with the outer layer of the skin, which consists of dead cells. Only the dead cells react with DHA, so the color gradually fades as the dead cells slough off and are replaced. This process generally leads to the fading of chemical tans within a few weeks. Another problem with chemical tans is uneven skin color. Areas of skin such as elbows and

knees, which contain a thicker layer of dead cells, may absorb and react with more tanning lotion and become darker than other areas.

Perhaps the greatest problem with chemical tans is the false sense of security they might give. Some people with chemical tans think it is safe to go into the sun and get a deeper tan. This isn't true. Sunlight presents the same hazards to chemically tanned skin that it does to untanned skin.

Some DHA-containing products.

Also notice in Table 14.2 that the boiling points of the aldehyde and ketone are higher than that of the comparable alkane. This can be explained by differences in polarity. Whereas alkanes are nonpolar, the carbonyl group of aldehydes and ketones is polar due to the more electronegative oxygen atom:

$$\overset{\overset{\textstyle \delta^-}{O}}{\underset{\delta^+}{\overset{\|}{-C-}}}$$

The attractive forces between molecules possessing such dipoles are not as strong as hydrogen bonds, but they do cause aldehydes and ketones to boil at higher temperatures than the nonpolar alkanes. The graph in ▶ Figure 14.2 summarizes the boiling point comparison for several families of compounds.

Water is a polar solvent and would be expected to be effective in dissolving compounds containing polar carbonyl groups. Besides exhibiting dipolar attractions, the carbonyl oxygen also forms hydrogen bonds with water:

$$R-\overset{\overset{\textstyle O}{\|}}{C}-H \qquad\qquad R-\overset{\overset{\textstyle O}{\|}}{C}-R'$$

hydrogen bond *hydrogen bond*

As a result, low molecular weight aldehydes and ketones are water soluble (Table 14.2).

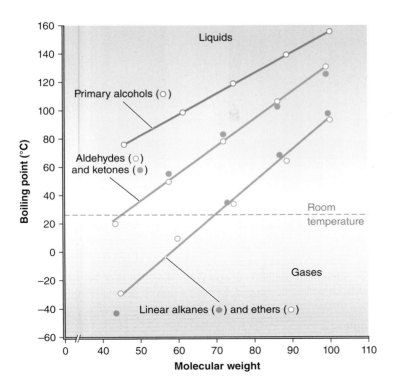

Figure 14.2 The boiling points of aldehydes and ketones are higher than those of alkanes and ethers but lower than those of alcohols of comparable molecular weights.

14.3 Chemical Properties

Learning Objective

4. Write key reactions for aldehydes and ketones.

Oxidation

We learned in Section 13.4 that when aldehydes are prepared by oxidizing primary alcohols with $KMnO_4$ or $K_2Cr_2O_7$, the reaction may continue and produce carboxylic acids. Ketones are prepared similarly, but they are much less susceptible to further oxidation, especially by mild oxidizing agents:

$$\textbf{General reaction: } \underset{\substack{\text{primary} \\ \text{alcohol}}}{R - CH_2 - OH} \xrightarrow{(O)} \underset{\text{aldehyde}}{R - \overset{\overset{O}{\|}}{C} - H} \xrightarrow{(O)} \underset{\substack{\text{carboxylic} \\ \text{acid}}}{R - \overset{\overset{O}{\|}}{C} - OH} \quad (14.1)$$

$$\textbf{General reaction: } \underset{\substack{\text{secondary} \\ \text{alcohol}}}{R - \overset{\overset{OH}{|}}{C}H - R'} \xrightarrow{(O)} \underset{\text{ketone}}{R - \overset{\overset{O}{\|}}{C} - R'} \xrightarrow{(O)} \text{no reaction} \quad (14.2)$$

The difference in reactivity toward oxidation is the chief reason why aldehydes and ketones are classified in separate families (see ▶ Figure 14.3).

Specific example:

$$\underset{\text{benzaldehyde}}{\text{benzaldehyde}} + (O) \longrightarrow \underset{\text{benzoic acid}}{\text{benzoic acid}} \quad (14.3)$$

 From left to right, three test tubes containing potassium dichromate ($K_2Cr_2O_7$), acetone, and benzaldehyde.

 After the addition of equal amounts of $K_2Cr_2O_7$ from the first test tube, the acetone remains unreacted, whereas the benzaldehyde is oxidized.

Figure 14.3 Attempted oxidation of acetone and oxidation of benzaldehyde. As the reaction proceeds, chromium is reduced, forming a grayish green precipitate.

Specific example:

$$CH_3 - \overset{\overset{\displaystyle O}{\|}}{C} - CH_3 + (O) \longrightarrow \text{no reaction} \qquad (14.4)$$

acetone

The oxidation of aldehydes occurs so readily that even atmospheric oxygen causes the reaction. A few drops of liquid benzaldehyde (Reaction 14.3) placed on a watch glass will begin to oxidize to solid benzoic acid within an hour. In the laboratory, it is not unusual to find that bottles of aldehydes that have been opened for a length of time contain considerable amounts of carboxylic acids.

> ▶ **LEARNING CHECK 14.3** Draw the structural formula for each product. Write "no reaction" if none occurs.
>
> **a.**
> $$CH_3CHCH_2 - \overset{\overset{\displaystyle O}{\|}}{C} - H + (O) \longrightarrow$$
> with CH_3 group on the second carbon
>
> **b.**
> cyclopentanone $+ (O) \longrightarrow$

The effectiveness of two common chemical reagents used to test for the presence of aldehydes—Tollens' reagent and Benedict's reagent—depends on the ease with which aldehydes are oxidized. In general, ketones fail to react with these same reagents.

Tollens' reagent is a mild oxidizing solution containing complexed Ag^+ ions. The oxidizing agent is the silver ion, which is reduced to metallic silver in the process and precipitates out (Reaction 14.5):

Tollens' reagent A mild oxidizing solution containing silver ions used to test for aldehydes.

$$R - \overset{\overset{\displaystyle O}{\|}}{C} - H \;+\; 2Ag(NH_3)_2^+ \;+\; 2OH^- \longrightarrow R - \overset{\overset{\displaystyle O}{\|}}{C} - O^-NH_4^+ \;+\; 3NH_3 \;+\; 2Ag \;+\; H_2O \quad (14.5)$$

an aldehyde Tollens' reagent a carboxylate salt silver

Birth Control: Progesterone Substitutes

The ketone *norethynodrel* is not a major industrial material, but in terms of social impact, it has had a profound influence since 1960. In that year, Enovid, with norethynodrel as the major component, became the first oral contraceptive for women approved by the FDA. Norethynodrel is effective

norethynodrel

progesterone

because it mimics the action of another ketone, *progesterone,* a hormone that causes changes in the wall of the uterus to prepare it to accept a fertilized egg and maintain the resulting pregnancy.

Norethynodrel establishes a state of false pregnancy; a woman ceases to ovulate and therefore cannot conceive. The pill (as this product is popularly called) has been used by millions of women and appears to be relatively safe even though some women experience undesirable side effects such as acne, hypertension, abnormal bleeding, or increased blood clotting. Women who suffer from these or other serious side effects should not take the pill. Women over the age of 40, particularly those who smoke or are overweight, are advised by the FDA to use contraceptive methods other than the pill.

Doctors sometimes prescribe higher doses of combined oral contraceptives for use as "morning after" pills, which are taken within 72 hours of unprotected intercourse to prevent any possibly fertilized egg from reaching the uterus. The FDA's Advisory Committee for Reproductive Health Drugs concluded that certain oral contraceptives are safe and effective for this type of use.

Another type of contraception is injectable progestin, a synthetic form of progesterone. Depo-Provera® is a product that is injected by a healthcare professional into the arm muscle or buttocks every 3 months. Depo-Provera prevents pregnancy in three ways. It changes the cervical mucus to help prevent sperm from reaching the egg, inhibits ovulation, and changes the uterine lining to prevent a fertilized egg from implanting in the uterus.

Long-term birth control for women became available in 1990 when the FDA approved under-the-skin implants that contain a slowly released contraceptive. In these devices, levonorgestrel (Norplant®, or the newer Norplant 2®), a synthetic compound similar to progesterone, is sealed inside small rubber rods about the size of matchsticks. The rods are implanted under the skin of the upper arm. Levonorgestrel is slowly released through the walls of the rods and prevents pregnancy for up to five years (for Norplant) or three years (for Norplant 2), with a failure rate of only 0.2%. Possible side effects from Norplant are vaginal bleeding, headaches, nausea, dizziness, and nervousness.

Depo-Provera is a contraceptive injection required four times a year to maintain its effectiveness.

When the reaction is carried out in a clean, grease-free glass container, the metallic silver deposits on the glass and forms a mirror. This reaction is used commercially to silver some mirrors (see ❱ Figure 14.4).

Figure 14.4 This young woman can see herself because the silver coating on the back of the mirror reflects light.

© Michael C. Slabaugh

Benedict's reagent A mild oxidizing solution containing Cu^{2+} ions used to test for the presence of aldehydes.

Benedict's reagent is a mild oxidizing solution containing Cu^{2+} ions. When an aldehyde oxidation takes place in an alkaline solution containing Cu^{2+}, a red precipitate of Cu_2O is produced:

$$\underset{\text{certain aldehydes}}{R-\overset{\overset{\displaystyle O}{\|}}{C}-H} \quad + \quad \underset{\substack{\text{Benedict's}\\\text{reagent}\\\text{(blue)}}}{2Cu^{2+}} \quad + \quad 5OH^- \longrightarrow \underset{\text{a carboxylate ion}}{R-\overset{\overset{\displaystyle O}{\|}}{C}-O^-} \quad + \quad \underset{\substack{\text{red}\\\text{precipitate}}}{Cu_2O} \quad + \quad 3H_2O \quad (14.6)$$

The presence of Cu^{2+} in Benedict's reagent causes this alkaline solution to have a bright blue color. A positive Benedict's test consists of the appearance of a colored (usually red) precipitate. All aldehydes give a positive Tollens' test, but only certain aldehydes and one type of easily oxidized ketone readily give a positive Benedict's test. The necessary structural features are shown.

A — an aldehyde with an adjacent carbonyl group

B — an aldehyde with an adjacent alcohol group

C — a ketone with an adjacent alcohol group

© Spencer L. Seager

1 From left to right, three test tubes containing Benedict's reagent, 0.5% glucose solution, and 2.0% glucose solution.

© Spencer L. Seager

2 The addition of Benedict's reagent from the first tube produces colors (due to the red Cu_2O) that indicate the amount of glucose present.

Figure 14.5 The Benedict's test for glucose.

The structural features **B** or **C** are found in a number of sugars, including glucose. Accordingly, Benedict's reagent reacts with glucose to produce a red precipitate of Cu_2O (see ▶ Figure 14.5).

The Addition of Hydrogen

In Section 12.3, we learned that addition reactions are common for compounds containing carbon–carbon double bonds. The same is true for the carbon–oxygen double bonds of

Unless otherwise noted all art on this page © Cengage Learning 2014

carbonyl groups. An important example is the addition of H_2 in the presence of catalysts such as nickel or platinum:

$$\textbf{General reaction:}\quad \underset{\text{aldehyde}}{R-\overset{\overset{\displaystyle O}{\|}}{C}-H} \;+\; H_2 \;\xrightarrow{\;Pt\;}\; \underset{\text{primary alcohol}}{R-\overset{\overset{\displaystyle OH}{|}}{\underset{\underset{\displaystyle H}{|}}{C}}-H} \qquad (14.7)$$

$$\textbf{General reaction:}\quad \underset{\text{ketone}}{R-\overset{\overset{\displaystyle O}{\|}}{C}-R'} \;+\; H_2 \;\xrightarrow{\;Pt\;}\; \underset{\text{secondary alcohol}}{R-\overset{\overset{\displaystyle OH}{|}}{\underset{\underset{\displaystyle H}{|}}{C}}-R'} \qquad (14.8)$$

$$\textbf{Specific example:}\quad \underset{\text{propanal}}{CH_3CH_2-\overset{\overset{\displaystyle O}{\|}}{C}-H} \;+\; H_2 \;\xrightarrow{\;Pt\;}\; \underset{\text{1-propanol}}{CH_3CH_2CH_2\overset{\overset{\displaystyle OH}{|}}{}} \qquad (14.9)$$

$$\textbf{Specific example:}\quad \underset{\text{acetone}}{CH_3-\overset{\overset{\displaystyle O}{\|}}{C}-CH_3} \;+\; H_2 \;\xrightarrow{\;Pt\;}\; \underset{\text{2-propanol}}{CH_3-\overset{\overset{\displaystyle OH}{|}}{CH}-CH_3} \qquad (14.10)$$

We see that the addition of hydrogen to an aldehyde produces a primary alcohol, whereas the addition to a ketone gives a secondary alcohol. Notice that these reactions are reductions that are essentially the reverse of the alcohol oxidations used to prepare aldehydes and ketones (Reactions 14.1 and 14.2).

▶ **LEARNING CHECK 14.4** Draw the structural formula for each product of the following reactions:

a.
$$CH_3CH_2-\overset{\overset{\displaystyle O}{\|}}{C}-CH_2CH_3 + H_2 \xrightarrow{\;Pt\;}$$

b.
$$+ H_2 \xrightarrow{\;Pt\;}$$

The Addition of Alcohols

Aldehydes react with alcohols to form **hemiacetals,** a functional group that is very important in carbohydrate chemistry (Chapter 17). Hemiacetals are usually not very stable and are difficult to isolate. With excess alcohol present and with an acid catalyst, however, a stable product called an acetal is formed:

hemiacetal
A compound that contains the

$$\text{functional group} -\overset{\overset{\displaystyle OH}{|}}{\underset{\underset{\displaystyle OR}{|}}{C}}-H$$

$$\underset{\substack{\text{General}\\\text{reaction:}}}{}\quad \underset{\text{aldehyde}}{R-\overset{\overset{\displaystyle O}{\|}}{C}-H} \;+\; \underset{\text{alcohol}}{R'-OH} \;\rightleftharpoons\; \underset{\substack{\text{hemiacetal}\\\text{intermediate}}}{R-\overset{\overset{\displaystyle OH}{|}}{\underset{\underset{\displaystyle OR'}{|}}{C}}-H} \;\overset{\substack{H^+ \text{ and}\\ R'-OH}}{\rightleftharpoons}\; \underset{\text{acetal}}{R-\overset{\overset{\displaystyle OR'}{|}}{\underset{\underset{\displaystyle OR'}{|}}{C}}-H} \;+\; H_2O \qquad (14.11)$$

Specific example:

$$CH_3 - \overset{\overset{\displaystyle O}{\|}}{C} - H \ + \ CH_3 - OH \ \rightleftharpoons \ CH_3 - \underset{\underset{\displaystyle OCH_3}{|}}{\overset{\overset{\displaystyle OH}{|}}{C}} - H \ \underset{CH_3 - OH}{\overset{H^+ \text{ and}}{\rightleftharpoons}} \ CH_3 - \underset{\underset{\displaystyle OCH_3}{|}}{\overset{\overset{\displaystyle OCH_3}{|}}{C}} - H \ + \ H_2O \qquad (14.12)$$

 acetaldehyde methanol hemiacetal acetal
 intermediate

acetal

A compound that contains the

$$-\underset{\underset{\displaystyle OR}{|}}{\overset{\overset{\displaystyle OR}{|}}{C}} - H \quad \text{arrangement of atoms.}$$

Hemiacetals contain an —OH group, hydrogen, and an —OR group on the same carbon. Thus, a hemiacetal appears to have alcohol and ether functional groups. **Acetals** contain a carbon that has a hydrogen and two —OR groups attached; they look like diethers:

$$CH_3 - \underset{\underset{\displaystyle OCH_3}{|}}{\overset{\overset{\displaystyle OH}{|}}{C}} - H \qquad\qquad CH_3 - \underset{\underset{\displaystyle OCH_3}{|}}{\overset{\overset{\displaystyle OCH_3}{|}}{C}} - H$$

hemiacetal carbon *acetal carbon*

To better understand the changes that have occurred, let's look first at hemiacetal formation and then at acetal formation. The first molecule of alcohol adds across the double bond of the aldehyde in a manner similar to other addition reactions:

— H attaches here

$$CH_3 - \overset{\overset{\displaystyle O}{\|}}{C} - H \ + \ CH_3 - O - H \ \rightleftharpoons \ CH_3 - \underset{\underset{\displaystyle OCH_3}{|}}{\overset{\overset{\displaystyle OH}{|}}{C}} - H \qquad (14.13)$$

— OCH$_3$ attaches here

hemiacetal

hemiketal

A compound that contains the

$$-\underset{\underset{\displaystyle OR}{|}}{\overset{\overset{\displaystyle OH}{|}}{C}} - \overset{|}{C} - \overset{|}{C} - \text{group.}$$

The second step, in which the hemiacetal is converted to an acetal, is like earlier substitution reactions. In this case, an —OCH$_3$ substitutes for an —OH:

$$CH_3 - \underset{\underset{\displaystyle OCH_3}{|}}{\overset{\overset{\displaystyle OH}{|}}{C}} - H \ + \ CH_3 - O - H \ \overset{H^+}{\rightleftharpoons} \ CH_3 - \underset{\underset{\displaystyle OCH_3}{|}}{\overset{\overset{\displaystyle OCH_3}{|}}{C}} - H \ + \ H - OH \qquad (14.14)$$

 hemiacetal acetal

ketal

A compound that contains the

$$-\underset{\underset{\displaystyle OR}{|}}{\overset{\overset{\displaystyle OR}{|}}{C}} - \overset{|}{C} - \overset{|}{C} - \text{group.}$$

In a very similar way, ketones can react with alcohols to form **hemiketals** and **ketals:**

hemiketal carbon *ketal carbon*

General reaction:

$$R - \overset{\overset{\displaystyle O}{\|}}{C} - R' \ + \ R'' - O - H \ \rightleftharpoons \ R - \underset{\underset{\displaystyle OR''}{|}}{\overset{\overset{\displaystyle OH}{|}}{C}} - R' \ \underset{R'' - OH}{\overset{H^+ \text{ and}}{\rightleftharpoons}} \ R - \underset{\underset{\displaystyle OR''}{|}}{\overset{\overset{\displaystyle OR''}{|}}{C}} - R' \ + \ H_2O \qquad (14.15)$$

 ketone alcohol hemiketal ketal
 intermediate

Specific example:

$$CH_3-\overset{\overset{\displaystyle O}{\|}}{C}-CH_3 \; + \; CH_3CH_2OH \; \rightleftharpoons \; CH_3-\overset{\overset{\displaystyle OH}{|}}{\underset{\underset{\displaystyle OCH_2CH_3}{|}}{C}}-CH_3 \; \xrightarrow[CH_3CH_2-OH]{H^+ \text{ and }} \; CH_3-\overset{\overset{\displaystyle OCH_2CH_3}{|}}{\underset{\underset{\displaystyle OCH_2CH_3}{|}}{C}}-CH_3 \; + \; H_2O \qquad (14.16)$$

acetone ethanol hemiketal intermediate ketal

▶ Example 14.3

Identify each of the following as a hemiacetal, hemiketal, acetal, ketal, or none of the above:

a. $CH_3-O-CH_2CH_2-OH$

b. $CH_3-O-\overset{\overset{\displaystyle OH}{|}}{C}HCH_3$

c. $CH_3CH_2-O-\overset{\overset{\displaystyle OCH_3}{|}}{\underset{\underset{\displaystyle CH_3}{|}}{C}}-CH_3$

d.

Solution

a. Look first at any structure to see if there is a carbon with two oxygens attached. Hemiacetals, hemiketals, acetals, and ketals are all alike in that regard. This compound has two oxygens, but they are on different carbons; thus it is none of the possibilities.

b. After finding a carbon with two oxygens attached, next look to see if one is an —OH. If it is, that makes it a hemiacetal or hemiketal. The third step is to look at the carbon containing the two oxygens. If it is attached to an —H, the compound was originally an aldehyde and not a ketone. Thus, this compound is a hemiacetal:

$$CH_3-O-\overset{\overset{\displaystyle OH \longleftarrow \textit{ one group is —OH}}{|}}{C}HCH_3$$

two oxygens and one hydrogen attached

c. There is a carbon with two oxygens attached and neither is an —OH. Thus, the compound is an acetal or ketal:

$$CH_3CH_2-O-\overset{\overset{\displaystyle OCH_3}{|}}{\underset{\underset{\displaystyle CH_3}{|}}{C}}-CH_3$$

no hydrogens attached

No hydrogens are attached to the carbon bonded to two oxygens. The compound is a ketal.

d. Two oxygens are attached to the same carbon. One group is an —OH. No hydrogens are attached to the central carbon. The compound is a hemiketal.

▶ **LEARNING CHECK 14.5** Draw the structural formula for the hemiacetal and hemiketal intermediates and for the acetal and ketal products of the following reactions. Label each structure as a hemiacetal, hemiketal, ketal, or acetal.

a.

$+ \; 2CH_3CH_2-OH \xrightarrow{H^+}$

b.

$+ \; 2CH_3-OH \xrightarrow{H^+}$

Some molecules contain both an —OH and a C=O group on different carbon atoms. In such cases, an intramolecular (within the molecule) reaction can occur, and a cyclic hemiacetal or hemiketal can be formed:

open-chain molecule containing an aldehyde and alcohol group

cyclic structure containing a hemiacetal group

(14.17)

Cyclic hemiacetals and hemiketals are much more stable than the open-chain compounds discussed earlier. In Chapter 17, we'll see that sugars such as glucose and fructose exist predominantly in the form of cyclic hemiacetals and hemiketals.

How Reactions Occur 14.1

Hemiacetal Formation

In the first step of the mechanism, the carbonyl oxygen is protonated:

The alcohol oxygen then bonds to the carbonyl carbon:

In the final step, a proton is given off to form the hemiacetal and regenerate the acid catalyst.

hemiacetal

In another reaction important in carbohydrate chemistry (Chapter 17), cyclic acetals and ketals may form from the hemistructures. As before, all reactions are reversible:

$$\text{cyclic hemiacetal} + CH_3OH \underset{}{\overset{H^+}{\rightleftharpoons}} \text{cyclic acetal} + H_2O \qquad (14.18)$$

▶ Example 14.4

Identify each of the following as a cyclic hemiacetal, hemiketal, acetal, or ketal:

a.

b.

c.

d.

Study Skills 14.1

A Reaction Map for Aldehydes and Ketones

This reaction map is designed to help you master organic reactions. Whenever you are trying to complete an organic reaction, use these two basic steps: (1) Identify the functional group that is to react, and (2) identify the reagent that is to react with the functional group. If the reacting functional group is an aldehyde or a ketone, find the reagent in the summary diagram, and use the diagram to predict the correct products.

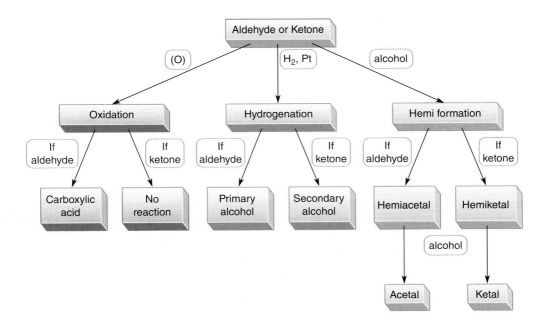

Solution

Use the same criteria that were applied to open-chain compounds in Example 14.3. Compound a has two oxygens attached to the same carbon. One is an —OH (hemiacetal or hemiketal). The central carbon has no hydrogens. Thus, the compound is a hemiketal. These criteria give the following results for each structure:

a.

hemiketal carbon

b.

*ketal carbon
(—OH absent,
—H absent)*

c.

*acetal carbon
(—OH absent,
—H present)*

d.

*hemiacetal carbon
(—OH present,
—H present)*

We have shown each of the reactions in acetal and ketal formation as being reversible. Simple hemiacetals and hemiketals are characteristically unstable and easily revert to the starting materials. Acetals and ketals are stable structures, but the reactions may be reversed by using water and an acid catalyst:

General
reaction:
$$R-\underset{\underset{OR'}{|}}{\overset{\overset{OR'}{|}}{C}}-H + H_2O \underset{}{\overset{H^+}{\rightleftarrows}} R-\overset{\overset{O}{\|}}{C}-H + 2R'-OH \qquad (14.19)$$

acetal aldehyde alcohol

General
reaction:
$$R-\underset{\underset{OR''}{|}}{\overset{\overset{OR''}{|}}{C}}-R' + H_2O \underset{}{\overset{H^+}{\rightleftarrows}} R-\overset{\overset{O}{\|}}{C}-R' + 2R''-OH \qquad (14.20)$$

ketal ketone alcohol

Specific
example:
$$CH_3-\underset{\underset{OCH_2CH_3}{|}}{\overset{\overset{OCH_2CH_3}{|}}{C}}-CH_3 + H_2O \underset{}{\overset{H^+}{\rightleftarrows}} CH_3-\overset{\overset{O}{\|}}{C}-CH_3 + 2CH_3CH_2-OH \qquad (14.21)$$

hydrolysis Bond breakage by reaction with water.

This type of reaction, in which water causes a compound to split into component substances, is called **hydrolysis.** It will be an important reaction to remember as we discuss, in later chapters, the chemistry of biomolecules such as carbohydrates, lipids, and proteins.

▶ **LEARNING CHECK 14.6** Draw the structural formulas needed to complete the following hydrolysis reactions:

a. $CH_3CH_2CH_2-\underset{\underset{OCH_2CH_3}{|}}{\overset{\overset{OCH_2CH_3}{|}}{C}}-H + H_2O \overset{H^+}{\rightleftarrows}$

b. (cyclopentane ring) $\underset{OCH_3}{\overset{OCH_3}{<}} + H_2O \overset{H^+}{\rightleftarrows}$

Vanilloids: Hot Relief from Pain

The word *vanilloids* might bring to mind images of vanilla-flavored candies or ice cream. However, vanilloids have properties very different from those of vanilla, and their inclusion in foods would result in a hot and spicy flavor that might even be extremely irritating, rather than a smooth vanilla flavor.

The best-known vanilloids are capsaicin and resiniferatoxin (RTX). Capsaicin is the compound in various types of hot peppers that gives them their characteristic hot and spicy flavor. It is used in a variety of products ranging from personal-defense pepper sprays to squirrel-proof birdseed. RTX is a powerful irritant extracted from a cactuslike plant, *Euphorbia resinifera.* The milky latex obtained from the plant is referred to in medical literature dating as far back as the first century. In these writings, it was described as a nose and skin irritant and as a treatment for chronic pain. In powdered form, RTX causes sneezing, a characteristic used by some practical jokers.

Structurally, molecules of capsaicin and RTX (not shown) are similar to those of vanillin in that they both have a homovanillyl group in their structure.

intolerable and unacceptable to patients. RTX fared better in the tests. It also relieved the condition, and caused only mild discomfort and an itching sensation with the first application.

Basic research has led to some important discoveries about these compounds. The gene for the capsaicin receptor has been cloned, making available the large quantities of the receptor needed to do further research and develop new drugs. For example, it has been found that the receptor responds not only to capsaicin but also to levels of heat that can damage tissue. It is suggested that possibly the reason hot peppers feel hot in the mouth is because they stimulate the same pain receptors that heat does.

Another important development is the discovery of a way to synthesize RTX in the laboratory. The availability of synthetic RTX may reduce the cost for the material and make possible further advances in the use of RTX in medicines.

vanillin

homovanillyl group

capsaicin

When either of the compounds is applied to the skin or mouth, a burning sensation results. This sensation is caused by the compounds bonding to receptors of small sensory neurons associated with the transmission of pain. Following repeated application of capsaicin or RTX, these neurons, or C sensory nerve fibers, become desensitized to the initial irritation or pain the compounds cause. This characteristic allows the compounds to be used topically to relieve chronic pain. Capsaicin is now used as an ingredient in a few OTC pain-relieving creams such as Capzasin-P, Heet, Menthacin, and Pain Doctor.

Both capsaicin and RTX have also been tested as treatments for a condition called *bladder hyperreflexia,* which is characterized by the urge to urinate even when there is very little urine in the bladder. Capsaicin effectively relieved the problem when it was instilled into the urinary bladder, but the first application caused an intense burning sensation that was

Hot peppers are a source of capsaicin.

▶ Example 14.5

Draw structural formulas for the products of the following reactions:

a.

+ CH_3CH_2OH $\overset{H^+}{\rightleftharpoons}$

b.

+ H_2O $\overset{H^+}{\rightleftharpoons}$

c.

+ H_2O $\overset{H^+}{\rightleftharpoons}$

Solution

a. The starting material is a cyclic hemiketal. Reaction with an alcohol produces a cyclic ketal by a substitution of —OCH_2CH_3 for the —OH:

+ CH_3CH_2O—H $\overset{H^+}{\rightleftharpoons}$ + H—OH

b. The starting compound is an acetal. Hydrolysis with water will form an aldehyde and two alcohol groups:

c. The starting compound is a ketal and upon hydrolysis will form a ketone and two alcohol groups:

▶ LEARNING CHECK 14.7
Identify each of the following as cyclic hemiacetals, hemiketals, acetals, or ketals and show structural formulas for the hydrolysis products:

a.

b.

Vitamin A and Birth Defects

Three active forms of vitamin A are known. One is the aldehyde called retinal. In the other two forms, the aldehyde group is replaced by an alcohol group (retinol) or a carboxylic acid group (retinoic acid).

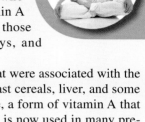

retinal

Vitamin A is an essential substance for healthy vision and skin, but sometimes too much of this good thing creates problems. A relationship between excessive vitamin A intake during pregnancy and birth defects has been recognized for some time. However, the minimum amount of vitamin A required to produce harmful effects is now believed to be much lower than was previously thought. According to a recent study, the consumption of vitamin A at or above 10,000 international units per day was linked to birth defects. A **vitamin international unit (IU)** is a measure of vitamin activity, determined by such biological methods as feeding a compound to vitamin-deprived animals and measuring growth. In the study, an increase in a variety of birth defects was detected in babies born to mothers who took more than 10,000 IU of vitamin A per day. The birth defects included those of the heart, brain, limbs, kidneys, and genitals.

The active forms of vitamin A that were associated with the defects are found in fortified breakfast cereals, liver, and some vitamin supplements. Beta-carotene, a form of vitamin A that has not been linked to birth defects, is now used in many prenatal vitamin supplements. Beta-carotene is a plant-based vitamin A source that is converted into an active form of vitamin A once ingested.

A maximum dose of 5000 IU of vitamin A during pregnancy is now recommended by the American College of Obstetricians and Gynecologists. In addition, the diet should contain plenty of fruits and vegetables that are naturally rich in beta-carotene (see Chemistry Around Us 12.2).

Many cereals are fortified with vitamin A.

Carrots are an excellent source of beta-carotene.

14.4 Important Aldehydes and Ketones

Learning Objective

5. Give specific uses for aldehydes and ketones.

vitamin international unit (IU)
A measure of vitamin activity, determined by biological methods.

Formaldehyde: $H-\overset{\overset{\displaystyle O}{\|}}{C}-H$

As seen with other functional classes, the most important compound of the class is usually the simplest member. Formaldehyde, the simplest aldehyde, is a gas at room temperature, but it is often supplied and used in the form of a 37% aqueous solution called *formalin*. This solution kills microorganisms and is effective in sterilizing surgical instruments.

It is also used to embalm cadavers. Formaldehyde is a key industrial chemical in the production of plastics such as Bakelite, the first commercial polymer invented in 1901, and Formica.

Acetone:
$$CH_3 - \overset{\overset{\displaystyle O}{\|}}{C} - CH_3$$

Judging from the quantity used, acetone is by far the most important of the ketones. Over 1 billion pounds are used annually in the United States. It is particularly useful as a solvent because it dissolves most organic compounds and yet it is miscible in water. It is widely used as a solvent for coatings, which range from nail polish to exterior enamel paints (see ▶ Figure 14.6).

Figure 14.6 Acetone is an excellent solvent for many organics, including nail polish. Why does acetone-based polish remover evaporate fairly quickly when used?

A number of naturally occurring aldehydes and ketones play important roles within living systems. The carbonyl functional group is fairly common in biological compounds. For example, progesterone and testosterone, female and male sex hormones, respectively, are both ketones.

Progesterone progesterone testosterone

Several naturally occurring aldehydes and ketones have very fragrant odors and are used in flavorings (see ▶ Figure 14.7 and ▶ Table 14.3).

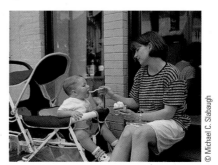

Figure 14.7 Vanilla ice cream owes its characteristic flavor to a special aldehyde.

TABLE 14.3 Some Fragrant Aldehydes and Ketones

Name	Structural Formula	Sources and Typical Uses
Vanillin		Vanilla bean; flavoring
Cinnamaldehyde		Oil of cinnamon; flavoring
Citral		Rinds of lemons, limes, and oranges; citrus flavoring
Biacetyl	$CH_3 - \overset{\overset{O}{\|\|}}{C} - \overset{\overset{O}{\|\|}}{C} - CH_3$	Butter; flavoring for margarines
Camphor		Camphor tree; characteristic medicinal odor; an ingredient in some inhalants
Menthone		Mint plants; peppermint flavoring

Case Study Follow-up

Ketones are partially broken-down fats. A buildup of ketones in blood can cause the body to produce high levels of uric acid, a risk factor for kidney stones (NIDDK, 2010). Uric acid kidney stones can be caused by ingestion of too much meat, as in this case study (NKUDIC, 2010).

According to the National Institute of Diabetes and Digestive and Kidney Diseases (NIDDK), to achieve slow and steady weight loss a person should not only consider a change in diet but also a weight-loss program that encourages healthy eating behaviors and moderately intense physical activity. This should then be followed by a plan to keep the weight off. Fad diets do not provide this. Programs such as Weight Watchers and the U.S. Government information website myplate.gov offer tools to manage weight in a healthy way. Healthy weight loss is a slow process. Many people need the help of a support group to continue with their weight-loss program in the long term.

Concept Summary

The Nomenclature of Aldehydes and Ketones

The functional groups characteristic of aldehydes and ketones are very similar; they both contain a carbonyl group:

$$\begin{array}{c} O \\ \parallel \\ -C- \end{array}$$

Aldehydes have a hydrogen attached to the carbonyl carbon,

$$\begin{array}{c} O \\ \parallel \\ -C-H \end{array}$$

whereas ketones have two carbons attached to the carbonyl carbon:

$$\begin{array}{c} O \\ | \quad \parallel \quad | \\ -C-C-C- \\ | \qquad | \end{array}$$

Objective 1, Exercise 14.4

The IUPAC ending for aldehyde names is *-al,* whereas that for ketones is *-one.*
Objective 2, Exercise 14.6

Physical Properties

Molecules of aldehydes and ketones cannot form hydrogen bonds with each other. As a result, they have lower boiling points than alcohols of similar molecular weight. Aldehydes and ketones have higher boiling points than alkanes of similar molecular weight because of the presence of the polar carbonyl group. The polarity of the carbonyl group and the fact that aldehydes and ketones can form hydrogen bonds with water explain why the low molecular weight compounds of these organic classes are water-soluble.
Objective 3, Exercise 14.16

Chemical Properties

Aldehydes and ketones are prepared by the oxidation of primary and secondary alcohols, respectively. Aldehydes can be further oxidized to carboxylic acids, but ketones resist oxidation. Thus, aldehydes are oxidized by Tollens' reagent (Ag^+) and Benedict's solution (Cu^{2+}), whereas ketones are not. A characteristic reaction of both aldehydes and ketones is the addition of hydrogen to the carbonyl double bond to form alcohols. In a reaction that is very important in sugar chemistry, an alcohol can add across the carbonyl group of an aldehyde to produce a hemiacetal. The substitution reaction of a second alcohol molecule with the hemiacetal produces an acetal. Ketones can undergo similar reactions to form hemiketals and ketals.
Objective 4, Exercise 14.42

Important Aldehydes and Ketones

Formaldehyde is a key industrial chemical in the production of plastics such as Bakelite and Formica. Acetone is an important solvent. Some naturally occurring aldehydes and ketones are important in living systems. Some function as sex hormones; others are used as flavorings.
Objective 5, Exercise 14.52

Key Terms and Concepts

Acetal (14.3)
Aldehyde (14.1)
Benedict's reagent (14.3)
Carbonyl group (Introduction)

Hemiacetal (14.3)
Hemiketal (14.3)
Hydrolysis (14.3)
Ketal (14.3)

Ketone (14.1)
Tollens' reagent (14.3)
Vitamin international unit (IU) (14.4)

Key Reactions

1.	Oxidation of an aldehyde to give a carboxylic acid (Section 14.3):	$$\underset{\displaystyle \overset{O}{\parallel}}{R-C-H} + (O) \longrightarrow \underset{\displaystyle \overset{O}{\parallel}}{R-C-OH}$$	Reaction 14.1
2.	Attempted oxidation of a ketone (Section 14.3):	$$\underset{\displaystyle \overset{O}{\parallel}}{R-C-R'} + (O) \longrightarrow \text{no reaction}$$	Reaction 14.2
3.	Hydrogenation of an aldehyde to give a primary alcohol (Section 14.3):	$$\underset{\displaystyle \overset{O}{\parallel}}{R-C-H} + H_2 \xrightarrow{\text{Pt}} R-\underset{\displaystyle \underset{H}{\mid}}{\overset{\displaystyle \overset{OH}{\mid}}{C}}-H$$	Reaction 14.7
4.	Hydrogenation of a ketone to give a secondary alcohol (Section 14.3):	$$\underset{\displaystyle \overset{O}{\parallel}}{R-C-R'} + H_2 \xrightarrow{\text{Pt}} R-\underset{\displaystyle \underset{H}{\mid}}{\overset{\displaystyle \overset{OH}{\mid}}{C}}-R'$$	Reaction 14.8
5.	Addition of an alcohol to an aldehyde to form a hemiacetal and then an acetal (Section 14.3):	$$\underset{\displaystyle \overset{O}{\parallel}}{R-C-H} + R'-OH \rightleftharpoons R-\underset{\displaystyle \underset{OR'}{\mid}}{\overset{\displaystyle \overset{OH}{\mid}}{C}}-H \xrightleftharpoons[]{\overset{H^+ \text{ and}}{R'-OH}} R-\underset{\displaystyle \underset{OR'}{\mid}}{\overset{\displaystyle \overset{OR'}{\mid}}{C}}-H + H_2O$$	Reaction 14.11
6.	Addition of an alcohol to a ketone to form a hemiketal and a ketal (Section 14.3):	$$\underset{\displaystyle \overset{O}{\parallel}}{R-C-R'} + R''-O-H \rightleftharpoons R-\underset{\displaystyle \underset{OR''}{\mid}}{\overset{\displaystyle \overset{OH}{\mid}}{C}}-R' \xrightleftharpoons[]{\overset{H^+ \text{ and}}{R''-OH}} R-\underset{\displaystyle \underset{OR''}{\mid}}{\overset{\displaystyle \overset{OR''}{\mid}}{C}}-R' + H_2O$$	Reaction 14.15
7.	Hydrolysis of an acetal to yield an aldehyde and two molecules of alcohol (Section 14.3):	$$R-\underset{\displaystyle \underset{OR'}{\mid}}{\overset{\displaystyle \overset{OR'}{\mid}}{C}}-H + H_2O \xrightleftharpoons{H^+} \underset{\displaystyle \overset{O}{\parallel}}{R-C-H} + 2R'-OH$$	Reaction 14.19
8.	Hydrolysis of a ketal to yield a ketone and two molecules of alcohol (Section 14.3):	$$R-\underset{\displaystyle \underset{OR''}{\mid}}{\overset{\displaystyle \overset{OR''}{\mid}}{C}}-R' + H_2O \xrightleftharpoons{H^+} \underset{\displaystyle \overset{O}{\parallel}}{R-C-R'} + 2R''-OH$$	Reaction 14.20

Exercises

The Nomenclature of Aldehydes and Ketones (Section 14.1)

14.1 What is the structural difference between an aldehyde and a ketone?

14.2 Draw structural formulas for an aldehyde and a ketone that contain the fewest number of carbon atoms possible.

14.3 Identify each of the following compounds as an aldehyde, a ketone, or neither:

a. $CH_3CH_2C-CH_2CH_3$ with O double bonded to C

b.

c.

d. cyclobutanone (square with =O)

e. benzene ring with CH_2C-H and O double bonded

f. NH_2-C-NH_2 with O double bonded

14.4 Identify each of the following compounds as an aldehyde, a ketone, or neither:

a. CH_3CH_2-C-H with O double bonded

b. $CH_3-C-O-CH_3$ with O double bonded

c. cyclopentanone (ring with =O)

d. $CH_3CH_2CH_2-C-OH$ with O double bonded

e. $CH_3CH_2-C-CH_3$ with O double bonded

f. $CH_3CH_2-C-NH_2$ with O double bonded

14.5 Assign IUPAC names to the following aldehydes and ketones:

a. CH_3-C-H with O double bonded

b. $CH_3CHCH_2CH-C-H$ with CH_3, CH_3 substituents and O double bonded

c. $CH_3CHCH_2-C-CH_3$ with CH_3 substituent and O double bonded

d. $CH_3CH_2CHCH_2-C-H$ with phenyl substituent and O double bonded

e. cyclopropane ring with =O and CH_3

14.6 Assign IUPAC names to the following aldehydes and ketones:

a. $CH_3CH_2CH_2-C-H$ with O double bonded

b. $CH_2CH_2CH-C-H$ with Br, Br substituents and O double bonded

c. $CH_3CHCH_2-C-CH_3$ with CH_3 substituent and O double bonded

d. cyclopentanone ring with Cl, Cl substituents and =O

e. benzene ring with $CH_2-C-CHCH_3$, CH_3 substituent and O double bonded

14.7 Draw structural formulas for each of the following compounds:

a. methanal

b. 3-ethyl-2-pentanone

c. 3-methylcyclohexanone

d. 2,4,6-trimethylheptanal

14.8 Draw structural formulas for each of the following compounds:

a. propanal

b. 3-methyl-2-butanone

c. 2,2-dimethylcyclopentanone

d. 3-bromo-4-phenylbutanal

14.9 Draw structural formulas and give IUPAC names for all the isomeric aldehydes and ketones that have the molecular formula $C_5H_{10}O$.

14.10 Draw structural formulas and give IUPAC names for all the isomeric aldehydes and ketones that have the molecular formula C_3H_6O.

14.11 Each of the following names is wrong. Give the structure and correct name for each compound.

a. 3-ethyl-2-butanone

b. 2-ethyl-propanal

c. 4-methyl-5-propyl-3-hexanone

d. 2-methyl-2-phenylethanal

14.12 Each of the following names is wrong. Give the structure and correct name for each compound.

a. 3-ethyl-2-methylbutanal

b. 2-methyl-4-butanone

c. 4,5-dibromocyclopentanone

Even-numbered exercises answered in Appendix B.
490 Blue-numbered exercises are more challenging.

Unless otherwise noted all art on this page © Cengage Learning 2014

Physical Properties (Section 14.2)

14.13 Why does hydrogen bonding *not* take place between molecules of aldehydes or ketones?

14.14 Most of the remaining water in washed laboratory glassware can be removed by rinsing the glassware with acetone (propanone). Explain how this process works (acetone is much more volatile than water).

14.15 The boiling point of propanal is 49°C, whereas the boiling point of propanol is 97°C. Explain this difference in boiling points.

14.16 Explain why propane boils at −42°C, whereas ethanal, which has the same molecular weight, boils at 20°C.

14.17 Use a dotted line to show hydrogen bonding between molecules in each of the following pairs:

a.
$$CH_3-\overset{\overset{\displaystyle O}{\|}}{C}-CH_3 \quad\text{and}\quad \overset{\displaystyle H}{\underset{\displaystyle H}{|}}O$$

b.
cyclopentyl–C(=O)–H and O with two H

14.18 Use a dotted line to show hydrogen bonding between molecules in each of the following pairs:

a. cyclohexanone and O with H, H

b. $CH_3CH_2-\overset{\overset{\displaystyle O}{\|}}{C}-H$ and $\overset{\displaystyle H}{\underset{\displaystyle H}{|}}O$

14.19 Arrange the following compounds in order of increasing boiling point:

a. cyclopentanone (O) b. cyclopentanol (OH) c. methylcyclopentane (CH₃)

14.20 The compounds menthone and menthol are fragrant substances present in an oil produced by mint plants:

menthone menthol

When pure, one of these pleasant-smelling compounds is a liquid at room temperature; the other is a solid. Identify the solid and the liquid and explain your reasoning.

Chemical Properties (Section 14.3)

14.21 Write an equation for the formation of the following compounds from the appropriate alcohol:

a. cyclopropyl ketone with CH₃

b. $CH_3-\overset{\overset{\displaystyle O}{\|}}{C}-\overset{\overset{\displaystyle Br}{|}}{C}HCH_3$

c. benzene ring with C(=O)–OH and CH₂CH₃

14.22 Write an equation for the formation of the following compounds from the appropriate alcohol:

a. $CH_3-\overset{\overset{\displaystyle O}{\|}}{C}-CH_2\overset{\overset{\displaystyle CH_3}{|}}{C}HCH_3$

b. cyclopentyl–C(=O)–H

c. cyclopentanone with CH₂CH₃

14.23 Identify the following structures as hemiacetals, hemiketals, or neither:

a. $CH_3-O-\overset{\overset{\displaystyle CH_3}{|}}{\underset{\underset{\displaystyle CH_3}{|}}{C}}-OH$

b. $CH_3CH_2\overset{\overset{\displaystyle OH}{|}}{C}H-OCH_2CH_3$

c. cyclopentane with OH and OCH₃

d. benzene ring with O–CH(OH)CH₂CH₃

14.24 Identify the following structures as hemiacetals, hemiketals, or neither:

a. $CH_3-\overset{\overset{\displaystyle OH}{|}}{C}H-OCH_3$

b. $CH_3CH_2\overset{\overset{\displaystyle OCH_3}{|}}{\underset{\underset{\displaystyle CH_3}{|}}{C}}-OH$

c. $CH_3\overset{\overset{\displaystyle OCH_3}{|}}{C}HCH_2-OH$

d. cyclopentane with OH and OCH₂CH₃

14.25 Label each of the following as acetals, ketals, or neither:

a. (cyclohexane ring with OCH$_3$ and OCH$_2$CH$_3$)

b. (cyclopentane ring with O—C(CH$_3$)(CH$_3$)—OCH$_3$)

c.
$$OCH_3$$
$$|$$
$$CH_2$$
$$|$$
$$OCH_2CH_3$$

14.26 Label each of the following as acetals, ketals, or neither:

a. (cyclohexane ring with OCH$_3$ and OCH$_2$CH$_3$)

b. (cyclohexane ring with O—C(OCH$_3$)(CH$_3$)—CH$_2$CH$_3$)

c.
$$OCH_3$$
$$|$$
$$CH_2—OCH_3$$

14.27 Label each of the following structures as a cyclic hemiacetal, hemiketal, acetal, ketal, or none of these:

a. b. c.

14.28 Label each of the following structures as a hemiacetal, hemiketal, acetal, ketal, or none of these:

a. b. c.

14.29 What two functional groups react to form the following?

a. A hemiacetal

b. An acetal

c. A ketal

d. A hemiketal

14.30 Hemiacetals are sometimes referred to as potential aldehydes. Explain.

14.31 Complete the following statements:

a. Oxidation of a secondary alcohol produces _____.

b. Oxidation of a primary alcohol produces an aldehyde that can be further oxidized to a _____.

c. Hydrogenation of a ketone produces _____.

d. Hydrogenation of an aldehyde produces _____.

e. Hydrolysis of an acetal produces _____.

f. Hydrolysis of a ketal produces _____.

14.32 What observation characterizes a positive Tollens' test?

14.33 Which of the following compounds will react with Tollens' reagent (Ag$^+$, NH$_3$, and H$_2$O)? For those that do react, draw a structural formula for the organic product.

a.
$$OH$$
$$|$$
$$CH_2—CH_2—CH_2—OCH_3$$

b.
$$O$$
$$||$$
$$H—C—CH_2—CH_2—CH_3$$

c.

d.

e.

14.34 Which of the following compounds will react with Tollens' reagent (Ag$^+$, NH$_3$, and H$_2$O)? For those that do react, draw a structural formula for the organic product.

a.

b.

c.
$$OH$$
$$|$$
$$CH_3—O—CHCH_3$$

d.
$$O$$
$$||$$
$$CH_3CH_2—C—H$$

e.
$$O$$
$$||$$
$$CH_3—C—CH_3$$

14.35 What is the formula of the precipitate that forms in a positive Benedict's test?

Unless otherwise noted all art on this page © Cengage Learning 2014

14.36 Not all aldehydes give a positive Benedict's test. Which of the following aldehydes do?

a. $CH_3CH_2-\overset{\overset{\displaystyle O}{\|}}{C}-H$

b. $\overset{\overset{\displaystyle O}{\|}}{C}-H$ (benzaldehyde)

c. $\overset{\overset{\displaystyle O}{\|}}{C}-\overset{\overset{\displaystyle O}{\|}}{C}-H$

d. $CH_3\overset{\overset{\displaystyle OH}{|}}{CH}-\overset{\overset{\displaystyle O}{\|}}{C}-H$

e. $CH_3-O-CH_2-\overset{\overset{\displaystyle O}{\|}}{C}-H$

14.37 A stockroom assistant prepares three bottles, each containing one of the following compounds:

$CH_3CH_2-\overset{\overset{\displaystyle O}{\|}}{C}-CH_3$ $CH_3CH_2CH_2\overset{\overset{\displaystyle O}{\|}}{CH}$ $CH_3CH_2\overset{\overset{\displaystyle O}{\|}}{CH}\underset{\underset{\displaystyle OH}{|}}{CH}$

However, the bottles are left unlabeled. Instead of discarding the samples, another assistant runs tests on the contents, using Tollens' and Benedict's reagents. Match the compound to the bottle, based on these results.

	Tollens' Reagent	**Benedict's Reagent**
Bottle A	A dark precipitate forms	A red-orange precipitate forms
Bottle B	No reaction	No reaction
Bottle C	A dark precipitate and slight mirror form	No reaction

14.38 Glucose, the sugar present within the blood, gives a positive Benedict's test. Circle the structural features that enable glucose to react.

$$\underset{\underset{\displaystyle CH_2}{|}}{OH}-\underset{\underset{\displaystyle CH}{|}}{OH}-\underset{\underset{\displaystyle CH}{|}}{OH}-\underset{\underset{\displaystyle CH}{|}}{OH}-\underset{\underset{\displaystyle CH}{|}}{OH}-\overset{\overset{\displaystyle O}{\|}}{C}-H$$

14.39 Fructose, present with glucose in honey, reacts with Benedict's reagent. Circle the structural features that enable fructose to react.

$$\underset{\underset{\displaystyle CH_2}{|}}{OH}-\underset{\underset{\displaystyle CH}{|}}{OH}-\underset{\underset{\displaystyle CH}{|}}{OH}-\underset{\underset{\displaystyle CH}{|}}{OH}-\overset{\overset{\displaystyle O}{\|}}{C}-\underset{\underset{\displaystyle CH_2}{|}}{OH}$$

14.40 Glucose can exist as a cyclic hemiacetal because one of the alcohol groups reacts with the aldehyde:

$$\underset{\underset{\displaystyle CH_2}{|}}{OH}-\underset{\underset{\displaystyle CH}{|}}{OH}-\underset{\underset{\displaystyle CH}{|}}{OH}-\underset{\underset{\displaystyle CH}{|}}{OH}-\underset{\underset{\displaystyle CH}{|}}{OH}-\overset{\overset{\displaystyle O}{\|}}{C}-H \rightleftharpoons$$

Draw an arrow to the carbon of the cyclic hemiacetal that was originally part of the aldehyde group. Circle the alcohol group in the open-chain structure that became a part of the cyclic hemiacetal.

14.41 After an intramolecular reaction, fructose forms a hemiketal:

$$\underset{\underset{\displaystyle CH_2}{|}}{OH}-\underset{\underset{\displaystyle CH}{|}}{OH}-\underset{\underset{\displaystyle CH}{|}}{OH}-\underset{\underset{\displaystyle CH}{|}}{OH}-\overset{\overset{\displaystyle O}{\|}}{C}-\underset{\underset{\displaystyle CH_2}{|}}{OH} \rightleftharpoons$$

Draw an arrow to the carbon of the cyclic hemiketal that was originally part of the ketone group. Circle the alcohol group in the open-chain structure that became part of the cyclic hemiketal.

14.42 Complete the following equations. If no reaction occurs, write "no reaction."

a. $+ H_2 \xrightarrow{Pt}$

b. $CH_3CH_2-\underset{\underset{\displaystyle CH_3}{|}}{\overset{\overset{\displaystyle OH}{|}}{C}}-OCH_3 + CH_3CH_2CH_2-OH \overset{H^+}{\rightleftharpoons}$

c. $CH_3CH_2-\overset{\overset{\displaystyle O}{\|}}{C}-H + 2CH_3\overset{\overset{\displaystyle OH}{|}}{CH}CH_3 \overset{H^+}{\rightleftharpoons}$

d. $CH_2-\overset{\overset{\displaystyle O}{\|}}{C}-H + (O) \longrightarrow$

e. $CH_3CH_2\underset{\underset{\displaystyle CH_3}{|}}{CH}-\overset{\overset{\displaystyle O}{\|}}{C}-H + H_2 \xrightarrow{Pt}$

14.43 Complete the following equations. If no reaction occurs, write "no reaction."

a. $CH_3CH_2-\overset{\overset{\displaystyle O}{\|}}{C}-CH_3 + H_2 \xrightarrow{Pt}$

b. $CH_3\underset{\underset{\displaystyle CH_3}{|}}{\overset{\overset{\displaystyle Br}{|}}{CH}}CH-\overset{\overset{\displaystyle O}{\|}}{C}-H + (O) \longrightarrow$

c. $\overset{\overset{\displaystyle O}{\|}}{C}-H + 2CH_3-OH \overset{H^+}{\rightleftharpoons}$

d. $+ (O) \longrightarrow$

e. $+ CH_3CH_2-OH \xrightarrow{H^+} \rightleftharpoons$

14.44 Describe the products that result when hydrogen (H_2) is added to alkenes, alkynes, aldehydes, and ketones. You might review Chapter 12 briefly.

14.45 Draw structural formulas for the products of the following hydrolysis reactions:

a. $\underset{\displaystyle CH_3CH-OCH_3}{\overset{\displaystyle OCH_2CH_3}{|}} + H_2O \xrightarrow{H^+} \rightleftharpoons$

b. $\begin{array}{c} OCH_3 \\ OCH_3 \end{array} + H_2O \xrightarrow{H^+} \rightleftharpoons$

c. $+ H_2O \xrightarrow{H^+} \rightleftharpoons$

d. $\underset{\displaystyle OCH_2CH_3}{\overset{\displaystyle CH_2-OCH_2CH_3}{|}} + H_2O \xrightarrow{H^+} \rightleftharpoons$

14.46 Draw structural formulas for the products of the following hydrolysis reactions:

a. $\begin{array}{c} OCH_2CH_3 \\ OCH_2CH_3 \end{array} + H_2O \xrightarrow{H^+} \rightleftharpoons$

b. $CH_3CH_2-\underset{\displaystyle CH_2CH_3}{\overset{\displaystyle OCH_3}{\underset{|}{\overset{|}{C}}}}-OCH_3 + H_2O \xrightarrow{H^+} \rightleftharpoons$

c. $CH_3CH_2CH_2O-CH_2-OCH_2CH_2CH_3 + H_2O \xrightarrow{H^+} \rightleftharpoons$

d. $CH_3O-\underset{\displaystyle OCH_3}{\overset{\displaystyle }{\underset{|}{CH}}}-CH_2CH_3 + H_2O \xrightarrow{H^+} \rightleftharpoons$

14.47 The following compounds are cyclic acetals or ketals. Write structural formulas for the hydrolysis products.

a. $+ H_2O \xrightarrow{H^+} \rightleftharpoons$

b. $+ H_2O \xrightarrow{H^+} \rightleftharpoons$

14.48 The following compounds are cyclic acetals or ketals. Write structural formulas for the hydrolysis products.

a. $+ H_2O \xrightarrow{H^+} \rightleftharpoons$

b. $+ H_2O \xrightarrow{H^+} \rightleftharpoons$

14.49 Write equations to show how the following conversions can be achieved. More than one reaction is required, and reactions from earlier chapters may be necessary.

a. $\longrightarrow$

b. $\longrightarrow$

14.50 Write equations to show how the following conversions can be achieved. More than one reaction is required, and reactions from earlier chapters may be necessary.

a. $CH_3CH_2CH_2-\overset{\displaystyle OH}{\underset{|}{}} \longrightarrow CH_3CH_2-\underset{\displaystyle OCH_2CH_3}{\overset{\displaystyle OCH_2CH_3}{\underset{|}{\overset{|}{CH}}}}$

b. $CH_3CH-\overset{\displaystyle O}{\underset{\displaystyle CH_3}{\underset{|}{\overset{\|}{C}}}}-CH_3 \longrightarrow CH_3\overset{\displaystyle CH_3}{\underset{|}{C}}=CH-CH_3$

Important Aldehydes and Ketones (Section 14.4)

14.51 Identify the most important aldehyde and ketone from Section 14.4 (on the basis of amount used), and list at least one characteristic for each that contributes to its usefulness.

14.52 Using Table 14.3, name an aldehyde or ketone used in the following ways:

 a. Peppermint flavoring

 b. Flavoring for margarines

 c. Cinnamon flavoring

 d. Vanilla flavoring

Additional Exercises

14.53 Arrange the following compounds starting with the carbon atom that is the most reduced and ending with the carbon that is the least reduced:

 a. $R-CH_2-OH$

 b. $R-\overset{\displaystyle O}{\overset{\|}{CH}}$

 c. $R-CH_3$

14.54
$$CH_3-\overset{\overset{\displaystyle O}{\|}}{C}-H \xrightarrow{(O)} CH_3-\overset{\overset{\displaystyle O}{\|}}{C}-OH$$

 acetaldehyde acetic acid

You need to produce 500 g of acetic acid using the reaction above. The actual yield of the reaction is 79.6% of the theoretical yield. How many grams of acetaldehyde do you need to start with to produce 500 g of acetic acid?

14.55
$$CH_3-\overset{\overset{\displaystyle O}{\|}}{C}-CH_3 + H_2O \rightleftharpoons$$

The addition of water to aldehydes and ketones occurs rapidly, although it is not thermodynamically favored. What would be the product for the reaction above? HINT: Think of the self-ionization of water and the polarity of the carbonyl group.

14.56 Draw the product that would result when 3-pentanone reacts with an excess of 1-propanol in the presence of an acid catalyst.

14.57 Formaldehyde levels above 0.10 mg/1000 L of ambient air can cause some humans to experience difficulty breathing. How many molecules of formaldehyde would be found in 1.0 L of air at this concentration?

Allied Health Exam Connection

The following questions are from these sources:

1. *Nursing School Entrance Exam* © 2005, Learning Express, LLC.

2. *McGraw-Hill's Nursing School Entrance Exams* by Thomas A. Evangelist, Tamara B. Orr and Judy Unrein © 2009, The McGraw-Hill Companies, Inc.

3. *NSEE Nursing School Entrance Exams*, 3rd Edition © 2009, Kaplan Publishing.

4. *Cliffs Test Prep: Nursing School Entrance Exams* by Fred N. Grayson © 2004, Wiley Publishing, Inc.

5. *Peterson's Master the Nursing School and Allied Health Entrance Exams*, 18th Edition by Marion F. Gooding © 2008, Peterson's, a Nelnet Company.

14.58 Identify the functional group designated by each of the following:

 a. RCHO

 b. ROH

 c.
$$R-\overset{\overset{\displaystyle O}{\|}}{C}-R'$$

14.59 Which of the following would be classified as a ketone?

 a.
$$H-\overset{\overset{\displaystyle H}{|}}{\underset{\underset{\displaystyle H}{|}}{C}}-\overset{\overset{\displaystyle H}{|}}{\underset{\underset{\displaystyle H}{|}}{C}}-\overset{\overset{\displaystyle H}{|}}{C}=O$$

 b.
$$H-\overset{\overset{\displaystyle H}{|}}{\underset{\underset{\displaystyle H}{|}}{C}}-\overset{\overset{\displaystyle O}{\|}}{C}-\overset{\overset{\displaystyle H}{|}}{\underset{\underset{\displaystyle H}{|}}{C}}-\overset{\overset{\displaystyle H}{|}}{\underset{\underset{\displaystyle H}{|}}{C}}-OH$$

 c.
$$H-\overset{\overset{\displaystyle H}{|}}{\underset{\underset{\displaystyle H}{|}}{C}}-\overset{\overset{\displaystyle O}{\|}}{C}-\overset{\overset{\displaystyle H}{|}}{\underset{\underset{\displaystyle H}{|}}{C}}-H$$

Chemistry for Thought

14.60 In the IUPAC name for the following ketone, it is not common to use a number for the position of the carbonyl group. Why not?
$$CH_3CH_2-\overset{\overset{\displaystyle O}{\|}}{C}-CH_3$$

14.61 Why can formaldehyde (CH_2O) be prepared in the form of a 37% solution in water, whereas decanal cannot?

14.62 Other addition reactions of aldehydes occur. Water, for example, adds to the carbonyl of trichloroacetaldehyde to form chloral hydrate, a strong hypnotic and sedative known as "knock-out drops" or (when mixed with alcohol) a "Mickey Finn." Complete the reaction by drawing the structural formula of chloral hydrate:

$$Cl-\overset{\overset{\displaystyle Cl}{|}}{\underset{\underset{\displaystyle Cl}{|}}{C}}-\overset{\overset{\displaystyle O}{\|}}{C}-H + H-OH \longrightarrow$$

 trichloroacetaldehyde chloral hydrate

14.63 In the labels of some consumer products, ketone components listed with an *-one* ending can be found. However, very few aldehyde-containing (*-al* ending) products are found. How can you explain this?

14.64 In Figure 14.6, it is noted that acetone is used as a solvent in fingernail polish remover. Why do you think fingernail polish remover evaporates fairly quickly when used?

14.65 Vanilla flavoring is either extracted from a tropical orchid or synthetically produced from wood pulp byproducts. What differences in chemical structure would you expect in these two commercial products: vanilla extract and imitation vanilla extract?

14.66 The structure of fructose in Exercise 14.39 reveals a ketone group and several alcohol groups. If the alcohol groups are referred to as hydroxys, give an IUPAC name for fructose.

14.67 The use of acetone in laboratory experiments must be carefully monitored because of the highly flammable nature of acetone. Give an equation for the combustion of acetone.

14.68 Look ahead to Chapter 17 and locate the structure of maltose in Section 17.7. Draw the structure of maltose and circle the acetal group.

Case Study

Dallas grew up on a farm. He learned to work hard and to just tough it out when he didn't feel well. After his 50th birthday, he started having frequent bouts of heartburn. No matter how hard he tried, the heartburn pain could not be ignored. He treated it by drinking baking soda in water, which helped a little, but not much. Then he tried liquid antacids and tablets, but his daughter was concerned because he seemed to be eating them like candy, and she convinced him to see a doctor. The doctor diagnosed Dallas with gastroesophageal reflux disease (GERD). The doctor explained to Dallas that the valve between his stomach and esophagus did not close tightly and that stomach acid was entering his esophagus and causing his pain. The doctor prescribed a proton-pump inhibitor to reduce the amount of acid produced and recommended that Dallas avoid certain foods. She also ordered an endoscopy to check for possible damage to the esophagus.

Can too many over-the-counter antacids be harmful? How can heartburn symptoms be distinguished from heart attack? What foods aggravate heartburn?

Follow-up to this Case Study appears at the end the chapter before the Concept Summary.

© iStockphoto.com/Fanelie Rosier

Learning Objectives

When you have completed your study of this chapter, you should be able to:

1 Write reaction equations that illustrate Arrhenius acid–base behavior. **(Section 9.1)**

2 Write reaction equations that illustrate Brønsted acid–base behavior, and identify Brønsted acids and bases from written reaction equations. **(Section 9.2)**

3 Name common acids. **(Section 9.3)**

4 Do calculations using the concept of the self-ionizaton of water. **(Section 9.4)**

5 Do calculations using the pH concept. **(Section 9.5)**

6 Write reaction equations that illustrate the characteristic reactions of acids. **(Section 9.6)**

7 Write reaction equations that represent neutralization reactions between acids and bases. **(Section 9.7)**

8 Write reaction equations that illustrate various ways to prepare salts, and do calculations using the concept of an equivalent of salt. **(Section 9.8)**

9 Demonstrate an understanding of the words *weak* and *strong* as applied to acids and bases. **(Section 9.9)**

10 Demonstrate an understanding of the titration technique used to analyze acids and bases. **(Section 9.10)**

11 Do calculations related to the analysis of acids and bases by titration. **(Section 9.11)**

12 Explain the concept of salt hydrolysis, and write equations to illustrate the concept. **(Section 9.12)**

13 Explain how buffers work, and write equations to illustrate their action. **(Section 9.13)**

A cids, bases, and salts are among the most common and important solutes found in solutions. Until late in the 19th century, these substances were characterized by such properties as taste and color changes induced in certain dyes. Acids taste sour; bases, bitter; and salts, salty. Litmus, a dye, is red in the presence of acids and blue in the presence of bases. These and other observations led to the correct conclusions that acids and bases are chemical opposites, and that salts are produced when acids and bases react with each other. Today, acids and bases are defined in more precise ways that are useful when studying their characteristics.

9.1 The Arrhenius Theory

Learning Objective

1. Write reaction equations that illustrate Arrhenius acid–base behavior.

In 1887, Swedish chemist Svante Arrhenius proposed a theory dealing with electrolytic dissociation. He defined **acids** as substances that dissociate when dissolved in water and produce hydrogen ions (H^+). Similarly, **bases** are substances that dissociate and release hydroxide ions (OH^-) into the solution. Hydrogen chloride (HCl) and sodium

Arrhenius acid Any substance that provides H^+ ions when dissolved in water.

Arrhenius base Any substance that provides OH^- ions when dissolved in water.

hydroxide (NaOH) are examples of an Arrhenius acid and base, respectively. They dissociate in water as follows:

$$HCl(aq) \rightarrow H^+(aq) + Cl^-(aq) \tag{9.1}$$

$$NaOH(aq) \rightarrow Na^+(aq) + OH^-(aq) \tag{9.2}$$

Note that the hydrogen ion is a bare proton, the nucleus of a hydrogen atom.

9.2 The Brønsted Theory

Learning Objective

2. Write reaction equations that illustrate Brønsted acid–base behavior, and identify Brønsted acids and bases from written reaction equations.

Arrhenius did not know that free hydrogen ions cannot exist in water. They covalently bond with water molecules to form hydronium ions (H_3O^+). The water molecules provide both electrons used to form the covalent bond:

$$H^+ + \ddot{\underset{H}{\text{O}}}-H \longrightarrow \left[H-\underset{H}{\overset{\cdot\cdot}{\text{O}}}-H \right]^+ \tag{9.3}$$

new bond

Or, more simply,

$$H^+(aq) + H_2O(\ell) \rightarrow H_3O^+(aq) \tag{9.4}$$

In 1923, Johannes Brønsted in Denmark and Thomas Lowry in England proposed an acid–base theory that took into account this behavior of hydrogen ions. They defined an **acid** as any hydrogen-containing substance that donates a proton (hydrogen ion) to another substance and a **base** as any substance that accepts a proton.

In conformity with this theory, the acidic behavior of covalently bonded HCl molecules in water is written

$$HCl(aq) + H_2O(\ell) \rightleftarrows H_3O^+(aq) + Cl^-(aq) \tag{9.5}$$

The HCl behaves as a Brønsted acid by donating a proton to a water molecule. The water molecule, by accepting the proton, behaves as a base.

The double arrows of unequal length in Equation 9.5 indicate that the reaction is reversible with the equilibrium lying far to the right. In actual water solutions, essentially 100% of the dissolved HCl is in the ionic form at equilibrium. Remember, both the forward and the reverse reactions are taking place at equilibrium (Section 8.6). When the reverse reaction occurs, hydronium ions donate protons to chloride ions to form HCl and H_2O molecules. Thus, H_3O^+ behaves as a Brønsted acid, and Cl^- behaves as a Brønsted base. We see from this discussion that when a substance like HCl behaves as a Brønsted acid by donating a proton, the species that remains (Cl^-) is a Brønsted base. The Cl^- is called the **conjugate base** of HCl. Every Brønsted acid and the base formed when it donates a proton is called a **conjugate acid–base pair.** Thus, in Equation 9.5, we see that HCl and Cl^- form a conjugate acid–base pair, as do H_3O^+ and H_2O for the reverse reaction. Notice that the acid and base in a conjugate acid–base pair differ only by a proton, H^+.

Brønsted acid Any hydrogen-containing substance that is capable of donating a proton (H^+) to another substance.

Brønsted base Any substance capable of accepting a proton from another substance.

conjugate base The species remaining when a Brønsted acid donates a proton.

conjugate acid–base pair A Brønsted acid and its conjugate base.

▶ Example 9.1

Identify all Brønsted acids, bases, and acid–base conjugate pairs in the reactions represented by the following equations:

a. $HNO_3(aq) + H_2O(\ell) \rightleftarrows H_3O^+(aq) + NO_3^-(aq)$
b. $HClO_4(aq) + H_2O(\ell) \rightleftarrows H_3O^+(aq) + ClO_4^-(aq)$
c. $NH_3(aq) + H_2O(\ell) \rightleftarrows OH^-(aq) + NH_4^+(aq)$

Solution

a. Nitric acid, HNO_3, behaves as a Brønsted acid by donating a proton to H_2O, a base, in the forward reaction. In the reverse reaction, H_3O^+, the conjugate acid of H_2O, donates a proton to NO_3^-, the conjugate base of HNO_3. In summary, the Brønsted acids are HNO_3 and H_3O^+, the Brønsted bases are H_2O and NO_3^-, and the conjugate acid–base pairs are HNO_3/NO_3^- and H_3O^+/H_2O:

$$HNO_3(aq) + H_2O(\ell) \rightleftharpoons H_3O^+(aq) + NO_3^-(aq)$$

acid base acid base

conjugate pair

conjugate pair

b. Similarly, perchloric acid ($HClO_4$) is a Brønsted acid, and H_2O is a Brønsted base (forward reaction). Also, H_3O^+ is a Brønsted acid, and the perchlorate ion (ClO_4^-) is a Brønsted base (reverse reaction). The conjugate acid–base pairs are $HClO_4/ClO_4^-$ and H_3O^+/H_2O:

$$HClO_4(aq) + H_2O(\ell) \rightleftharpoons H_3O^+(aq) + ClO_4^-(aq)$$

acid base acid base

conjugate pair

conjugate pair

c. In this reaction, water donates a proton instead of accepting one. Therefore, H_2O is a Brønsted acid, and ammonia (NH_3) is a Brønsted base (forward reaction). The ammonium ion (NH_4^+) is an acid, and the hydroxide ion (OH^-) is a base (reverse reaction). Note that an Arrhenius base was a substance that released the OH^-, whereas according to Brønsted, the OH^- is a base. The conjugate acid–base pairs are H_2O/OH^- and NH_4^+/NH_3:

$$NH_3(aq) + H_2O(\ell) \rightleftharpoons OH^-(aq) + NH_4^+(aq)$$

base acid base acid

conjugate pair

conjugate pair

▶ **LEARNING CHECK 9.1** Identify all Brønsted acids, bases, and acid–base conjugate pairs in the reactions represented by the following equations:

a. $HC_2H_3O_2(aq) + H_2O(\ell) \rightleftharpoons H_3O^+(aq) + C_2H_3O_2^-(aq)$

b. $NO_2^-(aq) + H_2O(\ell) \rightleftharpoons HNO_2(aq) + OH^-(aq)$

c. $HS^-(aq) + H_2O(\ell) \rightleftharpoons H_3O^+(aq) + S^{2-}(aq)$

9.3 Naming Acids

Learning Objective

3. Name common acids.

In Section 4.4, the rules for naming binary ionic compounds were given. The rules for naming binary covalent compounds and ionic compounds that contain polyatomic ions were discussed in Section 4.10. We now conclude our discussion of inorganic nomenclature by giving the rules used to name hydrogen-containing compounds that behave as acids. Examples of the two types of compounds that behave as acids were given in Section 9.2. Acids of the first type, represented by HCl, are compounds in which hydrogen is covalently bonded to a nonmetal. In acids of the second type, hydrogen is covalently bonded to a polyatomic ion. An example of the second type is HNO_3.

You probably recognized that HCl is a binary covalent compound that can be named by the rules given earlier in Section 4.10. According to those rules, HCl should be named hydrogen chloride. In fact, that is the correct name for the compound HCl that has not been dissolved in water and is represented in reaction equations by the notation HCl(g). Such compounds that have not been dissolved in water are said to be anhydrous (without water). However, when the gas is dissolved in water and represented in equations by the notation HCl(aq), it behaves as an acid and is given another name. The following rules are used to name acidic water solutions of such compounds:

1. The word *hydrogen* in the anhydrous compound name is dropped.
2. The prefix *hydro-* is attached to the stem of the name of the nonmetal that is combined with hydrogen.
3. The suffix *-ide* on the stem of the name of the nonmetal that is combined with hydrogen is replaced with the suffix *-ic*.
4. The word *acid* is added to the end of the name as a separate word.

▶ Example 9.2

Determine the name that would be given to each of the following binary covalent compounds in the anhydrous form and in the form of water solutions:

a. HCl (stomach acid)
b. H_2S (a gas produced when some sulfur-containing foods such as eggs decay)

Solution

a. The name of the anhydrous compound was given above as hydrogen chloride. The name of the water solution is obtained by dropping *hydrogen* from the anhydrous compound name and adding the prefix *hydro-* to the stem *chlor.* The *-ide* suffix on the *chlor* stem is replaced by the suffix *-ic* to give the name *hydrochloric.* The word *acid* is added, giving the final name *hydrochloric acid* for the water solution.
b. According to the rules of Section 4.10, the anhydrous compound name is hydrogen sulfide. The first two steps in obtaining the name of the water solution are to drop *hydrogen* and to add the prefix *hydro-* to the stem *sulf.* However, in acids involving sulfur as the nonmetal combined with hydrogen, the stem *sulf* is replaced by the entire name *sulfur* for pronunciation reasons. The next steps involve dropping the suffix *-ide,* adding the suffix *-ic,* and adding the word *acid.* The resulting name of the water solution is *hydrosulfuric acid.*

▶ LEARNING CHECK 9.2 Determine the name that would be given to each of the following binary covalent compounds in the anhydrous form and in the form of water solutions:

a. HI
b. HBr

Acids of the second type, in which hydrogen is covalently bonded to a polyatomic ion, have the same name in the anhydrous form and in the form of water solutions. The names for these acids are based on the name of the polyatomic ion to which the hydrogen is bonded. The rules are as follows:

1. All hydrogens that are written as the first part of the formula of the acid are removed. The hydrogens are removed in the form of H^+ ions.
2. The polyatomic ion that remains after the H^+ ions are removed is named by referring to sources such as Table 4.7.
3. When the remaining polyatomic ion has a name ending in the suffix *-ate,* the suffix is replaced by the suffix *-ic,* and the word *acid* is added.
4. When the remaining polyatomic ion has a name ending in the suffix *-ite,* the suffix is replaced by the suffix *-ous,* and the word *acid* is added.
5. If the polyatomic ion contains sulfur or phosphorus, the stems *-sulf* or *-phosph* that remain in Steps 3 or 4, when the suffixes *-ate* or *-ite* are replaced, are expanded for pronunciation reasons to *-sulfur* and *-phosphor* before the *-ic* or *-ous* suffixes are added.

▶ Example 9.3

Compounds derived from the acid H_3PO_4 serve numerous important functions in the body, including the control of acidity in urine and body cells and the storage of energy in the form of ATP. Name this important acid.

Solution

The removal of the three H^+ ions leaves behind the PO_4^{3-} polyatomic ion. This ion is named the phosphate ion in Table 4.7. According to Rules 1–4, the -*ate* suffix is replaced by the -*ic* suffix to give the name *phosphic acid*. However, Rule 5 must be used for this phosphorus-containing acid. The stem is expanded to *phosphor* to give the final name, *phosphoric acid*.

▶ **LEARNING CHECK 9.3** The acid H_2CO_3 is involved in many processes in the body, including the removal of CO_2 gas produced by cellular metabolism and the control of the acidity of various body fluids. Name this important acid.

9.4 The Self-Ionization of Water

Learning Objective

4. Do calculations using the concept of the self-ionization of water.

In Examples 9.1a and b, water behaved as a Brønsted base. In Example 9.1c, it was a Brønsted acid. But what happens when only pure water is present? The answer is that water behaves as both an acid and a base and undergoes a self- or auto-ionization. The equation representing this self-ionization is

$$H_2O(\ell) + H_2O(\ell) \rightleftarrows H_3O^+(aq) + OH^-(aq) \tag{9.6}$$

or

The transfer of a proton from one water molecule (the acid) to another (the base) causes one H_3O^+ and one OH^- to form. Therefore, in pure water the concentrations of H_3O^+ and OH^- must be equal. At 25°C these concentrations are 10^{-7} mol/L (M). Thus, the equilibrium position is far to the left, as indicated by the arrows in Equation 9.6. Unless noted otherwise, all concentrations and related terms in this chapter are given at 25°C.

The term **neutral** is used to describe any water solution in which the concentrations of H_3O^+ and OH^- are equal. Thus, pure water is neutral because each liter of pure water contains 10^{-7} mol H_3O^+ and 10^{-7} mol OH^-, at equilibrium. Although all water solutions are not necessarily neutral, it is true that in any solution that contains water, the product of the molar concentrations of H_3O^+ and OH^- is a constant. This becomes apparent by writing the equilibrium expression for Reaction 9.6:

neutral A term used to describe any water solution in which the concentrations of H_3O^+ and OH^- are equal. Also, a water solution with pH = 7.

$$K = \frac{[H_3O^+][OH^-]}{[H_2O][H_2O]} = \frac{[H_3O^+][OH^-]}{[H_2O]^2} \tag{9.7}$$

This expression contains the square of the concentration of water in the denominator. However, only a tiny amount of water actually reacts to form H_3O^+ and OH^- (10^{-7} mol/L), so the concentration of water remains essentially constant. Rearrangement of Equation 9.7 gives

$$K[H_2O]^2 = [H_3O^+][OH^-] \tag{9.8}$$

This equation may be written as

$$K[H_2O]^2 = K_w = [H_3O^+][OH^-] \tag{9.9}$$

ion product of water The equilibrium constant for the dissociation of pure water into H_3O^+ and OH^-.

acidic solution A solution in which the concentration of H_3O^+ is greater than the concentration of OH^-. Also, a solution in which pH is less than 7.

basic or alkaline solution A solution in which the concentration of OH^- is greater than the concentration of H_3O^+. Also, a solution in which pH is greater than 7.

where K_w is a new constant called the **ion product of water.** It is a constant because it is equal to the product of two constants, K and $[H_2O]^2$. At 25°C, K_w can be evaluated from the measured values of $[H_3O^+]$ and $[OH^-]$ in pure water.

$$K_w = [H_3O^+][OH^-] = (1.0 \times 10^{-7}\,\text{mol/L})(1.0 \times 10^{-7}\,\text{mol/L})$$
$$= 1.0 \times 10^{-14}\,(\text{mol/L})^2 \tag{9.10}$$

Equation 9.10 is valid not only for pure water but for any solution in which water is the solvent. Notice that we are including units for equilibrium constants in this discussion. This makes the calculation of concentrations easier to follow and understand.

A solution is classified as **acidic** when the concentration of H_3O^+ is greater than the concentration of OH^-. In a **basic** or **alkaline solution,** the concentration of OH^- is greater than that of H_3O^+. However, the product of the molar concentrations of H_3O^+ and OH^- will be $1.0 \times 10^{-14}\,(\text{mol/L})^2$ in either case. Many acidic and basic materials are found in the home (see ▶ Figure 9.1).

Figure 9.1 Acidic and basic materials are common in the home. Look at the photos, and note a single category to which most of the acidic materials belong, and one to which most of the basic materials belong.

Acidic materials found in the home.

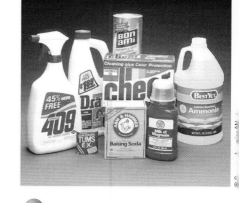
2 Basic or alkaline materials found in the home.

▶ Example 9.4

Classify each of the following solutions as acidic, basic, or neutral. Calculate the molar concentration of the ion whose concentration is not given.

a. $[H_3O^+] = 1.0 \times 10^{-4}$ mol/L
b. $[OH^-] = 1.0 \times 10^{-9}$ mol/L
c. $[OH^-] = 1.0 \times 10^{-6}$ mol/L

Solution

a. Because $[H_3O^+] = 1.0 \times 10^{-4}$ mol/L, a rearrangement of Equation 9.10 gives

$$[OH^-] = \frac{1.0 \times 10^{-14}\,(\text{mol/L})^2}{[H_3O^+]} = \frac{1.0 \times 10^{-14}\,(\text{mol/L})^2}{1.0 \times 10^{-4}\,\text{mol/L}}$$

$$= 1.0 \times 10.0^{-10}\,\text{mol/L}$$

Thus,

$$[H_3O^+] = 1.0 \times 10^{-4}\,\text{mol/L} \quad \text{and}$$

$$[OH^-] = 1.0 \times 10^{-10}\,\text{mol/L}$$

The solution is acidic because the $[H_3O^+]$ is greater than the $[OH^-]$; 1.0×10^{-4} is greater than 1.0×10^{-10}.

b. Similarly, $[OH^-] = 1.0 \times 10^{-9}$ mol/L; therefore,

$$[H_3O^+] = \frac{1.0 \times 10^{-14}\,(mol/L)^2}{[OH^-]} = \frac{1.0 \times 10^{-14}\,(mol/L)^2}{1.0 \times 10^{-9}\,mol/L}$$

$$= 1.0 \times 10.0^{-5}\,mol/L$$

This solution is also acidic because 1.0×10^{-5} is greater than 1.0×10^{-9}.

c. $[OH^-] = 1.0 \times 10^{-6}$ mol/L; therefore,

$$[H_3O^+] = \frac{1.0 \times 10^{-14}\,(mol/L)^2}{[OH^-]} = \frac{1.0 \times 10^{-14}\,(mol/L)^2}{1.0 \times 10^{-6}\,mol/L}$$

$$= 1.0 \times 10.0^{-8}\,mol/L$$

This solution is basic because the OH^- concentration (1.0×10^{-6} mol/L) is greater than the H_3O^+ concentration (1.0×10^{-8} mol/L).

▶ **LEARNING CHECK 9.4** Classify each of the following solutions as acidic, basic, or neutral. Calculate the molarity of the ion whose concentration is not given.

a. $[OH^-] = 1.0 \times 10^{-5}$ mol/L
b. $[H_3O^+] = 1.0 \times 10^{-9}$ mol/L
c. $[H_3O^+] = 1.0 \times 10^{-2}$ mol/L

9.5 The pH Concept

Learning Objective

5. Do calculations using the pH concept.

In Section 9.4, you learned that the concentration of H_3O^+ in pure water is 1.0×10^{-7} M. Chemists, technologists, and other laboratory personnel routinely work with solutions in which the H_3O^+ concentration may be anywhere from 10 to 10^{-14} M. Because of the inconvenience of working with numbers that extend over such a wide range, chemists long ago adopted a shortcut notation known as the pH. Mathematically, the **pH** is defined in terms of the negative logarithm (log) of $[H_3O^+]$ by the following two equations, where we now introduce the common practice of substituting H^+ for H_3O^+ to simplify equations:

pH The negative logarithm of the molar concentration of H^+ (H_3O^+) in a solution.

$$pH = -\log[H^+] \tag{9.11}$$

$$[H^+] = 1 \times 10^{-pH} \tag{9.12}$$

Thus, pH is simply the negative of the exponent used to express the hydrogen-ion concentration in moles per liter.

▶ **Example 9.5**

Express the following concentrations in terms of pH:

a. $[H^+] = 1 \times 10^{-5}$ mol/L
b. $[OH^-] = 1 \times 10^{-9}$ mol/L
c. $[H^+] = 1 \times 10^{-7}$ mol/L
d. $[H^+] = 1 \times 10^{-11}$ mol/L

Solution

a. pH is the negative of the exponent used to express $[H^+]$. Therefore, pH $= -(-5) = 5.0$
b. Here $[OH^-]$ is given, and $[H^+]$ must be calculated. We remember Equation 9.10 and get

$$[H^+] = \frac{1.0 \times 10^{-14} \, (mol/L)^2}{[OH^-]} = \frac{1.0 \times 10^{-14} \, (mol/L)^2}{1 \times 10^{-9} \, mol/L} = 1 \times 10^{-5} \, mol/L$$

Therefore, pH $= -(-5) = 5.0$
c. This pH $= -(-7) = 7.0$. $[H^+] = 1 \times 10^{-7}$ mol/L and corresponds to pure water and neutral solutions. Thus, a pH of 7 represents neutrality.
d. pH $= -(-11) = 11.0$

▶ **LEARNING CHECK 9.5** Express the following concentrations in terms of pH.

a. $[H^+] = 1 \times 10^{-14}$ mol/L
b. $[OH^-] = 1.0$ mol/L
c. $[OH^-] = 1 \times 10^{-8}$ mol/L

The pH value of 5.0 obtained in Example 9.5a corresponds to a solution in which the H^+ concentration is greater than the OH^- concentration. Thus, the solution is acidic. Any solution with a pH less than 7 is classified as acidic. Any solution with a pH greater than 7 is classified as basic or alkaline. The pH values of some familiar solutions are given in ▶ Table 9.1.

TABLE 9.1 Relationships Between $[H^+]$, $[OH^-]$, and pH

	$[H^+]$	$[OH^-]$	pH	Examples (solids are dissolved in water)
	10^{0}	10^{-14}	0	HCl (1 mol/L)
	10^{-1}	10^{-13}	1	Gastric juice
	10^{-2}	10^{-12}	2	Lemon juice
	10^{-3}	10^{-11}	3	Vinegar, carbonated drink Aspirin
	10^{-4}	10^{-10}	4	Orange juice Apple juice
	10^{-5}	10^{-9}	5	Black coffee
	10^{-6}	10^{-8}	6	Normal urine (average value) Milk, liquid dishwashing detergent
Neutral	10^{-7}	10^{-7}	7	Saliva, pure water Blood
	10^{-8}	10^{-6}	8	Soap (not synthetic detergent) Baking soda Phosphate-containing detergent
	10^{-9}	10^{-5}	9	Milk of magnesia Powdered household cleanser
	10^{-10}	10^{-4}	10	Phosphate-free detergent
	10^{-11}	10^{-3}	11	Household ammonia Liquid household cleaner
	10^{-12}	10^{-2}	12	
	10^{-13}	10^{-1}	13	NaOH (0.1 mol/L)
	10^{-14}	10^{0}	14	NaOH (1 mol/L)

▶ Example 9.6

Determine the H^+ and OH^- molar concentrations that correspond to the following pH values:

a. pH = 9.0
b. pH = 3.0
c. pH = 11.0

Solution

In each case, the relationships $[H^+] = 1 \times 10^{-pH}$ and $K_w = [H^+][OH^-] = 1.0 \times 10^{-14}$ $(mol/L)^2$ can be used. Note that we have substituted $[H^+]$ for $[H_3O^+]$ in Equation 9.10.

a. Because pH = 9.0, $[H^+] = 1 \times 10^{-pH} = 1 \times 10^{-9}$ mol/L

$$[OH^-] = \frac{K_w}{[H^+]} = \frac{1.0 \times 10^{-14}\,(mol/L)^2}{1 \times 10^{-9}\,mol/L} = 1 \times 10^{-5}\,mol/L$$

b. Because pH = 3.0, $[H^+] = 1 \times 10^{-pH} = 1 \times 10^{-3}$ mol/L

$$[OH^-] = \frac{K_w}{[H^+]} = \frac{1.0 \times 10^{-14}\,(mol/L)^2}{1 \times 10^{-3}\,mol/L} = 1 \times 10^{-11}\,mol/L$$

c. Because pH = 11.0, $[H^+] = 1 \times 10^{-pH} = 1 \times 10^{-11}$ mol/L

$$[OH^-] = \frac{K_w}{[H^+]} = \frac{1.0 \times 10^{-14}\,(mol/L)^2}{1 \times 10^{-11}\,mol/L} = 1 \times 10^{-3}\,mol/L$$

▶ **LEARNING CHECK 9.6** Determine the $[H^+]$ and $[OH^-]$ values that correspond to the following pH values:

a. pH = 10.0
b. pH = 4.0
c. pH = 5.0

It is apparent from Table 9.1 that not all solutions have pH values that are neat whole numbers. For example, the pH of vinegar is about 3.3. How do we deal with such numbers? The H^+ concentration of vinegar could be written $1 \times 10^{-3.3}$, but it is not convenient to work with exponents that are not whole numbers. When exact values are not needed, the pH, $[H^+]$, and so on can be expressed as a range. Thus, the H^+ concentration of vinegar is between 1×10^{-3} and 1×10^{-4} mol/L. Similarly, a solution with $[H^+] = 2 \times 10^{-5}$ mol/L has a pH between 4 and 5.

When more exact values are needed, we must work with logarithms. This is most easily done by using a hand calculator. A hydrogen-ion concentration is converted to pH by taking the logarithm and changing its sign. ▶ Table 9.2 gives the steps of a typical calculator procedure (what button is pushed, etc.) and a typical calculator readout or display for the conversion of $[H^+] = 3.6 \times 10^{-4}$ mol/L into pH. The pH from Table 9.2 would be recorded as 3.44.

▶ **LEARNING CHECK 9.7** Convert the following $[H^+]$ values into pH:

a. $[H^+] = 4.2 \times 10^{-5}$ mol/L
b. $[H^+] = 8.1 \times 10^{-9}$ mol/L

TABLE 9.2 Calculating pH from Molarity with a Calculator

Step	Calculator Procedure	Calculator Display
1. Enter 3.6	Press buttons 3, ., 6	3.6
2. Enter 10^{-4}	Press button that activates exponential mode (EE, Exp, etc.)	3.6^{00}
	Press 4	3.6^{04}
	Press change-sign button ($\pm$, etc.)	3.6^{-04}
3. Take logarithm	Press log button (log, etc.)	-3.4437
4. Change sign	Press change-sign button ($\pm$, etc.)	3.4437

Calculators can also be used to convert pH values into corresponding molar concentrations. The steps are given in ▶ Table 9.3 for the conversion of a pH value of 5.92 into $[H^+]$. As shown in Table 9.3, a pH of 5.92 corresponds to a $[H^+]$ of 1.2×10^{-6} mol/L. Note that the number of figures to the right of the decimal in a pH value should be the same as the number of significant figures in the $[H^+]$ value. Thus, the two figures to the right of the decimal in pH = 5.92 is reflected in the two significant figures in $[H^+] = 1.2 \times 10^{-6}$ mol/L.

TABLE 9.3 Calculating Molarity from pH with a Calculator

Step	Calculator Procedure	Calculator Display
1. Enter 5.92	Press 5, ., 9, 2	5.92
2. Change sign	Press change-sign button ($\pm$, etc.)	-5.92
3. Take antilog	Press antilog or 10^x button, or (more commonly) press inv. or 2^{nd} function button and then log button	.0000012 or 1.2^{-06}

▶ **LEARNING CHECK 9.8** Convert the following pH values into molar concentrations of H^+:

a. pH = 2.75
b. pH = 8.33

9.6 Properties of Acids

Learning Objective

6. Write reaction equations that illustrate the characteristic reactions of acids.

Acids and bases are used so often in most laboratories that stock solutions are kept readily available at each work space. The common solutions, their concentrations, and label designations are given in ▶ Table 9.4.

▶ Example 9.7

Describe how you would make 250 mL of 1 M HNO_3 by using a dilute HNO_3 stock solution.

Solution

According to Table 9.4, the dilute HNO_3 stock solution is 6 M. The volume of 6 M HNO_3 needed to make 250 mL of 1 M HNO_3 is obtained by using Equation 7.9. It must be remembered that this equation is useful only for dilution problems such as this one. The equation is not useful for calculations involving the volume of one solution that will react with a specific volume of a second solution (Sections 9.10 and 9.11).

$$C_c V_c = C_d V_d$$

$$(6 \text{ M}) V_c = (1 \text{ M})(250 \text{ mL})$$

$$V_c = \frac{(1 \text{ M})(250 \text{ mL})}{6 \text{ M}} = 41.7 \text{ mL}$$

Because the molarity is given using only one significant figure, the solution can be made without too much attention to volumetric flasks and the like. Thus, 42 mL of 6 M HNO_3 is measured with a graduated cylinder, and this is added to 208 mL of distilled water that has also been measured with a graduated cylinder.

▶ **LEARNING CHECK 9.9** Describe how you would prepare 500 mL of 3.0 M aqueous ammonia using a concentrated NH_3 stock solution (Table 9.4).

TABLE 9.4 Common Laboratory Acids and Bases

Name	Formula	Label Concentration	Molarity
Acids			
Acetic acid	$HC_2H_3O_2$	Glacial	18
Acetic acid	$HC_2H_3O_2$	Dilute	6
Hydrochloric acid	HCl	Concentrated	12
Hydrochloric acid	HCl	Dilute	6
Nitric acid	HNO_3	Concentrated	16
Nitric acid	HNO_3	Dilute	6
Sulfuric acid	H_2SO_4	Concentrated	18
Sulfuric acid	H_2SO_4	Dilute	3
Bases			
Aqueous ammonia[a]	NH_3	Concentrated	15
Aqueous ammonia	NH_3	None usually given	6
Sodium hydroxide	NaOH	None usually given	6

[a]Often erroneously called ammonium hydroxide and given the formula NH_4OH.

Different acids have different properties that make some more practical than others for specific uses. However, all acids have certain properties in common. Two of these were mentioned earlier—all acids taste sour and produce H_3O^+ ions when dissolved in water. In addition, all acids undergo characteristic double-replacement reactions with solid oxides, hydroxides, carbonates, and bicarbonates (see ▶ Figure 9.2).

Figure 9.2 The reaction of hydrochloric acid with three natural forms of CaCo₃. Left to right: limestone, marble, and eggshell.

$$2HCl(aq) + CuO(s) \rightarrow CuCl_2(aq) + H_2O(\ell) \qquad (9.13)$$
$$\text{copper}$$
$$\text{oxide}$$

$$2HCl(aq) + Ca(OH)_2(s) \rightarrow CaCl_2(aq) + 2H_2O(\ell) \qquad (9.14)$$
$$\text{calcium}$$
$$\text{hydroxide}$$

$$2HCl(aq) + CaCO_3(s) \rightarrow CaCl_2(aq) + CO_2(g) + H_2O(\ell) \qquad (9.15)$$
$$\text{calcium}$$
$$\text{carbonate}$$

$$2HCl(aq) + Sr(HCO_3)_2(s) \rightarrow SrCl_2(aq) + 2CO_2(g) + 2H_2O(\ell) \qquad (9.16)$$
$$\text{strontrium}$$
$$\text{bicarbonate}$$

Notice that the preceding reactions are written using molecular equations (Section 5.7).

Reactions involving ionic substances can also be written as total ionic equations or net ionic equations. Equation 9.13 is written in total ionic form in Equation 9.17.

$$\underbrace{2H^+(aq) + 2Cl^-(aq)}_{2HCl} + CuO(s) \longrightarrow \underbrace{Cu^{2+}(aq) + 2Cl^-(aq)}_{CuCl_2} + H_2O(\ell) \qquad (9.17)$$

We see that the chloride ions are spectator ions, so a net ionic equation can be written as shown in Equation 9.18.

$$2H^+(aq) + CuO(s) \rightarrow Cu^{2+}(aq) + H_2O(\ell) \qquad (9.18)$$

The general nature of the reaction is emphasized in the net ionic form because the H⁺ could come from any acid.

Remember that correctly written molecular equations must have their atoms balanced (Section 5.1). Total ionic and net ionic equations must also have their atoms balanced, but in addition the total charges on each side of the equation must balance. In Equation 9.18, for example, the two H⁺ ions provide two positive charges on the left, which are balanced by the two positive charges of Cu²⁺ on the right.

▶ Example 9.8

Write Equations 9.14 and 9.15 in total ionic and net ionic forms.

Solution

In Equation 9.14, HCl and $CaCl_2$ are soluble and ionizable.

Total ionic: $2H^+(aq) + 2Cl^-(aq) + Ca(OH)_2(s) \rightarrow Ca^{2+}(aq) + 2Cl^-(aq) + 2H_2O(\ell)$

The Cl^- is a spectator ion.

$\qquad$ Net ionic: $2H^+(aq) + Ca(OH)_2(s) \rightarrow Ca^{2+}(aq) + 2H_2O(\ell)$

In Equation 9.15, HCl and $CaCl_2$ are soluble and ionizable.

Total ionic: $2H^+(aq) + 2Cl^-(aq) + CaCO_3(s) \rightarrow Ca^{2+}(aq) + 2Cl^-(aq) + CO_2(g) + H_2O(\ell)$

Again, Cl^- is a spectator ion.

$\qquad$ Net ionic: $2H^+(aq) + CaCO_3(s) \rightarrow Ca^{2+}(aq) + CO_2(g) + H_2O(\ell)$

▶ **LEARNING CHECK 9.10** Write Equation 9.16 in total and net ionic forms. Consider HCl and $SrCl_2$ as soluble and ionizable.

Another property of acids is their ability to react with (and dissolve) certain metals to yield hydrogen gas. This is a redox reaction (Section 5.3), as evidenced by the change in oxidation number of hydrogen as the reaction takes place. In compounds such as acids, hydrogen has an oxidation number of $+1$. In hydrogen gas, the oxidation number is 0 (Section 5.3). Thus, hydrogen is reduced during the reaction, and, as shown by Equations 9.19 and 9.20, the metal is oxidized. The ability to reduce hydrogen ions to hydrogen gas is not the same for all metals. Some are such strong reducing agents that they can react with hydrogen ions of very low concentrations such as that found in water. Others are so weak as reducing agents that they cannot react with H^+ at the high concentration found in concentrated acids. These tendencies are represented by the **activity series** of metals shown in ▶ Table 9.5. The higher a metal is in the series, the more active it is as a reducing agent. Some typical reactions are given in Equations 9.19 and 9.20 (see ▶ Figure 9.3).

activity series A tabular representation of the tendencies of metals to react with H^+.

TABLE 9.5 The Activity Series of the Metals

Metal	Symbol	Comments
Potassium	K	React violently with cold water
Sodium	Na	
Calcium	Ca	Reacts slowly with cold water
Magnesium	Mg	React very slowly with steam, but quite rapidly in higher H^+ concentrations
Aluminum	Al	
Zinc	Zn	
Chromium	Cr	
Iron	Fe	React in moderately high H^+ concentrations
Nickel	Ni	
Tin	Sn	
Lead	Pb	
Copper	Cu	Do not react with H^+
Mercury	Hg	
Silver	Ag	
Platinum	Pt	
Gold	Au	

Figure 9.3 Metals vary in their ability to reduce hydrogen ions (H^+) to hydrogen gas (H_2). This difference is apparent when copper, iron, zinc, and magnesium (left to right) are put into hydrochloric acid solution (HCl) of the same molarity. Are these results consistent with Table 9.5? Explain.

$$\text{Molecular equation: } Zn(s) + 2HCl(aq) \rightarrow ZnCl_2(aq) + H_2(g) \qquad (9.19)$$

$$\text{Net ionic equation: } Zn(s) + 2H^+(aq) \rightarrow Zn^{2+}(aq) + H_2(g)$$

$$\text{Molecular equation: } 2K(s) + 2H_2O(\ell) \rightarrow 2KOH(aq) + H_2(g) \qquad (9.20)$$

$$\text{Net ionic equation: } 2K(s) + 2H_2O(\ell) \rightarrow 2K^+(aq) + 2OH^-(aq) + H_2(g)$$

▶ **LEARNING CHECK 9.11** Write molecular, total ionic, and net ionic equations to represent the following reactions:

a. Calcium (Ca) with cold water (NOTE: $Ca(OH)_2$ is not soluble in water.)
b. Mg with H_2SO_4 (NOTE: $MgSO_4$ is soluble and ionizable in water.)

9.7 Properties of Bases

Learning Objective

7. Write reaction equations that represent neutralization reactions between acids and bases.

neutralization reaction A reaction in which an acid and base react completely, leaving a solution that contains only a salt and water.

Solutions containing bases feel soapy or slippery and change the color of litmus from red to blue. Equation 9.14 illustrates their most characteristic chemical property—they react readily with acids. In most of the earliest acid–base reactions studied, the complete reaction of an acid with a base produced a neutral solution. For this reason, such reactions were often called **neutralization reactions** (see below). It is now known that many "neutralization" reactions do not produce neutral solutions (Section 9.12). However, the name for the reactions is still used. More than 20 billion pounds of sodium hydroxide (NaOH) is produced and used in the United States each year. This useful crystalline solid is quite soluble in water and dissociates to form basic solutions.

$$NaOH(s) + H_2O(\ell) \rightarrow Na^+(aq) + OH^-(aq) \qquad (9.21)$$

The neutralization reaction between NaOH and HCl is

Molecular equation: $HCl(aq) + NaOH(aq) \rightarrow NaCl(aq) + H_2O(\ell)$ (9.22)

Total ionic equation: $H^+(aq) + Cl^-(aq) + Na^+(aq) + OH^-(aq) \rightarrow$ (9.23)
$$Na^+(aq) + Cl^-(aq) + H_2O(\ell)$$

Net ionic equation: $H^+(aq) + OH^-(aq) \rightarrow H_2O(\ell)$ (9.24)

The molecular equation (9.22) illustrates the following statement, which is a common definition of neutralization: During a neutralization reaction, an acid and a base combine to form a salt and water. (More is said about salts in the next section.) The net ionic form of the equation (9.24) emphasizes the general nature of neutralization reactions: H^+ ions (from any source) react with OH^- (from any source) to form water.

Bases also react with fats and oils and convert them into smaller, soluble molecules. For this reason, most household cleaning products contain basic substances. For example, lye (NaOH) is the active ingredient in numerous drain cleaners, and many liquid household cleaners contain ammonia.

▶ **LEARNING CHECK 9.12** Write molecular, total ionic, and net ionic equations to represent neutralization reactions between the following acids and bases:

a. HNO_3 and NaOH
b. H_2SO_4 and KOH

9.8 Salts

Learning Objective

8. Write reaction equations that illustrate various ways to prepare salts, and do calculations using the concept of an equivalent of salt.

At room temperature, **salts** are solid ionic compounds that contain the **cation** (positive ion) of a base and the **anion** (negative ion) of an acid. Thus, ordinary table salt (NaCl) contains Na^+, the cation of NaOH, and Cl^-, the anion of HCl (look again at Equation 9.22). Similarly, $CuSO_4$ is a salt containing the cation of $Cu(OH)_2$ and the anion of H_2SO_4. You must be careful to think of the term *salt* in a general way, and not as representing only table salt (NaCl).

Some acids and bases are not stable enough to be isolated even though their salts are. For example, carbonic acid (H_2CO_3) cannot be isolated in the pure state. When it forms in water, it promptly decomposes:

$$H_2CO_3(aq) \rightleftharpoons H_2O(\ell) + CO_2(g) (9.25)$$

Despite this characteristic, salts of carbonic acid, such as Na_2CO_3 and $NaHCO_3$, are quite stable.

It is not necessary to identify the parent acid and base in order to write correct salt formulas or names. Just remember that the cation of a salt can be any positive ion except H^+, and it will usually be a simple metal ion or NH_4^+. The salt anion can be any negative ion except OH^-. Most of the polyatomic anions you will use were given earlier in Table 4.7. The rules for naming salts were given in Sections 4.4 and 4.10.

As previously observed, salts dissolved in solution are dissociated into ions. The salt can be recovered by evaporating away the water solvent. When this is done carefully, some salts retain specific numbers of water molecules as part of the solid crystalline structure. Such salts are called **hydrates,** and the retained water is called the **water of hydration.** Most hydrates lose all or part of the water of hydration when they are heated to moderate or high temperatures. A number of useful hydrates are given in ▶ Table 9.6.

salt A solid crystalline ionic compound at room temperature that contains the cation of a base and the anion of an acid.

cation A positively charged ion.

anion A negatively charged ion.

hydrate A salt that contains specific numbers of water molecules as part of the solid crystalline structure.

water of hydration Water retained as part of the solid crystalline structure of some salts.

TABLE 9.6 Some Useful and Common Hydrates

Formula	Chemical Name	Common Name	Uses
$CaSO_4 \cdot H_2O$	Calcium sulfate monohydrate	Plaster of Paris	Plaster, casts, molds
$CaSO_4 \cdot 2H_2O$	Calcium sulfate dihydrate	Gypsum	Casts, molds, wallboard
$MgSO_4 \cdot 7H_2O$	Magnesium sulfate heptahydrate	Epsom salts	Cathartic
$Na_2B_4O_7 \cdot 10H_2O$	Sodium tetraborate decahydrate	Borax	Laundry
$Na_2CO_3 \cdot 10H_2O$	Sodium carbonate decahydrate	Washing soda	Water softener
$Na_3PO_4 \cdot 12H_2O$	Sodium phosphate dodecahydrate	Trisodium phosphate (TSP)	Water softener
$Na_2SO_4 \cdot 10H_2O$	Sodium sulfate decahydrate	Glauber's salt	Cathartic
$Na_2S_2O_3 \cdot 5H_2O$	Sodium thiosulfate pentahydrate	Hypo	Film photography

Many salts occur in nature, and some are used as industrial raw materials. Examples are sodium chloride, NaCl (a source of Cl_2 and NaOH); calcium carbonate or limestone, $CaCO_3$ (a source of cement and building stone); and calcium phosphate or rock phosphate, $Ca_3(PO_4)_2$ (a source of fertilizer). In the laboratory, salts can be prepared by reacting a solution of an appropriate acid with a metal, a metal oxide, a metal hydroxide, a metal carbonate, or a metal bicarbonate. These reactions, given earlier as examples of acid properties (Equations 9.19, 9.13, 9.14, 9.15, 9.16), are given below in a general form:

$$\text{acid} + \text{metal} \rightarrow \text{salt} + H_2 \tag{9.26}$$

$$\text{acid} + \text{metal oxide} \rightarrow \text{salt} + H_2O \tag{9.27}$$

$$\text{acid} + \text{metal hydroxide} \rightarrow \text{salt} + H_2O \tag{9.28}$$

$$\text{acid} + \text{metal carbonate} \rightarrow \text{salt} + H_2O + CO_2 \tag{9.29}$$

$$\text{acid} + \text{metal bicarbonate} \rightarrow \text{salt} + H_2O + CO_2 \tag{9.30}$$

▶ Example 9.9

Write equations to represent the preparation of $Mg(NO_3)_2$, using Reactions 9.26 through 9.30. Use molecular equations to emphasize the salt formation.

Solution

In each case, a dilute solution of nitric acid (HNO_3) is reacted with magnesium metal or the appropriate magnesium compound:

$$2HNO_3(aq) + Mg(s) \rightarrow Mg(NO_3)_2(aq) + H_2(g)$$

$$2HNO_3(aq) + MgO(s) \rightarrow Mg(NO_3)_2(aq) + H_2O(\ell)$$

$$2HNO_3(aq) + Mg(OH)_2(s) \rightarrow Mg(NO_3)_2(aq) + 2H_2O(\ell)$$

$$2HNO_3(aq) + MgCO_3(s) \rightarrow Mg(NO_3)_2(aq) + H_2O(\ell) + CO_2(g)$$

$$2HNO_3(aq) + Mg(HCO_3)_2(s) \rightarrow Mg(NO_3)_2(aq) + 2H_2O(\ell) + 2CO_2(g)$$

▶ **LEARNING CHECK 9.13** Write balanced equations to represent the preparation of $AlCl_3$, using Reactions 9.26 through 9.30. Use molecular equations to emphasize the salt formation.

We have expressed the amounts of materials involved in chemical reactions primarily in terms of mass (grams) or number of moles. However, in certain applications, it is important to express the amount of salt in a solution in terms of the amount of electrical charge represented by the ions of the salt. This is especially true in medical applications, where the levels and balance of electrolytes in various body fluids are extremely important.

A unit that expresses the amount of ionic electrical charge for salts is the equivalent. One **equivalent of salt** is the amount that will produce 1 mol of positive (or negative) charges when dissolved and dissociated. To determine the amount of salt that represents 1 equivalent (eq), you must know what ions are produced when the salt dissociates. For example, potassium chloride (KCl), an electrolyte often administered to patients following surgery, dissociates as follows: $KCl(aq) \rightarrow K^+(aq) + Cl^-(aq)$. Thus, 1 mol, or 74.6 g, of solid KCl provides 1 mol of positive charges (1 mol of K^+ ions) when it dissolves and dissociates. Thus, 1 eq of KCl is equal to 1 mol, or 74.6 g, of KCl.

equivalent of salt The amount that will produce 1 mol of positive electrical charge when dissolved and dissociated.

▶ Example 9.10

Determine the number of equivalents and milliequivalents (meq) of salt contained in the following:

a. 0.050 mol KCl
b. 0.050 mol $CaCl_2$

Solution

a. As shown above, 1 mol KCl = 1 eq KCl. Therefore, 0.050 mol KCl = 0.050 eq KCl. Also, because 1 eq = 1000 meq,

$$0.050 \; \text{eq} \times \frac{1000 \; \text{meq}}{1 \; \text{eq}} = 50 \; \text{meq}$$

b. The dissociation reaction is

$$CaCl_2(aq) \rightarrow Ca^{2+}(aq) + 2Cl^-(aq)$$

Thus, we see that 1 mol $CaCl_2$ produces 1 mol Ca^{2+} or 2 mol of positive charges. Thus, 1 mol $CaCl_2$ = 2 eq $CaCl_2$. Therefore,

$$0.050 \; \text{mol} \; CaCl_2 \times \frac{2 \; \text{eq} \; CaCl_2}{1 \; \text{mol} \; CaCl_2} = 0.10 \; \text{eq} \; CaCl_2$$

Also, because 1 eq = 1000 meq,

$$0.10 \; \text{eq} \times \frac{1000 \; \text{meq}}{1 \; \text{eq}} = 1.0 \times 10^2 \; \text{meq}$$

Notice that we could have focused on the negative charges in either part above and still arrived at the same answers. In part a, 0.050 mol KCl produces 0.050 mol Cl^-, or 0.050 mol of negative charge. Similarly, in part b, 0.050 mol $CaCl_2$ produces 2×0.050, or 0.10 mol, Cl^- ions, or 0.10 mol of negative charge. We have arbitrarily chosen to use the positive charges, but either will work. Just remember that you do not count both the negative and positive charges for a salt.

▶ LEARNING CHECK 9.14 Determine the number of equivalents and milliequivalents in each of the following:

a. 0.10 mol NaCl
b. 0.10 mol $Mg(NO_3)_2$

▶ Example 9.11

A sample of blood serum contains 0.139 equivalents of Na^+ ion per liter of serum. Assume the Na^+ comes from dissolved NaCl, and calculate the number of equivalents, number of moles and number of grams of NaCl in 250 mL of the serum.

Solution

The Na^+ ion has a single charge, so we may write the following relationships:

$$1.00 \text{ mol NaCl} = 1.00 \text{ mol } Na^+ = 1.00 \text{ eq. } Na^+ = 1.00 \text{ eq NaCl}$$

These relationships provide numerous factors that can be used in the factor-unit method to solve problems. Two that will be used to solve these problems are:

$$\frac{1.00 \text{ eq NaCl}}{1.00 \text{ eq } Na^+} \quad \text{and} \quad \frac{1.00 \text{ mol NaCl}}{1.00 \text{ eq NaCl}}$$

The known quantity is 250 mL of serum. This is converted into equivalents of Na^+ by using the given concentration of $\dfrac{0.139 \text{ eq } Na^+}{L \text{ serum}}$ as the factor.

$$(0.250 \text{ L serum}) \times \frac{0.139 \text{ eq } Na^+}{1.00 \text{ L serum}} = 0.0347 \text{ eq } Na^+$$

This number of equivalents of Na^+ will now be converted into the quantities asked for by using the two factors given above, and a factor obtained from the formula weight for NaCl of 58.44 u.

$$(0.0347 \text{ eq } Na^+) \times \frac{1.00 \text{ eq NaCl}}{1.00 \text{ eq } Na^+} = 0.0347 \text{ eq NaCl}$$

$$(0.0347 \text{ eq NaCl}) \times \frac{1.00 \text{ mol NaCl}}{1.00 \text{ eq NaCl}} = 0.0347 \text{ mol NaCl}$$

$$(0.0347 \text{ mol NaCl}) \times \frac{58.44 \text{ g NaCl}}{1.00 \text{ mol NaCl}} = 2.03 \text{ g NaCl}$$

▶ **LEARNING CHECK 9.15** A sample of blood serum contains 0.103 equivalents of Cl^- ions per liter. Assume the Cl^- comes from dissolved NaCl and calculate the number of equivalents, number of moles, and number of grams of NaCl in 250 mL of serum.

9.9 The Strengths of Acids and Bases

Learning Objective

9. Demonstrate an understanding of the words *weak* and *strong* as applied to acids and bases.

strong acids and strong bases Acids and bases that dissociate (ionize) completely when dissolved to form a solution.

weak (or moderately weak) acids and bases Acids and bases that dissociate (ionize) less than completely when dissolved to form a solution.

When salts dissolve in water, they generally dissociate completely, but this is not true for all acids and bases. The acids and bases that do dissociate almost completely are classified as **strong acids** and **strong bases** (they are also strong electrolytes). Those that dissociate to a much smaller extent are called **weak** or **moderately weak,** depending on the degree of dissociation (they are also weak or moderately weak electrolytes). Examples of strong and weak acids are given in ▶ Table 9.7.

Carbon Dioxide in the Oceans

Carbon dioxide, CO_2, is generally recognized as an atmospheric greenhouse gas that contributes to global warming. Concerns are now being raised about the potential adverse impact of the dissolved CO_2 on the oceans of the world.

Measurements of CO_2 levels in the atmosphere begun in 1958 coupled with studies of air bubbles trapped in old glacial ice indicate that the concentration of CO_2 in the atmosphere remained essentially constant for several thousand years. However, in about 1800 the concentration began to increase rapidly as a result of the industrial revolution and the accompanying increase in the burning of fossil fuels to provide the energy needed to power machinery.

It is now estimated that about one-third of the CO_2 produced by burning fossil fuels in our highly industrialized, modern world ends up dissolved in the oceans of the world. This might seem to be a positive development because it reduces the amount of CO_2 contributing to global warming, but the results of continuing studies raise questions about the possible negative effects of this dissolved CO_2 on ocean ecosystems.

When CO_2 dissolves in water, it reacts with the water to form carbonic acid (Reaction 1).

$$1. \quad CO_2(g) + H_2O(\ell) \rightleftharpoons H_2CO_3(aq)$$

The carbonic acid dissociates into ions in two steps (Reactions 2 and 3).

$$2. \quad H_2CO_3(aq) \rightleftharpoons H^+(aq) + HCO_3^-(aq)$$

$$3. \quad HCO_3^-(aq) \rightleftharpoons H^+(aq) + CO_3^{2-}(aq)$$

Reaction 3 occurs only to a slight extent. The net effect of these two dissociation reactions is to increase the concentration of H^+ ions and decrease the pH of the oceans from their normal range of 8.0 – 8.3. According to one prediction, the pH range could decrease to 7.6 – 7.9 by the year 2100 if current trends continue.

The increase in H^+ concentration has the potential to be very harmful to some forms of marine life, especially those forms that use carbonate ions, CO_3^{2-}, to build their shells or other hard body parts out of calcium carbonate, $CaCO_3$. At first, this doesn't seem to make sense because, according to Reaction 3, the dissolved CO_2 actually forms CO_3^{2-} ions. However, as mentioned earlier, very little of the dissolved CO_2 actually undergoes Reaction 3. In fact, the extra H^+ ions added to the water from Reaction 2 actually react with CO_3^{2-} ions that are normally found in seawater, and convert them to HCO_3^- ions in a reaction that is the reverse of Reaction 3. This process thus reduces the concentration of CO_3^{2-} ions to levels lower than that normally found in seawater.

Scientists estimate that this mechanism could reduce the concentration of CO_3^{2-} ions in seawater to one-half its current value during the next 100 years if current trends continue. It is feared that such reductions will interfere with the growth and survival of carbonate-using organisms ranging in size from tiny phytoplankton that serve as major food sources for fish and marine mammals, to corals, the animals responsible for building huge coral reefs, the largest biological structures in the world.

Scientific research results such as these give us another reason to pause, seriously consider the negative impact of some of our modern practices on the world around us, and maybe even change some of those practices.

A Coral reef and a close-up of coral.

TABLE 9.7 Some Common Strong and Weak Acids

Name	Formula	% Dissociation[a]	K_a	Classification
Hydrochloric acid	HCl	100	Very large	Strong
Hydrobromic acid	HBr	100	Very large	Strong
Nitric acid	HNO_3	100	Very large	Strong
Sulfuric acid	H_2SO_4	100	Very large	Strong
Phosphoric acid	H_3PO_4	28	7.5×10^{-3}	Moderately weak
Sulfurous acid[b]	H_2SO_3	34	1.5×10^{-2}	Moderately weak
Acetic acid	$HC_2H_3O_2$	1.3	1.8×10^{-5}	Weak
Boric acid	H_3BO_3	0.01	7.3×10^{-10}	Weak
Carbonic acid[b]	H_2CO_3	0.2	4.3×10^{-7}	Weak
Nitrous acid[b]	HNO_2	6.7	4.6×10^{-4}	Weak

[a]Based on dissociation of one proton in 0.1 M solution at 25°C.

[b]Unstable acid.

A 0.10 M solution of hydrochloric acid could be prepared by dissolving 0.10 mol (3.7 g) of HCl gas in enough water to give 1.0 L of solution. According to Table 9.7, 100% of the dissolved gas would dissociate into H^+ and Cl^-. Thus, the concentration of H^+ in a 0.10 M HCl solution is 0.10 mol/L, and the pH is 1.00.

The strength of acids and bases is shown quantitatively by the value of the equilibrium constant for the dissociation reaction in water solutions. Equation 9.31 represents the dissociation of a general acid, HB, in water, where B^- represents the conjugate base of the acid:

$$HB(aq) + H_2O(\ell) \rightleftharpoons H_3O^+(aq) + B^-(aq) \tag{9.31}$$

The equilibrium expression for this reaction is

$$K = \frac{[H_3O^+][B^-]}{[HB][H_2O]} \tag{9.32}$$

In Equation 9.32, the brackets, again, represent molar concentrations of the materials in the solution. Only a tiny amount of the water in the solution actually enters into the reaction, so the concentration of water is considered to be constant (see Section 9.4). We can then write Equation 9.33, where K_a is a new constant called the **acid dissociation constant:**

acid dissociation constant The equilibrium constant for the dissociation of an acid.

$$K[H_2O] = K_a = \frac{[H_3O^+][B^-]}{[HB]} \tag{9.33}$$

In Equation 9.33, $[H_3O^+]$ and $[B^-]$ are, respectively, the equilibrium concentrations of the hydronium ion and the anion conjugate base that is characteristic of the acid. The [HB] represents the concentration of that part of the dissolved acid that remains undissociated in the equilibrium mixture. In solutions of strong acids, $[H_3O^+]$ and $[B^-]$ values are quite large, while [HB] has a value near 0, so K_a is quite large. In weak acids, [HB] has larger values, while $[H_3O^+]$ and $[B^-]$ are smaller, so K_a is smaller. Thus, the larger a K_a value, the stronger the acid it represents. This is illustrated by the K_a values given in Table 9.7. If we simplify by substituting H^+ for H_3O^+, introduced in Section 9.5, we obtain

$$K_a = \frac{[H^+][B^-]}{[HB]} \tag{9.34}$$

It is important to remember that the terms *weak* and *strong* apply to the extent of dissociation and not to the concentration of an acid or base. For example, gastric juice (0.05% HCl) is a dilute (not weak) solution of a strong acid.

▶ Example 9.12

Write dissociation reactions and expressions for K_a for each of the following weak acids:

a. Hydrocyanic acid (HCN)
b. Phosphoric acid (H_3PO_4) (1st H only)
c. Dihydrogen phosphate ion ($H_2PO_4^-$) (1st H only)

Solution

In each case, H^+ has been substituted for H_3O^+.

a. $HCN \leftrightharpoons H^+ + CN^-$; $K_a = \dfrac{[H^+][CN^-]}{[HCN]}$

b. $H_3PO_4 \leftrightharpoons H^+ + H_2PO_4^-$; $K_a = \dfrac{[H^+][H_2PO_4^-]}{[H_3PO_4]}$

c. $H_2PO_4^- \leftrightharpoons H^+ + HPO_4^{2-}$; $K_a = \dfrac{[H^+][HPO_4^{2-}]}{[H_2PO_4^-]}$

▶ **LEARNING CHECK 9.16** Write dissociation reactions and K_a expressions for the following weak acids:

a. Hydrogen phosphate ion (HPO_4^{2-})
b. Nitrous acid (HNO_2)
c. Hydrofluoric acid (HF)

Acid behavior is linked to the loss of protons. Thus, acids must contain hydrogen atoms that can be removed to form H^+. **Monoprotic acids** can lose only one proton per molecule, whereas **diprotic** and **triprotic** acids can lose two and three, respectively. For example, HCl is monoprotic, H_2SO_4 is diprotic, and H_3PO_4 is triprotic. Di- and triprotic acids dissociate in steps, as shown for H_2SO_4 in Equations 9.35 and 9.36:

$$H_2SO_4(aq) \rightleftharpoons H^+(aq) + HSO_4^-(aq) \tag{9.35}$$

$$HSO_4^-(aq) \leftrightharpoons H^+(aq) + SO_4^{2-}(aq) \tag{9.36}$$

The second proton is not as easily removed as the first because it must be pulled away from a negatively charged particle, HSO_4^-. Accordingly, HSO_4^- is a weaker acid than H_2SO_4.

The number of ionizable hydrogens cannot always be determined from the molecular formula for an acid. For example, acetic acid ($HC_2H_3O_2$) is monoprotic even though the molecule contains four hydrogen atoms. The dissociation of acetic acid is represented by Equation 9.37, where structural formulas are used to emphasize the different H atoms in the molecule:

$$
\begin{array}{c}
\quad\; H\quad O \\
\quad\; |\quad\; \| \\
H - C - C - O - H \quad \rightleftharpoons \quad H^+ + H - C - C - O^- \\
\quad\; | \\
\quad\; H
\end{array}
\qquad H^+ + \begin{array}{c} H\quad O \\ |\quad \| \\ H - C - C - O^- \\ | \\ H \end{array} \tag{9.37}
$$

Only the hydrogen bound to the oxygen is ionizable. Those hydrogens bound to C are too tightly held to be removed. ▶ Table 9.8 contains other examples, with the ionizable hydrogens shown in color.

monoprotic acid An acid that gives up only one proton (H^+) per molecule when dissolved.

diprotic acid An acid that gives up two protons (H^+) per molecule when dissolved.

triprotic acid An acid that gives up three protons (H^+) per molecule when dissolved.

TABLE 9.8 Examples of Monoprotic, Diprotic, and Triprotic Acids

Name	Formula	Structural Formula	Classification
Butyric acid	$HC_4H_7O_2$		Monoprotic
Carbonic acid	H_2CO_3		Diprotic
Formic acid	$HCHO_2$		Monoprotic
Nitric acid	HNO_3		Monoprotic
Phosphoric acid	H_3PO_4		Triprotic
Phosphorous acid	H_3PO_3		Diprotic

We have focused our attention on the strength of acids, using the extent of dissociation as a basis. However, all acid dissociations are reversible to some degree, and in the reverse reactions, anions produced by the forward reaction behave as Brønsted bases. What can be said about the strength of these bases? Because Brønsted acid–base behavior is really just competition for protons, we can answer this question by looking again at the simplified form of the equation for dissociation of a general acid:

$$HB(aq) \leftrightarrows H^+(aq) + B^-(aq) \tag{9.38}$$

We see from this equation that the strength of HB as an acid depends on how tightly the conjugate base B^- holds onto the proton. If HB is a strong acid, the conjugate base holds onto the proton only weakly. If HB is a weak acid, the conjugate base holds on more strongly, depending on the strength of HB. Thus, we have answered our earlier question. If HB is a strong acid, the H^+ is held only weakly by the B^-. We can conclude then that B^- is not strongly attracted to protons—it is a weak base. Conversely, if HB is a weak acid, the H^+ is held tightly by the B^-, and we conclude that B^- is more strongly attracted to protons—it is a stronger base than the B^- from a strong acid.

In general, the conjugate base anions produced by the dissociation of strong Brønsted acids are weak Brønsted bases. The conjugate base anions of weak acids are stronger bases, with their strengths dependent on the strength of the parent acid.

As you study this chapter, you will acquire a knowledge of the characteristic reactions of acids and the ability to write balanced equations for the reactions. In the Key Equations section at the end of the chapter, five characteristic reactions are summarized in item 3. One useful way to remember the reactions is to learn them as general word equations, such as

"An acid plus a metal gives a salt plus hydrogen gas"

rather than as specific equations such as $H_2SO_4(aq) + Zn(s) \rightarrow ZnSO_4(aq) + H_2(g)$. If you learn the general word equations and you recognize the starting materials for a reaction (such as an acid and a metal), you will know what the products will be (a salt and H_2 gas).

A second approach is to remember that all five of the general reactions of acids are either single-replacement

$$\text{acid} + \text{metal} \rightarrow \text{salt} + H_2$$

or double-replacement (the remaining four acid reactions in the Key Equations section). The formulas of the products of double-replacement reactions can be predicted by simply breaking each reactant into its positive and negative parts and recombining the parts in the other possible way (the positive part of one reactant with the negative part of the other reactant). For example, let's determine the products and the balanced equation for a reaction between H_2SO_4 and KOH. If you remember that H_2SO_4 is an acid and KOH is a base, the general word equation says the products will be a salt and water:

$$H_2SO_4(aq) + KOH(aq) \rightarrow \text{salt}(aq) + H_2O(\ell)$$

H_2SO_4 breaks apart to give H^+ and SO_4^{2-}; KOH breaks apart to give K^+ and OH^-. If we combine the positive part of the acid (H^+) with the negative part of the base (OH^-), we get the water (H_2O). A similar combination of the positive part

of the base (K^+) with the negative part of the acid (SO_4^{2-}) gives the salt. We must remember that the total charges of the combined parts must add up to 0. Thus, two K^+ will combine with one SO_4^{2-} to give the salt K_2SO_4. The balanced equation is

$$H_2SO_4(aq) + 2KOH(aq) \rightarrow K_2SO_4(aq) + 2H_2O(\ell)$$

As another example, consider a reaction between HBr and KOH. KBr breaks into H^+ and Br^-. KOH breaks into K^+ and OH^-. Now, switch the parts and recombine:

The products are KBr and H_2O, and the balanced equation is

$$HBr(aq) + KOH(aq) \rightarrow KBr(aq) + H_2O(\ell)$$

For a final example, let's try a reaction between HBr and $NaHCO_3$. The word equation predicts that the products should be a salt, water, and carbon dioxide gas. HBr breaks into H^+ and Br^-; $NaHCO_3$ breaks into Na^+ and HCO_3^-. Now, switch the parts and recombine:

The products are NaBr and H_2CO_3. However, H_2CO_3 is not stable; it decomposes to give H_2O and CO_2, the products predicted earlier. The balanced equation is

$$HBr(aq) + NaHCO_3(aq) \rightarrow NaBr(aq) + H_2O(\ell) + CO_2(g)$$

Ammonia (NH_3) is the weak base most often encountered in addition to the anions of strong acids. The dissociation reaction of gaseous NH_3 in water, given earlier in Example 9.1, is

$$NH_3(aq) + H_2O(\ell) \rightleftarrows NH_4^+(aq) + OH^-(aq) \tag{9.39}$$

The most common strong bases are the hydroxides of group IA(1) metals (NaOH, KOH, etc.) and the hydroxides of group IIA(2) metals ($Mg(OH)_2$, $Ca(OH)_2$, etc.).

▶ Example 9.13

Classify each of the following pairs by identifying the stronger of the pair according to the indicated behavior. Information from Tables 9.7 and 9.8 may be used.

a. H_3PO_4 and $H_2PO_4^-$ (acid)
b. $H_2PO_4^-$ and HPO_4^{2-} (base)
c. HNO_3 and HNO_2 (acid)

Do You Have Acid Reflux Disease?

The medical name for acid reflux disease is *gastroesophageal reflux disease,* which is often abbreviated and referred to as GERD. The disease is often mistaken for occasional heartburn and treated with over-the-counter remedies. GERD is the result of a malfunctioning muscle (the lower esophageal sphincter [LES] muscle) located at the bottom of the esophagus, just above the stomach. When operating normally, this muscle relaxes and opens to allow food to pass from the esophagus down into the stomach, then contracts to close the opening and prevent the acidic contents of the stomach from backing up into the esophagus.

When the muscle relaxes at inappropriate times, the acidic stomach contents get into the esophagus and cause the burning chest pain called heartburn. However, when this occurs repeatedly and frequently, the acidic stomach contents can also erode the lining of the esophagus. GERD is a complex condition with many degrees of severity, ranging from only frequent heartburn symptoms to erosive esophagitis, in which the esophagus can suffer different degrees of damage. In extreme cases of erosive esophagitis, ulcers develop in the esophagus and lead to esophageal bleeding that, if persistent and undetected, can lead to iron deficiency and anemia as well as extreme pain and weight loss. In some cases, severe GERD can lead to other serious medical conditions that require hospitalization and even surgery to correct.

Doctors often recommend lifestyle and dietary changes for most GERD patients, including the avoidance of foods and beverages that weaken the LES muscle. These foods include chocolate, peppermint, fatty foods, coffee, and alcoholic beverages. The use of foods and beverages that can irritate a damaged esophageal lining, such as acidic fruits and juices, pepper, and tomato products is also discouraged. GERD symptoms in overweight individuals often diminish when some weight is lost. Smokers who quit also generally gain some relief. Prescription medications that reduce the amount of acid in the stomach are also available. Two types of medication are available. Both types, called H2 blockers and proton (acid) pump inhibitors, decrease the amount of acid secreted into the stomach, but by different mechanisms.

The main symptom that may indicate the presence of GERD is frequent, persistent heartburn that occurs two or more times a week. Other symptoms include difficulty in swallowing and frequent belching and regurgitation. Less common symptoms that occur in some people resemble respiratory conditions and include a persistent sore throat, wheezing, chronic coughing, and hoarseness. Individuals who suspect they might be suffering from some degree of GERD should consult a physician to determine the extent of the disease and proper treatment.

GERD has many degrees of severity.

Solution

a. H_3PO_4 is stronger as an acid. In di- and triprotic acids, each proton in the removal sequence is harder to remove, so the corresponding acid is weaker.

b. The stronger acid produces the weaker anion base. Thus, $H_2PO_4^-$, the anion of the stronger acid H_3PO_4, would be a weaker base than HPO_4^{2-}, the anion of the weaker acid $H_2PO_4^-$. So HPO_4^{2-} is a stronger base than $H_2PO_4^-$.

c. HNO_3 is the stronger acid according to Table 9.7. Generally, when related acids (same atoms, etc.) are compared for strength, the one containing more oxygen atoms will be the stronger.

▶ LEARNING CHECK 9.17 Classify each of the following according to strength for the indicated behavior. If more than two are compared, list them with the strongest at the top and the weakest at the bottom. Use Tables 9.7 and 9.8 as needed.

a. $HClO$, $HClO_3$, $HClO_2$ (acid)
b. NO_2^- and NO_3^- (base)
c. $HC_2H_3O_2$ and $C_2H_3O_2^-$ (acid)

9.10 Analyzing Acids and Bases

Learning Objective

10. Demonstrate an understanding of the titration technique used to analyze acids and bases.

The analysis of solutions for the total amount of acid or base they contain is a regular activity in many laboratories. The total amount of acid in a solution is indicated by its capacity to neutralize a base. The pH is related to the acidity or concentration of H^+ in solution, while the capacity to neutralize a base depends on the total amount of H^+ available. For example, a 0.10 M acetic acid solution has an H^+ concentration of about 1.3×10^{-3} M (pH = 2.89). However, 1 L of the solution can neutralize 0.10 mol of OH^-, not just 1.3×10^{-3} mol. The reason is that the dissociation equilibrium of acetic acid is

$$HC_2H_3O_2(aq) \rightleftharpoons H^+(aq) + C_2H_3O_2^-(aq) \qquad (9.40)$$

As OH^- is added, H^+ reacts to form water (see Equation 9.24). The removal of H^+ causes the equilibrium of Reaction 9.40 to shift right in accordance with Le Châtelier's principle. The continued addition of OH^- and removal of H^+ will eventually cause all of the acetic acid molecules to dissociate and react.

A common procedure often used to analyze acids and bases is called **titration** (◗ Figure 9.4). Suppose the total acidity of an unknown acid solution needs to be determined. A known volume of the acidic solution is first measured out by drawing it up

titration An analytical procedure in which one solution (often a base) of known concentration is slowly added to a measured volume of an unknown solution (often an acid). The volume of the added solution is measured with a buret.

Figure 9.4 Titration.

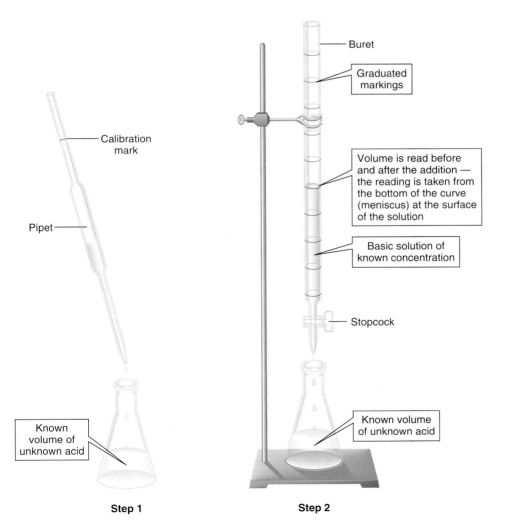

Buret

Graduated markings

Volume is read before and after the addition — the reading is taken from the bottom of the curve (meniscus) at the surface of the solution

Basic solution of known concentration

Stopcock

Calibration mark

Pipet

Known volume of unknown acid

Known volume of unknown acid

Step 1 **Step 2**

to the calibration mark of a pipet. This solution is placed in a container (Step 1). A basic solution of known concentration (a standard solution) is added to the acid solution in the container until the **equivalence point** is reached. This is the point where the unknown acid is completely reacted with base. The volume of base needed to reach the equivalence point is obtained from the buret readings.

To successfully complete a titration, the point at which the reaction is completed must somehow be detected. One way to do this is to add an indicator to the solution being titrated. An indicator is an organic compound that changes to different colors depending on the pH of its surroundings. An indicator is selected that will change color at a pH as close as possible to the pH the solution will have at the equivalence point. If the acid and base are both strong, the pH at that point will be 7. However, for reasons discussed later, the pH is not always 7 at the equivalence point. The point at which the indicator changes color and the titration is stopped is called the titration **endpoint.** ❱ Figure 9.5 gives the colors shown by a number of indicators at various pH values.

Figure 9.5 Indicators change color with changes in pH (the numbers across the bottom). Methyl red (top row) goes from red at low pH to yellow at higher pH. Bromthymol blue (middle row) goes from yellow to blue, and phenolphthalein (bottom row) goes from colorless to red. Which of the three indicators would be the best to use to differentiate between the solutions with pH values of 4 and 6?

Indicator papers (litmus paper, pH paper, etc.) are often used to make routine pH measurements. These papers are impregnated with one or more indicators that change to a variety of colors depending on the pH. However, indicators may not be practical under certain conditions. For example, there might not be any indicator that changes color close enough to the equivalence point, or the solution being titrated might be so highly colored that an indicator color change cannot be detected. Under such circumstances, a pH meter can be used. The electrodes of the meter are placed in the solution being titrated, and the pH is read directly (see ❱ Figure 9.6). The titration is continued until the meter reading matches the pH of the equivalence point.

© Spencer L. Seager

 At the beginning, the pH meter gives the pH of the acid solution being titrated.

 Partway through the titration, the pH meter reading is of a solution of un-reacted acid and the salt produced by the reaction.

 At the end of the titration, the pH meter gives the pH of the salt solution formed by the complete reaction of acid with base.

Figure 9.6 An acid–base titration using a pH meter to detect the equivalence point.

9.11 Titration Calculations

Learning Objective

11. Do calculations related to the analysis of acids and bases by titration.

Equations 9.41 and 9.42 represent the reactions that occur when solutions of nitric and sulfuric acid are titrated with sodium hydroxide:

$$HNO_3(aq) + NaOH(aq) \rightarrow H_2O(\ell) + NaNO_3(aq) \qquad (9.41)$$

$$H_2SO_4(aq) + 2NaOH(aq) \rightarrow 2H_2O(\ell) + Na_2SO_4(aq) \qquad (9.42)$$

One mole of HNO_3 requires 1 mol of NaOH for a complete reaction, but 1 mol of H_2SO_4 requires 2 mol of NaOH. Because these are solution reactions, stoichiometric calculations can be done using the methods described in Section 7.6.

▶ Example 9.14

Calculate the molarity of the HNO_3 and H_2SO_4 solutions involved in the following titrations:

a. A 25.0-mL sample of an HNO_3 solution requires the addition of 16.3 mL of 0.200 M NaOH to reach the equivalence point.

b. A 25.0-mL sample of an H_2SO_4 solution requires the addition of 32.6 mL of 0.200 M NaOH to reach the equivalence point.

Solution

In each case we know the volume of acid solution reacted. If we also knew the number of moles of acid in the volume of reacted solution, we could calculate the solution molarity by using Equation 7.5:

$$M = \frac{\text{moles of solute}}{\text{liters of solution}}$$

Therefore, our task will be to calculate the number of moles of acid reacted in each case. The methods described in Section 7.6 will be used. We will begin with the volume of NaOH solution used in each titration, and convert that volume to moles of acid using the factor-unit method.

a. Nitric acid

　Step 1. 0.0163 L NaOH solution

　Step 2. 0.0163 L NaOH solution 　　　　　　　　　　　　　　　$= \text{mol } HNO_3$

Step 3. $0.0163 \text{ L NaOH solution} \times \dfrac{0.200 \text{ mol NaOH}}{1 \text{ L NaOH solution}} \times \dfrac{1 \text{ mol HNO}_3}{1 \text{ mol NaOH}}$

$$= \text{mol HNO}_3$$

The factor $\dfrac{0.200 \text{ mol NaOH}}{1 \text{ L NaOH solution}}$ came from the molarity of the NaOH solution, and the factor $\dfrac{1 \text{ mol HNO}_3}{1 \text{ mol NaOH}}$ came from the 1 to 1 reaction ratio of HNO_3 with NaOH.

Step 4. $0.0163 \times \dfrac{0.200}{1} \times \dfrac{1 \text{ mol HNO}_3}{1} = 0.00326 \text{ mol HNO}_3$

This result tells us that the 25.0 mL titrated sample of HNO_3 contained 0.00326 moles of HNO_3. After converting the HNO_3 volume to liters, the molarity can be calculated:

$$M = \frac{\text{moles of HNO}_3}{\text{liters of HNO}_3 \text{ solution}} = \frac{0.00326 \text{ mol HNO}_3}{0.0250 \text{ L HNO}_3 \text{ solution}} = \frac{0.130 \text{ mol HNO}_3}{\text{L HNO}_3 \text{ solution}}$$

$$= 0.130 \text{ M HNO}_3$$

b. Sulfuric acid

This calculation follows the same pattern as the HNO_3 calculation, except for the fact that the reaction ratio of NaOH and H_2SO_4 is 2 mol of NaOH reacts with 1 mol of H_2SO_4. This gives a factor of $\dfrac{1 \text{ mol H}_2\text{SO}_4}{2 \text{ mol NaOH}}$ that will be used in step 3.

Step 1. $0.0326 \text{ L NaOH solution}$

Step 2. $0.0326 \text{ L NaOH solution}$ $= \text{mol H}_2\text{SO}_4$

Step 3. $0.0326 \text{ L NaOH solution} \times \dfrac{0.200 \text{ mol NaOH}}{1 \text{ L NaOH solution}} \times \dfrac{1 \text{ mol H}_2\text{SO}_4}{2 \text{ mol NaOH}}$

$$= \text{mol H}_2\text{SO}_4$$

Step 4. $0.0326 \times \dfrac{0.200}{1} \times \dfrac{1 \text{ mol H}_2\text{SO}_4}{2} = 0.00326 \text{ mol H}_2\text{SO}_4$

The molarity of the solution is calculated as before:

$$M = \frac{\text{moles of H}_2\text{SO}_4}{\text{liters of H}_2\text{SO}_4 \text{ solution}} = \frac{0.0326 \text{ mol H}_2\text{SO}_4}{0.0250 \text{ L H}_2\text{SO}_4 \text{ solution}} = \frac{0.130 \text{ mol H}_2\text{SO}_4}{\text{L H}_2\text{SO}_4 \text{ solution}}$$

$$= 0.130 \text{ M H}_2\text{SO}_4$$

Thus, we see that the two acid solutions have the same molar concentrations. Why did the second require twice the volume of NaOH solution for the titration?

▶ **LEARNING CHECK 9.18** Calculate the molarity of a solution of phosphoric acid (H_3PO_4) if a 25.0-mL sample of acid solution requires 14.1 mL of a 0.250 M NaOH solution to titrate to the equivalence point. The equation for the reaction is

$$H_3PO_4(aq) + 3NaOH(aq) \rightarrow 3H_2O(aq) + Na_3PO_4(aq)$$

9.12 Hydrolysis Reactions of Salts

Learning Objective

12. Explain the concept of salt hydrolysis, and write equations to illustrate the concept.

hydrolysis reaction Any reaction with water. For salts it is a reaction of the acidic cation and/or basic anion of the salt with water.

In general, a **hydrolysis reaction** is a reaction with water. Many types of hydrolysis reactions are known, but at this point we will discuss only one, the hydrolysis of salts. In Section 9.10, we said that the pH at the equivalence point is not 7 for all acid–base

titrations. However, we pointed out earlier that the only products of acid–base reactions are water and a salt. Therefore, it seems reasonable to conclude that some salts and water must interact (a hydrolysis reaction) and cause the solution pH to differ from that of pure water.

Suppose three solutions are prepared by dissolving equal molar amounts of sodium acetate, ammonium chloride, and sodium chloride in identical volumes of pure water. Measurement of pH shows that the sodium acetate solution is alkaline (pH higher than 7), the ammonium chloride solution is acidic (pH lower than 7), and the sodium chloride solution is neutral (pH = 7). The alkaline sodium acetate solution must contain more OH^- than H^+ ions. However, the only source of both ions in a solution of salt and water is the dissociation of water, so both should be present in equal amounts. The equation for the water dissociation is

$$H_2O(\ell) \rightleftharpoons H^+(aq) + OH^-(aq) \qquad (9.43)$$

The OH^- excess would result if something removed H^+ from this equilibrium, causing it to shift right and produce more OH^-. This is exactly what happens. The acetate anion is the conjugate base of a weak acid (acetic acid), and it is a strong enough Brønsted base to react with the H^+ ions of the above equilibrium:

$$C_2H_3O_2^-(aq) + H^+(aq) \rightarrow HC_2H_3O_2(aq) \qquad (9.44)$$

The overall result of this reaction can be seen by adding Equations 9.43 and 9.44:

$$H_2O(\ell) + C_2H_3O_2^-(aq) + H^+(aq) \rightarrow H^+(aq) + OH^-(aq) + HC_2H_3O_2(aq) \qquad (9.45)$$

Net reaction: $H_2O(\ell) + C_2H_3O_2^-(aq) \rightleftharpoons OH^-(aq) + HC_2H_3O_2^-(aq) \qquad (9.46)$

Now it can be seen that the excess OH^- comes from a reaction between the acetate ion and water. But what about the Na^+ ion that is also in the solution? Does it react with water? The Na^+ cation is the conjugate acid of the strong base NaOH. As a result, Na^+ is an extremely weak Brønsted acid and makes no contribution to the pH of the solution.

In general, salts influence the pH of water solutions as follows: (1) Salts containing an anion of a weak acid and a cation of a strong base will form alkaline water solutions. (2) Salts containing an anion of a strong acid and a cation of a weak base will form acidic solutions. (3) Salts containing an anion and a cation from equal-strength acids and bases (both weak or both strong) will form neutral solutions (see ❿ Figure 9.7).

Water
(H₂O)

Sodium Acetate
(CH₃COONa)

© Jeffrey M. Seager

Figure 9.7 Samples of pure water (left) and sodium acetate dissolved in water (right) behave differently when phenolphthalein indicator is added. The acetate ion hydrolyzes in water to form a basic solution that turns phenolphthalein to a pink color. Why didn't the Na^+ ion from the sodium acetate hydrolyze?

The acidic ammonium chloride solution is an example of the second category of salts, where the NH_4^+ cation is the conjugate acid of the weak base NH_3, and the Cl^- anion is the conjugate base of the strong acid HCl. The hydrolysis reaction is given in Equation 9.47, where H_3O^+ is used to emphasize the reaction with water:

$$NH_4^+(aq) + H_2O(\ell) \rightleftharpoons H_3O^+(aq) + NH_3(aq) \qquad (9.47)$$

The neutral sodium chloride solution is an example of the third category. Both NaOH and HCl are strong, and an NaCl solution is neutral.

▶ **LEARNING CHECK 9.19** Predict the relative pH value (higher than 7, lower than 7, etc.) for water solutions of the following salts. Table 9.7 may be useful.

a. Sodium nitrate ($NaNO_3$)
b. Sodium nitrite ($NaNO_2$)
c. Potassium borate (K_3BO_3)

9.13 Buffers

Learning Objective

13. Explain how buffers work, and write equations to illustrate their action.

buffer A solution with the ability to resist changing pH when acids (H^+) or bases (OH^-) are added.

Buffers are solutions that have the ability to resist changes in pH when acids or bases are added (see ▶ Figure 9.8). Most buffers consist of a pair of compounds, one with the ability to react with H^+ and the other with the ability to react with OH^-. An example is a mixture of acetic acid and its salt, sodium acetate. The acetate ion from sodium acetate is the conjugate base of acetic acid and reacts with any added acid (H^+ ions):

$$C_2H_3O_2^-(aq) + H^+(aq) \rightleftarrows HC_2H_3O_2(aq) \tag{9.48}$$

Any added base (OH^- ions) reacts with nonionized acetic acid molecules:

buffer capacity The amount of acid (H^+) or base (OH^-) that can be absorbed by a buffer without causing a significant change in pH.

$$HC_2H_3O_2(aq) + OH^-(aq) \rightleftarrows C_2H_3O_2^-(aq) + H_2O(\ell) \tag{9.49}$$

In this way, the buffer solution resists changes in pH. The amount of H^+ or OH^- that a buffer system can absorb without allowing significant pH changes to occur is called its **buffer capacity.**

① The solution on the left is not buffered; the one on the right is; universal indicator has been added to each solution.

② Sodium hydroxide has been added to each solution.

③ Hydrochloric acid has been added to two fresh samples that originally looked like the first pair of samples.

Figure 9.8 Buffered solutions resist changing pH when bases and acids are added. What observation of this experiment indicates that the pH of the buffered solutions did not change significantly when base or acid was added?

Buffered solutions are found extensively in the body, where they serve to protect us from the disastrous effects of large deviations in pH. An important buffer system in blood is composed of carbonic acid (H_2CO_3) and bicarbonate salts such as $NaHCO_3$. The unstable carbonic acid results when dissolved CO_2 reacts with water in the blood:

$$H_2O(\ell) + CO_2(aq) \rightleftharpoons H_2CO_3(aq) \tag{9.50}$$

Added H^+ is neutralized by reacting with HCO_3^- from the dissolved bicarbonate salts:

$$HCO_3^-(aq) + H^+(aq) \rightleftarrows H_2CO_3(aq) \tag{9.51}$$

The carbonic acid protects against added OH^-:

$$H_2CO_3(aq) + OH^-(aq) \rightleftharpoons HCO_3^-(aq) + H_2O(\ell) \qquad (9.52)$$

If large amounts of H^+ or OH^- are added to a buffer, the buffer capacity can be exceeded, the buffer system is overwhelmed, and the pH changes. For example, if large amounts of H^+ were added to the bicarbonate ion–carbonic acid buffer, Reaction 9.51 would take place until the HCO_3^- was depleted. The pH would then drop as additional H^+ ions were added. In blood, the concentration of HCO_3^- is ten times the concentration of H_2CO_3. Thus, this buffer has a greater capacity against added acid than against bases. This is consistent with the normal functions of the body that cause larger amounts of acidic than basic substances to enter the blood.

The pH of buffers can be calculated by using a form of Equation 9.34 that was given earlier and is repeated here:

$$K_a = \frac{[H^+][B^-]}{[HB]}$$

This equation can be rearranged to give

$$[H^+] = K_a \frac{[HB]}{[B^-]} \qquad (9.53)$$

Application of the logarithm concept to Equation 9.53 gives

$$pH = pK_a + \log \frac{[B^-]}{[HB]} \qquad (9.54)$$

In this equation, $pH = -\log[H^+]$ (Equation 9.11), and **pKa** $= -\log K_a$. Equation 9.54 is known as the **Henderson–Hasselbalch equation**; it is often used by biologists, biochemists, and others who frequently work with buffers. We see from Equation 9.54 that when the concentrations of a weak acid and its conjugate base (anion) are equal in a solution, the pH of the solution is equal to pK_a. When it is desired to produce a buffer with a pH different from the exact pK_a, Equation 9.54 indicates it can be done. An acid with a pK_a near the desired pH is selected, and the ratio of the concentrations of conjugate base (anion of the acid) and acid is adjusted to give the desired pH. When a weak acid and its salt (the source of the acid's conjugate base anion) are mixed in solution, you can generally assume that the amount of acid that dissociates is small and may be neglected. This means that the buffer concentrations of the acid and anion (the salt of acid) are "equal" to the made-up concentrations. ▶ Table 9.9 lists some weak acids, together with values of K_a and pK_a.

pKa The negative logarithm of K_a.

Henderson–Hasselbalch equation
A relationship between the pH of a buffer, pK_a, and the concentrations of acid and salt in the buffer.

▶ Example 9.15

a. Calculate the pH of a buffer solution that contains 0.10 mol acetic acid (CH_3COOH) and 0.10 mol sodium acetate (CH_3COONa) per liter.

b. What is the pH of a buffer in which the concentration of NaH_2PO_4 is 0.10 M and that of Na_2HPO_4 is 0.50 M?

c. A buffer system consisting of the ions $H_2PO_4^-$ and HPO_4^{2-} helps control the pH of urine. What value of the ratio $[HPO_4^{2-}]/[H_2PO_4^-]$ would be required to maintain a pH of 6.00, the average value for normal urine?

Solution

a. The acetic acid concentration is 0.10 M and that of its conjugate base, the acetate ion from the sodium acetate salt, is also 0.10 M. The pK_a for acetic acid is 4.74:

$$pH = pK_a + \log \frac{[CH_3COO^-]}{[CH_3COOH]} = 4.74 + \log\left(\frac{0.10 \text{ mol/L}}{0.10 \text{ mol/L}}\right)$$

$$= 4.74 + \log(1) = 4.74 + 0 = 4.74$$

TABLE 9.9 K_a and pK_a Values for Selected Weak Acids

Name	Formula	K_a	pK_a
Acetic acid[a]	CH_3COOH	1.8×10^{-5}	4.74
Ammonium ion	NH_4^+	5.6×10^{-10}	9.25
Boric acid	H_3BO_3	7.3×10^{-10}	9.14
Dihydrogen borate ion	$H_2BO_3^-$	1.8×10^{-13}	12.75
Hydrogen borate ion	HBO_3^{2-}	1.6×10^{-14}	13.80
Carbonic acid	H_2CO_3	4.3×10^{-7}	6.37
Bicarbonate ion	HCO_3^-	5.6×10^{-11}	10.25
Citric acid[a]	$C_3H_4(OH)(COOH)_3$	8.4×10^{-4}	3.08
Dihydrogen citrate ion[a]	$C_3H_4(OH)(COOH)_2COO^-$	1.8×10^{-5}	4.74
Hydrogen citrate ion[a]	$C_3H_4(OH)(COOH)(COO)_2^{2-}$	4.0×10^{-6}	5.40
Formic acid[a]	$HCOOH$	1.8×10^{-4}	3.74
Lactic acid[a]	$C_2H_4(OH)COOH$	1.4×10^{-4}	3.85
Nitrous acid	HNO_2	4.6×10^{-4}	3.33
Phosphoric acid	H_3PO_4	7.5×10^{-3}	2.12
Dihydrogen phosphate ion	$H_2PO_4^-$	6.2×10^{-8}	7.21
Hydrogen phosphate ion	HPO_4^{2-}	2.2×10^{-13}	12.66
Sulfurous acid	H_2SO_3	1.5×10^{-2}	1.82
Bisulfite ion	HSO_3^-	1.0×10^{-7}	7.00

[a]The hydrogen that ionizes in organic acids and ions is a part of a carboxylic acid group, represented by COOH.

We see that, as mentioned earlier, when the acid and conjugate base concentrations are equal, pH = pK_a.

b. In this case, both compounds are salts that produce the $H_2PO_4^-$ and HPO_4^{2-} ions. In such situations, the ion with more hydrogens will be the acid, and the one with fewer will be the anion or conjugate base. Therefore, the acid is $H_2PO_4^-$ at a concentration of 0.10 M, and the conjugate base or anion is HPO_4^{2-} at a concentration of 0.50 M. The pK_a for $H_2PO_4^-$ is 7.21:

$$pH = pK_a + \log \frac{[HPO_4^{2-}]}{[H_2PO_4^-]} = 7.21 + \log\left(\frac{0.50 \text{ mol/L}}{0.10 \text{ mol/L}}\right)$$

$$= 7.21 + \log(5.00) = 7.21 + 0.70 = 7.91$$

c. As in part (b), the acid is $H_2PO_4^-$ and the conjugate base is HPO_4^{2-}. The desired pH is 6.00. Substitution into Equation 9.54 gives

$$pH = pK_a + \log \frac{[HPO_4^{2-}]}{[H_2PO_4^-]}$$

$$6.00 = 7.21 + \log \frac{[HPO_4^{2-}]}{[H_2PO_4^-]}$$

$$6.00 - 7.21 = \log \frac{[HPO_4^{2-}]}{[H_2PO_4^-]}$$

$$-1.21 = \log \frac{[HPO_4^{2-}]}{[H_2PO_4^-]}$$

DR. MELINA JAMPOLIS

© Michael Roud Photography

Dr. Melina Jampolis is a San Francisco, California, physician nutrition specialist—a specialty practiced by only about 200 physicians in the United States. She focuses exclusively on nutrition for weight loss and disease prevention and treatment.

Ask an Expert 9.1

Q: Does diet play a role in peptic ulcer disease?

A: Peptic ulcer disease (PUD), which includes ulcer formation in the stomach or the duodenum (the first portion of the small intestine), affects a significant portion of the U.S. population and is the leading reason for gastrointestinal surgery. Since PUD affects your digestive tract, it makes sense that what you eat on a daily basis should impact the development of ulcer disease. However, direct associations between what many people believe to be ulcer-causing components of the diet and the development of PUD are surprisingly limited and inconsistent. Large observational studies have not established a direct link between the intake of alcohol, caffeine, or spicy foods and ulcer formation. This is true despite the fact that alcohol and caffeine are known to stimulate gastric acid secretion, which in turn makes ulcer symptoms worse and interferes with ulcer healing. Research over the past few decades has found that 80–90% of peptic ulcers are actually caused by a bacterium called *Helicobacter pylori* (*H. pylori*). So while diet might play a role, particularly in terms of ulcer healing, *H. pylori* infection is the primary cause of PUD.

Milk, which many people still mistakenly believe protects against or even helps to treat PUD, might actually increase its severity by causing an increase in acid secretion and masking ulcer symptoms. Masked symptoms allow the disease to progress without treatment. On the other hand, fermented milk products, including yogurt and cheese, have been associated with a reduction in PUD, possibly due to their antimicrobial properties. Research shows that probiotic strains, including *Lactobacillus* and *Bifidobacterium bifidum*, inhibit the growth of the *H. pylori*. These probiotic strains have also been shown to improve the effectiveness of treatment for *H. pylori* infection.

In the past, fiber consumption was discouraged for patients with PUD. Current research suggests that soluble fiber might actually play a protective role. In a large prospective study, those with the highest intakes of soluble fiber, particularly fiber from legumes, including beans, tofu, peanut butter, and nuts, had a 50% lower incidence of duodenal ulcer compared to those consuming the least amount of soluble fiber. Vegetable fiber and vitamin A intake also appear to exert a protective effect. Conversely, higher intakes of refined grains (which are lower in fiber) and refined sugar have been associated with a higher risk of duodenal ulcer disease.

Polyphenols, plant-based nutrients that play a role in decreasing the risk of numerous diseases, also appear to play an important role in ulcer prevention. Animal studies have shown that several different polyphenols help prevent PUD by increasing the formation of gut-protecting mucus; decreasing acid secretion; inhibiting the growth of *H. pylori*; and

Peptic Ulcer Disease

Fermented dairy products are good for PUD

Ginger is good for PUD

Fennel is good for PUD

Milk may increase the severity of PUD

Patients with PUD should avoid refined sugars

A
© Veronika Burmeister/Visuals Unlimited/Corbis

B
© tacar/Shutterstock.com

C
© Reika/Shutterstock.com

D
© Franco Deriu/Shutterstock. com

E
© Jiri Hera /Shutterstock.com

F
© Olga Danylenko /Shutterstock.com

acting as powerful antioxidants, which help protect the lining of the gut. Promising research in rats has shown a potential beneficial effect of numerous polyphenol-rich plant compounds, including ginger, fennel, and olive leaf extract.

Smoking has been strongly associated with the incidence of PUD through numerous mechanisms. On the other hand, physical activity has been shown to decrease the risk of duodenal ulcer. So, the adoption of a healthy lifestyle, including a diet containing a variety of fruits and vegetables, plenty of soluble fiber, and fermented dairy products with limited added sugar; not smoking; and exercising regularly can play a significant role in the prevention of ulcer disease.

At this point, we know the value of the log of the desired ratio. To get the ratio, we must evaluate the antilog of -1.21. Use Step 3 given in Table 9.3 to get 0.062 as the value of the ratio. This result says the ratio $[HPO_4^{2-}]/[H_2PO_4^-]$ must be 0.062. In other words, the HPO_4^{2-} concentration must be only about 0.06 times the value of the $H_2PO_4^-$ concentration. Any concentrations giving this ratio would be satisfactory. For example, if $[H_2PO_4^-] = 0.50$ M, then $[HPO_4^{2-}]$ would have to equal 0.062×0.5 M, or 0.031 M.

▶ LEARNING CHECK 9.20

a. What is the pH of a buffer solution in which formic acid (HCOOH) and sodium formate (HCOONa) are both at a concentration of 0.22 M?

b. What is the pH of a buffer solution that is 0.25 M in sulfurous acid (H_2SO_3) and 0.10 M in sodium bisulfite ($NaHSO_3$)?

c. A buffer system in the blood consists of the bicarbonate ion, HCO_3^-, and carbonic acid, H_2CO_3. What value of the ratio $[HCO_3^-]/[H_2CO_3]$ would be required to maintain blood at the average normal pH of 7.40?

Case Study Follow-up

Over-the-counter medications should be taken as directed. Some antacids contain large amounts of sodium, which might be problematic for someone on a sodium-restricted diet, and calcium-containing antacids might exacerbate existing kidney problems. Antacids should only be used for occasional relief. If a person is taking antacids on a daily basis for extended periods of time, a different medication, such as a proton-pump inhibitor, should be considered. Frequent long-lasting heartburn may indicate gastroesophageal reflux disease (GERD) (Mayo Clinic 2011).

Symptoms of heartburn include a burning sensation in the chest area occurring after a meal or while lying down, or a sour taste in the mouth from stomach acid. Heart attack symptoms might be mistaken for heartburn. However, if chest pain occurs during exercise; is accompanied by shortness of breath, nausea, or dizziness; and is radiating to the arm, neck, shoulder, or jaw, heart attack is a possibility—and emergency help should be sought immediately (Mayo Clinic, 2011).

Heartburn may be initiated or made worse by certain foods. Someone suffering from heartburn should avoid fatty foods, tomato sauce, chocolate, caffeine, and spicy foods. Other factors that aggravate heartburn are excess body weight, tight clothing, and lying down too soon after a meal. Maintaining a healthy weight and eating frequent small meals instead of infrequent large meals, especially before bedtime, will help control heartburn.

Concept Summary

The Arrhenius Theory

Svante Arrhenius defined acids as substances that dissociate in water to provide hydrogen ions (H^+), and bases as substances that dissociate in water to provide hydroxide ions, (OH^-).

Objective 1, **Exercise 9.2**

The Brønsted Theory

Johannes Brønsted and Thomas Lowry proposed a theory in which acids are defined as any hydrogen-containing substances capable of donating protons to other substances. Bases are substances that accept and form covalent bonds with protons. When a substance behaves as a Brønsted acid by donating a proton, the substance becomes a conjugate base.

Objective 2, **Exercises 9.6 and 9.10**

Naming Acids

Two types of acids are named differently. Water solutions of binary covalent compounds containing hydrogen and a nonmetal are named following the pattern hydro(stem)ic acid, where (stem) is the stem of the name of the nonmetal bonded to hydrogen. Acids in which hydrogen is bonded to polyatomic ions have names based on the name of the polyatomic ion to which hydrogen is bonded.

Objective 3, **Exercise 9.22**

The Self-Ionization of Water

Water, a hydrogen-containing material, is able to behave as both a Brønsted acid and a Brønsted base. In pure water, a small number of water molecules (10^{-7} mol/L) donate protons to other water molecules.

Objective 4, **Exercises 9.28a & b and 9.30a & b**

The pH Concept

The pH is the negative logarithm of the molar H^+ concentration of a solution. Solutions with pH values lower than 7 are acidic, those with pH values higher than 7 are basic or alkaline, and those with a pH value of 7 are neutral.

Objective 5, **Exercises 9.36 and 9.40**

Properties of Acids

All acids have certain characteristic properties that include (1) a sour taste; (2) a reaction with water to produce H_3O^+; (3) reactions with solid metallic oxides, hydroxides, carbonates, and bicarbonates; and (4) a reaction with certain metals to give hydrogen gas.

Objective 6, **Exercise 9.50**

Properties of Bases

Basic solutions feel soapy or slippery and change the color of litmus from red to blue. Their most characteristic chemical property is a neutralization reaction with acids to produce water and a salt.

Objective 7, **Exercise 9.60**

Salts

At room temperature, salts are solid crystalline substances that contain the cation of a base and the anion of an acid. Hydrated salts contain specific numbers of water molecules as a part of their crystalline structures. Salts can be prepared by reacting an appropriate acid with one of a number of other materials.

Objective 8, **Exercises 9.68 and 9.74**

The Strengths of Acids and Bases

Acids and bases that dissociate completely when dissolved in solution are called strong, and those that do not are called weak or moderately weak, depending on the degree of dissociation they undergo. Acid strength is indicated by the value of K_a, the acid dissociation constant. In general, polyprotic acids become weaker as an acid during each successive dissociation reaction. The Brønsted base produced by the dissociation of an acid has a strength opposite that of the acid. The acid strengths of cations produced by the dissociation of bases follow a similar pattern.

Objective 9, **Exercise 9.86**

Analyzing Acids and Bases

The neutralization reaction of acids and bases is used in a process called titration to analyze acids and bases. During a typical titration, a base solution of known concentration is added slowly to an acid solution of unknown concentration. The titration is stopped at the endpoint when a color change occurs in an indicator. The volumes of acid and base required are used to calculate the acid concentration.

Objective 10, **Exercise 9.92**

Titration Calculations

Titrations are used to determine the total amount of acid or base in solutions. Data collected from titrations are treated like other stoichiometric data in calculations.

Objective 11, **Exercises 9.98 and 9.100a**

Hydrolysis Reactions of Salts

The cation and anion of a salt may have the same or different Brønsted acid and base strengths. When they are the same, solutions of the salt have a pH of 7. When they are different, salt solutions have H^+ and OH^- concentrations that are unequal and pH values different than 7. The reactions of salt ions with water that cause these results are called hydrolysis reactions.

Objective 12, Exercise 9.108

Buffers

Solutions with the ability to maintain essentially constant pH values when acid (H^+) or base (OH^-) are added are called buffers. All buffers have a limit to the amount of acid or base they can absorb without changing pH. This limit is called the buffer capacity.

Objective 13, Exercise 9.116

Key Terms and Concepts

Acid dissociation constant (9.9)
Acidic solution (9.4)
Activity series (9.6)
Anion (9.8)
Arrhenius acid (9.1)
Arrhenius base (9.1)
Basic or alkaline solution (9.4)
Brønsted acid (9.2)
Brønsted base (9.2)
Buffer (9.13)
Buffer capacity (9.13)
Cation (9.8)

Conjugate acid–base pair (9.2)
Conjugate base (9.2)
Diprotic acid (9.9)
Endpoint of a titration (9.10)
Equivalence point of a titration (9.10)
Equivalent of salt (9.8)
Henderson–Hasselbalch equation (9.13)
Hydrate (9.8)
Hydrolysis reaction (9.12)
Ion product of water (9.4)
Monoprotic acid (9.9)
Neutral (9.4)

Neutralization reaction (9.7)
pH (9.5)
pK_a (9.13)
Salt (9.8)
Strong acids and strong bases (9.9)
Titration (9.10)
Triprotic acid (9.9)
Water of hydration (9.8)
Weak (or moderately weak) acids and bases (9.9)

Key Equations

1.	Relationship between [H^+] and [OH^-] in water solutions (Section 9.4):	$K_w = [H_3O^+][OH^-] = 1.0 \times 10^{-14}\ (\text{mol/L})^2$	Equation 9.10
2.	Relationships between pH and [H^+] (Section 9.5):	$pH = -\log[H^+]$ $[H^+] = 1 \times 10^{-pH}$	Equation 9.11 Equation 9.12
3.	General reactions of acids (Section 9.8):	acid + metal → salt + H_2 acid + metal oxide → salt + H_2O acid + metal hydroxide → salt + H_2O acid + metal carbonate → salt + H_2O + CO_2 acid + metal bicarbonate → salt + H_2O + CO_2	Equation 9.26 Equation 9.27 Equation 9.28 Equation 9.29 Equation 9.30
4.	Dissociation constant for acids (Section 9.9):	$K_a = \dfrac{[H^+][B^-]}{[HB]}$	Equation 9.34
5.	Calculation of buffer pH, Henderson–Hasselbalch equation (Section 9.13):	$pH = pK_a + \log\dfrac{[B^-]}{[HB]}$	Equation 9.54

Exercises

Even-numbered exercises are answered in Appendix B.

Blue-numbered exercises are more challenging.

The Arrhenius Theory (Section 9.1)

9.1 Write the dissociation equations for the following that emphasize their behavior as Arrhenius acids:

 a. HI

 b. HBrO

 c. HCN

 d. $HClO_2$

9.2 Write the dissociation equations for the following that emphasize their behavior as Arrhenius acids:

 a. $HBrO_2$

 b. HS^-

 c. HBr

 d. $HC_2H_3O_2$ (only the 1st listed H dissociates)

9.3 Each of the following produces a basic solution when dissolved in water. Identify those that behave as Arrhenius bases and write dissociation equations to illustrate that behavior.

 a. CsOH

 b. CH_3NH_2

 c. NH_3

 d. $Ca(OH)_2$

9.4 Each of the following produces a basic solution when dissolved in water. Identify those that behave as Arrhenius bases and write dissociation equations to illustrate that behavior.

 a. LiOH

 b. $C_2H_5NH_2$

 c. $Sr(OH)_2$

 d. $NaNH_2$

The Brønsted Theory (Section 9.2)

9.5 Identify each Brønsted acid and base in the following equations. Note that the reactions are assumed to be reversible.

 a. $HBr(aq) + H_2O(\ell) \rightleftarrows H_3O^+(aq) + Br^-(aq)$

 b. $H_2O(\ell) + N_3^-(aq) \rightleftarrows HN_3(aq) + OH^-(aq)$

 c. $H_2S(aq) + H_2O(\ell) \rightleftarrows H_3O^+(aq) + HS^-(aq)$

 d. $SO_3^{2-}(aq) + H_2O(\ell) \rightleftarrows HSO_3^-(aq) + OH^-(aq)$

 e. $HCN(aq) + H_2O(\ell) \rightleftarrows H_3O^+(aq) + CN^-(aq)$

9.6 Identify each Brønsted acid and base in the following equations. Note that the reactions are assumed to be reversible.

 a. $HC_2O_4^-(aq) + H_2O(\ell) \rightleftarrows H_3O^+(aq) + C_2O_4^{2-}(aq)$

 b. $HNO_2(aq) + H_2O(\ell) \rightleftarrows H_3O^+(aq) + NO_2^-(aq)$

 c. $PO_4^{3-}(aq) + H_2O(\ell) \rightleftarrows HPO_4^{2-}(aq) + OH^-(aq)$

 d. $H_2SO_3(aq) + H_2O(\ell) \rightleftarrows HSO_3^-(aq) + H_3O^+(\ell)$

 e. $F^-(aq) + H_2O(\ell) \rightleftarrows HF(aq) + OH^-(aq)$

9.7 Identify each conjugate acid–base pair in the equations of Exercise 9.5.

9.8 Identify each conjugate acid–base pair in the equations of Exercise 9.6.

9.9 Write equations to represent the Brønsted acid behavior for each of the following acids in water solution. Remember to represent the reactions as being reversible.

 a. HI

 b. HBrO

 c. HCN

 d. HSe^-

9.10 Write equations to represent the Brønsted acid behavior for each of the following acids in water solution. Remember to represent the reactions as being reversible.

 a. HF

 b. $HClO_3$

 c. HClO

 d. HS^-

9.11 Write a formula for the conjugate base formed when each of the following behaves as a Brønsted acid:

 a. HSO_3^-

 b. HPO_4^{2-}

 c. $HClO_3$

 d. $CH_3NH_3^+$

 e. $H_2C_2O_4$

9.12 Write a formula for the conjugate base formed when each of the following behaves as a Brønsted acid:

 a. HSO_4^-

 b. $CH_3NH_3^+$

 c. $HClO_4$

 d. NH_4^+

 e. HCl

9.13 Write a formula for the conjugate acid formed when each of the following behaves as a Brønsted base:

 a. NH_2^-

 b. CO_3^{2-}

 c. OH^-

 d. $(CH_3)_2NH$

 e. NO_2^-

9.14 Write a formula for the conjugate acid formed when each of the following behaves as a Brønsted base:

 a. HCO_3^-

 b. S^{2-}

 c. HS^-

 d. $HC_2O_4^-$

 e. $HN_2O_2^-$

9.15 The following reactions illustrate Brønsted acid–base behavior. Complete each equation.

 a. $HI(aq) + ? \rightarrow H_3O^+(aq) + I^-(aq)$

 b. $NH_3(\ell) + ? \rightarrow NH_4^+ + NH_2^-$

 c. $H_2C_2O_4(aq) + H_2O(\ell) \rightarrow ? + HC_2O_4^-(aq)$

 d. $H_2N_2O_2(aq) + H_2O(\ell) \rightarrow H_3O^+(aq) + ?$

 e. $? + H_2O(\ell) \rightarrow H_3O^+(aq) + CO_3^{2-}(aq)$

9.16 The following reactions illustrate Brønsted acid–base behavior. Complete each equation.

 a. $H_2AsO_4^-(aq) + ? \rightarrow NH_4^+(aq) + HAsO_4^{2-}(aq)$

 b. $C_6H_5NH_2(aq) + ? \rightarrow C_6H_5NH_3^+(aq) + OH^-(aq)$

 c. $S^{2-}(aq) + H_2O(\ell) \rightarrow ? + OH^-(aq)$

 d. $(CH_3)_2NH(aq) + ? \rightarrow (CH_3)_2NH_2^+(aq) + Br^-(aq)$

 e. $H_2PO_4^-(aq) + CH_3NH_2(aq) \rightarrow HPO_4^{2-}(aq) + ?$

9.17 Write equations to illustrate the acid–base reaction when each of the following pairs of Brønsted acids and bases are combined:

	Acid	*Base*
a.	$HOCl$	H_2O
b.	$HClO_4$	NH_3
c.	H_2O	NH_2^-
d.	H_2O	OCl^-
e.	$HC_2O_4^-$	H_2O

9.18 Write equations to illustrate the acid–base reaction of each of the following pairs of Brønsted acids and bases:

	Acid	*Base*
a.	HS^-	NH_3
b.	H_2O	ClO_3^-
c.	H_2O	NH_2^-
d.	HBO_3^{2-}	H_2O
e.	HNO_2	NH_3

Naming Acids (Section 9.3)

9.19 A water solution of HF gas is used to etch glass. Name the water solution as an acid.

9.20 Hydrogen cyanide, HCN, behaves in a water solution very much like the binary covalent compounds of hydrogen, but it liberates the cyanide ion, CN^-. Name the acidic water solution by following the rules for binary covalent compounds of hydrogen.

9.21 Name the following acids. Refer to Table 4.7 as needed.

 a. $H_2Se(aq)$

 b. $HClO_3$

 c. H_2SO_4

 d. HNO_3

9.22 Name the following acids. Refer to Table 4.7 as needed.

 a. $H_2Te(aq)$

 b. $HClO$

 c. H_2SO_3

 d. HNO_2

9.23 The acid $H_3C_6H_5O_7$ forms the citrate ion, $C_6H_5O_7^{3-}$, when all three hydrogens are removed. This acid is involved in an important energy-storing process in the body. Name the acid.

9.24 The acid $H_2C_4H_4O_4$ forms the succinate ion, $C_4H_4O_4^{2-}$, when both hydrogens are removed. This acid is involved in the same energy-storing process as the acid of Exercise 9.23. Name $H_2C_4H_4O_4$ as an acid.

9.25 Refer to Table 4.7, and write the formula for chromic acid.

9.26 Refer to Table 4.7, and write the formula for carbonic acid.

The Self-Ionization of Water (Section 9.4)

9.27 Calculate the molar concentration of OH^- in water solutions with the following H_3O^+ molar concentrations:

 a. 1.0×10^{-7}

 b. 3.2×10^{-3}

 c. 4.7×10^{-11}

 d. 1.2

 e. 0.043

9.28 Calculate the molar concentration of OH^- in water solutions with the following H_3O^+ molar concentrations:

 a. 0.044

 b. 1.3×10^{-4}

 c. 0.0087

 d. 7.9×10^{-10}

 e. 3.3×10^{-2}

9.29 Calculate the molar concentration of H_3O^+ in water solutions with the following OH^- molar concentrations:

 a. 1.0×10^{-7}

 b. 5.2×10^{-4}

 c. 9.9×10^{-10}

 d. 0.092

 e. 3.7

9.30 Calculate the molar concentration of H_3O^+ in water solutions with the following OH^- molar concentrations:

 a. 6.9×10^{-5}

 b. 0.074

 c. 4.9

 d. 1.7×10^{-3}

 e. 9.2×10^{-9}

9.31 Classify the solutions represented in Exercises 9.27 and 9.29 as acidic, basic, or neutral.

9.32 Classify the solutions represented in Exercises 9.28 and 9.30 as acidic, basic, or neutral.

The pH Concept (Section 9.5)

9.33 Classify solutions with the following characteristics as acidic, basic, or neutral:

 a. pH = 10

 b. pH = 4

 c. pH = 7.3

 d. pH = 6

9.34 Classify solutions with the following characteristics as acidic, basic, or neutral.

 a. pH = 4.7

 b. pH = 8.8

 c. pH = 1.5

 d. pH = 11

 e. pH = 5.9

9.35 Determine the pH of water solutions with the following characteristics. Classify each solution as acidic, basic, or neutral.

 a. $[H^+] = 1.0 \times 10^{-5}$

 b. $[OH^-] = 6.0 \times 10^{-3}$

 c. $[H^+] = [OH^-]$

 d. $[H^+] = 9.0 \times 10^{-4}$

 e. $[OH^-] = 3.0 \times 10^{-9}$

9.36 Determine the pH of water solutions with the following characteristics. Classify each solution as acidic, basic, or neutral.

 a. $[H^+] = 4.1 \times 10^{-9}$

 b. $[OH^-] = 9.4 \times 10^{-4}$

 c. $[OH^-] = 10[H^+]$

 d. $[H^+] = 2.3 \times 10^{-2}$

 e. $[OH^-] = 5.1 \times 10^{-10}$

9.37 Determine the pH of water solutions with the following characteristics. Classify each solution as acidic, basic, or neutral.

 a. $[H^+] = 3.7 \times 10^{-4}$

 b. $[H^+] = 7.4 \times 10^{-8}$

 c. $[H^+] = 1.9 \times 10^{-10}$

 d. $[OH^-] = 1.3 \times 10^{-1}$

 e. $[OH^-] = 6.8 \times 10^{-7}$

9.38 Determine the pH of water solutions with the following characteristics. Classify each solution as acidic, basic, or neutral.

 a. $[H^+] = 2.2 \times 10^{-3}$

 b. $[H^+] = 3.9 \times 10^{-12}$

 c. $[H^+] = 7.5 \times 10^{-6}$

 d. $[OH^-] = 2.5 \times 10^{-4}$

 e. $[OH^-] = 8.6 \times 10^{-10}$

9.39 Determine the $[H^+]$ value for solutions with the following characteristics:

 a. pH = 4.45

 b. pH = 13.12

 c. pH = 7.73

9.40 Determine the $[H^+]$ value for solutions with the following characteristics:

 a. pH = 9.27

 b. pH = 2.55

 c. pH = 5.42

9.41 Convert the following pH values into both $[H^+]$ and $[OH^-]$ values:

 a. pH = 8.00

 b. pH = 6.15

 c. pH = 1.30

9.42 Convert the following pH values into both $[H^+]$ and $[OH^-]$ values:

 a. pH = 3.95

 b. pH = 4.00

 c. pH = 11.86

9.43 The pH values listed in Table 9.1 are generally the average values for the listed materials. Most natural materials, such as body fluids and fruit juices, have pH values that cover a range for different samples. Some measured pH values for specific body fluid samples are given below. Convert each one to $[H^+]$, and classify the fluid as acidic, basic, or neutral.

 a. Blood, pH = 7.41

 b. Gastric juice, pH = 1.60

 c. Urine, pH = 5.93

 d. Saliva, pH = 6.85

 e. Pancreatic juice, pH = 7.85

9.44 The pH values listed in Table 9.1 are generally the average values for the listed materials. Most natural materials, such as body fluids and fruit juices, have pH values that cover a range for different samples. Some measured pH values for specific body fluid samples are given below. Convert each one to $[H^+]$, and classify the fluid as acidic, basic, or neutral.

 a. Bile, pH = 8.05

 b. Vaginal fluid, pH = 3.93

 c. Semen, pH = 7.38

 d. Cerebrospinal fluid, pH = 7.40

 e. Perspiration, pH = 6.23

9.45 The pH values of specific samples of food items are listed below. Convert each value to $[H^+]$, and classify the sample as acidic, basic, or neutral.

 a. Milk, pH = 6.39

 b. Coffee, pH = 5.10

 c. Orange juice, pH = 4.07

 d. Vinegar, pH = 2.65

9.46 The pH values of specific samples of food items are listed below. Convert each value to $[H^+]$, and classify the sample as acidic, basic, or neutral.

 a. Soft drink, pH = 2.91

 b. Tomato juice, pH = 4.11

 c. Lemon juice, pH = 2.32

 d. Grapefruit juice, pH = 3.07

Even-numbered exercises answered in Appendix B.

Properties of Acids (Section 9.6)

9.47 Using the information in Table 9.4, describe how you would prepare each of the following solutions.

 a. About 750 mL of 0.5 M H_2SO_4 from dilute sulfuric acid

 b. About 200 mL of 0.1 M NaOH from stock sodium hydroxide solution

 c. About 1.0 L of 1 M acetic acid from glacial acetic acid

9.48 Use the information in Table 9.4 and describe how you would prepare each of the following solutions.

 a. About 2 L of 3.0 M HNO_3 from dilute nitric acid solution

 b. About 500 mL of 1.5 M aqueous ammonia from concentrated aqueous ammonia solution

 c. About 5 L of 0.2 M HCl from concentrated hydrochloric acid solution

9.49 Write balanced molecular equations to illustrate the following characteristic reactions of acids, using nitric acid (HNO_3).

 a. Reaction with water to form hydronium ions

 b. Reaction with the solid oxide, CaO

 c. Reaction with the solid hydroxide, $Mg(OH)_2$

 d. Reaction with the solid carbonate, $CuCO_3$

 e. Reaction with the solid bicarbonate, $KHCO_3$

 f. Reaction with Mg metal

9.50 Write balanced molecular equations to illustrate the following characteristic reactions of acids, using sulfuric acid (H_2SO_4).

 a. Reaction with water to form hydronium ions

 b. Reaction with the solid oxide, CaO

 c. Reaction with the solid hydroxide, $Mg(OH)_2$

 d. Reaction with the solid carbonate, $CuCO_3$

 e. Reaction with the solid bicarbonate, $KHCO_3$

 f. Reaction with Mg metal

9.51 Write each molecular equation of Exercise 9.49 in total ionic and net ionic form. Use Table 7.4 to decide which products will be soluble.

9.52 Write each molecular equation of Exercise 9.50 in total ionic and net ionic form. Use Table 7.4 to decide which products will be soluble.

9.53 Write balanced molecular equations to illustrate five different reactions that could be used to prepare $BaCl_2$ from hydrochloric acid (HCl) and other appropriate substances.

9.54 Write balanced molecular equations to illustrate five different reactions that could be used to prepare $MgCl_2$ from hydrochloric acid (HCl) and other appropriate substances.

9.55 Write balanced molecular, total ionic, and net ionic equations to illustrate each of the following reactions. All the metals form 2+ ions.

 a. Zinc with H_2SO_4

 b. Magnesium with HCl

 c. Calcium with $HC_2H_3O_2$

9.56 Write balanced molecular, total ionic, and net ionic equations to illustrate each of the following reactions. All the metals form 2+ ions.

 a. Tin with H_2SO_3

 b. Magnesium with H_3PO_4

 c. Calcium with HBr

Properties of Bases (Section 9.7)

9.57 Write balanced molecular, total ionic, and net ionic equations to represent neutralization reactions between RbOH and the following acids. Use all H's possible for each acid.

 a. HCl

 b. HNO_3

 c. H_2SO_4

9.58 Write balanced molecular, total ionic, and net ionic equations to represent the neutralization reactions between RbOH and the following acids. Use all H's possible for each acid.

 a. HBr

 b. H_2SO_3

 c. H_3PO_3 (only two H's react)

9.59 Some polyprotic acids can form more than one salt, depending on the number of H's that react with base. Write balanced molecular, total ionic, and net ionic equations to represent the following neutralization reactions between KOH and

 a. H_2SO_4 (only react one H)

 b. H_2SO_4 (react both H's)

 c. H_3PO_4 (only react one H)

9.60 Some polyprotic acids can form more than one salt, depending on the number of H's that react with base. Write balanced molecular, total ionic, and net ionic equations to represent the following neutralization reactions between KOH and

 a. H_3PO_4 (react two H's)

 b. H_3PO_4 (react three H's)

 c. $H_2C_2O_4$ (react one H)

Salts (Section 9.8)

9.61 Identify with ionic formulas the cations and anions of the following salts:

 a. LiCl

 b. $Cu(NO_3)_2$

 c. $SrSO_4$

 d. K_3PO_4

 e. K_2HPO_4

 f. $CaCO_3$

9.62 Identify with ionic formulas the cations and anions of the following salts:

 a. $CuCl_2$

 b. $(NH_4)_2SO_4$

 c. Li_3PO_4

 d. $MgCO_3$

 e. $Ca(C_2H_3O_2)_2$

 f. KNO_3

9.63 Identify with formulas the acid and base from which the anion and cation of each salt in Exercise 9.61 was derived. Pay special attention to salts derived from polyprotic acids and be sure to list the acid formula with all H's.

9.64 Identify with formulas the acid and base from which the anion and cation of each salt in Exercise 9.62 was derived. Pay special attention to salts derived from polyprotic acids and be sure to list the acid formula with all H's.

9.65 Calculate the mass of water that would be released if the water of hydration were completely driven off 1.0 mol of (a) plaster of Paris and (b) gypsum (see Table 9.6). How would the products of these reactions compare?

9.66 Calculate the mass of water that would be released if the water of hydration were completely driven off 1.0 mol of (a) Epsom salts and (b) borax (see Table 9.6). How would the products of these reactions compare?

9.67 Write formulas for the acid and indicated solid that could be used to prepare each of the following salts:

 a. $CuCl_2$ (solid is an oxide)

 b. $MgSO_4$ (solid is a carbonate)

 c. LiBr (solid is a hydroxide)

9.68 Write formulas for the acid and indicated solid that could be used to prepare each of the following salts:

 a. $Mg(NO_3)_2$ (solid is a carbonate)

 b. $CaCl_2$ (solid is an oxide)

 c. Rb_2SO_4 (solid is a bicarbonate)

9.69 Write balanced molecular equations to illustrate each salt preparation described in Exercise 9.67.

9.70 Write balanced molecular equations to illustrate each salt preparation described in Exercise 9.68.

9.71 Determine the number of moles of each of the following salts that would equal 1 eq of salt:

 a. KNO_3

 b. Li_2CO_3

 c. $SrCl_2$

9.72 Determine the number of moles of each of the following salts that would equal 1 eq of salt:

 a. $CaCl_2$

 b. $Cu(NO_3)_2$

 c. $CrCl_3$

9.73 Determine the number of equivalents and milliequivalents in each of the following:

 a. 0.10 mol KI

 b. 0.25 mol $MgCl_2$

 c. 4.73×10^{-2} mol $AgNO_3$

9.74 Determine the number of equivalents and milliequivalents in each of the following:

 a. 0.22 mol $ZnCl_2$

 b. 0.45 mol CsCl

 c. 3.12×10^{-2} mol $Fe(NO_3)_2$

9.75 Determine the number of equivalents and milliequivalents in 5.00 g of each of the following salts. Include any waters of

hydration given in the salt formula when you calculate salt formula weights.

 a. NaCl

 b. $NaNO_3$

 c. Na_3PO_4

 d. $MgSO_4 \cdot 7H_2O$

9.76 Determine the number of equivalents and milliequivalents in 5.00 g of each of the following salts. Include any waters of hydration given in the salt formula when you calculate salt formula weights.

 a. $Na_2CO_3 \cdot 10H_2O$

 b. $CuSO_4 \cdot 5H_2O$

 c. Li_2CO_3

 d. NaH_2PO_4

9.77 A sample of intracellular fluid contains 45.1 meq/L of Mg^{2+} ion. Assume the Mg^{2+} comes from dissolved $MgCl_2$, and calculate the number of moles and number of grams of $MgCl_2$ that would be found in 250 mL of the intracellular fluid.

9.78 A sample of intracellular fluid contains 133 meq/L of K^+ ion. Assume the K^+ comes from dissolved K_2SO_4, and calculate the number of moles and number of grams of K_2SO_4 that would be found in 150 mL of the intracellular fluid.

The Strengths of Acids and Bases (Section 9.9)

9.79 Illustrate the difference between weak, moderately strong, and strong acids by writing dissociation reactions for the hypothetical acid HB, using arrows of various lengths.

9.80 The K_a values have been determined for four acids and are listed below. Arrange the acids in order of increasing acid strength (weakest first, strongest last).

$$\text{acid } A \ (K_a = 5.6 \times 10^{-5})$$
$$\text{acid } B \ (K_a = 1.8 \times 10^{-5})$$
$$\text{acid } C \ (K_a = 1.3 \times 10^{-4})$$
$$\text{acid } D \ (K_a = 1.1 \times 10^{-3})$$

9.81 Arrange the four acids classified as weak in Table 9.7 in order of increasing strength (weakest first, strongest last).

9.82 K_a values for four weak acids are given below:

$$\text{acid } A \ (K_a = 2.6 \times 10^{-4})$$
$$\text{acid } B \ (K_a = 3.7 \times 10^{-5})$$
$$\text{acid } C \ (K_a = 5.8 \times 10^{-4})$$
$$\text{acid } D \ (K_a = 1.5 \times 10^{-3})$$

 a. Arrange the four acids in order of increasing acid strength (weakest first, strongest last).

 b. Arrange the conjugate bases of the acids (identify as base A, etc.) in order of increasing base strength (weakest base first, strongest last).

9.83 Write dissociation reactions and K_a expressions for the following weak acids:

 a. Hypobromous acid, HBrO

 b. Sulfurous acid, H_2SO_3 (1st H only)

 c. Hydrogen sulfite ion, HSO_3^-

d. Hydroselenic acid, H_2Se (1st H only)

e. Arsenic acid, H_3AsO_4 (1st H only)

9.84 Write dissociation reactions and K_a expressions for the following weak acids:

a. Nitrous acid, HNO_2

b. Hydrogen carbonate ion, HCO_3^-

c. Dihydrogen phosphate ion, $H_2PO_4^-$ (1st H only)

d. Hydrogen sulfide ion, HS^-

e. Hypobromous acid, $HBrO$

9.85 Equal molar solutions are made of three monoprotic acids HA, HB, and HC. The pHs of the solutions are, respectively, 4.82, 3.16, and 5.47. Rank the acids in order of increasing acid strength and explain your reasoning.

9.86 If someone asked you for a weak acid solution, which of the following would you provide according to definitions in this chapter?

a. 0.05 M HCl

b. 20% acetic acid

If the individual really wanted the other solution, what term should have been used instead of *weak*?

9.87 Arsenic acid (H_3AsO_4) is a moderately weak triprotic acid. Write equations showing its stepwise dissociation. Which of the three anions formed in these reactions will be the strongest Brønsted base? Which will be the weakest Brønsted base? Explain your answers.

Analyzing Acids and Bases (Section 9.10)

9.88 Explain the purpose of doing a titration.

9.89 Describe the difference between the information obtained by measuring the pH of an acid solution and by titrating the solution with base.

9.90 Suppose a student is going to titrate an acidic solution with a base and just picks an indicator at random. Under what circumstances will (a) the endpoint and equivalence point be the same? (b) The endpoint and equivalence point be different?

9.91 Determine the number of moles of NaOH that could be neutralized by each of the following:

a. 1.00 L of 0.200 M HCl

b. 500 mL of 0.150 M HNO_3

9.92 Determine the number of moles of NaOH that could be neutralized by each of the following:

a. 250 mL of 0.400 M HBr

b. 750 mL of 0.300 M $HClO_4$

Titration Calculations (Section 9.11)

9.93 Write a balanced molecular equation to represent the neutralization reaction between NaOH and each of the following acids. React all of the acid H's.

a. Molybdic acid, H_2MoO_4

b. Permanganic acid, $HMnO_4$

c. Phosphoric acid, H_3PO_4

9.94 Write a balanced molecular equation to represent the neutralization reaction between NaOH and each of the following acids. React all of the acid H's.

a. Chromic acid, H_2CrO_4

b. Chloric acid, $HClO_3$

c. Arsenous acid, H_3AsO_3

9.95 Write a balanced molecular equation to represent the neutralization reaction between HCl and each of the following bases:

a. $Cd(OH)_2$

b. $Cr(OH)_3$

c. $Fe(OH)_2$

9.96 Write a balanced molecular equation to represent the neutralization reaction between HCl and the following bases:

a. $Sr(OH)_2$

b. $Ni(OH)_3$

c. $Zn(OH)_2$

9.97 A 25.00-mL sample of gastric juice is titrated with a 0.0210 M NaOH solution. The titration to the equivalence point requires 29.8 mL of NaOH solution. If the equation for the reaction is

$$HCl(aq) + NaOH(aq) \rightarrow NaCl(aq) + H_2O(\ell)$$

what is the molarity of HCl in the gastric juice?

9.98 A 25.00-mL sample of $H_2C_2O_4$ solution required 43.88mL of 0.1891 M NaOH solution to titrate it to the equivalence point. Calculate the molarity of the $H_2C_2O_4$ solution.

9.99 A 20.00-mL sample of each of the following acid solutions is to be titrated to the equivalence point using a 0.120 M NaOH solution. Determine the number of milliliters of NaOH solution that will be needed for each acid sample.

a. 0.180 M HCl

b. 0.180 M H_2SO_4

c. 0.100 M HCl

d. 10.00 g of H_3PO_4 in 250 mL of solution

e. 0.150 mol H_2MoO_4 in 500 mL of solution

f. 0.215 mol H_2MoO_4 in 700 mL of solution

9.100 A 20.00-mL sample of each of the following acid solutions is to be titrated to the equivalence point using a 0.120 M NaOH solution. Determine the number of milliliters of NaOH solution that will be needed for each acid sample.

a. 0.200 M $HClO_4$

b. 0.125 M H_2SO_4

c. 0.150 M $H_4P_2O_6$

d. 0.120 mol H_3PO_4 in 500 mL of solution

e. 6.25 g of H_2SO_4 in 250 mL of solution

f. 0.500 mol $HClO_3$ in 1.00 L of solution

9.101 The following acid solutions were titrated to the equivalence point with the base listed. Use the titration data to calculate the molarity of each acid solution.

 a. 25.00 mL of HI solution required 27.15 mL of a 0.250 M NaOH solution.

 b. 20.00 mL of H_2SO_4 solution required 11.12 mL of a 0.109 M KOH solution.

 c. 25.00 mL of gastric juice (HCl) required 18.40 mL of a 0.0250 M NaOH solution.

9.102 The following acid solutions were titrated to the equivalence point with the base listed. Use the titration data to calculate the molarity of each acid solution.

 a. 5.00 mL of dilute H_2SO_4 required 29.88 mL of a 1.17 M NaOH solution.

 b. 10.00 mL of vinegar (acetic acid) required 35.62 mL of a 0.250 M KOH solution.

 c. 10.00 mL of muriatic acid (HCl) used to clean brick and cement required 20.63 mL of a 6.00 M NaOH solution.

9.103 A 20.00-mL sample of diprotic oxalic acid ($H_2C_2O_4$) solution is titrated with a 0.250 M NaOH solution. A total of 27.86 mL of NaOH is required. Calculate:

 a. The number of moles of oxalic acid in the 20.00-mL sample.

 b. The molarity of the oxalic acid solution.

 c. The number of grams of oxalic acid in the 20.00-mL sample.

9.104 A sample of monoprotic benzoic acid weighing 0.5823 g is dissolved in about 25 mL of water. The solution is titrated to the equivalence point using 0.1021 M NaOH. The volume of base required is 46.75 mL. Calculate the molecular weight of the solid acid.

Hydrolysis Reactions of Salts (Section 9.12)

9.105 A solution of solid NH_4Cl dissolved in pure water is acidic (the pH is less than 7). Explain.

9.106 A solution of solid Na_2CO_3 dissolved in pure water has a pH significantly higher than the pH of pure water. Explain why.

9.107 Predict the relative pH (greater than 7, less than 7, etc.) for water solutions of the following salts. Table 9.9 may be useful. For each solution in which the pH is greater or less than 7, explain why and write a net ionic equation to justify your answer.

 a. Potassium sulfite, K_2SO_3

 b. Lithium nitrite, $LiNO_2$

 c. Sodium carbonate, Na_2CO_3

 d. Methylammonium chloride, CH_3NH_3Cl (CH_3NH_2 is a weak base)

9.108 Predict the relative pH (greater than 7, less than 7, etc.) for water solutions of the following salts. Table 9.9 may be useful. For each solution in which the pH is greater or less than 7, explain why and write a net ionic equation to justify your answer.

 a. Sodium hypochlorite, NaOCl (HOCl is a weak acid)

 b. Sodium formate, $NaCHO_2$

 c. Potassium nitrate, KNO_3

 d. Sodium phosphate, Na_3PO_4

9.109 A chemist has 20.00-mL samples of 0.100 M acid A and 0.100 M acid B in separate flasks. Both acids are monoprotic. Unfortunately,

the flasks were not labeled, so the chemist doesn't know which sample is in which flask. But fortunately, it is known that acid A is strong and acid B is weak. Before thinking about the problem, the chemist adds 20.00 mL of 0.100 M NaOH solution to each flask. Explain how the chemist could use a pH meter (or pH paper) to determine which flask originally contained which acid.

9.110 Explain why the hydrolysis of salts makes it necessary to have available in a laboratory more than one acid–base indicator for use in titrations.

9.111 How would the pH values of equal molar solutions of the following salts compare (highest, lowest, etc.)? NaH_2PO_4, Na_2HPO_4, and Na_3PO_4.

Buffers (Section 9.13)

9.112 Write equations similar to Equations 9.48 and 9.49 of the text to illustrate how a mixture of sodium hydrogen phosphate (Na_2HPO_4) and sodium dihydrogen phosphate (NaH_2PO_4) could function as a buffer when dissolved in water. Remember that phosphoric acid (H_3PO_4) ionizes in three steps.

9.113 Could a mixture of ammonia (NH_3), a weak base, and ammonium chloride (NH_4Cl) behave as a buffer when dissolved in water? Use reaction equations to justify your answer.

9.114 Some illnesses lead to a condition of excess acid (acidosis) in the body fluids. An accepted treatment is to inject solutions containing bicarbonate ions (HCO_3^-) directly into the bloodstream. Write an equation to show how this treatment would help combat the acidosis.

9.115 Calculate the pH of a buffer made by dissolving 1 mol formic acid (HCOOH) and 1 mol sodium formate (HCOONa) in 1 L of solution (see Table 9.9).

9.116 a. Calculate the pH of a buffer that is 0.1 M in lactic acid ($C_2H_4(OH)COOH$) and 0.1 M in sodium lactate, $C_2H_4(OH)COONa$.

 b. What is the pH of a buffer that is 1 M in lactic acid and 1 M in sodium lactate?

 c. What is the difference between the buffers described in parts a and b?

9.117 Which of the following weak acids and its conjugate base would you use to make a buffer with a pH of 5.00? Explain your reasons: acetic acid, nitrous acid, or formic acid.

9.118 Calculate the pH of buffers that contain the acid and conjugate base concentrations listed below.

 a. $[CH_3COOH] = 0.40$ M, $[CH_3COO^-] = 0.25$ M

 b. $[H_2PO_4^-] = 0.10$ M, $[HPO_4^{2-}] = 0.40$ M

 c. $[HSO_3^-] = 1.50$ M, $[SO_3^{2-}] = 0.20$ M

9.119 Calculate the pH of buffers that contain the acid and conjugate base concentrations listed below.

 a. $[HPO_4^{2-}] = 0.33$ M, $[PO_4^{3-}] = 0.52$ M

 b. $[HNO_2] = 0.029$ M, $[NO_2^-] = 0.065$ M

 c. $[HCO_3^-] = 0.50$ M, $[CO_3^{2-}] = 0.15$ M

9.120 What ratio of concentrations of NaH_2PO_4 and Na_2HPO_4 in solution would give a buffer with pH = 7.65?

9.121 A citric acid–citrate buffer has a pH of 3.20. You want to increase the pH to a value of 3.35. Would you add citric acid or sodium citrate to the solution? Explain.

Even-numbered exercises answered in Appendix B.

Additional Exercises

9.122 Consider the following reaction equation:

$$Cl^-(aq) + H_3O^+(aq) \rightarrow HCl(aq) + H_2O(\ell)$$

Draw Lewis structures (electron-dot formulas) for all the substances in the reaction equation, identify each reactant as a Brønsted acid or base, and then propose a definition for an acid and a base based on the ability of the substance to accept or donate a pair of electrons to form a covalent bond.

9.123 Consider the following dissociation reaction of a weak acid, HA:

$$HA(aq) + H_2O(\ell) \rightleftharpoons H_3O^+(aq) + A^-(aq)$$

It was determined that 2.63% of the acid in a 0.150 M solution of HA in water was dissociated. Calculate the pH of the 0.150 M solution.

9.124 The value of K_w for water varies with temperature. At 25°C, $K_w = 1.0 \times 10^{-14}$. At 50°C, $K_w = 5.5 \times 10^{-14}$. Calculate the pH of water at 50°C.

9.125 When sodium metal, Na, reacts with water, hydrogen gas, H_2, and sodium hydroxide, NaOH, in solution are produced. Write a balanced equation for the reaction, and explain how a basic solution is produced.

Allied Health Exam Connection

The following questions are from these sources:

1. *Nursing School Entrance Exam* © 2005, Learning Express, LLC.

2. *McGraw-Hill's Nursing School Entrance Exams* by Thomas A. Evangelist, Tamara B. Orr and Judy Unrein © 2009, The McGraw-Hill Companies, Inc.

3. *NSEE Nursing School Entrance Exams,* 3rd Edition © 2009, Kaplan Publishing.

4. *Cliffs Test Prep: Nursing School Entrance Exams* by Fred N. Grayson © 2004, Wiley Publishing, Inc.

5. *Peterson's Master the Nursing School and Allied Health Entrance Exams,* 18th Edition by Marion F. Gooding © 2008, Peterson's, a Nelnet Company.

9.126 An acid is a substance that dissociates in water into one or more _____ ions and one or more _____.

 a. hydrogen . . . anions

 b. hydrogen . . . cations

 c. hydroxide . . . anions

 d. hydroxide . . . cations

9.127 A base is a substance that dissociates in water into one or more _____ ions and one or more _____.

 a. hydrogen . . . anions

 b. hydrogen . . . cations

 c. hydroxide . . . anions

 d. hydroxide . . . cations

9.128 Which is true of alkaline solutions?

 a. More H^+ ion than OH^- ion

 b. Same amount of H^+ ion + OH^- ion

 c. More OH^- ion than H^+ ion

 d. None of the above

9.129 Which of the following is NOT an acid/conjugate base pair?

 a. HCN/CN^-

 b. H_2CO_3/OH^-

 c. H_2SO_4/HSO_4^-

 d. $H_3PO_4/H_2PO_4^-$

9.130 What is the formula of the hydronium ion?

 a. H^+

 b. NH_4^+

 c. H_3O^+

 d. H_2O^+

9.131 Which of the following substances has a pH closest to 7?

 a. ammonia

 b. blood

 c. lemon juice

 d. vinegar

9.132 Dissolving H_2SO_4 in water creates an acid solution by increasing the:

 a. sulfate ions

 b. water ions

 c. hydrogen ions

 d. oxygen ions

9.133 When a solution has a pH of 7, it is:

 a. a strong base

 b. a strong acid

 c. a weak base

 d. neutral

9.134 A common detergent has a pH of 11.0, so the detergent is:

 a. neutral

 b. acidic

 c. alkaline

 d. none of the above

9.135 In a 0.001 M solution of HCl, the pH is:

 a. 2

 b. −3

 c. 1

 d. 3

9.136 The pH of a blood sample is 7.40 at room temperature. The pOH is therefore:

 a. 6.60

 b. 7.40

 c. 6×10^{-6}

 d. 4×10^{-7}

9.137 As the concentration of hydrogen ions in a solution decreases:

 a. the pH numerically decreases

 b. the pH numerically increases

Even-numbered exercises answered in Appendix B.

c. the product of the concentrations $[H^+] \times [OH^-]$ comes closer to 1×10^{-14}

d. the solution becomes more acidic

9.138 Blood with a pH of 7.4 indicates that the blood sample is:

a. strongly acidic

b. strongly basic

c. weakly acidic

d. weakly basic

9.139 Atmospheric moisture (H_2O) combines with oxides of carbon, nitrogen, and sulfur (CO_2, NO_3 and SO_2) to produce:

a. alkaline precipitation

b. acid rain

c. alcohol

d. none of the above

9.140 Which of the following substances is most likely to taste sour?

a. NaOH

b. NaCl

c. NH_3

d. $HC_2H_3O_2$

9.141 Which of the following compounds would be classified as a salt?

a. Na_2CO_3

b. $Ca(OH)_2$

c. H_2CO_3

d. CH_3OH

9.142 A substance that functions to prevent rapid, drastic changes in the pH of a body fluid by changing strong acids and bases into weak acids and bases is called a(n):

a. salt

b. buffer

c. enzyme

d. coenzyme

9.143 Which one of the following equations represents neutralization?

a. $2Na + Cl_2 \rightarrow 2NaCl$

b. $CO_2 + H_2O \rightarrow H_2CO_3$

c. $HNO_3 + KOH \rightarrow KNO_3 + H_2O$

d. $CaO + H_2O \rightarrow Ca(OH)_2$

9.144 Which reaction below demonstrates a neutralization reaction?

a. $^{232}_{90}Th \rightarrow \, ^{228}_{88}Ra + \, ^{4}_{2}He$

b. $NaCl + H_2O \rightarrow HCl + NaOH$

c. $2HNO_3 + Mg(OH)_2 \rightarrow 2H_2O + Mg(NO_3)_2$

d. $CH_4 + 2O_2 \rightarrow CO_2 + 2H_2O$

9.145 In a titration of 40.0 mL of 0.20 M NaOH with 0.4 M HCl, what will be the final volume of the solution when the sodium hydroxide is completely neutralized?

a. 42 mL

b. 20 mL

c. 60 mL

d. 80 mL

9.146 When titrating 50 mL of 0.2 M HCl, what quantity of 0.5 M NaOH is needed to bring the solution to the equivalence point?

a. 80 mL

b. 40 mL

c. 20 mL

d. 10 mL

Chemistry for Thought

9.147 In an early industrial method, H_2SO_4 was manufactured in lead-lined chambers. Propose an explanation for this.

9.148 A saturated solution of solid $Ca(OH)_2$ in water has a $[OH^-]$ of only 2.50×10^{-2} M, and yet $Ca(OH)_2$ is a strong base. Explain this apparent contradiction.

9.149 Imagine that a solution of weak acid is being titrated with a strong base. Describe the substances present in the solution being titrated when it has been titrated halfway to the equivalence point. How is the pH of this half-titrated solution related to the pK_a for the weak acid?

9.150 Calculate K_a for the following weak acids based on the equilibrium concentrations and pH values given:

a. Benzoic acid, represented by HBz:

pH = 2.61, $[Bz^-] = 2.48 \times 10^{-3}$, [HBz] = 0.0975

b. Abietic acid, represented by HAb:

pH = 4.16, $[Ab^-] = 6.93 \times 10^{-5}$, [HAb] = 0.200

c. Cacodylic acid, represented by HCc:

pH = 3.55, $[Cc^-] = 0.000284$, [HCc] = 0.150

9.151 Bottles of ketchup are routinely left on the counters of cafés, yet the ketchup does not spoil. Why not?

9.152 Refer to Figure 9.2 and answer the question. What implications does this reaction have for the long-term durability of marble structures when exposed to acid rain?

9.153 Refer to Figure 9.3 and answer the question. Do you think the results would be the same if sulfuric acid (H_2SO_4) were substituted for the HCl? Explain.

9.154 Refer to Figure 9.5. Which of the three indicators would be the best to use to differentiate between the solutions with pH values of 4 and 6?

9.155 Refer to Figure 9.6 and explain why the pH reading of the meter might not be 7.00 at the equivalence point in a titration. Would the pH at the equivalence point be greater or less than 7 if hydrochloric acid were titrated with aqueous ammonia?

9.156 Refer to Figure 9.7 and answer the question. List at least two other ions that would behave like the Na^+ ion.

9.157 Refer to Figure 9.8 and answer the question. What color is universal indicator in acidic solutions? In basic solutions? Explain how you arrived at your conclusions.

© Tatiana Belova/Shutterstock.com

Case Study

The fragrance of the tobacco was tantalizing. When six-year-old Susan sat on her Grandpa's lap she loved to watch the flame pop in and out of the pipe bowl as he lit it. He could even blow smoke rings! All the grown-ups she knew smoked. When Susan was 16, she thought it would make her look older to smoke. She especially liked the skinny menthol cigarettes. Now Susan is 46; she has smoked for 30 years. At her last dental appointment, she was told she had a thickened white area on her right cheek and she was sent to an oral surgeon for a biopsy. The results were positive for squamous-cell carcinoma.

How can the health professionals working with Susan provide non-judgmental care, while at the same time encouraging her to make healthy changes? How can they ease her anxiety as she faces disfiguring surgery and the fear of living with cancer?

Follow-up to this Case Study appears at the end the chapter before the Concept Summary.

Learning Objectives

When you have completed your study of this chapter, you should be able to:

1 Assign IUPAC names and draw structural formulas for carboxylic acids. **(Section 15.1)**

2 Explain how hydrogen bonding affects the physical properties of carboxylic acids. **(Section 15.2)**

3 Recognize and write key reactions of carboxylic acids. **(Section 15.3)**

4 Assign common and IUPAC names to carboxylic acid salts. **(Section 15.4)**

5 Describe uses for carboxylate salts. **(Section 15.4)**

6 Recognize and write key reactions for ester formation. **(Section 15.5)**

7 Assign common and IUPAC names to esters. **(Section 15.6)**

8 Recognize and write key reactions of esters. **(Section 15.7)**

9 Write reactions for the formation of phosphate esters. **(Section 15.8)**

The tart flavor of foods that taste sour is generally caused by the presence of one or more carboxylic acids. Vinegar contains acetic acid, lemons and other citrus fruits contain citric acid (see ▶ Figure 15.1), and the tart taste of apples is caused by malic acid.

The characteristic functional group of **carboxylic acids** is the **carboxyl group:**

$$-\overset{\overset{\displaystyle O}{\|}}{C}-OH \qquad -COOH \quad \text{or} \quad -CO_2H$$

carboxyl group abbreviated forms

Carboxyl-containing compounds are found abundantly in nature (see ▶ Figure 15.2). Examples are lactic acid, which is formed in muscle cells during vigorous exercise, and citric acid, which is an important intermediate in cellular energy production, as well as a flavoring agent in citrus fruits (see ▶ Table 15.1).

Figure 15.1 Citrus fruits and juices are rich in citric acid. What flavor sensation is characteristic of acids?

carboxylic acid
An organic compound that contains the $-\overset{\overset{\displaystyle O}{\|}}{C}-OH$ functional group.

carboxyl group
The $-\overset{\overset{\displaystyle O}{\|}}{C}-OH$ group.

Figure 15.2 Rhubarb and spinach contain oxalic acid, a compound with two carboxyl groups. The nomenclature of dicarboxylic acids is not discussed here. What would you propose as the IUPAC ending for molecules with two carboxyl groups?

TABLE 15.1 Examples of Carboxylic Acids

Common Name	IUPAC Name	Structural Formula	Characteristics and Primary Uses
Formic acid	methanoic acid	$\overset{\displaystyle O}{\overset{\displaystyle \|}{H-C-OH}}$	Stinging agents of certain ants and nettles; used in food preservation
Acetic acid	ethanoic acid	$\overset{\displaystyle O}{\overset{\displaystyle \|}{CH_3-C-OH}}$	Active ingredient in vinegar; used in food preservation
Propionic acid	propanoic acid	$\overset{\displaystyle O}{\overset{\displaystyle \|}{CH_3CH_2-C-OH}}$	Salts used as mold inhibitors
Butyric acid	butanoic acid	$\overset{\displaystyle O}{\overset{\displaystyle \|}{CH_3(CH_2)_2-C-OH}}$	Odor-causing agent in rancid butter
Caproic acid	hexanoic acid	$\overset{\displaystyle O}{\overset{\displaystyle \|}{CH_3(CH_2)_4-C-OH}}$	Characteristic odor of Limburger cheese
Oxalic acid	ethanedioic acid	$\overset{\displaystyle O \quad O}{\overset{\displaystyle \| \quad \|}{HO-C-C-OH}}$	Present in leaves of some plants such as rhubarb and spinach; used as a cleaning agent for rust stains on fabric and porcelain
Citric acid	2-hydroxy-1,2,3-propane-tricarboxylic acid	$HO-\overset{O}{\overset{\|}{C}}-CH_2-\overset{OH}{\overset{\|}{\underset{\underset{O}{\overset{\|}{C}-OH}}{C}}}-CH_2-\overset{O}{\overset{\|}{C}}-OH$	Present in citrus fruits; used as a flavoring agent in foods; present in cells
Lactic acid	2-hydroxypropanoic acid	$CH_3\underset{\underset{OH}{\|}}{CH}-\overset{O}{\overset{\|}{C}}-OH$	Found in sour milk and sauerkraut; formed in muscles during exercise

15.1 The Nomenclature of Carboxylic Acids

Learning Objective

1. Assign IUPAC names and draw structural formulas for carboxylic acids.

Because of their abundance in nature, carboxylic acids were among the first organic compounds studied in detail. No systematic nomenclature system was then available, so the acids were usually named after some familiar source. Acetic acid,

$$\overset{\displaystyle O}{\overset{\displaystyle \|}{CH_3-C-OH}}$$
acetic acid

the sour constituent in vinegar (see ▶ Figure 15.3), is named after *acetum*, the Latin word for vinegar. Butyric acid occurs in rancid butter (the Latin word for butter is *butyrum*). Many of these common names are still widely used today (see Table 15.1). Carboxylic acids with long hydrocarbon chains, generally 12 to 20 carbon atoms, are called **fatty acids** (Chapter 18) because they were first isolated from natural fats. These acids, such as stearic acid with 18 carbons, are known almost exclusively by their common names.

Figure 15.3 Acetic acid is the active component in vinegar and a familiar laboratory weak acid.

© Cengage Learning/Charles D. Winters

fatty acid A long-chain carboxylic acid found in fats.

To name a carboxylic acid using the IUPAC system, the longest carbon chain including the carboxyl group is found and numbered. The numbering begins with the carboxyl carbon, so in monocarboxylic acids it is always located at the beginning of the chain, and no number is needed to locate it. The final -*e* of the parent hydrocarbon is dropped, and the ending -*oic* is added, followed by the word *acid*. Groups attached to the chain are named and located as before. Aromatic acids are given names derived from the parent compound, benzoic acid.

▶ Example 15.1

Use IUPAC rules to name the following carboxylic acids:

a. $CH_3CH_2-\overset{\overset{\displaystyle O}{\|}}{C}-OH$

b. $CH_3\underset{\underset{\displaystyle Br}{|}}{C}HCH_2-\overset{\overset{\displaystyle O}{\|}}{C}-OH$

c. $\overset{\overset{\displaystyle O}{\|}}{C}-OH$ (benzene ring with CH_3 at position 3)

Solution

a. The carbon chain contains three carbons. Thus, the name is based on the parent hydrocarbon, propane. The name is propanoic acid.

b. The chain contains four carbon atoms, and a bromine is attached to carbon number 3. The name is 3-bromobutanoic acid.

c. The aromatic acids are named as derivatives of benzoic acid. The carboxyl group is at position one, and the acid name is 3-methylbenzoic acid.

▶ LEARNING CHECK 15.1 Give the IUPAC name to the following:

a. $\overset{\overset{\displaystyle O}{\|}}{C}-OH$
$|$
$CH_3CH_2CHCH_3$

b. $\overset{\overset{\displaystyle O}{\|}}{C}-OH$ (benzene ring with Br and Br)

15.2 Physical Properties of Carboxylic Acids

Learning Objective

2. Explain how hydrogen bonding affects the physical properties of carboxylic acids.

Carboxylic acids with low molecular weights are liquids at room temperature and have characteristically sharp or unpleasant odors (see ▶ Table 15.2). Butyric acid, for example, is a component of perspiration and is partially responsible for the odor of locker rooms and unwashed socks. As the molecular weight of carboxylic acids increases, so does the boiling point. The heavier acids (containing more than ten carbons) are waxlike solids. Stearic acid ($C_{18}H_{36}O_2$), for example, is mixed with paraffin to produce a wax used to make candles.

When boiling points of compounds with similar molecular weights are compared, the carboxylic acids have the highest boiling points of any organic compounds we have studied so far (see ▶ Table 15.3 and ▶ Figure 15.4).

TABLE 15.2 Physical Properties of Some Carboxylic Acids

Common Name	Structural Formula	Boiling Point (°C)	Melting Point (°C)	Solubility (g/100 mL H₂O)
Formic acid	H—COOH	101	8	Infinite
Acetic acid	CH₃—COOH	118	17	Infinite
Propionic acid	CH₃—CH₂—COOH	141	−21	Infinite
Butyric acid	CH₃—(CH₂)₂—COOH	164	−5	Infinite
Valeric acid	CH₃—(CH₂)₃—COOH	186	−34	5
Caproic acid	CH₃—(CH₂)₄—COOH	205	−3	1
Caprylic acid	CH₃—(CH₂)₆—COOH	239	17	Insoluble
Capric acid	CH₃—(CH₂)₈—COOH	270	32	Insoluble
Lauric acid	CH₃—(CH₂)₁₀—COOH	299	44	Insoluble
Myristic acid	CH₃—(CH₂)₁₂—COOH	Decomposes	58	Insoluble
Palmitic acid	CH₃—(CH₂)₁₄—COOH	Decomposes	63	Insoluble
Stearic acid	CH₃—(CH₂)₁₆—COOH	Decomposes	71	Insoluble

TABLE 15.3 Boiling Points of Compounds with Similar Molecular Weight

Class	Compound	Molecular Weight	Boiling Point (°C)
Alkane	pentane	72	35
Ether	diethyl ether	74	35
Aldehyde	butanal	72	76
Alcohol	1-butanol	74	118
Carboxylic acid	propanoic acid	74	141

Figure 15.4 The boiling points of carboxylic acids are higher than those of all the other organic compounds studied thus far.

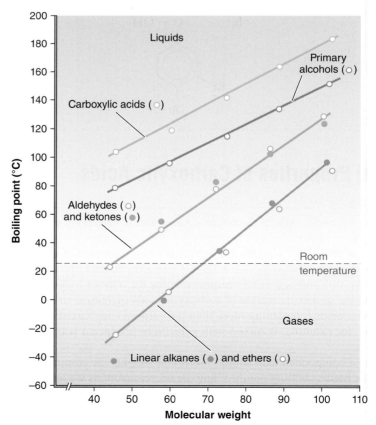

Alpha Hydroxy Acids in Cosmetics

Alpha-hydroxy acids occur in soured milk and many fruits as lactic acid. Tartaric acid occurs in grapes, malic acid is found in grapes and apples, citric acid is a common component of citrus fruits, and glycolic acid is found in sugar cane and sugar beets.

$$CH_3CH-\overset{\overset{\displaystyle O}{\|}}{C}-OH$$
$$\underset{\displaystyle OH}{|}$$

lactic acid

$$HO-\overset{\overset{\displaystyle O}{\|}}{C}-\overset{\overset{\displaystyle OH}{|}}{CH}-\overset{\overset{\displaystyle OH}{|}}{CH}-\overset{\overset{\displaystyle O}{\|}}{C}-OH$$

tartaric acid

$$CH_2-\overset{\overset{\displaystyle O}{\|}}{C}-OH$$
$$\underset{\displaystyle OH}{|}$$

glycolic acid

$$HO-\overset{\overset{\displaystyle O}{\|}}{C}-\overset{\overset{\displaystyle OH}{|}}{CH}CH_2-\overset{\overset{\displaystyle O}{\|}}{C}-OH$$

malic acid

Recently, alpha-hydroxy acids have been advertised as active ingredients in many cosmetics that claim to improve skin texture and tone, unblock or cleanse pores, improve oily skin or acne, and smooth fine lines and surface wrinkles. These cosmetics are most aggressively promoted for their antiwrinkle characteristics. The most commonly found alpha-hydroxy acids used in cosmetics are lactic acid and glycolic acid. These weak acids are thought to work by loosening the cells of the epidermis (outer layer of skin) and enhancing cell turnover by accelerating the flaking off of dead skin (exfoliating).

However, even though exfoliation may reveal healthier looking skin, the acid-containing cosmetics that speed up exfoliation may irritate the exposed skin and cause burning and stinging. In addition, new evidence indicates that alpha-hydroxy acids can increase the skin's sensitivity to sunlight and especially to the ultraviolet component of sunlight. In one industry-sponsored study, participants' skin was exposed to a 4% glycolic acid product twice daily for 12 weeks. Most of the participants developed minimal skin redness when exposed to 13% less UV radiation than normal, and three developed redness when exposed to 50% less UV light than normal. In another study, individuals who used an alpha-hydroxy acid product in the presence of UV radiation experienced twice the cell damage to their skin than others who were treated similarly with a non–alpha-hydroxy acid product.

Because of such test results, cosmetics companies have set guidelines suggesting that concentrations of alpha-hydroxy acids in skin products should be no more than 10% for over-the-counter use and no more than 30% for professional salon use. The acid content is included on the labels of many products, and manufacturers can also provide the information.

As people age, their skin naturally becomes more wrinkled. Several factors contribute to this result of the aging process. Skin becomes drier, thinner, and less elastic with age, and people with fair skin are more predisposed to these effects than are those with darker skin. Also, smoking and long-term overexposure to sunlight dramatically accelerate the wrinkling process. Thus, one of the best ways to slow down skin wrinkling is to protect the skin from the sun by wearing long-sleeved clothing, a hat, and a sunscreen that has at least an SPF 15 rating (see Chemistry and Your Health 12.1). Because many antiwrinkling cosmetics contain alpha-hydroxy acids, a sunscreen should always be worn when these products are used. Adequate protection from the sun is still the best wrinkle-prevention method available.

Cosmetic products with alpha-hydroxy acids.

For simple aliphatic compounds, the boiling points usually increase in this order: hydrocarbons and ethers, aldehydes and ketones, alcohols, and carboxylic acids. Carboxylic acids, like alcohols, can form intermolecular hydrogen bonds. It is this bonding that causes high boiling points. Acids have higher boiling points than alcohols with similar molecular weights because hydrogen-bonded acids are held together by two hydrogen bonds rather

than the one hydrogen bond that is characteristic of alcohols. A structure where two identical molecules are joined together is called a **dimer**:

dimer Two identical molecules bonded together.

$$R-C\overset{O \cdots H-O}{\underset{O-H \cdots O}{\diagdown}}C-R$$

Low molecular weight acids are very soluble in water (Table 15.2) because of hydrogen bonds that form between the carboxyl group and water molecules (intermolecular hydrogen bonds). As the length of the nonpolar hydrocarbon portion (the R group) of the carboxylic acid increases, the water solubility decreases. Carboxylic acids containing eight or more carbon atoms are not appreciably soluble in water and are considered to be insoluble.

Organic compounds may be arranged according to increasing water solubility as follows: hydrocarbons, ethers, aldehydes and ketones, alcohols, and carboxylic acids. Because forces resulting from hydrogen bonding play important roles in determining both boiling points and water solubility, it is not surprising that the same order is generally observed for these two properties.

15.3 The Acidity of Carboxylic Acids

Learning Objective

3. Recognize and write key reactions of carboxylic acids.

carboxylate ion

$$O \atop \|$$

The $R-C-O^-$ ion that results from the dissociation of a carboxylic acid.

The most important chemical property of carboxylic acids is the acidic behavior implied by their name. The hydrogen attached to the oxygen of the carboxyl group gives carboxylic acids their acidic character. In water, this proton may leave the acid, converting it into a **carboxylate ion**. Reaction 15.1 gives the general reaction, and Reaction 15.2 gives a specific example:

General reaction:

$$\underset{\text{carboxylic acid}}{R-\overset{O}{\overset{\|}{C}}-O-H} + H_2O \rightleftharpoons \underset{\substack{\text{carboxylate} \\ \text{ion}}}{R-\overset{O}{\overset{\|}{C}}-O^-} + \underset{\substack{\text{hydronium} \\ \text{ion}}}{H_3O^+} \qquad (15.1)$$

Generally, carboxylic acids behave as weak acids. A 1-M solution of acetic acid, for example, is only about 0.5% dissociated.

Specific example:

$$\underset{\text{acetic acid}}{CH_3-\overset{O}{\overset{\|}{C}}-O-H} + H_2O \rightleftharpoons \underset{\text{acetate ion}}{CH_3-\overset{O}{\overset{\|}{C}}-O^-} + H_3O^+ \qquad (15.2)$$

It is important to realize that Reactions 15.1 and 15.2 are reversible. According to Le Châtelier's principle, the addition of H_3O^+ (low pH) should favor formation of the carboxylic acid, and removal of H_3O^+ by adding base (high pH) should favor formation of the carboxylate ion:

$$\underset{\substack{\text{carboxylic} \\ \text{acid}}}{R-\overset{O}{\overset{\|}{C}}-O-H} + H_2O \underset{\substack{\text{acidic conditions} \\ \text{(low pH)}}}{\overset{\substack{\text{basic conditions} \\ \text{(high pH)}}}{\rightleftarrows}} \underset{\substack{\text{carboxylate} \\ \text{ion}}}{R-\overset{O}{\overset{\|}{C}}-O^-} + H_3O^+ \qquad (15.3)$$

Thus, the pH of a solution determines the form in which a carboxylic acid exists in the solution. At pH 7.4, the normal pH of body fluids, the carboxylate form predominates. For example, citric acid in body fluids is often referred to as citrate. This is an important point for later chapters in biochemistry.

▶ **LEARNING CHECK 15.2** Pyruvic acid, an important intermediate in the energy-conversion reactions in living organisms, is usually called pyruvate because it is commonly in the carboxylate form. Draw the structure of pyruvate.

$$CH_3 - \overset{\overset{O}{\|}}{C} - \overset{\overset{O}{\|}}{C} - OH$$

pyruvic acid

Although they are weak, carboxylic acids react readily with strong bases such as sodium hydroxide or potassium hydroxide to form salts. Reaction 15.4 gives the general reaction, and Reactions 15.5 and 15.6 are two specific examples:

General reaction:

$$R - \overset{\overset{O}{\|}}{C} - O - H + NaOH \longrightarrow R - \overset{\overset{O}{\|}}{C} - O^- Na^+ + H_2O \qquad (15.4)$$

$$\text{carboxylic acid} \qquad\qquad \text{sodium carboxylate}$$

Specific examples:

$$CH_3 - \overset{\overset{O}{\|}}{C} - O - H + NaOH \longrightarrow CH_3 - \overset{\overset{O}{\|}}{C} - O^- Na^+ + H_2O \qquad (15.5)$$

$$\text{acetic acid} \qquad\qquad\qquad \text{sodium acetate}$$

benzoic acid → potassium benzoate

$$C_6H_5 - \overset{\overset{O}{\|}}{C} - O - H + KOH \longrightarrow C_6H_5 - \overset{\overset{O}{\|}}{C} - O^- K^+ + H_2O \qquad (15.6)$$

benzoic acid potassium benzoate

▶ **LEARNING CHECK 15.3** Write the structural formulas for the products of the following reaction:

$$CH_3CH_2CH_2 - \overset{\overset{O}{\|}}{C} - OH + NaOH \longrightarrow$$

15.4 Salts of Carboxylic Acids

Learning Objectives

4. Assign common and IUPAC names to carboxylic acid salts.
5. Describe uses for carboxylate salts.

Nomenclature

Both common names and IUPAC names are assigned to carboxylic acid salts by naming the metal first and changing the -*ic* ending of the acid name to -*ate*.

▶ **Example 15.2**

Give both a common name and an IUPAC name to the following salts:

$$\text{a. } CH_3 - \overset{\overset{\displaystyle O}{\|}}{C} - O^- Na^+ \qquad \text{b. } \underset{\bigcirc}{} \overset{\overset{\displaystyle O}{\|}}{C} - O^- K^+$$

Solution

a. This salt is formed from $CH_3 - \overset{\overset{\displaystyle O}{\|}}{C} - OH$, which is called acetic acid (common name) or ethanoic acid (IUPAC name). Thus, the salt is sodium acetate (common name) or sodium ethanoate (IUPAC name).

b. This compound is the potassium salt of benzoic acid (both the common and IUPAC names). The name is potassium benzoate.

▶ **LEARNING CHECK 15.4** Give the IUPAC name for the following salts:

$$\text{a. } \underset{CH_3}{\overset{\overset{\displaystyle O}{\|}}{\underset{\bigcirc}{C} - O^- Li^+}} \qquad \text{b. } CH_3CH_2CH_2 - \overset{\overset{\displaystyle O}{\|}}{C} - O^- Na^+$$

Carboxylic acid salts are solids at room temperature and are usually soluble in water because they are ionic. Even long-chain acids with an extensive nonpolar hydrocarbon portion can be solubilized by converting them into salts (Reaction 15.7):

$$CH_3(CH_2)_{16} - \overset{\overset{\displaystyle O}{\|}}{C} - O - H + NaOH \longrightarrow CH_3(CH_2)_{16} - \overset{\overset{\displaystyle O}{\|}}{C} - O^- Na^+ + H_2O \quad (15.7)$$

<div align="center">
stearic acid sodium stearate

(insoluble) (soluble)
</div>

Useful Carboxylic Acid Salts

A number of acid salts are important around the home. Sodium stearate $(CH_3(CH_2)_{16}COO^-Na^+)$ and other sodium and potassium salts of long-chain carboxylic acids are used as soaps (see ▶ Figure 15.5).

Figure 15.5 Soap products enable us to keep ourselves and our homes clean.

Calcium and sodium propanoate are used commercially as preservatives in bread, cakes, and cheese to prevent the growth of bacteria and molds (see ▶ Figure 15.6). The parent acid, CH_3CH_2COOH, occurs naturally in Swiss cheese. The labels for these bakery products often contain the common name propionate, rather than the IUPAC-acceptable name propanoate.

Figure 15.6 Propanoates extend the shelf life of bread, preventing the formation of mold.

Sodium benzoate, another common food preservative, occurs naturally in many foods, especially cranberries and prunes. It is used in bakery products, ketchup, carbonated beverages, and a host of other foods:

sodium benzoate

Zinc 10-undecylenate, the zinc salt of $CH_2 = CH(CH_2)_8COOH$, is commonly used to treat athlete's foot. One commercial product that contains zinc 10-undecylenate is Desenex®.

A mixture of sodium citrate and citric acid

citric acid

Citric acid

is widely used as a buffer to control pH. Products sold as foams or gels such as jelly, ice cream, candy, and whipped cream maintain their desirable characteristics only at certain pHs, which can be controlled by the citrate/citric acid buffer. This same buffer is used in medicines and in human blood that is used for transfusions. In blood, it also functions as an anticoagulant.

15.5 Carboxylic Esters

Learning Objective

6. Recognize and write key reactions for ester formation.

carboxylic ester
A compound with the

$$\overset{O}{\overset{\|}{-C-OR}}$$ functional group.

esterification The process of forming an ester.

ester linkage The carbonyl carbon–oxygen single bond of the ester group.

Figure 15.7 Esters are partially responsible for the fragrance of oranges, pears, bananas, pineapples, and strawberries.

A very important reaction occurs when carboxylic acids are heated with alcohols or phenols in the presence of an acid catalyst. A molecule of water splits out and a **carboxylic ester** is formed:

General reaction:

$$\overset{O}{\overset{\|}{R-C}}-OH + H-O-R' \underset{}{\overset{H^+,\ heat}{\rightleftarrows}} \overset{O}{\overset{\|}{R-C}}-O-R' + H_2O \qquad (15.8)$$

carboxylic acid alcohol or phenol carboxylic ester

As before, R′ indicates that the two R groups can be the same or different. The process of ester formation is called **esterification,** and the carbonyl carbon–oxygen single bond of the ester group is called the **ester linkage:**

$$\overset{O}{\overset{\|}{-C}}-O-\overset{|}{\underset{|}{C}}- \qquad \textit{ester linkage}$$

ester group

The ester functional group is a key structural feature in fats, oils, and other lipids (Chapter 18). Also widely found in fruits and flowers, many esters are very fragrant and represent some of nature's most pleasant odors (see ▶ Figure 15.7). Because of this characteristic, esters are commonly used as flavoring agents in foods and as scents in personal products.

Reactions 15.9 and 15.10 illustrate the formation of two widely used esters:

Specific examples:

$$\overset{O}{\overset{\|}{CH_3CH_2CH_2-C}}-OH + HO-CH_2CH_3 \rightleftarrows^{H^+} \overset{O}{\overset{\|}{CH_3CH_2CH_2-C}}-O-CH_2CH_3 + H_2O \quad (15.9)$$

butanoic acid ethyl alcohol ethyl butanoate (strawberry flavoring)

salicylic acid + HO—CH₃ ⇌$^{H^+}$ methyl salicylate (oil of wintergreen) + H₂O (15.10)

methyl alcohol

▶ Example 15.3

Give the structure of the ester formed in the following reactions:

a. $\overset{O}{\overset{\|}{CH_3-C}}-OH + CH_3-OH \underset{}{\overset{H^+,\ heat}{\rightleftarrows}}$

b. $\overset{O}{\overset{\|}{CH_3CH_2CH_2-C}}-OH + \langle\bigcirc\rangle-OH \underset{}{\overset{H^+,\ heat}{\rightleftarrows}}$

Solution

a. $CH_3-\overset{\overset{\displaystyle O}{\|}}{C}-OH + CH_3OH \underset{\longleftarrow}{\overset{H^+,\ heat}{\longrightarrow}} CH_3-\overset{\overset{\displaystyle O}{\|}}{C}-O-CH_3 + H_2O$

b. $CH_3CH_2CH_2-\overset{\overset{\displaystyle O}{\|}}{C}-OH + \langle\bigcirc\rangle-OH \underset{\longleftarrow}{\overset{H^+,\ heat}{\longrightarrow}} CH_3CH_2CH_2-\overset{\overset{\displaystyle O}{\|}}{C}-O-\langle\bigcirc\rangle + H_2O$

▶ **LEARNING CHECK 15.5** Give the structure of the products formed in the following reactions:

a. $CH_3CH_2-\overset{\overset{\displaystyle O}{\|}}{C}-OH$ and CH_3-OH

b. $CH_3-\overset{\overset{\displaystyle O}{\|}}{C}-OH$ and $\langle\bigcirc\rangle-OH$

c. $\langle\bigcirc\rangle-\overset{\overset{\displaystyle O}{\|}}{C}-OH$ and $CH_3\underset{\underset{\displaystyle CH_3}{|}}{CH}-OH$

Polyesters, which are found in many consumer products, are just what the name implies—polymers made by an esterification reaction. The process used is an example of **condensation polymerization,** in which monomers combine and form a polymer; a small molecule such as water is formed as well. This is in contrast to addition polymerization, in which all atoms of the alkene monomer are incorporated into the polymer (Section 12.4). In many condensation polymerization reactions, each monomer has two functional groups so that the chain can grow from either end. A typical example is the reaction of terephthalic acid and ethylene glycol:

$$n HO-\overset{\overset{\displaystyle O}{\|}}{C}-\langle\bigcirc\rangle-\overset{\overset{\displaystyle O}{\|}}{C}-OH + n HO-CH_2CH_2-OH \underset{\longleftarrow}{\overset{H^+,\ heat}{\longrightarrow}} \qquad (15.11)$$

terephthalic acid ethylene glycol

$$\left(\!O-\overset{\overset{\displaystyle O}{\|}}{C}-\langle\bigcirc\rangle-\overset{\overset{\displaystyle O}{\|}}{C}-O-CH_2CH_2\!\right)_{\!n} + n H_2O$$

polyethylene terephthalate (PET)

Molecules of product continue to react with available monomers until, finally, a polyester is formed with the general structure given above, where the *n* means that the unit in parentheses is repeated many times.

Over 3 billion pounds of the polyester PET are produced annually. Fibers are formed by melting the polymer and forcing the liquid through tiny holes in devices called spinnerettes. The resulting fibers are spun into thread or yarn and marketed under the trade names Dacron®, Fortrel®, and Terylene®, depending on the manufacturer. Typical uses include automobile tire cord and permanent-press clothing. In medicine, Dacron thread is used for sutures, and woven fabric is used to replace damaged or diseased sections of blood vessels and the esophagus. Dacron fibers are often blended with cotton to make a fabric that is

more comfortable to wear on hot, humid days than those containing 100% polyester and that retains the latter's wrinkle resistance. Besides being forced through spinnerettes, PET melts may be forced through a narrow slit to produce thin sheets or films called Mylar® (see ▶ Figure 15.8). This form of polyester is used extensively in the manufacture of magnetic tapes for tape recorders.

Figure 15.8 Mylar, a polyester developed by E. I. DuPont deNemours Co., was used to cover the wings and pilot's compartment of the Gossamer Albatross, the first human-powered aircraft to fly across the English Channel.

carboxylic acid chloride
An organic compound that contains

the $-\overset{\overset{\displaystyle O}{\|}}{C}-Cl$ functional group.

carboxylic acid anhydride
An organic compound that contains

the $-\overset{\overset{\displaystyle O}{\|}}{C}-O-\overset{\overset{\displaystyle O}{\|}}{C}-$ functional group.

Although many esters can be prepared by the method just outlined in Reaction 15.8, the reversible nature of the reaction does not always allow for good yields of product. Two compounds that are more reactive than carboxylic acids and that produce esters in good yield are **carboxylic acid chlorides** and **carboxylic acid anhydrides**:

$$R-\overset{\overset{\displaystyle O}{\|}}{C}-Cl$$
carboxylic acid chloride

$$R-\overset{\overset{\displaystyle O}{\|}}{C}-O-\overset{\overset{\displaystyle O}{\|}}{C}-R$$
carboxylic acid anhydride

These substances react vigorously with alcohols in a nonreversible manner.

General reactions:

$$R-\overset{\overset{\displaystyle O}{\|}}{C}-Cl + HO-R' \longrightarrow R-\overset{\overset{\displaystyle O}{\|}}{C}-O-R' + HCl \qquad (15.12)$$
acid chloride alcohol carboxylic ester

$$R-\overset{\overset{\displaystyle O}{\|}}{C}-O-\overset{\overset{\displaystyle O}{\|}}{C}-R + HO-R' \longrightarrow R-\overset{\overset{\displaystyle O}{\|}}{C}-O-R' + R-\overset{\overset{\displaystyle O}{\|}}{C}-OH \qquad (15.13)$$
carboxylic acid anhydride alcohol carboxylic ester carboxylic acid

Reactions 15.14 and 15.15 illustrate two specific examples. In another example, the laboratory synthesis of aspirin (Reaction 15.16), using acetic anhydride, gives excellent yields of the ester.

Specific reactions:

$$\underset{\text{acetyl chloride}}{CH_3-\overset{\displaystyle O}{\overset{\|}{C}}-Cl} + \underset{\substack{\text{ethyl} \\ \text{alcohol}}}{HO-CH_2CH_3} \longrightarrow \underset{\text{ethyl acetate}}{CH_3-\overset{\displaystyle O}{\overset{\|}{C}}-O-CH_2CH_3} + HCl \qquad (15.14)$$

$$\underset{\text{acetic anhydride}}{CH_3-\overset{\displaystyle O}{\overset{\|}{C}}-O-\overset{\displaystyle O}{\overset{\|}{C}}-CH_3} + \underset{\text{phenol}}{\text{(phenol ring with OH)}} \longrightarrow \underset{\text{phenyl acetate}}{CH_3-\overset{\displaystyle O}{\overset{\|}{C}}-O-\text{(phenyl ring)}} + \underset{\text{acetic acid}}{CH_3-\overset{\displaystyle O}{\overset{\|}{C}}-OH} \qquad (15.15)$$

▶ Example 15.4

Give the structure of the ester formed in the following reactions:

a. (benzene ring)$-\overset{\displaystyle O}{\overset{\|}{C}}-Cl$ + $CH_3CH_2-OH \longrightarrow$

b. $CH_3CH_2-\overset{\displaystyle O}{\overset{\|}{C}}-O-\overset{\displaystyle O}{\overset{\|}{C}}-CH_2CH_3$ + $CH_3CH_2-OH \longrightarrow$

Solution

a. The products are (benzene ring)$-\overset{\displaystyle O}{\overset{\|}{C}}-O-CH_2CH_3$ + HCl

b. The products are $CH_3CH_2-\overset{\displaystyle O}{\overset{\|}{C}}-O-CH_2CH_3$ + $CH_3CH_2-\overset{\displaystyle O}{\overset{\|}{C}}-OH$

The first product in each case is the ester.

▶ LEARNING CHECK 15.6

Write equations to represent ester formation when the following pairs of compounds are reacted:

a. (benzene ring)$-\overset{\displaystyle O}{\overset{\|}{C}}-O-\overset{\displaystyle O}{\overset{\|}{C}}-$(benzene ring) and CH_3-OH

b. $CH_3CH_2-\overset{\displaystyle O}{\overset{\|}{C}}-Cl$ and $CH_3\underset{\underset{\displaystyle CH_3}{|}}{CH}-OH$

15.6 The Nomenclature of Esters

Learning Objective

7. Assign common and IUPAC names to esters.

Esters are named by a common system as well as by IUPAC rules; the common names are used most often. It is helpful with both IUPAC and common names to think of the esters as being formed from a carboxylic acid, the

$$
\underset{\text{acid part}}{\underbrace{\text{R}-\overset{\overset{\displaystyle O}{\|}}{\text{C}}-}}\ \text{part: and an alcohol, the}\ -\text{OR}'\ \text{part:}\ \underset{\text{acid part}}{\underbrace{\text{R}-\overset{\overset{\displaystyle O}{\|}}{\text{C}}-}}\overset{\overset{\displaystyle alcohol\ part}{}}{\text{OR}'}
$$

The first word of the name of an ester is the name of the alkyl or aromatic group (R′) contributed by the alcohol. The second word is the carboxylic acid name, with the *-ic acid* ending changed to *-ate*. This is similar to the method used for naming carboxylic acid salts. Thus, an ester of acetic acid becomes an acetate, one of butyric acid becomes a butyrate, one of lactic acid becomes a lactate, and so on.

▶ Example 15.5

Give common and IUPAC names for the following esters:

a. CH$_3$—$\overset{\overset{\displaystyle O}{\|}}{\text{C}}$—O—CH$_3$

b. CH$_3$CH$_2$CH$_2$—$\overset{\overset{\displaystyle O}{\|}}{\text{C}}$—O—⟨O⟩

c. ⟨O⟩—$\overset{\overset{\displaystyle O}{\|}}{\text{C}}$—O—CH$_2CH_3$

Solution

a. The first word is methyl, which refers to the alcohol portion:

$$
\underset{\text{acetate (common name)}}{\underbrace{\text{CH}_3-\overset{\overset{\displaystyle O}{\|}}{\text{C}}-\text{O}}}-\overset{\overset{\displaystyle methyl}{}}{\text{CH}_3}
$$

ethanoate (IUPAC name)

The second word is derived from the name of the two-carbon carboxylic acid (acetic acid or ethanoic acid). Thus, we have methyl acetate (common name) and methyl ethanoate (IUPAC name).

b. $\underset{\text{butyrate (common name)}}{\underbrace{\text{CH}_3\text{CH}_2\text{CH}_2-\overset{\overset{\displaystyle O}{\|}}{\text{C}}-\text{O}}}-\overset{\overset{\displaystyle phenyl}{}}{⟨O⟩}$

butanoate (IUPAC name)

Thus, the two names are phenyl butyrate (common name) and phenyl butanoate (IUPAC name).

c.

$$\text{benzene ring}-\overset{\overset{\textstyle O}{\|}}{C}-O-\underset{\text{ethyl}}{\underline{CH_2CH_3}}$$

$$\underbrace{}_{benzoate}$$

Thus, we have ethyl benzoate (common name and IUPAC name).

▶ **LEARNING CHECK 15.7** Give both a common and the IUPAC names for each of the following esters:

a.

$$H-\overset{\overset{\textstyle O}{\|}}{C}-O-\underset{\underset{\textstyle CH_3}{|}}{CH}CH_3$$

b.

$$\text{phenyl}-\overset{\overset{\textstyle O}{\|}}{C}-OCH_3$$

15.7 Reactions of Esters

Learning Objective

8. Recognize and write key reactions of esters.

The most important reaction of carboxylic esters, both in commercial processes and in the body, involves the breaking of the ester linkage. The process is called either ester hydrolysis or saponification, depending on the reaction conditions.

Ester Hydrolysis

Ester hydrolysis is the reaction of an ester with water to break an ester linkage and produce an alcohol and a carboxylic acid. This process is simply the reverse of the esterification reaction (Reaction 15.8). Strong acids are frequently used as catalysts to hydrolyze esters:

General reaction:

$$\underset{\text{ester}}{R-\overset{\overset{\textstyle O}{\|}}{C}-OR'} + H-OH \overset{H^+}{\rightleftharpoons} \underset{\substack{\text{carboxylic} \\ \text{acid}}}{R-\overset{\overset{\textstyle O}{\|}}{C}-OH} + \underset{\substack{\text{alcohol} \\ \text{or phenol}}}{R'-OH} \qquad (15.17)$$

Specific example:

$$\underset{\text{ethyl acetate}}{CH_3-\overset{\overset{\textstyle O}{\|}}{C}-O-CH_2CH_3} + H-OH \overset{H^+}{\rightleftharpoons} \underset{\text{acetic acid}}{CH_3-\overset{\overset{\textstyle O}{\|}}{C}-OH} + \underset{\text{ethyl alcohol}}{CH_3CH_2-OH} \qquad (15.18)$$

Aspirin: Should You Take a Daily Dose?

Aspirin, an ester of salicylic acid first prepared in 1893, is remarkably versatile. In the body it reduces fever but does not reduce normal body temperature. It also relieves a variety of simple pains such as headache, sprain, and toothache, and is an anti-inflammatory agent often used to treat arthritis.

prevent esophageal and colorectal cancers. This indication is very significant because colorectal cancer is the second leading cancer killer after lung cancer. Researchers theorize that the aspirin exerts this effect by blocking the production of hormone-like prostaglandins, which in turn inhibits the growth of tumors. Such research may ultimately lead to the use of aspirin therapy to prevent colorectal cancer, but no official health agency has yet made such a recommendation.

| salicylic acid | acetic anhydride | | acetylsalicylic acid (aspirin) | acetic acid |

Americans consume an estimated 80 billion aspirin tablets each year. The *Physicians' Desk Reference* lists more than 50 OTC drugs in which aspirin is the principal ingredient. Yet, despite the fact that aspirin has been in routine use for nearly a century, scientific journals continue to publish reports about new uses for this old remedy.

In recent years, researchers have discovered one particular effect of aspirin in the body that helps explain its benefits as well as some of its side effects: Aspirin interferes with the clotting action of blood. When blood vessels are injured and bleed, cells in the blood called platelets accumulate at the injury site and clump together to form a plug that seals the opening in the blood vessel. Aspirin reduces the ability of the platelets to clump together, thereby reducing the tendency of blood to clot. In this same way, aspirin may help reduce or prevent clots from forming in arteries that are narrowed by diseases such as atherosclerosis. A heart attack results when a coronary artery that provides blood to the heart is blocked by a blood clot. One study shows that aspirin reduces the chances of having a second heart attack by more than 30%. Other studies suggest that aspirin use helps prevent a first heart attack in healthy individuals, and aspirin can also help prevent first or recurrent strokes of the type caused by blood clots that block the blood supply to the brain.

The same process that reduces blood clotting is also responsible for some of the undesirable side effects of using aspirin. It is known that aspirin use causes increased rates of gastrointestinal bleeding and hemorrhagic stroke (stroke caused by a ruptured blood vessel in the brain). Heavy aspirin use before surgery can present a danger because it increases the risk of severe bleeding after the operation.

Recent research reported in medical journals provides evidence of another important medical use of aspirin that is not related to its ability to inhibit blood clotting: Aspirin helps

Most doctors recognize that the majority of their patients with coronary artery disease benefit from daily aspirin therapy. When such therapy is recommended, a low dose of 81 mg per day (one baby aspirin) is generally used. Because the long-term, regular use of aspirin poses risks of serious bleeding, the decision to begin such a program should be made only after consultation with a physician.

A variety of aspirin products is available.

Notice that when ester linkages break during hydrolysis, the elements of water (—OH and —H) are attached to the ester fragments to form the acid and alcohol (Reaction 15.17). The breaking of a bond and the attachment of the elements of water to the fragments are characteristic of all hydrolysis reactions.

The human body and other biological organisms are constantly forming and hydrolyzing a variety of esters. The catalysts used in these cellular processes are very efficient protein catalysts called enzymes (Chapter 20). Animal fats and vegetable oils are esters. Their enzyme-catalyzed hydrolysis is an important process that takes place when they are digested.

▶ **LEARNING CHECK 15.8** Give the structure of the products formed in the following hydrolysis reaction:

$$
\underset{}{\text{C6H5}}-\overset{\overset{\text{O}}{\|}}{\text{C}}-\text{O}-\text{CH}_2\text{CH}_2\text{CH}_3
$$

$$
+ \text{H}_2\text{O} \underset{}{\overset{\text{H}^+}{\rightleftarrows}}
$$

Saponification

Like ester hydrolysis, **saponification** results in a breaking of the ester linkage and produces an alcohol and a carboxylic acid (see Section 18.4 for more on saponification). However, unlike ester hydrolysis, saponification is done in solutions containing strong bases such as potassium or sodium hydroxide. The carboxylic acid is converted to a salt under these basic conditions.

saponification The basic cleavage of an ester linkage.

General reaction:

$$
\underset{\text{ester}}{\text{R}-\overset{\overset{\text{O}}{\|}}{\text{C}}-\text{O}-\text{R}'} + \text{NaOH} \longrightarrow \underset{\substack{\text{carboxylic} \\ \text{acid salt}}}{\text{R}-\overset{\overset{\text{O}}{\|}}{\text{C}}-\text{O}^-\text{Na}^+} + \underset{\text{alcohol}}{\text{R}'-\text{OH}} \qquad (15.19)
$$

ecific example:

$$
\underset{\text{methyl benzoate}}{\overset{\overset{\text{O}}{\|}}{\text{C}}-\text{O}-\text{CH}_3} + \text{NaOH} \longrightarrow \underset{\text{sodium benzoate}}{\overset{\overset{\text{O}}{\|}}{\text{C}}-\text{O}^-\text{Na}^+} + \underset{\text{methyl alcohol}}{\text{CH}_3-\text{OH}} \qquad (15.20)
$$

We will see in Chapter 18 that saponification of fats and oils is important in the production of soaps.

A Reaction Map for Carboxylic Acids

We hope you have become familiar with the reaction maps of Chapters 12, 13, and 14 and have found them useful in solving problems. Another reaction map is given below.

It includes the key reactions of this chapter and should be useful as you answer questions and prepare for exams.

How Reactions Occur 15.1

Ester Saponification

The cleavage of an ester linkage under basic conditions is initiated by the attraction of the carbonyl carbon for hydroxide:

$$CH_3 - C(\!=\!\!O) - O - CH_3 \rightleftharpoons CH_3 - \overset{:\ddot{O}:^-}{\underset{OH}{C}} - O - CH_3$$

$$:\ddot{O}H^-$$

As the —OH group bonds to the carbonyl carbon, the double bond must break (two electrons move to the carbonyl oxygen) so that carbon does not possess five bonds.

In the next step of the mechanism, the electrons reestablish the double bond. Once again, carbon will have five bonds if there is not a simultaneous bond breakage. In this case, it is the ester linkage that is cleaved:

$$CH_3 - \overset{:\ddot{O}:^-}{\underset{OH}{C}} - O - CH_3 \rightleftharpoons CH_3 - \overset{O}{\overset{\|}{C}} - OH + {}^-:\ddot{O} - CH_3$$

carboxylic acid strong base

A carboxylic acid is formed momentarily but it quickly donates its proton to the strongly basic anion:

$$CH_3 - \overset{O}{\overset{\|}{C}} - OH + {}^-:\ddot{O} - CH_3 \longrightarrow$$

$$CH_3 - \overset{O}{\overset{\|}{C}} - O^- + CH_3 - OH$$

carboxylate product alcohol product

If the source of hydroxide for the reaction was sodium hydroxide, the carboxylate product would be coupled with the positive sodium ion to form the salt.

▶ **LEARNING CHECK 15.9** Give structural formulas for the products of the following saponification reactions.

a.
$$CH_3CH_2-\overset{\overset{\displaystyle O}{\|}}{C}-O-\underset{\underset{\displaystyle CH_3}{|}}{CH}CH_3 + NaOH \longrightarrow$$

b.
$$\text{C}_6H_5-\overset{\overset{\displaystyle O}{\|}}{C}-O-CH_2CH_3 + KOH \longrightarrow$$

15.8 Esters of Inorganic Acids

Learning Objective

9. Write reactions for the formation of phosphate esters.

We have defined a carboxylic ester as the product of a reaction between a carboxylic acid and an alcohol. Alcohols can also form **esters** by reacting with inorganic acids such as sulfuric, nitric, and phosphoric acids. The most important of these in biochemistry are the esters of phosphoric acid (H_3PO_4):

ester A compound in which the —OH of an acid is replaced by an —OR.

General reaction:

$$R-OH + HO-\overset{\overset{\displaystyle O}{\|}}{\underset{\underset{\displaystyle OH}{|}}{P}}-OH \rightleftarrows R-O-\overset{\overset{\displaystyle O}{\|}}{\underset{\underset{\displaystyle OH}{|}}{P}}-OH + H_2O \qquad (15.21)$$

<div align="center">alcohol phosphoric acid phosphate ester</div>

Specific example:

$$CH_3CH_2-OH + HO-\overset{\overset{\displaystyle O}{\|}}{\underset{\underset{\displaystyle OH}{|}}{P}}-OH \rightleftarrows CH_3CH_2-O-\overset{\overset{\displaystyle O}{\|}}{\underset{\underset{\displaystyle OH}{|}}{P}}-OH + H_2O \qquad (15.22)$$

Because phosphoric acid has three —OH groups, it can form mono-, di-, and triesters:

$$RO-\overset{\overset{\displaystyle O}{\|}}{\underset{\underset{\displaystyle OH}{|}}{P}}-OH \qquad RO-\overset{\overset{\displaystyle O}{\|}}{\underset{\underset{\displaystyle OH}{|}}{P}}-OR' \qquad RO-\overset{\overset{\displaystyle O}{\|}}{\underset{\underset{\displaystyle OR''}{|}}{P}}-OR'$$

<div align="center">monoester, diester, triester,
one R group two R groups three R groups</div>

Mono- and diesters are essential to life and represent some of the most important biological molecules. An example of an important monoester is glucose-6-phosphate, which represents the first intermediate compound formed when glucose is oxidized to supply energy for the body (Chapter 23):

$$\text{glucose-6-phosphate}$$

glucose-6-phosphate

At body pH, the two —OH groups of the phosphoric acid are ionized, and the phosphate group has a charge of 2^-. Examples of important diesters include the phospholipids (Chapter 18) and the nucleic acids (Chapter 21).

As we study key compounds in the storage and transfer of chemical energy in living systems (Chapter 22), we will encounter phosphate esters in which two or three phosphate groups are linked. These **phosphoric anhydrides** are referred to as diphosphates and triphosphates.

phosphoric anhydride A compound that contains the

group.

a diphosphate ester a triphosphate ester

Adenosine diphosphate (ADP) and adenosine triphosphate (ATP) are the most important of these compounds. We will study their rather complex structures in more detail in Section 22.7. For now, note the ester linkages in each structure and the presence of the di- and triphosphate groups. Again, at the pH of body fluids, the —OH groups attached to the phosphorus lose H^+ and acquire negative charges.

ADP

ATP

Nitroglycerin in Dynamite and in Medicine

Nitroglycerin is a nitrate ester resulting from the reaction of nitric acid and glycerol:

$$
\begin{array}{ccc}
CH_2-OH & & CH_2-O-NO_2 \\
| & & | \\
CH-OH + 3HO-NO_2 \rightleftharpoons & CH-O-NO_2 + 3H_2O \\
| & & | \\
CH_2-OH & & CH_2-O-NO_2 \\
\text{glycerol} \quad \text{nitric acid} & & \text{nitroglycerin}
\end{array}
$$

First made in 1846 by the Italian chemist Sobrero, nitroglycerin was discovered to be a powerful explosive with applications in both war and peace. However, as a shock-sensitive, unstable liquid, nitroglycerin proved to be extremely dangerous to manufacture and handle. The Swedish chemist Alfred Nobel later perfected its synthesis and devised a safe method for handling it. Nobel mixed nitroglycerin with a clay-like absorbent material. The resulting solid, called dynamite, is an explosive that is much less sensitive to shock than liquid nitroglycerin. Dynamite is still one of the most important explosives used for mining, digging tunnels, and blasting hills for road building.

Surprising as it may seem, nitroglycerin is also an effective medicine. It is used to treat patients with angina pectoris—sharp chest pains caused by an insufficient supply of oxygen to the heart muscle. Angina pectoris is usually found in patients with coronary artery diseases, such as arteriosclerosis (hardening of the arteries). During overexertion or excitement, the partially clogged coronary arteries prevent the heart from getting an adequate supply of oxygenated blood, and pain results.

Nitroglycerin relaxes cardiac muscle and causes a dilation of the arteries, thus increasing blood flow to the heart and relieving the chest pains.

Nitroglycerin (combined with other substances to render it nonexplosive) can be administered in small tablets, which are placed under the tongue during an attack of angina. The nitroglycerin is rapidly absorbed into the bloodstream and finds its way to the heart muscle within seconds. It can also be applied directly to the skin as a cream or absorbed through the skin from a transdermal patch attached to the skin. This last delivery system is a recent development that allows the nitroglycerin to be continuously absorbed for 24 hours.

A transdermal patch allows nitroglycerin to be absorbed through the skin.

Case Study Follow-up

Tobacco use is the most common preventable cause of death in the United States. About half of all smokers will die from smoking-related problems (NIH, 2011). Quitting provides immediate health benefits that increase the longer the person abstains from tobacco use. To successfully stop smoking, a person must often use a multifaceted approach involving medication, lifestyle changes, exercise, and emotional support.

A large amount of information and support is available for smokers and other patients diagnosed with cancer as they face treatment. Healthcare professionals can provide important psychological and emotional support to patients as well as physical care. Judgmental attitudes only serve to increase a patient's anxiety and feelings of guilt, which in turn can trigger addictive behavior such as smoking. A positive supportive attitude is more helpful and appropriate. The American Cancer Institute has free detailed information available about every conceivable type of cancer and its treatment, as well as referrals for many types of support. Encouraging the patient to learn as much as possible about her or his condition is invaluable.

The Nomenclature of Carboxylic Acids

The characteristic functional group of carboxylic acids is the carboxyl group

$$
\begin{matrix}
O \\
\parallel \\
- C - OH
\end{matrix}
$$

Many of the simpler carboxylic acids are well known by common names. In the IUPAC system, the ending of *-oic acid* is used in the names of these compounds. Aromatic acids are named as derivatives of benzoic acid.
Objective 1 (Section 15.1), Exercise 15.6

Physical Properties of Carboxylic Acids

At room temperature, low molecular weight carboxylic acids are liquids with distinctively sharp or unpleasant odors. High molecular weight, long-chain acids are wax-like solids. Carboxylic acids are quite effective in forming dimers, two molecules held together by hydrogen bonds. Thus, they have relatively high boiling points, and those with lower molecular weights are soluble in water.
Objective 2 (Section 15.2), Exercise 15.10

The Acidity of Carboxylic Acids

Soluble carboxylic acids behave as weak acids; they dissociate only slightly in water to form an equilibrium mixture with the carboxylate ion. The equilibrium concentrations of the carboxylic acid and the carboxylate ion depend on pH. At low pH, the acid form predominates, and at pH 7.4 (the pH of cellular fluids) and above, the carboxylate ion predominates. Carboxylic acids react with bases to produce carboxylate salts and water.
Objective 3 (Section 15.3), Exercise 15.26

Salts of Carboxylic Acids

The carboxylate salts are named by changing the *-ic* ending of the acid to *-ate*. **Objective 4 (Section 15.4), Exercise 15.28** The ionic nature of the salts makes them water soluble. A number of carboxylate salts are useful as food preservatives, soaps, and medicines.
Objective 5 (Section 15.4), Exercise 15.32

Carboxylic Esters

Carboxylic acids, acid chlorides, and acid anhydrides react with alcohols to produce esters. **Objective 6 (Section 15.5), Exercise 15.36** Polyesters result from the reaction of dicarboxylic acids and diols. Polyesters are an example of condensation polymers; these are produced when monomers react to form a polymer plus a small molecule such as water. Many esters are very fragrant and represent some of nature's most pleasant odors. Because of this characteristic, esters are widely used as flavoring agents.

The Nomenclature of Esters

Both common and IUPAC names for esters are formed by first naming the alkyl group of the alcohol portion followed by the name of the acid portion in which the *-ic acid* ending has been changed to *-ate*.
Objective 7 (Section 15.6), Exercise 15.46

Reactions of Esters

Esters can be converted back to carboxylic acids and alcohols under either acidic or basic conditions. Hydrolysis, the reaction with water in the presence of acid, produces the carboxylic acid and alcohol. Saponification occurs in the presence of base to produce the carboxylate salt and alcohol.
Objective 8 (Section 15.7), Exercise 15.54

Esters of Inorganic Acids

Alcohols can also form esters by reacting with inorganic acids such as phosphoric acid. **Objective 9 (Section 15.8), Exercise 15.56** Phosphate esters represent some of the most important biological compounds.

Key Terms and Concepts

Carboxyl group (Introduction)
Carboxylate ion (15.3)
Carboxylic acid (Introduction)
Carboxylic acid anhydride (15.5)
Carboxylic acid chloride (15.5)

Carboxylic ester (15.5)
Condensation polymerization (15.5)
Dimer (15.2)
Ester (15.8)
Esterification (15.5)

Ester linkage (15.5)
Fatty acid (15.1)
Phosphoric anhydride (15.8)
Saponification (15.7)

Key Reactions

1.	Dissociation of a carboxylic acid to give a carboxylate ion (Section 15.3):	$$R - \overset{\overset{\textstyle O}{\|}}{C} - O - H + H_2O \rightleftarrows R - \overset{\overset{\textstyle O}{\|}}{C} - O^- + H_3O^+$$	Reaction 15.1
2.	Reaction of a carboxylic acid with base to produce a carboxylate salt plus water (Section 15.3):	$$R - \overset{\overset{\textstyle O}{\|}}{C} - O - H + NaOH \longrightarrow R - \overset{\overset{\textstyle O}{\|}}{C} - O^-Na^+ + H_2O$$	Reaction 15.4
3.	Reaction of a carboxylic acid with an alcohol to produce an ester plus water (Section 15.5):	$$R - \overset{\overset{\textstyle O}{\|}}{C} - OH + H - O - R' \underset{}{\overset{H^+, \text{ heat}}{\rightleftarrows}} R - \overset{\overset{\textstyle O}{\|}}{C} - O - R' + H_2O$$	Reaction 15.8
4.	Reaction of a carboxylic acid chloride with an alcohol to produce an ester plus hydrogen chloride (Section 15.5):	$$R - \overset{\overset{\textstyle O}{\|}}{C} - Cl + HO - R' \longrightarrow R - \overset{\overset{\textstyle O}{\|}}{C} - O - R' + HCl$$	Reaction 15.12
5.	Reaction of a carboxylic acid anhydride with an alcohol to produce an ester plus a carboxylic acid (Section 15.5):	$$R - \overset{\overset{\textstyle O}{\|}}{C} - O - \overset{\overset{\textstyle O}{\|}}{C} - R + HO - R' \longrightarrow R - \overset{\overset{\textstyle O}{\|}}{C} - O - R' + R - \overset{\overset{\textstyle O}{\|}}{C} - OH$$	Reaction 15.13
6.	Ester hydrolysis to produce a carboxylic acid and alcohol (Section 15.7):	$$R - \overset{\overset{\textstyle O}{\|}}{C} - OR' + H - OH \overset{H^+}{\rightleftarrows} R - \overset{\overset{\textstyle O}{\|}}{C} - OH + R' - OH$$	Reaction 15.17
7.	Ester saponification to give a carboxylate salt and alcohol (Section 15.7):	$$R - \overset{\overset{\textstyle O}{\|}}{C} - OR' + NaOH \longrightarrow R - \overset{\overset{\textstyle O}{\|}}{C} - O^-Na^+ + R' - OH$$	Reaction 15.19
8.	Phosphate ester formation (Section 15.8):	$$R - OH + HO - \underset{\underset{\textstyle OH}{\|}}{\overset{\overset{\textstyle O}{\|}}{P}} - OH \rightleftarrows R - O - \underset{\underset{\textstyle OH}{\|}}{\overset{\overset{\textstyle O}{\|}}{P}} - OH + H_2O$$	Reaction 15.21

Exercises

Even-numbered exercises are answered in Appendix B.

Blue-numbered exercises are more challenging.

The Nomenclature of Carboxylic Acids (Section 15.1)

15.1 What is the structure of the carboxylic acid functional group? How does it differ from the structure of an alcohol and from that of an aldehyde or a ketone?

15.2 What structural features are characteristic of fatty acids? Why are fatty acids given that name?

15.3 What compound is responsible for the sour or tart taste of Italian salad dressing (vinegar and oil)?

15.4 What carboxylic acid is present in sour milk and sauerkraut?

15.5 Write the correct IUPAC name for each of the following:

a. $CH_3CH_2CH_2 - \overset{\overset{O}{\|}}{C} - OH$

b. $CH_3 - O - CH_2CH_2 - \overset{\overset{O}{\|}}{C} - OH$

c. $CH_3\overset{\overset{CH_3}{|}}{C}H\overset{}{C}HCH_2 - \overset{\overset{O}{\|}}{C} - OH$ with Br below

d. benzene ring with $\overset{\overset{O}{\|}}{C} - OH$ and CH_2CH_3

e. $CH_3\overset{\overset{O}{\|}\ C - OH}{C}HCH_2CH_2 - Br$

15.6 Write the correct IUPAC name for each of the following:

a. $CH_3\overset{}{C}H - \overset{\overset{O}{\|}}{C} - OH$ with CH_3 below

b. $Br - CH_2CH_2CH_2 - \overset{\overset{O}{\|}}{C} - OH$

c. benzene ring with $\overset{\overset{O}{\|}}{C} - OH$ and $\overset{}{C}HCH_3$ with CH_3 below

d. $CH_3CH_2\overset{\overset{OCH_3}{|}}{C}HCH_2 - \overset{\overset{O}{\|}}{C} - OH$

e. benzene ring with $CH_2CH_2CH_2 - \overset{\overset{O}{\|}}{C} - OH$

15.7 Write a structural formula for each of the following:

a. hexanoic acid

b. 4-bromo-3-methylpentanoic acid

c. o-ethylbenzoic acid

15.8 Write a structural formula for each of the following:

a. pentanoic acid

b. 2-bromo-3-methylhexanoic acid

c. 4-propylbenzoic acid

Physical Properties of Carboxylic Acids (Section 15.2)

15.9 Of the classes of organic compounds studied so far, which have particularly unpleasant odors?

15.10 Which compound in each of the following pairs would you expect to have the higher boiling point? Explain your answer.

a. acetic acid or 1-propanol

b. propanoic acid or butanone

c. acetic acid or butyric acid

15.11 List the following compounds in order of increasing boiling point:

a. pentanal

b. hexane

c. 1-pentanol

d. butanoic acid

15.12 Draw the structure of the dimer formed when two molecules of propanoic acid hydrogen bond with each other.

15.13 The two isomers propanoic acid and methyl acetate are both liquids. One boils at 141°C, the other at 57°C.

$$CH_3CH_2 - \overset{\overset{O}{\|}}{C} - OH \qquad CH_3 - \overset{\overset{O}{\|}}{C} - OCH_3$$
propanoic acid methyl acetate

a. Predict which compound boils at 57°C and which at 141°C. Explain your reasoning.

b. Which of these two compounds would you predict to be more soluble in water? Explain.

15.14 Caproic acid, a six-carbon acid, has a solubility in water of 1 g/100 mL of water (Table 15.2). Which part of the structure of caproic acid is responsible for its solubility in water, and which part prevents greater solubility?

15.15 Why are acetic acid, sodium acetate, and sodium caprate all soluble in water, whereas capric acid, a 10-carbon fatty acid, is not?

15.16 List the following compounds in order of increasing water solubility:

 a. ethoxyethane

 b. propanoic acid

 c. pentane

 d. 1-butanol

15.17 List the following compounds in order of increasing water solubility:

 a. hexane **c.** 2-pentanone

 b. 1-pentanol **d.** valeric acid

The acidity of carboxylic acids (section 15.3)

15.18 Draw the structural formula for the carboxylate ion of propanoic acid.

15.19 What is the most important chemical property of carboxylic acids?

15.20 As we discuss the cellular importance of lactic acid in a later chapter, we will refer to this compound as lactate. Explain why.

$$CH_3-\overset{\overset{\displaystyle OH}{|}}{CH}-\overset{\overset{\displaystyle O}{\|}}{C}-OH$$

lactic acid

15.21 Write an equation to illustrate the equilibrium that is present when propanoic acid is dissolved in water. What structure predominates when OH^- is added to raise the pH to 12? What structure predominates as acid is added to lower the pH to 2?

15.22 Draw a structural formula that shows which form of butyric acid would predominate at a pH of 2.

15.23 Complete each of the following reactions:

 a. $CH_3(CH_2)_7-\overset{\overset{\displaystyle O}{\|}}{C}-OH + NaOH \longrightarrow$

 b.
$+ KOH \longrightarrow$

15.24 Complete each of the following reactions:

 a. $CH_3CH_2-\overset{\overset{\displaystyle O}{\|}}{C}-OH + NaOH \longrightarrow$

 b. $CH_3\overset{\overset{\displaystyle OH}{|}}{CH}-\overset{\overset{\displaystyle O}{\|}}{C}-OH + KOH \longrightarrow$

15.25 Write a balanced equation for the reaction of propanoic acid with each of the following:

 a. KOH

 b. H_2O

 c. NaOH

15.26 Write a balanced equation for the reaction of acetic acid with each of the following:

 a. NaOH

 b. KOH

 c. $Ca(OH)_2$

Salts of Carboxylic Acids (Section 15.4)

15.27 Give the IUPAC name for each of the following:

 a. $CH_3CH_2-\overset{\overset{\displaystyle O}{\|}}{C}-O^-Na^+$ **c.**

 b. $CH_3\overset{\overset{\displaystyle CH_3}{|}}{CH}-\overset{\overset{\displaystyle O}{\|}}{C}-O^-K^+$

15.28 Give the IUPAC name for each of the following:

 a. $CH_3\overset{\overset{\displaystyle Br}{|}}{CH}CH_2-\overset{\overset{\displaystyle O}{\|}}{C}-O^-Na^+$

 b. $(H-\overset{\overset{\displaystyle O}{\|}}{C}-O^-)_2Ca^{2+}$

 c.

15.29 Draw structural formulas for the following:

 a. sodium methanoate

 b. calcium 3-methylbutanoate

 c. potassium p-propylbenzoate

15.30 Draw structural formulas for the following:

 a. potassium ethanoate

 b. sodium m-methylbenzoate

 c. sodium 2-methylbutanoate

15.31 Name each of the following:

 a. The sodium salt of valeric acid

 b. The magnesium salt of lactic acid

 c. The potassium salt of citric acid

15.32 Give the name of a carboxylic acid or carboxylate salt used in each of the following ways:

 a. As a soap

 b. As a general food preservative used to pickle vegetables

 c. As a preservative used in soft drinks

 d. As a treatment for athlete's foot

 e. As a mold inhibitor used in bread

 f. As a food additive noted for its pH buffering ability

Carboxylic Esters (Section 15.5)

15.33 Which of the following compounds are esters?

 a. C₆H₅ group — CH₂ — O — CH₂ — OH

 b.
$$CH_3 - \overset{\overset{\displaystyle O}{\|}}{C} - O - CH_2CH_3$$

 c.
$$CH_3CH_2 - \underset{\underset{\displaystyle OCH_3}{|}}{CH} - OCH_3$$

 d.
ring — O — $\overset{\overset{\displaystyle O}{\|}}{C}$ — CH₃

 e.
$$CH_3 - O - CH_2 - \overset{\overset{\displaystyle O}{\|}}{C} - CH_2 - OH$$

 f.
ring — $\overset{\overset{\displaystyle O}{\|}}{C}$ — O — CH₂CH₃

15.34 For each ester in Exercise 15.33, draw a circle around the portion that came from the acid and use an arrow to point out the *ester linkage.*

15.35 Complete the following reactions:

 a.
ring — $\overset{\overset{\displaystyle O}{\|}}{C}$ — OH + CH₃CH — OH $\underset{}{\overset{H^+, \text{ heat}}{\rightleftharpoons}}$ with CH₃ below

 b.
ring — $\overset{\overset{\displaystyle O}{\|}}{C}$ — Cl + CH₃CH — OH $\longrightarrow$ with CH₃ below

 c.
ring — $\overset{\overset{\displaystyle O}{\|}}{C}$ — O — $\overset{\overset{\displaystyle O}{\|}}{C}$ — ring + CH₃ — OH $\longrightarrow$

15.36 Complete the following reactions:

 a.
$$CH_3 - \overset{\overset{\displaystyle O}{\|}}{C} - O - \overset{\overset{\displaystyle O}{\|}}{C} - CH_3 + CH_3 - OH \longrightarrow$$

 b.
$$CH_3CH - \overset{\overset{\displaystyle O}{\|}}{C} - OH + \text{(ring—CH}_2\text{—OH)} \overset{H^+, \text{ heat}}{\rightleftharpoons}$$
with CH₃ below

 c.
$$CH_3CH - \overset{\overset{\displaystyle O}{\|}}{C} - Cl + \text{(ring—OH)} \longrightarrow$$
with CH₃ below

15.37 Using the alcohol CH₃CH₂—OH, show three different starting compounds that may be used to synthesize the ester:

$$CH_3CH_2CH_2 - \overset{\overset{\displaystyle O}{\|}}{C} - O - CH_2CH_3$$

15.38 Give the structures of the ester that forms when propanoic acid is reacted with the following:

 a. methyl alcohol

 b. phenol

 c. 2-methyl-1-propanol

15.39 The structures of two esters used as artificial flavorings are given below. Write the structure of the acid and the alcohol from which each ester could be synthesized.

 a. Pineapple flavoring,

$$CH_3CH_2CH_2 - \overset{\overset{\displaystyle O}{\|}}{C} - O - CH_2CH_2CH_2CH_3$$

 b. Apple flavoring,

$$CH_3CH_2CH_2 - \overset{\overset{\displaystyle O}{\|}}{C} - O - CH_3$$

15.40 Heroin is formed by reacting morphine with 2 mol of

$$CH_3 - \overset{\overset{\displaystyle O}{\|}}{C} - Cl$$
to form the diester. Show the structure of heroin.

morphine

15.41 How do the acids and alcohols involved in polyester formation differ from those that commonly form simple esters?

15.42 Draw the structure of the repeating monomer unit in the polyester formed in the condensation of oxalic acid and 1,3-propanediol.

$$HO-\overset{\overset{O}{\|}}{C}-\overset{\overset{O}{\|}}{C}-OH + \overset{\overset{OH}{|}}{CH_2}-\overset{\overset{OH}{|}}{CH_2}-CH_2 \rightleftharpoons$$

The Nomenclature of Esters (Section 15.6)

15.43 Assign common names to the following esters. Refer to Table 15.1 for the common names of the acids.

a. $H-\overset{\overset{O}{\|}}{C}-O-CH_2CH_3$

b. $CH_3(CH_2)_4-\overset{\overset{O}{\|}}{C}-O-\overset{\overset{}{\underset{\underset{CH_3}{|}}{CHCH_3}}}{}$

15.44 Assign common names to the following esters. Refer to Table 15.1 for the common names of the acids.

a. $CH_3\overset{}{\underset{\underset{OH}{|}}{CH}}-\overset{\overset{O}{\|}}{C}-O-CH_2CH_3$

b. $CH_3CH_2CH_2-\overset{\overset{O}{\|}}{C}-O-CH_2CH_2CH_3$

15.45 Give the IUPAC name for each of the following:

a. $CH_3CH_2CH_2-\overset{\overset{O}{\|}}{C}-O-CH_2CH_3$

b. $\overset{\overset{O}{\|}}{C}-O-\overset{}{\underset{\underset{CH_3}{|}}{CHCH_3}}$ (with CH_3 on benzene ring)

15.46 Give the IUPAC name for each of the following:

a. $CH_3\overset{}{\underset{\underset{CH_3}{|}}{CH}}-\overset{\overset{O}{\|}}{C}-OCH_3$

b. $\overset{\overset{O}{\|}}{C}-O-CH_2CH_3$ (benzene ring with two Cl substituents)

15.47 Assign IUPAC names to the simple esters produced by a reaction between ethanoic acid and the following:

a. ethanol

b. 1-propanol

c. 1-butanol

15.48 Assign common names to the simple esters produced by a reaction between methanol and the following:

a. propionic acid

b. butyric acid

c. lactic acid

15.49 Draw structural formulas for the following:

a. methyl ethanoate

b. propyl 2-bromobenzoate

c. ethyl 3,4-dimethylpentanoate

15.50 Draw structural formulas for the following:

a. phenyl formate

b. methyl 4-nitrobenzoate

c. ethyl 2-chloropropanoate

Reactions of Esters (Section 15.7)

15.51 Define and compare the terms *ester hydrolysis* and *saponification*.

15.52 Write equations for the hydrolysis and saponification of ethyl acetate:

$$CH_3-\overset{\overset{O}{\|}}{C}-OCH_2CH_3$$

15.53 Complete the following reactions:

a. $CH_3CH_2\overset{}{\underset{\underset{CH_3}{|}}{CH}}-\overset{\overset{O}{\|}}{C}-O-CH_2CH_3 + NaOH \longrightarrow$

b. $CH_3(CH_2)_{10}-\overset{\overset{O}{\|}}{C}-O-CH_2CHCH_3 + H_2O \overset{H^+}{\rightleftharpoons}$ (with benzene ring)

15.54 Complete the following reactions:

a. $CH_3(CH_2)_{16}-\overset{\overset{O}{\|}}{C}-O-CH_2CH_3 + NaOH \longrightarrow$

b. $CH_3\overset{}{\underset{\underset{CH_3}{|}}{CH}}-\overset{\overset{O}{\|}}{C}-O-\bigcirc + H_2O \overset{H^+}{\rightleftharpoons}$

Esters of Inorganic Acids (Section 15.8)

15.55 Glyceraldehyde-3-phosphate, an important compound in the cellular oxidation of carbohydrates, is an ester of phosphoric acid and glyceraldehyde.

$$
\begin{array}{c}
O\!\!=\!\!\underset{|}{C}\!-\!H \\
H-\underset{|}{C}-OH \quad O \\
CH_2-O-\overset{\|}{\underset{|}{P}}-O^- \\
O^-
\end{array}
$$

 a. Give the structure of glyceraldehyde.

 b. Why is glyceraldehyde-3-phosphate shown with a 2^- charge?

15.56 Dihydroxyacetone reacts with phosphoric acid to form the monoester called dihydroxyacetone phosphate. Complete the reaction for its formation.

$$
\underset{\text{dihydroxyacetone}}{CH_2-\overset{O}{\overset{\|}{C}}-CH_2} + HO-\overset{O}{\underset{OH}{\overset{\|}{P}}}-OH \longrightarrow
$$

(with OH groups: $\overset{OH}{|}\ \overset{OH}{|}$ on the CH_2 carbons)

15.57 Give the structure for the following:

 a. monoethyl phosphate (with a 2^- charge)

 b. monoethyl diphosphate (with a 3^- charge)

 c. monoethyl triphosphate (with a 4^- charge)

Additional Exercises

15.58 Explain how a sodium bicarbonate ($NaHCO_3$) solution can be used to distinguish between a carboxylic acid solution and an alcohol solution.

15.59 The following reaction requires several steps. Show the reagents you would use and draw structural formulas for intermediate compounds formed in each step.

$$
H_2C\!=\!CH_2 \longrightarrow CH_3\overset{O}{\overset{\|}{C}}-O-CH_2CH_3
$$

15.60 Draw the structural formula and give the IUPAC name for the ester that results when 3-ethylhexanoic acid reacts with phenol.

15.61 How many mL of a 0.100 M NaOH solution would be needed to titrate 0.156 g of butanoic acid to a neutral pH endpoint?

15.62 Identify two things that can be done to the following equilibrium to achieve 100% conversion of butanoic acid to ethyl butanoate.

$$
CH_3CH_2CH_2\overset{O}{\overset{\|}{C}}-OH + CH_3CH_2OH \rightleftharpoons
$$
$$
CH_3CH_2CH_2\overset{O}{\overset{\|}{C}}-O-CH_2CH_3 + H_2O
$$

Allied Health Exam Connection

The following questions are from these sources:

1. *Nursing School Entrance Exam* © 2005, Learning Express, LLC.

2. *McGraw-Hill's Nursing School Entrance Exams* by Thomas A. Evangelist, Tamara B. Orr and Judy Unrein © 2009, The McGraw-Hill Companies, Inc.

3. *NSEE Nursing School Entrance Exams,* 3rd Edition © 2009, Kaplan Publishing.

4. *Cliffs Test Prep: Nursing School Entrance Exams* by Fred N. Grayson © 2004, Wiley Publishing, Inc.

5. *Peterson's Master the Nursing School and Allied Health Entrance Exams,* 18th Edition by Marion F. Gooding © 2008, Peterson's, a Nelnet Company.

15.63 Identify the functional group designated by each of the following:

 a. ROR

 b. RCOOH

 c. R

 d. RCHO

 e. $R-\overset{O}{\overset{\|}{C}}-R'$

15.64 Rank the following compounds from the one containing the greatest polarity to the one with the least polarity. Also, rank the compounds in order of increasing boiling points.

 a. CH_3CH_2-OH

 b. CH_3-O-CH_3

 c. $CH_3CH_2CH_3$

 d. CH_3COOH

15.65 Fats belong to the class of organic compounds represented by the general formula, $RCOOR'$, where R and R' represent hydrocarbon groups; therefore, fats are:

 a. ethers

 b. soaps

 c. esters

 d. lipases

Chemistry for Thought

15.66 Citric acid is often added to carbonated beverages as a flavoring. Why is citric acid viewed as a "safe" food additive?

15.67 Ester formation (Reaction 15.8) and ester hydrolysis (Reaction 15.17) are exactly the same reaction only written in reverse. What determines which direction the reaction proceeds and what actually forms?

15.68 Write a mechanism for the following reaction. Show the final location of the oxygen atom in the second color.

$$
CH_3CH_2-\overset{O}{\overset{\|}{C}}-O-CH_3 + NaOH \longrightarrow
$$

15.69 Answer the question in Figure 15.1. What flavor sensation is characteristic of acids?

15.70 Oxalic acid, the substance mentioned in Figure 15.2, has two carboxyl groups. If you were to give this compound an IUPAC name, what ending would be appropriate?

15.71 Why is it safe for us to consume foods like vinegar that contain acetic acids?

15.72 A Dacron patch is sometimes used in heart surgery. Why do polyesters like the Dacron patch resist hydrolysis reactions that would result in deterioration of the patch?

15.73 Citrus fruits such as grapefruit and oranges may be kept for several weeks without refrigeration. Offer some possible reasons why the spoilage rate is not higher.

15.74 In Section 18.3, locate the structure of a triglyceride. Draw its structure and circle the ester linkages.

15.75 Section 21.2 shows a tetranucleotide structure. Draw a portion of the structure and circle the portion representing the phosphate diester.

16 Amines and Amides

© iStockphoto.com/Kenneth Sponsler

Case Study

Koji was a rambunctious 6-year-old. His mother, Masumi, and her friend went to the park and let their children play together. Koji and his friend Ben were exploring the edge of the park, their "magical forest." They gathered sticks and built a fort—such fun! That night, however, Koji broke out in an itchy rash. An Internet search led Masumi to conclude it was poison ivy. Calamine lotion and antihistamines were recommended. She rushed to the store, where she bought supplies to treat the rash. She gave Koji a generic allergy medication containing diphenhydramine then slathered him with the pink lotion. The next morning she had trouble waking him, and he went right back to sleep. The doctor she called instructed her to bring him to the hospital along with bottles of any medications he had been given. Masumi was told that Koji had been overdosed with antihistamine. Not only had Masumi given him too much oral medication for his weight, she had not noticed that the lotion she gave him contained diphenhydramine as well as calamine. Koji was treated and expected to recover from the frightening ordeal.

How can the public be better educated about using remedies that contain mixtures of common medications? Are mixed medications a good idea? What are the symptoms of antihistamine overdose?

Follow-up to this Case Study appears at the end the chapter before the Concept Summary.

Learning Objectives

When you have completed your study of this chapter, you should be able to:

1 Given structural formulas, classify amines as primary, secondary, or tertiary. **(Section 16.1)**

2 Assign common and IUPAC names to simple amines. **(Section 16.2)**

3 Discuss how hydrogen bonding influences the physical properties of amines. **(Section 16.3)**

4 Recognize and write key reactions for amines. **(Section 16.4)**

5 Name amines used as neurotransmitters. **(Section 16.5)**

6 Give uses for specific biological amines. **(Section 16.6)**

7 Assign IUPAC names for amides. **(Section 16.7)**

8 Show the formation of hydrogen bonds with amides. **(Section 16.8)**

9 Give the products of acidic and basic hydrolysis of amides. **(Section 16.9)**

The effectiveness of a wide variety of important medicines depends either entirely or partly on the presence of a nitrogen-containing group in their molecules. Nitrogen-containing functional groups are found in more medications than any other type of functional group. In this chapter, we will study two important classes of organic nitrogen compounds, the amines and the amides.

Both amines and amides are abundant in nature, where they play important roles in the chemistry of life. Our study of these two functional classes will help prepare us for later chapters dealing with amino acids, proteins, and nucleic acids and provide a basis for understanding the structures and chemistry of a number of medicines.

16.1 Classification of Amines

Learning Objective

1. Given structural formulas, classify amines as primary, secondary, or tertiary.

amine An organic compound derived by replacing one or more of the hydrogen atoms of ammonia with alkyl or aromatic groups, as in RNH_2, R_2NH, and R_3N.

primary amine An amine having one alkyl or aromatic group bonded to nitrogen, as in $R-NH_2$.

secondary amine An amine having two alkyl or aromatic groups bonded to nitrogen, as in R_2NH.

tertiary amine An amine having three alkyl or aromatic groups bonded to nitrogen, as in R_3N.

Amines are organic derivatives of ammonia, NH_3, in which one or more of the hydrogens are replaced by an aromatic or alkyl group (R). Like alcohols, amines are classified as primary, secondary, or tertiary on the basis of molecular structure. However, the classification is done differently. When classifying amines, the number of groups (R) that have replaced hydrogens in the NH_3 is counted. The nitrogen atom in a **primary amine** is bonded to one R group. The nitrogen in **secondary amines** is bonded to two R groups, and that of **tertiary amines** is bonded to three R groups. These amine subclasses are summarized in ▶ Table 16.1.

TABLE 16.1 Subclasses of Amines

Subclass	General Formula	Example
Primary (1°)	R—N—H \| H	CH_3—N—H \| H
Secondary (2°)	R—N—R′ \| H	CH_3—N—CH_3 \| H
Tertiary (3°)	R—N—R′ \| R″	CH_3—N—CH_3 \| CH_3

▶ **LEARNING CHECK 16.1** Classify each of the following amines as primary, secondary, or tertiary:

a. $CH_3 - \overset{\overset{\displaystyle H}{\displaystyle |}}{N} - CH_2CH_3$

b. ⬡$-N-H$

c. ⬡$-N-CH_3$ with CH_3 below N

16.2 The Nomenclature of Amines

Learning Objective

2. Assign common and IUPAC names to simple amines.

Several approaches are used in naming amines. Common names are used extensively for those with low molecular weights. These are named by alphabetically linking the names of the alkyl or aromatic groups bonded to the nitrogen and attaching the suffix *-amine*. The name is written as one word, and the prefixes *di-* and *tri-* are used when identical alkyl groups are present. Some examples are

CH_3-NH_2
methylamine

$CH_3-NH-CH_3$
dimethylamine

$CH_3CH_2-NH-CH_3$
ethylmethylamine

▶ LEARNING CHECK 16.2 Assign a common name to the following amines:

a. $CH_3CH_2CH_2-NH_2$　　**b.** ⬡$-NH-CH_3$　　**c.** $CH_3-\underset{\underset{\displaystyle CH_3}{|}}{N}-CH_3$

An IUPAC approach for naming amines is similar to that for alcohols. The root name is determined by the longest continuous chain of carbon atoms. The -e ending in the alkane name is changed to –amine. The position of the amino group on the chain is shown by a number. Numbers are also used to locate other substituents on the carbon chain. An italic capital N is used as a prefix for a substituent on nitrogen.

$CH_3CH_2CH_2\underset{\underset{\displaystyle NH_2}{|}}{C}HCH_3$ 　　$\underset{\underset{\displaystyle CH_3CHCH_2CH_2}{}}{\overset{\overset{\displaystyle CH_3 \quad NH_2}{|\quad\quad|}}{}}$ 　　$\underset{\underset{\displaystyle CH_3CH_2CHCH_3}{}}{\overset{\overset{\displaystyle NHCH_3}{|}}{}}$

2-pentanamine 　　　3-methyl-1-butanamine 　　N-methyl-2-butanamine

▶ LEARNING CHECK 16.3 Give an IUPAC name for the following amines:

a. $CH_3CH_2CH_2CH_2-NH_2$　　**b.** $CH_3CH_2CH_2\underset{\underset{\displaystyle NHCH_3}{|}}{C}H_2$

Aromatic amines are usually given names (both common and IUPAC) based on aniline, the simplest aromatic amine. They are named as substituted anilines, and an italic capital N is used to indicate that an alkyl group is attached to the nitrogen and not to the ring. If two groups are attached to the nitrogen, an italic capital N is used for each one. Some examples are

⬡NH_2　　　⬡$-NH-CH_3$　　　⬡$\overset{\displaystyle -NH-CH_3}{-CH_2CH_3}$　　　⬡$-\underset{\underset{\displaystyle CH_3}{}}{\overset{\overset{\displaystyle CH_3}{|}}{N}}-CH_3$

aniline 　　N-methylaniline 　　2-ethyl-N-methylaniline 　　N,N-dimethylaniline

▶ LEARNING CHECK 16.4 Name the following amines as derivatives of aniline:

a. ⬡$-NH-CH_2CH_3$　　**c.** ⬡$\overset{\displaystyle NH_2}{\underset{\displaystyle CH_2CH_3}{-CH_3}}$

b. ⬡$-\underset{\underset{\displaystyle }{}}{\overset{\overset{\displaystyle CH_3}{|}}{N}}-CH_2CH_3$

DR. MELINA B. JAMPOLIS, M.D.

© Michael Roud Photography

Dr. Melina B. Jampolis, M.D. is a Los Angeles, California, Physician Nutrition Specialist—a specialty practiced by only a few hundred physicians in the United States. She focuses exclusively on nutrition for weight loss and disease prevention and treatment.

Ask an Expert 16.1

Q: Does caffeine help with weight loss?

A: Caffeine, a synthetic and naturally occurring alkaloid, is found in numerous plant products including kola nuts, cacao bean, yerba mate, guarana berries, and the two most common dietary sources, roasted coffee beans and tea leaves. It is also included in many energy drinks and weight-reducing supplements due to its ability to stimulate the sympathetic nervous system, thereby boosting metabolism and increasing lipolysis, the breakdown of fat. Caffeine is also a well-established ergogenic aid that enhances athletic performance and decreases fatigue by increasing mental alertness and improving the utilization of fat as fuel during exercise.

Although numerous studies have found that caffeine does increase daily caloric expenditure, the effect is modest in terms of weight loss. One study showed that after consuming 300 mg of caffeine (the amount in three regular cups of coffee), overweight subjects burned 79 more calories during the following 24 hours. When you consider that most weight-loss programs recommend a 500 calorie deficit per day in order to lose one pound of fat per week, it is clear that eating a lower calorie diet and exercising regularly are far more effective in terms of weight loss than caffeine consumption. In addition, most of the coffee drinks, bottled teas, and energy drinks that Americans consume contain far more than 79 calories, so their metabolism-boosting effect is completely offset by the additional calories ingested.

In terms of weight loss, the research is somewhat more promising when caffeine is combined with other bioactive ingredients. In particular, research looking at the combination of green tea catechins (GTCs), polyphenols found in unfermented tea leaves, and caffeine has shown positive results in terms of weight loss, especially metabolically toxic visceral adiposity, commonly referred to as "belly fat." Similar to caffeine, GTCs stimulate the central nervous system, so they might have a synergistic effect in terms of boosting metabolism and improving fat oxidation. In addition, GTC might decrease appetite and nutrient absorption, which might contribute further to their role in weight loss.

Epigallocatechin gallate (EGCG) is the most abundant catechin in green tea and is often found in extract form in weight-loss supplements. A recent study found a modest but significant reduction in body mass index, body weight, and waist circumference when GTCs were combined with caffeine, but not when they were consumed alone. Most of the research on GTCs has been done with green tea extracts because the higher doses required for weight loss would be very difficult to obtain from simply drinking green tea. The optimal dose of GTC plus caffeine for weight loss has not been established, and a supplement might not be as effective if you are already consuming several cups of coffee per day.

So, if your goal is weight loss, caffeine alone probably won't help very much. If a little caffeine motivates you to exercise—or gives you a pre-workout boost, allowing you to exercise more effectively—there is no harm in drinking a cup of coffee or green tea (without a lot of sugar or cream) before workouts. In terms of supplements, the modest effect (often achieved at high financial cost) and the variability in quality and amount of active ingredient make them difficult to recommend for most people trying to lose weight. If you are watching what you eat and exercising regularly, or if you have hit a weight-loss plateau, they might be worth a try, but the effects will probably be modest at best. And if caffeine in any form interferes with your sleep, this could have a negative impact on weight loss because sleep deprivation has been shown in numerous studies to correlate with weight gain.

Tea is a common source of c

16.3 Physical Properties of Amines

Learning Objective

3. Discuss how hydrogen bonding influences the physical properties of amines.

The simple, low molecular weight amines are gases at room temperature (see ▶ Table 16.2). Heavier, more complex compounds are liquids or solids.

TABLE 16.2 Properties of Some Amines

Name	Structure	Melting Point (°C)	Boiling Point (°C)
methylamine	$CH_3 - NH_2$	−94	−6
ethylamine	$CH_3CH_2 - NH_2$	−81	17
dimethylamine	$CH_3 - NH - CH_3$	−93	7
diethylamine	$CH_3CH_2 - NH - CH_2CH_3$	−48	56
trimethylamine	$CH_3 - \underset{\underset{CH_3}{\mid}}{N} - CH_3$	−117	3
triethylamine	$CH_3CH_2 - \underset{\underset{CH_2CH_3}{\mid}}{N} - CH_2CH_3$	−114	89

Like alcohols, primary and secondary amines form hydrogen bonds among themselves:

$$CH_3 - \underset{\underset{H}{\mid}}{N} - H \cdots \underset{\underset{H}{\mid}}{\overset{\overset{H}{\mid}}{N}} - CH_3$$

Because nitrogen is less electronegative than oxygen, the hydrogen bonds formed by amines are weaker than those formed by alcohols. For this reason, the boiling points of primary and secondary amines are usually somewhat lower than the boiling points of alcohols with similar molecular weights. Tertiary amines cannot form hydrogen bonds among themselves (because the nitrogen has no attached hydrogen atom), and their boiling points are similar to alkanes that have about the same molecular weights.

Amines with fewer than six carbon atoms are generally soluble in water as a result of hydrogen bond formation between amine functional groups and water molecules. This is true for tertiary as well as primary and secondary amines (see ▶ Figure 16.1).

1° amine 2° amine 3° amine

Figure 16.1 Hydrogen bonding between amines in water.

Low molecular weight amines have a sharp, penetrating odor similar to that of ammonia. Somewhat larger amines have an unpleasant odor reminiscent of decaying

fish. In fact, some amines are partially responsible for the odor of decaying animal tissue. Two such compounds have especially descriptive common names—putrescine and cadaverine:

$$H_2N—CH_2CH_2CH_2CH_2—NH_2$$
putrescine
(1,4-diaminobutane)

$$H_2N—CH_2CH_2CH_2CH_2CH_2—NH_2$$
cadaverine
(1,5-diaminopentane)

▶ **LEARNING CHECK 16.5** Draw structural formulas to show how each of the following amines forms hydrogen bonds with water:

a. $CH_3—\overset{\displaystyle |}{\underset{\displaystyle H}{N}}—H$ **b.** $CH_3CH_2—\overset{\displaystyle |}{\underset{\displaystyle CH_3}{N}}—CH_3$

16.4 Chemical Properties of Amines

Learning Objective

4. Recognize and write key reactions for amines.

Amines undergo many chemical reactions, but we will limit our study to the two most important properties of amines: basicity and amide formation.

Basicity and Amine Salts

The single most distinguishing feature of amines is their behavior as weak bases. They are the most common organic bases. We know from inorganic chemistry that ammonia behaves as a Brønsted base by accepting protons, and in the process becomes a conjugate acid. The reaction of NH_3 with HCl gas illustrates this point (Reaction 16.1):

$$\underset{\text{ammonia}}{H—\overset{\displaystyle |}{\underset{\displaystyle H}{N}}:} + H—Cl \longrightarrow \left[\underset{\substack{\text{ammonium}\\\text{ion}}}{H—\overset{\displaystyle |}{\underset{\displaystyle H}{N}}—H}\right]^{+} + \underset{\substack{\text{chloride}\\\text{ion}}}{Cl^{-}} \qquad (16.1)$$

We also remember from inorganic chemistry that Brønsted bases such as ammonia react with water to liberate OH^- ions (Reaction 16.2):

$$\underset{\text{ammonia}}{H—\overset{\displaystyle |}{\underset{\displaystyle H}{N}}:} + \underset{\text{water}}{H—OH} \rightleftharpoons \left[\underset{\substack{\text{ammonium}\\\text{ion}}}{H—\overset{\displaystyle |}{\underset{\displaystyle H}{N}}—H}\right]^{+} + \underset{\substack{\text{hydroxide}\\\text{ion}}}{OH^{-}} \qquad (16.2)$$

Because the amines are derivatives of ammonia, they react in similar ways. In water, they produce OH^- ions:

General reaction: $R—NH_2 + H_2O \rightleftharpoons R—NH_3^{+} + OH^{-}$ (16.3)

Specific reaction: $\underset{\text{methylamine}}{CH_3—NH_2} + H_2O \rightleftharpoons \underset{\substack{\text{methylammonium}\\\text{ion}}}{CH_3—NH_3^{+}} + OH^{-}$ (16.4)

▶ Example 16.1

Complete the following reaction:

$$CH_3-NH-CH_3 + H_2O \rightleftharpoons$$

Solution

Primary, secondary, and tertiary amines are all basic and exhibit the same reaction in water.

$$CH_3-NH-CH_3 + H_2O \rightleftharpoons CH_3-\overset{+}{N}H_2-CH_3 + OH^-$$

▶ **LEARNING CHECK 16.6** Complete the following reactions:

a. $CH_3-\underset{\underset{CH_3}{|}}{N}-CH_2CH_3 + H_2O \rightleftharpoons$
b. ⬡$-NH_2 + H_2O \rightleftharpoons$

All amines behave as weak bases and form salts when they react with acids such as HCl:

General reaction:	$R-NH_2 + HCl \rightarrow R-NH_3{}^+Cl^-$	(16.5)
	amine acid amine salt	

Specific example:	$CH_3-NH_2 + HCl \rightarrow CH_3-NH_3{}^+Cl^-$	(16.6)
	methylamine methylammonium chloride	

Other acids, such as sulfuric, nitric, phosphoric, and carboxylic acids (Reaction 16.7), also react with amines to form salts:

$$CH_3CH_2-NH_2 + CH_3COOH \rightarrow CH_3CH_2-NH_3{}^+CH_3COO^- \qquad (16.7)$$

ethylamine acetic acid ethylammonium acetate

▶ **LEARNING CHECK 16.7** Complete the following reactions:

a. ⬡$-NH-CH_3 + HCl \longrightarrow$

b. ⬠$-NH_2$ $+ CH_3CH_2COOH \longrightarrow$

As we have seen, amine salts may be named by changing "amine" to "ammonium" and adding the name of the negative ion derived from the acid. Some more examples are

$$CH_3-\underset{\underset{CH_2CH_3}{|}}{\overset{\overset{CH_3}{|}}{N}}-H^+Br^- \qquad\qquad (CH_3CH_2)_3NH^+CH_3COO^-$$

 ethyldimethylammonium bromide triethylammonium acetate

Amine salts have physical properties characteristic of other ionic compounds. They are white crystalline solids with high melting points. Because they are ionic, amine salts are more soluble in water than the parent amines. For this reason, amine drugs

are often given in the form of salts because they will dissolve in body fluids (see ▶ Figure 16.2).

Figure 16.2 Each of these OTC medications contains an amine salt as the active ingredient.

$$\text{morphine (water insoluble)} + H_2SO_4 \longrightarrow \text{morphine sulfate (water soluble)} \qquad (16.8)$$

morphine
(water insoluble)

morphine sulfate
(water soluble)

Amine salts are easily converted back to amines by adding a strong base:

$$R-NH_3^+Cl^- + NaOH \rightarrow R-NH_2 + H_2O + NaCl \qquad (16.9)$$

The form in which amines occur in solutions is pH dependent, just as is the case for carboxylic acids (Section 15.3). In solutions of high H^+ (low pH), the salt form of amines predominates. In solutions of high OH^- (high pH), the amine form is favored:

$$R-NH_2 \underset{OH^-}{\overset{H^+}{\rightleftarrows}} R-NH_3^+ \qquad (16.10)$$

amine amine salt
(high pH) (low pH)

The amine cations in the salts we have discussed to this point have one, two, or three alkyl groups attached to the nitrogen:

$$R-\overset{+}{N}H_3^+ \qquad R-\overset{+}{N}H_2-R' \qquad R-\overset{+}{N}H-R' \\ \qquad\qquad\qquad\qquad\qquad\qquad | \\ \qquad\qquad\qquad\qquad\qquad\qquad R''$$

primary amine secondary amine tertiary amine
cation cation cation

It is also possible to have amine cations in which four alkyl groups or benzene rings are attached to the nitrogen. An example is:

$$\left[CH_3CH_2-\overset{\overset{\displaystyle CH_2CH_3}{|}}{\underset{\underset{\displaystyle CH_3}{|}}{N}}-CH_2CH_3 \right]^+ \quad Cl^-$$

triethylmethylammonium chloride

quaternary ammonium salt An ionic compound containing a positively charged ion in which four alkyl or aromatic groups are bonded to nitrogen, as in R_4N^+.

These salts are called **quaternary ammonium salts** and are named the same way as other amine salts. Unlike other amine salts, quaternary salts contain no hydrogen attached to the nitrogen that can be removed by adding a base. Thus, quaternary salts are present in solution in only one form, which is independent of the pH of the solution.

Choline is an important quaternary ammonium ion that is a component of certain lipids (Section 18.6); acetylcholine is a compound involved in the transmission of nerve impulses from one cell to another (Section 16.5):

$$\left[HO-CH_2CH_2-\overset{\overset{\displaystyle CH_3}{|}}{\underset{\underset{\displaystyle CH_3}{|}}{N}}-CH_3 \right]^+ \qquad \left[CH_3-\overset{\overset{\displaystyle O}{\|}}{C}-O-CH_2CH_2-\overset{\overset{\displaystyle CH_3}{|}}{\underset{\underset{\displaystyle CH_3}{|}}{N}}-CH_3 \right]^+$$

choline cation acetylcholine cation

Some quaternary ammonium salts are important because they have disinfectant properties. For example, benzalkonium chloride (Zephiran®) is a well-known antiseptic compound that kills many pathogenic (disease-causing) bacteria and fungi on contact:

$$\left[\underset{\displaystyle}{\bigcirc\!\!\!\!\bigcirc} - CH_2 - \underset{\underset{CH_3}{|}}{\overset{\overset{CH_3}{|}}{N}} - R \right]^{+} \quad Cl^{-}$$

Zephiran chloride
(R represents a long alkyl chain)

Its detergent action destroys the membranes that coat and protect the microorganisms. Zephiran® chloride is recommended as a disinfectant solution for skin and hands prior to surgery and for the sterile storage of instruments. The trade names of some other anti-infectives that contain quaternary ammonium salts are Phemerol®, Bactine®, and Ceepryn®.

Amide Formation

Amines react with acid chlorides or acid anhydrides to form amides. The characteristic functional group of **amides** is a carbonyl group attached to nitrogen. The single bond linking the carbonyl carbon and nitrogen atoms in the group is called an **amide linkage:**

$$\overset{\overset{\displaystyle O}{\|}}{-C} - \underset{|}{N} - \quad \textit{amide linkage}$$

amide functional group

Amides may be thought of as containing an ammonia or amine portion and a portion derived from a carboxylic acid:

$$\overset{\overset{\displaystyle O}{\|}}{-C} - \underset{|}{N} -$$

from a carboxylic acid

from ammonia or an amine

However, we've seen that the reaction of an amine with a carboxylic acid normally produces a salt and not an amide. For this reason, the preparation of amides requires the more reactive acid chlorides or acid anhydrides.

Both primary and secondary amines can be used to prepare amides in this manner, a method similar to the formation of esters (Section 15.5). Tertiary amines, however, do not form amides because they lack a hydrogen atom on the nitrogen.

General reactions:

$$R - \overset{\overset{\displaystyle O}{\|}}{C} - Cl \ + \ R' - \underset{\underset{H}{|}}{N} - H \ \longrightarrow \ R - \overset{\overset{\displaystyle O}{\|}}{C} - \underset{\underset{H}{|}}{N} - R' \ + \ HCl \qquad (16.11)$$

acid chloride amine amide

$$R - \overset{\overset{\displaystyle O}{\|}}{C} - O - \overset{\overset{\displaystyle O}{\|}}{C} - R \ + \ R' - \underset{\underset{H}{|}}{N} - H \ \longrightarrow \ R - \overset{\overset{\displaystyle O}{\|}}{C} - \underset{\underset{H}{|}}{N} - R' \ + \ R - \overset{\overset{\displaystyle O}{\|}}{C} - OH \qquad (16.12)$$

acid anhydride amine amide carboxylic acid

amide
An organic compound having the functional group

$$-\overset{\overset{\displaystyle O}{\|}}{C} - \underset{|}{N} - .$$

amide linkage The carbonyl carbon–nitrogen single bond of the amide group.

Specific examples:

$$CH_3-\overset{\overset{O}{||}}{C}-O-\overset{\overset{O}{||}}{C}-CH_3 \ + \ H-\overset{\overset{H}{|}}{N}-H \ \longrightarrow \ CH_3-\overset{\overset{O}{||}}{C}-\overset{\overset{}{\underset{\underset{H}{|}}{N}}}{\underset{}{|}}-H \ + \ CH_3-\overset{\overset{O}{||}}{C}-OH$$

(16.13)

acetic anhydride ammonia acetamide acetic acid

benzoyl chloride methylamine N-methylbenzamide
(a 1° amine)

(16.14)

benzoyl chloride dimethylamine N,N-dimethylbenzamide
(a 2° amine)

(16.15)

> ▶ **LEARNING CHECK 16.8** Complete the following reactions:
>
> a. $CH_3-\overset{\overset{O}{||}}{C}-O-\overset{\overset{O}{||}}{C}-CH_3 \ + \ CH_3CH_2CH_2-NH_2 \ \longrightarrow$
>
> b. $CH_3CH_2-\overset{\overset{O}{||}}{C}-Cl \ + \ NH_3 \ \longrightarrow$

Reaction of diacid chlorides with diamines produces polyamides that, like poly-esters, are condensation polymers. The repeating units in polyamides are held together by amide linkage. An example is the formation of nylon, shown in Reaction 16.16 and ▶ Figure 16.3.

$$n Cl-\overset{\overset{O}{||}}{C}-(CH_2)_4-\overset{\overset{O}{||}}{C}-Cl \ + \ nH_2N-(CH_2)_6-NH_2 \ \longrightarrow$$

adipoyl chloride hexamethylenediamine

$$---\overset{\overset{O}{||}}{C}-(CH_2)_4-\overset{\overset{O}{||}}{C}-NH-(CH_2)_6-NH-\overset{\overset{O}{||}}{C}-(CH_2)_4-\overset{\overset{O}{||}}{C}-NH-(CH_2)_6-NH--- \ + \ nHCl$$

amide linkages *amide linkage*

polyamide nylon

(16.16)

Three billion pounds of nylon and related polyamides are produced annually. About 60% of that total goes to make the nylon fiber used in home furnishings such as carpet. The remainder is used largely as a textile fiber in clothing (shirts, dresses, stockings, underwear, etc.) and as tire cord. Minor but important uses include fasteners, rope, parachutes, paintbrushes, and electrical parts (see ▶ Figure 16.4). In medicine, nylon is used in specialized tubing. Nylon sutures were the first synthetic sutures and are still used.

© Joel Gordon

1 The reactants occupy separate immiscible layers. Hexamethylene-diamine is dissolved in water (bottom layer), and adipoyl chloride is dissolved in hexane (top layer). The two compounds react at the interface between the two layers to form a film of nylon, which is lifted by forceps.

© Joel Gordon

2 The rotating tube winds the nylon strand, which continues to form at the interface in the beaker.

Figure 16.3 The preparation of nylon.

Figure 16.4 Parachutes made of nylon fabric.

© Danshutter/Shutterstock.com

Aspirin Substitutes

Even though aspirin is an excellent and useful drug (see Chemistry and Your Health 15.1), it occasionally produces adverse effects that cannot be tolerated by some people. These effects include gastrointestinal bleeding and such allergic reactions as skin rashes and asthmatic attacks. Children who are feverish with influenza or chickenpox should not be given aspirin because of a strong correlation with Reye's syndrome, a devastating illness characterized by liver and brain dysfunction.

The amide *acetaminophen,* marketed under trade names such as Tylenol®, Excedrin Aspirin Free®, Panadol®, and Anacin-3®, is an effective aspirin substitute available for use in such situations.

In 1984, it became available in an over-the-counter (OTC) form under trade names such as Advil®, Ibuprin®, Mediprin®, and Motrin IB®. Ibuprofen is thought to be somewhat superior to aspirin as an anti-inflammatory drug, but it has about the same effectiveness as aspirin in relieving mild pain and reducing fever.

In 1994, the FDA approved another compound for sale as an over-the-counter pain reliever. *Naproxen,* marketed under the trade names Aleve® and Anaprox®, exerts its effects for a longer time in the body (8–12 hours per dose) than ibuprofen (4–6 hours per dose) or aspirin and acetaminophen (4 hours per dose). However, the chances for causing slight intestinal bleeding and stomach upset are greater with naproxen than with ibuprofen, and naproxen is not recommended for use by children under age 12.

acetaminophen

naproxen

Acetaminophen does not irritate the intestinal tract and yet has comparable analgesic (pain-relieving) and antipyretic (fever-reducing) effects. Acetaminophen is available in a stable liquid form suitable for administration to children and other patients who have difficulty taking tablets or capsules. Unlike aspirin, acetaminophen has virtually no anti-inflammatory effect and is therefore a poor substitute for aspirin in the treatment of inflammatory disorders such as rheumatoid arthritis. The overuse of acetaminophen has been linked to liver and kidney damage.

Ibuprofen, a carboxylic acid rather than an amide, is a drug with analgesic, antipyretic, and anti-inflammatory properties that was available for decades only as a prescription drug under the trade name Motrin®.

Ketoprofen, another pain reliever, became available for OTC sales in 1996. This compound, sold under the trade names Orudis KT® and Actron®, has the advantage of requiring very small doses when compared to other pain-relieving products. A dose of ketoprofen is 12.5 mg, compared to doses of 200–500 mg for the other products. The tiny, easy-to-swallow tablet is a characteristic emphasized by the manufacturers in advertising. The side effects of ketoprofen are similar to those of aspirin and ibuprofen, so ketoprofen should not be used by people known to have problems with either of these other two compounds.

ibuprofen

ketoprofen

Silk and wool are natural polyamides that we classify as proteins (discussed in detail in Chapter 19). For now, note the repeating units and amide linkages characteristic of proteins as shown in the following portion of a polyamide protein chain:

$$---NH-CH-\overset{\overset{\displaystyle O}{\displaystyle \|}}{C}-NH-CH-\overset{\overset{\displaystyle O}{\displaystyle \|}}{C}-NH-CH-\overset{\overset{\displaystyle O}{\displaystyle \|}}{C}-NH-CH-\overset{\overset{\displaystyle O}{\displaystyle \|}}{C}---$$

R R′ R″ R‴

amide linkages

16.5 Amines as Neurotransmitters

Learning Objective

5. Name amines used as neurotransmitters.

Neurotransmitters, the chemical messengers of the nervous system, carry nerve impulses from one nerve cell (neuron) to another. A neuron consists of a bulbous body called the soma (or cell body) attached to a long stemlike projection called an axon (see ▶ Figure 16.5). Numerous short extensions called dendrites are attached to the large bulbous end of the soma, and filaments called synaptic terminals are attached to the end of the axon. At low magnification, the synaptic terminals of one neuron's axon appear to be attached to the dendrites of an adjacent neuron. However, upon further magnification, a small gap called a synapse is visible between the synaptic terminals of the axon and the dendrites of the next neuron.

neurotransmitter A substance that acts as a chemical bridge in nerve impulse transmission between nerve cells.

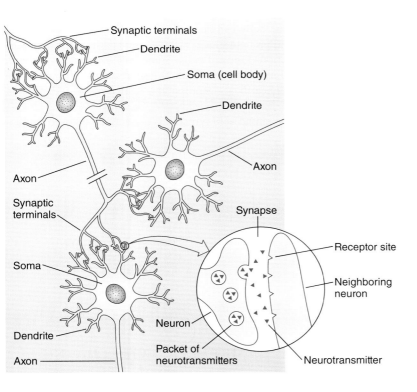

Figure 16.5 A nerve cell and the transmission of a nerve signal.

Molecules of a neurotransmitter are stored in small pockets in the axon near the synapse. These pockets release neurotransmitter molecules into the synapse when an electrical current flows from the soma, along the axon to the synaptic terminals. The electrical current is generated by the exchange of positive and negative ions across membranes. The released neurotransmitter molecules diffuse across the synapse and bind to receptors

on the dendrites of the next neuron. Once the neurotransmitter binds to the receptor, the message has been delivered. The receiving cell then sends an electrical current down its own axon until a synapse is reached, and a neurotransmitter delivers the message across the synapse to the next neuron. In the central nervous system—the brain and spinal cord—the most important neurotransmitters are acetylcholine and three other amines: norepinephrine, dopamine, and serotonin:

norepinephrine

dopamine

serotonin

acetylcholine cation

Neurotransmitters are not only chemical messengers for the nervous system, they may also be partly responsible for our moods. A simplified biochemical theory of mental illness is based on two amines found in the brain. The first is norepinephrine (NE). When an excess of norepinephrine is formed in the brain, the result is a feeling of elation. Extreme excesses of NE can even induce a manic state, while low NE levels may be a cause of depression.

At least six different receptors in the body can be activated by norepinephrine and related compounds. A class of drugs called beta blockers reduces the stimulant action of epinephrine and norepinephrine on various kinds of cells. Some beta blockers are used to treat cardiac arrhythmias, angina, and hypertension (high blood pressure). They function by slightly decreasing the force of each heartbeat. Depression is sometimes a side effect of using such drugs.

In a complex, multistep process, the amino acid tyrosine is used in the body to synthesize norepinephrine:

tyrosine

dopa

dopamine

norepinephrine

Each step in the process is catalyzed by at least one enzyme, and each of the intermediates formed in the synthesis has physiological activity. Dopa is used as a treatment for

We have discussed four different reactions of amines. When trying to decide what happens in a reaction, remember to focus on the functional groups. After identifying an amine as a starting material, next decide what other reagent is involved and which of the four pathways is appropriate.

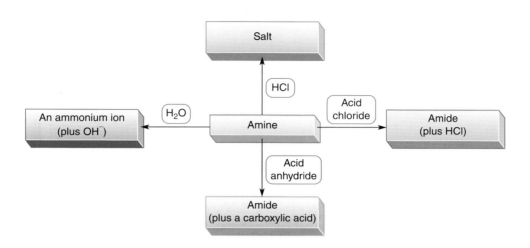

Parkinson's disease, and dopamine has been used to treat low blood pressure. Tyrosine is an essential amino acid that must be obtained from the diet, so what we eat may make a direct contribution to our mental health.

The second amine often associated with the biochemical theory of mental illness is serotonin. Like norepinephrine, it also functions as a neurotransmitter. Serotonin is produced in the body from the amino acid tryptophan:

tryptophan → serotonin

Serotonin

Serotonin has been found to influence sleeping, the regulation of body temperature, and sensory perception, but its exact role in mental illness is not yet clear. Unusually low levels of 5-hydroxyindoleacetic acid, a product of serotonin utilization, are characteristically found in the spinal fluid of victims of violent suicide. Drugs that mimic serotonin are sometimes used to treat depression, anxiety, and obsessive-compulsive disorder. Serotonin blockers are used to treat migraine headaches and relieve the nausea that accompanies cancer chemotherapy. A better understanding of the biochemistry of the brain may lead to better medications for treating various forms of mental illness.

16.6 Other Biologically Important Amines

Learning Objective

6. Give uses for specific biological amines.

Epinephrine

Epinephrine, or adrenaline, has a molecular structure similar to that of norepinephrine. The difference is that epinephrine contains an *N*-methyl group:

epinephrine
(adrenaline)

Epinephrine is more important as a hormone than as a neurotransmitter. It is synthesized in the adrenal gland and acts to increase the blood level of glucose, a key source of energy for body processes. The release of epinephrine—usually in response to pain, anger, or fear—provides glucose for a sudden burst of energy. For this reason, epinephrine has been called the fight-or-flight hormone.

Epinephrine also raises blood pressure. It does this by increasing the rate and force of heart contractions and by constricting the peripheral blood vessels. Injectable local anesthetics usually contain epinephrine because it constricts blood vessels in the vicinity of the injection. This prevents the blood from rapidly "washing" the anesthetic away and prolongs the anesthetic effect in the target tissue. Epinephrine is also used to reduce hemorrhage, treat asthma attacks, and combat anaphylactic shock (collapse of the circulatory system).

Amphetamines

Amphetamine (also known as Benzedrine®) is a powerful nervous system stimulant with an amine structure similar to that of epinephrine:

amphetamine
(Benzedrine®)

epinephrine
(adrenaline)

Notice that both compounds contain an aromatic ring attached to a substituted ethylamine. That structural arrangement, sometimes referred to as a phenethylamine, is apparently an essential feature of several physiologically active compounds. These structural similarities lead to similar behaviors in the body: Both compounds raise the glucose level in the blood and increase pulse rate and blood pressure. Other closely related phenethylamine compounds, such as Methedrine®, also act as powerful nervous system stimulants. Compounds of this type can be thought of as being derived from amphetamine and as a result are sometimes collectively referred to as **amphetamines:**

N-methylamphetamine
(Methedrine®, or "speed")

Amphetamine

amphetamines A class of drugs structurally similar to epinephrine, used to stimulate the central nervous system.

Amphetamines are used both legally (as prescribed by a physician) and illegally to elevate mood or reduce fatigue. In the drug culture, amphetamine tablets go by such names as bennies, pep pills, reds, red devils, speed, dexies, and uppers. Some amphetamines (known as STP, speed, and mescaline) cause hallucinations. The abuse of such drugs results in severe detrimental effects on both the body and the mind. They are addictive and concentrate in the brain and nervous system. Abusers often experience long periods of sleeplessness, weight loss, and paranoia. Abusers of amphetamines often compound their problems by taking other drugs in order to prevent the "crash," or deep depression, brought on by discontinuation of the drug.

Alkaloids

Plants are the sources of some of the most powerful drugs known. Numerous primitive tribes in the world possess knowledge about the physiological effects that result from eating or chewing the leaves, roots, flowers or bark of certain plants. The effects vary from plant species to plant species. Some cure diseases; others, such as opium, are addictive drugs. Still others are deadly poisons, such as the leaves of the belladonna plant and the hemlock herb. The substances responsible for these marked physiological effects are often nitrogen-containing compounds called **alkaloids.** The name, which means alkali-like, reflects the fact that these amine compounds are weakly basic.

alkaloids A class of nitrogen-containing organic compounds obtained from plants.

The molecular structures of alkaloids vary from simple to complex. Two common and relatively simple alkaloids are nicotine, which is found in tobacco, and caffeine, which is present in coffee and cola drinks:

nicotine Nicotine

caffeine Caffeine

Many people absorb nicotine into their bodies as a result of smoking or chewing tobacco. In small doses, nicotine behaves like a stimulant and is not especially harmful. However, it is habit-forming, and habitual tobacco users are exposed to other harmful substances such as tars, carbon monoxide, and polycyclic carcinogens.

Besides coffee and cola drinks, other sources of caffeine are tea, chocolate, and cocoa. Caffeine is a mild stimulant of the respiratory and central nervous systems, the reason for its well-known side effects of nervousness and insomnia. These characteristics, together with its behavior as a mild diuretic, account for the use of caffeine in a wide variety of products, including pain relievers, cold remedies, diet pills, and "stay-awake" pills (No-Doz®). Because caffeine is considered to be a drug, pregnant women should be prudent about how much caffeine they consume. Like most other drugs, caffeine enters the bloodstream, crosses the placental barrier, and reaches the fetus.

A number of alkaloids are used medicinally. Quinine, for example, is used to treat malaria. Atropine is used as a preoperative drug to relax muscles and reduce the secretion of saliva in surgical patients, and to dilate the pupil of the eye in patients undergoing eye examinations.

quinine atropine

Energy Drinks: Are They Really Harmless as a Source of Energy?

Energy for use in the human body is provided by consuming and metabolizing carbohydrates, proteins, and fat. The energy content of such consumed materials is usually given in units of calories. The primary "energy-providing" active ingredients in energy drinks are caffeine (1,3,7-trimethylxanthine, $C_8H_{10}N_4O_2$) and sugar. Caffeine is an alkaloid with no caloric value while sugar provides large amounts of calories but no other nutrients. For this reason, energy provided by sugar is often called "empty calories." In nature, caffeine is produced by plants such as *Coffea arabica* (coffee), *Camellia sinensis* (tea), and *Theobroma cacao* (cocoa). The plants produce caffeine to prevent insects and fungi from feeding on them. When animals, including humans, consume caffeine, it doesn't provide energy, but acts as a stimulant which increases the heart rate and produces a temporary boost in alertness. Sugar does provide energy, but it is in a short-lived temporary form commonly referred to as a "sugar high."

Caffeine has been consumed in many cultures for centuries in the form of tea and coffee, but something has changed. If you shop at grocery or convenience stores, you cannot help noticing the large number of energy drinks being promoted. These drinks come in brightly colored and even fluorescent cans displaying intense graphics to draw attention. Whose attention are they trying to get? If you analyze the marketing strategies, the target audience consists of teenagers and young adults.

So what is the big deal? Although there is still plenty of debate about caffeine and its effects on the body, empirical evidence has shown that large quantities can cause significant health and behavioral problems. For instance, too much caffeine can result in nervousness and insomnia. The insomnia causes fatigue, leading to more caffeine consumption, more insomnia, more lack of sleep, irritability, and so on. Additionally, increased caffeine consumption appears to correlate with an increase in bone loss and occasionally, abnormal heart rhythms. Addiction to caffeine is possible, with unpleasant symptoms resulting upon cessation of use.

Other implications associated with the consumption of energy drinks are often indirect. Life is full of tradeoffs and energy drinks are no exception. When people reach for an energy drink, they neglect healthful beverages such as water, milk, or juice. Instead of obtaining water, calcium, vitamin D, or nutrients from the above-mentioned beverages, they are drinking an "energy" drink consisting primarily of water and large quantities of caffeine and sugar. The excessive sugar consumption will have adverse long-term effects upon health. For example, high sugar diets are known to increase the risk of obesity, osteoporosis, and type 2 diabetes.

So, the next time you feel fatigued, drink a cool, refreshing glass of water and rest for a few minutes. If you feel you must drink something to awaken the senses, try a cup of green tea without sugar. Tea contains no empty calories and provides antioxidants. Most importantly, remember that the best way to stay healthy and energized is to eat a nutritious diet while getting plenty of rest and exercise.

A number of energy drinks are widely available in grocery and convenience stores.

Some sports drinks are formulated to replenish fluids as well as provide carbohydrates for energy.

Opium, the dried juice of the poppy plant, has been used for centuries as a painkilling drug. It contains numerous alkaloids, including morphine and its methyl ether, codeine. Both are central nervous system depressants, with codeine being much weaker. They exert a soothing effect on the body when administered in sufficient amounts. These properties make them useful as painkillers. Morphine is especially useful in this regard, being one of the most effective painkillers known. Codeine is used in some cough syrups to depress the action of the cough center in the brain. The major drawback to using these drugs is that they are all addictive. Heroin, a derivative of morphine, is one of the more destructive hard drugs used illegally in our society. A substantial number of addicts commit crimes to support their habits.

Morphine

morphine codeine heroin

16.7 The Nomenclature of Amides

Learning Objective

7. Assign IUPAC names for amides.

Simple amides are named after the corresponding carboxylic acids by changing the -*ic* ending (common names) or the -*oic* ending (IUPAC names) of the acid to -*amide*. Common names are used more often than IUPAC names. Some examples of the assignment of such names follow:

$$H-\overset{\overset{\displaystyle O}{\|}}{C}-OH \longrightarrow H-\overset{\overset{\displaystyle O}{\|}}{C}-NH_2$$

Common name formic acid formamide
IUPAC name methanoic acid methanamide

$$CH_3-\overset{\overset{\displaystyle O}{\|}}{C}-OH \longrightarrow CH_3-\overset{\overset{\displaystyle O}{\|}}{C}-NH_2$$

Common name acetic acid acetamide
IUPAC name ethanoic acid ethanamide

$$\text{C}_6\text{H}_5-\overset{\overset{\displaystyle O}{\|}}{C}-OH \longrightarrow \text{C}_6\text{H}_5-\overset{\overset{\displaystyle O}{\|}}{C}-NH_2$$

Common name benzoic acid benzamide
IUPAC name benzoic acid benzamide

a. Give the IUPAC name for the following simple amide:

$$CH_3CH_2CH_2-\overset{\overset{\displaystyle O}{\|}}{C}-NH_2$$

b. What is the IUPAC name for the simple amide derived from hexanoic acid?

If alkyl groups are attached to the nitrogen atom of amides (substituted amides), the name of the alkyl group precedes the name of the amide, and an italic capital *N* is used to indicate that the alkyl group is bonded to the nitrogen.

See the following examples.

$$H-\overset{\overset{\displaystyle O}{\|}}{C}-NH-CH_3$$

$$CH_3-\overset{\overset{\displaystyle O}{\|}}{\underset{\underset{\displaystyle CH_3}{|}}{C}}-N-CH_3$$

$$\overset{\overset{\displaystyle O}{\|}}{\underset{\underset{\displaystyle CH_3}{|}}{C}}-N-CH_2CH_3$$

Common name	*N*-methylformamide	*N,N*-dimethylacetamide	*N*-ethyl-*N*-methylbenzamide
IUPAC name	*N*-methylmethanamide	*N,N*-dimethylethanamide	*N*-ethyl-*N*-methylbenzamide

▶ **LEARNING CHECK 16.10** Give either a common name or the IUPAC name for each of the following amides:

a. $CH_3-\overset{\overset{\displaystyle O}{\|}}{\underset{\underset{\displaystyle CH_2CH_3}{|}}{C}}-N-CH_2CH_3$

b. $CH_3CH_2CH_2-\overset{\overset{\displaystyle O}{\|}}{C}-NH-CH_2\overset{\overset{\displaystyle CH_3}{|}}{C}HCH_3$

c. $\overset{\overset{\displaystyle O}{\|}}{\underset{\underset{\displaystyle CH_2CH_3}{|}}{C}}-N-$

d. $\overset{\overset{\displaystyle O}{\|}}{C}-NH-CH_3$ with CH_3 substituent

16.8 Physical Properties of Amides

Learning Objective

8. Show the formation of hydrogen bonds with amides.

Formamide is a liquid at room temperature. It is the only unsubstituted amide that is a liquid; all others are solids.

Unsubstituted amides can form a complex network of intermolecular hydrogen bonds (see ▶ Figure 16.6). It is this characteristic that causes melting points of these substances to be so high.

The substitution of alkyl or aromatic groups for hydrogen atoms on the nitrogen reduces the number of intermolecular hydrogen bonds that can form and causes the melting points to decrease. Thus, disubstituted amides often have lower melting and boiling points than monosubstituted and unsubstituted amides. We'll see in Chapter 19 that hydrogen bonding between amide groups is important in maintaining the shape of protein molecules.

Amides are rather water soluble, especially those containing fewer than six carbon atoms. This solubility results from the ability of amides to form hydrogen bonds with water. Even disubstituted amides do this because of the presence of the carbonyl oxygen (see ▶ Figure 16.7).

Figure 16.6 Intermolecular hydrogen bonding in an unsubstituted amide.

Figure 16.7 Hydrogen bonding between water.

A. an unsubstituted amide

B. a disubstituted amide

▶ **LEARNING CHECK 16.11** Show how the amide below can form the following:

a. Intermolecular hydrogen bonds with other amide molecules
b. Hydrogen bonds with water molecules

$$CH_3 - \overset{\overset{\displaystyle O}{\|}}{C} - \underset{\underset{\displaystyle H}{|}}{N} - CH_3$$

16.9 **Chemical Properties of Amides**

Learning Objective

9. Give the products of acidic and basic hydrolysis of amides.

Neutrality

Because basicity is the most important property of amines, it is only natural to wonder if amides are also basic. The answer is no. Although they are formed from carboxylic acids and basic amines, amides are neither basic nor acidic; they are neutral. The carbonyl group bonded to the nitrogen has destroyed the basicity of the original amine, and the nitrogen of the amine has replaced the acidic —OH of the carboxylic acid.

Amide Hydrolysis

The most important reaction of amides is hydrolysis. This reaction corresponds to the reverse of amide formation; the amide is cleaved into two compounds, a carboxylic acid and an amine or ammonia:

$$R-\overset{\overset{\displaystyle O}{\|}}{C}-NH-R' + H_2O \xrightarrow[\text{Heat}]{\substack{\text{Acid} \\ \text{or} \\ \text{base}}} R-\overset{\overset{\displaystyle O}{\|}}{C}-OH + R'-NH_2 \quad (16.17)$$

cleavage here

amide carboxylic acid amine

As with hydrolysis of carboxylic esters, amide hydrolysis requires the presence of a strong acid or base, and the nature of the final products depends on which of these reactants is used. Notice in the following examples that under acidic conditions, the salt of the amine is produced along with the carboxylic acid, and under basic conditions, the salt of the carboxylic acid is formed along with the amine. Also, notice that heat is required for the hydrolysis of amides.

General reactions:

$$R-\overset{\overset{\displaystyle O}{\|}}{C}-NH-R' + H_2O + HCl \xrightarrow{\text{Heat}} R-\overset{\overset{\displaystyle O}{\|}}{C}-OH + R'-NH_3^+Cl^- \quad (16.18)$$

amide carboxylic acid amine salt

$$R-\overset{\overset{\displaystyle O}{\|}}{C}-NH-R' + NaOH \xrightarrow{\text{Heat}} R-\overset{\overset{\displaystyle O}{\|}}{C}-O^-Na^+ + R'-NH_2 \quad (16.19)$$

amide carboxylate salt amine

Specific examples:

$$CH_3-\overset{\overset{\displaystyle O}{\|}}{C}-NH_2 + H_2O + HCl \xrightarrow{\text{Heat}} CH_3-\overset{\overset{\displaystyle O}{\|}}{C}-OH + NH_4^+Cl^- \quad (16.20)$$

acetamide acetic acid ammonium chloride

$$CH_3-\overset{\overset{\displaystyle O}{\|}}{C}-NH-CH_3 + H_2O + HCl \xrightarrow{\text{Heat}} CH_3-\overset{\overset{\displaystyle O}{\|}}{C}-OH + CH_3-NH_3^+Cl^- \quad (16.21)$$

N-methylacetamide acetic acid methylammonium chloride

$$CH_3-\overset{\overset{\displaystyle O}{\|}}{C}-NH-CH_3 + NaOH \xrightarrow{\text{Heat}} CH_3-\overset{\overset{\displaystyle O}{\|}}{C}-O^-Na^+ + CH_3-NH_2 \quad (16.22)$$

N-methylacetamide sodium acetate methylamine

Because the form in which carboxylic acids and amines occur in solution depends on the solution pH, one of the hydrolysis products must always be in the form of a salt.

► LEARNING CHECK 16.12 Complete the following hydrolysis reactions:

a.

$$\underset{\text{(benzene ring)}}{\bigcirc}\overset{\overset{\displaystyle O}{\displaystyle \|}}{C}-NH-CH_2CH_3 \quad + \; H_2O \; + \; HCl \xrightarrow{\text{Heat}}$$

b.

$$\underset{\text{(benzene ring)}}{\bigcirc}\overset{\overset{\displaystyle O}{\displaystyle \|}}{C}-NH-CH_2CH_3 \quad + \; NaOH \xrightarrow{\text{Heat}}$$

Amide hydrolysis, a very important reaction in biochemistry, is a central reaction in the digestion of proteins and the breakdown of proteins within cells. However, most amide hydrolysis in the body is catalyzed by enzymes rather than by strong acids or bases.

Because of their physiological properties, a number of amides play valuable roles in medicine. ► Table 16.3 lists some of these important compounds.

TABLE 16.3 Some Important Amides in Medicine

Structure	Generic Name (Trade Name)	Use
	thiopental (Pentothal®)	Intravenous anesthesia
	amobarbital (Amytal®)	Treatment of insomnia
	diazepam (Valium®)	Tranquilizer
	ampicillin (Polycillin®)	Antibiotic

Case Study Follow-up

In addition to helpful information on its website, the U. S. Food and Drug Administration has an educational pamphlet entitled *Medicines in My Home* (FDA, 2009). It can be viewed online or printed for distribution in doctor's offices, clinics, or schools. Many schools conduct education during the last week of October to help kids stay drug free, known as Red Ribbon Week. Educating children about over-the-counter (OTC) medications could easily be incorporated into such existing programs. Clinics that provide educational materials about OTC medications also provide a valuable public service.

Over-the-counter remedies that are mixtures of more than one medication can be convenient for the consumer. However, they significantly increase the choices available and can add to confusion. Since the chance of adverse reactions increases with the number of medications taken, combined medications can be problematic. Educating the public about the effects of medications and their common and chemical names is of utmost importance.

Unfortunately, antihistamine overdose is common. The list of symptoms include agitation, blurred vision, coma, confusion, convulsions, delirium, diarrhea, drowsiness, dry mouth, flushing, inability to urinate, incoherence, lack of sweat, fever, nausea, rapid heart rate, stomach pain, and unsteadiness. The patient may be treated with activated charcoal, oxygen, IV fluids, and gastric lavage. If the patient survives the first 24 hours after an antihistamine overdose, fatalities are rare (NIH, 2010).

Concept Summary

Classification of Amines

Amines are organic derivatives of ammonia in which one or more of the ammonia hydrogens are replaced by alkyl or aromatic groups. Amines are classified as primary, secondary, or tertiary, depending on the number of groups (one, two, or three) attached to the nitrogen.

Objective 1 (Section 16.1), Exercise 16.4

The Nomenclature of Amines

Common names are given to simple amines by adding the ending -*amine* to the names of the alkyl groups attached to the nitrogen. In IUPAC names, the -*e* ending in the alkane name is changed to -*amine*. Aromatic amines are named as derivatives of aniline.

Objective 2 (Section 16.2), Exercises 16.8 and 16.10

Physical Properties of Amines

Primary and secondary amines have boiling points slightly lower than those of corresponding alcohols. Tertiary amines have boiling points similar to those of alkanes. Low molecular weight amines are water-soluble.

Objective 3 (Section 16.3), Exercises 16.16 and 16.18

Chemical Properties of Amines

Amines are weak bases. They react with water to liberate hydroxide ions, and they react with acids to form salts. Amines react with acid chlorides and acid anhydrides to form amides.

Objective 4 (Section 16.4), Exercise 16.26

Amines as Neurotransmitters

Neurotransmitters are the chemical messengers of the nervous system. They carry nerve impulses from one nerve cell (neuron) to another. The most important neurotransmitters are acetylcholine and three other amines: norepinephrine, dopamine, and serotonin.

Objective 5 (Section 16.5), Exercise 16.38

Other Biologically Important Amines

Four neurotransmitters are acetylcholine, norepinephrine, dopamine, and serotonin. Epinephrine is also known as the fight-or-flight hormone. The amphetamines have structures similar to that of epinephrine. Alkaloids are nitrogen-containing compounds isolated from plants. They exhibit a variety of physiological effects on the body. Examples of alkaloids include nicotine, caffeine, quinine, atropine, morphine, and codeine.

Objective 6 (Section 16.6), Exercises 16.40 and 16.44

The Nomenclature of Amides

Amides are named by changing the *-ic acid* or *-oic acid* ending of the carboxylic acid portion of the compound to *-amide*. Groups attached to the nitrogen of the amide are denoted by an italic capital *N* that precedes the name of the attached group.

Objective 7 (Section 16.7), Exercise 16.46

Physical Properties of Amides

Low molecular weight amides are water-soluble due to the formation of hydrogen bonds. The melting and boiling points of unsubstituted amides are higher than those of comparable substituted amides due to intermolecular hydrogen bonding.

Objective 8 (Section 16.8), Exercise 16.50

Chemical Properties of Amides

Amides undergo hydrolysis in acidic conditions to yield a carboxylic acid and an amine salt. Hydrolysis under basic conditions produces a carboxylate salt and an amine.

Objective 9 (Section 16.9), Exercise 16.52

Key Terms and Concepts

Alkaloids (16.6)
Amide (16.4)
Amide linkage (16.4)
Amine (16.1)

Amphetamines (16.6)
Neurotransmitter (16.5)
Primary amine (16.1)
Quaternary ammonium salt (16.4)

Secondary amine (16.1)
Tertiary amine (16.1)

Key Reactions

1.	Reaction of amines with water (Section 16.4):	$R-NH_2 + H_2O \rightleftharpoons R-NH_3^+ + OH^-$	Reaction 16.3
2.	Reaction of amines with acids (Section 16.4):	$R-NH_2 + HCl \rightarrow R-NH_3^+ + Cl^-$	Reaction 16.5
3.	Conversion of amine salts back to amines (Section 16.4):	$R-NH_3^+Cl^- + NaOH \rightarrow R-NH_2 + H_2O + NaCl$	Reaction 16.9
4.	Reaction of amines with acid chlorides to form amides (Section 16.4):	$R-\overset{\overset{\displaystyle O}{\|}}{C}-Cl \; + \; R'-\underset{\underset{\displaystyle H}{\|}}{N}-H \longrightarrow R-\overset{\overset{\displaystyle O}{\|}}{C}-\underset{\underset{\displaystyle H}{\|}}{N}-R' \; + \; HCl$	Reaction 16.11
5.	Reaction of amines with acid anhydrides to form amides (Section 16.4):	$R-\overset{\overset{\displaystyle O}{\|}}{C}-O-\overset{\overset{\displaystyle O}{\|}}{C}-R + R'-\underset{\underset{\displaystyle H}{\|}}{N}-H \rightarrow R-\overset{\overset{\displaystyle O}{\|}}{C}-\underset{\underset{\displaystyle H}{\|}}{N}-R' + R-\overset{\overset{\displaystyle O}{\|}}{C}-OH$	Reaction 16.12
6.	Acid hydrolysis of amides (Section 16.9):	$R-\overset{\overset{\displaystyle O}{\|}}{C}-NH-R' + H_2O + HCl \xrightarrow{\text{Heat}} R-\overset{\overset{\displaystyle O}{\|}}{C}-OH + R'-NH_3^+Cl^-$	Reaction 16.18
7.	Basic hydrolysis of amides (Section 16.9):	$R-\overset{\overset{\displaystyle O}{\|}}{C}-NH-R' + NaOH \xrightarrow{\text{Heat}} R-\overset{\overset{\displaystyle O}{\|}}{C}-O^-Na^+ + R'-NH_2$	Reaction 16.19

Exercises

Even-numbered exercises are answered in Appendix B.

Blue-numbered exercises are more challenging.

Classification of Amines (Section 16.1)

16.1 What is the difference among primary, secondary, and tertiary amines in terms of bonding to the nitrogen atom?

16.2 Give a general formula for a primary amine, a secondary amine, and a tertiary amine.

16.3 Classify each of the following as a primary, secondary, or tertiary amine:

a. $CH_3CH_2-\underset{\underset{\displaystyle CH_3}{\|}}{N}-CH_2CH_3$ c. (benzene ring with $NH-CH_3$)

b. $CH_3-\overset{\overset{\displaystyle CH_3}{\|}}{\underset{\underset{\displaystyle CH_3}{\|}}{C}}-NH_2$ d. (pyrrolidine ring with $N-CH_3$)

16.4 Classify each of the following as a primary, secondary, or tertiary amine:

a. $CH_3CH_2-NH-CH_2CH_3$

b. (benzene ring)$-\underset{\underset{\displaystyle CH_3}{\|}}{N}-CH_2CH_3$

c. $CH_3CH_2\underset{\underset{\displaystyle CH_3}{\|}}{CH}-NH_2$

d. (pyrrolidine ring with $\overset{\overset{\displaystyle H}{\|}}{N}$)

16.5 Draw structural formulas for all amines that have the molecular formula $C_4H_{11}N$. Label each one as a primary, secondary, or tertiary amine.

16.6 Draw structural formulas for the four amines that have the molecular formula C_3H_9N. Label each one as a primary, secondary, or tertiary.

The Nomenclature of Amines (Section 16.2)

16.7 Give each of the following amines a common name by adding the ending -*amine* to alkyl group names:

a. CH_3CHCH_3 (with NH_2 attached)

b. $NH-CH_2CH_3$ (phenyl ring attached)

c. $CH_3CH_2CH_2-N-CH_3$ (with CH_2CH_3 below N)

16.8 Give each of the following amines a common name by adding the ending -*amine* to alkyl group names:

a. $CH_3-NH-CHCH_3$ (with CH_3 below)

b. (phenyl ring)$-N-CH_2CH_3$ (with CH_3 below N)

c. $CH_3CH_2CH_2CH_2-NH_2$

16.9 Give each of the following amines an IUPAC name:

a. CH_3CHCH_3 (with NH_2 above)

b. CH_3CCH_3 (with NH_2 above and CH_3 below)

c. $CH_3CH_2CH_2$ (with $NH-CH_2CH_3$ above)

16.10 Give each of the following amines an IUPAC name:

a. $CH_3CH_2CHCH_2-NH_2$ (with CH_3 above)

b. (cyclobutane ring with NH_2)

c. (cyclobutane ring with $NH-CH_3$)

16.11 Name the following aromatic amines as derivatives of aniline:

a. (phenyl ring)$-NH-CHCH_3$ (with CH_3 below)

b. (phenyl ring)$-N-CH_2CH_3$ (with CH_3 above N)

16.12 Name the following aromatic amines as derivatives of aniline:

a. (phenyl ring)$-NH-CH_2CH_2CH_3$

b. (phenyl ring)$-N-CH_3$ (with CH_3 below N)

16.13 Name each of the following amines by one of the methods used in Exercises 16.7, 16.9, and 16.11:

a. CH_3-C-NH_2 (with CH_3 above and CH_3 below)

b. $CH_3CH_2-N-CH_2CH_3$ (with phenyl ring below N)

c. (phenyl ring with NH_2 and Cl)

d. $CH_3CHCH_2CHCH_3$ (with CH_3 and NH_2 above)

16.14 Draw the structural formula for each of the following amines:

a. 3-ethyl-2-pentanamine

b. *m*-ethylaniline

c. *N,N*-diphenylaniline

16.15 Draw the structural formula for each of the following amines:

a. 2,3-dimethyl-1-butanamine

b. *p*-propylaniline

c. *N,N*-dimethylaniline

Physical Properties of Amines (Section 16.3)

16.16 Explain why all classes of low molecular weight amines are water soluble.

16.17 Why are the boiling points of amines lower than those of corresponding alcohols?

16.18 Why are the boiling points of tertiary amines lower than those of corresponding primary and secondary amines?

16.19 Draw diagrams similar to Figure 16.1 to illustrate hydrogen bonding between the following compounds:

a. $CH_3CH_2-N-CH_3$ (with H above N) and $CH_3CH_2-N-CH_3$ (with H above N)

b. (pyrrolidine ring with N-H) and H_2O

16.20 Draw diagrams similar to Figure 16.1 to illustrate hydrogen bonding between the following compounds:

a. $CH_3CH_2-NH-CH_3$ and H_2O

b. (pyrrolidine ring with N-H) and (pyrrolidine ring with N-H)

16.21 Arrange the following compounds in order of increasing boiling point:

a. $CH_3CH_2CH_2—NH_2$

b. $CH_3—\overset{\displaystyle |}{\underset{\displaystyle CH_3}{N}}—CH_3$

c. $CH_3CH_2CH_2—OH$

16.22 Arrange the following compounds in order of increasing boiling point:

a. [structure: benzene ring with CH₃, CH₃, and NH₂ substituents]

b. [structure: benzene ring with N(CH₃)—CH₃ substituent]

c. [structure: benzene ring with NH—CH₃ and CH₃ substituents]

Chemical Properties of Amines (Section 16.4)

16.23 Explain why $CH_3—NH_2$ is a Brønsted base.

16.24 When diethylamine is dissolved in water, the solution becomes basic. Write an equation to account for this observation.

16.25 Complete the following equations. If no reaction occurs, write "no reaction."

a. [cyclopentane ring with $\overset{\displaystyle O}{\overset{\displaystyle \|}{C}}—Cl$] $+ NH_3 \longrightarrow$

b. [benzene ring]$—\overset{\displaystyle |}{\underset{\displaystyle CH_3}{N}}—CH_3 + CH_3\overset{\displaystyle O}{\overset{\displaystyle \|}{C}}—OH \longrightarrow$

c. $CH_3CH_2—\overset{\displaystyle |}{\underset{\displaystyle CH_3}{N}}—CH_3 + CH_3—\overset{\displaystyle O}{\overset{\displaystyle \|}{C}}—Cl \longrightarrow$

d. [pyrrolidine ring]$N—H + HCl \longrightarrow$

e. [pyrrolidine ring]$N—H + H_2O \rightleftharpoons$

f. $CH_3CH_2—\overset{\displaystyle |}{\underset{\displaystyle CH_3}{N}}{H_2}^+Cl^- + NaOH \longrightarrow$

16.26 Complete the following equations. If no reaction occurs, write "no reaction."

a. $CH_3CH_2CH_2CH_2—NH_2 + HCl \rightarrow$

b. [cyclopentane ring with NH_2]$+ H_2O \rightleftharpoons$

c. [cyclopentane ring with NH_2] $+ CH_3\overset{\displaystyle O}{\overset{\displaystyle \|}{C}}—OH \longrightarrow$ [cyclopentane ring with ${NH_3}^+Cl^-$]

d. $CH_3CHCH_3 + NaOH \longrightarrow$

e. $CH_3\overset{\displaystyle |}{\underset{\displaystyle CH_3}{CH}}—\overset{\displaystyle O}{\overset{\displaystyle \|}{C}}—Cl + CH_3—NH_2 \longrightarrow$

f. [benzene ring]$—\overset{\displaystyle O}{\overset{\displaystyle \|}{C}}—O—\overset{\displaystyle O}{\overset{\displaystyle \|}{C}}—$[benzene ring]$ + NH_3 \longrightarrow$

16.27 How does the structure of a quaternary ammonium salt differ from the structure of a salt of a tertiary amine?

16.28 Why are amine drugs commonly administered in the form of their salts?

16.29 Write an equation to show how the drug dextromethorphan, a cough suppressant, could be made more water soluble.

dextromethorphan

16.30 Write equations for two different methods of synthesizing the following amide:

$$CH_3—\overset{\displaystyle O}{\overset{\displaystyle \|}{C}}—\overset{\displaystyle |}{\underset{\displaystyle CH_3}{N}}—CH_3$$

16.31 Write structures for the chemicals needed to carry out the following conversions:

a. [benzene ring with NH_2] $\rightarrow$ [benzene ring with ${NH_3}^+$] $CH_3—\overset{\displaystyle O}{\overset{\displaystyle \|}{C}}—O^-$

b. $CH_3—NH_2 \longrightarrow$ [benzene ring]$—\overset{\displaystyle O}{\overset{\displaystyle \|}{C}}—NH—CH_3$

c. $CH_3\overset{\displaystyle |}{\underset{\displaystyle CH_3}{CH}}—NH_2 \rightarrow CH_3\overset{\displaystyle |}{\underset{\displaystyle CH_3}{CH}}—{NH_3}^+ + OH^-$

16.32 Write structures for the chemicals needed to carry out the following conversions:

a. (benzene ring)—$NH_3^+Cl^- \longrightarrow$ (benzene ring)—NH_2

b. $CH_3CH_2-\overset{\overset{\displaystyle O}{\|}}{C}-Cl \longrightarrow CH_3CH_2-\overset{\overset{\displaystyle O}{\|}}{C}-NH_2$

c. $CH_3-\underset{\underset{\displaystyle CH_3}{|}}{NH} \longrightarrow CH_3-\underset{\underset{\displaystyle CH_3}{|}}{NH_2^+}Cl^-$

Amines as Neurotransmitters (Section 16.5)

16.33 Describe the general structure of a neuron.

16.34 What term is used to describe the gap between one neuron and the next?

16.35 Name the two amino acids that are starting materials for the synthesis of neurotransmitters.

16.36 Name the two amines often associated with the biochemical theory of mental illness.

16.37 What role do neurotransmitters play in nerve impulse transmission?

16.38 List four neurotransmitters important in the central nervous system.

Other Biologically Important Amines (Section 16.6)

16.39 Why is epinephrine called the fight-or-flight hormone?

16.40 Describe one clinical use of epinephrine.

16.41 What are the physiological effects of amphetamines on the body?

16.42 What is the source of alkaloids?

16.43 Why are alkaloids weakly basic?

16.44 Give the name of an alkaloid for the following:

 a. Found in cola drinks

 b. Used to reduce saliva flow during surgery

 c. Present in tobacco

 d. A cough suppressant

 e. Used to treat malaria

 f. An effective painkiller

The Nomenclature of Amides (Section 16.7)

16.45 Assign IUPAC names to the following amides:

a. $CH_3CH_2\underset{\underset{\displaystyle CH_2CH_3}{|}}{CH}-\overset{\overset{\displaystyle O}{\|}}{C}-NH_2$

b. $CH_3CH_2CH_2-\overset{\overset{\displaystyle O}{\|}}{C}-NH$—(benzene ring)

c. (benzene ring)—$\overset{\overset{\displaystyle O}{\|}}{C}-NH-\underset{\underset{\displaystyle CH_3}{|}}{CH}CH_3$

d. $CH_3CH_2-\overset{\overset{\displaystyle O}{\|}}{C}-\underset{\underset{\displaystyle CH_3}{|}}{N}-CH_3$

16.46 Assign IUPAC names to the following amides:

a. $CH_3CH_2CH_2-\overset{\overset{\displaystyle O}{\|}}{C}-NH-CH_3$

b. $CH_3-\overset{\overset{\displaystyle O}{\|}}{C}-\underset{\underset{\displaystyle CH_3}{|}}{N}-CH_3$

c. (benzene ring with CH_3)—$\overset{\overset{\displaystyle O}{\|}}{C}-NH_2$

d. $CH_3CH_2\underset{\underset{\displaystyle CH_3}{|}}{CH}-\overset{\overset{\displaystyle O}{\|}}{C}-NH_2$

16.47 Draw structural formulas for the following amides:

 a. benzamide

 b. *N*-methylethanamide

 c. *N*-methyl-3-phenylbutanamide

16.48 Draw structural formulas for the following amides:

 a. propanamide

 b. *N*-ethylpentanamide

 c. *N,N*-dimethylmethanamide

Physical Properties of Amides (Section 16.8)

16.49 Draw diagrams similar to those in Figure 16.1 to illustrate hydrogen bonding between the following molecules:

a. $CH_3-\overset{\overset{\displaystyle O}{\|}}{C}-\underset{\underset{\displaystyle CH_3}{|}}{N}-CH_3$ and H_2O

b. $CH_3-\overset{\overset{\displaystyle O}{\|}}{C}-NH_2$ and $CH_3-\overset{\overset{\displaystyle O}{\|}}{C}-NH_2$

16.50 Draw diagrams similar to those in Figure 16.1 to illustrate hydrogen bonding between the following molecules:

a. (cyclopentane ring)—$\overset{\overset{\displaystyle O}{\|}}{C}-NH_2$ and H_2O

b. $CH_3\underset{\underset{\displaystyle CH_3}{|}}{CH}-\overset{\overset{\displaystyle O}{\|}}{C}-NH_2$ and $CH_3\underset{\underset{\displaystyle CH_3}{|}}{CH}-\overset{\overset{\displaystyle O}{\|}}{C}-NH_2$

16.51 Explain why the boiling points of disubstituted amides are often lower than those of unsubstituted amides.

Chemical Properties of Amides (Section 16.9)

16.52 Complete the following reactions:

a. $CH_3 - \overset{\displaystyle O}{\overset{\displaystyle \|}{C}} - NH - CH_2CH_3 + NaOH \xrightarrow{\text{Heat}}$

b. $CH_3CH_2 - \overset{\displaystyle O}{\overset{\displaystyle \|}{C}} - NH_2 + H_2O + HCl \xrightarrow{\text{Heat}}$

16.53 Complete the following reactions:

a.

b.

16.54 One of the most successful mosquito repellents has the following structure and name. What are the products of the basic hydrolysis of *N,N*-diethyl-*m*-toluamide?

N,N-diethyl-*m*-toluamide

16.55 What are the products of the acid hydrolysis of the local anesthetic lidocaine?

lidocaine (Xylocaine)

Additional Exercises

16.56 The following molecular formulas represent saturated amine compounds or unsaturated amine compounds that contain C=C bonds. Determine whether each compound is saturated and, if not, how many C=C bonds are present.

a. $C_4H_{11}N$

b. $C_5H_{12}N_2$

c. C_4H_7N

16.57 16.50 mL of 0.100 M HCl was needed to titrate 0.216 g of an unknown amine to a neutral pH endpoint. What is the molecular weight of the amine? Assume the compound only contains one nitrogen atom and there are no other reactive groups present.

16.58 What products would result from the hydrolysis with NaOH of nylon 66 (polymer shown here)?

16.59 Finely ground plant material can be treated with a base to aid in the extraction of alkaloids present in the tissue. Explain why.

16.60 After a nerve impulse occurs, excess acetylcholine cation molecules in the synapse are hydrolyzed in about 10^{-6} seconds by the enzyme cholinesterase. What products are formed? HINT: Identify the functional group that can undergo hydrolysis (upon the addition of water).

acetylcholine cation

Allied Health Exam Connection

The following questions are from these sources:

1. *Nursing School Entrance Exam* © 2005, Learning Express, LLC.

2. *McGraw-Hill's Nursing School Entrance Exams* by Thomas A. Evangelist, Tamara B. Orr and Judy Unrein © 2009, The McGraw-Hill Companies, Inc.

3. *NSEE Nursing School Entrance Exams,* 3rd Edition © 2009, Kaplan Publishing.

4. *Cliffs Test Prep: Nursing School Entrance Exams* by Fred N. Grayson © 2004, Wiley Publishing, Inc.

5. *Peterson's Master the Nursing School and Allied Health Entrance Exams,* 18th Edition by Marion F. Gooding © 2008, Peterson's, a Nelnet Company.

16.61 Define neurotransmitter.

16.62 Give general chemical formulas for a primary, a secondary, and a tertiary amine.

16.63 The stimulant in coffee is:

 a. tannic acid

 b. theobromine

 c. theophylline

 d. caffeine

16.64 What are the most likely products of a reaction between $CH_3CH_2NH_2$ and H_2O?

 a. $CH_3CH_2NH_3{}^+ + OH^-$

 b. $(CH_3)_2NH_2{}^+ + OH^-$

 c. $CH_3CH_2NH_2OH^- + H^+$

 d. $(CH_2)NH_2{}^- + H_3O^+$

Chemistry for Thought

16.65 Why might it be more practical for chemical suppliers to ship amines as amine salts?

16.66 Give structural formulas for the four-carbon diamine and the four-carbon diacid chloride that would react to form nylon.

16.67 Why might it be dangerous on a camping trip to prepare a salad using an unknown plant?

16.68 One of the active ingredients in Triaminic® cold syrup is listed as chlorpheniramine maleate. What does the word *maleate* indicate about the structure of this active ingredient?

16.69 Write reactions to show how the following conversion can be achieved. An amine reagent is required, and reactions from earlier chapters are necessary.

$$CH_3CH_2-OH \longrightarrow CH_3-NH_3^+ \, CH_3-\overset{\displaystyle O}{\overset{\|}{C}}-O^-$$

16.70 In Figure 16.2, several products are shown that contain amine salts. Sometimes the active ingredients are given common names ending in hydrochloride. What acid do you think is used to prepare an amine hydrochloride salt?

16.71 In Section 21.1, several components of nucleic acids, DNA and RNA, are identified as "bases." What molecular feature of these substances might explain why they are referred to as bases?

16.72 The hydrolysis of amides requires rather vigorous conditions of strong acid or base and heat. What technique might be employed to achieve hydrolysis under milder conditions?

16.73 Alkaloids can be extracted from plant tissues using dilute hydrochloric acid. Why does the use of acid enhance their water solubility?

Chirality: The Handedness of Molecules

15

Charles D. Winters

Median cross section through the shell of a chambered nautilus found in the deep waters of the Pacific Ocean. The shell shows handedness; this cross section is a left-handed spiral.

15.1 What Is Enantiomerism?

In Chapters 11 through 14, we studied two types of stereoisomers, namely the *cis-trans* isomers of certain disubstituted cycloalkanes and appropriately substituted alkenes. Recall that stereoisomers have the same connectivity of their atoms but a different orientation of their atoms in space.

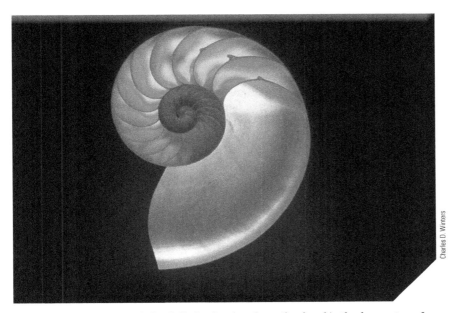

cis-1,2-Dimethyl-cyclohexane

trans-1,2-Dimethyl-cyclohexane

cis-2-Butene

trans-2-Butene

In this chapter, we study the relationship between objects and their **mirror images**; that is, we study stereoisomers called enantiomers and diastereomers. Figure 15.1 summarizes the relationship among these isomers and those we studied in Chapters 11 through 14.

OWL

Sign in to OWL at **www.cengage.com/owl** to view tutorials and simulations, develop problem-solving skills, and complete online homework assigned by your professor.

FIGURE 15.1 Relationships among isomers. In this chapter, we study enantiomers and diastereomers.

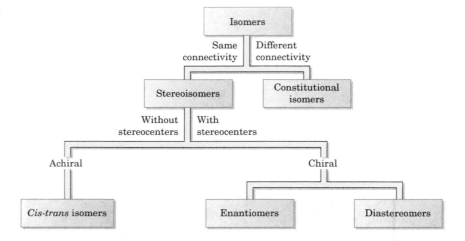

The significance of enantiomers is that, except for inorganic compounds and a few simple organic compounds, the vast majority of molecules in the biological world show this type of isomerism. Furthermore, approximately one half of all medications used to treat humans display this property.

As an example of enantiomerism, let us consider 2-butanol. As we discuss this molecule, we will focus on carbon 2, the carbon bearing the —OH group. What makes this carbon interesting is the fact that it has four different groups bonded to it: CH_3, H, OH, and CH_2CH_3.

$$OH$$
$$|$$
$$CH_3CHCH_2CH_3$$
2-Butanol

This structural formula does not show the three-dimensional shape of 2-butanol or the orientation of its atoms in space. To do so, we must consider the molecule as a three-dimensional object. On the left is what we will call the "original molecule" and a ball-and-stick model of it. In this drawing, the —OH and —CH_3 groups are in the plane of the paper, —H is behind the plane (shown as a broken wedge), and —CH_2CH_3 is in front of it (shown as a solid wedge). In the middle is a mirror. On the right is a **mirror image** of the original molecule along with a ball-and-stick model of the mirror image. Every molecule—and, in fact, every object in the world around us—has a mirror image.

The question we now need to ask is "What is the relationship between the original molecule of 2-butanol and its mirror image?" To answer this question, we need to imagine that we can pick up the mirror image and move it in 3-D space in any way we wish. If we can move the mirror image in space and find that it fits over the original molecule so that every bond, atom, and detail of the mirror image matches exactly the bonds, atoms, and

details of the original, then the two are **superposable**. In other words, the mirror image and the original represent the same molecule; they are merely oriented differently in space. If, however, no matter how we turn the mirror image in space, it will not fit exactly on the original with every detail matching, then the two are **nonsuperposable**; they are different molecules.

One way to see that the mirror image of 2-butanol is not superposable on the original molecule is illustrated in the following drawings. Imagine that we hold the mirror image by the C—OH bond and rotate the bottom part of the molecule by 180° about this bond. The —OH group retains its position in space, but the —CH₃ group, which was to the right and in the plane of the paper, remains in the plane of the paper but is now to the left. Similarly, the —CH₂CH₃ group, which was in front of the plane of the paper and to the left, is now behind the plane and to the right.

OH
|
H_3C—C⟍H
 CH_2CH_3

Original molecule

180° OH
 |
CH_3CH_2 H⟍C CH_3

Mirror image of
original molecule

rotate about the
C—OH bond by 180° ⟶

OH
|
H_3C—C⟍CH_2CH_3
 H

Mirror image
rotated by 180°

Now move the mirror image in space and try to fit it on the original molecule so that all bonds and atoms match.

Mirror image
turned by 180° ⟶

OH
|
H_3C—C⟍CH_2CH_3
 H

Original molecule ⟶

OH
|
H_3C—C⟍H
 CH_2CH_3

Charles D. Winters

The threads of a drill or screw twist along the axis of the helix, and some plants climb by sending out tendrils that twist helically. The drill bit shown here has a left-handed twist, and the tendril has a right-handed twist.

By turning the mirror image as we did, its —OH and —CH₃ groups now fit exactly on top of the —OH and —CH₃ groups of the original molecule. However, the —H and the —CH₂CH₃ groups of the two do not match. The —H is away from us in the original but toward us in the mirror image; the —CH₂CH₃ group is toward us in the original but away from us in the mirror image. We conclude that the original molecule of 2-butanol and its mirror image are nonsuperposable and therefore are different compounds.

To summarize, we can turn and rotate the mirror image of 2-butanol in any direction in space, but as long as no bonds are broken and rearranged, we can make only two of the four groups bonded to carbon 2 of the mirror image coincide with those on its original molecule. Because 2-butanol and its mirror image are not superposable, they are isomers. Isomers such as these are called **enantiomers**. Enantiomers, like gloves, always occur in pairs.

The terms "superposable" and "superimposable" mean the same thing and are both used currently.

Enantiomers Stereoisomers that are nonsuperposable mirror images; refers to a relationship between pairs of objects

(a) (b)

FIGURE 15.2 Mirror images. (a) Two woodcarvings. The mirror images cannot be superposed on the actual model. The man's right arm rests on the camera in the mirror image, but in the actual statue, the man's left arm rests on the camera. (b) Left- and right-handed sea shells. If you cup a right-handed shell in your right hand with your thumb pointing from the narrow end to the wide end, the opening will be on your right.

Chiral From the Greek *cheir*, "hand"; an object that is not superposable on its mirror image

Objects that are not superposable on their mirror images are said to be **chiral** (pronounced "ki-ral," rhymes with spiral; from the Greek: *cheir*, "hand"); that is, they show handedness. We encounter chirality in three-dimensional objects of all sorts. Our left hand is chiral, and so is our right hand. Thus, our hands have an enantiomeric relationship. A spiral binding on a notebook is chiral. A machine screw with a right-handed twist is chiral. A ship's propeller is chiral. As you examine the objects in the world around you, you will undoubtedly conclude that the vast majority of them are chiral.

The most common cause of enantiomerism in organic molecules is the presence of a carbon with four different groups bonded to it. Let us examine this statement further by considering 2-propanol, which has no such carbon atom. In this molecule, carbon 2 is bonded to three different groups, but no carbon is bonded to four different groups.

On the left is a three-dimensional representation of 2-propanol; on the right is its mirror image. Also shown are ball-and-stick models of each molecule.

Original molecule Mirror image

The question we now ask is "What is the relationship of the mirror image to the original?" This time, let us rotate the mirror image by 120° about the C—OH bond and then compare it to the original. After performing this rotation, we see that all atoms and bonds of the mirror image fit exactly on the original. Thus, the structures we first drew for the original molecule and its mirror image are, in fact, the same molecule—just viewed from different perspectives (Figure 15.3).

If an object and its mirror image are superposable, then they are identical and enantiomerism is not possible. We say that such an object is **achiral**

Achiral An object that lacks chirality; an object that is superposable on its mirror image

OH

H_3C — C — H / CH_3

Original molecule

120 OH

H — C — CH₃ / H_3C

Mirror image of original molecule

Rotate the mirror image by 120° about the C—OH bond ⟶

OH

H_3C — C — H / CH_3

Mirror image rotated by 120°

FIGURE 15.3 Rotation of the mirror image about the C—OH bond by 120° does not change the configuration of the stereocenter, but makes it easier to see that the mirror image is superposable on the original molecule.

(without chirality); that is, it has no handedness. Examples of achiral objects include an undecorated cup, an unmarked baseball bat, a regular tetrahedron, a cube, and a sphere.

To repeat, the most common cause of chirality in organic molecules is a tetrahedral carbon atom with four different groups bonded to it. We call such a chiral carbon atom a **stereocenter**. 2-Butanol has one stereocenter; 2-propanol has none. As another example of a molecule with a stereocenter, let us consider 2-hydroxypropanoic acid, more commonly named lactic acid. Lactic acid is a product of anaerobic glycolysis. (See Section 28.2 and Chemical Connections 28A.) It is also what gives sour cream its sour taste.

Figure 15.4 shows three-dimensional representations of lactic acid and its mirror image. In these representations, all bond angles about the central carbon atom are approximately 109.5° and the four bonds from it are directed toward the corners of a regular tetrahedron. Lactic acid displays enantiomerism or chirality; that is, the original molecule and its mirror image are not superposable but rather are different compounds.

Stereocenter A tetrahedral carbon atom that has four different groups bonded to it

FIGURE 15.4 Three-dimensional representations of lactic acid and its mirror image.

An equimolar mixture of two enantiomers is called a **racemic mixture**, a term derived from the name racemic acid (Latin: *racemus*, "a cluster of grapes"). Racemic acid is the name originally given to the equimolar mixture of the enantiomers of tartaric acid that forms as a by-product during the fermentation of grape juice to produce wine.

Racemic mixture A mixture of equal amounts of two enantiomers

How To . . .

Draw Enantiomers

Now that we know what enantiomers are, we can think about how to represent their three-dimensional structures on a two-dimensional surface. Let us take one of the enantiomers of 2-butanol as an example.

Following are a molecular model of one enantiomer and four different three-dimensional representations of it:

(1) (2) (3) (4)

In our initial discussions of 2-butanol, we used representation (1) to show the tetrahedral geometry of the stereocenter. In this representation, two groups (OH and CH_3) are in the plane of the paper, one (CH_2CH_3) is coming out of the plane toward us, and one (H) is behind the plane and going away from us. We can turn representation (1) slightly in space and tip it a bit to place the carbon framework in the plane of the paper. Doing so gives us representation (2), in which there are still two groups in the plane of the paper, one coming toward us and one going away from us.

For an even more abbreviated representation of this enantiomer of 2-butanol, we can change representation (2) into the line-angle formula (3). Although we do not normally show hydrogens in a line-angle formula, we do so here just to remind ourselves that the fourth group on the stereocenter is really there and that it is H. Finally, we can carry the abbreviation a step further and write 2-butanol as the line-angle formula (4). Here, we omit the H on the stereocenter, but we know that it must be there (carbon needs four bonds), and we know that it must be behind the plane of the paper. Clearly, the abbreviated formulas (3) and (4) are the easiest to write, and we will rely on this type of representation throughout the remainder of the text.

When you have to write three-dimensional representations of stereocenters, try to keep the carbon framework in the plane of the paper and the other two atoms or groups of atoms on the stereocenter toward and away from you, respectively. Using representation (4) as a model, we get the following alternative representations of its mirror image:

One enantiomer
of 2-butanol

Alternative representations of
its mirror image

Example 15.1 Drawing Mirror Images

Each of the following molecules has one stereocenter marked by an asterisk. Draw three-dimensional representations for the enantiomers of each molecule.

(a) $CH_3\overset{*}{C}HCH_2CH_3$

(b)

Strategy

First, draw the carbon stereocenter showing the tetrahedral orientation of its four bonds. One way to do this is to draw two bonds in the plane of the paper, a third bond toward you in front of the plane, and the fourth bond away from you behind the plane. Next, place the four groups bonded to the stereocenter on these positions. This completes the stereodrawing of one enantiomer. To draw the other enantiomer, interchange any two of the groups on the original stereodrawing.

Solution

To draw an original of (a), for example, place the CH_3 and CH_2CH_3 groups in the plane of the paper. Place H away from you and the Cl toward you; this orientation gives the enantiomer of (a) on the left. Its mirror image is on the right.

(a)

(b)

Problem 15.1

Each of the following molecules has one stereocenter marked by an asterisk. Draw three-dimensional representations for the enantiomers of each molecule.

(a)

(b) $CH_3\overset{*}{C}HCHCH_3$

15.2 How Do We Specify the Configuration of a Stereocenter?

Because enantiomers are different compounds, each must have a different name. The over-the-counter drug ibuprofen, for example, displays enantio-merism and can exist as the pair of enantiomers shown here:

The inactive enantiomer
of ibuprofen

The active enantiomer
of ibuprofen

Only one enantiomer of ibuprofen is biologically active. It reaches thera-peutic concentrations in the human body in approximately 12 minutes, whereas the racemic mixture takes approximately 30 minutes to achieve this feat. However, in this case, the inactive enantiomer is not wasted. The body converts it to the active enantiomer, but this process takes time.

What we need is a system to designate which enantiomer of ibuprofen (or one of any other pair of enantiomers, for that matter) is which without having to draw and point to one or the other of the enantiomers. To do so, chemists have developed the **R,S system**. The first step in assigning an R or S configuration to a stereocenter is to arrange the groups bonded to it in order of priority. Priority is based on atomic number: The higher the atomic number, the higher the priority. If a priority cannot be assigned on the basis of the atoms bonded directly to the stereocenter, look at the next atom or set of atoms and continue to the first point of difference; that is, continue until you can assign a priority.

Table 15.1 shows the priorities of the most common groups we encounter in organic and biochemistry. In the R,S system, a $C{=}O$ is treated as if car-bon were bonded to two oxygens by single bonds; thus, $CH{=}O$ has a higher priority than $-CH_2OH$, in which carbon is bonded to only one oxygen.

R,S system A set of rules for specifying the configuration about a stereocenter

Table 15.1 *R,S* Priorities of Some Common Groups

Atom or Group	Reason for Priority: First Point of Difference (Atomic Number)
— I	iodine (53)
— Br	bromine (35)
— Cl	chlorine (17)
— SH	sulfur (16)
— OH	oxygen (8)
— NH₂	nitrogen (7)
$\overset{O}{\overset{\|}{—\text{COH}}}$	carbon to oxygen, oxygen, then oxygen (6 ⟶ 8, 8, 8)
$\overset{O}{\overset{\|}{—\text{CNH}_2}}$	carbon to oxygen, oxygen, then nitrogen (6 ⟶ 8, 8, 7)
$\overset{O}{\overset{\|}{—\text{CH}}}$	carbon to oxygen, oxygen, then hydrogen (6 ⟶ 8, 8, 1)
— CH₂OH	carbon to oxygen (6 ⟶ 8)
— CH₂NH₂	carbon to nitrogen (6 ⟶ 7)
— CH₂CH₃	carbon to carbon (6 ⟶ 6)
— CH₂H	carbon to hydrogen (6 ⟶ 1)
— H	hydrogen (1)

Increasing priority →

Example 15.2 Using the *R,S* System

Assign priorities to the groups in each set.
(a) —CH_2OH and —CH_2CH_2OH
(b) —CH_2CH_2OH and —CH_2NH_2

Strategy and Solution

(a) The first point of difference is O of the —OH group compared to C of the —CH_2OH group.

First point of
difference

—CH_2OH —CH_2CH_2OH
Higher priority Lower priority

(b) The first point of difference is C of the CH_2OH group compared to N of the NH_2 group.

First point of
difference

—CH_2CH_2OH —CH_2NH_2
Lower priority **Higher priority**

Problem 15.2

Assign priorities to the groups in each set.

(a) —CH_2OH and —$CH_2CH_2\overset{\displaystyle O}{\overset{\|}{C}}OH$

(b) —CH_2NH_2 and —$CH_2\overset{\displaystyle O}{\overset{\|}{C}}OH$

To assign an *R* or *S* configuration to a stereocenter:

1. Assign a priority from 1 (highest) to 4 (lowest) to each group bonded to the molecule's stereocenter.
2. Orient the molecule in space so that the lowest-priority group (4) is directed away from you, as would be, for instance, the steering column of a car. The three higher-priority groups (1–3) then project toward you, as would the spokes of a steering wheel.
3. Read the three groups projecting toward you in order from highest (1) to lowest (4) priority.
4. If reading the groups 1-2-3 proceeds in a clockwise direction (to the right), the configuration is designated as **R** (Latin: *rectus*, "straight"); if reading the groups 1-2-3 proceeds in a counterclockwise direction (to the left), the configuration is **S** (Latin: *sinister*, "left"). You can also visualize this system as follows: Turning the steering wheel to the right equals *R,* and turning it to the left equals *S.*

Group of lowest
priority points
away from you

R Used in the *R,S* system to show that when the lowest-priority group is away from you, the order of priority of groups on a stereocenter is clockwise

S Used in the *R,S* system to show that when the lowest-priority group is away from you, the order of priority of groups on a stereocenter is counterclockwise

Example 15.3 Assigning an *R* or *S* Configuration

Assign an *R* or *S* configuration to each stereocenter.

(a) 2-Butanol (b) Alanine

Strategy and Solution

View each molecule through the stereocenter and along the bond from the stereocenter to the group of lowest priority.

(a) The order of decreasing priority about the stereocenter in this enantiomer of 2-butanol is —OH > —CH₂CH₃ > —CH₃ > —H. Therefore, view the molecule along the C—H bond with the H pointing away from you. Reading the other three groups in the order 1-2-3 follows in the clockwise direction. Therefore, the configuration is *R* and this enantiomer is (*R*)-2-butanol.

(R)-2-Butanol

With —H, the lowest-priority group, pointing away from you, this is what you see

(b) The order of decreasing priority in this enantiomer of alanine is —NH₂ > —COOH > —CH₃ > —H. View the molecule along the C—H bond with H pointing away from you. Reading the groups in the order 1-2-3 follows in a clockwise direction; therefore, the configuration is *R* and this enantiomer is (*R*)-alanine.

(R)-Alanine

With —H, the lowest-priority group, pointing away from you, this is what you see

Problem 15.3

Assign an *R* or *S* configuration to the single stereocenter in glyceraldehyde, the simplest carbohydrate (Chapter 20).

$$\underset{\text{Glyceraldehyde}}{\overset{\displaystyle HO}{\underset{\displaystyle}{H}}\text{—C—}\overset{\displaystyle \overset{O}{\parallel}}{C}\text{—H}}$$

Glyceraldehyde

Now let us return to our three-dimensional drawing of the enantiomers of ibuprofen and assign each an R or S configuration. In order of decreasing priority, the groups bonded to the stereocenter are —COOH (1) > —C_6H_5 (2) > —CH_3 (3) > H (4). In the enantiomer on the left, reading the groups on the stereocenter in order of priority is clockwise, and therefore, this enantiomer is (R)-ibuprofen. Its mirror image is (S)-ibuprofen.

(R)-Ibuprofen
(the inactive enantiomer)

(S)-Ibuprofen
(the active enantiomer)

The R,S system can be used to specify the configuration of any stereocenter in any molecule. It is not, however, the only system used for this purpose. There is also a D,L system, which is used primarily to specify the configuration of carbohydrates (Chapter 20) and amino acids (Chapter 22).

In closing, note that the purpose of Section 15.2 is to show you how chemists assign a configuration to a stereocenter that specifies the relative orientation of the four groups on the stereocenter. What is important is that when you see a name such as (S)-Naproxen or (R)-Plavix, you realize that the compound is chiral and that the compound is not a racemic mixture. Rather, it is a pure enantiomer. We use the symbol (R,S) to show that a compound is a racemic mixture, as for example, (R,S)-Naproxen.

15.3 How Many Stereoisomers Are Possible for Molecules with Two or More Stereocenters?

For a molecule with n stereocenters, the maximum number of stereoisomers possible is 2^n. We have already verified that for a molecule with one stereocenter, $2^1 = 2$ stereoisomers (one pair of enantiomers) are possible. For a molecule with two stereocenters, a maximum of $2^2 = 4$ stereoisomers (two pairs of enantiomers) is possible; for a molecule with three stereocenters, a maximum of $2^3 = 8$ stereoisomers (four pairs of enantiomers) is possible; and so forth.

A. Molecules with Two Stereocenters

We begin our study of molecules with two stereocenters by considering 2,3,4-trihydroxybutanal, a molecule with two stereocenters.

$$CHO$$
$$|$$
$$*CHOH$$
$$|$$
$$*CHOH$$
$$|$$
$$CH_2OH$$

2,3,4-Trihydroxybutanal
(2 stereocenters;
4 stereoisomers
are possible)

The maximum number of stereoisomers possible for this molecule is $2^2 = 4$, each of which is drawn in Figure 15.5.

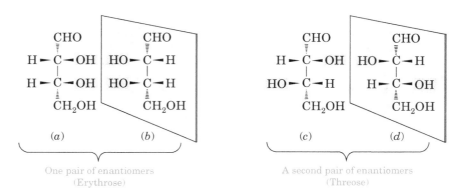

FIGURE 15.5 The four stereoisomers of 2,3,4-trihydroxybutanal.

Stereoisomers (a) and (b) are nonsuperposable mirror images and are, therefore, a pair of enantiomers. Stereoisomers (c) and (d) are also nonsuperposable mirror images and are a second pair of enantiomers. We describe the four stereoisomers of 2,3,4-trihydroxybutanal by saying that they consist of two pairs of enantiomers. Enantiomers (a) and (b) are named **erythrose**. Erythrose is synthesized in erythrocytes (red blood cells); hence the derivation of its name. Enantiomers (c) and (d) are named **threose**. Erythrose and threose belong to the class of compounds called carbohydrates, which we will discuss in Chapter 20.

We have specified the relationship between (a) and (b) and that between (c) and (d). What is the relationship between (a) and (c), between (a) and (d), between (b) and (c), and between (b) and (d)? The answer is that they are **diastereomers**—stereoisomers that are not mirror images.

Diastereomers Stereoisomers that are not mirror images

Example 15.4 Enantiomers and Diastereomers

1,2,3-Butanetriol has two stereocenters (carbons 2 and 3); thus, $2^2 = 4$ stereoisomers are possible for it. Following are three-dimensional representations for each.

$$
\begin{array}{cccc}
\text{CH}_2\text{OH} & \text{CH}_2\text{OH} & \text{CH}_2\text{OH} & \text{CH}_2\text{OH} \\
\text{H}\!-\!\text{C}\!-\!\text{OH} & \text{H}\!-\!\text{C}\!-\!\text{OH} & \text{HO}\!-\!\text{C}\!-\!\text{H} & \text{HO}\!-\!\text{C}\!-\!\text{H} \\
\text{HO}\!-\!\text{C}\!-\!\text{H} & \text{H}\!-\!\text{C}\!-\!\text{OH} & \text{HO}\!-\!\text{C}\!-\!\text{H} & \text{H}\!-\!\text{C}\!-\!\text{OH} \\
\text{CH}_3 & \text{CH}_3 & \text{CH}_3 & \text{CH}_3 \\
(1) & (2) & (3) & (4)
\end{array}
$$

(a) Which stereoisomers are pairs of enantiomers?
(b) Which stereoisomers are diastereomers?

Strategy

First, identify those structures that are mirror images. These, then, are the pairs of enantiomers. All other pairs of structures are diastereomers.

Solution

(a) Enantiomers are stereoisomers that are nonsuperposable mirror images. Compounds (1) and (4) are one pair of enantiomers and compounds (2) and (3) are a second pair of enantiomers.

(b) Diastereomers are stereoisomers that are not mirror images. Compounds (1) and (2), (1) and (3), (2) and (4), and (3) and (4) are diastereomers.

The diagram shows the relationship among these four stereoisomers.

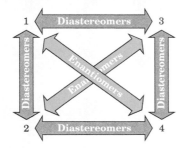

Problem 15.4

3-Amino-2-butanol has two stereocenters (carbons 2 and 3); thus, $2^2 = 4$ stereoisomers are possible for it.

$$
\begin{array}{cccc}
\text{CH}_3 & \text{CH}_3 & \text{CH}_3 & \text{CH}_3 \\
\text{H}\!-\!\text{C}\!-\!\text{OH} & \text{H}\!-\!\text{C}\!-\!\text{OH} & \text{HO}\!-\!\text{C}\!-\!\text{H} & \text{HO}\!-\!\text{C}\!-\!\text{H} \\
\text{H}_2\text{N}\!-\!\text{C}\!-\!\text{H} & \text{H}\!-\!\text{C}\!-\!\text{NH}_2 & \text{H}\!-\!\text{C}\!-\!\text{NH}_2 & \text{H}_2\text{N}\!-\!\text{C}\!-\!\text{H} \\
\text{CH}_3 & \text{CH}_3 & \text{CH}_3 & \text{CH}_3 \\
(1) & (2) & (3) & (4)
\end{array}
$$

(a) Which stereoisomers are pairs of enantiomers?
(b) Which sets of stereoisomers are diastereomers?

We can analyze chirality in cyclic molecules with two stereocenters in the same way we analyzed it in acyclic compounds.

Example 15.5 Enentriomerism in Cyclic Compounds

How many stereoisomers are possible for 3-methylcyclopentanol?

Strategy and Solution

Carbons 1 and 3 of this compound are stereocenters. Therefore, $2^2 = 4$ stereoisomers are possible for this molecule. The *cis* isomer exists as one pair of enantiomers, the *trans* isomer exists as a second pair of enantiomers.

cis-2-Methylcyclopentanol
(a pair of enantiomers)

trans-2-Methylcyclopentanol
(a second pair of enantiomers)

Problem 15.5

How many stereoisomers are possible for 3-methylcyclohexanol?

Example 15.6 Locating Stereocenters

Mark the stereocenters in each compound with an asterisk. How many stereoisomers are possible for each?

OH

(a)

.CH₃
CH₃

OH

(b)

OH O
 ‖
CH₃—CH—CH—COH
 |
 NH₂

(c)

Strategy

A stereocenter is a carbon atom that has four different groups bonded to it. Therefore, you are being asked to identify each carbon bonded to four different groups.

Solution

Each stereocenter is marked with an asterisk, and the number of stereoisomers possible for it appears under each compound. In (a), the carbon bearing the two methyl groups is not a stereocenter; this carbon has only three different groups bonded to it.

(a)

OH

*

.CH₃
CH₃

$2^1 = 2$

(b)

OH

*

*

$2^2 = 4$

(c) CH₃—CH—CH—COH

OH O
 *| *| ‖
CH₃—CH—CH—COH
 |
 NH₂

$2^2 = 4$

Problem 15.6

Mark all stereocenters in each compound with an asterisk. How many stereoisomers are possible for each?

(a)

HO

HO

NH₂
 |
CH₂CHCOOH

(b) CH₂=CHCHCH₂CH₃

OH
|

(c)

OH

NH₂

B. Molecules with Three or More Stereocenters

The 2^n rule applies equally well to molecules with three or more stereocenters. The following disubstituted cyclohexanol has three stereocenters, each marked with an asterisk. A maximum of $2^3 = 8$ stereoisomers is possible for this molecule. Menthol, one of the eight, has the configuration shown in the middle and on the right. Menthol is present in peppermint and other mint oils.

2-Isopropyl-5-methylcyclohexanol
(three stereocenters;
eight stereoisomers
are possible)

Menthol
(one of the eight
possible stereoisomers)

Menthol drawn as a
chair conformation
(note that the three groups
on the cyclohexane ring
are all equatorial)

Chiral Drugs

Some common drugs used in human medicine—for example, aspirin—are achiral. Others, such as the penicillin and erythromycin classes of antibiotics and the drug Captopril, are chiral and are sold as single enantiomers. Captopril is very effective for the treatment of high blood pressure and congestive heart failure. It is manufactured and sold as the (S,S)-stereoisomer.

Captopril

A large number of chiral drugs, however, are sold as racemic mixtures. The popular analgesic ibuprofen (the active ingredient in Motrin, Advil, and many other non-aspirin analgesics) is an example.

Recently, the U.S. Food and Drug Administration established new guidelines for the testing and marketing of chiral drugs. After reviewing these guidelines, many drug companies have decided to develop only single enantiomers of new chiral drugs.

In addition to regulatory pressure, pharmaceutical developers must deal with patent considerations. If a company has a patent on a racemic mixture of a drug, a new patent can often be taken out on one of its enantiomers.

Test your knowledge with Problem 15.30.

Cholesterol, a more complicated molecule, has eight stereocenters. To identify them, remember to add an appropriate number of hydrogens to complete the tetravalence of each carbon you think might be a stereocenter.

Cholesterol has eight stereocenters: 256 stereoisomers are possible

This is the stereoisomer found in human metabolism

15.4 What Is Optical Activity, and How Is Chirality Detected in the Laboratory?

A. Plane-Polarized Light

As we have already established, the two members of a pair of enantiomers are different compounds, and we must expect, therefore, that some of their properties differ. One such property relates to their effect on the plane of polarized light. Each member of a pair of enantiomers rotates the plane of polarized light; for this reason, each enantiomer is said to be **optically active**. To understand how optical activity is detected in the laboratory, we must first understand what plane-polarized light is and how a polarimeter, the instrument used to detect optical activity, works.

Ordinary light consists of waves vibrating in all planes perpendicular to its direction of propagation. Certain materials, such as a Polaroid sheet (a plastic film like that used in polarized sunglasses), selectively transmit

Optically active Showing that a compound rotates the plane of polarized light

FIGURE 15.6 Schematic diagram of a polarimeter with its sample tube containing a solution of an optically active compound. The analyzer has been turned clockwise by α degrees to restore the light field.

light waves vibrating only in parallel planes. Electromagnetic radiation vibrating in only parallel planes is said to be **plane polarized**.

B. A Polarimeter

Plane-polarized light Light with waves vibrating in only parallel planes

A **polarimeter** consists of a light source emitting unpolarized light, a polarizer, an analyzer, and a sample tube (Figure 15.6). If the sample tube is empty, the intensity of light reaching the detector (in this case, your eye) is at its maximum when the axes of the polarizer and analyzer are parallel to each other. If the analyzer is turned either clockwise or counterclockwise, less light is transmitted. When the axis of the analyzer is at right angles to the axis of the polarizer, the field of view is dark (no light passes through).

When a solution of an optically active compound is placed in the sample tube, it rotates the plane of the polarized light. If it rotates the plane clockwise, we say it is **dextrorotatory**; if it rotates the plane counterclockwise, we say it is **levorotatory**. Each member of a pair of enantiomers rotates the plane of polarized light by the same number of degrees, but in opposite directions. If one enantiomer is dextrorotatory, the other is levorotatory. Thus, racemic mixtures (as well as achiral compounds) do not display optical activity.

Dextrorotatory The clockwise (to the right) rotation of the plane of polarized light in a polarimeter

Levorotatory The counterclockwise (to the left) rotation of the plane of polarized light in a polarimeter

The number of degrees by which an optically active compound rotates the plane of polarized light is called its **specific rotation** and is given the symbol $[\alpha]$. Specific rotation is defined as the observed rotation of an optically active substance at a concentration of 1 g/mL in a sample tube that is 10 cm long. A dextrorotatory compound is indicated by a plus sign in parentheses, (+), and a levorotatory compound is indicated by a minus sign in parentheses, (−). It is common practice to report the temperature (in °C) at which the measurement is made and the wavelength of light used. The most common wavelength of light used in polarimetry is the sodium D line, the same wavelength responsible for the yellow color of sodium-vapor lamps.

The (+) enantiomer of lactic acid is produced by muscle tissue in humans. The (−) enantiomer is found in sour cream and sour milk.

Following are specific rotations for the enantiomers of lactic acid measured at 21°C and using the D line of a sodium-vapor lamp as the light source:

COOH
|
H₃C—C"""H
 ＼OH

(S)-(+)-Lactic acid
$[\alpha]_D^{21} = +2.6°$

COOH
|
H""C—CH₃
HO

(R)-(−)-Lactic acid
$[\alpha]_D^{21} = -2.6°$

15.5 What Is the Significance of Chirality in the Biological World?

Except for inorganic salts and a few low-molecular-weight organic substances, the majority of molecules in living systems—both plant and animal—are chiral. Although these molecules can exist as a number of stereoisomers, almost invariably, only one stereoisomer is found in nature. Of course, instances do occur in which more than one stereoisomer is found, but these isomers rarely exist together in the same biological system.

A. Chirality in Biomolecules

Perhaps the most conspicuous examples of chirality among biological molecules are the enzymes, all of which have many stereocenters. Consider chymotrypsin, an enzyme in the intestines of animals that catalyzes the digestion of proteins (Chapter 23). Chymotrypsin has 251 stereocenters. The maximum number of stereoisomers possible is 2^{251}—a staggeringly large number, almost beyond comprehension. Fortunately, nature does not squander its precious energy and resources unnecessarily; any given organism produces and uses only one of these stereoisomers.

B. How an Enzyme Distinguishes Between a Molecule and Its Enantiomer

An enzyme catalyzes a biological reaction of a molecule by first positioning the molecule at a **binding site** on the enzyme surface. An enzyme with specific binding sites for three of the four groups on a stereocenter can distinguish between a chiral molecule and its enantiomer or one of its diastereomers. Assume, for example, that an enzyme involved in catalyzing a reaction of glyceraldehyde has three binding sites: one specific for —H, a second specific for —OH, and a third specific for —CHO. Assume further that the three sites are arranged on the enzyme surface as shown in Figure 15.7. The enzyme can distinguish (R)-glyceraldehyde (the natural or biologically active form) from its enantiomer because the natural enantiomer can be adsorbed with three groups interacting with their appropriate binding sites; for the S enantiomer, at best only two groups can interact with these three binding sites.

Because interactions between molecules in living systems take place in a chiral environment, it should come as no surprise that a molecule and its enantiomer will elicit a different physiological response when compared to the same molecule's diastereomer. As we have already seen, (S)-ibuprofen is

The horns of this African Gazelle show chirality; one horn is the mirror image of the other.

(R)-Glyceraldehyde
fits the three binding
sites on surface

(S)-Glyceraldehyde
fits only two of the
three binding sites

FIGURE 15.7 A schematic diagram of an enzyme surface that can interact with (R)-glyceraldehyde at three binding sites, but with (S)-glyceraldehyde at only two of these sites.

active as a pain and fever reliever, while its R enantiomer is inactive. The S enantiomer of the closely related analgesic naproxen is also the active pain reliever of this compound, but its R enantiomer is a liver toxin!

(S)-Ibuprofen (S)-Naproxen

Summary

Section 15.1 What Is Enantiomerism?

- A **mirror image** is the reflection of an object in a mirror.
- **Enantiomers** are a pair of stereoisomers that are nonsuperposable mirror images.
- A **racemic mixture** contains equal amounts of two enantiomers and does not rotate the plane of polarized light.
- **Diastereomers** are stereoisomers that are not mirror images.
- An object that is not superposable on its mirror image is said to be **chiral**; it has handedness. An **achiral** object lacks chirality (handedness); that is, it has a superposable mirror image.
- The most common cause of chirality in organic molecules is the presence of a tetrahedral carbon atom with four different groups bonded to it. Such a carbon is called a **stereocenter**.

Section 15.2 How Do We Specify the Configuration of a Stereocenter?

- We use the **R,S system** to specify the configuration of a stereocenter.

Section 15.3 How Many Stereoisomers Are Possible for Molecules with Two or More Stereocenters?

- For a molecule with n stereocenters, the maximum number of stereoisomers possible is 2^n.

Section 15.4 What Is Optical Activity, and How Is Chirality Detected in the Laboratory?

- Light with waves that vibrate in only parallel planes is said to be **plane polarized**.
- We use a **polarimeter** to measure optical activity. A compound is said to be **optically active** if it rotates the plane of polarized light.
- If a compound rotates the plane clockwise, it is **dextrorotatory**; if it rotates the plane counterclockwise, it is **levorotatory**.
- Each member of a pair of enantiomers rotates the plane of polarized light an equal number of degrees, but in opposite directions.

Section 15.5 What Is the Significance of Chirality in the Biological World?

- An enzyme catalyzes biological reactions of molecules by first positioning them at binding sites on its surface. An enzyme with binding sites specific for three of the four groups on a stereocenter can distinguish between a molecule and its enantiomer or one of its diastereomers.

Problems

Orange-numbered problems are applied.

References to previous chapters are given in parentheses.

Section 15.1 What Is Enantiomerism?

15.7 Answer true or false.
 (a) The *cis* and *trans* stereoisomers of 2-butene are achiral.
 (b) The carbonyl carbon of an aldehyde, ketone, carboxylic acid, or ester cannot be a stereocenter.
 (c) Stereoisomers have the same connectivity of their atoms.
 (d) Constitutional isomers have the same connectivity of their atoms.
 (e) An unmarked cube is achiral.
 (f) A human foot is chiral.
 (g) Every object in nature has a mirror image.
 (h) The most common cause of chirality in organic molecules is the presence of a tetrahedral carbon atom with four different groups bonded to it.
 (i) If a molecule is not superposable on its mirror image, the molecule is chiral.

15.8 What does the term "chiral" mean? Give an example of a chiral molecule.

15.9 What does the term "achiral" mean? Give an example of an achiral molecule.

15.10 Define the term "stereoisomer." Name three types of stereoisomers.

15.11 In what way are constitutional isomers different from stereoisomers? In what way are they the same?

15.12 Which of the following objects are chiral (assume that there is no label or other identifying mark)?
(a) Pair of scissors (b) Tennis ball
(c) Paper clip (d) Beaker
(e) The swirl created in water as it drains out of a sink or bathtub

15.13 2-Pentanol is chiral, but 3-pentanol is not. Explain.

15.14 2-Butene exists as a pair of *cis-trans* isomers. Is *cis*-2-butene chiral? Is *trans*-2-butene chiral? Explain.

15.15 Explain why the carbon of a carbonyl group cannot be a stereocenter.

15.16 Which of the following compounds contain stereocenters?
(a) 2-Chloropentane (b) 3-Chloropentane
(c) 3-Chloro-1-butene (d) 1,2-Dichloropropane

15.17 Which of the following compounds contain stereocenters?
(a) Cyclopentanol
(b) 1-Chloro-2-propanol
(c) 2-Methylcyclopentanol
(d) 1-Phenyl-1-propanol

15.18 Using only C, H, and O, write structural formulas for the lowest-molecular-weight chiral molecule of each class.
(a) Alkane (b) Alkene
(c) Alcohol (d) Aldehyde
(e) Ketone (f) Carboxylic acid

15.19 Draw the mirror image for each molecule:

(a) H₃C — C with OH, COOH, H (b) H—C—OH with CHO, CH₂OH

(c) [ring structure with O, OH, H] (d) [cyclohexane with OH, CH₃]

15.20 Draw the mirror image for each molecule:

(a) H₂N — C — H with COOH, CH₃ (b) [ring with H, OH]

(c) [sugar structure with CH₂OH, O, OH, HO, H, OH] (d) H₃C — [cyclopentane] — NH₂

Section 15.3 How Many Stereoisomers Are Possible for Molecules with Two or More Stereocenters?

15.21 Answer true or false.
(a) For a molecule with two stereocenters, $2^2 = 4$ stereoisomers are possible.
(b) For a molecule with three stereocenters, $3^2 = 9$ stereoisomers are possible.
(c) Enantiomers, like gloves, occur in pairs.
(d) 2-Pentanol and 3-pentanol are both chiral and show enantiomerism.
(e) 1-Methylcyclohexanol is achiral and does not show enantiomerism.
(f) Diastereomers are stereoisomers that are not mirror images.

15.22 Mark each stereocenter in these molecules with an asterisk. Note that not all contain stereocenters.

15.23 Mark each stereocenter in these molecules with an asterisk. Note that not all contain stereocenters.

15.24 Label all stereocenters in each molecule with an asterisk. How many stereoisomers are possible for each molecule?

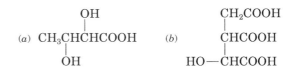

(a) CH₃CHCHCOOH with OH, OH (b) CH₂COOH, CHCOOH, HO—CHCOOH

(c) [cyclohexane with OH and isopropyl] (d) [cyclohexene with methyl and isopropyl]

15.25 Label all stereocenters in each molecule with an asterisk. How many stereoisomers are possible for each molecule?

(a)

(b)

(c)

(d)

15.26 For centuries, Chinese herbal medicine has used extracts of *Ephedra sinica* to treat asthma. The asthma-relieving component of this plant is ephedrine, a very potent dilator of the air passages of the lungs. The naturally occurring stereoisomer is levorotatory and has the following structure.

Ephedrine $[\alpha]_D^{25} = -41°$

(a) Mark each stereocenter in epinephrine with an asterisk.
(b) How many stereoisomers are possible for this compound?

15.27 The specific rotation of naturally occurring ephedrine, shown in Problem 15.26, is −41°. What is the specific rotation of its enantiomer?

15.28 What is a racemic mixture? Is a racemic mixture optically active? That is, will it rotate the plane of polarized light?

Section 15.4 What Is Optical Activity, and How Is Chirality Detected in the Laboratory?

15.29 Answer true or false.
(a) If a chiral compound is dextrorotatory, its enantiomer is levorotatory by the same number of degrees.
(b) A racemic mixture is optically inactive.
(c) All stereoisomers are optically active.
(d) Plane-polarized light consists of light waves vibrating in parallel planes.

Chemical Connections

15.30 (Chemical Connections 15A) What does it mean to say that a drug is *chiral*? If a drug is chiral, will it be optically active? That is, will it rotate the plane of polarized light?

15.31 (Chemical Connections 15A) When a successful drug is discovered, there often follows an effort to synthesize compounds closely related in structure to the original, in hopes of discovering new drugs that are even more effective. Following are structural

formulas for Captopril and three related angiotensin converting enzyme (ACE) inhibitors, which are used to treat hypertension. Which of these three are chiral, and how many stereoisomers are possible for each? Compare these three structures with that of Captopril and determine the similarities in structure among the four drugs.

Captopril

Quinapril (Accupril)

Enalopril (Altace)

Ramipril (Vasotec)

Additional Problems

15.32 Which of the eight alcohols with a molecular formula of $C_5H_{12}O$ are chiral?

15.33 Write the structural formula of an alcohol with the molecular formula $C_6H_{14}O$ that contains two stereocenters.

15.34 Which carboxylic acids with a molecular formula of $C_6H_{12}O_2$ are chiral?

15.35 Following are structural formulas for three of the drugs most widely prescribed to treat depression. Label all stereocenters in each and state the number of stereoisomers possible for each.

(a)

Fluoxetine
(Prozac)

(b)

Sertraline
(Zoloft)

(c)

Paroxetine
(Paxil)

15.36 Label the four stereocenters in amoxicillin, which belongs to the family of semisynthetic penicillins.

Amoxicillin

15.37 Consider a cyclohexane ring substituted with one hydroxyl group and one methyl group. Draw a structural formula for a compound of this composition that:

(a) Does not show *cis-trans* isomerism and has no stereocenters.

(b) Shows *cis-trans* isomerism but has no stereocenters.

(c) Shows *cis-trans* isomerism and has two stereocenters.

15.38 The next time you have the opportunity to view a collection of seashells that have a helical twist, study the chirality (handedness) of their twists. For each kind of shell, do you find an equal number of left-handed and right-handed twists or, for example, do they all have the same handedness?

15.39 The next time you have an opportunity to examine any of the seemingly endless varieties of blond spiral pasta (rotini, fusilli, radiatori, tortiglione, and so forth), examine their twists. Do the twists of any one kind all have a right-handed twist or a left-handed twist, or are they a racemic mixture?

15.40 Think about the helical coil of a telephone cord or the spiral binding on a notebook. Suppose that you view the spiral from one end and find that it has a left-handed twist. If you view the same spiral from the other end, does it have a left-handed twist from that end as well or does it have a right-handed twist?

15.41 Compound **A**(C_5H_8) is not optically active and cannot be separated into enantiomers. It reacts with bromine in carbon tetrachloride to discharge the purple color of bromine and form Compound **B**$(C_5H_8Br_2)$. When Compound **A** is treated with H_2 in the presence of a transition metal catalyst, it is converted to compound **C**(C_5H_{10}). When treated with HCl, compound **A** is converted to compound **D**(C_5H_9Cl). Given this information, propose structural formulas for compounds **A**, **B**, **C**, and **D**. *Hint*: There are at least three possibilities for Compound **A** and, in turn, three possibilities for Compounds **B**, **C**, and **D**.

Looking Ahead

15.42 Following is a chair conformation of glucose, the most prevalent carbohydrate in the biological world (Chapter 20).

(a) Identify the five stereocenters in this molecule.

(b) How many stereoisomers are possible?

(c) How many pairs of enantiomers are possible?

15.43 Triamcinolone acetonide, the active ingredient in Azmacort Inhalation Aerosol, is a steroid used to treat bronchial asthma.

Triamcinolone acetonide

(a) Label the eight stereocenters in this molecule.

(b) How many stereoisomers are possible for it? (Of these, the stereoisomer with the configuration shown here is the active ingredient in Azmacort.)

Challenge Problems

15.44 Consider the structure of the immunosuppressant *FK-506*, a molecule shown to disrupt calcineurin-mediated signal transduction in *T*-lymphocytes.

(a) What is the molecular formula of this immunosuppressant? (Chapter 10)

(b) How many stereocenters are present in *FK-506*? Determine the maximum number of stereoisomers possible.

(c) Identify and label the various functional groups present. (Chapter 10)

(d) Consider the two carbons in this structure labeled with asterisks (*). Determine the absolute configuration of each stereocenter.

(e) *FK-506* has been shown to exhibit moderate solubility in various organic solvents. Is this immunosuppressant expected to be soluble in ethanol (CH_3CH_2OH)? (Chapter 6)

(f) Consider the carbon atom labeled "**1**." What is the geometry and approximate bond angle of this carbon atom? (Chapter 3)

(g) Draw the alternative chair conformations of the cyclohexane ring at the lower right of *FK-506* and label the more stable conformation. (Chapter 11)

(h) Are there any aromatic components present in *FK-506*? (Chapter 13)

(i) Patients taking *FK-506* have reported several side effects from this medication, including headaches, nausea or diarrhea, and slight shaking. Would you expect the enantiomer of this drug to result in the same side effects?

15.45 *Oseltamivir* (sold under the trade name *Tamiflu*®) is a prescription antiviral drug that is used in the treatment of both *Influenza virus Type A* and *Influenzavirus Type B*.

(a) Identify the various functional groups present in *Oseltamivir*. Is the amine group primary, secondary, or tertiary? (Chapter 10)

(b) What is the molecular formula of *Oseltamivir*? (Chapter 10)

(c) Place a check mark in the box next to all the words that describe *Oseltamivir*:

☐ Chiral

☐ Achiral

☐ Optically active

☐ Optically inactive

☐ Racemic

(d) Label all stereocenters (if any) present in *Oseltamivir* as either *R* or *S*.

(e) Draw an enantiomer of *Oseltamivir*.

(f) Draw a diastereomer of *Oseltamivir*.

(g) *Oseltamivir* is synthesized starting from shikimic acid, which can be partially hydrogenated to form the compound shown below on the right. Draw alternative chair conformations of this molecule and label the more stable and less stable conformations. (Chapter 11)

(h) What is the maximum number of stereoisomers possible for *Oseltamivir*?

15.46 Consider *Lunesta*, a nonbenzodiazepine hypnotic agent (i.e., sleep-inducing drug) that is frequently advertised on TV commercials. Answer the following questions with respect to the given structure:

(a) Determine the molecular formula for *Lunesta*. (Chapter 10)

(b) Identify the functional groups present in *Lunesta*. (Chapter 10)

(c) How many of *Lunesta's* rings are aromatic? (Chapter 13)

(d) Fill in the blanks as shown: *Lunesta* has _____ stereocenter(s) and therefore _____ possible stereoisomer(s). Of the possible stereocenter(s), _____ is/are *R* and _____ is/are *S*.

(e) Does *Lunesta* have an enantiomer? Does it have a diastereomer?

(f) Which of the following is true about an enantiomer of *Lunesta*? Identify all that apply:

(1) The enantiomer rotates plane-polarized light in the opposite direction as *Lunesta*.

(2) The enantiomer is a mirror image of *Lunesta*.

(3) The enantiomer has the opposite biological effects as *Lunesta* (i.e., it keeps you awake).

(4) *Lunesta* does not have an enantiomer.

(g) Draw an enantiomer of *Lunesta*.

(h) Examine the derivative of the representation of the six-membered ring found in *Lunesta*. Draw the alternative chair conformations of this ring and label the more stable chair conformation. (Chapter 11)

H_3C ••••◁ ▷•••• COOH

17 Carbohydrates

© fredredhat/Shutterstock.com

Case Study

Flu season had just begun, and a wave of infection was making its way through the daycare center. Rayla was 3 years old, and this was her first year of preschool. With only a 24-hour incubation period, the virus spread fast. It hit Rayla hard. She was vomiting, with diarrhea and a fever. Her mother tried to get her to eat, but Rayla couldn't keep anything down. The doctor recommended clear liquids for the first 24 hours, then the BRAT diet (bananas, rice, applesauce, and toast), followed by yogurt and a normal diet as soon as Rayla could tolerate it. The doctor explained that dehydration was the first concern and that it was also important to introduce carbohydrates for energy then add protein and fat for nutrition. The key was the careful introduction of foods as rapidly as Rayla could tolerate them, but not so quickly as to trigger more stomach upset. Rayla's mother was surprised that she was not supposed to give her daughter food for 24 hours, but the treatment plan really helped. Rayla was back at pre-school in a few days.

What foods qualify as clear liquids? How much juice should be given to a sick child? When are flu symptoms dangerous?

Follow-up to this Case Study appears at the end the chapter before the Concept Summary.

Learning Objectives

When you have completed your study of this chapter, you should be able to:

1 Describe the four major functions of carbohydrates in living organisms. **(Section 17.1)**

2 Classify carbohydrates as monosaccharides, disaccharides, or polysaccharides. **(Section 17.1)**

3 Identify molecules possessing chiral carbon atoms. **(Section 17.2)**

4 Use Fischer projections to represent D and L compounds. **(Section 17.3)**

5 Classify monosaccharides as aldoses or ketoses, and classify them according to the number of carbon atoms they contain. **(Section 17.4)**

6 Write reactions for monosaccharide oxidation and glycoside formation. **(Section 17.5)**

7 Describe uses for important monosaccharides. **(Section 17.6)**

8 Draw the structures and list sources and uses for important disaccharides. **(Section 17.7)**

9 Write reactions for the hydrolysis of disaccharides. **(Section 17.7)**

10 Describe the structures and list sources and uses for important polysaccharides. **(Section 17.8)**

C arbohydrates are compounds of tremendous biological and commercial importance. Widely distributed in nature, they include such familiar substances as cellulose, table sugar, and starch (see ❱ Figure 17.1). Carbohydrates have four important functions in living organisms:

- To provide energy through their oxidation.
- To supply carbon for the synthesis of cell components.
- To serve as a stored form of chemical energy.
- To form a part of the structural elements of some cells and tissues.

With carbohydrates, we begin our study of **biomolecules**, substances closely associated with living organisms. All life processes, as far as we know, involve carbohydrates and other biomolecules, including lipids, proteins, and nucleic acids. Biomolecules are organic because they are compounds of carbon, but they are also a starting point for **biochemistry**, the chemistry of living organisms. Thus, these chapters on biomolecules represent an overlap of two areas of chemistry: organic and biochemistry.

biomolecule A general term referring to organic compounds essential to life.

biochemistry A study of the compounds and processes associated with living organisms.

17.1 Classes of Carbohydrates

Learning Objectives

1. Describe the four major functions of carbohydrates in living organisms.
2. Classify carbohydrates as monosaccharides, disaccharides, or polysaccharides.

The name *carbohydrate* comes from an early observation that heating these compounds produced water and a black residue of carbon, which was incorrectly interpreted to mean that they were hydrates of carbon.

Figure 17.1 Starches like pasta, bread, and rice are examples of carbohydrates.

© James Noble/Corbis

The most striking chemical characteristic of carbohydrates is the large number of functional groups they have. For example, ribose has a functional group on every carbon atom of its five-carbon chain:

$$
\begin{array}{c}
\overset{\displaystyle H}{\underset{\displaystyle}{\diagdown}}\!\!C\!\!\overset{\displaystyle O}{\diagup} \\
| \\
H-C-OH \\
| \\
H-C-OH \\
| \\
H-C-OH \\
| \\
CH_2OH
\end{array}
$$

ribose

carbohydrate A polyhydroxy aldehyde or ketone, or substance that yields such compounds on hydrolysis.

monosaccharide A simple carbohydrate most commonly consisting of three to six carbon atoms.

disaccharide A carbohydrate formed by the combination of two monosaccharides.

polysaccharide A carbohydrate formed by the combination of many monosaccharide units.

In addition to —OH groups, most carbohydrates have as part of their molecular structure a carbonyl group—either an aldehyde (sometimes shown as —CHO) or a ketone functional group. This is the origin of the modern definition: **Carbohydrates** are polyhydroxy aldehydes or ketones, or substances that yield such compounds on hydrolysis.

Carbohydrates can be classified according to the size of the molecules. **Monosaccharides** consist of a single polyhydroxy aldehyde or ketone unit. **Disaccharides** are carbohydrates composed of two monosaccharide units linked together chemically. Oligosaccharides (less common and of minor importance) contain from three to ten units. **Polysaccharides** consist of very long chains of linked monosaccharide units (see ▶ Figure 17.2).

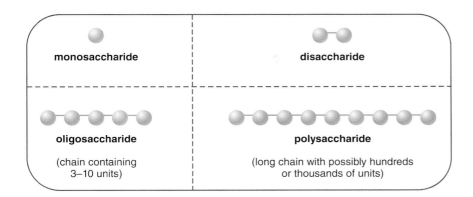

Figure 17.2 Carbohydrate classification.

monosaccharide

disaccharide

oligosaccharide

(chain containing 3–10 units)

polysaccharide

(long chain with possibly hundreds or thousands of units)

17.2 The Stereochemistry of Carbohydrates

Learning Objective

3. Identify molecules possessing chiral carbon atoms.

Glyceraldehyde, the simplest carbohydrate, exhibits a fascinating stereoisomerism shown by many organic compounds but especially characteristic of carbohydrates and many other natural substances. Glyceraldehyde can exist in two isomeric forms that are mirror images of each other (see ▶ Figure 17.3). Mirror-image isomers, called **enantiomers,** have the same molecular and structural formulas but different spatial arrangements of their atoms. No amount of rotation can convert one of these structures into the other. The molecules can be compared to right and left hands, which are also mirror images of each other (see ▶ Figure 17.4). Test this yourself. Put your right hand up to a mirror, and verify that its mirror image is the same as the direct image of your left hand.

enantiomers Stereoisomers that are mirror images.

L-glyceraldehyde **Mirror** D-glyceraldehyde

Figure 17.3 Enantiomers of glyceraldehyde. The designations L and D are discussed in Section 17.3.

Mirror Right hand

Figure 17.4 The reflection of a right hand is a left hand.

Compare your right hand with the right hand of a friend. Note that they can be overlapped or superimposed (see ▶ Figure 17.5). Now try to rotate or twist your right and left hands so that one is superimposed on the other and turned the exact same way. It cannot be done. Even if you place your hands palm-to-palm so the profiles superimpose, the nails are on the wrong sides. The same thing happens when you try to put a left-hand glove on your right hand.

When an object cannot be superimposed on its mirror image, the object is said to be **chiral.** Thus, a hand, a glove, and a shoe are chiral objects; they cannot be superimposed on their mirror images. However, a drinking glass, a sphere, and a cube are achiral objects because they can be superimposed on their mirror images.

chiral A descriptive term for compounds or objects that cannot be superimposed on their mirror image.

Figure 17.5 Two right hands can be superimposed; a right hand and a left hand cannot.

Many molecules in addition to glyceraldehyde are chiral, but fortunately it is not necessary to try to superimpose them on their mirror images in order to determine whether or not they are chiral. An organic molecule that contains a carbon atom attached to four different groups will be chiral and thus will have two non-superimposable mirror images. A carbon atom with four different groups attached is called a **chiral carbon.**

The center carbon of glyceraldehyde

chiral carbon A carbon atom with four different groups attached.

$$\boxed{CHO}$$
$$\boxed{H} - C - \boxed{OH}$$
$$\boxed{CH_2OH}$$

is chiral because it is attached to CHO, H, OH, and CH_2OH groups. Like your hands, the two enantiomers of glyceraldehyde are nonsuperimposable mirror images. No matter how hard we try, there is no way, short of breaking bonds, to superimpose the four groups so that they coincide.

Because the presence of a single chiral carbon atom gives rise to stereoisomerism, it is important to be able to recognize one when you see it. It is really not difficult. If a carbon atom is connected to four different groups, no matter how slight the differences, it is a chiral carbon. If any two groups are identical, it is not a chiral carbon.

▶ Example 17.1

Which of the following compounds contain a chiral carbon?

a. CH$_3$CHCH$_3$
 |
 OH

b. CH$_3$CHCH$_2$CH$_3$
 |
 OH

c. CH$_3$CCH$_2$CH$_3$
 ‖
 O

d. OH
 |
 CH — CH$_2$
 ╱ ╲
 CH$_2$ O
 ╲ ╱
 CH$_2$ — CH$_2$

Solution

It may help to draw the structures in a more complete form.

a. The central carbon atom has one H, one OH, but two CH$_3$ groups attached. It is not chiral. Neither of the other two carbons has four different groups.

$$\begin{array}{c} H \\ | \\ CH_3 - C - CH_3 \\ | \\ OH \end{array}$$

b. The central carbon atom has one H, one OH, one CH_3, and one CH_2CH_3 group attached. Both CH_3 and CH_2CH_3 are bonded to the central carbon atom through a carbon atom. However, when analyzing for chiral carbons, we look at the entire collection of atoms in a group and not just at the four atoms directly bonded. Thus, CH_3 and CH_2CH_3 groups are different (as are H and OH), so the central carbon (identified by an asterisk) is chiral. None of the other carbons are chiral.

$$CH_3 - \overset{\displaystyle H}{\underset{\displaystyle OH}{\overset{|}{\underset{|}{C^*}}}} - CH_2CH_3$$

c. The carbonyl carbon is attached to only three groups, so it is not chiral, even though the three groups are different. None of the other carbons have four different groups attached.

$$CH_3 - \underset{\displaystyle O}{\overset{\displaystyle \|}{C}} - CH_2 - CH_3$$

d. The rules are no different for carbons in rings. There is a chiral carbon marked with an asterisk. H and OH are two of the groups. As we proceed around the ring, $-CH_2-O-$ (the third group) is encountered in the clockwise direction and $-CH_2-CH_2-$ (the fourth group) in the counterclockwise direction.

$$
\begin{array}{c}
OH \\
| \\
{}^*CH - CH_2 \\
\diagup \qquad \diagdown \\
CH_2 \qquad\quad O \\
\diagdown \qquad \diagup \\
CH_2 - CH_2
\end{array}
$$

▶ **LEARNING CHECK 17.1** Which of the carbon atoms shown in color is chiral?

a.
$$
\begin{array}{l}
CH_2OH \\
| \\
CH - OH \\
| \\
CH_2OH
\end{array}
$$

b.
$$
\begin{array}{l}
CHO \\
| \\
CH - OH \\
| \\
CH - OH \\
| \\
CH_2OH
\end{array}
$$

c.
$$
\begin{array}{l}
CH_2OH \\
| \\
C = O \\
| \\
CH - OH \\
| \\
CH_2OH
\end{array}
$$

d.
$$
\begin{array}{c}
CH_2OH \\
| \\
CH - O \\
\diagup \qquad \diagdown \\
CH_2 \qquad\quad CH_2 \\
\diagdown \qquad \diagup \\
CH_2 - CH_2
\end{array}
$$

Organic molecules (and especially carbohydrates) may contain more than one chiral carbon. Erythrose, for example, has two chiral carbon atoms:

$$
\begin{array}{c}
OH \quad\; OH \quad\; OH \\
| \qquad\; | \qquad\; | \\
CH_2 - \underset{*}{CH} - \underset{*}{CH} - CHO
\end{array}
$$

erythrose

Identify the chiral carbons in glucose:

$$
\begin{array}{c}
\underset{1}{C} \overset{H}{} \overset{O}{} \\
H - \underset{2}{C} - OH \\
HO - \underset{3}{C} - H \\
H - \underset{4}{C} - OH \\
H - \underset{5}{C} - OH \\
\underset{6}{C}H_2OH
\end{array}
$$

Solution

Carbon number 1 is not chiral, because it has only three groups attached to it:

Carbon atoms 2, 3, 4, and 5 are chiral because they each have four different groups attached:

Carbon number 6 is not chiral because two of the four attached groups are the same.

When a molecule contains more than one chiral carbon, the possibility exists for two arrangements of attached groups at each chiral carbon atom. Thus, nearly all molecules having two chiral carbon atoms exist as two pairs of enantiomers, for a total of four stereoisomers. In a similar manner, when there are three chiral carbons present, there are eight stereoisomers (four pairs of enantiomers). The general formula is

$$\text{Maximum number of possible stereoisomers} = 2^n$$

where n is the number of chiral carbon atoms.

> **Example 17.3**

How many stereoisomers are possible for a molecule that contains four chiral carbons such as glucose?

Solution

Stereoisomers $= 2^n$

$$n = 4 \text{ chiral carbons}$$

$$2^4 = 2 \times 2 \times 2 \times 2 = 16$$

> **LEARNING CHECK 17.3** How many stereoisomers are possible for the following?

$$\underset{|}{\overset{OH}{CH_2}} - \underset{|}{\overset{OH}{CH}} - \underset{|}{\overset{OH}{CH}} - \underset{|}{\overset{OH}{CH}} - CHO$$

17.3 Fischer Projections

Learning Objective

4. Use Fischer projections to represent D and L compounds.

It is time-consuming to draw molecules in the three-dimensional shapes shown for the two enantiomers of glyceraldehyde in Figure 17.3, but there is a way to represent these mirror images in two dimensions. Emil Fischer, a German chemist known for pioneering work in carbohydrate chemistry, introduced a method late in the 19th century. His two-dimensional structures, called **Fischer projections,** are illustrated in ▶ Figure 17.6 for glyceraldehyde.

 In Fischer projections, the chiral carbon is represented by the intersection of two lines. If the compound is a carbohydrate, the carbonyl group is placed at or near the top. The molecule is also positioned so that the two bonds coming toward you out of the plane of the paper are drawn horizontally in the Fischer projection. The two bonds projecting away from you into the plane of the paper are drawn vertically. Thus, when you see a Fischer projection, you must realize that the molecule has a three-dimensional shape with horizontal bonds coming toward you and vertical bonds going away from you.

Fischer projection A method of depicting three-dimensional shapes for chiral molecules.

Figure 17.6 Ball-and-stick models (Top) and Fischer projections (Bottom) of the two enantiomers of glyceraldehyde.

L-glyceraldehyde D-glyceraldehyde

Mirror

Fischer designated the two enantiomers of glyceraldehyde as L and D compounds. Using this system, we can represent the isomers of similar compounds by the direction of bonds about the chiral carbon. A small capital L is used to indicate that an —OH group (or another functional group) is on the left of the chiral carbon when the carbonyl is at the top. A small capital D means the —OH is on the right of the chiral carbon.

▶ Example 17.4

Draw Fischer projections for the D and L forms of the following:

a.

$$CH_3 - \overset{\overset{\displaystyle OH}{|}}{CH} - COOH$$

lactic acid

b.

$$CH_3 - \overset{\overset{\displaystyle NH_2}{|}}{CH} - COOH$$

alanine

Solution

a. The second carbon of lactic acid is chiral with four different groups attached: H, OH, CH_3, and COOH. The chiral carbon is placed at the intersection of two lines. Lactic acid is not an aldehyde, but it does contain a carbon–oxygen double bond (in the carboxyl group). This carboxyl group is placed at the top of the vertical line. The direction of the —OH groups on the chiral carbons determines the D and L notations:

COOH

HO———H

CH_3

L-lactic acid

COOH

H———OH

CH_3

D-lactic acid

Mirror

b. Similarly, the amino acid alanine has a chiral carbon and a carboxyl group. The direction of the —NH$_2$ group determines D and L notations:

$$
\begin{array}{ccc}
\text{COOH} & & \text{COOH} \\
| & & | \\
\text{H}_2\text{N} \!-\!\!\!-\!\! \text{H} & & \text{H} \!-\!\!\!-\!\! \text{NH}_2 \\
| & & | \\
\text{CH}_3 & & \text{CH}_3
\end{array}
$$

Mirror

L-alanine D-alanine

▶ **LEARNING CHECK 17.4** Draw Fischer projections for the D and L forms of the following:

$$
\begin{array}{cc}
\text{CH}_3 & \text{NH}_2 \\
| & | \\
\text{CH}_3\text{CH} \!-\! \text{CH} & \!-\! \text{COOH}
\end{array}
$$

The existence of more than one chiral carbon in a carbohydrate molecule could lead to confusion of D and L designations. This is avoided by focusing on the hydroxy group attached to the chiral carbon farthest from the carbonyl group. By convention, the D family of compounds is that in which this hydroxy group projects to the right when the carbonyl is "up." In the L family of compounds, it projects to the left:

D-erythrose L-erythrose D-glucose L-glucose

Notice that D and L compounds are mirror images of each other (enantiomers).

▶ **LEARNING CHECK 17.5** Identify each structure as D or L:

a.

$$
\begin{array}{c}
\text{CHO} \\
| \\
\text{HO} \!-\!\!\!-\!\! \text{H} \\
| \\
\text{HO} \!-\!\!\!-\!\! \text{H} \\
| \\
\text{HO} \!-\!\!\!-\!\! \text{H} \\
| \\
\text{CH}_2\text{OH}
\end{array}
$$

b.

$$
\begin{array}{c}
\text{CH}_2\text{OH} \\
| \\
\text{C} \!=\! \text{O} \\
| \\
\text{HO} \!-\!\!\!-\!\! \text{H} \\
| \\
\text{H} \!-\!\!\!-\!\! \text{OH} \\
| \\
\text{H} \!-\!\!\!-\!\! \text{OH} \\
| \\
\text{CH}_2\text{OH}
\end{array}
$$

c.

$$
\begin{array}{c}
\text{CHO} \\
| \\
\text{H} \!-\!\!\!-\!\! \text{OH} \\
| \\
\text{HO} \!-\!\!\!-\!\! \text{H} \\
| \\
\text{CH}_2\text{OH}
\end{array}
$$

The physical properties of the two compounds that make up a pair of D and L isomers (enantiomers) are generally the same. The only exception is the way solutions of the two compounds affect polarized light that is passed through them. Light is polarized by passing it through a special polarizing lens, such as those found in polarized sunglasses. When polarized light is passed through a solution of one enantiomer, the plane of polarization of the light is rotated to either the right or the left when viewed by looking toward the source of the light (see ▶ Figure 17.7). The enantiomer that rotates it to the left is called the **levorotatory** (to the left) or (−) enantiomer. The one that rotates it to the right is the **dextrorotatory** (to the right) or (+) enantiomer.

levorotatory Rotates plane-polarized light to the left.

dextrorotatory Rotates plane-polarized light to the right.

Figure 17.7 The rotation of plane-polarized light by the solution of an enantiomer.

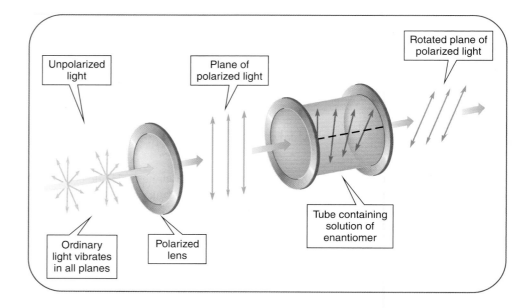

Unpolarized light

Plane of polarized light

Rotated plane of polarized light

Ordinary light vibrates in all planes

Polarized lens

Tube containing solution of enantiomer

The D and L designations do not represent the words *dextrorotatory* and *levorotatory* but only the spatial relationships of a Fischer projection. Thus, for example, some D compounds rotate polarized light to the right (dextrorotatory), and some rotate it to the left (levorotatory). The spatial relationships D and L and the rotation of polarized light are entirely different concepts and should not be confused with each other.

The property of rotating the plane of polarized light is called optical activity, and molecules with this property are said to be **optically active.** Measurements of optical activity are useful for differentiating between enantiomers.

Why is it so important to be able to describe stereoisomerism and recognize it in molecules? The reason stems from the fact that living organisms, both plant and animal, consist largely of chiral substances. Most of the compounds in natural systems—including biomolecules such as carbohydrates and amino acids—are chiral. Although these molecules can in principle exist as a mixture of stereoisomers, quite often only one stereoisomer is found in nature.

In some instances, two enantiomers are found in nature, but they are not found together in the same biological system. For example, lactic acid occurs naturally in both forms. The L-lactic acid is found in living muscle, whereas the D-lactic acid is present in sour milk. When we realize that only one enantiomer is found in a given biological system, it is not too surprising to find that the system can usually use or assimilate only one enantiomer. Humans utilize the D-isomers of monosaccharides and are unable to metabolize the L-isomers. The D form of glucose tastes sweet, is nutritious, and is an important component

optically active molecule A molecule that rotates the plane of polarized light.

of our diets. The L-isomer, on the other hand, is tasteless, and the body cannot use it. Yeast can ferment only D-glucose to produce alcohol, and most animals are able to utilize only L-amino acids in the synthesis of proteins.

17.4 Monosaccharides

Learning Objective

5. Classify monosaccharides as aldoses or ketoses, and classify them according to the number of carbon atoms they contain.

The simplest carbohydrates are the monosaccharides, consisting of a single polyhydroxy aldehyde or ketone unit. Monosaccharides are further classified according to the number of carbon atoms they contain (see ▶ Table 17.1). Thus, simple sugars containing three, four, five, and six carbon atoms are called, respectively, trioses, tetroses, pentoses, and hexoses. The presence of an aldehyde group in a monosaccharide is indicated by the prefix *aldo-*. Similarly, a ketone group is denoted by the prefix *keto-*. Thus, glucose is an aldo-hexose, and ribulose is a ketopentose:

TABLE 17.1 Monosaccharide Classification Based on the Number of Carbons in Their Chains

Number of Carbon Atoms	Sugar Class
3	Triose
4	Tetrose
5	Pentose
6	Hexose

```
        CHO                    CH₂OH
         |                       |
  H — C — OH               C = O
         |                       |
 HO — C — H              H — C — OH
         |                       |
  H — C — OH              H — C — OH
         |                       |
  H — C — OH                  CH₂OH
         |
      CH₂OH
  glucose, an              ribulose, a
  aldohexose               ketopentose
```

▶ **LEARNING CHECK 17.6** Classify each of the following monosaccharides by combining the aldehyde–ketone designation with terminology indicating the number of carbon atoms:

```
a.       CHO          b.     CH₂OH        c.        CHO
          |                     |                     |
    H — C — OH            C = O            HO — C — H
          |                     |                     |
   HO — C — H           H — C — OH          H — C — OH
          |                     |                     |
    H — C — OH              CH₂OH              CH₂OH
          |
       CH₂OH
```

Most monosaccharides are aldoses, and almost all natural monosaccharides belong to the D series. The family of D aldoses is shown in ▶ Figure 17.8. D-glyceraldehyde, the smallest monosaccharide with a chiral carbon, is the standard on which the whole series is based. Notice that the bottom chiral carbon in each compound is directed to the right. The 2^n formula tells us there must be 2 trioses, 4 tetroses, 8 pentoses, and 16 hexoses. Half of those are the D compounds shown in Figure 17.8. The other half (not shown) are the enantiomers or L compounds.

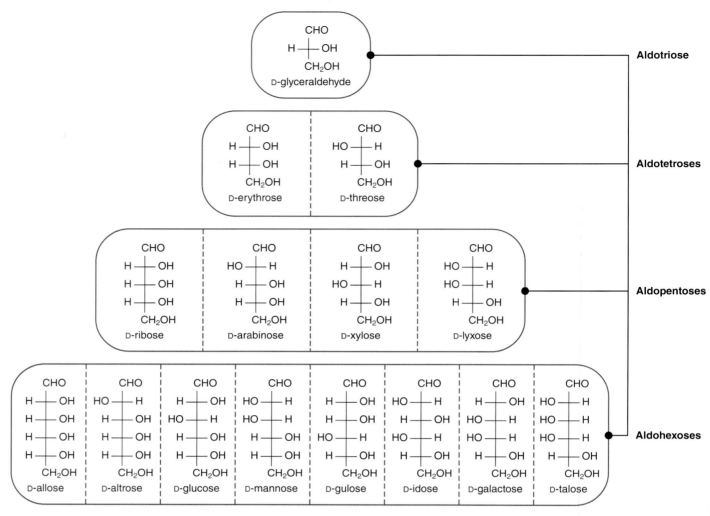

Figure 17.8 The family of D aldoses, shown in Fischer projections.

17.5 Properties of Monosaccharides

Learning Objective

6. Write reactions for monosaccharide oxidation and glycoside formation.

Physical Properties

Most monosaccharides (and disaccharides) are called sugars because they taste sweet. The degree of sweetness varies, as shown in ▶ Table 17.2. Fructose, the sweetest of the common sugars, is about 73% sweeter than sucrose, ordinary table sugar.

All carbohydrates are solids at room temperature, and because of the many —OH groups present, monosaccharide carbohydrates are extremely soluble in water. The —OH groups form numerous hydrogen bonds with the surrounding water molecules. In the body, this solubility allows carbohydrates to be transported rapidly in the circulatory system.

Chemical Properties, Cyclic Forms

So far we have represented the monosaccharides as open-chain polyhydroxy aldehydes and ketones. These representations are useful in discussing the structural features and stereochemistry of monosaccharides. However, we learned in Section 14.3 that aldehydes and ketones react with alcohols to form hemiacetals and hemiketals. When these functional

The Relative Sweetness of Sugars (Sucrose = 1.00)

Sugar	Relative Sweetness	Type
Lactose	0.16	Disaccharide
Galactose	0.22	Monosaccharide
Maltose	0.32	Disaccharide
Xylose	0.40	Monosaccharide
Glucose	0.74	Monosaccharide
Sucrose	1.00	Disaccharide
Invert sugar	1.30	Mixture of glucose and fructose
Fructose	1.73	Monosaccharide

groups are present in the same molecule, we noted that the result of their reaction is a stable cyclic structure. You should not be surprised then to find that all monosaccharides with at least five carbon atoms exist predominantly as cyclic hemiacetals and hemiketals.

To help depict the cyclization of glucose in Reaction 17.1, the open-chain structure has been bent around to position the functional groups in closer proximity. Notice the numbering of the carbon atoms that begins at the end of the chain, giving the lowest number to the carbonyl group carbon:

(17.1)

β-D-glucose α-D-glucose

In the reaction, the alcohol group on carbon 5 adds to the aldehyde group on carbon 1. The result is a **pyranose ring,** a six-membered ring containing an oxygen atom. The attached groups have been drawn above or below the plane of the ring. This kind of drawing, called **a Haworth structure,** is used extensively in carbohydrate chemistry. Note that as the reaction occurs, a new chiral carbon is produced at position 1. Thus, two stereoisomers are possible: one with the —OH group pointing down (the α form), and the other with the —OH group pointing up (the β form). The C-1 carbon is called an **anomeric carbon,** and

pyranose ring A six-membered sugar ring system containing an oxygen atom.

Haworth structure A method of depicting three-dimensional carbohydrate structures.

anomeric carbon An acetal, ketal, hemiacetal, or hemiketal carbon atom giving rise to two stereoisomers.

anomers Stereoisomers that differ in the three-dimensional arrangement of groups at the carbon of an acetal, ketal, hemiacetal, or hemiketal group.

the α and β forms are called **anomers.** Convenient condensed structures for the cyclic compounds omit the carbon atoms in the ring and the hydrogen atoms attached to the ring carbons, as shown in Reaction 17.2:

$$(17.2)$$

α-D-glucose (36%) D-glucose (0.02%) β-D-glucose (64%)

Thus, there are three forms of D-glucose: an open-chain structure and two ring forms. Because the reaction to form a cyclic hemiacetal is reversible, the three isomers of D-glucose are interconvertible. Studies indicate that the equilibrium distribution in water solutions is approximately 36% α-glucose, 0.02% open-chain form, and 64% β-glucose.

Other monosaccharides also form cyclic structures. However, some form five-membered rings, called **furanose rings,** rather than the six-membered kind. An example is D-fructose.

furanose ring A five-membered sugar ring system containing an oxygen atom.

The five-membered ring cyclization occurs like the ring formation in glucose. An alcohol adds across the carbonyl double bond (in this case, a ketone). The orientation of the —OH group at position 2 determines whether fructose is in the α or β form:

D-fructose

$$(17.3)$$

α-D-fructose β-D-fructose

In drawing cyclic Haworth structures of monosaccharides, certain rules should be followed so that all our structures will be consistent. First we must draw the ring with its oxygen to the back:

furanose ring pyranose ring

We must also put the anomeric carbon on the right side of the ring. Then we envision the ring as planar with groups pointing up or down. The terminal —CH_2OH group (position 6) is always shown above the ring for D-monosaccharides.

▶ Example 17.5

The aldohexose D-galactose exists predominantly in cyclic forms. Given the structure below, draw the Haworth structure for the anomer. Label the new compound as α or β.

Solution

Draw the pyranose ring with the oxygen atom to the back. Number the ring starting at the right side. Position number 1 will be the anomeric carbon. Place the —OH group at position 1 in the up direction (β form) so that it is the anomer of the given compound. Place groups at the other positions exactly as they are in the given compound. Remember that anomers differ only in the position of the OH attached to the anomeric carbon.

β-D-galactose

▶ **LEARNING CHECK 17.7** Draw the Haworth structure for the anomer of D-ribose. Label the new compound as α or β.

D-ribose

Oxidation

We learned in Section 14.3 that aldehydes and those ketones that contain an adjacent —OH group are readily oxidized by an alkaline solution of Cu^{2+} (Benedict's reagent). Open-chain forms of monosaccharides exist as aldehydes or hydroxyketones and are readily oxidized. As the oxidation proceeds, the cyclic forms in equilibrium are converted to open-chain forms (Le Châtelier's principle, Section 8.8) and also react.

Sugars that can be oxidized by weak oxidizing agents are called **reducing sugars.** Thus, all monosaccharides are reducing sugars.

reducing sugar A sugar that can be oxidized by Cu^{2+} solutions.

General reaction:

$$\text{Reducing sugar} \quad + \quad \underset{\substack{\text{(complex)}\\\text{deep blue solution}}}{Cu^{2+}} \quad \rightarrow \quad \text{oxidized compound} \quad + \quad \underset{\substack{\text{red-orange}\\\text{precipitate}}}{Cu_2O} \qquad (17.4)$$

Sugar-Free Foods and Diabetes

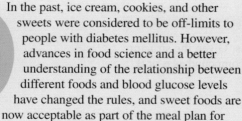

In the past, ice cream, cookies, and other sweets were considered to be off-limits to people with diabetes mellitus. However, advances in food science and a better understanding of the relationship between different foods and blood glucose levels have changed the rules, and sweet foods are now acceptable as part of the meal plan for people with diabetes. Diabetes is characterized by an impairment of the body's ability to utilize blood glucose.

Among the food science developments helpful to diabetics have been the discovery and commercial distribution of several synthetic noncarbohydrate sweetening agents. Three that have been approved by the American Diabetes Association are saccharin, acesulfame-K, and aspartame:

saccharin

aspartame

acesulfame-K

When compared with an equal weight of sucrose (table sugar), saccharin is about 450 times sweeter, acesulfame-K is about 200 times sweeter, and aspartame is about 180 times sweeter. Saccharin and acesulfame-K are noncaloric, whereas aspartame contributes very few calories when used in the quantities necessary to provide sweetness. Thus, these substances are useful dietary substitutes for sucrose or other calorie-laden sweeteners for people who wish to control calorie intake or for those who must avoid sugar, such as diabetics.

Until the approval of aspartame (trade name Nutrasweet®) in 1981, people with diabetes shopped for "dietetic" foods primarily in a special section of the supermarket. Aspartame vastly expanded the range of acceptable foods. Studies have verified its general safety when used in moderate amounts. The one exception is that it should not be used by individuals suffering from phenylketonuria (PKU), an inherited inability to metabolize phenylalanine properly. This condition is easily detected in newborn babies and infants, so routine screening is done shortly after birth.

In 1988, after six years of review, the FDA approved acesulfame-K under the trade name Sunette®. Coca-Cola® is using this artificial sweetener in a soft drink called Coca-Cola Zero®. Unlike aspartame, acesulfame-K is heat-stable and can survive the high temperatures of cooking processes.

Other sweeteners that have expanded the food options for diabetics are known as sugar alcohols. These are carbohydrate derivatives, such as sorbitol, in which the carbon–oxygen double bond of the aldehyde or ketone has been converted to an alcohol:

sorbitol

Sugar alcohols are incompletely absorbed during digestion and consequently contribute fewer calories than other carbohydrates. Sugar alcohols are found naturally in fruits. They are also produced commercially from carbohydrates for use in sugar-free candies, cookies, and chewing gum.

Specific example:

$$
\begin{array}{c}
\text{CHO} \\
|\\
\text{H}-\text{C}-\text{OH} \\
|\\
\text{HO}-\text{C}-\text{H} \\
|\\
\text{H}-\text{C}-\text{OH} \\
|\\
\text{H}-\text{C}-\text{OH} \\
|\\
\text{CH}_2\text{OH} \\
\text{D-glucose}
\end{array}
\;+\; Cu^{2+} \longrightarrow
\begin{array}{c}
\text{COOH} \\
|\\
\text{H}-\text{C}-\text{OH} \\
|\\
\text{HO}-\text{C}-\text{H} \\
|\\
\text{H}-\text{C}-\text{OH} \\
|\\
\text{H}-\text{C}-\text{OH} \\
|\\
\text{CH}_2\text{OH} \\
\text{D-gluconic} \\
\text{acid}
\end{array}
\;+\; Cu_2O
\qquad (17.5)
$$

Benedict's reagent is deep blue in color. As the open-chain form of a monosaccharide is oxidized, Cu^{2+} is reduced and precipitated as Cu_2O, a red-orange solid.

When we study energy transformations in cells (Chapters 22 and 23), we will encounter many reactions that involve the stepwise oxidation of carbohydrates to CO_2 and H_2O. The controlled oxidation of carbohydrates in the body serves as an important source of heat and other forms of energy.

Phosphate Esters

The hydroxy groups of monosaccharides can behave as alcohols and react with acids to form esters. Esters formed from phosphoric acid and various monosaccharides are found in all cells, and some serve as important intermediates in carbohydrate metabolism. The structures of two representative phosphate esters are shown below:

glucose 6-phosphate fructose 6-phosphate

Glycoside Formation

In Section 14.3, we learned that hemiacetals and hemiketals can react with alcohols in acid solutions to yield acetals and ketals, respectively. Thus, cyclic monosaccharides (hemiacetals and hemiketals) readily react with alcohols in the presence of acid to form acetals and ketals. The general name for these carbohydrate products is **glycosides.** The reaction of α-D-glucose with methanol is shown in Reaction 17.6.

glycoside Another name for a carbohydrate containing an acetal or ketal group.

α-D-glucose methyl α-D-glucopyranoside methyl β-D-glucopyranoside

glycosides

(17.6)

The hemiacetal in glucose is located at position 1, and the acetal thus forms at that same position. All the other —OH groups in glucose are ordinary alcohol groups and do not react under these conditions. As the glycoside reaction takes place, a new bond is established between the pyranose ring and the —OCH₃ groups. The new group may point up or down from the ring. Thus, a mixture of α- and β-glycosides is formed. The new carbon–oxygen–carbon linkage that joins the components of the glycoside is called a **glycosidic linkage.**

Although carbohydrate cyclic hemiacetals and hemiketals are in equilibrium with open-chain forms of the monosaccharides, the glycosides (acetals and ketals) are much more stable and do not exhibit open-chain forms. Therefore, glycosides of monosaccharides are not reducing sugars.

As we'll see later in this chapter, both disaccharides and polysaccharides are examples of glycosides in which monosaccharide units are joined together by acetal (glycosidic) linkages.

glycosidic linkage The carbon–oxygen–carbon linkage that joins the components of a glycoside to the ring.

▶ **LEARNING CHECK 17.8** Two glycosides are shown below. Circle any acetal or ketal groups and use an arrow to identify the glycosidic linkages.

a.

CH_2OH
HO O
OH
OCH_2CH_3
OH

b.

$HOCH_2$ O OCH_3
CH_2OH
HO OH

17.6 Important Monosaccharides

Learning Objective

7. Describe uses for important monosaccharides.

Ribose and Deoxyribose

Two pentoses, ribose and deoxyribose, are extremely important because they are used in the synthesis of nucleic acids (DNA and RNA), substances essential in protein synthesis and the transfer of genetic material (Chapter 21). Ribose (along with phosphate groups) forms the long chains that make up ribonucleic acid (RNA). Deoxyribose (along with phosphate groups) forms the long chains of deoxyribonucleic acid (DNA). Deoxyribose differs from ribose in that the OH group on carbon 2 has been replaced by a hydrogen atom (deoxy form).

$HOCH_2$ O OH
1
2
OH OH
β-D-ribose

$HOCH_2$ O OH
1
2 *two hydrogens at this position*
OH
β-D-deoxyribose

Glucose

Of the monosaccharides, the hexose glucose is the most important nutritionally and the most abundant in nature. Glucose is present in honey and fruits such as grapes, figs, and dates. Ripe grapes, for example, contain 20–30% glucose. Glucose is sometimes called dextrose. Glucose is also known as blood sugar because it is the sugar transported by the blood to body tissues to satisfy energy requirements (see ▶ Figure 17.9). Other sugars absorbed into the body must be converted to glucose by the liver. Glucose is commonly used as a sweetener in confections and other foods, including some baby foods.

Figure 17.9 A glucose solution prepared for intravenous use.

CH$_2$OH
O OH
OH
HO
OH

β-D-glucose

Galactose

Galactose is a hexose with a structure very similar to that of glucose. The only difference between the two is the orientation of the hydroxy group attached to carbon 4. Like glucose, galactose can exist in α, β, or open-chain forms; the β form is shown below:

^{6}CH$_2$OH
HO 5 O OH
—OH group
is down in —→ OH 1
glucose 4
3 2
OH

β-D-galactose

Galactose is synthesized in the mammary glands, where it is incorporated into lactose, the sugar found in milk. It is also a component of substances present in nerve tissue.

Fructose

Fructose (Section 17.5) is the most important ketohexose. It is also known as levulose and, because of its presence in many fruits, fruit sugar. It is present in honey in a 1:1 ratio with glucose and is abundant in corn syrup. This sweetest of the common sugars is important as a food sweetener because less fructose is needed than other sugars to achieve the same degree of sweetness.

17.7 Disaccharides

Learning Objectives

8. Draw the structures and list sources and uses for important disaccharides.
9. Write reactions for the hydrolysis of disaccharides.

Disaccharides are sugars composed of two monosaccharide units linked together by the acetal or ketal linkages described earlier. They can be hydrolyzed to yield their monosaccharide building blocks by boiling with dilute acid or reacting them with appropriate enzymes. Nutritionally, the most important members of this group are maltose, lactose, and sucrose.

Maltose

Maltose, also called malt sugar, contains two glucose units joined by a glycosidic linkage between carbon 1 of the first glucose unit and carbon 4 of the second unit (Reaction 17.7). The configuration of the linkage on carbon 1 in the glycosidic linkage between glucose units is α, and the linkage is symbolized α(1 → 4) to indicate this fact.

α(1 → 4) glycosidic linkage *a cyclic hemiacetal*

CH$_2$OH CH$_2$OH CH$_2$OH CH$_2$OH
O O O O
OH 1 + 4 OH 1 ⟶ OH 1 4 OH 1 + H$_2$O (17.7)
HO OH HO OH HO O OH
OH OH OH OH

α-D-glucose α-D-glucose maltose

Biomolecules: A New Focus

The chapters on organic chemistry (Chapters 11–16) were organized around the functional group concept. Each chapter dealt with a particular functional group or related groups. The nomenclature, properties, and uses of the compounds were discussed. The focus is different in this and the next four chapters (lipids, proteins, enzymes, and nucleic acids). Each of these chapters is devoted to a particular class of biomolecules—substances closely associated with life. Reactions and nomenclature receive much less emphasis; more time is spent describing structures and how they contribute to the processes of living organisms. Another key difference between these and earlier chapters is the reduced emphasis on mastering specific skills, such as solving numerical problems, balancing equations, and naming compounds. More attention should now be given to recognizing structures and understanding key terms and processes. It is a good time to increase your efforts to highlight important concepts in both the text and your lecture notes.

Notice that maltose contains both an acetal carbon (left glucose unit, position 1) and a hemiacetal carbon (right glucose unit, position 1). The —OH group at the hemiacetal position can point either up or down (the β is shown). The presence of a hemiacetal group also means that the right glucose ring can open up to expose an aldehyde group. Thus, maltose is a reducing sugar (Reaction 17.8).

(17.8)

maltose

Maltose, which is found in germinating grain, is formed during the digestion (hydrolysis) of starch to glucose. Its name is derived from the fact that during the germinating (or malting) of barley, starch is hydrolyzed, and the disaccharide is formed. On hydrolysis, maltose forms two molecules of D-glucose:

$$\text{maltose} + H_2O \xrightarrow{H^+} \text{D-glucose} + \text{D-glucose}$$ (17.9)

Lactose

Lactose, or milk sugar, constitutes 5% of cow's milk and 7% of human milk by weight (see ▶ Figure 17.10). Pure lactose is obtained from whey, the watery byproduct of cheese production. Lactose is composed of one molecule of D-galactose and one of D-glucose. The linkage between the two sugar units is β(1 → 4):

Figure 17.10 Cow's milk is about 5% lactose. What two products form when the lactose is hydrolyzed in the child's digestive system?

lactose

The presence of a hemiacetal group in the glucose unit makes lactose a reducing sugar.

Potato Comeback: The Healthy Side of Spuds

The potato, which originated in South America, has long had a stigma attached to it. The Spanish dispersed the potato beyond South America in the mid to late 1500s, but many people were initially reluctant to welcome the potato into their diets. This was due in part to the fact that it was known to be a member of the often toxic nightshade (Solanaceae) family, and it does indeed boast toxic leaves and stems. Also, it became associated with the lower-class population because it was easy to grow and could feed many for a relatively low cost. As a result, the "upper class" population avoided the potato for social reasons.

In modern times, being called a couch potato is considered to be an insult because it implies you are fat and lazy. But does eating potatoes make a person fat and lazy? Contrary to popular belief, the potato is not just a package of starch and other carbohydrates. It is true that a fried potato (as with any fried food) is not a healthy food choice because it becomes a vehicle for trans and saturated fats with the addition of butter, other fat-laden toppings, cheese, as well as excess sodium. Even a potato that is baked rather than fried can be corrupted from its pure nature when topped with sour cream, cheese, and bacon.

However, a potato plain and simple contains only 37 grams of carbohydrates while boasting 22 mg of vitamin C, 1.9 mg of iron, 4 g of protein, and more potassium than a banana (952 mg). If you leave the skin on a potato, it contains 4 g of fiber as well. The significance of these numbers becomes apparent when the following daily average requirements for adults age 25–50 are considered: 275–360 g carbohydrates, 60 mg vitamin C, 10–15 mg iron, 50–63 g protein, and 2200–3000 mg potassium.

So, enjoy your roasted, baked, microwaved, or boiled potatoes guilt-free when they are topped with low-fat options, such as low-fat plain yogurt instead of sour cream, or stuffed with steamed vegetables and savory herbs. As the world population continues to grow, the potato should be respected as a wonderful source of nutrition and calories. In fact, the potato provides twice the calories of wheat for the same amount of land used for cultivation.

While cheese is a common topping for potatoes, herbs or steamed vegetables would be more nutritious choices.

Sucrose

The disaccharide sucrose, common household sugar, is extremely abundant in the plant world. It occurs in many fruits, in the nectar of flowers (see ▶ Figure 17.11), and in the juices of many plants, especially sugar cane and sugar beets, the commercial sources. Sucrose contains two monosaccharides, glucose and fructose, joined together by a linkage that is α from carbon 1 of glucose and β from carbon 2 of fructose:

Figure 17.11 Hummingbirds depend on the sucrose and other carbohydrates of nectar for their energy.

CH_2OH

α-D-glucose unit

OH

HO

OH

O

$HOCH_2$

O

HO

β-D-fructose unit

CH_2OH

OH

sucrose

Neither ring in the sucrose molecule contains a hemiacetal or hemiketal group that is necessary for ring opening. This is true because the anomeric positions in both glucose and fructose are part of the glycosidic linkage that connects the rings to each other. Thus, in contrast to maltose and lactose, both rings of sucrose are locked in the cyclic form, and sucrose is therefore not a reducing sugar (see ▶ Figure 17.12).

1 From left to right, four test tubes containing Benedict's reagent, 2% maltose solution, 2% sucrose solution, and 2% lactose solution.

2 Both maltose and lactose are reducing sugars. The sucrose has remained unreacted.

invert sugar A mixture of equal amounts of glucose and fructose.

Figure 17.12 Benedict's test on disaccharides.

The hydrolysis of sucrose (see ▶ Figure 17.13) produces a 1:1 mixture of D-glucose and D-fructose called **invert sugar** (Reaction 17.10):

$$\text{sucrose} + \text{H}_2\text{O} \xrightarrow{\text{H}^+} \text{D-glucose} + \text{D-fructose} \qquad (17.10)$$

This mixture is sweeter than the original sucrose (see Table 17.2).

When sucrose is cooked with acid-containing fruits or berries, partial hydrolysis takes place, and some invert sugar is formed. The jams and jellies prepared in this manner are actually sweeter than the pure sugar originally put in them. ▶ Table 17.3 summarizes some features of the three disaccharides we have discussed.

Figure 17.13 Sucrose is hydrolyzed by bees in making honey. Why is honey sweeter than the starting sucrose?

TABLE 17.3 Some Important Disaccharides

Name	Monosaccharide Constituents	Glycoside Linkage	Source
Maltose	Two glucose units	$\alpha(1 \rightarrow 4)$	Hydrolysis of starch
Lactose	Galactose and glucose	$\beta(1 \rightarrow 4)$	Mammalian milk
Sucrose	Glucose and fructose	$\alpha\text{-}1 \rightarrow \beta\text{-}2$	Sugar cane and sugar beet juices

17.8 Polysaccharides

Learning Objective

10. Describe the structures and list sources and uses for important polysaccharides.

Just as two sugar units are linked together to form a dissacharide, additional units can be added to form higher saccharides. Nature does just this in forming polysaccharides, which

are condensation polymers containing thousands of units. Because of their size, polysaccharides are not water-soluble, but their many hydroxy groups become hydrated individually when exposed to water, and some polysaccharides form thick colloidal dispersions when heated in water. Thus, the polysaccharide known as starch can be used as a thickener in sauces, gravies, pie fillings, and other food preparations. As shown in ▶ Table 17.4, the properties of polysaccharides differ markedly from those of monosaccharides and disaccharides.

TABLE 17.4 Properties of Polysaccharides Compared with Those of Monosaccharides and Disaccharides

Property	Monosaccharides and Disaccharides	Polysaccharides
Molecular weight	Low	Very high
Taste	Sweet	Tasteless
Solubility in water	Soluble	Insoluble or form colloidal dispersions
Size of particles	Pass through a membrane	Do not pass through a membrane
Test with Cu^{2+} for reducing sugars	Positive (except for sucrose)	Negative

Starch

Starch is a polymer consisting entirely of D-glucose units. It is the major storage form of D-glucose in plants. Two starch fractions, amylose (10–20%) and amylopectin (80–90%), can usually be isolated from plants. Amylose is made up of long unbranched chains of glucose units connected by $\alpha(1 \rightarrow 4)$ linkages (see ▶ Figure 17.14). This is the same type of linkage found in maltose. The long chain, often containing between 1000 and 2000 glucose units, is flexible enough to allow the molecules to twist into the shape of a helix (see ▶ Figure 17.15A).

$\alpha(1 \rightarrow 4)$ linkage

Figure 17.14 The structure of amylose.

An important test for the presence of starch is the reaction that occurs between iodine, I_2, and the coiled form of amylose. The product of the reaction is deep blue in color (see ▶ Figure 17.16) and is thought to consist of the amylose helix filled with iodine molecules (see Figure 17.15B). This same iodine reaction is also widely used to monitor the hydrolysis of starch. The color gradually fades and finally disappears, as starch is hydrolyzed by either acid or enzymes to form dextrins (smaller polysaccharides), then maltose, and finally glucose. The disappearance of the blue iodine color is thought to be the result of the breakdown of the starch helix.

Figure 17.16 A dark bluish-black color is the characteristic result when a solution of iodine encounters the starch in potatoes. What other foods would you expect to give a positive starch test?

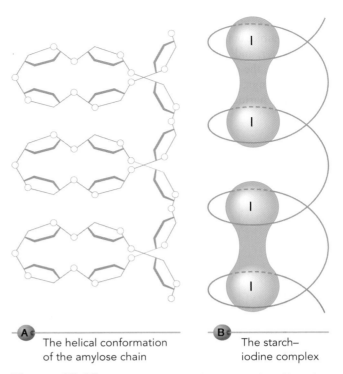

A The helical conformation of the amylose chain

B The starch–iodine complex

Figure 17.15 The molecular conformation of starch and the starch–iodine complex.

Amylopectin, the second component of starch, is not a straight-chain molecule like amylose but contains random branches. The branching point is the $\alpha(1 \rightarrow 6)$ glycosidic linkage (see ▶ Figure 17.17). There are usually 24 to 30 D-glucose units, all connected by $\alpha(1 \rightarrow 4)$ linkages, between each branch point of amylopectin. These branch points give amylopectin the appearance of a bushy molecule (Figure 17.17). Amylopectin contains as many as 10^5 glucose units in one gigantic molecule.

Figure 17.17 The partial structure of an amylopectin molecule. Glycogen has a similar structure.

Glycogen

The polysaccharide glycogen is sometimes called animal starch because it is a storage carbo-hydrate for animals that is analogous to the starch of plants. It is especially abundant in the liver and muscles, where excess glucose taken in by an animal is stored for future use. On hydrolysis, glycogen forms D-glucose, which helps maintain the normal blood sugar level and provide the muscles with energy. Structurally, glycogen is very similar to amylopectin, containing both $\alpha(1 \rightarrow 4)$ and $\alpha(1 \rightarrow 6)$ linkages between glucose units (see ❱ Figure 17.18). The main difference between amylopectin and glycogen is that glycogen is even more highly branched; there are only 8 to 12 D-glucose units between branch points.

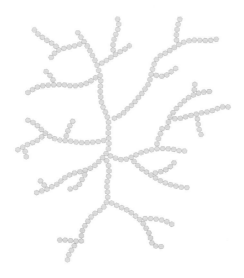

Figure 17.18 A simplified representation of the branched polysaccharide glycogen (branches every 8–12 glucose units). Amylo-pectin is much less densely branched (branches every 24–30 glucose units). Each small hexagon represents a single glucose unit.

Cellulose

Cellulose is the most important structural polysaccharide and is the single most abun-dant organic compound on Earth (see ❱ Figure 17.19). It is the material in plant cell walls that provides strength and rigidity. Wood is about 50% cellulose. Like amylose, cellulose is a linear polymer consisting of D-glucose units joined by the $1 \rightarrow 4$ linkage. It may contain from 300 to 3000 glucose units in one molecule. The main structural difference

Figure 17.19 Cellulose and the plant kingdom are responsible for much of the world's natural beauty.

DR. MELINA B. JAMPOLIS, M.D.

Dr. Melina B. Jampolis, M.D. is a Los Angeles, California, Physician Nutrition Specialist—a specialty practiced by only a few hundred physicians in the United States. She focuses exclusively on nutrition for weight loss and disease prevention and treatment.

Ask an Expert 17.1

Q: Is high-fructose corn syrup worse for your health than table sugar?

A: High-fructose corn syrup (HFCS) is a low-cost liquid sweetener that was first introduced in the United States in the late 1960s. It is made from a mixture of corn-starch and water by chemically reacting the mixture using enzymes as catalysts. The reaction converts the mixture into a liquid that contains water, glucose, and fructose in various ratios depending on the reaction conditions and the enzymes used. There are two common types of HFCS. HFCS-55, found mostly in soft drinks, contains 55% fructose and 42% glucose (the remaining 3% is made up of starch-like glucose polymers). HFCS-42, found in processed foods including ice cream and baked goods, contains 42% fructose and 53% glucose (the remaining 5% is made up of glucose polymers). Sucrose, commonly known as table sugar, contains 50% glucose and 50% fructose. The only major chemical difference between sucrose and HFCS is the presence of a chemical bond in sucrose linking together glucose and fructose to form a disaccharide. This bond is easily broken by enzymes located in the small intestine. In HFCS, glucose and fructose exist in free-monosaccharide form. Also unlike sucrose, HFCS is stable in an acidic environment (such as soft drinks), has a lower freezing point, and occurs as a syrup rather than a granular solid that has to be dissolved in water before use. These characteristics, in addition to its low cost and widespread availability due to government corn subsidies, make it very appealing to the food and beverage industry. Its use grew exponentially for the 35 years after its introduction, but in the mid 2000s, leading nutrition experts began to suspect that the rapid rise in obesity in the United States during the same time period might be connected to our increased consumption of HFCS.

Our body does not process HFCS the same way it processes regular table sugar. Some scientists believe that HFCS may contribute to obesity disrupting normal metabolic function.

Mountain Dew contains high amounts of high fructose corn syrup.

However, this hypothesis has not been clinically substantiated and is the subject of ongoing discussion and continued research. Most experts now believe that due to the similarities in the chemical structure of HFCS and sucrose, HFCS does not uniquely contribute to the obesity epidemic. They argue that it is the overall high sugar, fat, and calorie intake from the average U.S. diet that is responsible. Nutrition experts agree that fructose consumption from both HFCS and sucrose is particularly damaging when it occurs in high doses. Because fructose is absorbed via passive rather than active transport, it is rapidly taken up by the liver and bypasses a key regulatory step in glycolysis. This can lead to increased fat production in the liver. High fructose intake, particularly from sugar or HFCS-sweetened beverages, has been associated with significant increases in obesity (particularly abdominal obesity), fatty liver disease, and metabolic syndrome, a condition that often leads to type 2 diabetes.

Until research uncovers more convincing evidence pointing to a uniquely detrimental effect of HFCS compared to sucrose, the best approach is to limit overall added sugar consumption, particularly in the form of sugar-sweetened beverages including sodas, fruit drinks, "energy" drinks, and sugar-filled water. As a category these account for the greatest percentage of added sugar intake in the United States.

between amylose and cellulose is that all the $1 \rightarrow 4$ glycosidic linkages in cellulose are β instead of α (see ▶ Figure 17.20). This seemingly small difference causes tremendous differences between amylose and cellulose. The shapes of the molecules are quite different. The $\alpha(1 \rightarrow 4)$-linked amylose tends to form loose spiral structures (Figure 17.15), whereas $\beta(1 \rightarrow 4)$-linked cellulose tends to form extended straight chains. These chains become aligned side by side to form well-organized, water-insoluble fibers in which the hydroxy groups form numerous hydrogen bonds with the neighboring chains. These parallel chains of cellulose confer rigidity and strength to the molecules.

Figure 17.20 The structure of cellulose.

Second, although starch with its a linkages is readily digestible, humans and other animals lack the necessary enzymes to hydrolyze the β linkages of cellulose. Thus, cellulose passes unchanged through the digestive tract and does not contribute to the caloric value of food. However, it still serves a useful purpose in digestion. Cellulose, a common constituent of dietary fiber, is the roughage that provides bulk, stimulates contraction of the intestines, and aids the passage of food through the digestive system.

Animals that use cellulose as a food do so only with the help of bacteria that possess the necessary enzymes for breakdown. Herbivores such as cows, sheep, and horses are animals in this category. Each has a colony of such bacteria somewhere in the digestive system and uses the simple carbohydrates resulting from the bacterial hydrolysis of cellulose. Fortunately, the soil also contains organisms with appropriate enzymes. Otherwise, debris from dead plants would accumulate rather than disappear through biodegradation.

Case Study Follow-up

Liquids such as water, sports drinks, broth, and plain gelatin, which are easily digested and leave no residue in the intestinal tract, are considered to be clear liquids. A clear liquid diet cannot supply adequate nutrition and should not be continued for more than a few days (Mayo Clinic, 2011). Juice that contains no pulp such as apple, grape, or cranberry is considered to be a clear liquid. Any liquid, whether juice or water, should be given to a sick child only in small amounts so as not to trigger nausea. Popsicles are a good alternative to liquids because they take longer to ingest.

"Stomach flu" is the common term used for symptoms that typically include nausea, vomiting, diarrhea, and fever. It is not the same as influenza virus infection, which affects the respiratory system. What most people are referring to when they use the term "stomach flu" is viral gastroenteritis. Signs of severe gastroenteritis requiring medical attention in infants include fever of over 102°F, no wet diapers for 6 hours, sunken fontanel, crying without tears, dry mouth, bloody stools, vomiting that lasts more than several hours, and lethargy. For children, the warning signs are similar: dehydration, fever, excessive vomiting, and bloody stools. In adults, the fever can be as high as 104°F, and vomiting continuing for more than two days is cause for concern (Mayo Clinic, 2011).

Concept Summary

Classes of Carbohydrates

Carbohydrates are polyhydroxy aldehydes or ketones, or substances that yield such compounds on hydrolysis. Carbohydrates are used as energy sources, biosynthetic intermediates, energy storage, and structural elements in organisms. **Objective 1 (Section 17.1), Exercise 17.2.** Carbohydrates can exist either as single units (monosaccharides) or joined together in molecules ranging from two units (disaccharides) to hundreds of units (polysaccharides).
Objective 2 (Section 17.1), Exercise 17.4

The Stereochemistry of Carbohydrates

Carbohydrates, along with many other natural substances, exhibit a type of isomerism in which two isomers are mirror images of each other. The two isomers are called enantiomers and contain a chiral carbon atom. **Objective 3 (Section 17.2), Exercise 17.8.** When a molecule has more than one chiral carbon, the maximum number of stereoisomers possible is 2^n, where n is the number of chiral carbons.

Fischer Projections

A useful way of depicting the structure of chiral molecules employs crossed lines (Fischer projections) to represent chiral carbon atoms. The prefixes D- and L- are used to distinguish between enantiomers. **Objective 4 (Section 17.3), Exercise 17.12.** Signs indicating the rotation of plane-polarized light to the right ($+$) or to the left ($-$) may also be used to designate enantiomers.

Monosaccharides

Monosaccharides that contain an aldehyde group are called aldoses, whereas those containing a ketone group are ketoses. Monosaccharides are also classified by the number of carbon atoms as trioses, tetroses, etc. **Objective 5 (Section 17.4), Exercise 17.22.** Most natural monosaccharides belong to the D family.

Properties of Monosaccharides

Monosaccharides are sweet-tasting solids that are very soluble in water. Noncarbohydrate low-calorie sweeteners such as aspartame have been developed as sugar substitutes. Pentoses and hexoses form cyclic hemiacetals or hemiketals whose structures can be represented by Haworth structures. Two isomers referred to as anomers (the α and β forms) are produced in the cyclization reaction. All monosaccharides are oxidized by Benedict's reagent and are called reducing sugars. Monosaccharides can react with alcohols to produce acetals or ketals that are called glycosides.
Objective 6 (Section 17.5), Exercise 17.34

Important Monosaccharides

Ribose and deoxyribose are important as components of nucleic acids. The hexoses glucose, galactose, and fructose are the most important nutritionally and the most abundant in nature. Glucose, also known as blood sugar, is transported within the bloodstream to body tissues, where it supplies energy.
Objective 7 (Section 17.6), Exercise 17.37

Disaccharides

Glycosidic linkages join monosaccharide units together to form disaccharides. Three important disaccharides are maltose (two glucose units $\alpha(1 \rightarrow 4)$-linked), lactose (a galactose linked to glucose by a $\beta(1 \rightarrow 4)$ glycosidic linkage), and sucrose (α-glucose joined to β-fructose). **Objective 8, (Section 17.7), Exercise 17.44.** Hydrolysis of disaccharides produces monosaccharides.
Objective 9 (Section 17.7), Exercise 17.52

Polysaccharides

Cellulose, starch, and glycogen are three important polysaccharides. Starch is the major storage form of glucose in plants, whereas glycogen is the storage form of glucose in animals. Cellulose is the structural material of plants.
Objective 10 (Section 17.8), Exercise 17.54

Key Terms and Concepts

Anomeric carbon (17.5)
Anomers (17.5)
Biochemistry (Introduction)
Biomolecule (Introduction)
Carbohydrate (17.1)
Chiral (17.2)
Chiral carbon (17.2)
Dextrorotatory (17.3)

Disaccharide (17.1)
Enantiomers (17.2)
Fischer projection (17.3)
Furanose ring (17.5)
Glycoside (17.5)
Glycosidic linkage (17.5)
Haworth structure (17.5)
Invert sugar (17.7)

Levorotatory (17.3)
Monosaccharide (17.1)
Optically active molecule (17.3)
Polysaccharide (17.1)
Pyranose ring (17.5)
Reducing sugar (17.5)

Key Reactions

1.	Oxidation of a sugar (Section 17.5):	reducing sugar + Cu^{2+} → oxidized compound + Cu_2O	Reaction 17.4
2.	Glycoside formation (Section 17.5):	monosaccharide + alcohol $\xrightarrow{H^+}$ acetals or ketals	
3.	Hydrolysis of disaccharides (Section 17.7):	disaccharide + H_2O $\xrightarrow[\text{enzymes}]{H^+ \text{ or}}$ two monosaccharides	

Exercises

Classes of Carbohydrates (Section 17.1)

17.1 What are the four important roles of carbohydrates in living organisms?

17.2 Describe whether each of the following substances serves primarily as an energy source, a form of stored energy, or a structural material (some serve as more than one):

 a. cellulose **c.** glycogen

 b. sucrose, table sugar **d.** starch

17.3 What are the structural differences among monosaccharides, disaccharides, and polysaccharides?

17.4 Match the terms *carbohydrate, monosaccharide, disaccharide,* and *polysaccharide* to each of the following (more than one term may fit):

 a. table sugar

 b.

 c. starch

 d. fructose

 e. cellulose

 f.

 g. glycogen

 h. amylose

17.5 Define *carbohydrate* in terms of the functional groups present.

The Stereochemistry of Carbohydrates (Section 17.2)

17.6 Why are carbon atoms 1 and 3 of glyceraldehyde not considered chiral?

17.7 Locate the chiral carbon in amphetamine and identify the four different groups attached to it.

17.8 Which of the following molecules can have enantiomers? Identify any chiral carbon atoms.

 a. $CH_3CH_2-CH-CH_2CH_3$ with OH

 b. $CH_3CH_2-CH-\overset{O}{\overset{\|}{C}}-CH_3$ with OH

 c.

17.9 Which of the following molecules can have enantiomers? Identify any chiral carbon atoms.

 a. $CH_2=CH-CH-CH_3$ with OH

 b. $CH_3-\overset{OH}{\overset{\|}{CH}}-CH_2-\overset{O}{\overset{\|}{C}}-H$

 c.

Fischer Projections (Section 17.3)

17.10 Explain what the following Fischer projection denotes about the three-dimensional structure of the compound:

17.11 Identify each of the following as a D or an L form and draw the structural formula of the enantiomer:

 a.

 b.

17.12 Identify each of the following as a D or an L form and draw the structural formula of the enantiomer:

a.
```
        CHO
HO ———— H
HO ———— H
H  ———— OH
        CH₂OH
```

b.
```
        CH₂OH
        C = O
H  ———— OH
HO ———— H
HO ———— H
        CH₂OH
```

17.13 Draw Fischer projections for both the D and L isomers of the following:

a. 2,3-dihydroxypropanoic acid

b. 2-chloro-3-hydroxypropanoic acid

17.14 Draw Fischer projections for both the D and L isomers of the following amino acids:

```
Alanine,   H₂N—CH—COOH
                 |
a.               CH₃
```

```
Leucine,   H₂N—CH—COOH
                 |
b.               CH₂
                 |
                 CH
                /  \
             CH₃    CH₃
```

17.15 How many chiral carbon atoms are there in each of the following sugars? How many stereoisomers exist for each compound?

```
     OH   OH   OH   O
     |    |    |    ||
a.   CH₂ — CH — CH — C — H
```

```
     OH   O   OH   OH   OH
     |    ||   |    |    |
b.   CH₂ — C — CH — CH — CH — CH₃
```

17.16 How many chiral carbon atoms are there in each of the following sugars? How many stereoisomers exist for each compound?

```
a.   OH   OH   OH   O
     |    |    |    ||
     CH₂ — CH — CH — C — CH₂ — OH
```

```
b.   OH   OH   OH   OH
     |    |    |    |
     CH₂ — CH — CH — CH — CHO
```

17.17 How many aldoheptoses are possible? How many are the D form and how many the L form?

17.18 How many aldopentoses are possible? How many are the D form and how many the L form?

17.19 Why is the study of chiral molecules important in biochemistry?

17.20 What physical property is characteristic of optically active molecules?

Monosaccharides (Section 17.4)

17.21 Classify each of the following monosaccharides as an aldo- or keto-triose, tetrose, pentose, or hexose:

a.
```
        CHO
H  ———— OH
H  ———— OH
HO ———— H
HO ———— H
        CH₂OH
```

b.
```
        CH₂OH
        C = O
H  ———— OH
H  ———— OH
        CH₂OH
```

17.22 Classify each of the following monosaccharides as an aldo- or keto-triose, tetrose, pentose, or hexose:

a.
```
        CH₂OH
        C = O
H  ———— OH
HO ———— H
        CH₂OH
```

b.
```
        CHO
H  ———— OH
H  ———— OH
H  ———— OH
        CH₂OH
```

17.23 Draw Fischer projections of any aldotetrose and any ketopentose.

Properties of Monosaccharides (Section 17.5)

17.24 Explain why certain carbohydrates are called sugars.

17.25 Explain why monosaccharides are soluble in water.

17.26 Using a Fischer projection of a glucose molecule, identify the site(s) on the molecule where water can hydrogen-bond.

17.27 Identify each of the following as an α or a β form and draw the structural formula of the other anomer:

a. CH₂OH ...

b. HOCH₂ ... OH ... CH₂OH

17.28 Identify each of the following as an α or a β form and draw the structural formula of the other anomer:

a. CH₂OH ...

b. HOCH₂ ... OH ...

17.29 The structure of talose differs from galactose only in the direction of the —OH group at position 2. Draw and label Haworth structures for α- and β-talose.

17.30 The structure of mannose differs from glucose only in the direction of the —OH group at position 2. Draw and label Haworth structures for α- and β-mannose.

17.31 What is the difference between pyranose and furanose rings?

17.32 An unknown sugar failed to react with a solution of Cu^{2+}. Classify the compound as a reducing or nonreducing sugar.

17.33 Explain how the cyclic compound β-D-galactose can react with Cu^{2+} and be classified as a reducing sugar.

17.34 Complete the following reactions:

a.

b.

c.

17.35 Use an arrow to identify the glycosidic linkage in each of the following:

a.

b.

Important Monosaccharides (Section 17.6)

17.36 What monosaccharides are used in the synthesis of nucleic acids?

17.37 Explain why D-glucose can be injected directly into the bloodstream to serve as an energy source.

17.38 Give two other names for D-glucose.

17.39 Which of the following are ketohexoses?

 a. glucose **b.** fructose **c.** galactose

17.40 How do the hexoses glucose and galactose differ structurally?

17.41 Give the natural sources for each of the following:

 a. glucose **b.** fructose **c.** galactose

17.42 Explain why fructose can be used as a low-calorie sweetener.

Disaccharides (Section 17.7)

17.43 What one monosaccharide is a component of all three of the disaccharides sucrose, maltose, and lactose?

17.44 Identify a disaccharide that fits each of the following:

 a. The most common household sugar

 b. Formed during the digestion of starch

 c. An ingredient of human milk

 d. Found in germinating grain

 e. Hydrolyzes when cooked with acidic foods to give invert sugar

 f. Found in high concentrations in sugar cane

17.45 What type of linkage is broken when disaccharides are hydrolyzed to monosaccharides?

17.46 Explain the process of how the hemiacetal group of a lactose molecule is able to react with Benedict's reagent.

17.47 Why is invert sugar sweeter than sucrose?

17.48 Sucrose and honey are commonly used sweeteners. Suppose you had a sweet-tasting water solution that contained either honey or sucrose. How would you chemically determine which sweetener was present?

17.49 Draw Haworth projection formulas of the disaccharides maltose and sucrose. Label the hemiacetal, hemiketal, acetal, or ketal carbons.

17.50 Using structural characteristics, show why

 a. lactose is a reducing sugar.

 b. sucrose is not a reducing sugar.

17.51 What type of linkage, for example, $\alpha(1 \to 4)$, is present in the following?

 a. lactose **b.** maltose **c.** sucrose

17.52 The disaccharide melibiose is present in some plant juices.

 a. What two monosaccharides are formed on hydrolysis of melibiose?

 b. Is melibiose a reducing sugar? Explain.

 c. Describe the glycosidic linkage between the two monosaccharide units.

Polysaccharides (Section 17.8)

17.53 Match the following structural characteristics to the polysaccharides amylose, amylopectin, glycogen, and cellulose (a characteristic may fit more than one):

 a. Contains both $\alpha(1 \to 4)$ and $\alpha(1 \to 6)$ glycosidic linkages

 b. Is composed of glucose monosaccharide units

Even-numbered exercises answered in Appendix B.

Unless otherwise noted all art on this page © Cengage Learning 2014

c. Contains acetal linkages between monosaccharide units

d. Is composed of highly branched molecular chains

e. Is composed of unbranched molecular chains

f. Contains only $\alpha(1 \rightarrow 4)$ glycosidic linkages

g. Contains only $\beta(1 \rightarrow 4)$ glycosidic linkages

17.54 Name a polysaccharide that fits each of the following:

a. The unbranched polysaccharide in starch

b. A polysaccharide widely used as a textile fiber

c. The most abundant polysaccharide in starch

d. The primary constituent of paper

e. A storage form of carbohydrates in animals

17.55 Polysaccharides are abundant in celery, and yet celery is a good snack for people on a diet. Explain why.

Additional Exercises

17.56 There are two solutions:

(1) a 10% (w/v) water–glucose solution

(2) a 10% (w/v) water–maltose solution

Can you differentiate between the two solutions based on boiling points? Explain your answer.

17.57 Why does one mole of D-glucose only react with one mole of methanol (instead of two) to form an acetal?

17.58 If 100 g of sucrose is completely hydrolyzed to invert sugar, how many grams of glucose will be present?

17.59 Hexanal and 1-hexanol are liquids at room temperature, but glucose (a hexose) is a solid. Give two reasons that may explain this phenomenon.

17.60 Look at Figure 7.15 "Osmosis through carrot membranes." Suppose maltose was used instead of molasses in the demonstration and the solution level rose 5 cm above the carrot in the tube. Next, maltase, an enzyme that hydrolyzes the glycosidic linkage, was added to the solution. What would happen to the solution level in the tube? Explain your reasoning.

Allied Health Exam Connection

The following questions are from these sources:

1. *Nursing School Entrance Exam* © 2005, Learning Express, LLC.

2. *McGraw-Hill's Nursing School Entrance Exams* by Thomas A. Evangelist, Tamara B. Orr and Judy Unrein © 2009, The McGraw-Hill Companies, Inc.

3. *NSEE Nursing School Entrance Exams,* 3rd Edition © 2009, Kaplan Publishing.

4. *Cliffs Test Prep: Nursing School Entrance Exams* by Fred N. Grayson © 2004, Wiley Publishing, Inc.

5. *Peterson's Master the Nursing School and Allied Health Entrance Exams,* 18th Edition by Marion F. Gooding © 2008, Peterson's, a Nelnet Company.

17.61 The molecular formula for glucose is $C_6H_{12}O_6$, and the molecular formula for fructose is $C_6H_{12}O_6$. Which of the following describe glucose and fructose?

a. stereoisomers

c. hexoses

b. isomers

d. anomers

17.62 Which of the following are composed of long chains of glucose molecules?

a. cellulose

b. starch

c. cholesterol

d. glycogen

17.63 Identify each of the following as a monosaccharide or a disaccharide. If it is a disaccharide, identify the individual monosaccharide components.

a. dextrose

d. maltose

b. fructose

e. lactose

c. sucrose

f. ribose

17.64 What is the general type of reaction used to decompose sucrose to glucose + fructose?

17.65 Glucose is a reducing sugar, which if boiled in Benedict's reagent, produces an orange to brick-red color. What chemical species is being reduced during the reaction?

17.66 Which polysaccharide is a branched polymer of glucose found in the liver and muscle cells?

a. amylase

b. cellulose

c. glycogen

d. amylopectin

Chemistry for Thought

17.67 Suppose human intestinal bacteria were genetically altered so they could hydrolyze the β linkages of cellulose. Would the results be beneficial? Explain.

17.68 A sample of starch is found to have a molecular weight of 2.80×10^5 u. How many glucose units are present in a molecule of the starch?

17.69 The open-chain form of glucose constitutes only a small fraction of any glucose sample. Yet, when Cu^{2+} is used to oxidize the open-chain form, nearly all the glucose in a sample reacts. Use Le Châtelier's principle to explain this observation.

17.70 Aspartame (Nutrasweet) contains calories and yet is used in diet drinks. Explain how a drink can contain aspartame as a sweetener and yet be low in calories.

17.71 From Figure 17.10, what two products form when the lactose in cow's milk is hydrolyzed in a child's digestive system?

17.72 Answer the question raised in Figure 17.16. What foods in addition to potatoes would you expect to give a positive starch test?

17.73 Amylopectin is a component of starch, yet it does not give a positive iodine test (turn bluish-black) for the presence of starch when it is tested in its pure form. Why?

17.74 Amylose is a straight-chain glucose polymer similar to cellulose. What would happen to the longevity of paper manufactured with amylose instead of cellulose?

17.75 Raffinose, a trisaccharide found in some plants, contains three monosaccharide components: galactose, glucose, and fructose. Disregarding the types of linkages, how many possible structures are there for raffinose?

18 Lipids

Case Study

Jamal ran cross-country for his high school track team 18 years ago and had regularly placed at statewide competitions. Now, family and work concerns made keeping fit difficult. Competition had been a powerful motivating factor for him in his teens, and Jamal thought training for a marathon might get him back on track. He set a goal of running a marathon for his 35th birthday. His wife encouraged him to get a physical first. The doctor ordered a fasting lipoprotein profile. Jamal's results were LDL 169 mg/dL, HDL 50 mg/dL, total cholesterol 189 mg/dL, and triglycerides 155 mg/dL. These levels of total cholesterol and triglycerides are considered elevated for Jamal's age. The doctor explained that exercise and a healthy diet would work together to lower his total cholesterol and increase his high-density lipoprotein (HDL). Now he had even more motivation to hit the track!

What is the difference between "good" and "bad" cholesterol? What role do triglycerides play in heart health?

Follow-up to this Case Study appears at the end the chapter before the Concept Summary.

Learning Objectives

When you have completed your study of this chapter, you should be able to:

1 Classify lipids as saponifiable or nonsaponifiable and list five major functions of lipids. **(Section 18.1)**

2 Describe four general characteristics of fatty acids. **(Section 18.2)**

3 Draw structural formulas of triglycerides given the formulas of the component parts. **(Section 18.3)**

4 Describe the structural similarities and differences of fats and oils. **(Section 18.3)**

5 Write key reactions for fats and oils. **(Section 18.4)**

6 Compare the structures of fats and waxes. **(Section 18.5)**

7 Draw structural formulas and describe uses for phosphoglycerides. **(Section 18.6)**

8 Draw structural formulas and describe uses for sphingolipids. **(Section 18.7)**

9 Describe the major features of cell membrane structure. **(Section 18.8)**

10 Identify the structural characteristic typical of steroids and list important groups of steroids in the body. **(Section 18.9)**

11 Name the major categories of steroid hormones. **(Section 18.10)**

12 Describe the biological importance and therapeutic uses of the prostaglandins. **(Section 18.11)**

The group of compounds called lipids is made up of substances with widely different compositions and structures. Unlike carbohydrates, which are defined in terms of structure, lipids are defined in terms of a physical property—solubility. Lipids are biological molecules that are insoluble in water but soluble in nonpolar solvents. Lipids are the waxy, greasy, or oily compounds found in plants and animals (see ▶ Figure 18.1 and ▶ Figure 18.2). Lipids repel water, a useful characteristic of protective wax coatings found on some plants. Fats and oils are energy-rich and have relatively low densities. These properties account for their use as storage forms of energy in plants and animals. Still other lipids are used as structural components, especially in the formation of cellular membranes.

Figure 18.1 Waxes form a protective coating on these leaves.

Figure 18.2 Thick layers of fat help insulate penguins against low temperatures.

18.1 Classification of Lipids

Learning Objective

1. Classify lipids as saponifiable or nonsaponifiable and list the major functions of lipids.

lipid A biological compound that is soluble only in nonpolar solvents.

simple lipid An ester-containing lipid with just two types of components: an alcohol and one or more fatty acids.

complex lipid An ester-containing lipid with more than two types of components: an alcohol, fatty acids—plus others.

Lipids are grouped into two main classes: saponifiable lipids and nonsaponifiable lipids. Saponification refers to the process in which esters are hydrolyzed under basic conditions (Section 15.7). Triglycerides, waxes, phospholipids, and sphingolipids are esters and thus all belong to the first class. Nonsaponifiable lipids are not esters and cannot be hydrolyzed. Steroids and prostaglandins belong to this class. ▶ Figure 18.3 summarizes the classification of different types of lipids. Notice from the figure that saponifiable lipids are further classified into categories of simple and complex, based on the number of components in their structure. **Simple lipids** contain just two types of components (fatty acids and an alcohol), whereas **complex lipids** contain more than two (fatty acids, an alcohol, plus other components).

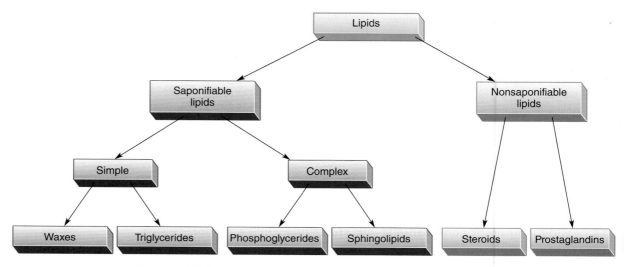

Figure 18.3 The major types of lipids.

18.2 Fatty Acids

Learning Objective

2. Describe four general characteristics of fatty acids.

Prior to discussing the chemical structures and properties of the saponifiable lipids, it is useful to first describe the chemistry of fatty acids, the fundamental building blocks of many lipids. Fatty acids (defined in Section 15.1) are long-chain carboxylic acids, as shown in ▶ Figure 18.4. It is the long nonpolar tails of fatty acids that are responsible for

Figure 18.4 The molecular structure of fatty acids: **A** lauric acid and **B** a simplified diagram of a fatty acid with a nonpolar tail and a polar head.

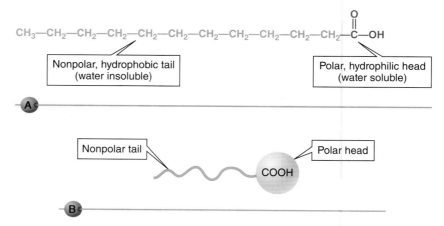

most of the fatty or oily characteristics of fats. The carboxyl group, or polar head of fatty acids, is very hydrophilic under conditions of physiological pH, where it exists as the carboxylate anion —COO$^-$.

In aqueous solution, the ions of fatty acids associate with one another in a rather unique way. The ions form spherical clusters, called **micelles,** in which the nonpolar chains extend toward the interior of the structure away from water, and the polar carboxylate groups face outward in contact with the water. Some micelles are large on a molecular scale and contain hundreds or even thousands of fatty acid molecules. The nonpolar chains in a micelle are held together by weak dispersion forces. The structure of a micelle in a radial cross section is shown in ▶ Figure 18.5. Micelle formation and structure are important in a number of biological functions, such as the transport of insoluble lipids in the blood (Section 24.1).

micelle A spherical cluster of molecules in which the polar portions of the molecules are on the surface and the nonpolar portions are located in the interior.

Figure 18.5 A cross section of a fatty acid micelle.

Hydrophilic groups

Hydrophobic groups

The fatty acids found in natural lipids have several characteristics in common:

1. They are usually straight-chain carboxylic acids (no branching).
2. The sizes of most common fatty acids range from 10 to 20 carbons.
3. Fatty acids usually have an even number of carbon atoms (including the carboxyl group carbon).
4. Fatty acids can be saturated (containing no double bonds between carbons) or unsaturated (containing one or more double bonds between carbons). Apart from the carboxyl group and double bonds, there are usually no other functional groups present.

▶ Table 18.1 lists some important fatty acids, along with their formulas and melting points.

Unsaturated fatty acids usually contain double bonds in the cis configuration.

$$\underset{\text{long chain}}{\overset{\text{H}}{\diagdown}}\text{C}=\text{C}\underset{\text{long chain}}{\overset{\text{H}}{\diagup}}$$

This configuration creates a long characteristic bend, or kink, in the fatty acid chain that is not found in saturated fatty acids.

These kinks prevent unsaturated fatty acid chains from packing together as closely as do the chains of saturated acids (see ▶ Figure 18.6). As a result, the intermolecular forces are weaker, and unsaturated fatty acids have lower melting points and are usually liquids at room temperature. For example, the melting point of stearic acid (18 carbons) is 71°C, whereas that of oleic acid (18 carbons with one cis double bond) is 13°C. The melting point of linoleic acid (18 carbons and two double bonds) is even lower (−5°C). Chain length also affects the melting point, as illustrated by the fact that palmitic acid (16 carbons) melts at 7°C lower than stearic acid (18 carbons).

TABLE 18.1 Some Important Fatty Acids

Compound Type and Number of Carbons	Name	Formula	Melting Point (°C)	Common Sources
Saturated				
14	Myristic acid	$CH_3(CH_2)_{12}—COOH$	54	Butterfat, coconut oil, nutmeg oil
16	Palmitic acid	$CH_3(CH_2)_{14}—COOH$	63	Lard, beef fat, butterfat, cottonseed oil
18	Stearic acid	$CH_3(CH_2)_{16}—COOH$	70	Lard, beef fat, butterfat, cottonseed oil
20	Arachidic acid	$CH_3(CH_2)_{18}—COOH$	76	Peanut oil
Monounsaturated				
16	Palmitoleic acid	$CH_3(CH_2)_5CH=CH(CH_2)_7—COOH$	−1	Cod liver oil, butterfat
18	Oleic acid	$CH_3(CH_2)_7CH=CH(CH_2)_7—COOH$	13	Lard, beef fat, olive oil, peanut oil
Polyunsaturated				
18	Linoleic acid[a]	$CH_3(CH_2)_4(CH=CHCH_2)_2(CH_2)_6—COOH$	−5	Cottonseed oil, soybean oil, corn oil, linseed oil
18	Linolenic acid[b]	$CH_3CH_2(CH=CHCH_2)_3(CH_2)_6—COOH$	−11	Linseed oil, corn oil
20	Arachidonic acid[a]	$CH_3(CH_2)_4(CH=CHCH_2)_4(CH_2)_2—COOH$	−50	Corn oil, linseed oil, animal tissues
20	Eicosapentaenoic acid[b]	$CH_3CH_2(CH=CHCH_2)_5(CH_2)_2—COOH$		Fish oil, seafoods
22	Docosahexaenoic acid[b]	$CH_3CH_2(CH=CHCH_2)_6CH_2—COOH$		Fish oil, seafoods

[a]Omega-6 fatty acid.
[b]Omega-3 fatty acid.

Figure 18.6 Space-filling models of fatty acids. Unsaturated fatty acids do not pack as tightly as saturated acids, and their melting points are lower than those of saturated acids.

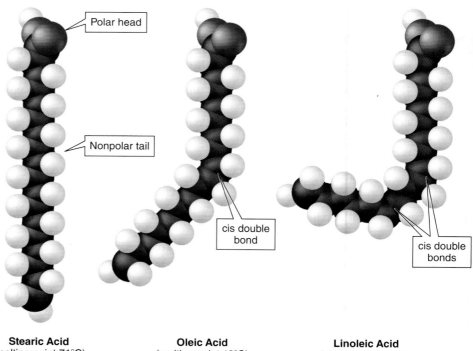

Stearic Acid (melting point 71°C)

Oleic Acid (melting point 13°C)

Linoleic Acid (melting point −5°C)

The presence of double bonds and the length of fatty acid chains in membrane lipids partly explain the fluidity of biological membranes, an important feature discussed in Section 18.8.

The human body can synthesize all except two of the fatty acids it needs. These two, linoleic acid and linolenic acid, are polyunsaturated fatty acids that contain 18 carbon atoms (Table 18.1). Because they are not synthesized within the body and must be obtained from the diet, they are called **essential fatty acids.** Both are widely distributed in plant and fish oils. In the body, both acids are used to produce hormonelike substances that regulate a wide range of functions and characteristics, including blood pressure, blood clotting, blood lipid levels, the immune response, and the inflammation response to injury and infection.

Linolenic acid is called an omega-3 fatty acid, which means that the endmost double bond is three carbons from the methyl end of the chain:

$$CH_3—CH_2—(CH=CHCH_2)_3—(CH_2)_6—COOH$$
linolenic acid

In linoleic acid, an omega-6 fatty acid, the endmost double bond is located six carbons from the methyl end of the chain. Both linoleic and linolenic acids can be converted to other omega-3 and omega-6 fatty acids.

Omega-3 fatty acids have been a topic of interest in medicine since 1985. In that year, researchers reported the results of a study involving natives of Greenland. These individuals have a very low death rate from heart disease, even though their diet is very high in fat. Studies led researchers to conclude that the abundance of fish in the diet of the Greenland natives was involved. Continuing studies led to a possible involvement of the omega-3 fatty acids in the oil of the fish, which may decrease serum cholesterol and triglyceride levels.

A recent five-year study on the benefits of omega-3 fatty acids involved 18,000 patients with unhealthy cholesterol levels. At the end of the study, those patients receiving omega-3 fatty acids had superior cardiovascular function, and nonfatal coronary events were significantly reduced.

essential fatty acid A fatty acid needed by the body but not synthesized within the body.

18.3 The Structure of Fats and Oils

Learning Objectives

3. Draw structural formulas of triglycerides given the formulas of the component parts.
4. Describe the structural similarities and differences of fats and oils.

Animal fats and vegetable oils are the most widely occurring lipids. Chemically, fats and oils are both esters, and as we learned in Chapter 15, esters consist of an alcohol portion and an acid portion. In fats and oils, the alcohol portion is always derived from glycerol, and the acid portion is furnished by fatty acids. Because glycerol has three —OH groups, a single molecule of glycerol can be attached to three different acid molecules. An example is the esterification reaction of stearic acid and glycerol:

$$
\begin{array}{l}
CH_2—OH \quad HO—\overset{\displaystyle O}{\overset{\displaystyle \|}{C}}—C_{17}H_{35} \quad CH_2—O—\overset{\displaystyle O}{\overset{\displaystyle \|}{C}}—C_{17}H_{35} \\[2mm]
\quad\;\; \\
CH—OH + HO—\overset{\displaystyle O}{\overset{\displaystyle \|}{C}}—C_{17}H_{35} \rightarrow CH—O—\overset{\displaystyle O}{\overset{\displaystyle \|}{C}}—C_{17}H_{35} + 3H_2O \quad (18.1)\\[2mm]
\quad\;\; \\
CH_2—OH \quad HO—\overset{\displaystyle O}{\overset{\displaystyle \|}{C}}—C_{17}H_{35} \quad CH_2—O—\overset{\displaystyle O}{\overset{\displaystyle \|}{C}}—C_{17}H_{35}
\end{array}
$$

glycerol stearic acid glyceryl tristearate
(1 molecule) (3 molecules) (a triglyceride — 1 molecule)

The following diagram may help you remember the components of a triglyceride.

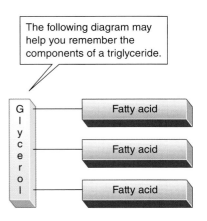

triglyceride or triacylglycerol
A triester of glycerol in which all three alcohol groups are esterified.

The resulting esters are called **triglycerides** or **triacylglycerols.**

The fatty acid components in naturally occurring triglyceride molecules are rarely identical (as in the case of glyceryl tristearate). In addition, natural triglycerides (fats and oils) are usually mixtures of different triglyceride molecules. Butterfat, for example, contains at least 14 different fatty acid components.

▶ **LEARNING CHECK 18.1** Write one structure (several possibilities exist) for a triglyceride derived from stearic acid, oleic acid, and palmitic acid.

fat A triglyceride that is a solid at room temperature.

oil A triglyceride that is a liquid at room temperature.

With some exceptions, triglycerides that come from animals other than fish are solids at room temperature and are called **fats.** Triglycerides from plants or fish are liquids at room temperature and are usually referred to as **oils.** Although both fats and oils are triglycerides, they differ structurally in one important respect—the degree of unsaturation. As shown in ▶ Figure 18.7, animal fats contain primarily triglycerides of long-chain saturated fatty acids (higher melting points). In contrast, vegetable oils, such as corn oil and sunflower oil, consist of triglycerides containing unsaturated fatty acids (lower melting points) (see ▶ Figure 18.8). Thus, we see that the structural and physical properties of fatty acids determine the properties of the triglycerides derived from them.

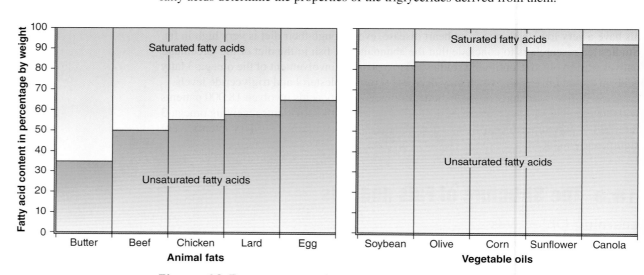

Figure 18.7 A comparison of saturated and unsaturated fatty acids in some foods.

Figure 18.8 Sunflowers are an important crop in some regions of the country because the seeds are a good source of unsaturated oils. Why do you think seeds are rich in oils?

Excessive fat in the diet is recognized as one risk factor influencing the development of chronic disease. The main concern about excessive dietary fat, especially saturated fat, centers on its role in raising blood cholesterol levels (Section 18.9). High blood cholesterol is a recognized risk factor in the development of coronary heart disease, the leading cause of death in Americans every year.

18.4 Chemical Properties of Fats and Oils

Learning Objective

5. Write key reactions for fats and oils.

The chemical properties of triglycerides are typical of esters and alkenes because these are the two functional groups present.

Hydrolysis

Hydrolysis is one of the most important reactions of fats and oils, just as it was for carbohydrates. The treatment of fats or oils with water and an acid catalyst causes them to hydrolyze to form glycerol and fatty acids. This reaction is simply the reverse of ester formation:

$$
\begin{array}{l}
\text{CH}_2-\text{O}-\overset{\displaystyle \overset{\text{O}}{\|}}{\text{C}}-(\text{CH}_2)_{14}\text{CH}_3 \\[2mm]
\text{CH}-\text{O}-\overset{\displaystyle \overset{\text{O}}{\|}}{\text{C}}-(\text{CH}_2)_7\text{CH}=\text{CH}(\text{CH}_2)_7\text{CH}_3 \qquad +\ 3\text{H}_2\text{O} \xrightarrow[\substack{\text{or}\\ \text{lipase}}]{\text{H}^+} \\[2mm]
\text{CH}_2-\text{O}-\overset{\displaystyle \overset{\text{O}}{\|}}{\text{C}}-(\text{CH}_2)_6(\text{CH}_2\text{CH}=\text{CH})_2(\text{CH}_2)_4\text{CH}_3
\end{array}
$$

(18.2)

$$
\begin{array}{l}
\text{CH}_2-\text{OH} \\
\text{CH}-\text{OH} \qquad + \\
\text{CH}_2-\text{OH}
\end{array}
\left\{
\begin{array}{l}
\text{CH}_3(\text{CH}_2)_{14}-\overset{\displaystyle \overset{\text{O}}{\|}}{\text{C}}-\text{OH} \\
\qquad\qquad \text{palmitic acid} \\[2mm]
\text{CH}_3(\text{CH}_2)_7\text{CH}=\text{CH}(\text{CH}_2)_7-\overset{\displaystyle \overset{\text{O}}{\|}}{\text{C}}-\text{OH} \\
\qquad\qquad \text{oleic acid} \\[2mm]
\text{CH}_3(\text{CH}_2)_4(\text{CH}=\text{CHCH}_2)_2(\text{CH}_2)_6-\overset{\displaystyle \overset{\text{O}}{\|}}{\text{C}}-\text{OH} \\
\qquad\qquad \text{linoleic acid}
\end{array}
\right.
$$

glycerol

Enzymes (lipases) of the digestive system also catalyze the hydrolysis process. This reaction represents the only important change that takes place in fats and oils during digestion. The breakdown of cellular fat deposits to supply energy also begins with the lipase-catalyzed hydrolysis reaction.

▶ **LEARNING CHECK 18.2** Write the structures of the hydrolysis products of the following reaction:

$$
\begin{array}{l}
\text{CH}_2-\text{O}-\overset{\displaystyle \overset{\text{O}}{\|}}{\text{C}}-(\text{CH}_2)_7\text{CH}=\text{CH}(\text{CH}_2)_7\text{CH}_3 \\[2mm]
\text{CH}-\text{O}-\overset{\displaystyle \overset{\text{O}}{\|}}{\text{C}}-(\text{CH}_2)_{14}\text{CH}_3 \qquad\qquad +\ 3\text{H}_2\text{O} \xrightarrow{\text{H}^+} \\[2mm]
\text{CH}_2-\text{O}-\overset{\displaystyle \overset{\text{O}}{\|}}{\text{C}}-(\text{CH}_2)_{16}\text{CH}_3
\end{array}
$$

Saponification

When triglycerides are reacted with a strong base, the process of saponification (soap making) occurs. In this commercially important reaction, the products are glycerol and the salts of fatty acids, which are also called **soaps** (Reaction 18.3).

soap A salt of a fatty acid often used as a cleaning agent.

$$
\begin{array}{l}
CH_2-O-\overset{\displaystyle O}{\overset{\|}{C}}-(CH_2)_{14}CH_3 \\
\quad\quad\quad \overset{\displaystyle O}{} \\
CH-O-\overset{\displaystyle O}{\overset{\|}{C}}-(CH_2)_7CH=CH(CH_2)_7CH_3 \;+\; 3NaOH \longrightarrow \\
\quad\quad\quad\quad\quad\quad\quad\quad\quad\quad\quad\quad\quad \text{strong base}\\
CH_2-O-\overset{\displaystyle O}{\overset{\|}{C}}-(CH_2)_6(CH_2CH=CH)_2(CH_2)_4CH_3
\end{array}
\tag{18.3}
$$

$$
\begin{array}{l}
CH_2-OH \\
CH-OH \quad + \\
CH_2-OH \\
\text{glycerol}
\end{array}
\left\{
\begin{array}{l}
CH_3(CH_2)_{14}-\overset{\displaystyle O}{\overset{\|}{C}}-O^-Na^+ \\
\text{sodium palmitate} \\
CH_3(CH_2)_7CH=CH(CH_2)_7-\overset{\displaystyle O}{\overset{\|}{C}}-O^-Na^+ \\
\text{sodium oleate} \\
CH_3(CH_2)_4(CH=CHCH_2)_2(CH_2)_6-\overset{\displaystyle O}{\overset{\|}{C}}-O^-Na^+ \\
\text{sodium linoleate}
\end{array}
\right.
$$

soaps

The salts obtained from saponification depend on the base used. Sodium salts, known as hard salts, are found in most cake soap used in the home. Potassium salts, soft soaps, are used in some shaving creams and liquid soap preparations.

In traditional soap making, animal fat is the source of triglycerides, and lye (crude NaOH) or an aqueous extract of wood ashes is the source of the base. The importance of soap making was amply proved after the soap maker's art was lost with the fall of the Roman Empire. The soapless centuries between A.D. 500 and 1500 were notorious for the devastating plagues that nearly depopulated an unsanitary western Europe.

▶ **LEARNING CHECK 18.3** Write structures for the products formed when the following triglyceride is saponified using NaOH:

$$
\begin{array}{l}
CH_2-O-\overset{\displaystyle O}{\overset{\|}{C}}-(CH_2)_{16}CH_3 \\
\\
CH-O-\overset{\displaystyle O}{\overset{\|}{C}}-(CH_2)_7CH=CH(CH_2)_7CH_3 \\
\\
CH_2-O-\overset{\displaystyle O}{\overset{\|}{C}}-(CH_2)_7CH=CH(CH_2)_7CH_3
\end{array}
$$

Hydrogenation

In Chapter 12, we learned that double bonds can be reduced to single bonds by treatment with hydrogen (H_2) in the presence of a catalyst. An important commercial reaction of fats and oils uses this same hydrogenation process, in which some of the fatty acid double bonds are converted to single bonds. The result is a decrease in the degree of unsaturation and a corresponding increase in the melting point of the fat or oil (Figure 18.6). The peanut oil in many popular brands of peanut butter has been partially hydrogenated to convert the oil to a semisolid that does not separate. Hydrogenation is most often used in the production of semisolid cooking shortenings (such as Crisco®, Spry®, and Fluffo®) or margarines from liquid vegetable oils (see ▶ Figure 18.9).

Partially hydrogenated vegetable oils were developed in part to help displace highly saturated animal fats used in frying, baking, and spreads. It is important not to complete the reaction and totally saturate all the double bonds. If this is done, the product is hard and waxy—not the smooth, creamy product desired by consumers. Equation 18.4 gives an example in which some of the double bonds react, showing one of the possible products.

Figure 18.9 Hydrogenation of vegetable oils is used to prepare both shortenings and margarines. How do oils used in automobiles differ chemically from these vegetable oils?

$$
\begin{array}{l}
CH_2 - O - \overset{\displaystyle O}{\overset{\|}{C}} - (CH_2)_{14}CH_3 \\
\quad \overset{\displaystyle O}{\overset{\|}{}} \\
CH - O - \overset{\|}{C} - (CH_2)_7CH = CH(CH_2)_7CH_3 \; + \; 2H_2 \\
\quad \overset{\displaystyle O}{\overset{\|}{}} \\
CH_2 - O - \overset{\|}{C} - (CH_2)_6(CH_2 CH = CH)_2(CH_2)_4CH_3
\end{array}
\xrightarrow{\;\text{Ni}\;}
\begin{array}{l}
CH_2 - O - \overset{\displaystyle O}{\overset{\|}{C}} - (CH_2)_{14}CH_3 \\
\quad \overset{\displaystyle O}{\overset{\|}{}} \\
CH - O - \overset{\|}{C} - (CH_2)_7CH = CH(CH_2)_7CH_3 \\
\quad \overset{\displaystyle O}{\overset{\|}{}} \\
CH_2 - O - \overset{\|}{C} - (CH_2)_6(CH_2 CH_2 CH_2)_2(CH_2)_4CH_3
\end{array}
\tag{18.4}
$$

▶ **LEARNING CHECK 18.4** If an oil with the following structure is completely hydrogenated, what is the structure of the product?

$$
\begin{array}{l}
CH_2 - O - \overset{\displaystyle O}{\overset{\|}{C}} - (CH_2)_7CH = CH(CH_2)_7CH_3 \\[1em]
CH - O - \overset{\displaystyle O}{\overset{\|}{C}} - (CH_2)_7CH = CHCH_2CH = CHCH_2CH = CHCH_2CH_3 \\[1em]
CH_2 - O - \overset{\displaystyle O}{\overset{\|}{C}} - (CH_2)_7CH = CHCH_2CH = CH(CH_2)_4CH_3
\end{array}
$$

During hydrogenation, some fatty acid molecules in the common cis configuration (Section 18.2) are isomerized into trans fatty acids. The main sources of trans fatty acids in the diet are stick margarine, shortening, and high-fat baked goods. Recent clinical studies have shown that blood cholesterol levels may be raised by the consumption of trans fatty acids (see Chemistry and Your Health 18.1). Current dietary advice is to reduce the consumption of saturated fatty acids and products that contain significant amounts of trans fatty acids.

A Reaction Map for Triglycerides

We've discussed three different reactions of triglycerides. Remember, when you're trying to decide what happens in a reaction, focus attention on the functional groups. After identifying a triglyceride as a starting material, next decide what other reagent is involved and which of the three pathways is appropriate.

18.5 Waxes

Learning Objective

6. Compare the structures of fats and waxes.

wax An ester of a long-chain fatty acid and a long-chain alcohol.

Waxes represent a second group of simple lipids that, like fats and oils, are esters of fatty acids. However, the alcohol portion of waxes is derived from long-chain alcohols (12–32 carbons) rather than glycerol. Beeswax, for example, contains a wax with the following structure:

$$CH_3(CH_2)_{14} - \overset{\overset{\displaystyle O}{\displaystyle \|}}{C} - O - (CH_2)_{29}CH_3$$

palmitic acid portion long-chain alcohol portion

Waxes are water-insoluble and not as easily hydrolyzed as fats and oils; consequently, they often occur in nature as protective coatings on feathers, fur, skin, leaves, and fruits. Sebum, a secretion of the sebaceous glands of the skin, contains many different waxes. It keeps the skin soft and prevents dehydration. Waxes are used commercially to make cosmetics, candles, ointments, and protective polishes.

18.6 Phosphoglycerides

Learning Objective

7. Draw structural formulas and describe uses for phosphoglycerides.

phosphoglyceride A complex lipid containing glycerol, fatty acids, phosphoric acid, and an aminoalcohol component.

phospholipid A phosphorus-containing lipid.

Phosphoglycerides are complex lipids that serve as the major components of cell membranes. Phosphoglycerides and related compounds are also referred to as **phospholipids.** In these compounds, one of the —OH groups of glycerol is joined by an ester linkage to phosphoric acid, which in turn is linked to another alcohol (usually an aminoalcohol).

Performance Enhancing Steroids

We humans will sometimes do foolish things to our bodies in order to enhance our appearance. When money and/or fame are to be gained, as in athletics, performance enhancement has sometimes been taken to extremes. Numerous athletic records involving strength or endurance exist under a cloud of suspicion of possible drug-induced performance enhancement. Included in this category are the record number of home runs hit in a major league baseball season, the longest distance a woman has thrown the discus in the Olympics, and the number of times a person has won a long-distance bicycling race.

Often, the enhancement is accomplished by the use of steroid compounds such as testosterone, the principal male sex hormone. Testosterone is responsible for the secondary sex changes that occur in males as they reach puberty. Testosterone is also produced by females, but only in amounts about 5% that of males. In both sexes, testosterone influences energy levels and protects the body from developing osteoporosis.

The performance enhancement characteristics of testosterone are the result of it being an anabolic steroid. Anabolic compounds, including steroids, promote the growth of body tissues such as bone and muscle. So, an athlete undergoing athletic training coupled with anabolic steroid use tends to build up muscle and bone tissue much more rapidly than an athlete training without the steroids. One downside for female athletes using testosterone in amounts exceeding the levels normally present in their bodies is the development of male characteristics such as facial hair, voice lowering, and a diminishing in breast size.

Testosterone is not the only anabolic steroid to have been used by athletes attempting to improve their performance. The primary four-ring steroid structure (see Section 18.9) can be chemically modified with relative ease by chemists. As a result, numerous "designer" steroids have been developed. In order to be useful to competitive athletes, the desirable characteristics of such modified steroids are their behavior as anabolic compounds and the difficulty of detecting them in the urine samples collected from the winners of athletic events. Fortunately, chemists have been generally able to keep a step or two ahead of the "designers" as far as detection is concerned. One example of how designer testosterone is differentiated from testosterone produced naturally in the body is the ratio of the amount of the two carbon isotopes, $^{12}_6C$ and $^{13}_6C$, found in the testosterone. The natural testosterone produced in the body is slightly richer in $^{13}_6C$ than is any designer testosterone. The difference can be detected by appropriate analysis techniques, and the illegal users identified and disqualified.

Some sports records are under a cloud of suspicion.

Anabolic compounds promote growth of bone and muscle.

Urine samples can be tested for the presence of steroids.

The other two —OH groups of glycerol are linked to fatty acids, resulting in the following general structure:

a phosphoglyceride

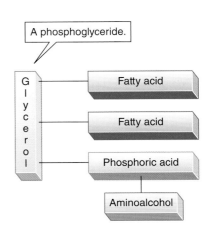

A phosphoglyceride.

Glycerol — Fatty acid

Glycerol — Fatty acid

Glycerol — Phosphoric acid

— Aminoalcohol

The most abundant phosphoglycerides have one of the alcohols choline, ethanolamine, or serine attached to the phosphate group. These aminoalcohols are shown below in charged forms:

$$HO-CH_2CH_2-\overset{+}{N}(CH_3)_3 \qquad HO-CH_2CH_2-\overset{+}{N}H_3 \qquad HO-CH_2\overset{|}{C}H-\overset{+}{N}H_3$$

<table>
<tr><td>choline
(a quaternary
ammonium cation)</td><td>ethanolamine
(cation form)</td><td>serine
(two ionic groups
present)</td></tr>
</table>

lecithin A phosphoglyceride containing choline.

A typical phosphoglyceride is phosphatidylcholine, which is commonly called **lecithin**:

$$^1CH_2-O-\overset{\overset{O}{\|}}{C}-(CH_2)_{16}CH_3$$
$$^2CH-O-\overset{\overset{O}{\|}}{C}-(CH_2)_7CH=CHCH_2CH=CH(CH_2)_4CH_3$$
$$^3CH_2-O-\overset{\overset{O}{\|}}{\underset{\underset{O^-}{|}}{P}}-O-CH_2CH_2-\overset{+}{N}(CH_3)_3$$

phosphatidylcholine

All phosphoglycerides that contain choline are classified as lecithins. Because different fatty acids may be bonded at positions 1 and 2 of the glycerol, a number of different lecithins are possible. Note that the lecithin shown contains a negatively charged phosphate group and a positively charged quaternary nitrogen. These charges make that end of the molecule strongly hydrophilic, whereas the rest of the molecule is hydrophobic. This structure of lecithins enables them to function as very important structural components of most cell membranes (Section 18.8). It also allows lecithins to function as emulsifying and micelle-forming agents. Such micelles play an important role in the transport of lipids in the blood (Chapter 24). Lecithin (phosphatidylcholine) is commercially extracted from soybeans for use as an emulsifying agent in food. It gives a smooth texture to such products as margarine and chocolate candies (see ▶ Figure 18.10).

cephalin A phosphoglyceride containing ethanolamine or serine.

Phosphoglycerides in which the alcohol is ethanolamine or serine, rather than choline, are called **cephalins.** They are found in most cell membranes and are particularly abundant

Figure 18.10 Some common foods containing lecithins as emulsifying agents.

in brain tissue. Cephalins are also found in blood platelets, where they play an important role in the blood-clotting process. A typical cephalin is represented as:

$$CH_2-O-\overset{\overset{\displaystyle O}{\|}}{C}-(CH_2)_{14}CH_3$$

$$CH-O-\overset{\overset{\displaystyle O}{\|}}{C}-(CH_2)_7CH=CH(CH_2)_7CH_3$$

$$CH_2-O-\overset{\overset{\displaystyle O}{\|}}{\underset{\underset{\displaystyle O^-}{\|}}{P}}-O-CH_2\overset{\overset{\displaystyle +}{}}{CH}-\overset{}{\underset{\underset{\displaystyle COO^-}{\|}}{NH_3}}$$

Note the presence of the negatively charged phosphate and carboxyl groups and positively charged nitrogen. This characteristic allows cephalins, like the lecithins, to function as emulsifiers.

> ▶ **LEARNING CHECK 18.5** Draw a typical structure for a cephalin containing the cation of ethanolamine:
>
> $$HO-CH_2CH_2-\overset{+}{N}H_3$$

18.7 Sphingolipids

Learning Objective

8. Draw structural formulas and describe uses for sphingolipids.

Sphingolipids, a second type of complex lipid found in cell membranes, do not contain glycerol. Instead, they contain sphingosine, a long-chain unsaturated aminoalcohol. This substance and a typical sphingolipid, called a sphingomyelin, are represented below:

sphingolipid A complex lipid containing the aminoalcohol sphingosine.

$$CH_3(CH_2)_{12}CH=CH-CH-OH$$
$$|$$
$$CH-NH_2$$
$$|$$
$$CH_2OH$$

sphingosine

$$CH_3(CH_2)_{12}CH=CH-CH-OH$$

fatty acid

$$CH-NH-\overset{\overset{\displaystyle O}{\|}}{C}-(CH_2)_7CH=CH(CH_2)_7CH_3$$

$$CH_2-O-\overset{\overset{\displaystyle O}{\|}}{\underset{\underset{\displaystyle O^-}{\|}}{P}}-O-CH_2CH_2\overset{+}{N}(CH_3)_3$$

phosphate *choline*

sphingomyelin

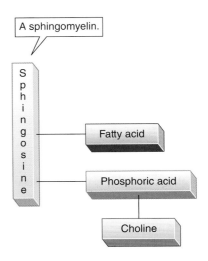

A sphingomyelin.

Sphingosine — Fatty acid
Sphingosine — Phosphoric acid — Choline

In sphingomyelin, choline is attached to sphingosine through a phosphate group. A single fatty acid is also attached to the sphingosine, but an amide linkage is involved instead of an ester linkage. A number of sphingomyelins are known; they differ only in the fatty acid component. Large amounts of sphingomyelins are found in brain and nerve tissue and in the protective myelin sheath that surrounds nerves.

glycolipid A complex lipid containing a sphingosine, a fatty acid, and a carbohydrate.

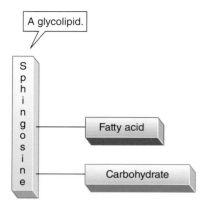

A glycolipid.

Sphingosine — Fatty acid

Sphingosine — Carbohydrate

Glycolipids are another type of sphingolipid. Unlike sphingomyelins, however, these complex lipids contain carbohydrates (usually monosaccharides such as glucose or galactose). Glycolipids are often called cerebrosides because of their abundance in brain tissue. The structure of a typical cerebroside is

$$CH_3(CH_2)_{12}CH = CH - CH - OH$$

fatty acid

$$CH - NH - \overset{\overset{\displaystyle O}{\|}}{C} - (CH_2)_7 CH = CH(CH_2)_7 CH_3$$

CH₂OH CH₂

HO O O

D-galactose

OH

OH

a cerebroside

Notice that, unlike the sphingomyelins, cerebrosides do not contain phosphate.

Several human diseases are known to result from an abnormal accumulation of sphingomyelins and glycolipids in the body (see ▶ Table 18.2). Research has shown that each of these diseases is the result of an inherited absence of an enzyme needed to break down these complex lipids.

TABLE 18.2 Diseases Originating from Abnormal Metabolism and Accumulation of Glycolipids and Sphingomyelins

Disease	Organs(s) Affected	Type of Lipid Accumulated
Tay-Sachs	Brain	Glycolipid (ganglioside G_{M2})
Gaucher's	Spleen, liver	Cerebrosides containing glucose
Niemann-Pick	Several, particularly liver and spleen	Sphingomyelins

18.8 **Biological Membranes**

Learning Objective

9. Describe the major features of cell membrane structure.

Cell Structure

Two cell types are found in living organisms: prokaryotic and eukaryotic. **Prokaryotic cells,** comprising bacteria and cyanobacteria (blue-green algae), are smaller and less complex than eukaryotic cells. The more complex **eukaryotic cells** make up the tissues of all other organisms, including humans. Both types of cells are essentially tiny membrane-enclosed units of fluid containing the chemicals involved in life processes. In addition, eukaryotic cells contain small bodies called **organelles,** which are suspended in the cellular fluid, or cytoplasm. Organelles are the sites of many specialized functions in eukaryotes. The most prominent organelles and their functions are listed in ▶ Table 18.3. Membranes perform two vital functions in living organisms: The external cell membrane acts as a selective barrier between the living cell and its environment, and internal membranes surround some organelles, creating cellular compartments that have separate organization and functions.

prokaryotic cell A simple unicellular organism that contains no nucleus and no membrane-enclosed organelles.

eukaryotic cell A cell containing membrane-enclosed organelles, particularly a nucleus.

organelle A specialized structure within a cell that performs a specific function.

TABLE 18.3 The Functions of Some Cellular Organelles

Organelle	Function
Endoplasmic reticulum	Synthesis of proteins, lipids, and other substances
Lysosome	Digestion of substances taken into cells
Microfilaments and microtubules	Cellular movements
Mitochondrion	Cellular respiration and energy production
Nucleus	Contains hereditary material (DNA), which directs protein synthesis
Plastids	Contains plant pigments such as chlorophyll (photosynthesis)
Ribosome	Protein synthesis

Membrane Structure

Most cell membranes contain about 60% lipid and 40% protein. Phosphoglycerides (such as lecithin and cephalin), sphingomyelin, and cholesterol are the predominant types of lipids found in most membranes. Precisely how the lipids and proteins are organized to form membranes has been the subject of a great deal of research. A widely accepted model called the **fluid-mosaic model** is diagrammed in ▶ Figure 18.11. The lipids are organized

fluid-mosaic model A model of membrane structure in which proteins are embedded in a flexible lipid bilayer.

Figure 18.11 The fluid-mosaic model of membrane structure. Phosphoglycerides are the chief lipid component. They are arranged in a bilayer. Proteins float like icebergs in a sea of lipid.

lipid bilayer A structure found in membranes, consisting of two sheets of lipid molecules arranged so that the hydrophobic portions are facing each other.

in a **bilayer** in which the hydrophobic chains extend toward the inside of the bilayer, and the hydrophilic groups (the phosphate groups and other polar groups) are oriented toward the outside, where they come in contact with water (see ▶ Figure 18.12). Like the micelle structure discussed in Section 18.2, a lipid bilayer is a very stable arrangement where "like" associates with "like." The hydrophobic tails of the lipids are protected from water, and the hydrophilic heads are in a position to interact with water. When a lipid bilayer is broken and the interior hydrocarbon tails are exposed to water, the resulting repulsion causes the bilayer to re-form, and the break seals spontaneously.

Figure 18.12 The lipid bilayer model. Circles represent the polar portion of phosphoglycerides. The hydrocarbon "tails" are within the interior of the bilayer.

Nonpolar tails

Polar head

Membrane lipids usually contain unsaturated fatty acid chains that fit into bilayers more loosely than do saturated fatty acids (Section 18.2). This increases the flexibility or fluidity of the membrane. Some of the proteins in the membrane float in the lipid bilayer like icebergs in the sea, whereas others extend completely through the bilayer. The lipid molecules are free to move laterally within the bilayer like dancers on a crowded dance floor—hence the term "fluid mosaic."

18.9 Steroids

Learning Objective

10. Identify the structural characteristic typical of steroids and list important groups of steroids in the body.

steroid A compound containing four rings fused in a particular pattern.

Steroids exhibit the distinguishing feature of other lipids: They are soluble in nonpolar solvents. Structurally, however, they are completely different from the lipids already discussed. **Steroids** have as their basic structure a set of three six-membered rings and a single five-membered ring fused together:

steroid ring system

Cholesterol

The most abundant steroid in the human body, and the most important, is cholesterol:

$$CH_3 \qquad CH_3$$
$$CH(CH_2)_3CHCH_3$$
$$CH_3$$

$$CH_3$$

HO

cholesterol

Algae in Your Fuel Tank

According to some experts, the worldwide production of petroleum has peaked and will decrease from this time forward. Whether or not you agree with this, it is a fact that petroleum is not a renewable material and will inevitably run out at some point in the future. As the supply goes down, prices will go up, as they did in 2011 when record-breaking prices for crude oil were reached.

One promising renewable substitute for some petroleum-based fuel is referred to as *biodiesel*, a vehicle and heating fuel that can be made from vegetable oils and animal fats. Chemically, both fats and oils are triglycerol esters of carboxylic fatty acids. Under appropriate catalytic conditions, these fats and oils can be reacted with methanol to produce a mixture of glycerol and methyl esters of the fatty acids. When the glycerol is removed from the mixture, the remaining mixture of fatty acid methyl esters is a liquid that is suitable for use as a fuel in diesel engines. Unlike petroleum, the source of this fuel is renewable, since the raw materials are oils derived from plants and fats obtained from animals that feed on plants.

A relatively recent development in research has focused on microalgae as a potential plant source for biodiesel. Microalgae are one-celled microorganisms that grow in water and undergo photosynthesis. There are several advantages to using algae as a source of fuel. Some algae species have significantly higher oil content than other types of plants. Green algae, for example, grow rapidly, and as much as 60% of their dry weight can be oils. Another advantage of algae as a fuel source is the large amount of algae that can be produced per acre compared to other types of plants. Still another advantage is that the water in which algae grow can be fresh, brackish, or salty and it

can even be waste water. A final advantage widely believed, but not yet confirmed by research, is that the use of algae-based fuel would result in only a tiny fraction of the net released greenhouse gases per mile driven that come from the use of traditional petroleum-based fuels.

Pond algae being harvested.

Cholesterol is an essential component of cell membranes and is a precursor for other important steroids, including bile salts, male and female sex hormones, vitamin D, and the adrenocorticoid hormones (Section 18.10). Cholesterol for use in these important functions is synthesized in the liver. Additional amounts of cholesterol are present in the foods we eat.

On the other side of the coin, cholesterol has received much attention because of a correlation between its levels in the blood and the disease known as atherosclerosis, or hardening of the arteries (Section 24.1). Although our knowledge of the role played by cholesterol in atherosclerosis is incomplete, it is now considered advisable to reduce the amount of cholesterol in the foods we eat. In addition, reducing the amount of saturated fatty acids in the diet appears to lower cholesterol production by the body.

Bile Salts

Bile is a yellowish-brown or green liver secretion that is stored and concentrated in the gallbladder. The entry of partially digested fatty food into the small intestine causes the gallbladder to contract and empty bile into the intestine. Bile does not catalyze any digestive reactions, but it is important in lipid digestion. Fats are more difficult to hydrolyze than starch and proteins because they are not soluble in water. In the watery medium of the digestive system, fats tend to form large globules with a limited surface area exposed to attack by

DR. MELINA B. JAMPOLIS, M.D.

© Michael Roud Photography

Dr. Melina B. Jampolis, M.D. is a Los Angeles, California, Physician Nutrition Specialist—a specialty practiced by only a few hundred physicians in the United States. She focuses exclusively on nutrition for weight loss and disease prevention and treatment.

Ask an Expert 18.1

Q: How significantly can diet really lower cholesterol?

A: Hippocrates said, "Let food be thy medicine and medicine be thy food." Unfortunately, the majority of Americans, and their physicians, do not follow this advice. According to a 2010 report from the National Center for Health Statistics, one in four Americans over the age of 45 takes a cholesterol-reducing statin medication—which can have detrimental side effects—rather than maintaining healthy cholesterol levels through diet. Many mistakenly believe that diet is simply not as effective as medication in terms of cholesterol reduction, but a series of recent studies suggests otherwise. Although no single food is as effective as the powerful statin drugs, research investigating a dietary portfolio of cholesterol-lowering foods has shown very promising results, with far fewer side effects and at far less cost.

Products containing plant sterols.

One study, published in a major nutrition journal in 2005, involved 34 people with high cholesterol. They were divided into three groups, then randomly placed into three different treatment scenarios. They followed each treatment for one month, during which all food and medication was provided and monitored. The control treatment involved placing the subjects on a very low saturated fat diet. The second treatment combined a very low saturated fat diet with a 20 mg dose of a popular statin medication. The third treatment combined a very low saturated fat diet with a special diet containing specific "doses" of cholesterol-lowering foods that included the following:

1. *Plant sterols (1.0 gram for every 1,000 calories consumed)* Plant sterols are plant-based compounds that compete with cholesterol for absorption in the gut, thereby lowering blood cholesterol levels. They are found naturally in plants in much smaller doses, so supplementation or fortification is required for higher doses. This study used margarine enhanced with plant sterols.
2. *Soy-protein foods (including soy milk and soy burgers)* 21.4 grams per 1,000 calories
3. *Almonds (14 grams per 1,000 calories)*
4. *Viscous fiber (10 grams per 1,000 calories)* Viscous fiber is a type of dietary fiber that forms a gel in solution with water. The dietary sources used in this study included oats, barley, psyllium, okra, and eggplant. Other good sources of soluble fiber not included in this study include beans, legumes, citrus fruit, and apples.

Soy milk is made from soybeans.

Ask an Expert 18.1 *(continued)*

After one month of following the control diet, participants lowered their LDL (low-density lipoprotein, or "bad" cholesterol) by an average of 8.5 percent. After one month of taking the statin medication, the second group lowered their LDL by an average of 33.3 percent, and after one month of incorporating the special diet, subjects in the third group showed an average LDL reduction of 29.6 percent. One fourth of the participants in the third group actually achieved their lowest LDL levels on record after following the special diet for one month.

The following year, the researchers tested the special diet of the third group in the real world. They prescribed the same special diet, this time without providing food, to 66 people with high cholesterol for one year. Overall, the subjects showed an average of 13 percent reduction in LDL. One third achieved a greater than 20 percent reduction in LDL, and success was directly related to how closely the participants followed the diet. The researchers went on to show that adding strawberries, an excellent source of antioxidants, helped further protect the heart by decreasing oxidative damage due to LDL cholesterol, a major risk factor in the progression of heart disease.

It seems as though Hippocrates had the right idea. By incorporating these heart-healthy foods into your diet regularly, along with exercise, maintaining a healthy weight, and not smoking, you can significantly lower cholesterol and improve your heart health.

Almonds may help lower cholesterol levels.

Beans and certain grains are sources of viscous fiber.

the digestive juices. The chief constituents of bile are the bile salts and two waste components: cholesterol and bile pigments. One of the principal bile salts is sodium glycocholate:

$$\text{OH} \quad \overset{\displaystyle CH_3}{\underset{\displaystyle CH_3}{|}}\,CHCH_2CH_2 - \overset{\displaystyle O}{\overset{||}{C}} - NHCH_2COO^- Na^+$$

sodium glycocholate

The bile salts act much like soaps; they emulsify the lipids and break the large globules into many smaller droplets. After such action, the total amount of lipid is still the same, but a much larger surface area is available for the hydrolysis reactions. Some researchers feel that bile salts also remove fatty coatings from particles of other types of food and thus aid in their digestion.

A second function of bile salts is to emulsify cholesterol found in the bile. Excess body cholesterol is concentrated in bile and is passed into the small intestine for excretion. If

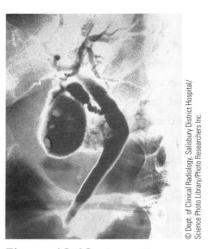

Figure 18.13 Three gallstones (green) in a gallbladder (red).

hormone A chemical messenger secreted by specific glands and carried by the blood to a target tissue, where it triggers a particular response.

cholesterol levels become too high in the bile, or if the concentration of bile salts is too low, the cholesterol precipitates and forms gallstones (see ▶ Figure 18.13). The most common gallstones contain about 80% cholesterol and are colored by entrapped bile pigments.

The passage of a gallstone from the gallbladder down the common bile duct to the intestine causes excruciating pain. Sometimes one or more stones become lodged in the duct and prevent bile from passing into the duodenum, and fats can no longer be digested normally. A person afflicted with this condition feels great pain and becomes quite nauseated and ill. Bile pigments are absorbed into the blood, the skin takes on a yellow coloration, and the stool becomes gray-colored because of lack of excreted bile pigments. If the condition becomes serious, both the gallbladder and the stones can be surgically removed.

18.10 Steroid Hormones

Learning Objective

11. Name the major categories of steroid hormones.

A number of steroids in the body serve important roles as **hormones.** The two major categories of steroid hormones are the adrenocorticoid hormones and the sex hormones.

Adrenocorticoid Hormones

Adrenal glands are small mounds of tissue located at the top of each kidney. The outer layer of the gland, the adrenal cortex, produces a number of potent steroid hormones, the adrenocorticoids. They are classified into two groups according to function: Mineralocorticoids regulate the concentration of ions (mainly Na^+) in body fluids, and glucocorticoids enhance carbohydrate metabolism.

Cortisol, the major glucocorticoid, functions to increase the glucose and glycogen concentrations in the body. This is accomplished by the conversion of lactate and amino acids from body proteins into glucose and glycogen. The reactions take place in the liver under the influence of cortisol.

cortisol

Cortisol and its ketone derivative, cortisone, exert powerful anti-inflammatory effects in the body. These, or similar synthetic derivatives such as prednisolone, are used to treat inflammatory diseases such as rheumatoid arthritis and bronchial asthma.

cortisone

prednisolone

By far the most important mineralocorticoid is aldosterone, which influences the absorption of Na^+ and Cl^- in kidney tubules. An increase in the level of the hormone results in a corresponding increase in absorption of Na^+ and Cl^-. Because the concentration of Na^+ in tissues influences the retention of water, aldosterone is involved in water balance in the body.

aldosterone

Sex Hormones

The testes and ovaries produce steroids that function as sex hormones. Secondary sex characteristics that appear at puberty, including a deep voice, beard, and increased muscular development in males and a higher voice, increased breast size, and lack of facial hair in females, develop under the influence of these sex hormones.

The testes in males perform two functions: One is to produce sperm; the other is to produce male sex hormones (androgens), the most important of which is testosterone. Testosterone promotes the normal growth of the male genital organs and aids in the development of secondary sex characteristics.

Testosterone testosterone methandrostenolone

Growth-promoting (anabolic) steroids, including the male hormone testosterone and its synthetic derivatives such as methandrostenolone (Dianabol), are among the most widely used drugs banned by sports-governing organizations because they are alleged to be dangerous and to confer an unfair advantage to users. These drugs, used by both male and female athletes, promote muscular development without excessive masculinization. Their use is particularly prevalent in sports where strength and muscle mass are advantageous, such as weight lifting, track-and-field events like the shot put and hammer throw, and body building.

The side effects of anabolic steroids range from acne to deadly liver tumors. Effects on the male reproductive system include testicular atrophy, a decrease in sperm count, and, occasionally, temporary infertility.

The primary female sex hormones are the estrogens estradiol and estrone, and progesterone. Estrogens and progesterone are important in the reproductive process. Estrogens are involved in egg (ovum) development in the ovaries, and progesterone causes changes

Olive Oil: A Heart-Healthy Lipid

When individuals decide to go on a weight-loss diet, they often focus primarily on the caloric content of food. When this is done, highly caloric lipids—fats and oils—are usually among the first foods to be eliminated from the diet. While this makes sense from a calorie-counting perspective, it might not when other factors are considered, such as the health benefits of some eliminated lipids.

Olive oil is a good example of a lipid that provides numerous health benefits when included in the diet. The main type of lipid found in all types of olive oil is monounsaturated fatty acids, or MUFAs, with the 18-carbon oleic acid being the predominant component (see Table 18.1 for its formula). MUFAs are considered to be healthy lipids. There is evidence that dietary MUFAs help lower total cholesterol levels in the body, and especially the levels of undesirable low-density lipoproteins (LDLs). Some research results show that MUFAs may help maintain normal blood clotting and normal blood pressure and may aid in the control of blood sugar levels.

Olive oil is also known as a good source of potent antioxidants called polyphenols, which are thought to help slow the development of atherosclerosis, or narrowing of the arteries. There is even some evidence suggesting that olive oil in the diet may provide protection against age-related dementia, Alzheimer's disease, and some types of cancer.

In spite of all this good news, the high calorie content of olive oil should not be overlooked. It is important to pay attention to serving sizes and to remember to consume olive oil in place of and not in addition to other high-calorie foods. If this is not done, the beneficial health gains might be nullified by unhealthy weight gain.

Numerous health benefits are associated with olive oil.

in the wall of the uterus to prepare it to accept a fertilized egg and maintain the resulting pregnancy.

estradiol

estrone

progesterone

18.11 Prostaglandins

Learning Objective

12. Describe the biological importance and therapeutic uses of the prostaglandins.

This group of compounds was given its name because the first prostaglandins were identified from the secretions of the male prostate gland. Recent research has identified as many as 20 prostaglandins in a variety of tissues within both males and females.

Prostaglandins are cyclic compounds synthesized in the body from the 20-carbon unsaturated fatty acid arachidonic acid. Prostaglandins are designated by codes that refer to the ring substituents and the number of side-chain double bonds. For example, prostaglandin E_2 (PGE$_2$) has a carbonyl group on the ring and a side chain containing two double bonds:

prostaglandin A substance derived from unsaturated fatty acids, with hormonelike effects on a number of body tissues.

$$\text{PGE}_2 \qquad (18.5)$$

$$\text{PGF}_{2\alpha} \qquad (18.6)$$

Prostaglandins are similar to hormones in the sense that they are intimately involved in a host of body processes. Clinically, it has been found that prostaglandins are involved in almost every phase of the reproductive process; they can act to regulate menstruation, prevent conception, and induce uterine contractions during childbirth. Certain prostaglandins stimulate blood clotting. They also lead to inflammation and fever. It has been found that aspirin inhibits prostaglandin production. This explains in part why aspirin is such a powerful drug in the treatment of inflammatory diseases such as arthritis.

From a medical viewpoint, prostaglandins have enormous therapeutic potential. For example, PGE$_2$ and PGF$_2$ induce labor and are used for therapeutic abortion in early pregnancy. PGE$_2$ in aerosol form is used to treat asthma; it opens up the bronchial tubes by relaxing the surrounding muscles. Other prostaglandins inhibit gastric secretions and are used in treating peptic ulcers. Many researchers believe that when prostaglandins are fully understood, they will be found useful for treating a much wider variety of ailments.

Case Study Follow-up

High-density lipoproteins are considered "good cholesterol" and low-density lipoproteins "bad" cholesterol. Some remember the difference by thinking, "H is for health and L is for lethal." HDL levels should be above 40 mg/dL and LDL levels should be below 130 mg/dL for a total cholesterol below 200 mg/dL. Elevated LDL cholesterol is the primary target of cholesterol-lowering therapies (nicotinic acid, bile sequestering, or statin medications).

If more calories are consumed than are calories used, the body stores the excess in the form of triglycerides. Triglycerides are stored in fat cells and converted to energy between meals. Eating refined foods containing sugar or white flour can contribute to elevated levels of triglycerides in the blood. High triglycerides levels (over 150 mg/dL) may contribute to atherosclerosis (hardening of the arteries). Lifestyle choices that contribute to lowering total cholesterol levels, such as a diet low in saturated fat and adequate exercise, tend to lower triglyceride levels as well.

Concept Summary

Classification of Lipids

Lipids are a family of naturally occurring compounds grouped together on the basis of their relative insolubility in water and solubility in nonpolar solvents. Lipids are energy-rich compounds that are used as waxy coatings, energy storage compounds, and as structural components by organisms. Lipids are classified as saponifiable (ester-containing) or nonsaponifiable. Saponifiable lipids are further classified as simple or complex, depending on the number of structural components.

Objective 1 (Section 18.1), Exercises 18.2 and 18.4

Fatty Acids

A fatty acid consists of a long nonpolar chain of carbon atoms, with a polar carboxylic acid group at one end. Most natural fatty acids contain an even number of carbon atoms. They may be saturated, unsaturated, or polyunsaturated (containing two or more double bonds).

Objective 2 (Section 18.2), Exercise 18.6

The Structure of Fats and Oils

Triglycerides or triacylglycerols in the form of fats and oils are the most abundant lipids. Fats and oils are simple lipids that are esters of glycerol and fatty acids. **Objective 3 (Section 18.3), Exercise 18.14.** The difference between fats and oils is the melting point, which is essentially a function of the fatty acids in the compound.

Objective 4 (Section 18.3), Exercise 18.12

Chemical Properties of Fats and Oils

Fats and oils can be hydrolyzed in the presence of acid to produce glycerol and fatty acids. When the hydrolysis reaction is carried out in the presence of a strong base, salts of the fatty acids (soaps) are produced. During hydrogenation, some multiple bonds of unsaturated fatty acids contained in fats or oils are reacted with hydrogen and converted to single bonds.

Objective 5 (Section 18.4), Exercise 18.18

Waxes

Waxes are simple lipids composed of a fatty acid esterified with a long-chain alcohol. **Objective 6 (Section 18.5), Exercise 18.24.** Waxes are insoluble in water and serve as protective coatings in nature.

Phosphoglycerides

Phosphoglycerides consist of glycerol esterified to two fatty acids and phosphoric acid. The phosphoric acid is further esterified to choline (in the lecithins) and to ethanolamine or serine (in the cephalins). The phosphoglycerides are particularly important in membrane formation.

Objective 7 (Section 18.6), Exercises 18.28 and 18.30

Sphingolipids

These complex lipids contain a backbone of sphingosine rather than glycerol and only one fatty acid component. They are abundant in brain and nerve tissue.

Objective 8 (Section 18.7), Exercise 18.34

Biological Membranes

Membranes surround tissue cells as a selective barrier, and they encase the organelles found in eukaryotic cells. Membranes contain both proteins and lipids. According to the fluid-mosaic model, the lipids are arranged in a bilayer fashion with the hydrophobic portions on the inside of the bilayer. Proteins float in the bilayer.

Objective 9 (Section 18.8), Exercise 18.42

Steroids

Steroids are compounds that have four rings fused together in a specific way. The most abundant steroid in humans is cholesterol, which serves as a starting material for other important steroids such as bile salts, adrenocorticoid hormones, and sex hormones.

Objective 10 (Section 18.9), Exercises 18.44 and 18.46

Steroid Hormones

Hormones are chemical messengers, synthesized by specific glands, that affect various target tissues in the body. The adrenal cortex produces a number of steroid hormones that regulate carbohydrate utilization (the glucocorticoids) and electrolyte balance (the mineralocorticoids). The testes and ovaries produce steroid hormones that determine secondary sex characteristics and regulate the reproductive cycle in females.

Objective 11 (Section 18.10), Exercise 18.50

Prostaglandins

These compounds are synthesized from the 20-carbon fatty acid arachiodonic acid. They exert many hormone-like effects on the body and are used therapeutically to induce labor, treat asthma, and control gastric secretions.

Objective 12 (Section 18.11), Exercise 18.58

Key Terms and Concepts

Cephalin (18.6)
Complex lipid (18.1)
Essential fatty acid (18.2)
Eukaryotic cell (18.8)
Fat (18.3)
Fluid-mosaic model (18.8)
Glycolipid (18.7)
Hormone (18.10)

Lecithin (18.6)
Lipid (18.1)
Lipid bilayer (18.8)
Micelle (18.2)
Oil (18.3)
Organelle (18.8)
Phosphoglyceride (18.6)
Phospholipid (18.6)

Prokaryotic cell (18.8)
Prostaglandin (18.11)
Simple lipid (18.1)
Soap (18.4)
Sphingolipid (18.7)
Steroid (18.9)
Triglyceride or triacylglycerol (18.3)
Wax (18.5)

Key Reactions

1. Hydrolysis of a triglyceride to glycerol and fatty acids—general reaction (Section 18.4):

2. Saponification of a triglyceride to glycerol and fatty acid salts—general reaction (Section 18.4):

3. Hydrogenation of a triglyceride—general reaction (Section 18.4):

$$
\begin{array}{l}
CH_2-O-\overset{\displaystyle O}{\overset{\|}{C}}-R \\[2mm]
CH-O-\overset{\displaystyle O}{\overset{\|}{C}}-(CH_2)_7CH=CH(CH_2)_7CH_3 + H_2 \xrightarrow{\ Ni\ } \\[2mm]
CH_2-O-\overset{\displaystyle O}{\overset{\|}{C}}-R
\end{array}
\qquad
\begin{array}{l}
CH_2-O-\overset{\displaystyle O}{\overset{\|}{C}}-R \\[2mm]
CH-O-\overset{\displaystyle O}{\overset{\|}{C}}-(CH_2)_{16}CH_3 \\[2mm]
CH_2-O-\overset{\displaystyle O}{\overset{\|}{C}}-R
\end{array}
$$

Exercises

Even-numbered exercises are answered in Appendix B.

Blue-numbered exercises are more challenging.

Introduction and Classification of Lipids (Section 18.1)

18.1 What is the basis for deciding if a substance is a lipid?

18.2 List two major functions of lipids in the human body.

18.3 What functional group is common to all saponifiable lipids?

18.4 Classify the following as saponifiable or nonsaponifiable lipids:

 a. A steroid **d.** A phosphoglyceride

 b. A wax **e.** A glycolipid

 c. A triglyceride **f.** A prostaglandin

Fatty Acids (Section 18.2)

18.5 Draw the structure of a typical saturated fatty acid. Label the polar and nonpolar portions of the molecule. Which portion is hydrophobic? Hydrophilic?

18.6 Describe four structural characteristics exhibited by most fatty acids.

18.7 Describe the structure of a micelle formed by the association of fatty acid molecules in water. What forces hold the micelle together?

18.8 Name two essential fatty acids, and explain why they are called essential.

18.9 Indicate whether each of the following fatty acids is saturated or unsaturated. Which of them are solids and which are liquids at room temperature?

 a. $CH_3(CH_2)_{14}COOH$

 b. $CH_3(CH_2)_4CH=CHCH_2CH=CH(CH_2)_7COOH$

 c. $CH_3(C_{14}H_{24})COOH$

 d. $CH_3(C_{10}H_{20})COOH$

18.10 Explain why the melting points of unsaturated fatty acids are lower than those of saturated fatty acids.

18.11 What structural feature of a fatty acid is responsible for the name omega-3 fatty acid?

The Structure of Fats and Oils (Section 18.3)

18.12 How are fats and oils structurally similar? How are they different?

18.13 From Figure 18.7, arrange the following substances in order of increasing percentage of unsaturated fatty acids: chicken fat, beef fat, corn oil, butter, and sunflower oil.

18.14 Draw the structure of a triglyceride that contains one myristic acid, one palmitoleic acid, and one linoleic acid. Identify the ester bonds.

18.15 From what general source do triglycerides tend to have more saturated fatty acids? More unsaturated fatty acids?

18.16 The percentage of fatty acid composition of two triglycerides is reported below. Predict which triglyceride has the lower melting point.

	Palmitic Acid	Stearic Acid	Oleic Acid	Linoleic Acid
Triglyceride A	20.4	28.8	38.6	10.2
Triglyceride B	9.6	7.2	27.5	55.7

18.17 Why is the amount of saturated fat in the diet a health concern?

Chemical Properties of Fats and Oils (Section 18.4)

18.18 What process is used to prepare a number of useful products such as margarines and cooking shortenings from vegetable oils?

18.19 Write equations for the following reactions using the oil shown below:

$$
\begin{array}{l}
CH_2-O-\overset{\displaystyle O}{\overset{\|}{C}}-(CH_2)_7CH=CH(CH_2)_7CH_3 \\[2mm]
CH-O-\overset{\displaystyle O}{\overset{\|}{C}}-(CH_2)_7CH=CH(CH_2)_7CH_3 \\[2mm]
CH_2-O-\overset{\displaystyle O}{\overset{\|}{C}}-(CH_2)_{16}CH_3
\end{array}
$$

 a. Lipase-catalyzed hydrolysis

 b. Saponification

 c. Hydrogenation

18.20 Why is the hydrogenation of vegetable oils of great commercial importance?

18.21 In general terms, name the products of the reactions below:

 a. Acid hydrolysis of a fat

 b. Acid hydrolysis of an oil

 c. Saponification of a fat

 d. Saponification of an oil

18.22 Write reactions to show how each of the following products might be prepared from a typical triglyceride present in the source given. Use Table 18.1 as an aid:

 a. Glycerol from beef fat

 b. Stearic acid from beef fat

 c. A margarine from corn oil

 d. Soaps from lard

Waxes (Section 18.5)

18.23 Draw the structure of a wax formed from oleic acid and cetyl alcohol $(CH_3(CH_2)_{14}CH_2\!-\!OH)$.

18.24 Like fats, waxes are esters of long-chain fatty acids. What structural difference exists between them that warrants placing waxes in a separate category?

18.25 Draw the structure of a wax formed from stearic acid and 1-dodecanol $(CH_3(CH_2)_{10}CH_2\!-\!OH)$

18.26 What role do waxes play in nature?

Phosphoglycerides (Section 18.6)

18.27 How do phosphoglycerides differ structurally from triglycerides?

18.28 Draw the general block diagram structure of a phosphoglyceride.

18.29 Draw the structure of a phosphoglyceride containing ethanolamine:

$$HO\!-\!CH_2CH_2\!-\!\overset{+}{N}H_3$$

Is it a lecithin or a cephalin?

18.30 Describe two biological roles served by the lecithins.

18.31 Draw the structure of a lecithin. What structural features make lecithin an important commercial emulsifying agent in certain food products?

18.32 What is the structural difference between a lecithin and a cephalin?

18.33 Where are cephalins found in the human body?

Sphingolipids (Section 18.7)

18.34 Draw the general block diagram structure of a sphingolipid.

18.35 List two structural differences between sphingolipids and phosphoglycerides.

18.36 List three diseases caused by abnormal metabolism and accumulation of sphingolipids.

18.37 Describe the structural similarities and differences between the sphingomyelins and the glycolipids.

18.38 Give another name for glycolipids. In what tissues are they found?

Biological Membranes (Section 18.8)

18.39 Where would you find membranes in a prokaryotic cell? Where would you find membranes in a eukaryotic cell? What functions do the membranes serve?

18.40 What three classes of lipids are found in membranes?

18.41 How does the polarity of the phosphoglycerides contribute to their function of forming cell membranes?

18.42 Describe the major features of the fluid-mosaic model of cell membrane structure.

Steroids (Section 18.9)

18.43 Why is it suggested that some people restrict cholesterol intake in their diet?

18.44 Draw the characteristic chemical structure that applies to all steroid molecules.

18.45 Explain how bile salts aid in the digestion of lipids.

18.46 List three important groups of compounds the body synthesizes from cholesterol. Give the location in bodily tissues where cholesterol is an essential component.

18.47 What symptoms might indicate the presence of gallstones in the gallbladder?

18.48 What is the major component in gallstones?

Steroid Hormones (Section 18.10)

18.49 What is a hormone? What are the two major categories of steroid hormones?

18.50 Name the two groups of adrenocorticoid hormones, give a specific example of each group, and explain the function of those compounds in the body.

18.51 How are testosterone and progesterone structurally similar? How are they different?

18.52 Name the primary male sex hormone and the three principal female sex hormones.

18.53 Why do athletes use anabolic steroids? What side effects are associated with their use?

18.54 What role do the estrogens and progesterone serve in preparation for pregnancy?

Prostaglandins (Section 18.11)

18.55 How are prostaglandins differentiated from each other?

18.56 What compound serves as a starting material for prostaglandin synthesis?

18.57 What body processes appear to be regulated in part by prostaglandins?

18.58 Name three therapeutic uses of prostaglandins.

Additional Exercises

18.59 Unsaturated fatty acids are susceptible to oxidation, which causes rancidity in food products. Suggest a way to decrease the amount of oxidative rancidity occurring in a food product.

18.60 A red-brown solution of bromine (Br_2) was added to a lipid, and the characteristic red-brown bromine color disappeared. What can be deduced about the lipid structure from this information?

18.61 Which of the following waxes would have the lowest melting point? Explain your answer.

a. $CH_3(CH_2)_{14} - \overset{\overset{\displaystyle O}{\|}}{C} - O - (CH_2)_{29}CH_3$

b. $CH_3(CH_2)_7CH = CH(CH_2)_5 - \overset{\overset{\displaystyle O}{\|}}{C} - O - (CH_2)_{29}CH_3$

18.62 Suggest a reason why complex lipids, such as phosphoglycerides and sphingomyelin, are more predominant in cell membranes than simple lipids.

18.63 Many esters are pleasantly fragrant. Examples include esters that are partially responsible for the smell of oranges and strawberries. What is the main difference between a fragrant ester and a wax? Explain why some esters are fragrant and waxes are not especially aromatic.

Allied Health Exam Connection

The following questions are from these sources:

1. *Nursing School Entrance Exam* © 2005, Learning Express, LLC.

2. *McGraw-Hill's Nursing School Entrance Exams* by Thomas A. Evangelist, Tamara B. Orr and Judy Unrein © 2009, The McGraw-Hill Companies, Inc.

3. *NSEE Nursing School Entrance Exams,* 3rd Edition © 2009, Kaplan Publishing.

4. *Cliffs Test Prep: Nursing School Entrance Exams* by Fred N. Grayson © 2004, Wiley Publishing, Inc.

5. *Peterson's Master the Nursing School and Allied Health Entrance Exams,* 18th Edition by Marion F. Gooding © 2008, Peterson's, a Nelnet Company.

18.64 Fats belong to the class of organic compounds represented by the general formula, RCOOR′, where R and R′ represent hydrocarbon groups. What is the name of the functional group present in fats? What functional group is common to all saponifiable lipids?

18.65 Identify each of the following characteristics as describing an unsaturated fatty acid or a saturated fatty acid:

a. Contains more hydrogen atoms

b. Is more healthy

c. More plentiful in plant sources

d. Is usually a solid at room temperature

18.66 Identify which sex hormones (testosterone, estrogens, or progesterone) are produced in:

a. The ovaries

b. The testes

18.67 Substance X passes through a cell membrane easily. Substance X would best be described as:

a. Hydrophilic or hydrophobic

b. Polar or nonpolar

c. A lipid or a protein

18.68 In diseases of the gallbladder, which of the following nutrients is limited in its digestibility? Explain your choice(s).

a. Starches

b. Proteins

c. Fats

18.69 Steroids are classified as:

a. carbohydrates

b. nucleic acids

c. lipids

d. proteins

18.70 Accumulation of cholesterol leads to the hardening of the arteries. This is called:

a. vasoconstriction

b. venipuncture

c. atherosclerosis

d. hypertension

18.71 Cholesterol, in spite of its bad reputation, is an essential component of:

a. microtubules

b. the cell membrane

c. ribosomes

d. cytosol

18.72 Bile is manufactured in the:

a. duodenum

b. liver

c. gall bladder

d. pancreas

18.73 The basic structure of cell membranes is a:

a. protein bilayer

b. protein-impregnated phospholipid bilayer

c. carbohydrate bilayer

d. phospholipid bilayer

18.74 The mineralocorticoid _____ is a product of the adrenal cortex.

a. epinephrine

b. norepinephrine

c. ACTH

d. aldosterone

18.75 Which cell type has a nucleus?

a. bikaryotic

b. prokaryotic

c. eukaryotic

d. postkaryotic

18.76 The cells of a human body are:

 a. bikaryotic cells

 b. prokaryotic cells

 c. unkaryotic cells

 d. eukaryotic cells

Chemistry for Thought

18.77 Gasoline is soluble in nonpolar solvents. Why is gasoline not classified as a lipid?

18.78 The structure of cellular membranes is such that ruptures are closed naturally. Describe the molecular forces that cause the closing to occur.

18.79 In Figure 18.7, the five vegetable oils listed are derived from seeds. Why do you think seeds are rich in oils?

18.80 Answer the question asked in Figure 18.9. How do oils used in automobiles differ chemically from vegetable oils?

18.81 Why doesn't honey dissolve beeswax?

18.82 In Figure 18.5 (where the nonpolar tails are together), why is the structure more stable than a structure in which the polar heads are together?

18.83 Why are there so many structurally different kinds of lipids?

18.84 In what ways are the structural features of lecithin similar to those of a soap?

18.85 When a doughnut is placed on a napkin, the napkin will often absorb a liquid and appear "moist." What is most likely the nature of the liquid?

Case Study

Linda was a beautiful, slender woman who looked much younger than her 67 years. Most of her life she had been careful to watch her weight and maintain her figure. She went to the gym regularly and considered herself quite fit. Recently, however, she had been diagnosed with osteopenia, lower-than-optimal bone density, which can progress to the more serious condition of osteoporosis, low bone density. Her doctor not only recommended calcium and vitamin D supplements but also increased protein intake. It seemed odd to Linda that he would recommend protein if the problem was her bone density. He explained that she was at an even greater risk of fracture if she did not have adequate muscle mass. The idea of increased intake of any food was difficult for the weight-conscious woman to accept. She had worked hard to limit her intake of dairy products or fattening nuts, and she didn't even care for meat.

How can Linda receive an adequate amount of protein without gaining too much weight? How many grams of protein per kilogram of body weight should an older woman consume? How can a person tell the difference between weight consciousness and anorexia?

Follow-up to this Case Study appears at the end the chapter before the Concept Summary.

Learning Objectives

When you have completed your study of this chapter, you should be able to:

1. Identify the characteristic parts of alpha-amino acids. **(Section 19.1)**

2. Draw structural formulas to illustrate the various ionic forms assumed by amino acids. **(Section 19.2)**

3. Write reactions to represent the formation of peptides and proteins. **(Section 19.3)**

4. Describe uses for important peptides. **(Section 19.4)**

5. Describe proteins in terms of the following characteristics: size, function, classification as fibrous or globular, and classification as simple or conjugated. **(Section 19.5)**

6. Explain what is meant by the primary structure of proteins. **(Section 19.6)**

7. Describe the role of hydrogen bonding in the secondary structure of proteins. **(Section 19.7)**

8. Describe the role of side-chain interactions in the tertiary structure of proteins. **(Section 19.8)**

9. Explain what is meant by the quaternary structure of proteins. **(Section 19.9)**

10. Describe the conditions that can cause proteins to hydrolyze or become denatured. **(Section 19.10)**

T he name *protein*, coined more than 100 years ago, is derived from the Greek *proteios*, which means "of first importance," and is appropriate for these most important of all biological compounds. Proteins are indispensable components of all living things, where they play crucial roles in all biological processes. In this chapter, we begin with a discussion of the structures and chemistry of the common amino acids, then progress to show how combinations of amino acids form large molecules called peptides and larger molecules called proteins.

19.1 The Amino Acids

Learning Objective

1. Identify the characteristic parts of alpha-amino acids.

Structure

All proteins, regardless of their origin or biological function, are structurally similar. They are polymers consisting of chains of amino acids chemically bound to each other. As the name implies, an amino acid is an organic compound that contains both an amino group and a carboxylate group in ionic form (Section 19.2). Hundreds of different amino acids, both synthetic and naturally occurring, are known, but only 20 are commonly found in natural proteins. The amino acids in proteins are called **alpha (α)-amino acids** because the amino group is attached to the α carbon (the carbon next to the carboxylate group),

alpha-amino acid An organic compound containing both an amino group and a carboxylate group, with the amino group attached to the carbon next to the carboxylate group.

$$H_2N-CH-\overset{\overset{\displaystyle O}{\|}}{C}-O^-$$
$$\underset{\underset{\displaystyle CH_2}{\diagdown \diagup}}{CH_2 \quad CH_2}$$

The structure of proline differs slightly from the general formula because the amino group and R group are part of a ring.

as shown in ▶ Figure 19.1. Each amino acid has a characteristic side chain, or R group, that imparts chemical individuality to the molecule. These R side chains contain different structural features, such as aromatic rings, —OH groups, —NH_3^+ groups, and —COO^- groups. This variety in side chains causes differences in the properties of the individual amino acids and the proteins containing different combinations of them.

Figure 19.1 The general structure of α-amino acids shown in ionic form.

The polarity of the R groups is an important characteristic and is the basis for classifying amino acids into the four groups shown in ▶ Table 19.1: neutral and nonpolar side chains, neutral but polar side chains, basic side chains, and acidic side chains. Note that acidic side chains contain a carboxylate group and that basic side chains contain an additional amino group. The three-letter and one-letter abbreviations that are used to represent amino acids are given after the names:

cysteine (Cys) C

glutamine (Gln) Q

asparagine (Asn) N

Stereochemistry

A glance at the general formula for the 20 amino acids

shows that with the exception of glycine, in which the R group is —H, there are four different groups attached to the α carbon. Thus, 19 of the 20 amino acids contain a chiral α carbon atom and can exist as two enantiomers; these are the L and D forms:

an L-amino acid

a D-amino acid

As we saw when we studied carbohydrates, one of the two possible forms usually predominates in natural systems. With few exceptions, the amino acids found in living systems exist in the L form.

TABLE 19.1 The Common Amino Acids of Proteins. Below each Amino Acid are its Name, its Three-Letter Abbreviation, and its One-Letter Abbreviation

NEUTRAL, NONPOLAR SIDE CHAINS

Glycine (Gly) G

Alanine (Ala) A

Valine (Val) V

Leucine (Leu) L

Isoleucine (Ile) I

Phenylalanine (Phe) F

Proline (Pro) P

Methionine (Met) M

NEUTRAL, POLAR SIDE CHAINS

Serine (Ser) S

Threonine (Thr) T

Tyrosine (Tyr) Y

Tryptophan (Trp) W

Cysteine (Cys) C

Asparagine (Asn) N

Glutamine (Gln) Q

BASIC, POLAR SIDE CHAINS

ACIDIC, POLAR SIDE CHAINS

Histidine (His) H

Lysine (Lys) K

Arginine (Arg) R

Aspartate (Asp) D

Glutamate (Glu) E

19.2 Zwitterions

Learning Objective

2. Draw structural formulas to illustrate the various ionic forms assumed by amino acids.

zwitterion A dipolar ion that carries both a positive and a negative charge as a result of an internal acid–base reaction in an amino acid molecule.

The structural formulas used to this point have shown amino acids in an ionized form. The fact that amino acids are white crystalline solids with relatively high melting points and high water solubilities suggests that they exist in an ionic form. Studies of amino acids confirm that this is true both in the solid state and in solution. The presence of a carboxyl group and a basic amino group in the same molecule makes possible the transfer of a hydrogen ion in a kind of internal acid–base reaction (Reaction 19.1). The product of this reaction is a dipolar ion called a **zwitterion.**

$$H_2N-\overset{\displaystyle |}{\underset{\displaystyle R}{CH}}-\overset{\displaystyle O}{\overset{\displaystyle ||}{C}}-OH \rightarrow \overset{+}{H_3N}-\overset{\displaystyle |}{\underset{\displaystyle R}{CH}}-\overset{\displaystyle O}{\overset{\displaystyle ||}{C}}-O^- \qquad (19.1)$$

<div align="center">
nonionized form

(does not exist)

zwitterion

(present in solids

and solutions)
</div>

The structure of an amino acid in solution varies with the pH of the solution. For example, if the pH of a solution is lowered by adding a source of H_3O^+, such as hydrochloric acid, the carboxylate group ($-COO^-$) of the zwitterion can pick up a proton to form $-COOH$ (Reaction 19.2):

$$\overset{+}{H_3N}-\overset{\displaystyle |}{\underset{\displaystyle R}{CH}}-\overset{\displaystyle O}{\overset{\displaystyle ||}{C}}-O^- + H_3O^+ \rightarrow \overset{+}{H_3N}-\overset{\displaystyle |}{\underset{\displaystyle R}{CH}}-\overset{\displaystyle O}{\overset{\displaystyle ||}{C}}-OH + H_2O \qquad (19.2)$$

<div align="center">
zwitterion

(0 net charge)

(positive net charge)
</div>

The zwitterion form has a net charge of 0, but the form in acid solution has a net positive charge.

When the pH of the solution is increased by adding OH^-, the $-NH_3^+$ of the zwitterion can lose a proton, and the zwitterion is converted into a negatively charged form (Reaction 19.3):

$$\overset{+}{H_3N}-\overset{\displaystyle |}{\underset{\displaystyle R}{CH}}-\overset{\displaystyle O}{\overset{\displaystyle ||}{C}}-O^- + OH^- \rightarrow H_2N-\overset{\displaystyle |}{\underset{\displaystyle R}{CH}}-\overset{\displaystyle O}{\overset{\displaystyle ||}{C}}-O^- + H_2O \qquad (19.3)$$

<div align="center">
zwitterion

(0 net charge)

(negative net charge)
</div>

Changes in pH also affect acidic and basic side chains and those proteins in which they occur. Thus, all amino acids exist in solution in ionic forms, but the actual form (and charge) is determined by the solution pH.

Because amino acids assume a positively charged form in acidic solutions and a negatively charged form in basic solutions, it seems reasonable to assume that at some pH between the acidic and basic extremes the amino acid will have no net charge (it will be a zwitterion). This assumption is correct, and the pH at which the zwitterion forms is called the **isoelectric point.** Each amino acid has a unique and characteristic isoelectric point; those with neutral R groups are all near a pH of 6 (that of glycine, e.g., is at pH 6.06), those with basic R groups have higher values (that of lysine is at pH 9.47), and

isoelectric point The characteristic solution pH at which an amino acid has a net charge of 0.

the two acidic amino acids have lower values (that of aspartate is at pH 2.98). Proteins, which are composed of amino acids, also have characteristic isoelectric points.

The ability of amino acids and some proteins to react with both H_3O^+ and OH^-, as shown by Reactions 19.2 and 19.3, allows solutions of amino acids or proteins to behave as buffers. The buffering action of blood proteins is one of their most important functions.

▶ Example 19.1

Draw the structure of the amino acid leucine

$$\overset{+}{H_3N} - CH - \overset{\overset{\displaystyle O}{\|}}{C} - O^-$$
$$\quad\quad\quad | $$
$$\quad\quad CH_2$$
$$\quad\quad\quad | $$
$$\quad\quad CH$$
$$\quad\quad / \quad \backslash$$
$$\quad CH_3 \quad CH_3$$

a. in acidic solution at a pH below the isoelectric point;
b. in basic solution at a pH above the isoelectric point.

Solution

a. In acidic solution, the carboxylate group of the zwitterion picks up a proton.

$$\overset{+}{H_3N} - CH - \overset{\overset{\displaystyle O}{\|}}{C} - O^- + H_3O^+ \rightarrow \overset{+}{H_3N} - CH - \overset{\overset{\displaystyle O}{\|}}{C} - OH + H_2O$$
$$\quad\quad | \quad\quad\quad\quad\quad\quad\quad\quad\quad\quad\quad\quad | $$
$$\quad CH_2 \quad\quad\quad\quad\quad\quad\quad\quad\quad\quad\quad CH_2$$
$$\quad\quad | \quad\quad\quad\quad\quad\quad\quad\quad\quad\quad\quad\quad | $$
$$\quad CH \quad\quad\quad\quad\quad\quad\quad\quad\quad\quad\quad\quad CH$$
$$\quad / \quad \backslash \quad\quad\quad\quad\quad\quad\quad\quad\quad\quad / \quad \backslash$$
$$CH_3 \quad CH_3 \quad\quad\quad\quad\quad\quad\quad\quad CH_3 \quad CH_3$$

b. In basic solution, the $\overset{+}{H_3N}$— group of the zwitterion loses a proton.

$$\overset{+}{H_3N} - CH - \overset{\overset{\displaystyle O}{\|}}{C} - O^- + OH^- \rightarrow H_2N - CH - \overset{\overset{\displaystyle O}{\|}}{C} - O^- + H_2O$$
$$\quad\quad | \quad\quad\quad\quad\quad\quad\quad\quad\quad\quad\quad\quad | $$
$$\quad CH_2 \quad\quad\quad\quad\quad\quad\quad\quad\quad\quad\quad CH_2$$
$$\quad\quad | \quad\quad\quad\quad\quad\quad\quad\quad\quad\quad\quad\quad | $$
$$\quad CH \quad\quad\quad\quad\quad\quad\quad\quad\quad\quad\quad\quad CH$$
$$\quad / \quad \backslash \quad\quad\quad\quad\quad\quad\quad\quad\quad\quad / \quad \backslash$$
$$CH_3 \quad CH_3 \quad\quad\quad\quad\quad\quad\quad\quad CH_3 \quad CH_3$$

▶ LEARNING CHECK 19.1 Draw the structure of the amino acid serine

$$\overset{+}{H_3N} - CH - \overset{\overset{\displaystyle O}{\|}}{C} - O^-$$
$$\quad\quad\quad | $$
$$\quad\quad CH_2 - OH$$

a. in acidic solution at a pH below the isoelectric point;
b. in basic solution at a pH above the isoelectric point.

19.3 Reactions of Amino Acids

Learning Objective

3. Write reactions to represent the formation of peptides and proteins.

Amino acids can undergo reactions characteristic of any functional group in the molecule. This includes reactions of the carboxylate group, the amino group, and any other functional groups attached to the R side chain. However, two reactions are of special interest because of their influence in determining protein structure.

Oxidation of Cysteine

Cysteine, the only sulfhydryl (—SH)-containing amino acid of the 20 commonly found in proteins, has a chemical property not shared by the other 19. We learned in Section 13.9 that a sulfhydryl group can easily be oxidized to form a disulfide bond (—S—S—). Thus, two cysteine molecules react readily to form a disulfide compound called cystine. The disulfide, in turn, is easily converted to —SH groups by the action of reducing agents:

cysteine → cystine (19.4)

As will be seen, this reaction is important in establishing the structure of some proteins.

Peptide Formation

In Section 16.4 we noted that amides could be thought of as being derived from a carboxylic acid and an amine (Reaction 19.5), although in actual practice the acid chlorides or acid anhydrides are generally used.

$$\underset{\substack{\text{a carboxylic} \\ \text{acid}}}{R-\overset{\overset{\displaystyle O}{\|}}{C}-OH} + \underset{\text{an amine}}{R'-NH_2} \xrightarrow{\text{Heat}} \underset{\text{an amide}}{R-\overset{\overset{\displaystyle O}{\|}}{C}-NH-R'} + H_2O \qquad (19.5)$$

amide linkage

In the same hypothetical way, it is possible to envision the carboxylate group of one amino acid reacting with the amino group of a second amino acid. For example, glycine could combine with alanine:

peptide linkage

glycine alanine glycylalanine (a dipeptide) (19.6)

Dr. Melina Jampolis is a San Francisco, California, physician nutrition specialist—a specialty practiced by only about 200 physicians in the United States. She focuses exclusively on nutrition for weight loss and disease prevention and treatment.

Ask an Expert 19.1

Q: Can a higher protein diet help me lose weight?

A: There is extensive debate among experts over which type of diet is the most effective for weight loss. Protein has several potential benefits due to its effect on hunger, metabolism, and body composition. Of the three macronutrients—protein, carbohydrates, and fat—protein has the greatest ability to satisfy hunger, which is critical for dieters. Dietary protein functions by triggering a greater release of the powerful appetite-suppressing hormone peptide YY (PYY), which communicates with the brain to decrease hunger. Studies have found that eating larger amounts of protein, especially at breakfast, helps improve hunger control throughout the day.

Protein can also boost metabolism slightly, which is particularly important during dieting, when metabolism can drop significantly. The total metabolic rate, or the number of calories you burn each day, includes three components: resting metabolic rate (RMR, the calories your body, including all of your organs, needs to function at rest), physical activity (the component over which you have the most control), and the thermic effect of feeding (the calories burned as a result of the digestion and processing of foods that you consume). Although the thermic effect of feeding represents only about 10% of your daily caloric expenditure, research shows that protein boosts the thermic effect of eating significantly more than carbohydrates and fat do. This enables you to burn more calories by consuming slightly more protein with each meal. The effect is fairly small, however, and can easily be negated by overconsumption of calories. So, it is important to eat a slightly higher percentage of protein without increasing total calories.

Protein satisfies hunger.

Dietary protein may help increase abdominal fat loss.

Protein may also benefit metabolism through its impact on body composition. Research has shown that protein in the diet can help maintain lean body mass during weight loss, particularly when combined with resistance training. If and when weight is regained, one study showed that by eating just 3% more protein, the regained weight was more likely to be muscle than fat. Lean body mass, which includes muscle, bone, and water, is one of the only components of RMR that you can control to some extent. Therefore, preserving muscle may help minimize the drop in metabolism both during and after weight loss, which can improve both weight loss and weight maintenance. In addition, research suggests that consuming a higher percentage of protein may help increase abdominal fat loss, particularly in women who tend to carry

Dietary protein can help maintain lean body mass.

Ask an Expert 19.1 (continued)

fat around their midsection rather than their hips and thighs. Higher protein diets may also help lower triglycerides more effectively in women with excess belly fat.

Finally, eating slightly more protein during weight loss may help preserve bone mineral content, which is particularly important in women as they get older and their risk of osteoporosis increases. If you have kidney problems, however, consuming higher amounts of protein is not recommended because it can worsen kidney disease.

The bottom line is that calories count the most when it comes to losing weight. However, consuming a slightly higher percentage of protein (25–30%) while consuming fewer calories may make weight loss slightly easier and more sustainable. For optimal health, make sure to consume mainly low-fat and plant-based protein.

dipeptide A compound formed when two amino acids are bonded by an amide linkage.

Compounds of this type made up of two amino acids are called **dipeptides,** and the amide linkage that holds them together is called a **peptide linkage** or **peptide bond.**

It is important to realize that a different dipeptide could also form by linking glycine and alanine the other way (alanine on the left in this case):

$$\overset{+}{H_3N}-\underset{\underset{CH_3}{|}}{CH}-\overset{\overset{O}{||}}{C}-O^- + \overset{+}{H_3N}-CH_2-\overset{\overset{O}{||}}{C}-O^- \longrightarrow \overset{+}{H_3N}-\underset{\underset{CH_3}{|}}{CH}-\overset{\overset{O}{||}}{C}\overset{\textit{peptide linkage}}{-}NH-CH_2-\overset{\overset{O}{||}}{C}-O^- + H_2O \quad (19.7)$$

alanine glycine alanylglycine

peptide linkage or peptide bond The amide linkage between amino acids that results when the amino group of one acid reacts with the carboxylate group of another.

Glycylalanine and alanylglycine are structural isomers of each other, and each has a unique set of properties. The reactions to form these and other dipeptides are more complex than Reactions 19.6 and 19.7 imply. In nature, these processes are carried out according to genetic information using a mechanism we shall examine in Section 21.8.

The presence of amino and carboxylate groups on the ends of dipeptides allows for the attachment of a third amino acid to form a tripeptide. For example, valine could be attached to alanylglycine:

peptide An amino acid polymer of short chain length.

polypeptide An amino acid polymer of intermediate chain length containing up to 50 amino acid residues.

$$\overset{+}{H_3N}-\underset{\underset{CH_3}{|}}{CH}-\overset{\overset{O}{||}}{C}\overset{\textit{two peptide linkages}}{-}NH-CH_2-\overset{\overset{O}{||}}{C}-NH-\underset{\underset{\underset{CH_3}{|}}{\underset{CH-CH_3}{|}}}{CH}-\overset{\overset{O}{||}}{C}-O^- + H_2O$$

alanylglycylvaline, a tripeptide (19.8)

protein An amino acid polymer made up of more than 50 amino acids.

amino acid residue An amino acid that is a part of a peptide, polypeptide, or protein chain.

N-terminal residue An amino acid on the end of a chain that has an unreacted or free amino group.

C-terminal residue An amino acid on the end of a chain that has an unreacted or free carboxylate group.

More amino acids can react in the same way to form a tetrapeptide, a pentapeptide, and so on, until a chain of hundreds or even thousands of amino acids has formed. The compounds with shortest chains are often simply called **peptides,** those with longer chains are called **polypeptides,** and those with still longer chains are called **proteins.** Chemists differ about where to draw the lines in the use of these names, but generally polypeptide chains with more than 50 amino acids are called proteins. However, the terms *protein* and *polypeptide* are often used interchangeably.

Amino acids that have been incorporated into chains are called **amino acid residues.** The amino acid residue with an unreacted or free amino group at the end of the chain is designated the **N-terminal residue,** and, according to convention, it is written on the left end of the peptide chain. Similarly, the residue with a free carboxylate group at the other end of the chain is the **C-terminal residue;** it is written on the right end of the chain. Thus,

alanine is the N-terminal residue and valine is the C-terminal residue in the tripeptide alanylglycylvaline:

*alanine, the
N-terminal
residue*
$$H_3\overset{+}{N} - CH - \overset{\overset{\textstyle O}{\|}}{C} - NH - CH_2 - \overset{\overset{\textstyle O}{\|}}{C} - NH - CH - \overset{\overset{\textstyle O}{\|}}{C} - O^-$$
*valine, the
C-terminal
residue*

with CH₃ below the first CH, and CH–CH₃ with CH₃ below the third CH.

Peptides are named by starting at the N-terminal end of the chain and listing the amino acid residues in order from left to right. Structural formulas and even full names for large peptides become very unwieldy and time-consuming to write. This is simplified by representing peptide and protein structures in terms of three-letter abbreviations for the amino acid residues with dashes to show peptide linkages. Thus, the structure of glycylalanine is represented by Gly-Ala. The isomeric dipeptide, alanylglycine, is Ala-Gly. In this case, alanine is the N-terminal residue, and glycine is the C-terminal residue.

The tripeptide alanylglycylvaline can be represented by Ala-Gly-Val. In addition to this sequence, five other arrangements of these three components are possible, and each one represents an isomeric tripeptide with different properties. These sequences are Ala-Val-Gly, Val-Ala-Gly, Val-Gly-Ala, Gly-Val-Ala, and Gly-Ala-Val.

Insulin, with 51 amino acids, has 1.55×10^{66} sequences possible! From these possibilities, the body reliably produces only one, which illustrates the remarkable precision of the life process. From the simplest bacterium to the human brain cell, only the amino acid sequences needed to form essential cell peptides are produced.

▶ LEARNING CHECK 19.2 Use Table 19.1 to draw the full structure of the following tetrapeptide. Label the N-terminal and C-terminal residues.

Phe-Cys-Ser-Ile

19.4 Important Peptides

Learning Objective

4. Describe uses for important peptides.

More than 200 peptides have been isolated and identified as essential to the proper functioning of the human body. The identity and sequence of amino acid residues in these peptides is extremely important to proper physiological function. Two well-known examples are vasopressin and oxytocin, which are hormones released by the pituitary gland. Each hormone is a nonapeptide (nine amino acid residues) with six of the residues held in the form of a loop by a disulfide bond (see ▶ Figure 19.2). The disulfide bond in these

vasopressin **oxytocin**

Figure 19.2 The structures of vasopressin and oxytocin. Differences are in amino acid residues 3 and 8. The normal carboxylate groups of the C-terminal residues (Gly) have been replaced by amide groups.

C-Reactive Protein: A Message from the Heart

The letters LDL and HDL followed by the word cholesterol are familiar to most health-conscious individuals. The letters stand for low-density lipoprotein and high-density lipoprotein, respectively, and it is also common knowledge that high LDL levels in the blood are dangerous and indicate possible heart disease. However, one of every four heart attack or stroke victims has a low LDL level, low blood pressure, does not smoke, is not diabetic, and has no other indication of cardiovascular disease—at least until recently. A protein discovered in the 1930s is gaining new prominence as a test for heart disease. The protein, called *C-reactive Protein* (CRP) is produced in the liver and passed into the bloodstream in response to any type of inflammation in the body. Many researchers now believe that inflammation is involved in cardiovascular disease.

An inexpensive test that measures the amount of CRP in the blood can detect inflammation when no other symptoms of cardiovascular disease exist. It is estimated that could help prevent up to 25% of all heart attacks. It should be stressed that the test is not an indicator of cardiovascular disease. It simply denotes inflammation and infection, which could be anywhere in the body and could be caused by many things. It cannot be a specific prognostic indicator and not a cure. Individuals who desire a healthy heart still need to eat wisely, avoid tobacco and other known harmful products, and exercise regularly. Regular exercise has been shown to reduce the level of CRP in the blood, which indicates a reduction in inflammation. It has also been shown that aspirin and similar drugs reduce inflammation, which provides an explanation for the accepted practice of taking a low dose of aspirin on a regular basis to help prevent heart attacks.

National guidelines are being developed to standardize CRP testing techniques and interpretation of the results. A paper published in the *New England Journal of Medicine* specifies three levels of risk that will probably be used as guidelines. Levels of CRP below one milligram per liter of blood are considered to be low. Levels between 1 and 3 mg/L are considered moderate, and levels above 3 mg/L are considered high.

Some factors suggest that CRP levels should not be used as the sole indicator of cardiovascular disease. For example, women tend to have higher CRP levels than men, but men have a higher incidence of cardiovascular disease. Also, women on hormone therapy seem to have abnormally high levels of CRP even in the absence of inflammation. Some researchers even suggest that CRP is just an indicator for some other factor, such as microbes that might be the real culprits, citing the atherosclerosis caused by syphilis as an example. In any case, the low cost of CRP testing coupled with the fact that many insurance plans will pay for it makes such testing a good idea.

Molecular models of C-reactive protein.

© Dr. Tim Evans/Photo Researchers, Inc.

disulfide bridge A bond produced by the oxidation of —SH groups on two cysteine residues. The bond loops or holds two peptide chains together.

hormones is formed by the oxidation of cysteine residues in the first and sixth positions (counting from the N-terminal end) of these peptide chains. In peptides and proteins, disulfide bonds such as these that draw a single peptide chain into a loop or hold two peptide chains together are called **disulfide bridges.**

Figure 19.2 shows that the structures of vasopressin and oxytocin differ only in the third and eighth amino acid residues of their peptide chains. The result of these variations is a significant difference in their biological functions. Vasopressin is known as antidiuretic hormone (ADH) because of its action in reducing the volume of urine formed, thus conserving the body's water. It also raises blood pressure. Oxytocin causes the smooth muscles of the uterus to contract and is often administered to induce labor. Oxytocin also acts on the smooth muscles of lactating mammary glands to stimulate milk ejection.

Another important peptide hormone is adrenocorticotropic hormone (ACTH). It is synthesized by the pituitary gland and consists of a single polypeptide chain of 39 amino acid residues with no disulfide bridges (see ▶ Figure 19.3). The major function of ACTH is to regulate the production of steroid hormones in the cortex of the adrenal gland. ▶ Table 19.2 lists these and some other important peptide or protein hormones.

Figure 19.3 The amino acid sequence of ACTH.

TABLE 19.2 Examples of Peptide or Protein Hormones

Name	Origin	Action
Adrenocorticotropic hormone (ACTH)	Pituitary	Stimulates production of adrenal hormones
Angiotensin II	Blood plasma	Causes blood vessels to constrict
Follicle-stimulating hormone (FSH)	Pituitary	Stimulates sperm production and follicle maturation
Gastrin	Stomach	Stimulates stomach to secrete acid
Glucagon	Pancreas	Stimulates glycogen metabolism in liver
Human growth hormone (HGH)	Pituitary	Stimulates growth and cell reproduction
Insulin	Pancreas	Controls metabolism of carbohydrates
Oxytocin	Pituitary	Stimulates contraction of uterus and other smooth muscles
Prolactin	Pituitary	Stimulates lactation
Somatostatin	Hypothalamus	Inhibits production of HGH
Vasopressin	Pituitary	Decreases volume of urine excreted

19.5 Characteristics of Proteins

Learning Objective

5. Describe proteins in terms of the following characteristics: size, function, classification as fibrous or globular, and classification as simple or conjugated.

Size

Proteins are extremely large natural polymers of amino acids with molecular weights that vary from about 6000 to several million u. The immense size of proteins (in the molecular sense) can be appreciated by comparing glucose with hemoglobin, a relatively small protein. Glucose has a molecular weight of 180 u, whereas the molecular weight of hemoglobin is 65,000 u (see ▶ Table 19.3). The molecular formula of glucose is $C_6H_{12}O_6$ and that of hemoglobin is $C_{2952}H_{4664}O_{832}N_{812}S_8Fe_4$.

Protein molecules are too large to pass through cell membranes and are contained inside the normal cells where they were formed. However, if cells become damaged by disease or trauma, the protein contents can leak out. Thus, persistent excessive amounts of proteins in the urine are indicative of damaged kidney cells. A routine urinalysis usually includes a test for protein. Similarly, a heart attack can be confirmed by the presence in the blood of certain proteins (enzymes) that are normally confined to cells in heart tissue (Section 20.9).

Acid–Base Properties

The 20 different R groups of amino acids are important factors in determining the physical and chemical properties of proteins that contain the amino acids. Acid–base behavior is

TABLE 19.3 Molecular Weights of Some Common Proteins

Protein	Molecular Weight (u)	Number of Amino Acid Residues
Insulin	6,000	51
Cytochrome c	16,000	104
Growth hormone	49,000	191
Hemoglobin	65,000	574
Hexokinase	96,000	730
Gamma globulin	176,000	1320
Myosin	800,000	6100

one of the most important of these properties. Proteins, like amino acids, take the form of zwitterions. The R groups of glutamate and aspartate contain —COO^- groups and provide H^+ ions, whereas the R groups of arginine and histidine are basic (see Table 19.1). Thus, proteins, like amino acids, have characteristic isoelectric points and can behave as buffers in solutions.

The tendency for large molecules such as proteins to remain in solution or form a stable colloidal dispersion depends to a large extent on the repulsive forces acting between molecules with like charges on their surfaces. When protein molecules are at a pH where they take forms that have a net positive or negative charge, the presence of these like charges causes the molecules to repel one another and remain dispersed. These repulsive forces are smallest at the isoelectric point, when the net molecular charges are essentially zero. Thus, protein molecules tend to clump together and precipitate from solutions in which the pH is equal to or close to the isoelectric point.

Protein Function

A large part of the importance of proteins results from the crucial roles they serve in all biological processes. The various functions of proteins are discussed below and summarized in ▶ Table 19.4.

1. **Catalytic function:** Nearly all the reactions that take place in living organisms are catalyzed by proteins functioning as enzymes. Without these catalytic proteins, biological reactions would take place too slowly to support life. Enzyme-catalyzed reactions range from relatively simple processes to the very complex, such as the duplication of hereditary material in cell nuclei. Enzymes are discussed in more detail in the next chapter.

2. **Structural function:** We saw in Section 17.8 that the main structural material for plants is cellulose. In the animal kingdom, structural materials other than the inorganic components of the skeleton are composed of protein. Collagen, a fiberlike protein, is responsible for the mechanical strength of skin and bone. Keratin, the chief constituent of hair, skin, and fingernails, is another example.

3. **Storage function:** Some proteins provide a way to store small molecules or ions. Ovalbumin, for example, is a stored form of amino acids that is used by embryos developing in bird eggs. Casein, a milk protein, and gliadin, in wheat seeds, are also stored forms of protein intended to nourish animals and plants, respectively. Ferritin, found in all cells of the body, attaches to iron ions and forms a storage complex in humans and other animals.

antibody A substance that helps protect the body from invasion by viruses, bacteria, and other foreign substances.

4. **Protective function: Antibodies** are tremendously important proteins that protect the body from disease. These highly specific proteins combine with and help destroy viruses, bacteria, and other foreign substances that get into the blood or tissue of the body. Blood clotting, another protective process, is carried out by the proteins thrombin and fibrinogen. Without this process, even small wounds would result in life-threatening bleeding.

TABLE 19.4 Biological Functions of Proteins

Function	Examples	Occurrence or Role
Catalysis	lactate dehydrogenase	Oxidizes lactic acid
	cytochrome c	Transfers electrons
	DNA polymerase	Replicates and repairs DNA
Structure	viral-coat proteins	Sheath around nucleic acid of viruses
	glycoproteins	Cell coats and walls
	α-keratin	Skin, hair, feathers, nails, and hooves
	β-keratin	Silk of cocoons and spiderwebs
	collagen	Fibrous connective tissue
	elastin	Elastic connective tissue
Storage	ovalbumin	Egg-white protein
	casein	A milk protein
	ferritin	Stores iron in the spleen
	gliadin	Stores amino acids in wheat
	zein	Stores amino acids in corn
Protection	antibodies	Form complexes with foreign proteins
	fibrinogen	Involved in blood clotting
	thrombin	Involved in blood clotting
Regulation	insulin	Regulates glucose metabolism
	growth hormone	Stimulates growth of bone
Nerve impulse transmission	rhodopsin	Involved in vision
	acetylcholine receptor protein	Impulse transmission in nerve cells
Movement	myosin	Thick filaments in muscle fiber
	actin	Thin filaments in muscle fiber
	dynein	Movement of cilia and flagella
Transport	hemoglobin	Transports O_2 in blood
	myoglobin	Transports O_2 in muscle cells
	serum albumin	Transports fatty acids in blood
	transferrin	Transports iron in blood
	ceruloplasmin	Transports copper in blood

5. **Regulatory function:** Numerous body processes are regulated by hormones, many of which are proteins. Examples are growth hormone, which regulates the growth rate of young animals, and thyrotropin, which stimulates the activity of the thyroid gland.

6. **Nerve impulse transmission:** Some proteins behave as receptors of small molecules that pass between gaps (synapses) separating nerve cells. In this way, they transmit nerve impulses from one nerve to another. Rhodopsin, a protein found in the rod cells of the retina of the eye, functions this way in the vision process.

7. **Movement function:** Every time we climb stairs, push a button, or blink an eye, we use muscles that have proteins as their major components. The proteins actin and myosin are particularly important in processes involving movement. They are long-filament proteins that slide along each other during muscle contraction.

8. **Transport function:** Numerous small molecules and ions are transported effectively through the body only after binding to proteins. For example, fatty acids are carried between fat (adipose) tissue and other tissues or organs by serum albumin, a blood protein. Hemoglobin, a well-known example, carries oxygen from the lungs to other body tissues, and transferrin is a carrier of iron in blood plasma.

Proteins perform other functions, but these are among the most important. It is easy to see that properly functioning cells of living organisms must contain many proteins. It has

Alzheimer's Disease

Alzheimer's disease is a progressive, degenerative disease that attacks the brain, causing impaired thinking, behavior, and memory. As the disease progresses, nerve cells in the brain degenerate, and the size of the brain actually decreases. About 4 million Americans suffer from this malady; it afflicts 1 in 10 people over age 65, and nearly half of all people over age 85. The disease, first identified by Alois Alzheimer in 1906, is best described by the words of one of its victims: "I have lost myself."

Some warning signs of Alzheimer's disease include difficulty in performing familiar tasks, language problems, disorientation related to time or place, poor or decreased quality of judgment, memory loss affecting job skills, problems with abstract thinking, misplacing things or putting them in inappropriate places, passivity and loss of initiative, and changes in mood, personality, or behavior. If several of these symptoms are present in an older person, a medical evaluation for Alzheimer's disease is in order.

The causes of the disease are under debate. Some researchers feel it is caused by the formation in the brain of fibrils (strands) and plaque deposits consisting largely of amyloid beta-protein. Others think the formation of tangles in a microtubule-associated protein called Tau is the culprit. Still others think both of these explanations are correct, and that the formation of abnormal amyloid beta strands causes the abnormal killer forms of the Tau protein to form. This position is supported by a recent study of the brains of aging rhesus monkeys. This study showed that amyloid beta-protein caused the same damage to the monkey brains that was found in the brains of Alzheimer's victims. In addition, the amyloid beta-protein caused changes in the Tau protein of the monkey brains that made it capable of forming tangles.

Currently, two drugs have been approved for use in treating Alzheimer's disease, Tacrine and Aricept, which treat some of the associated memory loss. Both drugs function by inhibiting the reuptake of acetylcholine in neural synapses. Unfortunately, they neither cure the disease nor slow its progress.

Current research is focused on preventing or reversing the process of changing normal amyloid protein into the deformed amyloid protein found in the brains of Alzheimer's patients. The α-helices of normal proteins are changed to β-pleated sheets in the abnormal proteins characteristic of the disease. In a recent promising study, an experimental peptide containing five amino acids was shown to mimic a region of amyloid beta-protein that regulates folding. However, the experimental peptide is so constructed that it prevents the other amino acids of amyloid beta-protein from folding into the β-pleated sheet conformation necessary to form amyloid beta-protein fibrils. In cell culture studies, the experimental peptide inhibited the formation of amyloid fibrils, broke down existing fibrils, and prevented the death of neurons. This type of promising discovery may eventually lead to a drug that can stop the progress—or even reverse the effects—of Alzheimer's disease.

A MRI showing brain atrophy in Alzheimer's disease.

© J. Cavallini/Custom Medical Stock Photo

been estimated that a typical human cell contains 9000 different proteins, and that a human body contains about 100,000 different proteins.

Classification

fibrous protein A protein made up of long rod-shaped or stringlike molecules that intertwine to form fibers.

globular protein A spherical protein that usually forms stable suspensions in water or dissolves in water.

Proteins can be classified by the functions just discussed. They can also be classified into two major types, fibrous and globular, on the basis of their structural shape. **Fibrous proteins** are made up of long rod-shaped or stringlike molecules that can intertwine with one another and form strong fibers. They are water-insoluble and are usually found as major components of connective tissue, elastic tissue, hair, and skin. Examples are collagen, elastin, and keratin (see ❱ Figure 19.4).

Globular proteins are more spherical and either dissolve in water or form stable suspensions in water. They are not found in structural tissue but are transport proteins, or

proteins that may be moved easily through the body by the circulatory system. Examples of these are hemoglobin and transferrin.

Another classification scheme for proteins is based on composition—proteins are either simple or conjugated. **Simple proteins** are those that contain only amino acid residues. **Conjugated proteins** contain amino acid residues and other organic or inorganic components. The non–amino acid parts of conjugated proteins are called **prosthetic groups.** The type of prosthetic group present is often used to further classify conjugated proteins. For example, proteins containing lipids, carbohydrates, or metal ions are called lipoproteins, glycoproteins, and metalloproteins, respectively. Thus, the iron-containing proteins hemoglobin and myoglobin are metalloproteins. ▎ Table 19.5 lists the common classes of conjugated proteins.

Figure 19.4 Animal hair and spiderwebs are constructed of the fibrous proteins α-keratin and β-keratin, respectively. What properties of fibrous proteins make hair, fur, and spiderwebs useful?

© Christina Slabaugh

TABLE 19.5 Conjugated Proteins

Class	Prosthetic Groups	Examples
Nucleoproteins	nucleic acids (DNA, RNA)	Viruses
Lipoproteins	lipids	Fibrin in blood, serum lipoproteins
Glycoproteins	carbohydrates	Gamma globulin in blood, mucin in saliva
Phosphoproteins	phosphate groups	Casein in milk
Hemoproteins	heme	Hemoglobin, myoglobin, cytochromes
Metalloproteins	iron	Ferritin, hemoglobin
	zinc	Alcohol dehydrogenase

simple protein A protein made up entirely of amino acid residues.

conjugated protein A protein made up of amino acid residues and other organic or inorganic components.

prosthetic group The non–amino acid parts of conjugated proteins.

Protein Structure

As you might expect, the structures of extremely large molecules, such as proteins, are much more complex than those of simple organic compounds. Many protein molecules consist of a chain of amino acids twisted and folded into a complex three-dimensional structure. This structural complexity imparts unique features to proteins that allow them to function in the diverse ways required by biological systems. To better understand protein function, we must look at four levels of organization in their structure. These levels are referred to as primary, secondary, tertiary, and quaternary.

19.6 The Primary Structure of Proteins

Learning Objective

6. Explain what is meant by the primary structure of proteins.

Every protein, be it hemoglobin, keratin, or insulin, has a similar backbone of carbon and nitrogen atoms held together by peptide bonds:

protein backbone (in color)

The difference in proteins is the variation in the length of the backbone and the sequence of the side chains (R groups) that are attached to the backbone. The order in which amino acid residues are linked together in a protein is called the **primary structure.** Each

primary protein structure The linear sequence of amino acid residues in a protein chain.

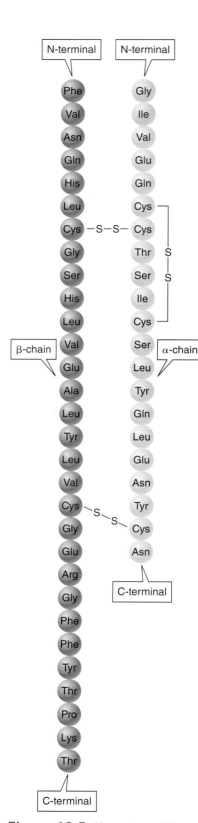

Figure 19.5 The amino acid sequence (primary structure) of human insulin.

different protein in a biological organism has a unique sequence of amino acid residues. It is this sequence that causes a protein chain to fold and curl into the distinctive shape that, in turn, enables the protein to function properly. As we will see in Section 19.10, a protein molecule that loses its characteristic three-dimensional shape cannot function.

Biochemists have devised techniques for finding the order in which the residues are linked together in protein chains. A few of the proteins whose primary structures are known are listed in ▶ Table 19.6.

TABLE 19.6 Some Proteins Whose Sequence of Amino Acids is Known	
Protein	**Number of Amino acid Residues**
Insulin	51
Hemoglobin	
α-chain	141
β-chain	146
Myoglobin	153
Human growth hormone	191
Trypsinogen	229
Carboxypeptidase A	307
Gamma globulin	1320

▶ Figure 19.5 shows the primary structure of human insulin. Notice that the individual molecules of this hormone consist of two chains having a total of 51 amino acid residues. In the molecule, two disulfide bridges hold the chains together, and there is one disulfide linkage within a chain. Insulin plays an essential role in regulating the use of glucose by cells. Diabetes mellitus can result when the body does not produce enough insulin or when cells do not respond to the insulin that is produced.

As we saw in the case of vasopressin and oxytocin (Section 19.4), small changes in amino acid sequence can cause profound differences in the functioning of proteins. For example, a minor change in sequence in the blood protein hemoglobin causes the fatal sickle-cell disease.

19.7 The Secondary Structure of Proteins

Learning Objective

7. Describe the role of hydrogen bonding in the secondary structure of proteins.

If the only structural characteristics of proteins were their amino acid sequences (primary structures), all protein molecules would consist of long chains arranged in random fashion. However, protein chains fold and become aligned in such a way that certain orderly patterns result. These orderly patterns, referred to as **secondary structures,** result from hydrogen bonding and include the α-helix (alpha-helix) and the β-pleated (beta-pleated) sheet.

The α-Helix

In 1951, American chemists Linus Pauling and Robert Corey suggested that proteins could exist in the shape of an **α-helix,** a form in which a single protein chain twists so that it resembles a coiled helical spring (see ▶ Figure 19.6). The chain is held in the helical shape

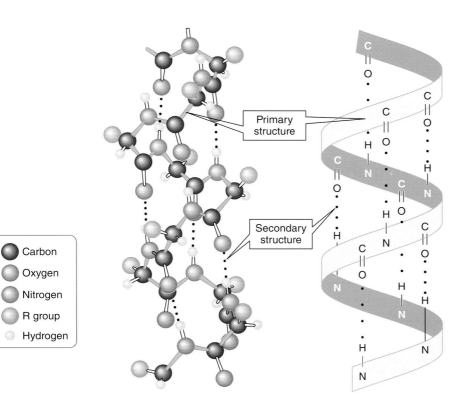

Figure 19.6 Two representations of the a-helix, showing hydrogen bonds between amide groups.

Carbon
Oxygen
Nitrogen
R group
Hydrogen

Primary structure

Secondary structure

by numerous intramolecular hydrogen bonds between carbonyl oxygens and amide hydrogens in adjacent turns of the helical backbone:

$$-\text{C}=\text{O} \cdots \text{H}-\text{N}-$$

The carbonyl group of each amino acid residue is hydrogen bonded to the amide hydrogen of the amino acid that is four residues away in the chain; thus, all amide groups in the helix are hydrogen bonded (Figure 19.6). The protein backbone forms the coil, and the side chains (R groups) extend outward from the coil.

Six years after Pauling and Corey proposed the α-helix, its presence in proteins was detected. Since that time it has been found that the amount of α-helical content is quite variable in proteins. In some it is the major structural component, whereas in others a random coil predominates and there is little or no α-helix coiling.

In the proteins α-keratin (found in hair), myosin (found in muscle), epidermin (found in skin), and fibrin (found in blood clots), two or more helices interact (supracoiling) to form a cable (see ▶ Figure 19.7). These cables make up bundles of fibers that lend strength to the tissue in which they are found.

Figure 19.7 The supracoiling of three α-helices in the keratins of hair and wool.

The β-Pleated Sheet

A less common type of secondary structure is found in some proteins. This type, called a **β-pleated sheet,** results when several protein chains lie side by side and are held in position by hydrogen bonds between the carbonyl oxygens of one chain and the amide hydrogens of an adjacent chain (see ▶ Figure 19.8).

secondary protein structure The arrangement of protein chains into patterns as a result of hydrogen bonds between amide groups of amino acid residues in the chain. The common secondary structures are the α-helix and the β-pleated sheet.

α-helix The helical structure in proteins that is maintained by hydrogen bonds.

β-pleated sheet A secondary protein structure in which protein chains are aligned side by side in a sheetlike array held together by hydrogen bonds.

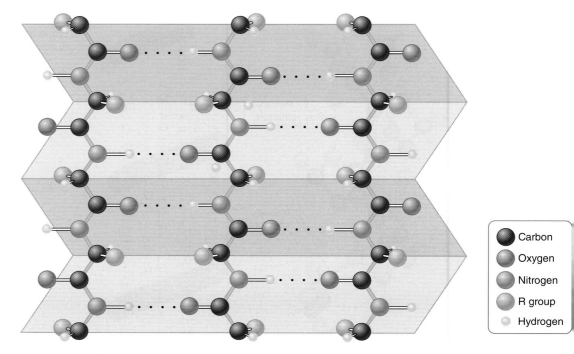

Figure 19.8 The β-pleated sheet. The four dots show hydrogen bonds between adjacent protein chains.

The β-pleated sheet is found extensively only in the protein of silk. However, a number of proteins in which a single polypeptide chain forms sections of a β-pleated sheet structure by folding back on itself are known. ▶ Figure 19.9 depicts a protein chain exhibiting the β-pleated sheet, the α-helix, and other structural conformations. Note the position of the hydrogen bonds in the two secondary structures.

Figure 19.9 A segment of a protein showing areas of α-helical, β-pleated sheet, and coil molecular structure.

Sickle-Cell Disease

Hemoglobin is composed of four polypeptide chains: two α-chains, each containing 141 amino acid residues, and two β-chains, each containing 146 amino acid residues (Figure 19.12). Hemoglobin is located in red blood cells and performs the life-sustaining function of transporting oxygen from the lungs to the cells and carbon dioxide from the cells to the lungs. In some individuals, the hemoglobin molecules have a slightly different sequence of amino acid residues. It is the so-called abnormal human hemoglobins that have attracted particular attention because of the diseases associated with them. One of the best-known abnormal hemoglobins (designated HbS) differs from the normal type (HbA) by only one amino acid residue in each of the two β-chains. In HbS, the glutamate in the sixth position of normal HbA is replaced by a valine residue:

	4	5	6	7	8	9
Normal HbA	—Thr—Pro—Glu—Glu—Lys—Ala—					
Sickle-cell HbS	—Thr—Pro—Val—Glu—Lys—Ala—					

This difference affects only two positions in a molecule containing 574 amino acid residues, and yet it is enough to result in a very serious disease, sickle-cell disease.

When combined with oxygen, the red blood cells of people with sickle-cell disease have the flat, disklike shape of normal red blood cells. However, after they give up their oxygen, red blood cells containing HbS hemoglobin become distorted into a characteristic sickle shape. These sickled cells tend to clump together and wedge in capillaries, particularly in the spleen, and cause excruciating pain. Cells blocking capillaries are rapidly destroyed, and the loss of red blood cells causes anemia. Children with sickle-cell disease have an 80% lower chance of surviving to adulthood than unafflicted children.

Sickle-cell anemia is a genetic disease that can be identified by screening a blood sample for abnormal hemoglobin. A person with an HbS gene from one parent and a normal HbA gene from another parent (a heterozygote) is said to have the sickle-cell trait. About 40% of the hemoglobin in these individuals is HbS, but there are generally no ill effects. A person with HbS genes from both parents (a homozygote) is said to have sickle-cell disease, and all of his or her hemoglobin is HbS. Laboratory screening tests to separate HbA and HbS proteins can easily determine whether prospective parents carry the sickle-cell trait.

There is an intriguing relationship between the sickle-cell trait and malaria resistance. In some parts of the world, up to 20% of the population has the sickle-cell trait. The trait produces an increased resistance to one type of malaria because the malarial parasite cannot feed on the hemoglobin in sickled red blood cells. Individuals with sickle-cell disease die young, while those without the sickle-cell trait also have a high probability of dying prematurely, but from malaria. Occupying the middle ground are those with the sickle-cell trait who do not suffer much from the effects of sickle-cell disease and also avoid the ravages of malaria.

Scanning electron micrograph of normal red blood cells (round shape) in the midst of sickled cells (crescent shape).

19.8 The Tertiary Structure of Proteins

Learning Objective

8. Describe the role of side-chain interactions in the tertiary structure of proteins.

Tertiary structure, the next higher level of complexity in protein structure, refers to the bending and folding of the protein into a specific three-dimensional shape. This bending and folding may seem rather disorganized, but nevertheless it results in a favored arrangement for a given protein.

The tertiary structure results from interactions between the R side chains of the amino acid residues. These R-group interactions are of four types:

tertiary protein structure A specific three-dimensional shape of a protein resulting from interactions between R groups of the amino acid residues in the protein.

1. **Disulfide bridges:** As in the structure of insulin (Figure 19.5), a disulfide linkage can form between two cysteine residues that are close to each other in the same chain or between cysteine residues in different chains. The existence and location of these

disulfide bridges is a part of the tertiary structure because these interactions hold the protein chain in a loop or some other three-dimensional shape.

2. **Salt bridges:** These interactions are a result of ionic bonds that form between the ionized side chain of an acidic amino acid ($-COO^-$) and the side chain of a basic amino acid ($-NH_3^+$).

3. **Hydrogen bonds:** Hydrogen bonds can form between a variety of side chains, especially those that possess the following functional groups:

$$-OH \qquad -NH_2 \qquad \overset{\displaystyle O}{\underset{\displaystyle \parallel}{-C}}-NH_2$$

One possible interaction, between the $-OH$ groups of two serine residues, is shown in ▶ Figure 19.10. We saw in Section 19.7 that hydrogen bonding also determines the secondary structure of proteins. The distinction is that the tertiary hydrogen bonding occurs between R groups, whereas in secondary structures, the hydrogen bonding is between backbone $-C=O$ and $-N$ groups.

Figure 19.10 R-group interactions leading to tertiary protein structure.

Disulfide bridge

Cys —S—S— Cys

Phe

Hydrophobic interactions

Phe

Protein backbone

Asp —COO⁻ H₃N⁺— Lys

Salt bridge

Ser

Hydrogen bond

Ser

4. **Hydrophobic interactions:** These result when nonpolar groups are either attracted to one another or forced together by their mutual repulsion of aqueous solvent. Interactions of this type are common between R groups such as the nonpolar phenyl rings of phenylalanine residues (Figure 19.10). This is illustrated by the compact structure of globular proteins in aqueous solutions (see ▶ Figure 19.11). Much like in the

Figure 19.11 A globular protein with a hydrophobic region on the inside and polar groups on the outside extending into the aqueous surroundings.

Aqueous region

Hydrophobic region

fatty acid micelles in Section 18.2, the globular shape results because polar groups are pointed outward toward the aqueous solvent, and nonpolar groups are pointed inward, away from the water molecules. This type of interaction is weaker than the other three, but it usually acts over large surface areas so that the net effect is an interaction strong enough to stabilize the tertiary structure.

The interactions leading to tertiary protein structures are summarized in Figure 19.10.

▶ **LEARNING CHECK 19.3** What kind of R-group interaction might be expected if the following side chains were in close proximity?

a. $-\underset{\underset{\text{CH}_3}{|}}{\text{CH}}\text{CH}_2\text{CH}_3$ and $-\underset{\underset{\text{CH}_3}{|}}{\text{CH}}\text{CH}_2\text{CH}_3$

b. $-\underset{\underset{\text{O}}{\|}}{\text{C}}-\text{NH}_2$ and $-\text{C}_6\text{H}_4-\text{OH}$

c. $-\text{CH}_2-\underset{\underset{\text{O}}{\|}}{\text{C}}-\text{O}^-$ and $-\text{CH}_2\text{CH}_2\text{CH}_2\text{CH}_2-\text{NH}_3^+$

19.9 The Quaternary Structure of Proteins

Learning Objective

9. Explain what is meant by the quaternary structure of proteins.

Many functional proteins contain two or more polypeptide chains held together by forces such as ionic attractions, disulfide bridges, hydrogen bonds, and hydrophobic forces. Each of the polypeptide chains, called **subunits,** has its own primary, secondary, and tertiary structure. The arrangement of subunits to form the larger protein is called the **quaternary structure** of the protein.

subunit A polypeptide chain having primary, secondary, and tertiary structural features that is a part of a larger protein.

quaternary protein structure The arrangement of subunits that form a larger protein.

Study Skills 19.1

Visualizing Protein Structure

A visual aid to help you "see" protein structure and remember the difference between primary, secondary, and tertiary structure is the cord of a telephone receiver. The chainlike primary structure is represented by the long straight cord. The coiling of the cord into a helical arrangement represents the secondary structure, and the tangled arrangement the cord adopts after the receiver has been used several times is the tertiary structure.

Primary structure

Secondary structure

Tertiary structure

Hemoglobin is a well-known example of a protein exhibiting quaternary structure. Hemoglobin is made of four chains (subunits): two identical chains (called alpha) containing 141 amino acid residues each and two other identical chains (beta) containing 146 residues each. Each of these four hemoglobin subunits contains a heme group (a planar ring structure centered around an iron atom, shown in ❱ Figure 19.12B) located in crevices near the exterior of the molecule. The hemoglobin molecule is nearly spherical with the four subunits held together rather tightly by hydrophobic forces. A schematic drawing of the quaternary structure of hemoglobin is shown in Figure 19.12A.

A Hemoglobin exhibits quaternary structure with two α-chains and two β-chains. The purple disks are heme groups.

B A heme group.

Figure 19.12 The structure of hemoglobin.

19.10 Protein Hydrolysis and Denaturation

Learning Objective

10. Describe the conditions that can cause proteins to hydrolyze or become denatured.

Hydrolysis

We learned in Section 16.8 that amides can be hydrolyzed by aqueous acid or base. The amide linkages of peptides and proteins also show this characteristic. As a result, the heating of a peptide or protein in the presence of acid or base causes it to break into smaller peptides, or even amino acids, depending on the hydrolysis time, temperature, and pH.

$$\text{protein} + H_2O \xrightarrow[\text{OH}^-]{H^+ \text{ or}} \text{smaller peptides} \xrightarrow[\text{OH}^-]{H^+ \text{ or}} \text{amino acids} \qquad (19.9)$$

The process of protein digestion (Section 22.6) involves hydrolysis reactions that are catalyzed by enzymes in the digestive tract. In Chapter 24, we'll also see that the hydrolysis of cellular proteins to amino acids is an ongoing process as the body resynthesizes needed molecules and tissues.

Denaturation

Proteins are maintained in their natural three-dimensional conformation, or **native state,** by stable secondary and tertiary structures and through the aggregation of subunits in quaternary structures. If proteins are exposed to physical or chemical conditions, such as extreme temperatures or pH values that disrupt these stabilizing structures, the folded native structure breaks down and the protein takes on a random, disorganized conformation (see ▶ Figure 19.13). This process, called **denaturation,** causes the protein to become inactive, and it may precipitate because hydrophobic residues are likely to be exposed to the aqueous surroundings. The change of egg white from a clear, jellylike material to a white

native state The natural three-dimensional conformation of a functional protein.

denaturation The process by which a protein loses its characteristic native structure and function.

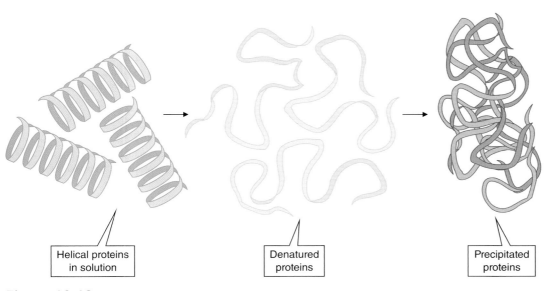

| Helical proteins in solution | Denatured proteins | Precipitated proteins |

Figure 19.13 Protein denaturation and coagulation of the proteins.

Figure 19.14 Denaturing the protein in eggs.

solid when heated is an example of this process (see ▶ Figure 19.14). Denaturation also explains why most proteins are biologically active only over a narrow temperature range, typically 0°C–40°C. Temperatures higher than those normal for a living organism can cause intramolecular vibrations to become so intense that hydrogen bonds or other stabilizing forces are disrupted and denaturation results.

The correlation between denaturation and loss of biological activity is clearly illustrated by the common methods used to kill microorganisms and deactivate their toxins. Most bacterial toxins, which are proteins, lose their ability to cause disease when they are heated. For example, the toxic protein excreted by *Clostridium botulinum* is responsible for botulism, an often fatal form of food poisoning. This dangerous substance loses its toxic properties after being heated at 100°C for a few minutes. Heating also deactivates the toxins of the bacteria that cause diphtheria and tetanus. Heat denaturation is used to prepare vaccines against these particular diseases. The deactivated (denatured) toxin can no longer cause the symptoms of the disease to appear, but it can stimulate the body to produce substances that induce immunity to the functional toxins. It is well known that high temperatures have been used for many years in hospitals and laboratories to sterilize surgical instruments and glassware that must be germ-free. The high temperatures denature and deactivate proteins needed within the germ cells for survival.

Similar changes in protein conformation resulting in denaturation can be brought about by heavy-metal ions such as Hg^{2+}, Ag^+, and Pb^{2+} that interact with —SH groups and carboxylate (—COO^-) groups. Organic materials containing mercury (mercurochrome and merthiolate) were once commonly used as antiseptics in the home to treat minor skin abrasions because they denature proteins in bacteria. Mercury, silver, and lead salts are also poisonous to humans for the same reason: They deactivate critical proteins we need to live. Large doses of raw egg white and milk are often given to victims of heavy-metal poisoning. The proteins in the egg and milk bind to the metal ions and form a precipitate. The metal-containing precipitate is removed from the stomach by pumping or is ejected by induced vomiting. If the precipitated protein is not removed, it will be digested, and the toxic metal ions will be released again.

Some of the various substances and conditions that will denature proteins are summarized in ▶ Table 19.7.

TABLE 19.7 Substances and Conditions that Denature Proteins

Substance or Condition	Effect on Proteins
Heat and ultraviolet light	Disrupt hydrogen bonds and ionic attractions by making molecules vibrate too violently; produce coagulation, as in cooking an egg
Organic solvents (ethanol and others miscible with water)	Disrupt hydrogen bonds in proteins and probably form new ones with the proteins
Strong acids or bases	Disrupt hydrogen bonds and ionic attractions; prolonged exposure results in hydrolysis of protein
Detergents	Disrupt hydrogen bonds, hydrophobic interactions, and ionic attractions
Heavy-metal ions (Hg^{2+}, Ag^+, Pb^{2+})	Form bonds to thiol groups and precipitate proteins as insoluble heavy-metal salts

Case Study Follow-up

Bone is approximately 50% protein matrix. Recent evidence suggests that increased dietary protein is important for the elderly because the ability to build bone and muscle from available dietary protein decreases with age. Some suggest increasing the RDA (recommended daily allowance) for older individuals from .8g protein /kg bodyweight to 1.0–1.2 g /kg per day (Kerstetter et al. 2009). For a 120 lb woman, 65g of protein would meet the higher recommendation. With a caloric value of 260 calories, 65 grams of protein could cause an undesirable weight gain if it is merely added to an existing diet. However, careful substitution could increase protein intake without causing a weight gain. A woman not wishing to gain weight, but advised to make such a change in her diet, should evaluate whether weight maintenance is the most healthful decision. A height/weight ratio, or body mass index (BMI), is helpful in making the determination. A BMI of 18.5–24.9 is recommended (USNHH, 2011). If the BMI is within a healthy range, then she would need to substitute the increased protein in place of fat or carbohydrates in the existing diet. If the BMI is below 18.5, then the protein should be added to the existing diet. If she is unwilling to maintain a healthy weight, psychological counseling could help her understand the reasons for her behavior. Failure to maintain a weight that is at least 85% of normal is evidence of an eating disorder. Sensitive management of such patients is vital considering the health risks of anorexia.

Concept Summary

The Amino Acids

All proteins are polymers of amino acids, which are bifunctional organic compounds that contain both an amino group and a carboxylate group. Differences in the R groups of amino acids cause differences in the properties of amino acids and proteins.
Objective 1 (Section 19.1), Exercise 19.2

Zwitterions

The presence of both amino groups and carboxyl groups in amino acids makes it possible for amino acids to exist in several ionic forms, including the form of a zwitterion. Objective 2 (Section 19.2), Exercise 19.12 The zwitterion is a dipolar form in which the net charge on the ion is zero.

Reactions of Amino Acids

Amino acids can undergo reactions characteristic of any functional group in the molecule. Two important reactions are the reaction of two cysteine molecules to form a disulfide, and the reaction of amino groups and carboxylate groups of different molecules to form peptide (amide) linkages.
Objective 3 (Section 19.3), Exercise 19.16

Important Peptides

More than 200 peptides have been shown to be essential for the proper functioning of the human body. Hormones are among the peptides for which functions have been identified.
Objective 4 (Section 19.4), Exercise 19.22

Concept Summary (continued)

Characteristics of Proteins

Proteins are large polymers of amino acids. Acidic and basic properties of proteins are determined by the acidic or basic character of the R groups of the amino acids constituting the protein. Proteins perform numerous important functions in the body. Proteins are classified structurally as fibrous or globular. They are classified on the basis of composition as simple or conjugated.

Objective 5 (Section 19.5), Exercises 19.30 and 19.32

The Primary Structure of Proteins

The primary structure of a protein is the sequence of amino acids in the polymeric chain. This gives all proteins an identical backbone of carbon and nitrogen atoms held together by peptide linkages. The difference in proteins is the sequence of R groups attached to the backbone.

Objective 6 (Section 19.6), Exercise 19.34

The Secondary Structure of Proteins

Protein chains are held in characteristic shapes called secondary structures by hydrogen bonds. Two specific structures that have been identified are the α-helix and the β-pleated sheet.

Objective 7 (Section 19.7), Exercise 19.38

The Tertiary Structure of Proteins

A third level of complexity in protein structure results from interactions between the R groups of protein chains. These interactions include disulfide bridges, salt bridges, hydrogen bonds, and hydrophobic attractions.

Objective 8 (Section 19.8), Exercise 19.42

The Quaternary Structure of Proteins

Some functional proteins consist of two or more polypeptide chains held together by forces such as ionic attractions, disulfide bridges, hydrogen bonds, and hydrophobic forces. The arrangement of these polypeptides to form the functional protein is called the quaternary structure of the protein.

Objective 9 (Section 19.9), Exercise 19.46

Protein Hydrolysis and Denaturation

The peptide (amide) linkages of peptides and proteins can be hydrolyzed under appropriate conditions. This destroys the primary structure and produces smaller peptides or amino acids. The characteristic secondary, tertiary, and quaternary structures of proteins can also be disrupted by certain physical or chemical conditions such as extreme temperatures or pH values. The disruption of these structures is called denaturation and causes the protein to become nonfunctional and, in some cases, to precipitate.

Objective 10 (Section 19.10), Exercise 19.50

Key Terms and Concepts

Alpha-amino acid (19.1)
α-helix (19.7)
Amino acid residue (19.3)
Antibody (19.5)
β-pleated sheet (19.7)
Conjugated protein (19.5)
C-terminal residue (19.3)
Denaturation (19.10)
Dipeptide (19.3)

Disulfide bridge (19.4)
Fibrous protein (19.5)
Globular protein (19.5)
Isoelectric point (19.2)
Native state (19.10)
N-terminal residue (19.3)
Peptide (19.3)
Peptide linkage (peptide bond) (19.3)
Polypeptide (19.3)

Primary protein structure (19.6)
Prosthetic group (19.5)
Protein (19.3)
Quaternary protein structure (19.9)
Secondary protein structure (19.7)
Simple protein (19.5)
Subunit (19.9)
Tertiary protein structure (19.8)
Zwitterion (19.2)

Key Reactions

1. Formation of a zwitterion (Section 19.2): $$H_2N-CH-\underset{\underset{R}{\mid}}{\overset{\overset{O}{\parallel}}{C}}-OH \rightarrow \overset{+}{H_3N}-CH-\underset{\underset{R}{\mid}}{\overset{\overset{O}{\parallel}}{C}}-O^-$$	Reaction 19.1
2. Conversion of a zwitterion to a cation in an acidic solution (Section 19.2): $$\overset{+}{H_3N}-CH-\underset{\underset{R}{\mid}}{\overset{\overset{O}{\parallel}}{C}}-O^- + H_3O^+ \rightarrow \overset{+}{H_3N}-CH-\underset{\underset{R}{\mid}}{\overset{\overset{O}{\parallel}}{C}}-OH + H_2O$$	Reaction 19.2
3. Conversion of a zwitterion to an anion in a basic solution (Section 19.2): $$\overset{+}{H_3N}-CH-\underset{\underset{R}{\mid}}{\overset{\overset{O}{\parallel}}{C}}-O^- + OH^- \rightarrow H_2N-CH-\underset{\underset{R}{\mid}}{\overset{\overset{O}{\parallel}}{C}}-O^- + H_2O$$	Reaction 19.3
4. Oxidation of cysteine to cystine (Section 19.3): $$\overset{+}{H_3N}-CH-\overset{\overset{O}{\parallel}}{C}-O^- \quad \overset{+}{H_3N}-CH-\overset{\overset{O}{\parallel}}{C}-O^-$$ with CH_2, SH, SH, CH_2 groups $+ (O) \xrightarrow{\text{Oxidation}}$ with CH_2, S, S, CH_2 groups $+ H_2O$	Reaction 19.4
5. Formation of a peptide linkage—general reaction (Section 19.3): $$\overset{+}{H_3N}-CH-\underset{\underset{R}{\mid}}{\overset{\overset{O}{\parallel}}{C}}-O^- + \overset{+}{H_3N}-CH-\underset{\underset{R'}{\mid}}{\overset{\overset{O}{\parallel}}{C}}-O^- \rightarrow \overset{+}{H_3N}-CH-\underset{\underset{R}{\mid}}{\overset{\overset{O}{\parallel}}{C}}-NH-CH-\underset{\underset{R'}{\mid}}{\overset{\overset{O}{\parallel}}{C}}-O^- + H_2O$$	Reaction 19.6
6. Hydrolysis of proteins in acid or base (Section 19.10): $$\text{protein} + H_2O \xrightarrow[\text{OH}^-]{\text{H}^+ \text{ or}} \text{smaller peptides} \xrightarrow[\text{OH}^-]{\text{H}^+ \text{ or}} \text{amino acids}$$	Reaction 19.9

Exercises

The Amino Acids (Section 19.1)

19.1 Draw the structure of hexanoic acid. Label the alpha carbon.

19.2 What functional groups are found in all amino acids?

19.3 Identify the R group of the side chain in the following amino acids that results in the side-chain classification indicated in parentheses (see Table 19.1):

 a. tyrosine (neutral, polar)

 b. glutamate (acidic, polar)

 c. methionine (neutral, nonpolar)

 d. histidine (basic, polar)

 e. cysteine (neutral, polar)

 f. valine (neutral, nonpolar)

19.4 Draw structural formulas for the following amino acids, identify the chiral carbon atom in each one, and circle the four different groups attached to the chiral carbon.

 a. threonine

 b. aspartate

 c. serine

 d. phenylalanine

19.5 Draw structural formulas for the following amino acids, identify the chiral carbon atom in each one, and circle the four different groups attached to the chiral carbon.

 a. alanine

 b. tryptophan

 c. histidine

 d. glutamate

19.6 Isoleucine contains two chiral carbon atoms. Draw the structural formula for isoleucine twice. In the first, identify one of the chiral carbons and circle the four groups attached to it. In the second, identify the other chiral carbon and circle the four groups attached to it.

19.7 Draw Fischer projections representing the D and L forms of the following:

 a. aspartate

 b. phenylalanine

19.8 Draw Fischer projections representing the D and L forms of the following:

 a. cysteine

 b. glutamate

Zwitterions (Section 19.2)

19.9 What is meant by the term *zwitterion?*

19.10 What characteristics indicate that amino acids exist as zwitterions?

19.11 What is meant by the term *isoelectric point?*

19.12 Write structural formulas to show the form the following amino acids would have in a solution with a pH higher than the amino acid isoelectric point:

 a. cysteine

 b. alanine

19.13 Write structural formulas to show the form the following amino acids would have in a solution with a pH lower than the amino acid isoelectric point:

 a. phenylalanine

 b. leucine

19.14 Write ionic equations to show how serine acts as a buffer against the following added ions:

 a. OH^-

 b. H_3O^+

Reactions of Amino Acids (Section 19.3)

19.15 Write two reactions to represent the formation of the two dipeptides that form when valine and serine react.

19.16 Write a complete structural formula and an abbreviated formula for the tripeptide formed from aspartate, cysteine, and valine in which the C-terminal residue is cysteine and the N-terminal residue is valine.

19.17 Write a complete structural formula and an abbreviated formula for the tripeptide formed from tyrosine, serine, and phenylalanine in which the C-terminal residue is serine and the N-terminal residue is phenylalanine.

19.18 Write abbreviated formulas for the six isomeric tripeptides of alanine, phenylalanine, and arginine.

19.19 Write abbreviated formulas for the six isomeric tripeptides of asparagine, glutamate, and proline.

19.20 How many tripeptide isomers that contain one residue each of valine, phenylalanine, and lysine are possible?

19.21 How many tripeptide isomers that contain one glycine residue and two alanine residues are possible?

Important Peptides (Section 19.4)

19.22 What special role does the amino acid cysteine have in the peptides vasopressin and oxytocin?

19.23 What is the difference between a peptide and a protein?

Characteristics of Proteins (Section 19.5)

19.24 Explain why the presence of certain proteins in body fluids such as urine or blood can indicate that cellular damage has occurred in the body.

19.25 Write equations to show how a protein containing both lysine and aspartate could act as a buffer against the following added ions:

a. OH^-

b. H_3O^+

19.26 Explain why a protein is least soluble in an aqueous medium that has a pH equal to the isoelectric point of the protein.

19.27 Wool is a protein used as a textile fiber. Classify the protein of wool into a category of Table 19.4.

19.28 List the eight principal functions of proteins.

19.29 Classify each of the following proteins into one of the eight functional categories of proteins:

a. insulin

b. collagen

c. hemoglobin

d. cytochrome c

e. α-keratin

f. serum albumin

19.30 For each of the following two proteins listed in Table 19.4, predict whether it is more likely to be a globular or a fibrous protein. Explain your reasoning.

a. collagen

b. lactate dehydrogenase

19.31 For each of the following two proteins listed in Table 19.4, predict whether it is more likely to be a globular or a fibrous protein. Explain your reasoning.

a. elastin

b. ceruloplasmin

19.32 Differentiate between simple and conjugated proteins.

19.33 Give one example of a conjugated protein that contains the following prosthetic group:

a. iron

b. lipid

c. phosphate group

d. carbohydrate

e. heme

The Primary Structure of Proteins (Section 19.6)

19.34 Describe what is meant by the term *primary structure of proteins.*

19.35 What type of bonding is present to account for the primary structure of proteins?

19.36 Write the structure for a protein backbone. Make the backbone long enough to attach four R groups symbolizing amino acid side chains.

The Secondary Structure of Proteins (Section 19.7)

19.37 Describe the differences between alpha and beta secondary structures of proteins.

19.38 What type of bonding between amino acid residues is most important in holding a protein or polypeptide in a specific secondary configuration?

19.39 Describe what is meant by "supracoiling" in proteins.

The Tertiary Structure of Proteins (Section 19.8)

19.40 How do hydrogen bonds involved in tertiary protein structures differ from those involved in secondary structures?

19.41 Which amino acids have side-chain groups that can form salt bridges?

19.42 Refer to Table 19.1 and list the type of side-chain interaction expected between the side chains of the following pairs of amino acid residues.

a. tyrosine and glutamine

b. aspartate and lysine

c. leucine and isoleucine

d. phenylalanine and valine

19.43 Which amino acids have side-chain groups that can participate in hydrogen bonding?

19.44 A globular protein in aqueous surroundings contains the following amino acid residues: phenylalanine, methionine, glutamate, lysine, and alanine. Which amino acid side chains would be directed toward the inside of the protein and which would be directed toward the aqueous surroundings?

The Quaternary Structure of Proteins (Section 19.9)

19.45 What is meant by the term *quaternary protein structure*?

19.46 What types of forces give rise to quaternary structure?

19.47 Describe the quaternary protein structure of hemoglobin.

19.48 What is meant by the term *subunit*?

Protein Hydrolysis and Denaturation (Section 19.10)

19.49 What is meant by the term *denaturation*?

19.50 Suppose a sample of a protein is completely hydrolyzed and another sample of the same protein is denatured. Compare the final products of each process.

19.51 As fish is cooked, the tissue changes from a soft consistency to a firm one. A similar change takes place when fish is pickled by soaking it in vinegar (acetic acid). In fact, some people prepare fish for eating by pickling instead of cooking. Propose an explanation of why the two processes give somewhat similar results.

19.52 In what way is the protein in a raw egg the same as that in a cooked egg?

19.53 In addition to emulsifying greasy materials, what other useful function might be served by a detergent used to wash dishes?

19.54 Once cooked, egg whites remain in a solid form. However, egg whites that are beaten to form meringue will partially change back to a jellylike form if allowed to stand for a while. Explain these behaviors using the concept of reversible protein denaturation.

19.55 Lead is a toxic material. What form of the lead is actually the harmful substance?

19.56 Explain how egg white can serve as an emergency antidote for heavy-metal poisoning.

Additional Exercises

19.57 A protein has a molecular weight of about 12,000 u. This protein contains 6.4% (w/w) sulfur in the form of cystine (the cysteine disulfide). How many cystine units are present in the protein?

19.58 Which amino acids could be referred to as derivatives of butanoic acid?

19.59 A Tyndall effect is observed as light is scattered as it passes through a small polypeptide–water mixture with a pH of 6.7. What can be deduced about the polypeptide's isoelectric point from this information?

19.60 What is the conjugate acid for the following zwitterion? What is the conjugate base for it?

$$\overset{+}{H_3N}-\overset{\overset{\displaystyle H}{|}}{\underset{\underset{\displaystyle R}{|}}{C}}-COO^-$$

19.61 The K_a values recorded for alanine are 5.0×10^{-3} and 2.0×10^{-10}. Why are two values recorded? What functional groups do the values correspond to? How many K_a values would be recorded for glutamate?

Allied Health Exam Connection

The following questions are from these sources:

1. *Nursing School Entrance Exam* © 2005, Learning Express, LLC.

2. *McGraw-Hill's Nursing School Entrance Exams* by Thomas A. Evangelist, Tamara B. Orr and Judy Unrein © 2009, The McGraw-Hill Companies, Inc.

3. *NSEE Nursing School Entrance Exams,* 3rd Edition © 2009, Kaplan Publishing.

4. *Cliffs Test Prep: Nursing School Entrance Exams* by Fred N. Grayson © 2004, Wiley Publishing, Inc.

5. *Peterson's Master the Nursing School and Allied Health Entrance Exams,* 18th Edition by Marion F. Gooding © 2008, Peterson's, a Nelnet Company.

19.62 _____ stimulates the smooth muscle of the uterine wall during the labor and delivery process. After delivery, it promotes the ejection of milk.

19.63 What functional groups are found in all amino acids? How many different amino acids are found in naturally occurring proteins?

19.64 Which of the following are true concerning the chemical bond that forms between the carboxyl (RCOOH) group of one amino acid and the amino (RC—NH$_2$) group of another?

 a. The bond is called a peptide bond.

 b. It is formed by inserting a water molecule between them.

 c. It is formed by a dehydration reaction.

 d. A polypeptide has more of these bonds than a protein.

19.65 Rank the following components of hemoglobin in decreasing amounts as would normally be found in a hemoglobin molecule:

 a. Iron atoms

 b. Amino acids

 c. Heme groups

19.66 Describe the quaternary protein structure of hemoglobin.

19.67 Complete degradation of a protein into individual amino acids involves (choose all that are correct):

 a. Removal of a water molecule from between two amino acids

 b. Addition of a water molecule between two amino acids

 c. A hydrolysis reaction

 d. The breaking of peptide linkage

19.68 Which is NOT a characteristic of proteins?

 a. They contain genetic information.

 b. They can act as hormones.

 c. They can catalyze chemical reactions.

 d. They act in cell membrane trafficking.

19.69 Which of the following describes the primary structure of proteins?

 a. The collective shape assumed by all of the chains in a protein containing multiple chains.

 b. The folding of an individual protein molecule.

 c. The regular repeated shape of the protein molecule's backbone.

 d. The sequence of amino acids bonded together by peptide bonds.

Chemistry for Thought

19.70 Some researchers feel that the "high" experienced by runners may be due to the brain's synthesis of peptides. Explain why this theory might be a reasonable explanation.

19.71 Suggest a reason why individuals with the sickle-cell trait might sometimes encounter breathing problems on high-altitude flights.

19.72 In Section 19.2, you learned that amino acids like alanine are crystalline solids with high melting points. However, the ethyl ester of alanine, which has a free NH_2 group, melts at only 87°C. Explain why the ethyl ester melts 200 degrees below the melting point of alanine.

19.73 Why do health care workers wipe a patient's skin with solutions of rubbing alcohol before giving injections?

19.74 Would you expect plasma proteins to be fibrous or globular? Explain.

19.75 Why must the protein drug insulin be given by injection rather than taken by mouth?

19.76 In Figure 19.4, it is noted that animal hair is made of fibrous proteins. What properties of fibrous proteins make hair, fur, and spiderwebs useful?

19.77 Why is it necessary that protein molecules be enormous?

19.78 Name two elements that are found in proteins but are not present in fats, oils, or carbohydrates.

20 Enzymes

© Doug Struthers/Getty Images

Case Study

Myocardial infarction sounded like a word from a foreign language or even a joke—Bob wasn't sure which. How could he, a 34-year-old construction worker, possibly be having a heart attack? When he complained of shoulder pain and nausea at work, his supervisor insisted on taking him to the ER. He had thought his boss was over-reacting, but now Bob realized the supervisor's caution saved his life. At the emergency room, an EKG and tests for the enzyme creatine phosphokinase and the protein troponin confirmed that his symptoms were indeed caused by heart attack. The doctor explained that Bob's genetic inheritance, his poor diet, and his smoking habit formed a deadly combination. In fact, for many men his age, death is the first "symptom" of heart attack. Immediate treatment saved his life. If Bob wanted to live to be an old man, he would need to change his diet and stop smoking.

What resources are available to help people like Bob stop smoking? How do heart attack symptoms differ for men and women? What role do diet and genetics play in cholesterol levels?

Follow-up to this Case Study appears at the end the chapter before the Concept Summary.

Learning Objectives

When you have completed your study of this chapter, you should be able to:

1 Describe the general characteristics of enzymes and explain why enzymes are vital in body chemistry. **(Section 20.1)**

2 Determine the function and/or substrate of an enzyme on the basis of its name. **(Section 20.2)**

3 Identify the general function of cofactors. **(Section 20.3)**

4 Use the lock-and-key theory to explain specificity in enzyme action. **(Section 20.4)**

5 List two ways of describing enzyme activity. **(Section 20.5)**

6 Identify the factors that affect enzyme activity. **(Section 20.6)**

7 Compare the mechanisms of competitive and noncompetitive enzyme inhibition. **(Section 20.7)**

8 Describe the three methods of cellular control over enzyme activity. **(Section 20.8)**

9 Discuss the importance of measuring enzyme levels in the diagnosis of disease. **(Section 20.9)**

The catalytic behavior of proteins acting as enzymes is one of the most important functions performed by cellular proteins. Without catalysts, most cellular reactions would take place much too slowly to support life (see ▶ Figure 20.1). With the exception of a few recently discovered RNA molecules (discussed in Chapter 21) that catalyze their own reactions, all enzymes are globular proteins. Enzymes are the most efficient of all known catalysts; some can increase reaction rates by 10^{20} times that of uncatalyzed reactions.

20.1 General Characteristics of Enzymes

Learning Objective

1. Describe the general characteristics of enzymes and explain why enzymes are vital in body chemistry.

Enzymes are well suited to their essential roles in living organisms in three major ways: They have enormous catalytic power, they are highly specific in the reactions they catalyze, and their activity as catalysts can be regulated.

Catalytic Efficiency

As we know, catalysts increase the rate of chemical reactions but are not used up in the process. Although a catalyst actually participates in a chemical reaction, it is not permanently modified and may be used again and again. Enzymes are true catalysts that speed

Figure 20.1 One miracle of life is that hundreds of chemical reactions take place simultaneously in each living cell; the activity of enzymes in the cells makes it all possible.

enzyme A biomolecule that catalyzes chemical reactions.

Figure 20.2 An energy diagram for a reaction when uncatalyzed and catalyzed.

chemical reactions by lowering activation energies (see ❱ Figure 20.2) and allowing reactions to achieve equilibrium more rapidly.

Many of the important enzyme-catalyzed reactions are similar to the reactions we studied in the chapters on organic chemistry: ester hydrolysis, alcohol oxidation, and so on. However, laboratory conditions cannot match what happens when these reactions are carried out in the body; enzymes cause such reactions to proceed under mild pH and temperature conditions. In addition, enzyme catalysis within the body can accomplish in seconds reactions that ordinarily take weeks or even months under laboratory conditions.

The influence of enzymes on the rates of reactions essential to life is truly amazing. A good example is the need to move carbon dioxide, a waste product of cellular respiration, out of the body. Before this can be accomplished, the carbon dioxide must be combined with water to form carbonic acid:

$$CO_2 + H_2O \xrightarrow{\text{carbonic anhydrase}} H_2CO_3 \tag{20.1}$$

In the absence of the appropriate enzyme, carbonic anhydrase, the formation of carbonic acid takes place much too slowly to support the required exchange of carbon dioxide between the blood and the lungs. But in the presence of carbonic anhydrase, this vital reaction proceeds rapidly. Each molecule of the enzyme can catalyze the formation of carbonic acid at the rate of 36 million molecules per minute.

Specificity

Enzyme specificity is a second characteristic that is important in life processes. Unlike other catalysts, enzymes are often quite specific in the type of reaction they catalyze and even the particular substance that will be involved in the reaction. For example, strong acids catalyze the hydrolysis of any amide, the dehydration of any alcohol, and a variety of other processes. However, the enzyme urease catalyzes only the hydrolysis of a single amide, urea (Reaction 20.2 and ❱ Figure 20.3):

$$\underset{\underset{\displaystyle \parallel}{\overset{\displaystyle O}{}}}{H_2N-C-NH_2} + H_2O \xrightarrow{\text{urease}} CO_2 + 2NH_3 \tag{20.2}$$

Figure 20.3 The hydrolysis of urea catalyzed by urease.

① The enzyme urease is added to a urea solution containing the indicator phenolphthalein.

② As urea is hydrolyzed, forming ammonia, the indicator turns pink. How else might the presence of ammonia be detected?

© Mark Slabaugh

absolute specificity The characteristic of an enzyme that it acts on one and only one substance.

relative specificity The characteristic of an enzyme that it acts on several structurally related substances.

This is an example of **absolute specificity,** the catalyzing of the reaction of one and only one substance. Other enzymes display **relative specificity** by catalyzing the reaction of structurally related substances. For example, the lipases hydrolyze lipids, proteases split up

proteins, and phosphatases hydrolyze phosphate esters. **Stereochemical specificity** extends even to enantiomers: D-amino acid oxidase will not catalyze the reactions of L-amino acids.

stereochemical specificity The characteristic of an enzyme that it is able to distinguish between stereoisomers.

Regulation

A third significant property of enzymes is that their catalytic behavior can be regulated. Even though each living cell contains thousands of different molecules that could react with each other in an almost unlimited number of ways, only a relatively small number of these possible reactions take place because of the enzymes present. The cell controls the rates of these reactions and the amount of any given product formed by regulating the action of the enzymes.

20.2 Enzyme Nomenclature and Classification

Learning Objective

2. Determine the function and/or substrate of an enzyme on the basis of its name.

Some of the earliest discovered enzymes were given names ending with -*in* to indicate their protein composition. For example, three of the digestive enzymes that catalyze protein hydrolysis are named pepsin, trypsin, and chymotrypsin.

The large number of enzymes now known has made it desirable to adopt a systematic nomenclature system known as the Enzyme Commission (EC) system. Enzymes are grouped into six major classes on the basis of the reaction catalyzed (see ▶ Table 20.1).

TABLE 20.1 The EC Classification of Enzymes

Group Name	Type of Reaction Catalyzed
Oxidoreductases	Oxidation–reduction reactions
Transferases	Transfer of functional groups
Hydrolases	Hydrolysis reactions
Lyases	Addition to double bonds or the reverse of that reaction
Isomerases	Isomerization reactions
Ligases	Formation of bonds with ATP cleavage[a]

[a]ATP is discussed in Chapter 22.

In the EC system, each enzyme has an unambiguous (and often long) systematic name that specifies the **substrate** (substance acted on), the functional group acted on, and the type of reaction catalyzed. All EC names end in -*ase*. The hydrolysis of urea provides a typical example:

substrate The substance that undergoes a chemical change catalyzed by an enzyme.

$$H_2N-\overset{\overset{\displaystyle O}{\|}}{C}-NH_2 + H_2O \xrightarrow{\text{enzyme}} CO_2 + 2NH_3 \qquad (20.3)$$

IEC name: urea amidohydrolase
Substrate: urea
Functional group: amide
Type of reaction: hydrolysis

Enzymes are also assigned common names, which are usually shorter and more convenient. Common names are derived by adding -*ase* to the name of the substrate or to a combination of the substrate name and type of reaction. For example, urea amidohydrolase is assigned the common name urease:

Substrate: urea
Common name: urea + ase = urease

Enzymes and Disease

A number of hereditary diseases appear to result from the absence of enzymes or from the presence of altered enzymes. These diseases are often referred to as **inborn errors of metabolism** (the term *metabolism* refers to all reactions occurring within a living organism).

An example of an inborn error of lipid metabolism is Gaucher's disease, characterized by symptoms that include an enlarged spleen and an enlarged liver. A large amount of glucocerebroside is found in fat deposits in these organs. Normally, these organs contain β-glucosidase, an enzyme that catalyzes the degradation of glucocerebrosides (Section 18.7), so that only small amounts of these lipids are normally present. However, the enzyme activity is impaired in Gaucher's disease, and the glucocerebrosides accumulate. Most people with the adult form of the disease do not require treatment; however, the infantile form produces mental retardation and often death.

The following table lists some diseases caused by enzyme deficiencies.

Disease	Deficient Enzyme
Albinism	tyrosinase
Galactosemia	galactose 1-phosphate uridyltransferase
Gaucher's disease	β-glucosidase
Homocystinuria	cystathionine synthetase
Maple syrup urine disease	amino acid decarboxylase
Methemoglobinemia	methemoglobin reductase
Niemann-Pick disease	sphingomyelinase
Phenylketonuria (PKU)	phenylalanine hydroxylase
Tay-Sachs disease	hexosaminidase A

An albino grey squirrel, showing a lack of pigmentation in the eyes, skin, and hair.

Microscopic view of a section of human liver with Gaucher's disease.

inborn error of metabolism A disease in which a genetic change causes a deficiency of a particular protein, often an enzyme.

The enzyme name *alcohol dehydrogenase* is an example of a common name derived from both the name of the substrate and the type of reaction:

Substrate: alcohol (ethyl alcohol)
Reaction type: dehydrogenation (removal of hydrogen)
Common name: alcohol dehydrogenation + ase = alcohol dehydrogenase

Throughout this text, we will refer to most enzymes by their accepted common names.

▶ **LEARNING CHECK 20.1** Predict the substrates for the following enzymes:

a. maltase
b. peptidase
c. glucose 6-phosphate isomerase

20.3 Enzyme Cofactors

Learning Objective

3. Identify the general function of cofactors.

In Section 19.5, we learned that proteins may be simple (containing only amino acid residues) or conjugated with a prosthetic group present. Many enzymes are simple proteins, whereas many others function only in the presence of specific nonprotein molecules or metal ions. If these nonprotein components are tightly bound to and form an integral part of the enzyme structure, they are true prosthetic groups. Often, however, a nonprotein component is only weakly bound to the enzyme and is easily separated from the protein structure. This type of nonprotein component is referred to as a **cofactor.** When the cofactor is an organic substance, it is called a **coenzyme.** The cofactor may also be an inorganic ion (usually a metal ion). The protein portion of enzymes requiring a cofactor is called the **apoenzyme.** Thus, the combination of an apoenzyme and a cofactor produces an active enzyme:

$$\text{apoenzyme} + \text{cofactor (coenzyme or inorganic ion)} \rightarrow \text{active enzyme} \qquad (20.4)$$

Typical inorganic ions are metal ions such as Mg^{2+}, Zn^{2+}, and Fe^{2+}. For example, the enzyme carbonic anhydrase functions only when Zn^{2+} is present, and rennin needs Ca^{2+} in order to curdle milk. Numerous other metal ions are essential for proper enzyme function in humans; hence, they are required for good health.

Like metal ions, the small organic molecules that act as coenzymes bind reversibly to an enzyme and are essential for its activity. An interesting feature of coenzymes is that many of them are formed in the body from vitamins (see ▶ Table 20.2), which explains why it is necessary to have certain vitamins in the diet for good health. For example, the coenzyme nicotinamide adenine dinucleotide (NAD^+), which is a necessary part of some enzyme-catalyzed oxidation–reduction reactions, is formed from the vitamin precursor nicotinamide. Reaction 20.5 shows the participation of NAD^+ in the oxidation of lactate by the enzyme lactate dehydrogenase (LDH). Like other cofactors, NAD^+ is written

cofactor A nonprotein molecule or ion required by an enzyme for catalytic activity.

coenzyme An organic molecule required by an enzyme for catalytic activity.

apoenzyme A catalytically inactive protein formed by removal of the cofactor from an active enzyme.

TABLE 20.2 Vitamins and their Coenzyme Forms

Vitamin	Coenzyme Form	Function
biotin	biocytin	Carboxyl group removal or transfer
folacin	tetrahydrofolic acid	One-carbon group transfer
lipoic acid	lipoamide	Acyl group transfer
niacin	nicotinamide adenine dinucleotide (NAD^+)	Hydrogen transfer
	nicotinamide adenine dinucleotide phosphate ($NADP^+$)	Hydrogen transfer
pantothenic acid	coenzyme A (CoA)	Acyl group carrier
pyridoxal, pyridoxamine, pyridoxine (B_6 group)	pyridoxal phosphate	Amino group transfer
riboflavin	flavin mononucleotide (FMN) flavin adenine dinucleotide (FAD)	Hydrogen transfer Hydrogen transfer
thiamin (B_1)	thiamin pyrophosphate (TPP)	Aldehyde group transfer
vitamin B_{12}	coenzyme B_{12}	Shift of hydrogen atoms between adjacent carbon atoms; methyl group transfer

ACE Inhibitors (Angiotensin-Converting Enzyme Inhibitors)

An important part of most medical checkups is the measurement of blood pressure. The reason for this is to detect the presence of hypertension or higher-than-normal blood pressure. Hypertension, a widespread health problem in our society, can cause other harmful health conditions such as kidney disease. The presence in the body of an octapeptide called angiostensin II causes high blood pressure by constricting the muscles that surround blood vessels. With the blood vessels constricted, the heart must work harder and exert higher pressure to pump blood through the cardiovascular system.

Angiotensin II is produced in the body by the enzyme-catalyzed conversion of angiotensin I to angiotensin II. The enzymes that catalyze the conversion are called angiotensin-converting enzymes or ACE. Doctors often administer angiotensin-converting enzyme inhibitors (ACE inhibitors) to patients with high blood pressure. ACE inhibitors lower blood pressure by hindering the activity of ACE which, in turn, slows the production of angiotensin II and consequently alleviates vascular constriction. Once the blood vessels dilate, the heart does not have to work as hard to pump the blood through the vascular system. In addition, ACE inhibitors have been shown to improve the health (and alleviate symptoms) of patients with chronic migraines, coronary artery disease, heart failure, and those that have had a heart attack.

There are several ACE inhibitors available with slight differences among them. Some function by blocking the activity of ACE in the blood while others do so in tissue instead. However, there is not yet any clear evidence to indicate that one type of ACE inhibitor is superior to another.

As with any medication, side effects and drug interactions can occur. Side effects include: dizziness, lightheadedness (caused by low blood pressure), changes in taste, headaches, loss of appetite, rash, and cough. More seriously, ACE inhibitors can cause elevated blood-potassium levels, angioedema, or, if taken while pregnant, birth defects. Drug interactions are also possible. For example, the effectiveness of ACE inhibitors may be reduced by the use of nonsteroidal anti-inflammatory medications such as ibuprofen. Therefore, it is important to fully discuss with your health professional the benefits and risks of taking an ACE inhibitor.

Checking blood pressure is an important part of a medical examination.

Drug blister packs are sometimes marked with days of the week to assist the user.

separately from the enzyme so that the change in its structure may be shown and to emphasize that the enzyme and cofactor are easily separated.

$$\underset{\text{lactate}}{CH_3-\overset{\overset{\displaystyle OH}{|}}{CH}-COO^-} + NAD^+ \underset{}{\overset{\text{lactate}}{\underset{\text{dehydrogenase}}{\rightleftharpoons}}} \underset{\text{pyruvate}}{CH_3-\overset{\overset{\displaystyle O}{||}}{C}-COO^-} + NADH + H^+ \quad (20.5)$$

We can see from the reaction that the coenzyme NAD^+ is essential because it is the actual oxidizing agent. NAD^+ is typical of coenzymes that often aid in the transfer of chemical groups from one compound to another. In Reaction 20.5, NAD^+ accepts hydrogen from lactate and will transfer it to other compounds in subsequent reactions. In Chapter 22, we will discuss in greater detail several coenzymes that act as shuttle systems in the exchange of chemical substances among various biochemical pathways.

20.4 The Mechanism of Enzyme Action

Learning Objective

4. Use the lock-and-key theory to explain specificity in enzyme action.

Although enzymes differ widely in structure and specificity, a general theory has been proposed to account for their catalytic behavior. Because enzyme molecules are large compared with the molecules whose reactions they catalyze (substrate molecules), it has been proposed that substrate and enzyme molecules come in contact and interact over only a small region of the enzyme surface. This region of interaction is called the **active site.**

The binding of a substrate molecule to the active site of an enzyme may occur through hydrophobic attraction, hydrogen bonding, and/or ionic bonding. The complex formed when a substrate and an enzyme bond is called the enzyme–substrate (ES) complex. Once this complex is formed, the conversion of substrate (S) to product (P) may take place:

active site The location on an enzyme where a substrate is bound and catalysis occurs.

General reaction:

$$E + S \rightleftharpoons ES \longrightarrow E + P \qquad (20.6)$$

enzyme substrate enzyme– enzyme product
 substrate
 complex

Specific example:

$$\text{Sucrase} + \text{sucrose} \rightleftharpoons \left\{ \begin{array}{c} \text{sucrase–} \\ \text{sucrose} \\ \text{complex} \end{array} \right\} \longrightarrow \text{sucrase} + \text{glucose} + \text{fructose} \qquad (20.7)$$

enzyme substrate enzyme products

The chemical transformation of the substrate occurs at the active site, usually aided by enzyme functional groups that participate directly in the making and breaking of chemical bonds. After chemical conversion has occurred, the product is released from the active site, and the enzyme is free for another round of catalysis.

An extension of the theory of ES complex formation is used to explain the high specificity of enzyme activity. According to the **lock-and-key theory,** enzyme surfaces will accommodate only those substrates having specific shapes and sizes. Thus, only specific substrates "fit" a given enzyme and can form complexes with it (see ▶ Figure 20.4A).

A limitation of the lock-and-key theory is the implication that enzyme conformations are fixed or rigid. However, research results suggest that the active sites of some enzymes are not rigid. This is taken into account in a modification of the lock-and-key theory known as the **induced-fit theory,** which proposes that enzymes have somewhat flexible conformations that may adapt to incoming substrates. The active site has a shape that becomes complementary to that of the substrate only after the substrate is bound (see ▶ Figure 20.4B).

lock-and-key theory A theory of enzyme specificity proposing that a substrate has a shape fitting that of the enzyme's active site, as a key fits a lock.

induced-fit theory A theory of enzyme action proposing that the conformation of an enzyme changes to accommodate an incoming substrate.

A In the **lock-and-key model**, the rigid enzyme and substrate have matching shapes.

B In the **induced-fit model**, the flexible enzyme changes shape to match the substrate.

Figure 20.4 Models representing enzyme action.

20.5 Enzyme Activity

Learning Objective

5. List two ways of describing enzyme activity.

enzyme activity The rate at which an enzyme catalyzes a reaction.

turnover number The number of molecules of substrate acted on by one molecule of enzyme per minute.

Enzyme activity refers in general to the catalytic ability of an enzyme to increase the rate of a reaction. The amazing rate (36 million molecules per minute) at which one molecule of carbonic anhydrase converts carbon dioxide to carbonic acid was mentioned earlier. This rate, called the **turnover number,** is one of the highest known for enzyme systems. More common turnover numbers for enzymes are closer to 10^3/min, or 1000 reactions per minute. Nevertheless, even such low numbers dramatize the speed with which a small number of enzyme molecules can transform a large number of substrate molecules. ▶ Table 20.3 gives the turnover numbers of several enzymes.

TABLE 20.3 Examples of Enzyme Turnover Numbers

Enzyme	Turnover Number (per minute)	Reaction Catalyzed
carbonic anhydrase	36,000,000	$CO_2 + H_2O \rightleftharpoons H_2CO_3$
catalase	5,600,000	$2H_2O_2 \rightleftharpoons 2H_2O + O_2$
cholinesterase	1,500,000	Hydrolysis of acetylcholine
chymotrypsin	6,000	Hydrolysis of specific peptide bonds
DNA polymerase I	900	Addition of nucleotide monomers to DNA chains
lactate dehydrogenase	60,000	pyruvate + NADH + H$^+$ $\rightleftharpoons$ lactate + NAD$^+$
penicillinase	120,000	Hydrolysis of penicillin

Experiments that measure enzyme activity are called *enzyme assays.* Assays for blood enzymes are routinely performed in clinical laboratories. Such assays are often done by determining how fast the characteristic color of a product forms or the color of a substrate decreases. Reactions in which protons (H$^+$) are produced or used up can be followed by measuring how fast the pH of the reacting mixture changes with time.

Because some clinical assays are done many times a day, the procedures for running the assays have been automated and computerized. The determined enzyme activity levels are usually reported in terms of **enzyme international units (IU),** which define enzyme activity as the amount of enzyme that will convert a specified amount of substrate to a product within a certain time.

enzyme international unit (IU) A quantity of enzyme that catalyzes the conversion of 1 μmol of substrate per minute under specified conditions.

One standard international unit (1 IU) is the quantity of enzyme that catalyzes the conversion of 1 micromole (μmol) of substrate per minute under specified reaction conditions. Thus, unlike the turnover number, which is a constant characteristic for one molecule of a particular enzyme, international units measure how much enzyme is present. For example, an enzyme preparation with an activity corresponding to 40 IU contains a concentration of enzyme 40 times greater than the standard. This is a useful way to measure enzyme activity because the level of enzyme activity compared with normal activity is significant in the diagnosis of many diseases (Section 20.9).

▶ **LEARNING CHECK 20.2** Differentiate between the terms *turnover number* and *enzyme international unit.*

20.6 Factors Affecting Enzyme Activity

Learning Objective

6. Identify the factors that affect enzyme activity.

Several factors affect the rate of enzyme-catalyzed reactions. The most important factors are enzyme concentration, substrate concentration, temperature, and pH. In this section, we'll look at each of these factors in some detail. In Section 20.7, we'll consider another very important factor, the presence of enzyme inhibitors.

Enzyme Concentration

In an enzyme-catalyzed reaction, the concentration of enzyme is normally very low compared with the concentration of substrate. When the enzyme concentration is increased, the concentration of ES also increases in compliance with reaction rate theory:

$$E + S \rightleftharpoons ES$$
increased [E] gives more [ES]

Thus, the availability of more enzyme molecules to catalyze a reaction leads to the formation of more ES and a higher reaction rate. The effect of enzyme concentration on the rate of a reaction is shown in ❯ Figure 20.5. As the figure indicates, the rate of a reaction is directly proportional to the concentration of the enzyme—that is, if the enzyme concentration is doubled, the rate of conversion of substrate to product is also doubled.

Figure 20.5 The dependence of reaction rate (initial velocity) on enzyme concentration.

Substrate Concentration

As shown in ❯ Figure 20.6, the concentration of substrate significantly influences the rate of an enzyme-catalyzed reaction. Initially, the rate is responsive to increases in substrate concentration. However, at a certain concentration, the rate levels out and remains constant. This maximum rate (symbolized by V_{max}) occurs because the enzyme is saturated with substrate and cannot work any faster under the conditions imposed.

Temperature

Enzyme-catalyzed reactions, like all chemical reactions, have rates that increase with temperature (see ❯ Figure 20.7). However, because enzymes are proteins, there is a temperature limit beyond which the enzyme becomes vulnerable to denaturation. Thus, every enzyme-catalyzed reaction has an **optimum temperature,** usually in the range 25°C–40°C. Above or below that value, the reaction rate will be lower. This effect is illustrated in Figure 20.7.

optimum temperature The temperature at which enzyme activity is highest.

The Effect of pH

The graph of enzyme activity as a function of pH is somewhat similar to the behavior as a function of temperature (see ❯ Figure 20.8). Notice in Figure 20.8 that an enzyme is most effective in a narrow pH range and is less active at pH values lower or higher than this optimum. This variation in enzyme activity with changing pH may be due to the influence

Figure 20.6 The dependence of reaction rate (initial velocity) on substrate concentration.

Figure 20.7 The effect of temperature on enzyme-catalyzed reaction rates.

Figure 20.8 A typical plot of the effect of pH on reaction rate.

optimum pH The pH at which enzyme activity is highest.

Figure 20.9 Pickles are prepared under acidic conditions. Why do they resist spoilage?

© Mark Slabaugh

of pH on acidic and basic side chains within the active site. In addition, most enzymes are denatured by pH extremes. The resistance of pickled foods (see ❯ Figure 20.9) to spoilage is due to the enzymes of microorganisms being less active under acidic conditions.

Many enzymes have an **optimum pH** near 7, the pH of most biological fluids. However, the optimum pH of a few is considerably higher or lower than 7. For example, pepsin, a digestive enzyme of the stomach, shows maximum activity at a pH of about 1.5, the pH of gastric fluids. ❯ Table 20.4 lists optimum pH values for several enzymes.

TABLE 20.4 Examples of Optimum pH for Enzyme Activity

Enzyme	Source	Optimum pH
pepsin	Gastric mucosa	1.5
β-glucosidase	Almond	4.5
sucrase	Intestine	6.2
urease	Soybean	6.8
catalase	Liver	7.3
succinate dehydrogenase	Beef heart	7.6
arginase	Beef liver	9.0
alkaline phosphatase	Bone	9.5

❯ **LEARNING CHECK 20.3** Indicate how each of the following affects the rate of an enzyme-catalyzed reaction:

a. Increase in enzyme concentration
b. Increase in substrate concentration
c. Increase in temperature
d. Increase in pH

20.7 Enzyme Inhibition

Learning Objective

7. Compare the mechanisms of competitive and noncompetitive enzyme inhibition.

enzyme inhibitor A substance that decreases the activity of an enzyme.

An **enzyme inhibitor** is any substance that can decrease the rate of an enzyme-catalyzed reaction. An understanding of enzyme inhibition is important for several reasons. First, the characteristic function of many poisons and some medicines is to inhibit one or more enzymes and to decrease the rates of the reactions they catalyze. Second, some substances normally found in cells inhibit specific enzyme-catalyzed reactions and thereby provide a means for the internal regulation of cellular metabolism.

Enzyme inhibitors are classified into two categories, reversible and irreversible, on the basis of how they behave at the molecular level.

Irreversible Inhibition

An irreversible inhibitor forms a covalent bond with a specific functional group of the enzyme and as a result renders the enzyme inactive. A number of very deadly poisons act as irreversible inhibitors.

The cyanide ion (CN^-) is an example of an irreversible enzyme inhibitor. It is extremely toxic and acts very rapidly. The cyanide ion interferes with the operation of an iron-containing enzyme called cytochrome oxidase. The ability of cells to use oxygen depends on the action of cytochrome oxidase. When the cyanide ion reacts with the iron of this enzyme, it forms a very stable complex (Reaction 20.8), and the enzyme can no longer function properly. As a result, cell respiration stops, causing death in a matter of minutes.

Enzyme Discovery Heats Up

Enzymes provide the same advantages to a commercial process as they do to a living organism. They are highly specific and extremely fast-acting catalysts. The use of enzymes in commercial industrial processes is developing rapidly and has a potentially bright future because of the existence of enzymes in microorganisms that thrive in extreme environments. Such enzymes have been called **extremozymes** because of the extreme conditions under which they function. These conditions include temperatures greater than 100°C in hot springs and deep-sea thermal vents, or below 0°C in Antarctic waters. Some enzymes function under immense pressure on the ocean floor, whereas others are unaffected by extremes of pH and salt concentrations in solution.

One goal of current research is to obtain useful enzymes from extremophiles, the microbes that function in these extreme environments. The process used by one company to obtain commercially useful enzymes consists of the following steps:

1. Biomass samples are obtained from the extreme environment.
2. DNA is extracted from the biomass and purified.
3. Fragments of the purified DNA are cloned to produce large libraries of genes.
4. The cloned genes are screened to find any that are coded to produce enzymes.
5. The DNA sequence is determined for any genes that are coded to produce enzymes.
6. The DNA sequence for enzyme-coded genes is cloned to produce large amounts of the gene, which in turn is inserted into organisms and used to produce large amounts of the enzyme.
7. The enzyme is optimized by random DNA mutations.

The last step is particularly interesting. An organism's DNA is randomly mutated over several generations. Offspring from each generation are selected that produce a specific enzyme with activity greater than or different from that of the enzyme from the previous generation. This technique, known as *mutagenesis,* is used to alter enzymes so they will perform new tasks or do old ones better.

Because extremozymes function under conditions that are so far removed from normal, research into their behavior is intense. One of the research goals is to develop ways to use enzyme catalysis in industrial processes that require extreme temperatures or pH. One example is the current use of heat-stable DNA polymerase in the DNA replication technique called the polymerase chain reaction (Section 21.3). Another research goal is to develop enzyme-catalyzed industrial processes that don't generate large amounts of undesirable waste material. For example, an esterase that catalyzes the hydrolysis of the antibiotic intermediate *p*-nitrobenzyl ester was developed. That hydrolysis reaction was usually done using catalytic zinc and organic solvents in a process that generated a lot of industrial waste. Some other applications being considered are the use of hydrolases at high temperature in the food-processing industry and the use of heat-stable enzymes in the production of corn syrup.

Extremozymes enable microorganisms to survive in the harsh environment of deep-sea thermal vents.

$$\underset{\substack{\text{cytochrome}\\\text{oxidase}}}{\text{Cyt—Fe}^{3+}} + \underset{\substack{\text{cyanide}\\\text{ion}}}{\text{CN}^-} \rightarrow \underset{\text{stable complex}}{\text{Cyt—Fe—CN}^{2+}} \qquad (20.8)$$

extremozyme A nickname for certain enzymes isolated from microorganisms that thrive in extreme environments.

Any antidote for cyanide poisoning must be administered quickly. One antidote is sodium thiosulfate (the "hypo" used in the developing of photographic film). This substance converts the cyanide ion to a thiocyanate ion that does not bind to the iron of cytochrome oxidase.

$$\underset{\text{cyanide}}{\text{CN}^-} + \underset{\text{thiosulfate}}{\text{S}_2\text{O}_3^{2-}} \rightarrow \underset{\text{thiocyanate}}{\text{SCN}^-} + \underset{\text{sulfite}}{\text{SO}_3^{2-}} \qquad (20.9)$$

The toxicity of heavy metals such as mercury and lead is due to their ability to render the protein part of enzymes ineffective. These metals act by combining with the —SH groups found on many enzymes (Reaction 20.10). In addition, as we learned in Chapter 19, metals can cause nonspecific protein denaturation. Both mercury and lead poisoning can cause permanent neurological damage.

$$\text{active enzyme} \qquad \qquad \text{inactive enzyme}$$

$$(20.10)$$

Heavy-metal poisoning is treated by administering chelating agents—substances that combine with the metal ions and hold them very tightly. One effective antidote is the chelating agent ethylenediaminetetraacetic acid, or EDTA, which will chelate all heavy metals except mercury.

The calcium salt of EDTA is administered intravenously. In the body, calcium ions of the salt are displaced by heavy-metal ions, such as lead, that bind to the chelate more tightly. The lead–EDTA complex is soluble in body fluids and is excreted in the urine.

$$\text{CaEDTA}^{2-} + \text{Pb}^{2+} \rightarrow \text{PbEDTA}^{2-} + \text{Ca}^{2+} \qquad (20.11)$$

Not all enzyme inhibitors act as poisons toward the body; some, in fact, are useful therapeutic agents. Sulfa drugs and the group of compounds known as penicillins are two well-known families of **antibiotics** that inhibit specific enzymes essential to the life processes of bacteria. The first penicillin was discovered in 1928 by Alexander Fleming. He noticed that the bacteria on a culture plate did not grow in the vicinity of a mold that had contaminated the culture; the mold was producing penicillin. The general penicillin structure is shown in ▶ Table 20.5, along with four widely used forms. Penicillins interfere with transpeptidase, an enzyme that is important in bacterial cell wall construction. The inability to form strong cell walls prevents the bacteria from surviving.

antibiotic A substance produced by one microorganism that kills or inhibits the growth of other microorganisms.

TABLE 20.5 Four Widely Used Penicillins

General penicillin structure

Name	Year Marketed	Side Chain (R—)	Comments
Penicillin G	1943	benzyl CH₂— group	Usually given by injection
Penicillin V	1953	phenoxymethyl O—CH₂— group	An oral penicillin; resistant to stomach hydrolysis
Methicillin	1960	2,6-dimethoxyphenyl (OCH₃, OCH₃) group	Given by injection
Ampicillin	1961	α-aminobenzyl CH—NH₂ group	Given by injection or taken orally; effective against a broad spectrum of organisms

Avoiding Mercury in Fish

Most healthful diets extol the wisdom of eating fish. After all, fish contain high-quality protein and other essential nutrients, are low in saturated fat, and contain omega-3 fatty acids. However, a growing concern in the United States is that the health benefits of eating fish might be undermined by the level of mercury contained in some types. Mercury, especially in the form of compounds, is recognized as a powerful neural toxin. Women who are pregnant, women who may become pregnant, women who are nursing infants, and young children are especially susceptible to the negative side effects of dietary mercury. Unfortunately, this is the group of people who would benefit most from consuming fish as part of a well-balanced diet.

Women who eat a large amount of fish during pregnancy, or even as little as a single serving of highly contaminated fish, run the risk of exposing their developing child to excessive levels of mercury. Compounds of the toxic metal can cross the placenta and harm the brain and nervous system of the rapidly developing child. Exposure to mercury while in the womb has been associated with learning deficiencies, delayed mental development, and other neurological problems in children.

Mercury occurs naturally in the environment and is emitted from sources such as coal-fired power plants. Mercury that falls to earth can accumulate in mud and sediments of streams and oceans where it can be converted by microorganisms to compounds such as methylmercury. These compounds find their way into fish, and since fish store mercury in their bodies because they are incapable of excreting it, the mercury content is amplified when larger fish eat smaller fish in the food chain. Thus, the greatest accumulations are found in fish that are highest in the food chain. Fish like tuna, sea bass, and halibut show some of the worst contamination as a result of this process.

One interpretation of a survey conducted by the U.S. Environmental Protection Agency (EPA), www.epa.gov/ost/fish, found that more than half the fish in the nation's lakes and reservoirs

contain mercury compounds at levels that exceed government standards for children and for women of child-bearing age.

The following guidelines are helpful in deciding what and how much fish to eat weekly. By following these guidelines, individuals are able to reap the benefits of eating fish, while avoiding excessive exposure to the harmful effects of mercury.

- Avoid shark, swordfish, king mackerel, or tilefish.
- Eat up to 12 ounces (two average meals) a week of the following fish and shellfish that are lower in mercury: Shrimp, canned light tuna, salmon, pollock, and catfish. Albacore ("white") tuna has more mercury than canned light tuna so no more than 6 ounces (an average meal) of albacore tune should be eaten per week.
- Check local advisories about the safety of fish caught in local lakes, rivers, and coastal areas. If no advice is available, eat up to 6 ounces per week of fish caught in these waters, but don't consume any other fish during that week.

For more information about choosing fish that are low in mercury and that are obtained using sustainable fishing practices, check out Seafood Watch guides at www.montereybayaquarium.org/cr/seafoodwatch.aspx, also available as an iPhone app. These seafood guides are available by region in a wallet-sized foldout that makes a perfect grocery store shopping companion.

Also helpful:

Mercury Pollution from Power Plants by State
 http://ewg.org/node/8150
How Much Tuna Can You Eat Safely?—Tuna Calculator
 http://ewg.org/tunacalculator

Fish is an important part of a healthful diet.

There are now guidelines limiting the amount of tuna that should be consumed in a weekly period.

Reversible Inhibition

A reversible inhibitor (in contrast to one that is irreversible) reversibly binds to an enzyme. An equilibrium is established; therefore, the inhibitor can be removed from the enzyme by shifting the equilibrium:

$$E + I \rightleftharpoons EI$$

There are two types of reversible inhibitors: competitive and noncompetitive.

A **competitive inhibitor** binds to the active site of an enzyme and thus "competes" with substrate molecules for the active site. Competitive inhibitors often have molecular structures that are similar to the normal substrate of the enzyme. The competitive inhibition of succinate dehydrogenase by malonate is a classic example. Succinate dehydrogenase catalyzes the oxidation of the substrate succinate to form fumarate by transferring two hydrogens to the coenzyme FAD:

$$
\begin{array}{c}
\text{COO}^- \\
| \\
\text{CH}_2 \\
| \\
\text{CH}_2 \\
| \\
\text{COO}^- \\
\text{succinate}
\end{array}
+ \text{FAD}
\xrightarrow{\text{succinate dehydrogenase}}
\begin{array}{c}
\text{COO}^- \\
| \\
\text{CH} \\
|| \\
\text{HC} \\
| \\
\text{COO}^- \\
\text{fumarate}
\end{array}
+ \text{FADH}_2
\qquad (20.12)
$$

Malonate, having a structure similar to succinate, competes for the active site of succinate dehydrogenase and thus inhibits the enzyme:

$$
\begin{array}{c}
\text{COO}^- \\
| \\
\text{CH}_2 \\
| \\
\text{CH}_2 \\
| \\
\text{COO}^- \\
\text{succinate}
\end{array}
\qquad
\begin{array}{c}
\text{COO}^- \\
| \\
\text{CH}_2 \\
| \\
\text{COO}^- \\
\text{malonate}
\end{array}
$$

The action of sulfa drugs on bacteria is another example of competitive enzyme inhibition. Folic acid, a substance needed for growth by some disease-causing bacteria, is normally synthesized within the bacteria by a chemical process that requires p-aminobenzoic acid. Because sulfanilamide, the first sulfa drug, resembles p-aminobenzoic acid and competes with it for the active site of the bacterial enzyme involved, it can prevent bacterial growth (see ▶ Figure 20.10). This is possible because the enzyme binds readily to either of these

Figure 20.10 Structural relationships of sulfanilamide, p-aminobenzoic acid, and folic acid.

molecules. Therefore, the introduction of large quantities of sulfanilamide into a patient's body causes most of the active sites to be bound to the wrong (from the bacterial viewpoint) substrate. Thus, the synthesis of folic acid is stopped or slowed, and the bacteria are prevented from multiplying. Meanwhile, the normal body defenses work to destroy them.

Human beings also require folic acid, but they get it from their diet. Consequently, sulfa drugs exert no toxic effect on humans. However, one danger of sulfa drugs, or of any antibiotic, is that excessive amounts can destroy important intestinal bacteria that perform many symbiotic, life-sustaining functions. Although sulfa drugs have largely been replaced by antibiotics such as the penicillins and tetracyclines, some are still used in treating certain bacterial infections, such as those occurring in the urinary tract.

The nature of competitive inhibition is represented in ▶ Figure 20.11. There is competition between the substrate and the inhibitor for the active site. Once the inhibitor combines with the enzyme, the active site is blocked, preventing further catalytic action.

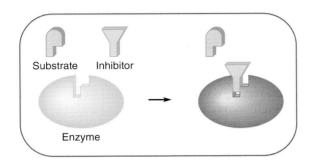

Substrate Inhibitor

Enzyme

Figure 20.11 The behavior of competitive inhibitors. The active site is occupied by the inhibitor, and the substrate is prevented from bonding.

Competitive inhibition can be reversed by increasing the concentration of substrate and letting Le Châtelier's principle operate. This is illustrated by the following equilibria that would exist in a solution containing enzyme (E), substrate (S), and competitive inhibitor (I):

$$\text{equilibrium 1:} \quad E + S \xrightleftharpoons{\text{Increasing [S]}} ES$$

$$\text{equilibrium 2:} \quad E + I \underset{\text{Decreasing [E]}}{\rightleftharpoons} EI$$

If the concentration of substrate is increased, then according to Le Châtelier's principle, the first equilibrium should shift to the right. As it does, the concentration of enzyme decreases, which causes equilibrium 2 to shift to the left. The overall effect is that the concentration of ES has increased while the concentration of EI has decreased. Thus, the competition between inhibitor and substrate is won by whichever molecular species is in greater concentration.

A **noncompetitive inhibitor** bears no resemblance to the normal enzyme substrate and binds reversibly to the surface of an enzyme at a site other than the catalytically active site (see ▶ Figure 20.12). The interaction between the enzyme and the noncompetitive inhibitor causes the three-dimensional shape of the enzyme and its active site to change. The enzyme no longer binds the normal substrate, or the substrate is improperly bound in a way that prevents the catalytic groups of the active site from participating in catalyzing the reaction.

noncompetitive inhibitor An inhibitor that binds to the enzyme at a location other than the active site.

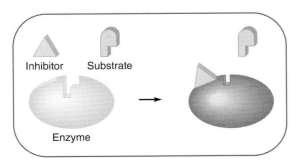

Inhibitor Substrate

Enzyme

Figure 20.12 The behavior of noncompetitive inhibitors. The inhibitor bonds to the enzyme at a site other than the active site and changes the shape of the active site.

Unlike competitive inhibition, noncompetitive inhibition cannot be reversed by the addition of more substrate because additional substrate has no effect on the enzyme-bound inhibitor (it can't displace the inhibitor because it can't bond to the site occupied by the inhibitor).

> **▶ LEARNING CHECK 20.4** Compare a noncompetitive and a competitive inhibitor with regard to the following:
>
> **a.** Resemblance to substrate
> **b.** Binding site on the enzyme
> **c.** The effect of increasing substrate concentration

20.8 The Regulation of Enzyme Activity

Learning Objective

8. Describe the three methods of cellular control over enzyme activity.

Enzymes work together in an organized yet complicated way to facilitate all the biochemical reactions needed by a living organism. For an organism to respond to changing conditions and cellular needs, very sensitive controls over enzyme activity are required. We will discuss three mechanisms by which this is accomplished: activation of zymogens, allosteric regulation, and genetic control.

The Activation of Zymogens

zymogen or proenzyme The inactive precursor of an enzyme.

A common mechanism for regulating enzyme activity is the synthesis of enzymes in the form of inactive precursors called **zymogens** or **proenzymes.** Some enzymes in their active form would degrade the internal structures of the cells and, ultimately, the cells themselves. Such enzymes are synthesized and stored as zymogens. When the active enzyme is needed, the stored zymogen is released from storage and activated at the location of the reaction. Activation usually involves the cleavage of one or more peptide bonds of the zymogen. The digestive enzymes pepsin, trypsin, and chymotrypsin and several of the enzymes involved in blood clotting are produced and activated this way. Trypsinogen, the inactive form of trypsin, is synthesized in the pancreas and activated in the small intestine by the hydrolysis of a single peptide bond. The products are the active enzyme (trypsin) and a hexapeptide:

$$\text{trypsinogen} + H_2O \xrightarrow{\text{enteropeptidase}} \text{trypsin} + \text{hexapeptide} \qquad (20.13)$$

Several examples of zymogens are listed in ▶ Table 20.6.

TABLE 20.6 Examples of Zymogens

Zymogen	Active Enzyme	Function
chymotrypsinogen	chymotrypsin	Digestion of proteins
pepsinogen	pepsin	Digestion of proteins
procarboxypeptidase	carboxypeptidase	Digestion of proteins
proelastase	elastase	Digestion of proteins
prothrombin	thrombin	Blood clotting
trypsinogen	trypsin	Digestion of proteins

Allosteric Regulation

A second method of enzyme regulation involves the combination of the enzyme with some other compound such that the three-dimensional conformation of the enzyme is altered and its catalytic activity is changed. Compounds that alter enzymes this way are called **modulators** of the activity; they may increase the activity (activators) or decrease the activity (inhibitors). The noncompetitive inhibitors we studied in Section 20.7 are examples of modulators. Enzymes that have a quaternary protein structure with distinctive binding sites for modulators are referred to as **allosteric enzymes.** These variable-rate enzymes are often located at key control points in cellular processes. In general, **activators** act as signals for increased production, whereas inhibitors are used to stop the formation of excess products.

An excellent example of allosteric regulation—the control of an allosteric enzyme—is the five-step synthesis of the amino acid isoleucine (see ▶ Figure 20.13). Threonine deaminase, the enzyme that catalyzes the first step in the conversion of threonine to isoleucine, is subject to inhibition by the final product, isoleucine. The structures of isoleucine and threonine are quite different, so isoleucine is not a competitive inhibitor. Also, the site to which isoleucine binds to the enzyme is different from the enzyme active site that binds to threonine. This second site, called the allosteric site, specifically recognizes isoleucine, whose presence there induces a change in the conformation of the enzyme such that threonine binds poorly to the active site. Thus, isoleucine exerts an inhibiting effect on the enzyme activity. As a result, the reaction slows as the concentration of isoleucine increases, and no excess isoleucine is produced. When the concentration of isoleucine falls to a low enough level, the enzyme becomes more active, and more isoleucine is synthesized. This type of allosteric regulation in which the enzyme that catalyzes the first step of a series of reactions is inhibited by the final product is called **feedback inhibition.**

modulator A substance that binds to an enzyme at a location other than the active site and alters the catalytic activity.

allosteric enzyme An enzyme with quaternary structure whose activity is changed by the binding of modulators.

activator A substance that binds to an allosteric enzyme and increases its activity.

feedback inhibition A process in which the end product of a sequence of enzyme-catalyzed reactions inhibits an earlier step in the process.

Figure 20.13 The allosteric regulation of threonine deaminase by isoleucine, an example of feedback inhibition.

The control of enzyme activity by allosteric regulation of key enzymes is of immense benefit to an organism because it allows the concentration of cellular products to be maintained within very narrow limits.

Genetic Control

One way to increase production from an enzyme-catalyzed reaction, given a sufficient supply of substrate, is for a cell to increase the number of enzyme molecules present. The synthesis of all proteins, including enzymes, is under genetic control by nucleic acids (Chapter 21). An example of the genetic control of enzyme activity involves **enzyme induction,** the synthesis of enzymes in response to a temporary need of the cell.

enzyme induction The synthesis of an enzyme in response to a cellular need.

A Summary Chart of Enzyme Inhibitors

At this point in your study of enzymes, a summary chart is a useful tool for representing the various types of enzyme inhibitors in a compact, easy-to-review way.

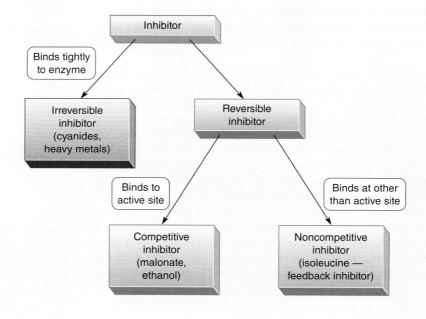

The first demonstrated example of enzyme induction came from studies conducted in the 1950s on the bacterium *Escherichia coli*. β-galactosidase, an enzyme required for the utilization of lactose, catalyzes the hydrolysis of lactose to D-galactose and D-glucose.

In the absence of lactose in the growth medium, there were fewer than ten β-galactosidase molecules per cell of *E. coli*. However, if *E. coli* are added to a lactose-containing medium, within minutes the bacterium begins to produce thousands of molecules of β-galactosidase. This is an example of enzyme induction. If lactose is removed from the growth medium, the production of β-galactosidase again falls back to a low level.

The biological significance of the genetic control of enzyme activity is that it allows an organism to adapt to environmental changes. The coupling of genetic control and allosteric regulation of enzyme activity puts the cellular processes in the body under constant control.

20.9 Medical Application of Enzymes

Learning Objective

9. Discuss the importance of measuring enzyme levels in the diagnosis of disease.

Enzymes in Clinical Diagnosis

Certain enzymes are normally found almost exclusively inside tissue cells and are released into the blood and other biological fluids only when these cells are damaged or destroyed. Because of the normal breakdown and replacement of tissue cells that go on constantly, the blood serum contains these enzymes but at very low concentrations—often a million times lower than the concentration inside cells. However, blood serum levels of cellular enzymes increase significantly when excessive cell injury or destruction occurs, or when cells grow rapidly as a result of cancer. Changes in blood serum concentrations of specific enzymes can be used clinically to detect cell damage or uncontrolled growth, and even to suggest the site of the damage or cancer. Also, the extent of cell damage can often be estimated by the magnitude of the serum concentration increase above normal levels. For these reasons, the measurement of enzyme concentrations in blood serum and other biological fluids has become a major diagnostic tool, particularly in diagnosing diseases of the heart, liver, pancreas, prostate, and bones. In fact, certain enzyme determinations are performed so often that they have become routine procedures in the clinical chemistry laboratory. ▶ Table 20.7 lists some enzymes used in medical diagnosis.

TABLE 20.7 Diagnostically Useful Assays of Blood Serum Enzymes

Enzyme	Pathological Condition
acid phosphatase	Prostate cancer
alkaline phosphatase (ALP)	Liver or bone disease
amylase	Diseases of the pancreas
creatine kinase (CK)	Heart attack
aspartate transaminase (AST)	Heart attack or hepatitis
alanine transaminase (ALT)	Hepatitis
lactate dehydrogenase (LDH)	Heart attack, liver damage
lipase	Acute pancreatitis
lysozyme	Monocytic leukemia

Isoenzymes

Lactate dehydrogenase (LDH) and creatine kinase (CK), two of the enzymes listed in Table 20.7, are particularly useful in clinical diagnosis because each occurs in multiple forms called **isoenzymes.** Although all forms of a particular isoenzyme catalyze the same reaction, their molecular structures are slightly different and their locations within the body tissues may vary.

isoenzyme A slightly different form of the same enzyme produced by different tissues.

Probably the most fully studied group of isoenzymes is that of lactate dehydrogenase (LDH). The quaternary structure of the enzyme consists of four subunits that are of two different types. One is labeled H because it is the predominant subunit present in the LDH enzyme found in heart muscle cells. The other, labeled M, predominates in other muscle cells. There are five possible ways to combine these four subunits to form the enzyme (see ▶ Figure 20.14). Each combination has slightly different properties, which allows them to be separated and identified by electrophoresis.

Figure 20.14 Isomeric forms (isoenzymes) of lactate dehydrogenase.

▶ Table 20.8 shows the distribution of the five LDH isoenzymes in several human tissues. Notice that each type of tissue has a distinct pattern of isoenzyme percentages. Liver and skeletal muscle, for example, contain particularly high percentages of LDH_5. Also notice the differences in LDH_1 and LDH_2 levels in heart and skeletal muscles.

TABLE 20.8 Tissue Distribution of LDH Isoenzymes

Tissue	LDH_1 (%)	LDH_2 (%)	LDH_3 (%)	LDH_4 (%)	LDH_5 (%)
Brain	23	34	30	10	3
Heart	50	36	9	3	2
Kidney	28	34	21	11	6
Liver	4	6	17	16	57
Lung	10	20	30	25	15
Serum	28	41	19	7	5
Skeletal muscle	5	5	10	22	58

Because of the difference in tissue distribution of LDH isoenzymes, serum levels of LDH are used in the diagnosis of a wide range of diseases: anemias involving the rupture of red blood cells, acute liver diseases, congestive heart failure, and muscular diseases such as muscular dystrophy. This wide range of diseases makes an LDH assay a good initial diagnostic test. Elevated levels of LDH_1 and LDH_2, for example, indicate myocardial infarction, whereas elevated LDH_5 indicates possible liver damage. If LDH activity is elevated, then this and other isoenzyme assays can be used to pinpoint the location and type of disease more accurately.

Case Study Follow-up

Middle-aged men are the stereotypical models of heart disease, but many younger men and women experience heart attack. Men typically report a feeling of pressure and crushing chest pain just prior to a heart attack. Women most frequently experience unusual fatigue and sleep disturbance, as well as shortness of breath and anxiety, preceding a heart attack. Women as well as men might experience jaw, arm, back, or chest pain; sweating; and nausea. Women typically postpone seeking treatment for up to two weeks after experiencing symptoms (Albarron, 2007, Løvlien et al., 2006). Cardiac events are frequently misdiagnosed in women and younger men (NHLBI, 2011).

Diet, genetic inheritance, or both may cause hypercholesterolemia (high cholesterol). Familial hypercholesterolemia is caused by mutations in several genes. These mutations cause a decrease in the number of low-density lipoprotein receptors (LDLR), the main carrier of cholesterol in the blood. The condition is more prevalent in Afrikaner, Finnish, French Canadian, and Lebanese populations. However, the majority of hypercholesterolemia is caused by lifestyle choices—diet, exercise, and smoking. (USNLM, 2007).

Concept Summary

General Characteristics of Enzymes

Enzymes are highly efficient protein catalysts involved in almost every biological reaction. They are often quite specific in terms of the substance acted on and the type of reaction catalyzed.

Objective 1 (Section 20.1), Exercise 20.2

Enzyme Nomenclature and Classification

Enzymes are grouped into six major classes on the basis of the type of reaction catalyzed. Common names for enzymes often end in *-ase* and are based on the substrate and/or the type of reaction catalyzed.

Objective 2 (Section 20.2), Exercise 20.12

Enzyme Cofactors

Cofactors are nonprotein molecules required for an enzyme to be active. Cofactors are either organic (coenzymes) or inorganic ions.

Objective 3 (Section 20.3), Exercise 20.14

The Mechanism of Enzyme Action

The behavior of enzymes is explained by a theory in which the formation of an enzyme–substrate complex is assumed to occur. The specificity of enzymes is explained by the lock-and-key theory and the induced-fit theory.

Objective 4 (Section 20.4), Exercise 20.20

Enzyme Activity

The catalytic ability of enzymes is described by turnover number and enzyme international units. Experiments that measure enzyme activity are referred to as enzyme assays.

Objective 5 (Section 20.5), Exercise 20.26

Concept Summary (continued)

Factors Affecting Enzyme Activity

The catalytic activity of enzymes is influenced by numerous factors. The most important are substrate concentration, enzyme concentration, temperature, and pH.
Objective 6 (Section 20.6), Exercise 20.28

Enzyme Inhibition

Chemical substances called inhibitors decrease the rates of enzyme-catalyzed reactions. Irreversible inhibitors render enzymes permanently inactive and include several very toxic substances such as the cyanide ion and heavy-metal ions. Reversible inhibitors are of two types: competitive and noncompetitive.
Objective 7 (Section 20.7), Exercise 20.34

The Regulation of Enzyme Activity

Three mechanisms of cellular control over enzyme activity exist. One method involves the synthesis of enzyme precursors called zymogens, which are activated when needed by the cell. The second mechanism relies on the binding of small molecules (modulators), which increase or decrease enzyme activity. Genetic control of enzyme synthesis, the third method, regulates the amount of enzyme available.
Objective 8 (Section 20.8), Exercise 20.38

Medical Applications of Enzymes

Numerous enzymes have become useful as aids in diagnostic medicine. The presence of specific enzymes in body fluids such as blood has been related to certain pathological conditions.
Objective 9 (Section 20.9), Exercise 20.46

Key Terms and Concepts

Absolute specificity (20.1)
Activator (20.8)
Active site (20.4)
Allosteric enzyme (20.8)
Antibiotic (20.7)
Apoenzyme (20.3)
Coenzyme (20.3)
Cofactor (20.3)
Competitive inhibitor (20.7)
Enzyme (20.1)

Enzyme activity (20.5)
Enzyme induction (20.8)
Enzyme inhibitor (20.7)
Enzyme international unit (IU) (20.5)
Extremozyme (20.7)
Feedback inhibition (20.8)
Inborn error of metabolism (20.3)
Induced-fit theory (20.4)
Isoenzymes (20.9)
Lock-and-key theory (20.4)

Modulator (20.8)
Noncompetitive inhibitor (20.7)
Optimum pH (20.6)
Optimum temperature (20.6)
Relative specificity (20.1)
Stereochemical specificity (20.1)
Substrate (20.2)
Turnover number (20.5)
Zymogen or proenzyme (20.8)

Key Reactions

1. Formation of an active enzyme (Section 20.3):	apoenzyme + cofactor (coenzyme or inorganic ion) → active enzyme	Reaction 20.4
2. Mechanism of enzyme action (Section 20.4):	$E + S \rightleftarrows ES \rightarrow E + P$	Reaction 20.6

Exercises

Even-numbered exercises are answered in Appendix B.

Blue-numbered exercises are more challenging.

General Characteristics of Enzymes (Section 20.1)

20.1 What is the role of enzymes in the body?

20.2 List two ways that enzyme catalysis of a reaction is superior to normal laboratory conditions.

20.3 What is the relationship between an enzyme and the energy of activation for a reaction?

20.4 Why are so many different enzymes needed?

20.5 Define what is meant by the term *enzyme specificity.*

20.6 Define what is meant by the term *absolute specificity.*

20.7 List three ways in which enzymes are particularly well suited for their essential roles in living organisms.

Enzyme Nomenclature and Classification (Section 20.2)

20.8 What is the ending of EC names and most common names of enzymes?

20.9 What is the relationship between urea and urease? Between maltose and maltase?

20.10 Match the following enzymes and substrates:

Enzyme	Substrate
a. sucrase	maltose
b. amylase	amylose
c. lactase	sucrose
d. maltase	arginine
e. arginase	lactose

20.11 Match the following general enzyme names and reactions catalyzed:

Enzyme	Reaction Catalyzed
a. decarboxylase	formation of ester linkages
b. phosphatase	removal of carboxyl groups from compounds
c. peptidase	hydrolysis of peptide linkages
d. esterase	hydrolysis of phosphate ester linkages

20.12 Because one substrate may undergo a number of reactions, it is often convenient to use an enzyme nomenclature system that includes both the substrate name (or general type) and the type of reaction catalyzed. Identify the substrate and type of reaction for the following enzyme names:

a. succinate dehydrogenase

b. L-amino acid reductase

c. cytochrome oxidase

d. glucose-6-phosphate isomerase

Enzyme Cofactors (Section 20.3)

20.13 Some enzymes consist of protein plus another component. Which of the terms *cofactor* or *coenzyme* correctly describes each of the following nonprotein components?

a. an inorganic ion

b. a nonspecific component

c. an organic material

d. nicotinic acid,

20.14 What are the relationships among the terms *cofactor, active enzyme,* and *apoenzyme*?

20.15 State the relationship between vitamins and enzyme activity.

20.16 List some typical inorganic ions that serve as cofactors.

20.17 What vitamins are required for FAD and NAD^+ formation?

The Mechanism of Enzyme Action (Section 20.4)

20.18 Explain what is meant by the following equation:
$$E + S \rightleftarrows ES \rightarrow E + P$$

20.19 In what way are the substrate and active site of an enzyme related?

20.20 How is enzyme specificity explained by the lock-and-key theory?

20.21 Compare the lock-and-key theory with the induced-fit theory.

20.22 An enzyme can catalyze reactions involving propanoic acid, butanoic acid, and pentanoic acid. Would the lock-and-key theory or the induced-fit theory best explain this enzyme's mechanism of action? Why?

Enzyme Activity (Section 20.5)

20.23 List two ways of describing enzyme activity.

20.24 What observations may be used in experiments to determine enzyme activity?

20.25 Define the term *turnover number.*

20.26 What is an enzyme international unit? Why is the international unit a useful method of expressing enzyme activity in medical diagnoses?

Factors Affecting Enzyme Activity (Section 20.6)

20.27 Use graphs to illustrate enzyme activity as a function of the following:

a. substrate concentration

b. enzyme concentration

c. pH

d. temperature

20.28 Write a single sentence to summarize the information of each graph in Exercise 20.27.

20.29 What happens to the rate of an enzyme-catalyzed reaction as substrate concentration is raised beyond the saturation point?

20.30 How might V_{max} for an enzyme be determined?

20.31 How would you expect hypothermia to affect enzyme activity in the body?

20.32 When handling or storing solutions of enzymes, the pH is usually kept near 7.0. Explain why.

Enzyme Inhibition (Section 20.7)

20.33 Distinguish between irreversible and reversible enzyme inhibition.

20.34 Distinguish between competitive and noncompetitive enzyme inhibition.

20.35 How does each of the following irreversible inhibitors interact with enzymes?

 a. cyanide

 b. heavy-metal ions

20.36 List an antidote for each of the two poisons in Exercise 20.35 and describe how each functions.

The Regulation of Enzyme Activity (Section 20.8)

20.37 Why is the regulation of enzyme activity necessary?

20.38 List three mechanisms for the control of enzyme activity.

20.39 Describe the importance of zymogens in the body. Give an example of an enzyme that has a zymogen.

20.40 The clotting of blood occurs by a series of zymogen activations. Why are the enzymes that catalyze blood clotting produced as zymogens?

20.41 What type of enzyme possesses a binding site for modulators?

20.42 Name and contrast the two types of modulators.

20.43 Explain how feedback enzyme inhibition works and why it is advantageous for the cell.

20.44 What is meant by genetic control of enzyme activity and enzyme induction?

Medical Application of Enzymes (Section 20.9)

20.45 Why are enzyme assays of blood serum useful in a clinical diagnosis?

20.46 How is each of the following enzyme assays useful in diagnostic medicine?

 a. CK

 b. ALP

 c. amylase

20.47 What are isoenzymes? List two examples of isoenzymes.

20.48 Why is an LDH assay a good initial diagnostic test?

20.49 What specific enzyme assays are particularly useful in diagnosing liver damage or disease?

Additional Exercises

20.50 Carboxypeptidase is a proteolytic enzyme that cleaves the C-terminal amino acid residue from a polypeptide. The amino acid arginine is found in the active site of carboxypeptidase and is responsible for holding the C-terminal end of the polypeptide in place so the cleavage of the peptide bond can occur. What type of interaction occurs between the C-terminal end of the polypeptide and the arginine side chain?

20.51 An enzyme preparation that decarboxylates butanoic acid has an activity of 50 IU. How many grams of butanoic acid will this enzyme preparation decarboxylate in 10 minutes? Assume an unlimited supply of substrate.

20.52 Propanoic acid chloride was found to react with the side chain of a serine residue on an enzyme to cause irreversible inhibition of that enzyme. Suggest a mechanism of how this occurs.

$$CH_3CH_2\overset{\displaystyle O}{\overset{\displaystyle \|}{C}}-Cl$$

20.53 1.0×10^{12} enzyme molecules were added to 1.0 L of substrate solution with an initial pH of 7.0. After 1.0 minute, the solution had a pH of 6.0. Assume an unlimited supply of substrate and any change in hydrogen ion concentration was due to the following reaction.

$$\text{Substrate} \xrightarrow{\text{enzyme}} \text{Product} + H^+$$

 a. What was the change in H^+ concentration?

 b. How many molecules of substrate were reacted to cause this change in H^+ concentration?

 c. What is the turnover number of this enzyme?

20.54 The following reaction has come to equilibrium and it is found that there are 100 times as many molecules of A as there are of B in the solution.

$$A \rightleftharpoons B$$

An enzyme that catalyzes this reaction is then added to the solution. In which direction will the equilibrium shift?

Allied Health Exam Connection

The following questions are from these sources:

1. *Nursing School Entrance Exam* © 2005, Learning Express, LLC.

2. *McGraw-Hill's Nursing School Entrance Exams* by Thomas A. Evangelist, Tamara B. Orr and Judy Unrein © 2009, The McGraw-Hill Companies, Inc.

3. *NSEE Nursing School Entrance Exams,* 3rd Edition © 2009, Kaplan Publishing.

4. *Cliffs Test Prep: Nursing School Entrance Exams* by Fred N. Grayson © 2004, Wiley Publishing, Inc.

5. *Peterson's Master the Nursing School and Allied Health Entrance Exams,* 18th Edition by Marion F. Gooding © 2008, Peterson's, a Nelnet Company.

Even-numbered exercises answered in Appendix B.
678 Blue-numbered exercises are more challenging.

Unless otherwise noted all art on this page © Cengage Learning 2014

20.55 Which of the following is not a characteristic of enzymes?

a. They are macromolecules.

b. They act on substances.

c. They are phospholipids.

d. They initiate and decelerate chemical reactions.

e. They act as catalysts.

20.56 The human body has an average pH of about 7 and a temperature of about 37°C. Use graphs to illustrate enzyme activity in the human body as a function of the following:

a. Substrate concentration

b. Enzyme concentration

c. pH (include pH optimum value)

d. Temperature (include temperature optimum value)

20.57 Look at Table 20.4 and identify the proteolytic enzyme that begins protein digestion in the stomach. Does this name use an EC name ending?

20.58 Saliva contains mucus, water, and _____, which partially digests polysaccharides. Fill in the blank with the correct response from below:

a. lipase

b. amylase

c. trypsin

d. insulin

20.59 Most human enzymes function best in the temperature range of:

a. 0–10°C

b. 10–25°C

c. 25–40°C

d. 40–55°C

20.60 The site on an enzyme molecule that does the catalytic work is called the:

a. binding site

b. allosteric site

c. lock

d. active site

20.61 The process by which an enzyme acts on the substrate can be described by the:

a. lock-and-key model

b. enzyme-and-substrate model

c. enzyme folding model

d. catalytic model

20.62 In the multienzyme sequence shown below, molecules of D are able to fit to the enzyme E_1 and prevent the conversion of A to B. What is this action of E called?

$$A \xrightarrow{E_1} B \xrightarrow{E_2} C \xrightarrow{E_3} D$$

a. effector inhibition

b. allosteric inhibition

c. feedback inhibition

d. competitive inhibition by nonproduct

Chemistry for Thought

20.63 Explain how the pasteurization of milk utilizes one of the factors that influence enzyme activity.

20.64 Explain how food preservation by freezing utilizes one of the factors that influence enzyme activity.

20.65 Some pottery glazes contain lead compounds. Why would it be unwise to use such pottery to store or serve food?

20.66 Urease can catalyze the hydrolysis of urea, but not the hydrolysis of methyl urea. Why?

20.67 The active ingredient in meat tenderizer is the enzyme papain, a protease. Explain how treating meat with this material before cooking would make it more tender.

20.68 Why are enzymes that are used for laboratory or clinical work stored in refrigerators?

20.69 Describe the differences between graphs showing temperature versus reaction rate for an enzyme-catalyzed reaction and an uncatalyzed reaction.

20.70 Answer the question associated with Figure 20.3. How else might ammonia be detected?

20.71 In Figure 20.9, it is noted that pickles resist spoilage. Why is that true for this acidic food?

20.72 One of the steps in preparing frozen corn for the grocery market involves "blanching" (briefly placing the corn in boiling water). Why is blanching necessary?

20.73 What experiment would you conduct to determine if an inhibitor is competitive or noncompetitive?

20.74 Why might an enzyme be selected over an inorganic catalyst for a certain industrial process?

20.75 Enzymes are enormous molecules, and yet the active site is relatively small. Why is a huge molecule necessary for enzymes?

21 Nucleic Acids and Protein Synthesis

Case Study

DNA (deoxyribonucleic acid) carries the hereditary information and is found in every cell. Rachel never really thought about it until her gynecologist informed her that she was at risk to be a carrier of the trait for Tay-Sachs disease. The doctor said that since she and her husband had Eastern European ancestry, they might want to consider a blood test to determine whether they carried the mutated gene that causes Tay-Sachs. Children with the disease develop normally at first but later develop blindness, deafness, retardation, and usually die by age 4. If they both had the gene, there would be a 25% chance in each pregnancy that the child would be affected. Rachel's religious beliefs prohibited terminating a pregnancy. She had several options to consider: letting things take their natural course and accepting any child in good health or not, considering adoption, or childlessness. Rachel wasn't even sure she wanted to know if she carried the gene.

Should Rachel and her husband see a genetic counselor? Does the gynecologist have the right or responsibility to offer advice or just to offer information?

Follow-up to this Case Study appears at the end the chapter before the Concept Summary.

Learning Objectives

When you have completed your study of this chapter, you should be able to:

1 Identify the components of nucleotides and correctly classify the sugars and bases. **(Section 21.1)**

2 Describe the structure of DNA. **(Section 21.2)**

3 Outline the process of DNA replication. **(Section 21.3)**

4 Contrast the structures of DNA and RNA and list the function of the three types of cellular RNA. **(Section 21.4)**

5 Describe what is meant by the terms *transcription* and *translation*. **(Section 21.5)**

6 Describe the process by which RNA is synthesized in cells. **(Section 21.6)**

7 Explain how the genetic code functions in the flow of genetic information. **(Section 21.7)**

8 Outline the process by which proteins are synthesized in cells. **(Section 21.8)**

9 Describe how genetic mutations occur and how they influence organisms. **(Section 21.9)**

10 Describe the technology used to produce recombinant DNA. **(Section 21.10)**

O ne of the most remarkable properties of living cells is their ability to produce nearly exact replicas of themselves through hundreds of generations. Such a process requires that certain types of information be passed unchanged from one generation to the next. The transfer of necessary genetic information to new cells is accomplished by means of biomolecules called **nucleic acids.** The high molecular weight compounds represent coded information, much as words represent information in a book. It is the nearly infinite variety of possible structures that enables nucleic acids to represent the huge amount of information that must be transmitted sexually or asexually to reproduce a living organism. This information controls the inherited characteristics of the individuals in the new generation and determines the life processes as well (see ▶ Figure 21.1).

nucleic acid A biomolecule involved in the transfer of genetic information from existing cells to new cells.

Figure 21.1 Nucleic acids passed from the parents to offspring determine the inherited characteristics.

21.1 Components of Nucleic Acids

Learning Objective

1. Identify the components of nucleotides and correctly classify the sugars and bases.

Nucleic acids are classified into two categories: **ribonucleic acid (RNA),** found mainly in the cytoplasm of living cells, and **deoxyribonucleic acid (DNA),** found primarily in the nuclei of cells. Both DNA and RNA are polymers, consisting of long, linear molecules. The repeating structural units, or monomers, of the nucleic acids are called **nucleotides.** Nucleotides, however, are composed of three simpler components: a heterocyclic base, a sugar, and a phosphate (see ◗ Figure 21.2). These components will be discussed individually.

Figure 21.2 The composition of nucleic acids.

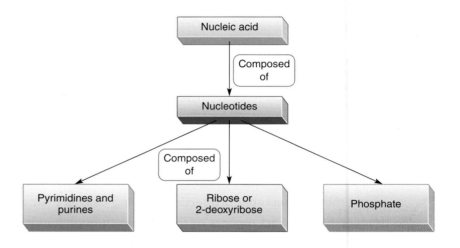

Each of the five bases commonly found in nucleic acids are heterocyclic compounds that can be classified as either a pyrimidine or a purine, the parent compounds from which the bases are derived:

pyrimidine purine

The three pyrimidine bases are uracil, thymine, and cytosine, usually abbreviated U, T, and C. Adenine (A) and guanine (G) are the two purine bases. Adenine, guanine, and cytosine are found in both DNA and RNA, but uracil is ordinarily found only in RNA, and thymine only in DNA. Structural formulas of the five bases are given in ◗ Figure 21.3.

The sugar component of RNA is D-ribose, as the name ribonucleic acid implies. In deoxyribonucleic acid (DNA), the sugar is D-deoxyribose. Both sugars occur in the β-configuration.

HO—CH₂ OH HO—CH₂ OH ← *β-configuration*

OH OH OH *no* —OH *group*

D-ribose D-deoxyribose

Figure 21.3 The major bases of nucleic acids.

Phosphate, the third component of nucleotides, is derived from phosphoric acid (H_3PO_4), which under cellular pH conditions exists in ionic form:

The formation of a nucleotide from these three components is represented in Reaction 21.1:

In a nucleotide, the base is always attached to the $1'$ position of the sugar, and the phosphate is generally located at the $5'$ position. The carbon atoms in the sugar are designated with a number followed by a prime to distinguish them from the atoms in the bases.

Because the nucleotide of Reaction 21.1 contains ribose as the sugar, the nucleotide must be one found in RNA. The general structure of a nucleotide can be represented as

$$^-O-\overset{\overset{\displaystyle O}{\|}}{\underset{\underset{\displaystyle O^-}{|}}{P}}-O-CH_2$$

base

OH — *OH present in RNA*

or

phosphate — sugar — base

21.2 The Structure of DNA

Learning Objective

2. Describe the structure of DNA.

DNA molecules, among the largest molecules known, contain between 1 and 100 million nucleotide units. The nucleotides are joined together in nucleic acids by phosphate groups that connect the 5′ carbon of one nucleotide to the 3′ carbon of the next. These linkages are referred to as *phosphodiester bonds*. The result is a chain of alternating phosphate and sugar units to which the bases are attached. The sugar–phosphate chain is referred to as the **nucleic acid backbone,** and it is constant throughout the entire DNA molecule (see ▶ Figure 21.4). Thus, one DNA molecule differs from another only in the sequence, or order of attachment, of the bases along the backbone. Just as the amino acid sequence of a protein determines the primary structure of the protein, the order of the bases provides the primary structure of DNA.

nucleic acid backbone The sugar–phosphate chain that is common to all nucleic acids.

Figure 21.4 The nucleic acid backbone.

phosphate — sugar — phosphate — sugar — phosphate — sugar

▶ Figure 21.5 shows the structure of a tetranucleotide that represents a partial structural formula of a DNA molecule. The end of the polynucleotide segment of DNA in Figure 21.5 that has no nucleotide attached to the 5′ CH₂ is called the 5′ end of the segment. The other end of the chain is the 3′ end. By convention, the sequence of bases along the backbone is read from the 5′ end to the 3′ end. Because the backbone structure along the chain does not vary, a polynucleotide structure may conveniently be abbreviated by giving only the sequence of the bases along the backbone. For example, ACGT represents the tetranucleotide in Figure 21.5.

▶ **LEARNING CHECK 21.1** Draw the structural formula for a trinucleotide portion of DNA with the sequence CTG. Point out the 5′ and 3′ ends of the molecule. Indicate with arrows the phosphodiester linkages. Enclose the nucleotide corresponding to T in a box with dotted lines.

The Secondary Structure of DNA

The secondary structure of DNA was proposed in 1953 by American molecular biologist James D. Watson and English biologist Francis H. C. Crick (see ▶ Figure 21.6). This was perhaps the greatest discovery of modern biology, and it earned its discoverers the Nobel Prize in Physiology or Medicine in 1962.

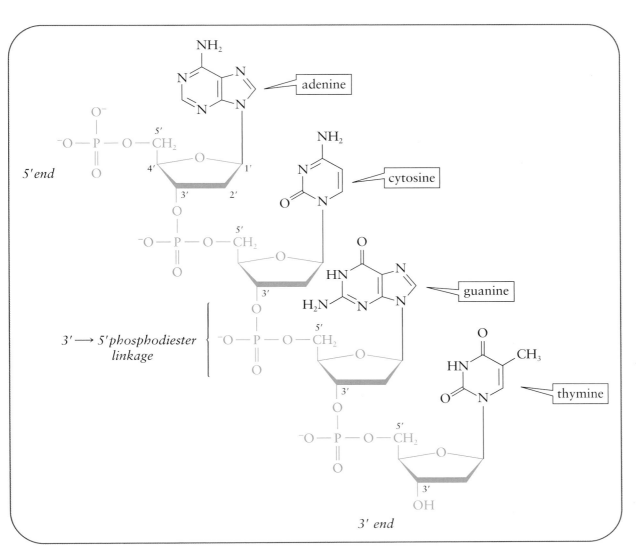

Figure 21.5 The structure of ACGT, a tetranucleotide segment of DNA. The nucleic acid backbone is in color.

Figure 21.6 J. D. Watson (left) and F. H. C. Crick (right), working in the Cavendish Laboratory at Cambridge, England, built scale models of the DNA double helix based on the X-ray crystallography data of M. H. F. Wilkins and Rosalind Franklin.

The model of DNA established by Watson and Crick was based on key contributions of other researchers, including the analysis of the base composition of DNA. The analysis of DNA from many different forms of life revealed an interesting pattern. The relative amounts of each base often varied from one organism to another, but in all DNA the percentages of adenine and thymine were always equal to each other as were the percentages of guanine and cytosine. For example, human DNA contains 20% guanine, 20% cytosine, 30% adenine, and 30% thymine. Watson and Crick concluded from these and other types of data that DNA is composed of two strands entwined around each other in a double helix, as shown in ▶ Figure 21.7.

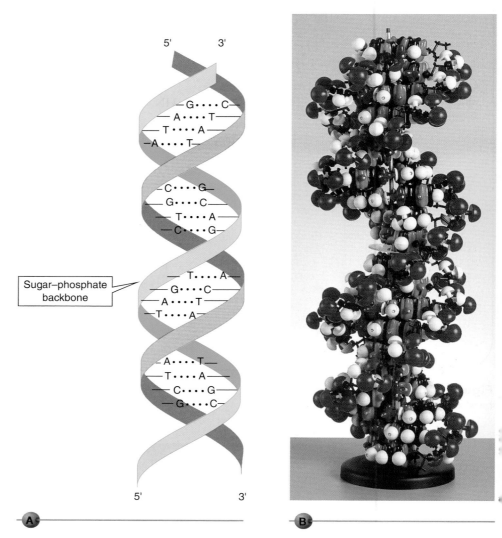

Figure 21.7 The double helix of DNA: Ⓐ a schematic drawing and Ⓑ a three-dimensional molecular model. Both representations show the bases pointing toward the center of the helix away from the sugar–phosphate backbone.

The two intertwined polynucleotide chains of the DNA double helix run in opposite (antiparallel) directions. Thus, each end of the double helix contains the 5′ end of one chain and the 3′ end of the other. The sugar–phosphate backbone is on the outside of the helix, and the bases point inward. The unique feature of the Watson and Crick structure is the way in which the chains are held together to form the double helix. They theorized that the DNA structure is stabilized by hydrogen bonding between the bases that extend inward from the sugar–phosphate backbone (see ▶ Figure 21.8). The spacing in the interior of the

double helix is such that adenine always hydrogen bonds to thymine, and guanine always hydrogen bonds to cytosine. Thus, in double-helical DNA, wherever there is an adenine on one strand of the helix, there must be a thymine on the other strand, and similarly for guanine and cytosine. The two DNA strands with these matched sequences are said to be **complementary** to each other.

complementary DNA strands Two strands of DNA in a double-helical form such that adenine and guanine of one strand are matched and hydrogen bonded to thymine and cytosine, respectively, of the second strand.

Figure 21.8 Base pairing. Hydrogen bonding between complementary base pairs holds the two strands of a DNA molecule together.

▶ Example 21.1

One strand of a DNA molecule has the base sequence CCATTG. What is the base sequence for the complementary strand?

Solution

Three things must be remembered and used to solve this problem: (1) The base sequence of a DNA strand is always written from the 5′ end to the 3′ end; (2) adenine (A) is always paired with its complementary base thymine (T), and guanine (G) is always paired with its complement cytosine (C); and (3) in double-stranded DNA, the two strands run in opposite directions, so that the 5′ end of one strand is associated with the 3′ end of the other strand. These three ideas lead to the following:

Original strand: 5′ end C–C–A–T–T–G 3′ end
Complementary strand: 3′ end G–G–T–A–A–C 5′ end

Nucleic Acid Supplements

Because of the fundamental roles nucleic acids play in life itself, it is not surprising that many claims of health benefits related to these substances have been made. As a result of these claims, DNA, RNA, and their various derivatives are well represented on the dietary supplement shelves of retailers. In addition, numerous shampoos and other cosmetics that contain DNA and RNA are also available. The idea behind the use of such products is that as we age, our DNA/RNA becomes depleted or defective, and must be replaced if good health is to be maintained or restored. It has been suggested that injections or oral supplements could be used to accomplish the replacement.

The health benefits claimed for such therapy include slowing the aging process, improving memory and mental processes, stimulating the immune system, and fighting cancer. There has been almost universal doubt about such health benefits, especially if the nucleic acids were taken orally. It has been argued that these substances would be destroyed during digestion and therefore could not reach target organs and tissues of the body.

Only very recently have reports been made of scientific evidence that nucleic acid supplementation might provide some benefits in terms of positively influencing the immune response of the body. Evidence to support the claims of slowing the aging process and improving memory and mental processes is very inconclusive and not promising at this time. There has

been very little investigation of the anti-cancer properties of RNA and DNA in their native forms. However, some synthetic forms of the nucleic acid have been studied in this regard and some promising results have been obtained in the treatment of specific types of cancer.

The only negative claim about using nucleic acid supplements is that they may produce excessive uric acid and promote or aggravate gout. Because of this, anyone with gout or a tendency to develop it should not use nucleic acid supplements without first obtaining a physician's approval.

Dietary supplements containing nucleic acids.

When we follow convention and write the sequence of the complementary strand in the 5′ to 3′ direction, it becomes

$$5' \, C–A–A–T–G–G \, 3'$$

▶ **LEARNING CHECK 21.2** Write the complementary base sequence for the DNA strand TTACG.

21.3 DNA Replication

Learning Objective

3. Outline the process of DNA replication.

DNA is responsible for one of the most essential functions of living organisms, the storage and transmission of hereditary information. A human cell normally contains 46 structural units called **chromosomes** (see ▶ Figure 21.9). Each chromosome contains one molecule of DNA coiled tightly about a group of small, basic proteins called histones. Individual sections of DNA molecules make up **genes,** the fundamental units of heredity. In Section 21.5, you'll learn that each gene directs the synthesis of a specific protein. The number of genes contained in the structural unit of an organism varies with the type of organism. For example, a virus, the smallest structure known to carry genetic information, is thought

chromosome A tightly packed bundle of DNA and protein that is involved in cell division.

gene An individual section of a chromosomal DNA molecule that is the fundamental unit of heredity.

Figure 21.9 Chromosomes.
A The 46 chromosomes of a
human cell. **B** Each chromosome
is a protein-coated strand of multi-
coiled DNA.

Chromosome

© L. Lisco and D. W. Fawcett/Visuals Unlimited

A

DNA double helix

Histones

B

to contain from a few to several hundred genes. A bacterial cell, such as *Escherichia coli
(E. coli),* contains about 1000 genes, whereas a human cell contains approximately 25,000.

One of the elegant features of the Watson–Crick three-dimensional structure for DNA
was that it provided the first satisfactory explanation for the transmission of hereditary
information—it explained how DNA is duplicated for the next generation.

The process by which an exact copy of DNA is produced is called **replication.** It
occurs when two strands of DNA separate and each serves as a template (pattern) for
the construction of its own complement. The process generates new DNA double-
stranded molecules that are exact replicas of the original DNA molecule. A schematic
diagram of the replication process is presented in ▶ Figure 21.10. Notice that the two
daughter DNA molecules have exactly the same base sequences as the original parent
DNA. Notice, too, that each daughter contains one strand of the parent and one new
strand that is complementary to the parent strand. This type of replication is called
semiconservative replication.

replication The process by which
an exact copy of a DNA molecule is
produced.

semiconservative replication A
replication process that produces
DNA molecules containing one strand
from the parent and a new strand that
is complementary to the strand from
the parent.

Figure 21.10 A schematic diagram of the replication of DNA.

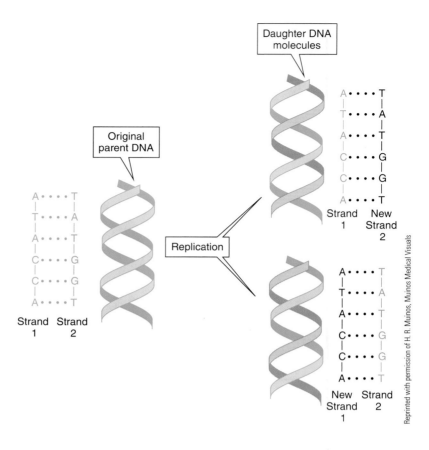

The process of replication can be viewed as occurring in three steps.

Step 1. Unwinding of the double helix: Replication begins when the enzyme helicase catalyzes the separation and unwinding of the nucleic acid strands at a specific point along the DNA helix. In this process, hydrogen bonds between complementary base pairs are broken, and the bases that were formerly in the center of the helix are exposed. The point where this unwinding takes place is called a **replication fork** (see ▶ Figure 21.11).

replication fork A point where the double helix of a DNA molecule unwinds during replication.

Step 2. Synthesis of DNA segments: DNA replication takes place along both nucleic acid strands separated in Step 1. The process proceeds from the 3′ end toward the 5′ end of the exposed strand (the template). Because the two strands are antiparallel, the synthesis of new nucleic acid strands proceeds toward the replication fork on one exposed strand and away from the replication fork on the other strand (Figure 21.11). New (daughter) DNA strands form as nucleotides, complementary to those on the exposed strands, and are linked together under the influence of the enzyme DNA polymerase. Notice that the daughter chain grows from the 5′ end toward the 3′ end as the process moves from the 3′ end of the exposed (template) strand toward the 5′ end. As the synthesis proceeds, a second replication fork is created when a new section of DNA unwinds. The daughter strand that was growing toward the first replication fork continues growing smoothly toward the new fork. However, the other daughter strand was growing away from the first fork. A new segment of this strand begins growing from the new fork but is not initially bound to the segment that grew from the first fork. Thus, as the parent DNA progressively unwinds, this daughter strand is synthesized as a series of fragments that are bound together in Step 3. The gaps or breaks between segments in this daughter strand are called nicks, and the

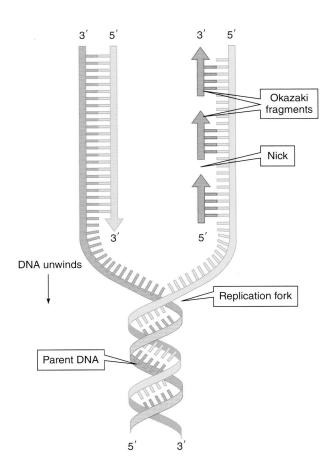

Figure 21.11 The replication of DNA. Both new strands are growing in the 59 to 39 direction.

DNA fragments separated by the nicks are called **Okazaki fragments** after their discoverer, Reiji Okazaki (Figure 21.11).

Step 3. Closing the nicks: One daughter DNA strand is synthesized without any nicks, but the Okazaki fragments of the other strand must be joined together. An enzyme called DNA ligase catalyzes this final step of DNA replication. The result is two DNA double-helical molecules that are identical.

Observations with an electron microscope show that the replication of DNA molecules in eukaryotic cells occurs simultaneously at many points along the original DNA molecule. These replication zones blend together as the process of replication continues. This is necessary if long molecules are to be replicated rapidly. For example, it is estimated that the replication of the largest chromosome in *Drosophila* (the fruit fly) would take more than 16 days if there were only one origin for replication. Research results indicate that the actual replication is accomplished in less than 3 minutes because it takes place simultaneously at more than 6000 replication forks per DNA molecule. ▶ Figure 21.12 shows a schematic diagram in which replication is proceeding at several points in the DNA chain.

A knowledge of the DNA replication process led scientist Kary Mullis in 1983 to a revolutionary laboratory technique called the *polymerase chain reaction (PCR)*. The PCR technique mimics the natural process of replication, in which the DNA double helix unwinds. As the two strands separate, DNA polymerase makes a copy using each strand as a template. To perform PCR, a small quantity of the target DNA is added to a test tube along with a buffered solution containing DNA polymerase; the cofactor $MgCl_2$, which is needed by the polymerase to function; the four nucleotides; the four building blocks; and primers. The primers are short polynucleotide segments that will bind to the separated

Okazaki fragment A DNA fragment produced during replication as a result of strand growth in a direction away from the replication fork.

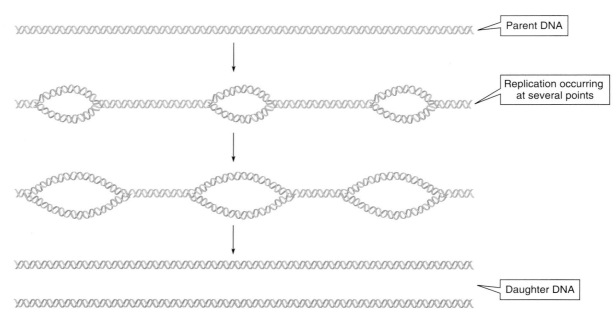

Parent DNA

Replication occurring at several points

Daughter DNA

Figure 21.12 A schematic representation of eukaryotic chromosome replication. The new DNA is shown in purple.

DNA strands and serve as starting points for new chain growth. The PCR mixture is taken through three-step replication cycles:

1. Heat (94°C–96°C) is used for one to several minutes to unravel (denature) the DNA into single strands.
2. The tube is cooled to 50°C–65°C for one to several minutes, during which the primers hydrogen-bond to the separated strands of target DNA.
3. The tube is heated to 72°C for one to several minutes, during which time the DNA polymerase synthesizes new strands.

Each cycle doubles the amount of DNA. Following 30 such cycles, a theoretical amplification factor of 1 billion is attained.

Almost overnight, PCR became a standard research technique for detecting all manner of mutations associated with genetic disease (Section 21.9). PCR can also be used to detect the presence of unwanted DNA, as in the case of a bacterial or viral infection. Conventional tests that involve the culture of microorganisms or the use of antibodies can take weeks to perform. PCR offers a fast and simple alternative. The ability of PCR to utilize degraded DNA samples and sometimes the DNA from single cells is of great interest to forensic scientists. PCR has also permitted DNA to be amplified from some unusual sources, such as extinct mammals, Egyptian mummies, and ancient insects trapped in amber.

21.4 Ribonucleic Acid (RNA)

Learning Objective

4. Contrast the structures of DNA and RNA and list the function of the three types of cellular RNA.

RNA, like DNA, is a long, unbranched polymer consisting of nucleotides joined by $3' \rightarrow 5'$ phosphodiester bonds. The number of nucleotides in an RNA molecule ranges from as few as 73 to many thousands. The primary structure of RNA differs from that of DNA in two ways. As we learned in Section 21.1, the sugar unit in RNA is ribose rather than deoxyribose. The other difference is that RNA contains the base uracil (U) instead of thymine (T).

The Clone Wars

Any gardener who has used a cutting from one plant to grow an identical plant has created a clone of the original plant, since clones are organisms that contain identical DNA. Based on that definition, identical twins are essentially clones of each other. The first successful laboratory cloning of an animal involved a tadpole, and occurred in 1952. It took more than 40 years of research before a mammal, Dolly the sheep, was cloned from an adult cell rather than an embryonic cell. Since that success in 1996, numerous other successful mammalian clonings have been achieved in the laboratory.

Research into cloning methods and procedures continues today and has proved to be a sensitive ethical and societal issue. A repeatedly asked question is: Why do it? Supporters of the practice give numerous answers to the question, including the need to save rare or endangered animal species, and the need to produce more quality food for an ever-increasing world population.

The cloning procedure involves three basic steps. First, a donor cell is obtained from an animal that is to be cloned. Next, an egg cell is obtained from an animal that will act as the surrogate mother for the cloned animal. The DNA-containing nucleus of the egg cell is removed and replaced with the nucleus (and the DNA) from the donor cell of the animal being cloned. Finally, the modified egg cell is re-implanted in the surrogate mother, and the embryo, which now contains DNA identical to that of the donor animal, develops. The resulting cloned animal is an exact genetic copy of the donor animal and has all the properties, characteristics, etc., of the donor animal.

This cloning technique has already been used to produce cloned copies of two endangered species of cows: the guar, an ox-like animal from India, and the banteng, a cow from southeast Asia. The San Diego Zoo maintains a "frozen zoo" that contains preserved frozen cells of animals that can be used as future sources of DNA to reproduce or expand the numbers of selected animals.

The high cost of cloning has not prevented some enterprising individuals from commercializing the process. For example, a California company will clone your favorite pet for a nominal fee of $50,000. Surprisingly (or not for pet lovers), the company has had some customers interested in paying for their services.

The obvious extension of this technique to the cloning of humans is the basis for strong opposition from some individuals and organizations. They take the position that no one should play God and create animals, especially humans, even if it is scientifically possible. Cloning supporters point out that rather than creating humans, cloning could help humans have better-quality lives. They say that cloning is not an end in itself but can lead to scientific advances that will benefit human beings. One potential use in this category is to genetically engineer and then mass produce animals that can produce and secrete specific human proteins in their blood or milk. Potentially, such transgenic animals could produce therapeutic proteins for treating or studying human diseases. Another potential application is the use of cloning techniques to produce animal cells and organs that would not trigger the immune system of humans to reject such cells and organs used as transplants. Thus, an animal pancreas with such characteristics could be transplanted into a human suffering from diabetes and cure the disease.

It appears likely that disagreements about the appropriateness of conducting cloning research will continue. If cool heads prevail, a reasonable compromise will be found, and a level of research that provides minimal upset to opponents and maximum benefits to humanity in general will continue.

The first successfully cloned Afghan hound sits with his genetic father.

The secondary structure of RNA is also different from that of DNA. RNA molecules are single-stranded, except in some viruses. Consequently, an RNA molecule need not contain complementary base ratios of 1:1. However, RNA molecules do contain regions of double-helical structure where they form loops (see ❱ Figure 21.13). In these regions, adenine (A) pairs with uracil (U), and guanine (G) pairs with cytosine (C). The proportion of helical regions varies over a wide range depending on the kind of RNA studied, but a value of 50% is typical.

Figure 21.13 A portion of RNA that has folded back on itself and formed a double-helical region.

RNA is distributed throughout cells; it is present in the nucleus, the cytoplasm, and in mitochondria (Table 18.3; Section 22.7). Cells contain three kinds of RNA: messenger RNA (mRNA), ribosomal RNA (rRNA), and transfer RNA (tRNA). Each of these kinds of RNA performs an important function in protein synthesis.

Messenger RNA

messenger RNA (mRNA) RNA that carries genetic information from the DNA in the cell nucleus to the site of protein synthesis in the cytoplasm.

Messenger RNA (mRNA) functions as a carrier of genetic information from the DNA of the cell nucleus directly to the cytoplasm, where protein synthesis takes place. The bases of mRNA are in a sequence that is complementary to the base sequence of one of the strands of the nuclear DNA. In contrast to DNA, which remains intact and unchanged throughout the life of the cell, mRNA has a short lifetime—usually less than an hour. It is synthesized as needed and then rapidly degraded to the constituent nucleotides.

Ribosomal RNA

ribosomal RNA (rRNA) RNA that constitutes about 65% of the material in ribosomes, the sites of protein synthesis.

Ribosomal RNA (rRNA) constitutes 80–85% of the total RNA of the cell. It is located in the cytoplasm in organelles called **ribosomes,** which are about 65% rRNA and 35% protein. The function of ribosomes as the sites of protein synthesis is discussed in Section 21.8.

ribosome A subcellular particle that serves as the site of protein synthesis in all organisms.

Transfer RNA

transfer RNA (tRNA) RNA that delivers individual amino acid molecules to the site of protein synthesis.

Transfer RNA (tRNA) molecules deliver amino acids, the building blocks of proteins, to the site of protein synthesis. Cells contain at least one specific type of tRNA for each of the 20 common amino acids found in proteins. These tRNA molecules are the smallest of all the nucleic acids, containing 73–93 nucleotides per chain.

A comparison of RNA characteristics for the three different forms is summarized in ▶ Table 21.1.

TABLE 21.1 Different Forms of RNA Molecules in *Escherichia coli (E. coli)*

Class of RNA	% in Cells	Number of RNA Subtypes	Number of Nucleotides
Ribosomal RNA (rRNA)	80	3	120
			1700
			3700
Transfer RNA (tRNA)	15	46	73–93
Messenger RNA (mRNA)	5	Many	75–3000

Because of their small size, a number of tRNAs have been studied extensively. ▶ Figure 21.14 shows a representation of the secondary structure of a typical tRNA. This tRNA molecule, like all others, has regions where there is hydrogen bonding between complementary bases, and regions (loops) where there is no hydrogen bonding.

anticodon A three-base sequence in tRNA that is complementary to one of the codons in mRNA.

Two regions of tRNA molecules have important functions during protein synthesis. One of these regions, designated the **anticodon,** enables the tRNA to bind to mRNA

Figure 21.14 The typical tRNA cloverleaf structure.

during protein synthesis. The second important site is the 3′ end of the molecule, which binds to an amino acid and transports it to the site of protein synthesis. Each amino acid is joined to the 3′ end of its specific tRNA by an ester bond that forms between the carboxyl group of the amino acid and the 3′ hydroxy group of ribose. The reaction is catalyzed by an enzyme that matches tRNA molecules to their proper amino acids. These enzymes, which are very specific for both the structure of the amino acid and the tRNA, rarely cause a bond to form between an amino acid and the wrong tRNA. When a tRNA molecule is attached to its specific amino acid, it is said to be "activated" because it is ready to participate in protein synthesis. ▶ Figure 21.15 shows the general structure of an activated tRNA and a schematic representation that will be used in Section 21.8 to describe protein synthesis.

Figure 21.15 An activated tRNA: Ⓐ general structure and Ⓑ a schematic representation.

21.5 The Flow of Genetic Information

Learning Objective

5. Describe what is meant by the terms *transcription* and *translation*.

central dogma of molecular biology The well-established process by which genetic information stored in DNA molecules is expressed in the structure of synthesized proteins.

You learned in Section 21.3 that DNA is the storehouse of genetic information in the cell and that the stored information can be passed on to new cells as DNA undergoes replication. In this section, you will discover how the information stored in DNA is expressed within the cell.

This process of expression is so well established that it is called the **central dogma of molecular biology.** The accepted dogma, or principle, says that genetic information contained in DNA molecules is transferred to RNA molecules. The transferred information of RNA molecules is then expressed in the structure of synthesized proteins. In other words, the genetic information in DNA (genes) directs the synthesis of certain proteins. In fact, there is a specific DNA gene for every protein in the body. DNA does not direct the synthesis of carbohydrates, lipids, or the other nonprotein substances essential for life. However, these other materials are manufactured by the cell through reactions made possible by enzymes (proteins) produced under the direction of DNA. Thus, in this respect, the information stored in DNA really does determine every characteristic of the living organism.

transcription The transfer of genetic information from a DNA molecule to a molecule of messenger RNA.

Two steps are involved in the flow of genetic information: transcription and translation. In higher organisms (eukaryotes), the DNA containing the stored information is located in the nucleus of the cell, and protein synthesis occurs in the cytoplasm. Thus, the stored information must first be carried out of the nucleus. This is accomplished by **transcription,** or transferring the necessary information from a DNA molecule onto a molecule of messenger RNA. The appropriately named messenger RNA carries the information (the message) from the nucleus to the site of protein synthesis in the cellular cytoplasm.

translation The conversion of the code carried by messenger RNA into an amino acid sequence of a protein.

In the second step, the mRNA serves as a template on which amino acids are assembled in the proper sequence necessary to produce the specified protein. This takes place when the code or message carried by mRNA is **translated** into an amino acid sequence by tRNA. There is an exact word-to-word translation from mRNA to tRNA. Thus, each word in the mRNA language has a corresponding word in the amino acid language of tRNA. This communicative relationship between mRNA nucleotides and amino acids is called the *genetic code* (Section 21.7). ❱ Figure 21.16 summarizes the mechanisms for the flow of genetic information in the cell.

DNA
replication

DNA → Transcription → RNA → Translation → protein

Figure 21.16 The flow of genetic information in the cell.

21.6 Transcription: RNA Synthesis

Learning Objective

6. Describe the process by which RNA is synthesized in cells.

An enzyme called RNA polymerase catalyzes the synthesis of RNA. During the first step of the process, the DNA double helix begins to unwind at a point near the gene that is to be transcribed. Since the end product will be single-stranded, only one strand of the DNA molecule is transcribed. Ribonucleotides are linked together along the unwound DNA strand in a sequence determined by complementary base pairing of the DNA strand bases and ribonucleotide bases.

The DNA strand always has one sequence of bases recognized by RNA polymerase as the initiation or starting point. Starting at this point, the enzyme catalyzes the synthesis of mRNA in the 5′ to 3′ direction until it reaches another sequence of bases that designates the termination point. Because the complementary chains of RNA and DNA run in opposite directions, the enzyme must move along the DNA template in the 3′ to 5′ direction (see ▶ Figure 21.17). Once the mRNA molecule has been synthesized, it moves away from the DNA template, which then rewinds to form the original double-helical structure. Transfer RNA and ribosomal RNA are synthesized in the same way, with DNA serving as a template.

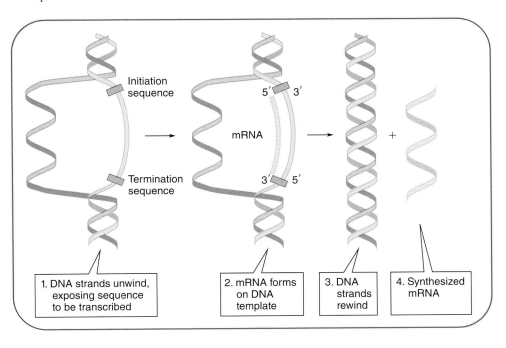

Figure 21.17 The synthesis of mRNA.

1. DNA strands unwind, exposing sequence to be transcribed
2. mRNA forms on DNA template
3. DNA strands rewind
4. Synthesized mRNA

▶ Example 21.2

Write the sequence for the mRNA that could be synthesized using the following DNA base sequence as a template:

$$5′ \qquad G–C–A–A–C–T–T–G \qquad 3′$$

Solution

RNA synthesis begins at the 3′ end of the DNA template and proceeds toward the 5′ end. The complementary RNA strand is formed from the bases C, G, A, and U. Uracil (U) is the complement of adenine (A) on the DNA template.

direction of strand →

DNA template: 5′ G–C–A–A–C–T–T–G 3′
New mRNA: 3′ C–G–U–U–G–A–A–C 5′

← direction of strand

Writing the sequence of the new mRNA in the 5′ to 3′ direction, it becomes:

5′ C–A–A–G–U–U–G–C 3′

▶ **LEARNING CHECK 21.3** Write the sequence for the mRNA that could be synthesized on the following DNA template:

5′ A–T–T–A–G–C–C–G 3′

Although the general process of transcription operates universally, there are differences in detail between the processes in prokaryotes and eukaryotes. The genes found in prokaryotic cells exist as a continuous segment of a DNA molecule. Transcription of this gene segment produces mRNA that undergoes translation into a protein almost immediately because there is no nuclear membrane in a prokaryotic cell separating DNA from the cytoplasm. In 1977, however, it was discovered that the genes of eukaryotic cells are segments of DNA that are "interrupted" by segments that do not code for amino acids. These DNA segments that carry no amino acid code are called **introns,** and the coded DNA segments are called **exons.**

When transcription occurs in the nuclei of eukaryotic cells, both introns and exons are transcribed. This produces what is called **heterogeneous nuclear RNA (hnRNA).** This long molecule of hnRNA then undergoes a series of enzyme-catalyzed reactions that cut and splice the hnRNA to produce mRNA (see ▶ Figure 21.18). The mRNA resulting from this process contains only the sequence of bases that actually codes for protein synthesis. Although the function of introns in eukaryotic DNA is not yet understood, it is an area of active research.

intron A segment of a eukaryotic DNA molecule that carries no codes for amino acids.

exon A segment of a eukaryotic DNA molecule that is coded for amino acids.

heterogeneous nuclear RNA (hnRNA) RNA produced when both introns and exons of eukaryotic cellular DNA are transcribed.

Figure 21.18 Segments of hnRNA formed from introns of eukaryotic cells are removed by special enzymes to produce mRNA.

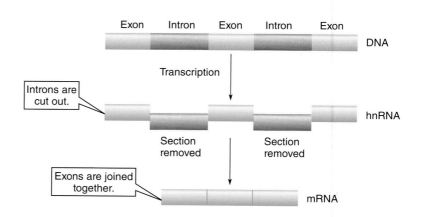

Is There a DNA Checkup in Your Future?

The human genome consists of the genetic material contained in the human body in the form of genes and control factors for the genes. These genes and control factors, the fundamental units of heredity, are made of DNA and are organized into the chromosomes found in each cell. The genes carry the codes, or directions, for the synthesis of every type of protein produced by the body.

Scientists around the world have been working for many years on the "human genome project," with the goal of identifying and determining the sequence of the approximately 3 billion letters of genetic code contained in the 20,000 genes of the human body. In June of 2000, scientists announced that the sequence of the complete human genome had been compiled. Today, that same work of reading a human genome—which required thousands of scientists much more than 10 years to accomplish at a cost of 2.7 billion dollars—can be done in one lab in a matter of days at a cost of less than $5,000.

What is the benefit of knowing the genome of a human? In 2000, only a handful of genes had been identified that were known to influence the development of common diseases such as heart disease, diabetes, and some cancers. Today, as a result of research in the human genome project, the number of such predictive genes has increased to 600–700 and involves more than 100 diseases.

While it is probably a number of years in the future, one clinical expectation from the human genome project is that physicians will one day be able to prescribe personal genome readings for patients. The results of such DNA checkups might allow physicians to precisely estimate individual risks for a significant number of common diseases and then provide advice on lifestyle changes, or even prescribe preventive medications.

In an ongoing project in this direction, research work is being done to sequence the complete genomes of 3,000 individuals. The goal is to identify genetic differences that predispose people to develop type 2 diabetes.

Efforts are also underway to reduce the costs associated with DNA-sequencing equipment and procedures to bring them in line with the costs of relatively routine diagnostic procedures such as MRI scans or endoscopy examinations. So, it appears probable that DNA checkups are likely to be in your future, especially if you are relatively young.

A researcher prepares a sample for DNA sequencing.

21.7 The Genetic Code

Learning Objective

7. Explain how the genetic code functions in the flow of genetic information.

Discovery of the Genetic Code

By 1961, it was clear that the sequence of bases in DNA serves to direct the synthesis of mRNA, and that the sequence of bases in mRNA corresponds to the order of amino acids in a particular protein. However, the genetic code, the exact relationship between mRNA sequences and amino acids, was unknown. At least 20 mRNA "words" are needed to represent uniquely each of the 20 amino acids found in proteins. If the mRNA words consisted of a single letter represented by a base (A, C, G, or U), only four amino acids could be uniquely represented. Thus, it was proposed that it is not one mRNA base but a combination of bases that codes for each amino acid. For example, if a code word consists of a sequence of two mRNA bases, there are $4^2 = 16$ possible combinations, so 16 amino acids could be represented uniquely. This is a more extensive code, but it still contains too few words to do the job for 20 amino acids. If the code consists of a sequence of three bases, there are 4^3 64 possible combinations, more than enough to specify uniquely each amino

acid in the primary sequence of a protein. Research has confirmed that nature does indeed use three-letter code words (a triplet code) to store and express genetic information. Each sequence of three nucleotide bases that represents code words on mRNA molecules is called a **codon.**

codon A sequence of three nucleotide bases that represents a code word on mRNA molecules.

After the discovery of three-letter codons, researchers were anxious to answer the next question: Which triplets of bases (codons) code for which amino acids? In 1961, Marshall Nirenberg and his coworkers at the National Institutes of Health (NIH) in Bethesda, Maryland, attempted to break the code in a very ingenious way. They made a synthetic molecule of mRNA consisting of uracil bases only. Thus, this mRNA contained only one codon, the triplet UUU. They incubated this synthetic mRNA with ribosomes, amino acids, tRNAs, and the appropriate enzymes for protein synthesis. The exciting result of this experiment was that a polypeptide that consisted only of phenylalanine was synthesized. Thus, the first word of the genetic code had been deciphered; UUU phenylalanine.

A series of similar experiments by Nirenberg and other researchers followed, and by 1967 the entire genetic code had been broken. The complete code is shown in ▶ Table 21.2.

TABLE 21.2 The Genetic Code: mRNA Codons for Each of the 20 Amino Acids

Amino Acid	Codons	Number of Codons
alanine	GCA, GCC, GCG, GCU	4
arginine	AGA, AGG, CGA, CGC, CGG, CGU	6
asparagine	AAC, AAU	2
aspartic acid	GAC, GAU	2
cysteine	UGC, UGU	2
glutamic acid	GAA, GAG	2
glutamine	CAA, CAG	2
glycine	GGA, GGC, GGG, GGU	4
histidine	CAC, CAU	2
isoleucine	AUA, AUC, AUU	3
leucine	CUA, CUC, CUG, CUU, UUA, UUG	6
lysine	AAA, AAG	2
methionine, initiation	AUG	1
phenylalanine	UUC, UUU	2
proline	CCA, CCC, CCG, CCU	4
serine	UCA, UCC, UCG, UCU, AGC, AGU	6
threonine	ACA, ACC, ACG, ACU	4
tryptophan	UGG	1
tyrosine	UAC, UAU	2
valine	GUA, GUC, GUG, GUU	4
Stop signals	UAG, UAA, UGA	3
Total number of codons		64

Three very important processes discussed in this chapter are replication, transcription, and translation. New terminology is always easier to learn if we can make associations with something we already know. See if these ideas help. To replicate means to copy or to repeat. Associate the word *replicate* with *repeat*.

For the processes of transcription and translation, think of an analogy with the English language. If you were to transcribe your lecture notes from a recording, you would rewrite them in the same language. In the same way, transcription of DNA to mRNA is a rewriting of the information using the same nucleic acid language. If you translated your lecture notes, you would convert them to another language, such as German. Translation of mRNA to an amino acid sequence is converting information from a nucleic acid language to a language of proteins.

Characteristics of the Genetic Code

The first important characteristic of the genetic code is that it applies almost universally. With very minor exceptions, the same amino acid is represented by the same three-base codon (or codons) in every organism.

Another interesting feature of the genetic code is apparent from Table 21.2. Most of the amino acids are represented by more than one codon, a condition known as *degeneracy*. Only methionine and tryptophan are represented by single codons. Leucine, serine, and arginine are the most degenerate, with each one represented by six codons. The remaining 15 amino acids are each coded for by at least two codons. Even though most amino acids are represented by more than one codon, it is significant that the reverse is not true—no single codon represents more than one amino acid. Each three-base codon represents one and only one amino acid.

Only 61 of the possible 64 base triplets represent amino acids. The remaining three (UAA, UAG, and UGA) are signals for chain terminations. They tell the protein-synthesizing process when the primary structure of the synthesized protein is complete and it is time to stop adding amino acids to the chain. These three codons are indicated in Table 21.2 as stop signals.

The presence of stop signals in the code implies that start signals must also exist. There is only one initiation (start) codon, AUG, which also is the codon for the amino acid methionine. AUG functions as an initiation codon only when it occurs as the first codon of a sequence. When this happens, protein synthesis begins at that point (Section 21.8).

These general features of the genetic code are summarized in ▶ Table 21.3.

TABLE 21.3 General Characteristics of the Genetic Code

Characteristic	Example
Codons are three-letter words	GCA = alanine
The code is degenerate	GCA, GCC, GCG, GCU all represent alanine
The code is precise	GCC represents only alanine
Chain initiation is coded	AUG
Chain termination is coded	UAA, UAG, and UGA
The code is almost universal	GCA = alanine, perhaps, in all organisms

21.8 Translation and Protein Synthesis

Learning Objective

8. Outline the process by which proteins are synthesized in cells.

To this point, you have become familiar with the molecules that participate in protein synthesis and the genetic code, the language that directs the synthesis. We now investigate the actual process by which polypeptide chains are assembled. There are three major stages in protein synthesis: initiation of the polypeptide chain, elongation of the chain, and termination of the completed polypeptide chain.

Initiation of the Polypeptide Chain

The first amino acid that starts the process of protein synthesis in prokaryotic (bacterial) cells is a derivative of methionine. This compound, N-formylmethionine, initiates the growing polypeptide chain as the N-terminal amino acid. The fact that most proteins do not have N-formylmethionine as the N-terminal amino acid indicates that when protein synthesis is completed, the N-formylmethionine is cleaved from the finished protein.

$$H-\overset{\overset{\displaystyle O}{\|}}{C}-NH-CH-\overset{\overset{\displaystyle O}{\|}}{C}-O^-$$

formyl group CH_2

CH_2-S-CH_3

N-formylmethionine
(fMet)

A ribosome comprises two subunits, a large subunit and a small subunit. The initiation process begins when mRNA is aligned on the surface of a small ribosomal subunit in such a way that the initiating codon, AUG, occupies a specific site on the ribosome called the P site (peptidyl site). When the AUG codon is used this way to initiate synthesis of a polypeptide chain in prokaryotic cells, it represents N-formylmethionine (fMet) instead of methionine. When AUG is located anywhere else on the mRNA, it simply represents methionine. For the eukaryotic cells of humans, AUG always specifies methionine even when it is the initiating codon. Next, a tRNA molecule with its attached fMet binds to the codon through hydrogen bonds. The resulting complex binds to the large ribosomal subunit to form a unit called an *initiation complex* (see ▶ Figure 21.19).

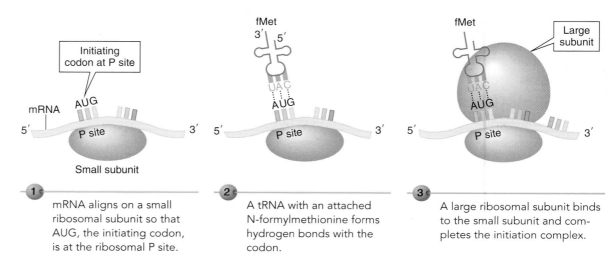

1 mRNA aligns on a small ribosomal subunit so that AUG, the initiating codon, is at the ribosomal P site.

2 A tRNA with an attached N-formylmethionine forms hydrogen bonds with the codon.

3 A large ribosomal subunit binds to the small subunit and completes the initiation complex.

Figure 21.19 Initiation complex formation.

Stem Cell Research

"**Stem cell** research" is a phrase many individuals are familiar with, but only understand in a superficial way. This ethically charged and very controversial research has great potential to provide treatments and possibly cures for serious conditions such as diabetes, heart disease, and Parkinson's disease. Despite this potential to benefit human society, numerous countries have limited and even banned specific practices associated with this research on the basis of ethical concerns.

Stem cells possess the unique capability to develop into many different types of cells found in the body. When a stem cell divides, each new cell has the ability to either remain as a stem cell or transform into another type of specialized cell such as a muscle cell, a red blood cell, or a brain cell. Because of this ability, stem cells can serve as a repair system for the body and theoretically divide without limit to replenish other cells that are lost through injury, disease, or normal wear and tear.

There are two types of stem cells: embryonic stem cells and adult stem cells. Human embryonic stem cells are thought to have much greater developmental potential than adult stem cells because they are *pluripotent,* which means they are able to develop into any type of cell. Adult stem cells are *multipotent,* meaning they can become cells corresponding to the type of tissue in which they reside.

After many years of research, it is now possible to isolate stem cells from human embryos and get them to multiply in the laboratory. These are called human embryonic stem cells. The embryos used in these studies were created by in vitro fertilization processes in order to treat infertility. When the embryos were no longer needed, they were donated for research with the informed consent of the donor.

The existence of two types of stem cells has prompted some critics of the embryonic cell research to ask why adult stem cells are not used instead of embryonic stem cells. Supporters of the research point out that embryonic stem cells have a much greater versatility because they can become any type of cell, not just the same type of cell as the cells of the tissue in which they are found. Embryonic stem cells could be used to treat a damaged organ, a broken bone, or an injured spinal cord. In some research, embryonic stem cells have been grown into heart muscle cells that clump together in a laboratory dish and pulse in unison. And when those heart cells were injected into mice and pigs with heart disease, they filled in for the injured or dead cells and accelerated the animal's recovery. Similar studies have suggested that embryonic stem cells have the potential to provide similar cures for conditions such as diabetes and spinal cord injury. In our society where waiting lists for donated organs are too long to help many patients, stem cell research could hold the answer.

A researcher prepares stem cells for culture.

© Darren Hauck/Getty Images

Elongation of the Chain

A second site, called the A site (aminoacyl site), is located on the mRNA–ribosome complex next to the P site. The A site is where an incoming tRNA carrying the next amino acid will bond. Each of the tRNA molecules representing the 20 amino acids can try to fit the A site, but only the one with the correct anticodon that is complementary to the next codon on the mRNA will fit properly.

Once at the A site, the second amino acid (in this case, phenylalanine) is linked to *N*-formylmethionine by a peptide bond whose formation is catalyzed by the enzyme peptidyl transferase (see ❱ Figure 21.20). After the peptide bond forms, the tRNA bound to the P site is "empty," and the growing polypeptide chain is now attached to the tRNA bound to the A site.

In the next phase of elongation, the whole ribosome moves one codon along the mRNA toward the 3′ end. As the ribosome moves, the empty tRNA is released from the P site, and tRNA attached to peptide chain moves from the A site and takes its place on the P site. This movement of the ribosome along the mRNA is called *translocation* and makes the A site available to receive the next tRNA with the proper anticodon.

stem cell An unspecialized cell that has the ability to replicate and differentiate, giving rise to a specialized cell.

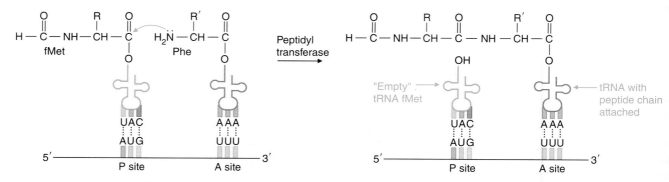

Figure 21.20 The amino acid at the P site bonds through a peptide bond to the amino acid at the A site.

The amino acid carried by this tRNA bonds to the peptide chain, and the elongation process is repeated. This occurs over and over until the entire polypeptide chain is synthesized. The elongation process is represented in ❱ Figure 21.21 for the synthesis of the tripeptide fMet—Phe—Val.

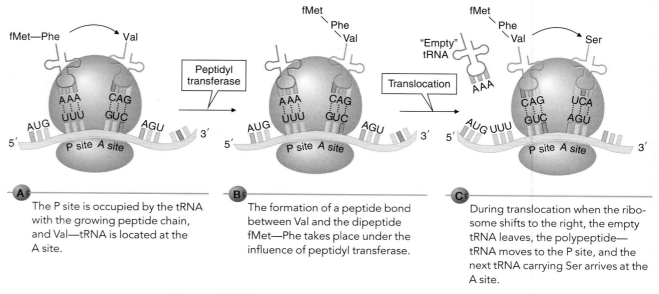

(A) The P site is occupied by the tRNA with the growing peptide chain, and Val—tRNA is located at the A site.

(B) The formation of a peptide bond between Val and the dipeptide fMet—Phe takes place under the influence of peptidyl transferase.

(C) During translocation when the ribosome shifts to the right, the empty tRNA leaves, the polypeptide—tRNA moves to the P site, and the next tRNA carrying Ser arrives at the A site.

Figure 21.21 Polypeptide chain elongation.

The Termination of Polypeptide Synthesis

The chain elongation process continues and polypeptide synthesis continues until the ribosome complex reaches a stop codon (UAA, UAG, or UGA) on the mRNA. At that point, a specific protein known as a termination factor binds to the stop codon and catalyzes the hydrolysis of the completed polypeptide chain from the final tRNA. The "empty" ribosome dissociates and can then bind to another strand of mRNA to once again begin the process of protein synthesis.

Several ribosomes can move along a single strand of mRNA one after another (see ❱ Figure 21.22). Thus, several identical polypeptide chains can be synthesized almost simultaneously from a single mRNA molecule. This markedly increases the efficiency of utilization of the mRNA. Such complexes of several ribosomes and mRNA are called **polyribosomes** or **polysomes.** Growing polypeptide chains extend from the ribosomes into the cellular cytoplasm and spontaneously fold to assume characteristic three-dimensional secondary and tertiary configurations.

polyribosome or polysome A complex of mRNA and several ribosomes.

Figure 21.22 A polyribosome, several ribosomes proceeding simultaneously along mRNA.

> ▶ **LEARNING CHECK 21.4** Write the primary structure of the polypeptide produced
> during translation of the following mRNA sequence:
>
> 5′ AUG–CAC–CAU–GUA–UUG–UGU–UAG 3′

21.9 Mutations

Learning Objective

9. Describe how genetic mutations occur and how they influence organisms.

In Section 21.3, we pointed out that the base-pairing mechanism provides a nearly perfect way to copy a DNA molecule during replication. However, not even the copying mechanism involved in DNA replication is totally error free. It is estimated that, on average, one in every 10^{10} bases of DNA (i.e., 1 in 10 billion) is incorrect. Any change resulting in an incorrect sequence of bases on DNA is called a **mutation.** The faithful transcription of mutated DNA leads to an incorrect base sequence in mRNA. This can lead to an incorrect amino acid sequence for a protein, or possibly the failure of a protein to be synthesized at all.

Some mutations occur naturally during DNA replication; others can be induced by environmental factors such as ionizing radiation (X-rays, ultraviolet light, gamma rays, etc.). Repeated exposure to X-rays greatly increases the rate of mutation. Thus, patients are given X-rays only when necessary, and technicians who administer X-rays remain behind protective barriers. A large number of chemicals (e.g., nitrous acid and dimethyl sulfate) can also induce mutations by reacting with DNA. Such chemicals are called **mutagens.**

Some mutations might be beneficial to an organism by making it more capable of surviving in its environment. Mutations may also occur without affecting an organism. Conversely, mutations may be lethal or produce genetic diseases whenever an important protein (or enzyme) is not correctly synthesized. Sickle-cell disease, phenylketonuria (PKU), hemophilia, muscular dystrophy, and many other disorders are results of such mutations that have become permanently incorporated into the genetic makeup of certain individuals.

mutation Any change resulting in an incorrect base sequence on DNA.

mutagen A chemical that induces mutations by reacting with DNA.

21.10 Recombinant DNA

Learning Objective

10. Describe the technology used to produce recombinant DNA.

Remarkable technology is available that allows segments of DNA from one organism to be introduced into the genetic material of another organism. The resulting new DNA (containing the foreign segment) is referred to as **recombinant DNA.** The application of this technology, commonly called *genetic engineering,* has produced major advances in

recombinant DNA DNA of an organism that contains genetic material from another organism.

Figure 21.23 This tomato, a beneficiary of genetic engineering, has an increased shelf life.

human health care and holds the promise for a future of exciting advances in biology, agriculture (see ▶ Figure 21.23), and many other areas of study.

An early success of genetic engineering was the introduction of the gene for human insulin into the DNA of the common bacterium *E. coli.* The bacterium then transcribed and translated the information carried by the gene and produced the protein hormone. By culturing such *E. coli,* it has become possible to produce and market large quantities of human insulin. The availability of human insulin is very important for diabetics allergic to the insulin traditionally used, which is isolated from the pancreatic tissue of slaughtered pigs or cattle. ▶ Table 21.4 lists several other medically important materials that have been produced through genetic engineering.

TABLE 21.4 Some Substances Produced by Genetic Engineering	
Substance	**Use**
Human insulin	Treatment of diabetes mellitus
Human growth hormone	Treatment of dwarfism
Interferon	Fights viral infections
Hepatitis B vaccine	Protection against hepatitis
Malaria vaccine	Protection against malaria
Tissue plasminogen activator	Promotes the dissolving of blood clots

Enzymes Used in Genetic Engineering

The discovery of restriction enzymes in the 1960s and 1970s made genetic engineering possible. Restriction enzymes, which are found in a wide variety of bacterial cells, catalyze the cleaving of DNA molecules. These enzymes are normally part of a mechanism that protects certain bacteria from invasion by foreign DNA such as that of a virus. In these bacteria, some of the bases in their DNA have methyl groups attached. For example, the following compounds are found:

<div style="text-align:center">1-methylguanine 5-methylcytosine</div>

The methylated DNA of these bacteria is left untouched by the restriction enzymes, but foreign DNA that lacks the methylated bases undergoes rapid cleavage of both strands and thus becomes nonfunctional. Because there is a "restriction" on the type of DNA allowed in the bacterial cell, the protective enzymes are called **restriction enzymes.**

Restriction enzymes act at sites on DNA called palindromes. In language, a palindrome is any word or phrase that reads the same in either direction, such as "radar" or "Madam, I'm Adam." For double-stranded DNA, a palindrome is a section in which the two strands have the same sequence but run in opposite directions. Examples of DNA palindromes follow; the arrows indicate the points of attack by restriction enzymes:

restriction enzyme A protective enzyme found in some bacteria that catalyzes the cleaving of all but a few specific types of DNA.

<div style="text-align:center">

↓ ↓

5′ C – C – G – C – G – G 3′　　5′ G – G – A – T – C – C 3′

3′ G – G – C – G – C – C 5′　　3′ C – C – T – A – G – G 5′

↑ ↑

</div>

DNA and the Crime Scene

DNA, commonly referred to as the blueprint of life, passes along hereditary information to offspring and directs all life processes. DNA also plays a key role in forensic science, made popular by TV shows such as *CSI: Crime Scene Investigation.* However, DNA fingerprinting isn't just a gimmick used in Hollywood scripts; it is a valuable tool in solving real-world crimes.

DNA profiling—also called DNA typing or DNA fingerprinting—is possible because most of the DNA molecule is common to all humans, but small parts of it differ from person to person. In fact, 99.9% of human DNA is identical, but 0.1% differs from person to person. Small as this difference seems, it is equivalent to 3 million bases in an individual DNA. Therefore, with the exception of identical twins, the DNA of every human is unique. Unlike a conventional fingerprint, which occurs only on the fingertips, a DNA fingerprint is identical for every cell of each tissue and organ of the person's body. Consequently, DNA fingerprinting has become the method of choice for identifying and distinguishing among individual human beings.

Law enforcement laboratories around the world routinely use DNA fingerprints to link suspects to crime-scene biological evidence such as blood, semen, or hair. DNA fingerprints used to establish paternity in custody and child-support litigations provide nearly perfect accuracy in parental identification. The U.S. armed services have switched from dog tags and dental records to DNA fingerprint records as a means to identify all personnel, including those killed in combat.

The use of DNA by the U.S. armed services has even made it possible to identify soldiers from past wars. In 1997, DNA collected from bones of American servicemen killed during the Vietnam War helped the Army identify the bodies. It wasn't the only method used in the identification process, but it provided conclusive evidence.

The technique of DNA fingerprinting involves cleaving DNA molecules at specific points using restriction enzymes. The mixture of DNA fragments is then separated into specific patterns by a process called gel electrophoresis. In this process, the cleaved DNA is put into a gel through which electricity is passed. The current organized the pieces of DNA in the gel by size. The resulting patterns are made visible by attaching radioactive reagents to the DNA fragments and exposing X-ray film to the results of the electrophoresis. The film shows a specific pattern of dark bands when it is developed.

The ability to obtain DNA fingerprints from exceedingly small tissue samples has become possible by using the polymerase chain reaction technique (Section 21.3).

The PCR technique allows billions of copies of a DNA sample to be prepared in a few hours. PCR enables researchers to study extremely faint and tiny traces of DNA obtained from biological samples, such as specks of dried blood, strands of hair, chips of bone, or even from fingerprints. PCR amplification of the DNA in a single sperm cell has been used to link suspects to rape victims. A single cell from saliva on the stamp of a letter bomb would provide enough DNA to help identify the person who licked the stamp.

These few examples illustrate the tremendous identification potential of the PCR technique coupled with the uniqueness of each individual's DNA. It is getting more and more difficult to hide.

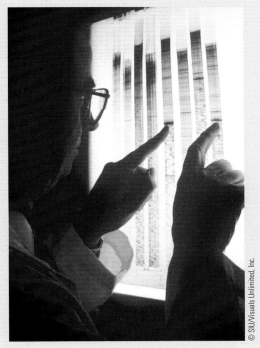

A researcher compares the patterns of dark bands produced by DNA fragments.

© SIU/Visuals Unlimited, Inc.

At least 100 bacterial restriction enzymes are known, and each catalyzes DNA cleavage in a specific and predictable way. These enzymes are the tools used to take DNA apart and reduce it to fragments of known size and nucleotide sequence.

Another set of enzymes important in genetic engineering, called DNA ligases, has been known since 1967. These enzymes normally function to connect DNA fragments during replication, and they are used in genetic engineering to put together pieces of DNA produced by restriction enzymes.

Plasmids

The introduction of a new DNA segment (gene) into a bacterial cell requires the assistance of a DNA carrier called a **vector.** The vector is often a circular piece of double-stranded DNA called a **plasmid.** Plasmids range in size from 2000 to several hundred thousand nucleotides and are found in the cytoplasm of bacterial cells. Plasmids function as accessories to chromosomes by carrying genes for the inactivation of antibiotics and the production of toxins. They have the unusual ability to replicate independently of chromosomal DNA. A typical bacterial cell contains about 20 plasmids and one or two chromosomes.

The Formation of Recombinant DNA

The recombinant DNA technique begins with the isolation of a plasmid from a bacterium. A restriction enzyme is added to the plasmid, which is cleaved at a specific site:

$$\sim G-G-A-T-C-C\sim \quad \xrightarrow{\text{restriction enzyme}} \quad \sim G \qquad G-A-T-C-C\sim$$
$$\sim C-C-T-A-G-G\sim \qquad\qquad \sim C-C-T-A-G \qquad\qquad\qquad G\sim$$

sticky ends

Because a plasmid is circular, cleaving it this way produces a double-stranded chain with two ends (see ▶ Figure 21.24). These are called "sticky ends" because each has one strand in which several bases are unpaired and ready to pair up with a complementary section if available.

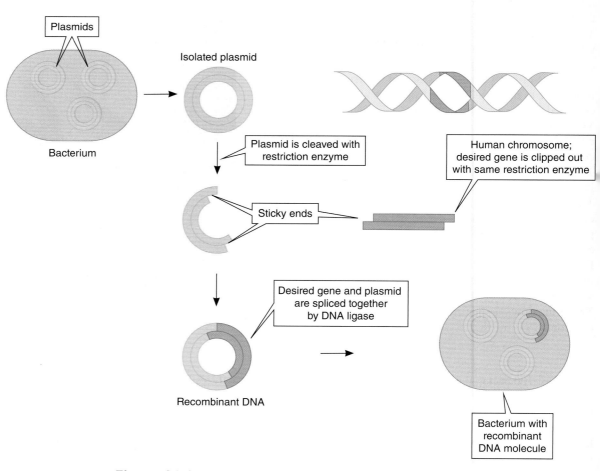

Figure 21.24 The formation of recombinant DNA.

Genetically Modified Foods

Many people think that the practice of genetically altering food is the result of recent discoveries in the science of genetics. The reality is that such bioengineering of food has been going on for centuries in the practices of cross-pollinating plants and selective crossbreeding of animals. These activities were done in successful attempts to produce plant and animal food sources with desirable characteristics.

The goals of bioengineering foods today are essentially the same as those earlier goals, but the goals are more sophisticated. Instead of focusing on such things as increased animal size or drought-resistant plants, today's bioengineering has goals such as producing plants that repel or kill insects that attack them or producing animals that yield meat low in artery-clogging fats.

The following successes serve to illustrate the tremendous potential of bioengineering in helping to alleviate an increasing problem of supplying the world's inhabitants with quality food. Corn is commonly modified by adding a gene that produces plants that kill corn-devouring caterpillars. A recently developed strain of rice contains genes that produce beta-carotene, the precursor of vitamin A, in the rice grains. When this so-called golden rice is substituted for regular rice as the major source of food in the diet, it can help prevent the onset of blindness in children that results from a vitamin A deficiency. Scientists have found a way to produce tomato plants that contain three times the normal level of lycopene, a known cancer-preventing compound.

In spite of this great potential, the bioengineering of food is not accepted as desirable by everyone. The extent of concern is not uniform. For example, there are few labeling guidelines for genetically modified food in the United States. The U.S. Food and Drug Administration only requires that food be labeled as genetically modified if the nutritional content of the food has been changed, or if a potential allergen (such as a peanut gene) has been added. By contrast, the European Union was concerned enough to place a moratorium on the imports of modified sweet corn from the United States. The import of other bioengineered crops has since been allowed.

The greatest concerns of opponents to bioengineered foods are related to human health. It is feared that genes introduced into plants from bacteria and viruses might accidentally make the plants into sources of protein allergens dangerous to humans. The well-known peanut proteins that are serious allergens to some people are sometimes used as an example. There could be other negative effects, as yet unknown, from introducing this recombinant genetic material into the human body.

It appears that bioengineering of foods holds great promise of providing significant benefits to humans. However, more education and research are needed to minimize concerns and demonstrate the safety of the procedure to those who are in doubt.

Tomatoes are one example of bioengineered foods in the marketplace.

The next step is to provide the sticky ends with complementary sections for pairing. A human chromosome is cleaved into several fragments using the same restriction enzyme. Because the same enzyme is used, the human DNA is cleaved such that the same sticky ends result:

$$G - A - T - C - C \thicksim\thicksim\thicksim\thicksim\thicksim\thicksim G$$
$$\text{human DNA segment}$$
$$G \thicksim\thicksim\thicksim\thicksim\thicksim\thicksim C - C - T - A - G$$

To splice the human gene into the plasmid, the two are brought together under conditions suitable for the formation of hydrogen bonds between the complementary bases of the sticky ends. The breaks in the strands are then joined by using DNA ligase, and the plasmid once again becomes a circular piece of double-stranded DNA that now incorporates both human and bacterial DNA (Figure 21.24); recombinant DNA has been formed.

Bacterial cells are bathed in a solution containing recombinant DNA plasmids, which diffuse into the cells. When the bacteria reproduce, they replicate all the genes, including the recombinant DNA plasmid. Bacteria multiply quickly, and soon a large number of

bacteria, all containing the modified plasmid, are manufacturing the new protein as directed by the recombinant DNA.

The use of this technology makes possible (in principle) the large-scale production of virtually any polypeptide or protein. By remembering the many essential roles these substances play in the body, it is easy to predict that genetic engineering will make tremendous contributions to improving health care in the future.

Case Study Follow-up

"Reproductive rights rest on the recognition of the basic right of all couples and individuals to decide freely and responsibly the number, spacing and timing of their children and to have the information and means to do so, and the right to attain the highest standard of sexual and reproductive health. They also include the right of all to make decisions concerning reproduction free of discrimination, coercion and violence" (UN, 1995). In light of the international definition of reproductive rights, responsibilities concerning reproductive decisions rest with the couple. Genetic counseling can be help those at risk of transmitting heritable diseases to make informed decisions.

According to the American Medical Association Medical Code of Ethics, physicians have several areas of responsibility concerning reproductive issues and genetic counseling. "Physicians engaged in genetic counseling are ethically obligated to provide prospective parents with the basis for an informed decision for childbearing. Counseling should include reasons for and against testing as well as discussion of inappropriate uses of genetic testing. Prenatal genetic testing is most appropriate for women or couples whose medical histories or family backgrounds indicate an elevated risk of fetal genetic disorders. Women or couples without an elevated risk of genetic disease may legitimately request prenatal diagnosis, provided they understand and accept the risks involved. When counseling prospective parents, physicians should avoid the imposition of their personal moral values and the substitution of their own moral judgment for that of the prospective parents" (AMA, 1994).

Concept Summary

Components of Nucleic Acids

Nucleic acids are classified into two categories: ribonucleic acids (RNA) and deoxyribonucleic acids (DNA). Both types are polymers made up of monomers called nucleotides. All nucleotides are composed of a pyrimidine or purine base, a sugar, and phosphate. The sugar component of RNA is ribose, and that of DNA is deoxyribose. The bases adenine, guanine, and cytosine are found in all nucleic acids. Uracil is found only in RNA, and thymine only in DNA.

Objective 1 (Section 21.1), Exercises 21.2 and 21.4

The Structure of DNA

The nucleotides of DNA are joined by linkages between phosphate groups and sugars. The resulting sugar–phosphate backbone is the same for all DNA molecules, but the order of attached bases along the backbone varies. This order of nucleotides with attached bases is the primary structure of nucleic acids. The secondary structure is a double-stranded helix held together by hydrogen bonds between complementary base pairs on the strands.

Objective 2 (Section 21.2), Exercise 21.10

DNA Replication

The replication of DNA occurs when a double strand of DNA unwinds at specific points. The exposed bases match up with complementary bases of nucleotides. The nucleotides bind together to form two new strands that are complementary to the strands that separated. Thus, the two new DNA molecules each contain one old strand and one new strand.

Objective 3 (Section 21.3), Exercise 21.20

Ribonucleic Acid (RNA)

Three forms of ribonucleic acid are found in cells: messenger RNA, ribosomal RNA, and transfer RNA. Each form serves an important function during protein synthesis. All RNA molecules are single stranded, but some contain loops or folds.

Objective 4 (Section 21.4), Exercises 21.26 and 21.28

The Flow of Genetic Information

The flow of genetic information occurs in two steps called transcription and translation. In transcription, information stored in DNA molecules is passed to molecules of messenger RNA. In translation, the messenger RNA serves as a template that directs the assembly of amino acids into proteins.

Objective 5 (Section 21.5), Exercise 21.32

Transcription: RNA Synthesis

The various RNAs are synthesized in much the same way as DNA is replicated. Nucleotides with complementary bases align themselves against one strand of a partially unwound DNA segment that contains the genetic information that is to be transcribed. The aligned nucleotides bond together to form the RNA. In eukaryotic cells, the produced RNA is heterogeneous and is cut and spliced after being synthesized to produce the functional RNA.

Objective 6 (Section 21.6), Exercise 21.34

The Genetic Code

The genetic code is a series of three-letter words that represent the amino acids of proteins as well as start and stop signals for protein synthesis. The letters of the words are the bases found on mRNA, and the words on mRNA are called codons. The genetic code is the same for all organisms and is degenerate for most amino acids.

Objective 7 (Section 21.7), Exercise 21.38

Translation and Protein Synthesis

The translation step in the flow of genetic information results in the synthesis of proteins. The synthesis takes place when properly coded mRNA forms a complex with the component of a ribosome. Transfer RNA molecules carrying amino acids align themselves along the mRNA in an order representing the correct primary structure of the protein. The order is determined by the matching of complementary codons on the mRNA to anticodons on the tRNA. The amino acids sequentially bond together to form the protein, which then spontaneously forms characteristic secondary and tertiary structures.

Objective 8 (Section 21.8), Exercise 21.44

Mutations

Any change that results in an incorrect sequence of bases on DNA is called a mutation. Some mutations occur naturally during DNA replication, whereas others are induced by environmental factors. Some mutations are beneficial to organisms; others may be lethal or result in genetic diseases.

Objective 9 (Section 21.9), Exercise 21.48

Recombinant DNA

The discovery and application of restriction enzymes and DNA ligases have resulted in a technology called genetic engineering. The primary activities of genetic engineers are the isolation of genes (DNA) that code for specific useful proteins and the introduction of these genes into the DNA of bacteria. The new (recombinant) DNA in the rapidly reproducing bacteria mediates production of the useful protein, which is then isolated for use.

Objective 10 (Section 21.10), Exercise 21.52

Key Terms and Concepts

Anticodon (21.4)
Central dogma of molecular biology (21.5)
Chromosome (21.3)
Codon (21.7)
Complementary DNA strands (21.2)
Deoxyribonucleic acid (DNA) (21.1)
Exon (21.6)
Gene (21.3)
Heterogeneous nuclear RNA (hnRNA) (21.6)
Intron (21.6)

Messenger RNA (mRNA) (21.4)
Mutagen (21.9)
Mutation (21.9)
Nucleic acid (Introduction)
Nucleic acid backbone (21.2)
Nucleotide (21.1)
Okazaki fragment (21.3)
Plasmid (21.10)
Polyribosome (polysome) (21.8)
Recombinant DNA (21.10)
Replication (21.3)

Replication fork (21.3)
Restriction enzyme (21.10)
Ribonucleic acid (RNA) (21.1)
Ribosomal RNA (rRNA) (21.4)
Ribosome (21.4)
Semiconservative replication (21.3)
Stem cell (21.8)
Transcription (21.5)
Transfer RNA (tRNA) (21.4)
Translation (21.5)
Vector (21.10)

Exercises

Even-numbered exercises are answered in Appendix B.

Blue-numbered exercises are more challenging.

Components of Nucleic Acids (Section 21.1)

21.1 What is the principal location of DNA within the eukaryotic cell?

21.2 Which pentose sugar is present in DNA? In RNA?

21.3 Name the three components of nucleotides.

21.4 Indicate whether each of the following is a pyrimidine or a purine:

a. guanine

b. thymine

c. uracil

d. cytosine

e. adenine

21.5 Which bases are found in DNA? In RNA?

21.6 Write the structural formula for the nucleotide thymidine 5′-monophosphate. The base component is thymine.

The Structure of DNA (Section 21.2)

21.7 In what way might two DNA molecules that contain the same number of nucleotides differ?

21.8 Identify the 3′ and 5′ ends of the DNA segment AGTCAT.

21.9 What data obtained from the chemical analysis of DNA supported the idea of complementary base pairing in DNA proposed by Watson and Crick?

21.10 Describe the secondary structure of DNA as proposed by Watson and Crick.

21.11 Describe the role of hydrogen bonding in the secondary structure of DNA.

21.12 How many total hydrogen bonds would exist between the following strands of DNA and their complementary strands?

a. CAGTAG

b. TTGACA

21.13 How many total hydrogen bonds would exist between the following strands of DNA and their complementary strands?

a. CACGGT

b. TTTAAA

21.14 A strand of DNA has the base sequence ATGCATC. Write the base sequence for the complementary strand.

21.15 A strand of DNA has the base sequence GATTCA. Write the base sequence for the complementary strand.

DNA Replication (Section 21.3)

21.16 What is a chromosome? How many chromosomes are in a human cell? What is the approximate number of genes in a human cell?

21.17 What is meant by the term *semiconservative replication*?

21.18 What is a replication fork?

21.19 Describe the function of the enzyme helicase in the replication of DNA.

21.20 List the steps involved in DNA replication.

21.21 What enzymes are involved in DNA replication?

21.22 In what direction is a new DNA strand formed?

21.23 Explain how the synthesis of a DNA daughter strand growing toward a replication fork differs from the synthesis of a daughter strand growing away from a replication fork.

21.24 The base sequence ACGTCT represents a portion of a single strand of DNA. Draw the complete double-stranded molecule for this portion of the strand and use the representation to illustrate the replication of the DNA strand. Be sure to clearly identify the nucleotide bases involved, the new strands formed, and the daughter DNA molecules.

21.25 Explain the origin of Okazaki fragments.

Ribonucleic Acid (RNA) (Section 21.4)

21.26 How does the sugar–phosphate backbone of RNA differ from the backbone of DNA?

21.27 Compare the secondary structures of RNA and DNA.

21.28 Briefly describe the characteristics and functions of the three types of cellular RNA.

21.29 Must the ratio of guanine to cytosine be 1:1 in RNA? Explain.

21.30 What are the two important regions of a tRNA molecule?

The Flow of Genetic Information (Section 21.5)

21.31 What is the central dogma of molecular biology?

21.32 In the flow of genetic information, what is meant by the terms *transcription* and *translation?*

Transcription: RNA Synthesis (Section 21.6)

21.33 Briefly describe the synthesis of mRNA in the transcription process.

21.34 Write the base sequence for the mRNA that would be formed during transcription from the DNA strand with the base sequence GCCATATTG.

21.35 Describe the differences in the transcription and translation processes as they occur in prokaryotic cells and eukaryotic cells.

21.36 What is the relationship among exons, introns, and hnRNA?

The Genetic Code (Section 21.7)

21.37 What is a codon?

21.38 For each of the following mRNA codons, give the tRNA anticodon and use Table 21.2 to determine the amino acid being coded for by the codon.

 a. UAU

 b. CAU

 c. UCA

 d. UCU

21.39 Describe the experiment that allowed researchers to first identify the codon for a specific amino acid.

21.40 Which of the following statements about the genetic code are true and which are false? Correct each false statement.

 a. Each codon is composed of four bases.

 b. Some amino acids are represented by more than one codon.

 c. All codons represent an amino acid.

 d. Each living species is thought to have its own unique genetic code.

 e. The codon AUG at the beginning of a sequence is a signal for protein synthesis to begin at that codon.

 f. It is not known if the code contains stop signals for protein synthesis.

Translation and Protein Synthesis (Section 21.8)

21.41 The β-chain of hemoglobin is a protein that contains 146 amino acid residues. What minimum number of nucleotides must be present in a strand of mRNA that is coded for this protein?

21.42 What is a polysome?

21.43 Beginning with DNA, describe in simple terms (no specific codons, etc.) how proteins are coded and synthesized.

21.44 List the three major stages in protein synthesis.

21.45 Does protein synthesis begin with the N-terminal or with the C-terminal amino acid?

21.46 What is meant by the terms *A site* and *P site?*

21.47 Beginning with DNA, describe specifically the coding and synthesis of the following tetrapeptide that represents the first four amino acid residues of the hormone oxytocin: Gly–Leu–Pro–Cys. Be sure to include processes such as formation of mRNA (use correct codons, etc.), attachment of mRNA to a ribosome, attachment of tRNA to mRNA-ribosome complex, and so on.

Mutations (Section 21.9)

21.48 What is a genetic mutation?

21.49 Briefly explain how genetic mutations can do the following:

 a. Harm an organism

 b. Help an organism

21.50 What is the result of a genetic mutation that causes the mRNA sequence GCC to be replaced by CCC?

Recombinant DNA (Section 21.10)

21.51 Explain the function and importance of restriction enzymes and DNA ligase in the formation of recombinant DNA.

21.52 Explain how recombinant DNA differs from normal DNA.

21.53 Explain what plasmids are and how they are used to get bacteria to synthesize a new protein that they normally do not synthesize.

21.54 List three substances likely to be produced on a large scale by genetic engineering, and give an important use for each.

Even-numbered exercises answered in Appendix B.

Blue-numbered exercises are more challenging. **713**

Unless otherwise noted all art on this page © Cengage Learning 2014

Additional Exercises

21.55 Explain how heating a double-stranded DNA fragment to 94°C–96°C when performing PCR causes the DNA to unravel into single strands.

21.56 Review Figure 21.5 and suggest a reaction that would be used to excise introns from hnRNA. Also suggest a reaction that would be used to join the exon segments together.

21.57 A segment of DNA has an original code of –ACA–. This segment was mutated to –AAA–. After the mutation occurred, the protein that was coded for was no longer able to maintain its tertiary structure. Explain why.

21.58 A species of bacteria can use sucrose as its sole source of carbon energy. The bacterial enzyme Q is used to hydrolyze sucrose into its constituent monosaccharides. In the absence of sucrose, there are fewer than 10 enzyme Q molecules in a bacterial cell. In the presence of sucrose there are more than several thousand enzyme molecules in a single cell. Enzyme Q does not exist as a zymogen.

 a. What are the constituent monosaccharides of sucrose?

 b. What is the specific type of enzyme regulation that controls enzyme Q?

 c. Suggest a mechanism of how this type of enzyme regulation occurs.

21.59 During DNA replication, about 1000 nucleotides are added per minute per molecule of DNA polymerase. The genetic material in a single human cell consists of about 3 billion nucleotides:

 a. How many years would it take one DNA polymerase enzyme to replicate the genetic material in one cell?

 b. How many DNA polymerase molecules would be needed to replicate a cell's genetic material in 10 minutes (assuming equidistance between replication forks)?

Allied Health Exam Connection

The following questions are from these sources:

1. *Nursing School Entrance Exam* © 2005, Learning Express, LLC.

2. *McGraw-Hill's Nursing School Entrance Exams* by Thomas A. Evangelist, Tamara B. Orr and Judy Unrein © 2009, The McGraw-Hill Companies, Inc.

3. *NSEE Nursing School Entrance Exams,* 3rd Edition © 2009, Kaplan Publishing.

4. *Cliffs Test Prep: Nursing School Entrance Exams* by Fred N. Grayson © 2004, Wiley Publishing, Inc.

5. *Peterson's Master the Nursing School and Allied Health Entrance Exams,* 18th Edition by Marion F. Gooding © 2008, Peterson's, a Nelnet Company.

21.60 Put the following terms in the correct order of information transfer according to the central dogma of molecular biology:

 RNA, DNA, protein

21.61 Which of the following are components of a nucleotide in a DNA molecule?

 a. Sugar

 b. A phospholipid

 c. A nitrogen base

21.62 Explain the function and importance of each of the following in the formation of recombinant DNA:

 a. Plasmid

 b. Restriction enzyme

 c. DNA ligase

21.63 The genes that encode for eukaryotic protein sequences are passed from one generation to the next via:

 a. other proteins

 b. rRNA

 c. tRNA

 d. DNA

21.64 Which base is found in DNA but not in RNA?

 a. thymine

 b. cytosine

 c. guanine

 d. adenine

21.65 Which of the following best describes tRNA?

 a. It is the site of rRNA synthesis.

 b. It is the product of transcription, and encodes for translated proteins.

 c. It binds specific amino acids and carries them to the ribosomes during protein synthesis.

 d. It contains the genome and is the site at which genes are used to make mRNA.

21.66 Which of the following is the site of protein synthesis within a eukaryotic cell?

 a. the ribosomes

 b. the nucleus

 c. the mitochondria

 d. the Golgi apparatus

21.67 In messenger RNA, a codon contains how many nucleotides?

 a. one

 b. two

 c. three

 d. four

Chemistry for Thought

21.68 Genetic engineering shows great promise for the future but has been controversial at times. Discuss with some classmates the pros and cons of genetic engineering. List two benefits and two concerns that come from your discussion.

21.69 Two samples of DNA are compared, and one has a greater percentage of guanine-cytosine base pairs. How should that greater percentage affect the attractive forces holding the double helix together?

21.70 If DNA replication were not semiconservative, what might be another possible structure for the daughter DNA molecules?

21.71 The genetic code contains three stop signals and 61 codons that code for 20 amino acids. From the standpoint of mutations, why are we fortunate that the genetic code does not have only the required 20 amino acid codons and 44 stop signals?

21.72 Azidothymidine (AZT), a drug used to fight HIV, is believed to act as an enzyme inhibitor. What type of enzyme inhibition is most likely caused by this drug?

21.73 If DNA specifies only the primary structure of a protein, how does the correct three-dimensional protein structure develop?

21.74 When were the first experiments carried out that produced genetically modified plants?

21.75 How does the DNA content determine what reactions occur within an organism?

21.76 What would be the ramifications if DNA were single stranded?

Case Study

Shani was shocked and disappointed. She had gone into labor at 32 weeks gestation, and her baby had been delivered by C-section. She had so wanted a natural birth! Now, just a few hours after the surgery, a lactation consultant was telling Shani that the best thing she could do for her baby was to breastfeed him. The consultant also said that because he was premature, her newborn would not be able to nurse for at least five weeks. However, they could feed her milk to him through a naso-gastric tube. The lactation consultant explained that breast milk contains the perfect balance of water, fat, protein, and antibodies, and that it changes over time to match the baby's changing needs. Shani should expect to pump eight times a day and one to two times at night. She was exhausted by the surgery but was determined to do the best for her baby. Even though she couldn't take her baby home, she could do something important to help him.

Why is breast milk a superior food for any baby, but especially a premature one? To what age of the child does the World Health Organization and the American Pediatric Association recommend breastfeeding?

Follow-up to this Case Study appears at the end the chapter before the Concept Summary.

Learning Objectives

When you have completed your study of this chapter, you should be able to:

1. Describe the difference between macronutrients and micronutrients in terms of amounts required and their functions in the body. (**Section 22.1**)

2. Describe the primary functions in the body of each macronutrient. (**Section 22.2**)

3. Distinguish between and classify vitamins as water-soluble or fat-soluble on the basis of name and behavior in the body. (**Section 22.3**)

4. List a primary function in the body for each major mineral. (**Section 22.4**)

5. Describe the major steps in the flow of energy in the biosphere. (**Section 22.5**)

6. Differentiate among metabolism, anabolism, and catabolism. (**Section 22.6**)

7. Outline the three stages in the extraction of energy from food. (**Section 22.6**)

8. Explain how ATP plays a central role in the production and use of cellular energy. (**Section 22.7**)

9. Explain the role of coenzymes in the common catabolic pathway. (**Section 22.8**)

The science of **nutrition** is an applied field that focuses on the study of food, water, and other nutrients and the ways in which living organisms utilize them. Nutrition scientists use the principles of nutrition to obtain answers to questions that have a great deal of practical significance. For example, they might try to determine the proper components of a sound diet, the best way to maintain proper body weight, or the foods and other nutrients needed by people with specific illnesses or injuries.

The fuels of the human body are the sugars, lipids, and proteins derived from food (see ▶ Figure 22.1). The reactions that release energy from these substances are among the body's most important biochemical processes. In this chapter, we will study an introduction to nutrition and how cells extract energy from food.

nutrition An applied science that studies food, water, and other nutrients and the ways living organisms use them.

© Michael C. Slabaugh

Figure 22.1 Carbohydrates, lipids, and proteins from food supply the energy for all of our activities.

22.1 **Nutritional Requirements**

Learning Objective

1. Describe the difference between macronutrients and micronutrients in terms of amounts required and their functions in the body.

A human body must be supplied with appropriate nutrients if it is to function properly and remain healthy. Some nutrients are required in relatively large amounts (gram quantities daily) because they provide energy and materials required to repair damaged tissue or build new tissue. These **macronutrients** are the carbohydrates, lipids, and proteins contained in food. **Micronutrients** are required by the body in only small amounts

macronutrient A substance needed by the body in relatively large amounts.

micronutrient A substance needed by the body only in small amounts.

reference daily intakes (RDI) A set of standards for protein, vitamins, and minerals used on food labels as part of the Daily Values.

daily reference values (DRV) A set of standards for nutrients and food components (such as fat and fiber) that have important relationships with health; used on food labels as part of the Daily Values.

daily values (DV) Reference values developed by the FDA specifically for use on food labels. The Daily Values represent two sets of standards: Reference Daily Intakes (RDI) and Daily Reference Values (DRV).

(milligrams or micrograms daily). The small quantities needed suggest correctly that at least some micronutrients are utilized in enzymes. Micronutrients are classified as either vitamins or minerals.

In addition to macro- and micronutrients, the human body must receive appropriate amounts of water and fiber. The importance of water becomes obvious when we learn that 45–75% of the human body mass is water. Fiber is an indigestible plant material composed primarily of cellulose. Fiber makes no contribution to the body in the form of macro- or micronutrients, but it prevents or relieves constipation by absorbing water and softening the stool for easier elimination.

A number of countries of the world have established nutritional guidelines for their citizens in an attempt to improve and maintain good national health. In the United States, the Nutrition Labeling and Education Act of 1990 brought sweeping changes to the regulations that define what is required on a food label. The official guidelines are called **Reference Daily Intakes (RDI)** for proteins and 19 vitamins and minerals, and **Daily Reference Values (DRV)** for other nutrients of public health importance. For simplicity, all reference values on food labels are referred to as **Daily Values (DV)** (see ❱ Figure 22.2). The Food and Drug Administration (FDA) decided to use 2000 calories as a standard for energy intake in calculating the DRVs. A 2000-calorie

Figure 22.2 An example of a food label.

diet is considered about right for many adults. Recall from Chapter 1 that the nutritional calorie is equal to 1 kilocalorie (kcal) of energy. The guidelines are reviewed and revised about every five years. The U.S. Department of Agriculture (USDA) has issued the food guide MyPlate, designed to replace the old MyPyramid posters with new recommendations (see ◗ Figure 22.3).

Courtesy of the USDA

Figure 22.3 The food guide Choose MyPlate developed by the U.S. Department of Agriculture. ChooseMyPlate.gov will help you select foods and amounts that are right for you.

22.2 The Macronutrients

Learning Objective

2. Describe the primary functions in the body of each macronutrient.

Carbohydrates

Carbohydrates are ideal energy sources for most body functions and also provide useful materials for the synthesis of cell and tissue components. These facts, plus the relatively low cost and ready availability of carbohydrates, have led to their worldwide use as the main dietary source of energy.

Despite their importance as a dominant source of energy, many people consider foods rich in carbohydrates to be inferior, at least in part because of their reputation for being fattening. It is now recognized that this reputation is generally not deserved. Most of the excess calories associated with eating carbohydrates are actually due to the high-calorie foods eaten *with* the carbohydrates—for example, potatoes and bread are often eaten with butter, a high-energy lipid.

Dietary carbohydrates are often classified as simple or complex. **Simple carbohydrates** are the sugars we classified earlier as monosaccharides and disaccharides (Chapter 17). **Complex carbohydrates** consist essentially of the polysaccharides amylose and amylopectin, which are collectively called starch. Cellulose, another polysaccharide, is also a complex carbohydrate; however, because it cannot be digested by humans, it serves a nonnutritive role as fiber.

Numerous nutritional studies include recommendations about dietary carbohydrates in their reports. One conclusion common to most of these studies is that a typical American diet does not include enough complex carbohydrates. These studies recommend that about 58% of daily calories should come from carbohydrate food. Currently, only about 46% of

simple carbohydrates
Monosaccharides and disaccharides, commonly called sugars.

complex carbohydrates The polysaccharides amylose and amylopectin, collectively called starch.

the typical diet comes from carbohydrates, and too much of that total comes from simple carbohydrates (see ▶ Figure 22.4).

Figure 22.4 **A** The composition of a typical American diet; **B** the composition of a healthful diet with lower fat intake and reduced levels of fat.

Lipids

Lipids, or fats, like carbohydrates, have a somewhat negative dietary image. In part, this is because the word *fat* has several meanings, and its relationship to health is sometimes misunderstood. In our modern society, some people think of fat as something to be avoided at all costs, regardless of body size.

As we saw in Chapter 18, a number of different substances are classified as lipids. However, about 95% of the lipids in foods and in our bodies are triglycerides, in which three fatty acid molecules are bonded to a molecule of glycerol by ester linkages. The fatty acids in triglycerides can be either saturated or unsaturated. Generally, triglycerides containing a high percentage of unsaturated fatty acids are liquids at room temperature and are called oils (see ▶ Figure 22.5). A higher concentration of saturated fatty acids causes triglyceride melting points to increase, and they are solids (fats) at room temperature.

Figure 22.5 Oil-fried foods are rich in triglycerides.

© Monkey Business Images, 2009. Used under license from Shutterstock.com

Lipids are important dietary constituents for a number of reasons: They are a concentrated source of energy and provide more than twice the energy of an equal mass of carbohydrate; they contain some fat-soluble vitamins and help carry them through the body; and some fatty acids needed by the body cannot be synthesized and must come from the diet—they are the essential fatty acids.

In addition to metabolic needs, dietary lipids are desirable for other reasons. Lipids improve the texture of foods, and absorb and retain flavors, thus making foods more palatable. Lipids are digested more slowly than other foods and therefore prolong **satiety,** a feeling of satisfaction and fullness after a meal.

satiety A state of satisfaction or fullness.

The essential fatty acids are the polyunsaturated linoleic and linolenic acids. Generally, vegetable oils are good sources of unsaturated fatty acids (see 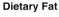 Figure 22.6). Some oils that are especially rich in linoleic acid come from corn, cottonseed, soybean, and wheat germ. Infants especially need linoleic acid for good health and growth; human breast milk contains a higher percentage of it than does cow's milk.

Dietary Fat

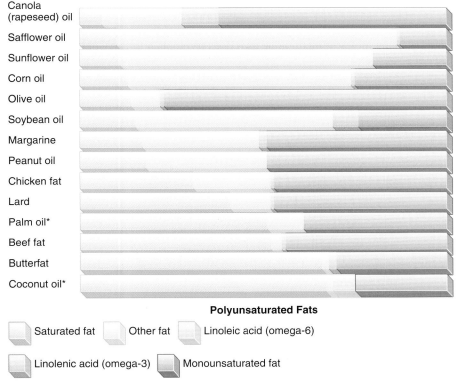

Figure 22.6 The fatty acid composition of common food fats.

We still do not have a complete understanding of the relationship between dietary lipids and health. A moderate amount of fat is needed in everyone's diet, but many people consume much more than required. Research results indicate a correlation between the consumption of too much fat, and fat of the wrong type (saturated fatty acids), and two of the greatest health problems: obesity and cardiovascular disease. Because of these results, there is a recommended reduction in the percentage of calories obtained from fats—from the national average of almost 42% to no more than 30%.

TABLE 22.1 The RDI for Protein

Group	RDI (g)
Pregnant women	60
Nursing mothers	65
Infants under age 1	14
Children age 1 to 4	16
Adults	50

essential amino acid An amino acid that cannot be synthesized within the body at a rate adequate to meet metabolic needs.

complete protein Protein in food that contains all essential amino acids in the proportions needed by the body.

TABLE 22.2 The Essential Amino Acids

Histidine
Isoleucine
Leucine
Lysine
Methionine
Phenylalanine
Threonine
Tryptophan
Valine

Proteins

Proteins are the only macronutrients for which an RDI has been established. The RDI varies for different groups of people, as shown in ▶ Table 22.1, which shows that nursing mothers have a greater need for protein than do other adults. This reflects one of the important uses of protein in the body, the production of new tissue as the body grows. In addition, proteins are needed for the maintenance and repair of cells and for the production of enzymes, hormones, and other important nitrogen-containing compounds of the body. Proteins can also be used to supply energy; they provide about 4 calories/gram, the same as carbohydrates. It is recommended that 12% of the calories obtained from food be obtained from dietary proteins (Figure 22.4).

As we learned in Chapter 19, proteins are natural polymers of amino acids joined by amide (or peptide) linkages. On digestion, proteins are broken down to individual amino acids that are absorbed into the body's amino acid pool and used for the purposes mentioned earlier. The **essential amino acids** listed in ▶ Table 22.2 must be obtained from the diet because they cannot be synthesized in the body in sufficient amounts to satisfy the body's needs.

The minimum quantity of each essential amino acid needed per day by an individual will vary, depending on the use in the body. For example, results of one study showed that young men need a daily average of only 7 g (0.034 mol) of tryptophan but 31 g (0.21 mol) of methionine. According to this study, the body of an average young man requires about seven times as many moles of methionine as it does tryptophan to carry out the processes involving amino acids.

Proteins in foods are classified as **complete proteins** if they contain all the essential amino acids in the proper proportions needed by the body. Protein foods that don't meet this requirement are classified as incomplete. Several protein-containing foods are shown in ▶ Figure 22.7.

8 g in 1 cup milk

3 g in 1 starch portion

2 g in $\frac{1}{2}$ cup vegetables

7 g in 1 oz meat

Figure 22.7 The protein content of several foods.

22.3 Micronutrients I: Vitamins

Learning Objective

3. Distinguish between and classify vitamins as water-soluble or fat-soluble on the basis of name and behavior in the body.

Vitamins are organic micronutrients that the body cannot produce in amounts needed for good health. The highly polar nature of some vitamins renders them water-soluble. Nine

water-soluble vitamins have been identified. Some are designated by names, some by letters, and some by letters and numbers. ▶ Table 22.3 presents the names nutritionists use (the "correct" names), along with other common names you will likely encounter in books and on product labels. With the exception of vitamin C, all water-soluble vitamins have been shown to function as coenzymes.

TABLE 22.3 Vitamin Sources, Functions, and Deficiency Conditions

Vitamin	Dietary Sources	Functions	Deficiency Conditions
Water-soluble			
B_1 (thiamin)	Bread, beans, nuts, milk, peas, pork, rice bran	Coenzyme in decarboxylation reactions	Beriberi: nausea, severe exhaustion, paralysis
B_2 (riboflavin)	Milk, meat, eggs, dark green vegetables, bread, beans, peas	Forms the coenzymes FMN and FAD, which are hydrogen transporters	Dermatitis (skin problems)
Niacin	Meat, whole grains, poultry, fish	Forms the coenzyme NAD^+, which is a hydride transporter	Pellagra: weak muscles, no appetite, diarrhea, dermatitis
B_6 (pyridoxine)	Meats, whole grains, poultry, fish	Coenzyme form carries amino and carboxyl groups	Dermatitis, nervous disorders
B_{12} (cobalamin)	Meat, fish, eggs, milk	Coenzyme in amino acid metabolism	Rare except in vegetarians; pernicious anemia
Folic acid	Leafy green vegetables, peas, beans	Coenzyme in methyl group transfers	Anemia
Pantothenic acid	All plants and animals, nuts; whole-grain cereals	Part of coenzyme A, acyl group carrier	Anemia
Biotin	Found widely; egg yolk, liver, yeast, nuts	Coenzyme form used in fatty acid synthesis	Dermatitis, muscle weakness
C (ascorbic acid)	Citrus fruits, tomatoes, green pepper, strawberries, leafy green vegetables	Synthesis of collagen for connective tissue	Scurvy: tender tissues; weak, bleeding gums; swollen joints
Fat-soluble			
A (retinol)	Eggs, butter, cheese, dark green and deep orange vegetables	Synthesis of visual pigments	Inflamed eye membranes, night blindness, scaliness of skin
D (calciferol)	Fish-liver oils, fortified milk	Regulation of calcium and phosphorus metabolism	Rickets (malformation of the bones)
E (tocopherol)	Whole-grain cereals, margarine, vegetable oil	Prevention of oxidation of vitamin A and fatty acids	Breakage of red blood cells
K	Cabbage, potatoes, peas, leafy green vegetables	Synthesis of blood-clotting substances	Blood-clotting disorders

Some vitamins (A, D, E, and K) have very nonpolar molecular structures and therefore dissolve only in nonpolar solvents. In the body, the nonpolar solvents are the lipids we have classified as fats, so these vitamins are called fat-soluble. The fat-soluble vitamins have diverse functions in the body, and they act somewhat like hormones (Table 22.3). Care must be taken to avoid overdoses of the fat-soluble vitamins. Toxic effects are known to occur, especially with vitamin A, when excess amounts of these vitamins accumulate in body tissue. Excesses of water-soluble vitamins are excreted readily through the kidneys and are not normally a problem.

The Ten Most Dangerous Foods to Eat While Driving

We don't often think of it, but every time we drive a car, we are maneuvering a two-ton piece of machinery at speeds up to 80 mph! And yet, as if that weren't enough, some drivers eat and drink as they do it! Exxon conducted a survey in 2001 and found that 70% of auto drivers eat while they are driving; 85% drink coffee, juice, or soda; and a few confessed they would use a microwave in the car if they could! The National Highway Traffic Safety Administration tracked 6.3 million auto crashes in one year, and attributed 25% to food and drink distractions.

With the hurried pace of society, it is no wonder many of us try to eat and drive at the same time. However, some foods and drinks have disaster written all over them when combined with driving. Liquids are especially problematic as they spill easily. Most drivers do not take time to pull over and clean up a mess, but instead continue to drive and simultaneously clean the car and/or themselves. According to studies, the following are the top ten food and drink culprits that contribute to causing accidents and collisions:

1. Coffee: It is usually way too hot and burns the mouth. The coffee also finds a way out of the cup and onto a clean white blouse.

© iStockphoto.com/Andyd

2. Hot Soup: It has the same problem as coffee because most people drink it.

© iStockphoto.com/Viktor Pravdica

3. Tacos: Notorious for coming apart at the first bite, most tacos end up scattered all over the seat, creating a salad bar effect.

© iStockphoto.com/DNY59

4. Chili: The spoon rarely makes it to the mouth without losing some of the food.

© iStockphoto.com/DNY59

5. Hamburgers: Our hands get greasy, and the mustard and ketchup squeeze out the other end, making steering almost impossible!

© iStockphoto.com/Kelly Cline

6. Barbecued food: It tastes good, but that slippery, messy sauce will end up everywhere!

© iStockphoto.com/Ryerson Clark

7. Fried chicken: The grease ends up on your hands, face, seat, and clothes. The steering wheel usually becomes greasy, which makes it nearly impossible to steer.

© iStockphoto.com/Robert Byron

8. Jelly or cream-filled doughnuts: No one has ever eaten these types of doughnuts without creating some sort of mess. Why would you want to try to eat them while driving a car?

© iStockphoto.com/tonyoquias

9. Soft drinks: They are subject to spills, and the carbonation can also trigger that moment when the nose gets all tingly and distracts you from your driving.

© iStockphoto.com/Vasko Miokovic

10. Chocolate: It tastes yummy but ends up all over the hands and everything you touch! If the car is warm, good luck trying to keep the chocolate from melting!

© iStockphoto.com/Picsfive

Vitamin Water: Beneficial or Not?

A typical human body is about two-thirds water by weight. In order to maintain good health, an adult must take in almost 2.5 liters of water daily in the form of beverages or food containing water. Vitamin water is a beverage composed primarily of water to which has been added small amounts of vitamins and flavoring agents, including non-caloric sweeteners. The motivation to use vitamin water seems obvious and reasonable. It provides part of the needed daily water intake, and part of the vitamins needed for good health. However, several questions can be asked about vitamin water use. Two common ones are (1) do vitamin water users run the risk of ingesting enough vitamins to cause vitamin toxicity and (2) do the benefits of vitamin water use justify the extra cost of vitamin water compared to ordinary water?

The vitamins in vitamin water are of two types (see Table 22.3). One type referred to as water-soluble includes vitamin C and all the B vitamins. The second type, called fat-soluble, includes vitamins A, E, D, and K. Water-soluble vitamins are known to degrade or break down when they are exposed to water for prolonged periods of time. This degradation speeds up in the presence of light and heat. So, unless vitamin water is reasonably fresh and has been protected from light and heat, it will contain significantly less of the vitamins than the amount listed on the label. The typical amount listed on the label of an 18 oz bottle indicates that it contains 100% of the recommended daily adult requirement of vitamin C and 40% of the daily requirement for the B vitamins and vitamin A. Another factor that reduces the probability of vitamin toxicity from vitamin water use is that fat-soluble vitamins are not well absorbed by the body unless they are consumed along with some fat. So, unless the vitamin water is accompanied by a fat-containing meal or snack, little of the fat-soluble vitamins will be absorbed into the body.

While this information appears to indicate minimal chances for vitamin toxicity to occur unless large amounts of vitamin water are consumed daily, the question still remains about whether the cost of the use of vitamin water as a source of vitamins is justified. The results of a quick survey of products available at a typical food store and drugstore provide an answer. The price of an 18 oz bottle of vitamin water at a food store was $1.00. The same amount of bottled water cost 27 cents. Remember, if it was fresh, the bottle of vitamin water provided 100% of the daily vitamin C requirement, but only 40% of the vitamin A and B requirements. The cost of one tablet of an adult multivitamin was about 6 cents, and the tablet provided more than 100% of the daily requirements for all the vitamins except A and K. Thus, an expenditure of 33 cents would provide all of the water and much more of the needed vitamins available in one bottle of vitamin water that would cost $1.00. So, unless the flavorings in vitamin water are important to you, bottled water and a daily multivitamin tablet make the most sense.

Vitamin Water is an expensive source of vitamins.

22.4 Micronutrients II: Minerals

Learning Objective

4. List a primary function in the body for each major mineral.

The word **mineral** is generally used to describe inorganic substances, often as if they were in the elemental form. Thus, we might hear that a food is a good source of phosphorus, when in fact the food does not contain elemental phosphorus, a caustic nonmetal, but probably contains phosphate ions such as HPO_4^{2-} and $H_2PO_4^-$ or, more likely, organic substances that contain phosphorus, such as nucleic acids and phospholipids.

In the body, the elements classified as minerals are never used in elemental form, but rather in the form of ions or compounds. They are classified as **major minerals** and **trace minerals** on the basis of the amount present in the body, as shown in ▶ Figure 22.8. In general, the major minerals are required in larger daily amounts than are the trace minerals.

mineral A metal or nonmetal used in the body in the form of ions or compounds.

major mineral A mineral found in the body in quantities greater than 5 g.

trace mineral A mineral found in the body in quantities smaller than 5 g.

For example, the RDIs for calcium and phosphorus, the major minerals found in the body in largest amounts, are 800 mg. The RDIs for iron and iodine, two of the trace minerals, are 10–18 mg and 0.12 mg, respectively. By way of comparison, the RDIs for vitamin C and niacin are, respectively, 55–60 mg and 18 mg.

Figure 22.8 Minerals in a 60-kg person. The major minerals are those present in amounts larger than 5 g (a teaspoon); only four of the numerous trace minerals are shown. Only calcium and phosphorus appear in amounts larger than a pound (454 g).

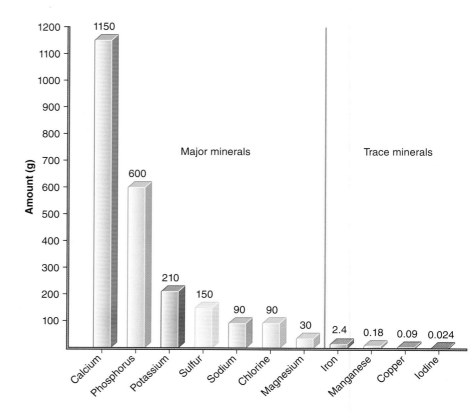

As shown in ◗ Table 22.4, the functions of minerals are consistent with their classification as major or trace and with the amount required daily in the diet. For example, compounds of some major minerals (Ca and P) are the primary inorganic structural components of bones and teeth. Other major minerals (Na, K, Cl, and Mg) form principal ions that are distributed throughout the body's various fluids. Some trace minerals are components of vitamins (Co), enzymes (Zn and Se), hormones (I), or specialized proteins (Fe and Cu). Thus, we see that even though trace minerals are required in small quantities, their involvement in critical enzymes, hormones, and the like makes them equally as important for good health as the major minerals.

22.5 The Flow of Energy in the Biosphere

Learning Objective

5. Describe the major steps in the flow of energy in the biosphere.

The sun is the ultimate source of energy used in all biological processes. The sun's enormous energy output is the result of the fusion of hydrogen atoms into helium atoms. The net reaction for this process is:

$$4H \xrightarrow{\text{nuclear fusion}} He + energy \qquad (22.1)$$

A portion of the liberated energy reaches Earth as sunlight and is absorbed by chlorophyll pigments in plants. In the plants, the energy drives the reactions of photosynthesis that

TABLE 22.4 Major and Trace Mineral Sources, Functions, and Deficiency Conditions

Mineral	Dietary Sources	Functions	Deficiency Conditions
Major minerals			
Calcium	Dairy foods, dark green vegetables	Bone and teeth formation, blood clotting, nerve impulse transmission	Stunted growth, rickets, weak and brittle bones
Chlorine	Table salt, seafood, meat	HCl in gastric juice, acid–base balance	Muscle cramps, apathy, reduced appetite
Magnesium	Whole-grain cereals, meat, nuts, milk, legumes	Activation of enzymes, protein synthesis	Inhibited growth, weakness, spasms
Phosphorus	Milk, cheese, meat, fish, grains, legumes, nuts	Enzyme component, acid–base balance, bone and tooth formation	Weakness, calcium loss, weak bones
Potassium	Meat, milk, many fruits, cereals, legumes	Acid–base and water balance, nerve function	Muscle weakness, paralysis
Sodium	Most foods except fruit	Acid–base and water balance, nerve function	Muscle cramps, apathy, reduced appetite
Sulfur	Protein foods	Component of proteins	Deficiencies are very rare
Trace minerals			
Arsenic[a]	Many foods	Growth and reproduction	Poor growth and reproduction
Cobalt	Meat, liver, dairy foods	Component of vitamin B_{12}	Pernicious anemia (vitamin-deficiency symptom)
Copper	Drinking water, liver, grains, legumes, nuts	Component of numerous enzymes, hemoglobin formation	Anemia, fragility of arteries
Chromium	Fats, vegetable oils, grains, meat	Enhances insulin action	Reduced ability to metabolize glucose
Fluorine	Drinking water, seafood, onions, spinach	Maintenance of bones and teeth	Higher frequency of tooth decay
Iodine	Iodized salt, fish, dairy products	Component of thyroid hormones	Hypothyroidism, goiter
Iron	Liver, lean meat, whole grains, dark green vegetables	Component of enzymes and hemoglobin	Anemia
Manganese	Grains, beet greens, legumes, fruit	Component of enzymes	Deficiencies are rare
Molybdenum	Legumes, cereals, organ meats, dark green vegetables	Component of enzymes	Deficiencies are rare
Nickel	Many foods	Needed for health of numerous tissues	Organ damage, deficiencies are rare
Selenium	Grains, meats, poultry, milk	Component of enzymes	Deficiencies are rare
Silicon[a]	Many foods	Bone calcification	Poor bone development, deficiencies are rare
Tin[a]	Many foods	Needed for growth	Poor growth
Vanadium[a]	Many foods	Growth, bone development, reproduction	Poor growth, bone development, and reproduction
Zinc	Milk, liver, shellfish, wheat bran	Component of numerous enzymes	Poor growth, lack of sexual maturation, loss of appetite, abnormal glucose tolerance

[a]Need and deficiency symptoms determined for animals, probable in humans, but not yet recognized.

convert carbon dioxide and water first into glucose, and then into starch, triglycerides, and other storage forms of energy. The net reaction for glucose production is:

$$6CO_2 + 6H_2O + energy \xrightarrow{\text{photosynthesis}} C_6H_{12}O_6 + 6O_2 \qquad (22.2)$$
$$\text{glucose}$$

All animals obtain energy either directly or indirectly from these energy stores in plants.

During **cellular respiration,** both plants and animals combine these energy-rich compounds with oxygen from the air, producing carbon dioxide and water, and releasing energy. Cellular respiration, which should not be confused with pulmonary respiration (breathing), is represented as:

cellular respiration The entire process involved in the use of oxygen by cells.

$$\text{glucose and other storage forms of energy} + O_2 \xrightarrow{\text{respiration}} CO_2 + H_2O + \text{energy released} \qquad (22.3)$$

A portion of the energy released during respiration is captured within the cells in the form of adenosine triphosphate (ATP), a chemical carrier of energy, from which energy can be obtained and used directly for the performance of biological work. The remainder of the energy from respiration is liberated as heat. Steps in the flow of energy in the biosphere are summarized in ❱ Figure 22.9.

Figure 22.9 Energy flow in the biosphere.

Notice in Figure 22.9 that atmospheric carbon dioxide is the initial source of carbon for carbohydrates. Another important feature of Figure 22.9 is that overall, the respiration process is the reverse of the photosynthetic process. Thus, some of Earth's carbon compounds are repeatedly recycled by living organisms (see ❱ Figure 22.10).

Figure 22.10 A simplified carbon cycle.

22.6 Metabolism and an Overview of Energy Production

Learning Objectives

6. Differentiate among metabolism, anabolism, and catabolism.
7. Outline the three stages in the extraction of energy from food.

Metabolism

Living cells are very active chemically, with thousands of different reactions occurring at the same time. The sum total of all the chemical reactions involved in maintaining a living cell is called **metabolism.** The reactions of metabolism are divided into two categories, catabolism and anabolism. **Catabolism** consists of all reactions that lead to the breakdown of biomolecules. **Anabolism** includes all reactions that lead to the synthesis of biomolecules. In general, energy is released during catabolism and required during anabolism.

A characteristic of all living organisms is a high degree of order in their structures and chemical processes. Even the simplest organisms exhibit an enormous array of chemical reactions that are organized into orderly, well-regulated sequences known as **metabolic pathways.** Each metabolic pathway consists of a series of consecutive chemical reactions or steps that convert a starting material into an end product. For example, two pathways that will be covered in Chapter 23 are the citric acid cycle and the electron transport chain.

Fortunately for those who study the biochemistry of living systems, a great many similarities exist among the major metabolic pathways found in all life forms. These similarities enable scientists to study the metabolism of simple organisms and use the results to help explain the corresponding metabolic pathways in more complex organisms, including humans. This text concentrates on human biochemistry, but you should realize that much of what is said about human metabolism can be applied equally well to the metabolism of most other organisms.

metabolism The sum of all reactions occurring in an organism.

catabolism All reactions involved in the breakdown of biomolecules.

anabolism All reactions involved in the synthesis of biomolecules.

metabolic pathway A sequence of reactions used to produce one product or accomplish one process.

The Catabolism of Food

The three stages involved in the catabolic extraction of energy from food are illustrated in ▶ Figure 22.11.

Figure 22.11 The three stages in the extraction of energy from food.

Stage I is digestion, in which large, complex molecules are chemically broken into relatively small, simple ones (see ❱ Figure 22.12). The most common reaction in digestion is hydrolysis, in which proteins are converted to amino acids, carbohydrates are converted to monosaccharides (primarily glucose, galactose, and fructose), and fats are converted to fatty acids and glycerol. The smaller molecules are then absorbed into the body through the lining of the small intestine.

Figure 22.12 The digestion of food involves enzyme-catalyzed hydrolysis reactions.

$$proteins \xrightarrow{\text{hydrolysis}} amino\ acids$$

$$disaccharides\ and\ polysaccharides \xrightarrow{\text{hydrolysis}} monosaccharides$$

$$fats\ and\ oils \xrightarrow{\text{hydrolysis}} fatty\ acids\ +\ glycerol$$

In Stage II, the small molecules from digestion are degraded to even simpler units, primarily the two-carbon acetyl portion of acetyl coenzyme A (acetyl CoA):

$$\underset{\text{acetyl}}{\underbrace{CH_3 - \overset{\overset{\textstyle O}{\|}}{C}}} - \underset{\text{coenzyme A}}{\underbrace{S - CoA}}$$

Some energy is released in the second stage, but much more is produced during the oxidation of the acetyl units of acetyl CoA in the third stage. Stage III consists of the citric acid cycle followed by electron transport and oxidative phosphorylation. Because the reactions of Stage III are the same regardless of the type of food being degraded, Stage III is sometimes referred to as the **common catabolic pathway.** Energy released during Stage III appears in the form of energy-rich molecules of ATP. The whole purpose of the catabolic pathway is to convert the chemical energy in foods to molecules of ATP. The common catabolic pathway will be covered in Chapter 23. Chapters 23–25 discuss the ways in which carbohydrates, lipids, and proteins provide molecules that are degraded by reactions of the common catabolic pathway.

common catabolic pathway The reactions of the citric acid cycle plus those of the electron transport chain and oxidative phosphorylation.

22.7 ATP: The Primary Energy Carrier

Learning Objective

8. Explain how ATP plays a central role in the production and use of cellular energy.

Certain bonds in ATP store the energy released during the oxidation of carbohydrates, lipids, and proteins. ATP molecules act as energy carriers and deliver the energy to the parts of the cell where energy is needed to power muscle contraction, biosynthesis, and other cellular work.

The Structure and Hydrolysis of ATP

The structure of the ATP molecule is relatively simple (see ❱ Figure 22.13). It consists of a heterocyclic base, adenine, bonded to the sugar ribose. Taken together, this portion of the molecule is called adenosine. The triphosphate portion is bonded to the ribose to give adenosine triphosphate, or ATP. At the cell pH of 7.4, all the protons of the triphosphate group are ionized, giving the ATP molecule a charge of -4. In the cell, ATP is complexed with Mg^{2+} in a 1:1 ratio. Thus, the 1:1 complex exhibits a net charge of -2. Two other triphosphates—GTP, containing the base guanine, and UTP, containing the base uracil—are important in carbohydrate metabolism (Chapter 23).

Figure 22.13 The structure of ATP.

The triphosphate end of ATP is the part of the molecule that is important in the transfer of biochemical energy. The key reaction in this energy delivery system is the transfer of a phosphoryl group, $-PO_3^{2-}$, from ATP to another molecule. For example, during the hydrolysis of ATP in water, a phosphoryl group is transferred from ATP to water. The products of this hydrolysis are adenosine diphosphate (ADP) and a phosphate ion, often referred to as an inorganic phosphate, P_i, or simply as *phosphate*.

$$\text{adenosine} - O - \overset{\overset{O}{\|}}{\underset{\underset{O^-}{|}}{P}} - O - \overset{\overset{O}{\|}}{\underset{\underset{O^-}{|}}{P}} - O - \overset{\overset{O}{\|}}{\underset{\underset{O^-}{|}}{P}} - O^- + H - OH \longrightarrow$$

ATP

$$\text{adenosine} - O - \overset{\overset{O}{\|}}{\underset{\underset{O^-}{|}}{P}} - O - \overset{\overset{O}{\|}}{\underset{\underset{O^-}{|}}{P}} - O^- + HO - \overset{\overset{O}{\|}}{\underset{\underset{O^-}{|}}{P}} - O^- + H^+ \qquad (22.4)$$

ADP inorganic phosphate (P_i)

The transfer of a phosphoryl group from ATP to water is accompanied by a release of energy. This energy is called free energy and is represented by the symbol ΔG. When energy is released by a reaction or process, ΔG will have a negative value. When energy is absorbed, ΔG will have a positive value. When ΔG is measured under standard conditions (temperature, concentration, etc.), it is represented by $\Delta G°$, and a superscript prime ($\Delta G°'$) is added if $\Delta G°$ is measured at body conditions. The liberated free energy is available for use by the cell to carry out processes requiring an input of energy. This energy-releasing hydrolysis reaction is represented by the following equation:

$$\text{ATP} + H_2O \rightarrow \text{ADP} + P_i + H^+ \quad \Delta G°' = -7.3 \text{ kcal/mol} \qquad (22.5)$$

Many other phosphate-containing compounds found in biological systems also liberate energy on hydrolysis. Several are listed in ▶ Table 22.5, along with values for their free standard energy of hydrolysis.

Compounds that liberate a great amount of free energy on hydrolysis are called **high-energy compounds.** Remember, a negative sign for $\Delta G°'$ means the energy is liberated when the reaction takes place. Thus, ATP ($\Delta G°' = -7.3$ kcal/mol) is considered a high-energy compound, but not the only one found in cells, as you can see from Table 22.5.

high-energy compound A substance that on hydrolysis liberates a great amount of free energy.

TABLE 22.5 Free Energy Changes for the Hydrolysis of Some Phosphate Compounds

Reaction			$\Delta G^{\circ\prime}$ (kcal/mol)
Phosphoenolpyruvate + H_2O	$\rightarrow$	pyruvate + phosphate	−14.8
Carbamoyl phosphate + H_2O	$\rightarrow$	ammonia + CO_2 + phosphate	−12.3
1,3-bisphosphoglycerate + H_2O	$\rightarrow$	3-phosphoglycerate + phosphate	−11.8
Phosphocreatine + H_2O	$\rightarrow$	creatine + phosphate	−10.3
ATP + H_2O	$\rightarrow$	ADP + phosphate	−7.3
ADP + H_2O	$\rightarrow$	AMP + phosphate	−7.3
Glucose-1-phosphate + H_2O	$\rightarrow$	glucose + phosphate	−5.0
AMP + H_2O	$\rightarrow$	adenosine + phosphate	−3.4
Glucose-6-phosphate + H_2O	$\rightarrow$	glucose + phosphate	−3.3
Glycerol-3-phosphate + H_2O	$\rightarrow$	glycerol + phosphate	−2.2

The hydrolysis of ATP to ADP is the principal energy-releasing reaction for ATP. However, some other hydrolysis reactions also play important roles in energy transfer. An example is the hydrolysis of ATP to adenosine monophosphate (AMP) and pyrophosphate (PP_i):

$$\text{ATP} + H_2O \rightarrow \text{AMP} + PP_i + 2H^+ \qquad \Delta G^{\circ\prime} = -10.9 \text{ kcal/mol} \qquad (22.7)$$

The reaction may also be written as:

Study Skills 22.1

Bioprocesses

The last four chapters of the text complete our study of the molecular basis of life. This chapter and the next three build on your knowledge of the biomolecules (carbohydrates, lipids, proteins, and nucleic acids) and examine the processes that support living organisms. Your attention should now be directed toward gaining an understanding of these processes, where they occur in the cell, their purpose, and, in some cases, key summary reactions.

A number of detailed pathways such as glycolysis, the fatty acid spiral, and the urea cycle will be presented. Don't let the numerous reactions in these pathways intimidate you. Although each reaction could be looked at individually, we have tried to help you focus your attention by emphasizing the overall importance of each pathway by identifying its purpose, cellular location, starting material, products, energy requirements, and regulation.

Calorie Language

In the United States, obesity is now considered to be a national problem. Many adults are overweight, obese, or even morbidly obese. Even more concerning is the increase in adolescent obesity. The concern with obesity is not an issue of vanity, but rather is an issue of health. Obesity is directly or indirectly linked to a wide array of serious negative health conditions that impact not only the health of individuals, but also the health of our society as a whole.

Part of the problem is the demand for quick and satisfying foods to fit into our hectic lives. It is easy to grab burgers, fries and a soda for the family at a fast food restaurant as we rush from school and the office to soccer games and ballet. But the tide is changing. People want healthier choices. As a result, fast food restaurants and prepackaged food industries are making changes. But, are these changes in our convenience foods really a significant improvement? Or, do they make us believe we are eating better when, in reality, we are simply trading one bad choice for another, but are unaware of it.

If we educate ourselves on the meaning of the new marketing language being used, we might avoid falling for misleading calorie content claims for foods. The following legal definitions will help you make more informed decisions about your foods.

- "Calorie free" – items contain less than 5 calories **per serving**
- "Low calorie" – items contain less than 40 calories **per serving**
- "Reduced" or "fewer calories" – items contain 25% **less calories than the original product**
- "Light" – items contain 50% less fat OR 1/3 the calories of the original product

The above terminology can be tricky and confusing especially when you need to break out a calculator and a scale to determine how many servings you are consuming and the total calories. Keep in mind that there are very few truly calorie-free items that we consume, aside from pure unadulterated water. For more information or if you need assistance wading through the nutrition labels of foods, check out the following website: www.http//mypyramid.gov.

Fast food restaurants are beginning to offer more healthful choices.

When the hydrolysis of ATP to AMP occurs during metabolism, it is usually followed by the immediate hydrolysis of the pyrophosphate, which releases even more free energy:

$$^-O-\overset{\overset{O}{\|}}{\underset{\underset{O^-}{|}}{P}}-O-\overset{\overset{O}{\|}}{\underset{\underset{O^-}{|}}{P}}-O^- + H_2O \longrightarrow 2HO-\overset{\overset{O}{\|}}{\underset{\underset{O^-}{|}}{P}}-O^- \qquad \Delta G^{\circ\prime} = -4.6 \text{ kcal/mol} \qquad (22.8)$$

$$PP_i \qquad\qquad\qquad P_i$$

The hydrolyses of ATP and related compounds are summarized in ▶ Table 22.6.

TABLE 22.6 Hydrolyses of Some ATP-Related Compounds

Reaction			$\Delta G^{\circ\prime}$ (kcal/mol)
ATP + H$_2$O	$\rightarrow$	ADP + P$_i$ + H$^+$	-7.3
ATP + H$_2$O	$\rightarrow$	AMP + PP$_i$ + 2H$^+$	-10.9
PP$_i$ + H$_2$O	$\rightarrow$	2P$_i$	-4.6
ADP + H$_2$O	$\rightarrow$	AMP + P$_i$ + H$^+$	-7.3

The ATP–ADP Cycle

In biological systems, ATP functions as an immediate donor of free energy rather than as a storage form of free energy. In a typical cell, an ATP molecule is hydrolyzed within one minute following its formation. Thus, the turnover rate of ATP is very high. For example, a resting human body hydrolyzes ATP at the rate of about 40 kg every 24 hours. During strenuous exertion, this rate of ATP utilization may be as high as 0.5 kg per minute. Motion, biosynthesis, and other forms of cellular work can occur only if ATP is continuously regenerated from ADP. ❱ Figure 22.14 depicts the central role served by the ATP–ADP cycle in linking energy production with energy utilization.

Figure 22.14 The ATP–ADP cycle. ATP, which supplies the energy for cellular work, is continuously regenerated from ADP during the oxidation of fuel molecules.

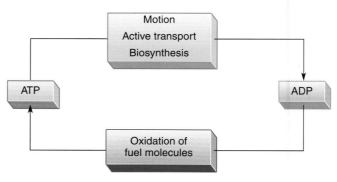

Mitochondria

mitochondrion A cellular organelle where reactions of the common catabolic pathway occur.

Enzymes that catalyze the formation of ATP, as well as the other processes in the common catabolic pathway, are all located within the cell in organelles called **mitochondria** (see ❱ Figure 22.15). Mitochondria are often called cellular "power stations" because they are the sites for most ATP synthesis in the cells.

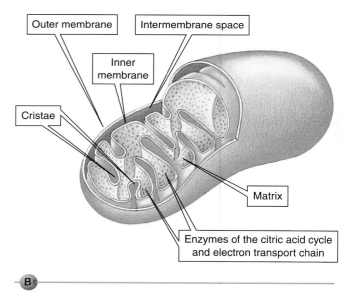

Figure 22.15 The mitochondrion: Ⓐ a photomicrograph; Ⓑ a schematic drawing, cut away to reveal the internal organization.

A mitochondrion contains both inner and outer membranes. As a result of extensive folding, the inner membrane has a surface area that is many times that of the outer membrane. The folds of the inner membrane are called *cristae,* and the gel-filled space that surrounds them is called the *matrix.* The enzymes for ATP synthesis (electron transport and oxidative phosphorylation) are located on the matrix side of the cristae. The enzymes for the citric acid cycle are found within the matrix, attached or near to the surface of the inner membrane. Thus, all the enzymes involved in the common catabolic pathway are in close proximity.

22.8 Important Coenzymes in the Common Catabolic Pathway

Learning Objective

9. Explain the role of coenzymes in the common catabolic pathway.

As discussed in Section 20.3, coenzymes often participate in enzyme-catalyzed reactions by acting as shuttle systems in the transfer of chemical groups from one compound to another. For example, a coenzyme may accept hydrogen from one compound and later donate hydrogen to another compound. We also pointed out that many important coenzymes are formed from vitamins. The three substances discussed in this section exhibit both of these coenzyme characteristics.

Coenzyme A

Coenzyme A is a central compound in metabolism. It is a part of acetyl coenzyme A (acetyl CoA), the substance formed from all foods as they pass through Stage II of catabolism (see ▶ Figure 22.16).

$$\left.\begin{array}{l}\text{Fatty acids and glycerol} \\ \text{Glucose and other sugars} \\ \text{Amino acids}\end{array}\right\} \longrightarrow \underset{\substack{\text{acetyl coenzyme A} \\ \text{(acetyl CoA)}}}{CH_3 - \overset{\overset{\displaystyle O}{\|}}{C} - S - CoA}$$

Figure 22.16 Stage II of the oxidation of foods. Acetyl CoA is formed as the pathways of catabolism converge.

Coenzyme A is derived from the B vitamin pantothenic acid (B5) (see ▶ Figure 22.17). It also contains two other components, a phosphate derivative of ADP and b-mercaptoethylamine. A key feature in the structure of coenzyme A is the presence of the sulfhydryl group (—SH), which is the reactive portion of the molecule. For this reason, coenzyme A is often abbreviated as CoA—SH.

Figure 22.17 The structure of coenzyme A. The sulfhydryl group (—SH) is the reactive site.

The letter *A* was included in the coenzyme name to signify its participation in the transfer of acetyl groups. It is now known that coenzyme A transfers acyl groups in general rather than just the acetyl group. This is demonstrated in fatty acid oxidations

(Section 24.4), fatty acid synthesis (Section 24.7), and other biological reactions. Acyl groups are linked to coenzyme A through the sulfur atom in a **thioester bond.**

$$\underset{\text{acyl CoA}}{R-\overset{\overset{\displaystyle O}{\parallel}}{C}-S-CoA} \qquad \underset{\text{acetyl CoA}}{CH_3-\overset{\overset{\displaystyle O}{\parallel}}{C}-S-CoA}$$

The Coenzymes NAD⁺ and FAD

The majority of energy for ATP synthesis is released when the oxygen we breathe is reduced. During that process, oxygen accepts electrons and hydrogen ions, and water is produced. The electrons come from the oxidation of fuel molecules, such as glucose, but the electrons are not transferred directly to the oxygen from the fuel molecules or their breakdown products. Instead, these substrates first transfer the electrons to special coenzyme carriers. The reduced forms of these coenzymes then transfer the electrons to oxygen through the reactions of the electron transport chain. ATP is formed from ADP and P$_i$ as a result of this flow of electrons.

The first of these coenzymes, nicotinamide adenine dinucleotide (NAD⁺), is a derivative of ADP and the vitamin nicotinamide (see ❚ Figure 22.18). The reactive site of NAD⁺ is located in the nicotinamide portion of the molecule. During the oxidation of a substrate, the nicotinamide ring of NAD⁺ accepts two electrons and one proton, which forms the reduced coenzyme NADH.

Figure 22.18 The structure of nicotinamide adenine dinucleotide (NAD⁺). The reactive site is in the nicotinamide part of the molecule.

$$
\begin{array}{c}
\text{NAD}^+ + 2e^- + H^+ \rightleftharpoons \text{NADH}
\end{array}
\tag{22.9}
$$

NAD$^+$ (oxidized form) NADH (reduced form)

A typical cellular reaction in which NAD$^+$ serves as an electron acceptor is the oxidation of an alcohol:

General reaction:

$$
\underset{\text{alcohol}}{R-\overset{OH}{\underset{H}{\overset{|}{\underset{|}{C}}}}-H} + \text{NAD}^+ \rightarrow \underset{\text{aldehyde}}{R-\overset{O}{\overset{\|}{C}}-H} + \text{NADH} + H^+
\tag{22.10}
$$

Specific example:

$$
\underset{\text{ethanol}}{CH_3CH_2-OH} + \text{NAD}^+ \xrightarrow{\underset{\text{dehydrogenase}}{\text{alcohol}}} \underset{\text{acetaldehyde}}{CH_3-\overset{O}{\overset{\|}{C}}-H} + \text{NADH} + H^+
\tag{22.11}
$$

In this reaction, one hydrogen atom of the alcohol substrate is directly transferred to NAD$^+$, whereas the other appears in solution as H$^+$. Both electrons lost by the alcohol have been transferred to the nicotinamide ring in NADH.

Biochemical reactions in which coenzymes participate are often written in a more concise way. For example, Reaction 22.10 may be written:

$$
R-\overset{OH}{\underset{H}{\overset{|}{\underset{|}{C}}}}-H \xrightarrow{\qquad} R-\overset{O}{\overset{\|}{C}}-H
\tag{22.12}
$$

NAD$^+$ NADH + H$^+$

This format allows for the separate emphasis of the oxidation reaction and the involvement of a coenzyme.

▶ **LEARNING CHECK 22.1** Write the following reaction in the normal form of a chemical equation:

$$
\begin{array}{c}
\overset{OH}{\underset{}{\overset{|}{CH}}}-COO^- \\
|\\
CH_2-COO^-
\end{array}
\xrightarrow{\qquad}
\begin{array}{c}
\overset{O}{\overset{\|}{C}}-COO^- \\
|\\
CH_2-COO^-
\end{array}
$$

NAD$^+$ NADH + H$^+$

Flavin adenine dinucleotide (FAD) is the other major electron carrier in the oxidation of fuel molecules. This coenzyme is a derivative of ADP and the vitamin riboflavin. The reactive site is located within the riboflavin ring system (see ▶ Figure 22.19).

Figure 22.19 The structure of flavin adenine dinucleotide (FAD). The reactive portion (shown in blue) is in the riboflavin ring system.

As in the reduction of NAD^+, substrates of enzymes that use FAD as the coenzyme give up two electrons to the coenzyme. However, unlike NAD^+, the FAD coenzyme accepts both of the hydrogen atoms lost by the substrate. Thus, the abbreviation for the reduced form of FAD is $FADH_2$:

$$+\ 2H^+\ +\ 2e^- \rightleftharpoons \tag{22.13}$$

FAD
(oxidized form)

$FADH_2$
(reduced form)

DR. MELINA JAMPOLIS

Dr. Melina Jampolis is a San Francisco, California, physician nutrition specialist—a specialty practiced by only about 200 physicians in the United States. She focuses exclusively on nutrition for weight loss and disease prevention and treatment.

Ask an Expert 22.1

Q: Is it better to take a fiber supplement or to eat fiber-fortified foods?

A: Added fiber is popping up in everything these days, including yogurt, ice cream, nutrition bars, cookies, juice, and even water. The health benefits of fiber are numerous and include promoting bowel health and regularity, cholesterol and blood sugar reduction, and increasing satiety, which can help with weight control. The recommended daily intake of fiber ranges between 25 and 38 grams per day, yet most Americans consume only about 12 grams per day. So, fiber-fortified foods or supplements could help us narrow the gap—right?

One problem with this idea is that added fibers, such as those found in many supplements or used to fortify foods, might not have the same health benefits as naturally occurring, or intact, fiber. Added fiber generally comes in the form of isolated fibers, which include inulin, polydextrose, and maltrodextrin. These fibers, also known as functional fiber, can be extracted from foods or chemically synthesized. Naturally occurring fiber-rich foods like whole grains, beans, fruits, nuts, seeds, and vegetables contain a variety of fiber types, often in a combination of water-soluble and insoluble fiber. These foods also contain vitamins, minerals, and phytonutrients, but isolated fibers offer only one type of fiber without the accompanying nutrients. In addition, they are often added to less nutrient-rich foods, so the potential health benefits, which have not been thoroughly investigated, are likely to be significantly less.

Isolated fibers do not appear to have the same benefit as intact soluble fiber in terms of cholesterol and blood sugar reduction. This is because they are not viscous, meaning they do not form a gel when added to water. Polydextrose, a synthetic indigestible glucose polymer, acts as a prebiotic, stimulating the growth of healthy probiotic bacteria in the colon. But, in high doses it can have a laxative or gas-producing effect. Inulin, a soluble, indigestible fructose polymer derived from chicory root, is also a prebiotic, thereby promoting bowel health. Inulin might also help with satiety, and some studies suggest it boosts the absorption of minerals, including calcium and magnesium. In higher doses, however, it too can cause gas, bloating, and diarrhea.

Fiber supplements vary in the types of fiber that they contain. Psyllium, a naturally occurring soluble fiber, has been studied extensively, and research suggests a benefit in terms of constipation prevention, cholesterol reduction, blood sugar control, and weight loss, particularly when combined with a healthy diet. It also seems to help those suffering from irritable bowel syndrome (IBS), a common condition associated with bowel irregularity, bloating, and abdominal pain.

There is no question that obtaining fiber directly from regular foods is optimal, but there are some cases in which a supplement or fortified food might be helpful. However, more research is needed to determine the health benefits of isolated fibers. If they are added to less-healthy products like frozen desserts, fruit drinks, baked goods, or sugary cereals, do not be fooled into believing that they balance out the negative aspect of these foods. And simply adding a fiber supplement to an unhealthy diet is much less beneficial than changing the diet to include more healthful foods.

Naturally occurring fiber-rich foods include whole grains, nuts, and seeds.

Fiber supplements may have certain health benefits.

The substrates for oxidation reactions in which FAD is the coenzyme differ from those involving NAD^+. FAD is often involved in oxidation reactions in which a $-CH_2-CH_2-$ portion of the substrate is oxidized to a double bond:

General reaction:

$$R-\underset{\underset{H}{|}}{\overset{\overset{H}{|}}{C}}-\underset{\underset{H}{|}}{\overset{\overset{H}{|}}{C}}-R + FAD \longrightarrow \underset{\text{unsaturated}}{R-CH=CH-R} + FADH_2 \quad (22.14)$$

saturated
(reduced)

unsaturated
(oxidized)

Specific example:

$$\underset{\text{butyryl CoA}}{CH_3CH_2CH_2-\overset{\overset{O}{\|}}{C}-S-CoA} \xrightarrow{\qquad FAD \qquad FADH_2 \qquad} CH_3CH=CH-\overset{\overset{O}{\|}}{C}-SCoA \quad (22.15)$$

▶ **LEARNING CHECK 22.2** Complete the following reactions:

a. $^-OOC-CH_2-CH_2-COO^- + FAD \longrightarrow$

b. $CH_3-\underset{\underset{OH}{|}}{CH}-COO^- + NAD^+ \longrightarrow$

Case Study Follow-up

The American Association of Pediatrics recommends exclusive breastfeeding during the first six months, then for at least one additional year, and as long thereafter as mutually desired by mother and child. "Human milk is species-specific, and all substitute feeding preparations differ markedly from it, making human milk uniquely superior for infant feeding. In addition, human milk–fed premature infants receive significant benefits with respect to parasite protection and improved developmental outcomes compared with formula-fed premature infants. Breastfeeding decreases the incidence of a wide range of diseases, is associated with lower rates of sudden infant death, and is associated with enhanced cognitive development" (AAP, 1997).

The World Health Organization recommends exclusive breastfeeding for the first six months and then continued breastfeeding along with other foods for two years or more. Breastfeeding should be "on demand" as often as the baby wants it day and night (WHO, 2011).

Concept Summary

Nutritional Requirements

Every human body requires certain amounts of various macro- and micronutrients, water, and fiber to function properly. **Objective 1 (Section 22.1), Exercise 22.2.** The amounts needed vary with a number of factors such as body size, age, and sex. Various countries have established nutritional guidelines in attempts to maintain good health for their citizens. In the United States, the Reference Daily Intake (RDI) and Daily Reference Values (DRV) are designed to represent appropriate nutrient intake for 95% of the population.

The Macronutrients

Macronutrients are substances required by the body in relatively large amounts. They are used by the body to provide energy and the materials necessary to form new or replacement tissue. The macronutrients are carbohydrates, lipids, and proteins. **Objective 2 (Section 22.2), Exercise 22.4.** An RDI has been established only for proteins, but other groups have recommended the amounts of carbohydrates, lipids, and proteins that should be included in the diet.

Micronutrients I: Vitamins

Vitamins are organic micronutrients that the body cannot produce in the amounts needed for good health. A number of vitamins have a high water solubility resulting from the highly polar nature of their molecules. All but one of the water-soluble vitamins are known to function as coenzymes in the body and are involved in many important metabolic processes. Fat-soluble vitamins have nonpolar molecular structures. As a result, they are insoluble in water but soluble in fat or other nonpolar solvents. Fat-soluble vitamins act somewhat like hormones in the body. Fat-soluble vitamins do not dissolve in water-based body fluids, so they are not excreted through the kidneys. Amounts in excess of bodily requirements are stored in body fat. Thus, it is much easier to produce toxic effects by overdosing with fat-soluble vitamins than with water-soluble vitamins. **Objective 3 (Section 22.3), Exercise 22.10**

Micronutrients II: Minerals

Minerals are inorganic substances needed by the body. Those present in the body in amounts equal to or greater than 5 g are called major minerals. Those present in smaller amounts are called trace minerals. Minerals perform many useful functions in the body. **Objective 4 (Section 22.4), Exercise 22.16**

The Flow of Energy in the Biosphere

Energy for all living processes comes from the sun. A portion of the sun's energy is trapped in the process of photosynthesis, which produces carbohydrates. We derive energy from the foods we eat: carbohydrates, lipids, and proteins. As these substances are oxidized, molecules of ATP that supply the energy needed for cellular processes are formed. **Objective 5 (Section 22.5), Exercise 22.24**

Metabolism and an Overview of Energy Production

Metabolism, the sum of all cellular reactions, involves the breakdown (catabolism) and synthesis (anabolism) of molecules. **Objective 6 (Section 22.6), Exercise 22.26.** There are three stages in the catabolism of foods to provide energy. In Stage I, digestion converts foods into smaller molecules. In Stage II, these smaller molecules are converted into two-carbon acetyl units that combine with coenzyme A, forming acetyl CoA. Stage III, which is called the common catabolic pathway, consists of the citric acid cycle followed by the electron transport chain and oxidative phosphorylation. The main function of catabolism is to produce ATP molecules. **Objective 7 (Section 22.6), Exercise 22.28**

ATP: The Primary Energy Carrier

Molecular ATP is the link between energy production and energy use in cells. ATP is called a high-energy compound because of the large amount of free energy liberated on hydrolysis. Cells are able to harness the free energy liberated by ATP to carry out cellular work. ATP is consumed immediately following its formation and is quickly regenerated from ADP as fuel molecules are oxidized. Mitochondria play a key role in energy production because they house the enzymes for both the citric acid cycle and the electron transport chain.

Objective 8 (Section 22.7), Exercise 22.34

Important Coenzymes in the Common Catabolic Pathway

Three very important coenzymes are involved in catabolism: coenzyme A, NAD^+, and FAD. Coenzyme A binds to the two-carbon fragments produced in Stage II to form acetyl CoA, the direct fuel of the citric acid cycle. NAD^+ and FAD are the oxidizing agents that participate in the oxidation reactions of the citric acid cycle. They transport hydrogen atoms and electrons from the citric acid cycle to the electron transport chain.

Objective 9 (Section 22.8), Exercise 22.46

Key Terms and Concepts

Anabolism (22.6)
Catabolism (22.6)
Cellular respiration (22.5)
Common catabolic pathway (22.6)
Complete protein (22.2)
Complex carbohydrate (22.2)
Daily Reference Values (DRV) (22.1)
Daily Values (DV) (22.1)

Essential amino acid (22.2)
High-energy compound (22.7)
Macronutrient (22.1)
Major mineral (22.4)
Metabolic pathway (22.6)
Metabolism (22.6)
Micronutrient (22.1)
Mineral (22.4)

Mitochondrion (22.7)
Nutrition (Introduction)
Reference Daily Intakes (RDI) (22.1)
Satiety (22.2)
Simple carbohydrates (22.2)
Thioester bond (22.8)
Trace mineral (22.4)

Key Reactions

1.	Photosynthesis (Section 22.5):	$6CO_2 + 6H_2O + energy \rightarrow C_6H_{12}O_6 \rightarrow 6O_2$	Reaction 22.2				
2.	Hydrolysis of ATP (Section 22.7):	$ATP + H_2O \rightarrow ADP + P_i + H^+$	Reaction 22.5				
3.	Oxidation by NAD^+ (Section 22.8):	$$\begin{array}{ccc} \overset{\displaystyle OH}{\underset{\displaystyle H}{R-\overset{	}{\underset{	}{C}}-H}} + NAD^+ \longrightarrow & R-\overset{\displaystyle O}{\overset{\|}{C}}-H + NADH + H^+ \end{array}$$	Reaction 22.10		
4.	Oxidation by FAD (Section 22.8):	$$R-\overset{\displaystyle H}{\underset{\displaystyle H}{\overset{	}{\underset{	}{C}}}}-\overset{\displaystyle H}{\underset{\displaystyle H}{\overset{	}{\underset{	}{C}}}}-R + FAD \longrightarrow R-CH=CH-R + FADH_2$$	Reaction 22.14

Exercises

Even-numbered exercises are answered in Appendix B.

Blue-numbered exercises are more challenging.

Nutritional Requirements (Section 22.1)

22.1 What is the principal component of dietary fiber?

22.2 What is the primary difference between a macronutrient and a micronutrient?

22.3 Explain the importance of sufficient fiber in the diet.

The Macronutrients (Section 22.2)

22.4 List two general functions in the body for each of the macronutrients.

22.5 For each of the following macronutrients, list a single food item that would be a good source:

 a. carbohydrate (simple)

 b. carbohydrate (complex)

 c. lipid

 d. protein

22.6 List the types of macronutrients found in each of the following food items. List the nutrients in approximate decreasing order of abundance (most abundant first, etc.).

 a. Potato chips

 b. Buttered toast

 c. Plain toast with jam

 d. Cheese sandwich

 e. A lean steak

 f. A fried egg

22.7 What makes a fatty acid essential? What are the essential fatty acids?

22.8 Use Figure 22.2 and list the Daily Values (DV) for fat, saturated fat, total carbohydrate, and fiber based on a 2000-calorie diet.

22.9 Use the Daily Values (DV) and the calories per gram conversions given in Figure 22.2 to calculate the number of calories in a 2000-calorie diet that should be from fat, saturated fat, and total carbohydrate.

Micronutrients I: Vitamins (Section 22.3)

22.10 Identify each of the following vitamins as water-soluble or fat-soluble.

 a. tocopherol **c.** folic acid

 b. niacin **d.** retinol

22.11 What general function is served by eight of the water-soluble vitamins?

22.12 Why is there more concern about large doses of fat-soluble vitamins than of water-soluble vitamins?

22.13 What fat-soluble vitamin or deficiency is associated with the following?

 a. Night blindness

 b. Blood clotting

 c. Calcium and phosphorus use in forming bones and teeth

 d. Preventing oxidation of fatty acids

22.14 What water-soluble vitamin deficiency is associated with the following?

 a. scurvy

 b. beriberi

 c. pernicious anemia

 d. pellagra

Micronutrients II: Minerals (Section 22.4)

22.15 What is the difference between a vitamin and a mineral?

22.16 List at least one specific function for each major mineral of the body.

22.17 What determines whether a mineral is classified as a major or trace mineral?

22.18 What are the general functions of trace minerals in the body?

22.19 How can the ingestion of a small lump of elemental sodium metal be toxic when sodium is a required major mineral?

The Flow of Energy in the Biosphere (Section 22.5)

22.20 What element serves as a fuel for the fusion process occurring on the sun?

22.21 What is the source of energy for life on Earth?

22.22 Write a net equation for the photosynthetic process.

22.23 Explain how Earth's supply of carbon compounds may be recycled by the processes of photosynthesis and respiration.

22.24 Describe in general terms the steps in the flow of energy from the sun to molecules of ATP.

Metabolism and an Overview of Energy Production (Section 22.6)

22.25 What is a metabolic pathway?

22.26 Classify catabolism and anabolism as synthetic or breakdown processes.

22.27 Outline the three stages in the extraction of energy from food.

22.28 Which stage of energy production is concerned primarily with the following?

 a. Formation of ATP

 b. Digestion of fuel molecules

 c. Consumption of O_2

 d. Generation of acetyl CoA

22.29 Explain why Stage III of energy production is referred to as the common catabolic pathway.

22.30 In terms of energy production, what is the main purpose of the catabolic pathway?

22.31 Would the digestion of protein to amino acids that are then used to build muscle in the body be considered a catabolic pathway? Why or why not?

ATP: The Primary Energy Carrier (Section 22.7)

22.32 Is ATP involved in anabolic processes or catabolic processes?

22.33 What do the symbols ATP, ADP, and AMP represent?

22.34 Explain why ATP is referred to as the primary energy carrier.

22.35 Using the partial structure shown below, write the structure of ATP, ADP, and AMP:

$$-\overset{\overset{\displaystyle O}{\|}}{\underset{\underset{\displaystyle O^-}{|}}{P}}-O-\text{adenosine}$$

22.36 What do the symbols P_i and PP_i represent?

22.37 Using symbolic formulas such as ADP and PP_i, write equations for the hydrolysis of ATP to ADP and the hydrolysis of ATP to AMP.

22.38 Using Table 22.5, explain why phosphoenolpyruvate is called a high-energy compound but glycerol 3-phosphate is not.

22.39 What does the symbol $\Delta G^{\circ\prime}$ represent? How does the sign for $\Delta G^{\circ\prime}$ indicate whether a reaction is exergonic or endergonic?

22.40 Which portion of the ATP molecule is particularly responsible for it being described as a high-energy compound?

22.41 Why is it more accurate to refer to ATP as a carrier or donor of free energy rather than as a storage form of free energy?

22.42 What is the role of mitochondria in the use of energy by living organisms?

22.43 Describe the importance and function of the ATP–ADP cycle.

22.44 Describe the structure of a mitochondrion and identify the location of enzymes important in energy production.

Important Coenzymes in the Common Catabolic Pathway (Section 22.8)

22.45 What coenzymes are produced by the body from the following vitamins?

 a. riboflavin

 b. pantothenic acid

 c. nicotinamide

22.46 What roles do the following coenzymes serve in the catabolic oxidation of foods?

 a. coenzyme A **b.** FAD **c.** NAD^+

22.47 Write the abbreviations for the oxidized and reduced forms of:

 a. flavin adenine dinucleotide

 b. nicotinamide adenine dinucleotide

22.48 Which compound is oxidized in the following reaction? Which compound is reduced?

$$^-OOC-CH_2-CH_2-COO^- + FAD \longrightarrow$$
$$^-OOC-CH=CH-COO^- + FADH_2$$

Even-numbered exercises answered in Appendix B.

22.49 Which compound is oxidized in the following reaction? Which compound is reduced?

$$CH_3CH_2-OH + NAD^+ \longrightarrow CH_3\overset{\overset{\displaystyle O}{\|}}{C}-H + NADH + H^+$$

22.50 Write balanced reactions for the following oxidations using NAD^+ or FAD:

 a. $HO-CH_2-COOH \rightarrow O=CH-COOH$

 b. $HO-CH_2CH_2-OH \rightarrow HO-CH=CH-OH$

22.51 Write balanced reactions for the following oxidations using NAD^+:

 a. $CH_3-\overset{\overset{\displaystyle OH}{|}}{CH}-COO^- \rightarrow CH_3-\overset{\overset{\displaystyle O}{\|}}{C}-COO^-$

 b. $CH_3-OH \rightarrow H-\overset{\overset{\displaystyle O}{\|}}{C}-H$

22.52 Draw abbreviated structural formulas to show the reactive portion of FAD and the reduced compound $FADH_2$.

Additional Exercises

22.53 Based on the solubility characteristics of vitamin B_1, would you expect to find it in the interior of an enzyme or on the exterior surface of the enzyme when it acts as a coenzyme?

22.54 Balance the following equation. How many electrons will be transferred to NADH?

$$CH_4 + O_2 + ____ NAD^+ \rightarrow CO_2 + ____ NADH + ____ H^+$$

22.55 Draw an energy diagram that depicts the two hydrolysis reactions of ATP below.

$$ATP \rightarrow ADP + P_i \rightarrow AMP + 2P_i$$

22.56 What would be the main process in the human body that would be interrupted by a deficiency of an essential amino acid? What specific part of that process would be affected?

22.57 Average 18-year-olds should get 1300 mg of calcium in their diet daily. Use Figure 22.8 and calculate the percentage of the daily intake that represents the total amount of calcium found in a 60-kg person.

Allied Health Exam Connection

The following questions are from these sources:

1. *Nursing School Entrance Exam* © 2005, Learning Express, LLC.

2. *McGraw-Hill's Nursing School Entrance Exams* by Thomas A. Evangelist, Tamara B. Orr and Judy Unrein © 2009, The McGraw-Hill Companies, Inc.

3. *NSEE Nursing School Entrance Exams,* 3rd Edition © 2009, Kaplan Publishing.

4. *Cliffs Test Prep: Nursing School Entrance Exams* by Fred N. Grayson © 2004, Wiley Publishing, Inc.

5. *Peterson's Master the Nursing School and Allied Health Entrance Exams,* 18th Edition by Marion F. Gooding © 2008, Peterson's, a Nelnet Company.

22.58 Identify which vitamin(s) is indicated by the following:

 a. The fat-soluble vitamins

 b. Thiamin

 c. A vitamin that helps prevent rickets

 d. A vitamin that helps clot blood

 e. A vitamin useful in combatting pernicious anemia

22.59 Answer the following:

 a. Which mineral is the most abundant in the human body?

 b. Which mineral is necessary for the proper functioning of the thyroid gland?

 c. Which mineral is necessary for the proper formation of hemoglobin?

 d. What is the difference between a vitamin and a mineral?

22.60 Which of the following are not a requirement for photosynthesis?

 a. oxygen

 b. carbon dioxide

 c. sunlight

 d. chlorophyll

22.61 With which organelle is the synthesis of ATP associated?

22.62 Use Figure 22.2 to determine which macronutrient would produce the greatest amount of energy from 1 gram of the macronutrient.

22.63 Outline the three stages in the extraction of energy from food. What type of chemical reaction occurs most often during digestion?

22.64 Amino acids that cannot be manufactured by the body are called:

 a. essential amino acids

 b. synthetic amino acids

 c. basic amino acids

 d. dependent amino acids

22.65 More than 90% of dietary fat is in the form of:

 a. triglycerides

 b. phospholipids

 c. cholesterol

 d. lipase

22.66 Water soluble vitamins include:

 a. vitamin A

 b. vitamin C

 c. vitamin D

 d. vitamin K

22.67 The chemical reaction that supplies immediate energy for muscular contractions can be summarized as:

 a. $ATP \rightarrow ADP + P$

 b. $lactic\ acid \rightarrow CO_2 + H_2O$

 c. $lactic\ acid \rightarrow glycogen$

 d. $glycogen \rightarrow ATP$

22.68 Which process does the following equation represent?

$$6CO_2 + light\ energy + 6H_2O \rightarrow C_6H_{12}O_6 + 6O_2$$

 a. glycolysis

 b. fermentation

 c. photosynthesis

 d. cellular respiration

Chemistry for Thought

22.69 At one time, a system of MDR (minimum daily requirement) values for nutrients was used. Why do you think Daily Values (DV) might be more informative and useful than MDRs?

22.70 Briefly explain why you think it would be undesirable or beneficial (decide which position to defend in each case) to follow a diet that is (a) extremely low in carbohydrates, (b) extremely low in lipids, or (c) extremely low in proteins.

22.71 Doughnuts, even those without frosting, are high in triglycerides. Explain.

22.72 One of the oils listed in Figure 22.6 is palm oil, which for several years was used in fast-food restaurants to fry potatoes. Why was this use considered an unhealthy practice?

22.73 In Figure 22.7, it is observed that vegetables are a source of protein. We most often think of meats, grains, and dairy products as sources of protein, but not vegetables. Use Table 19.4 to list the types of protein that might be found in vegetables.

22.74 Vitamin tablets and oranges are both plentiful sources of vitamin C. Why might an orange be better for you than taking a vitamin C tablet?

22.75 A cold cereal manufactured from corn is deficient in the amino acid lysine. What other foods in a breakfast meal might supply lysine?

22.76 The body has a storage capacity for excess carbohydrates and fats but not for excess proteins. What consequences does this fact have for a daily diet?

22.77 Which macronutrient is a major source of dietary sulfur?

Case Study

Natalie's husband is an F-16 pilot for the U.S. Air Force. They moved from a military base in humid San Antonio, Texas, to Tucson, Arizona. Natalie thought she was having difficulty adjusting to the dry climate. She was drinking large quantities of water and could not quench her thirst. She had also lost a few pounds. Could it be dehydration? Eventually she felt so ill that she visited the emergency room. The ER physician immediately suspected diabetic ketoacidosis and ordered blood and urine tests. The results supported a diagnosis of type 1 diabetes mellitus. Natalie now has to check her sugar levels before every meal and several times during the day, and she has an insulin pump. She tries to keep her blood sugar in the range of 90 mg/dL to 130 mg/dL before meals and below 180 mg/dL two hours after meals.

What should she do if her levels dip or go too high? What type of community support might be available to Natalie? How might Natalie's husband need support, since her diabetes diagnosis impacts his life well?

Follow-up to this Case Study appears at the end the chapter before the Concept Summary.

© iStockphoto.com/Mark Hatfield

Learning Objectives

When you have completed your study of this chapter, you should be able to:

1 Identify the products of carbohydrate digestion. **(Section 23.1)**

2 Explain the importance to the body of maintaining proper blood sugar levels. **(Section 23.2)**

3 List the starting material and products of the glycolysis pathway. **(Section 23.3)**

4 Describe how the glycolysis pathway is regulated in response to cellular needs. **(Section 23.3)**

5 Name the three fates of pyruvate. **(Section 23.4)**

6 Identify the two major functions of the citric acid cycle. **(Section 23.5)**

7 Describe how the citric acid cycle is regulated in response to cellular energy needs. **(Section 23.5)**

8 Explain the function of the electron transport chain and describe how electrons move down the chain. **(Section 23.6)**

9 List the major features of the chemi-osmotic hypothesis. **(Section 23.7)**

10 Calculate the amount of ATP produced by the complete oxidation of a mole of glucose. **(Section 23.8)**

11 Explain the importance of the processes of glycogenesis and glycogenolysis. **(Section 23.9)**

12 Describe gluconeogenesis and the operation of the Cori cycle. **(Section 23.10)**

13 Describe how hormones regulate carbohydrate metabolism. **(Section 23.11)**

C arbohydrates play major roles in cell metabolism. The central substance in carbohydrate metabolism is glucose; it is the key food molecule for most organisms. As the major carbohydrate metabolic pathways are discussed, you will see that each one involves either the use or the synthesis of glucose. You will also see how the chemical degradation of glucose provides energy in the cell, how glucose is stored, how the blood glucose level is regulated, and how diabetes results from changes in blood glucose regulation mechanisms.

23.1 The Digestion of Carbohydrates

Learning Objective

1. Identify the products of carbohydrate digestion.

The major function of dietary carbohydrates is to serve as an energy source. In a typical American diet, carbohydrates meet about 45–55% of the daily energy needs. Fats and proteins furnish the remaining energy. During carbohydrate digestion, di- and polysaccharides are hydrolyzed to monosaccharides, primarily glucose, fructose, and galactose:

$$\text{polysaccharides} + H_2O \xrightarrow{\text{digestion}} \text{glucose} \qquad (23.1)$$

$$\text{sucrose} + H_2O \xrightarrow{\text{digestion}} \text{glucose} + \text{fructose} \qquad (23.2)$$

$$\text{lactose} + H_2O \xrightarrow{\text{digestion}} \text{glucose} + \text{galactose} \qquad (23.3)$$

$$\text{maltose} + H_2O \xrightarrow{\text{digestion}} \text{glucose} \qquad (23.4)$$

Figure 23.1 Blood glucose levels.

blood sugar level The amount of glucose present in blood, normally expressed as milligrams per 100 mL of blood.

hypoglycemia A lower-than-normal blood sugar level.

hyperglycemia A higher-than-normal blood sugar level.

renal threshold The blood glucose level at which glucose begins to be excreted in the urine.

glucosuria A condition in which elevated blood sugar levels result in the excretion of glucose in the urine.

glycolysis A series of reactions by which glucose is oxidized to pyruvate.

After digestion is completed, glucose, fructose, and galactose are absorbed into the bloodstream through the lining of the small intestine and transported to the liver. In the liver, fructose and galactose are rapidly converted to glucose or to compounds that are metabolized by the same pathway as glucose.

23.2 Blood Glucose

Learning Objective

2. Explain the importance to the body of maintaining proper blood sugar levels.

Glucose is by far the most plentiful monosaccharide found in blood, and the term *blood sugar* usually refers to glucose. In adults, the normal **blood sugar level** measured after a fast of 8–12 hours is in the range of 70–110 mg/100 mL. (In clinical reports, such levels are often expressed in units of milligrams per deciliter, mg/dL.) The blood sugar level reaches a maximum of approximately 140–160 mg/100 mL about 1 hour after a carbohydrate-containing meal. It returns to normal after 2–2½ hours.

If a blood sugar level is below the normal fasting level, a condition called **hypoglycemia** exists. Because glucose is the only nutrient normally used by the brain for energy, mild hypoglycemia leads to dizziness and fainting as brain cells are deprived of energy. Severe hypoglycemia can cause convulsions and coma. When the blood glucose concentration is above normal, the condition is referred to as **hyperglycemia.** If blood glucose levels exceed approximately 180 mg/100 mL, the sugar is not completely reabsorbed by the kidneys, and glucose is excreted in the urine (see ❱ Figure 23.1). The blood glucose level at which this occurs is called the **renal threshold,** and the condition in which glucose appears in the urine is called **glucosuria.** Prolonged hyperglycemia at a glucosuric level must be considered serious because it indicates that something is wrong with the body's normal ability to control the blood sugar level.

The liver is the key organ involved in regulating the blood glucose level. The liver responds to the increase in blood glucose that follows a meal by removing glucose from the bloodstream. The removed glucose is primarily converted to glycogen or triglycerides for storage. Similarly, when blood glucose levels are low, the liver responds by converting stored glycogen to glucose and by synthesizing new glucose from noncarbohydrate substances.

23.3 Glycolysis

Learning Objectives

3. List the starting material and products of the glycolysis pathway.
4. Describe how the glycolysis pathway is regulated in response to cellular needs.

Glycolysis is an important part of the catabolic process by which the body gets energy from carbohydrates. It consists of a series of ten reactions, with the net result being the conversion of a glucose molecule into two molecules of pyruvate. All enzymes for glycolysis are present in the cellular cytoplasm. The ten reactions of glycolysis catalyzed by these enzymes are represented in ❱ Figure 23.2. The addition of all these reactions gives a net reaction for glycolysis:

$$\text{glucose} + 2P_i + 2ADP + 2NAD^+ \rightarrow$$
$$2 \text{ pyruvate} + 2ATP + 2NADH + 4H^+ + 2H_2O \qquad (23.5)$$

This equation indicates a net gain of 2 mol of ATP for every mole of glucose converted to pyruvate. In addition, 2 mol of the coenzyme NADH is formed when

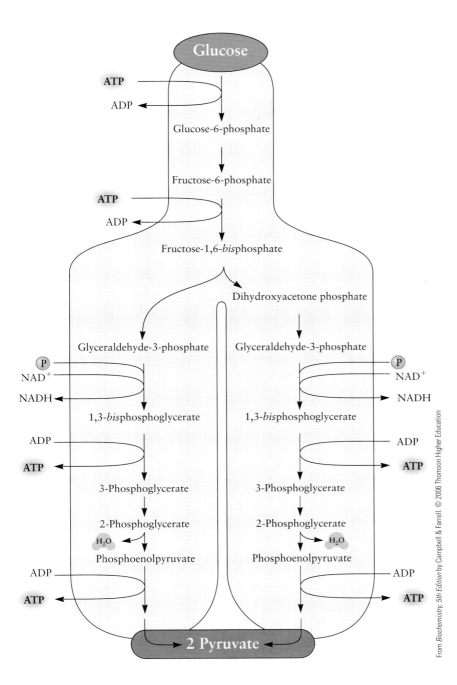

Figure 23.2 A summary of glycolysis. The Ⓟ stands for

$$-\overset{\overset{\displaystyle O^-}{|}}{\underset{\underset{\displaystyle O^-}{|}}{P}}=O$$

and the prefix "bis-" is used to denote two of these groups.

From *Biochemistry, 5th Edition* by Campbell & Farrell. © 2006 Thomson Higher Education

NAD^+ serves as an oxidizing agent in glycolysis. Fructose and galactose from digested food are both converted into intermediates that enter into the glycolysis pathway. Fructose enters glycolysis as dihydroxyacetone phosphate and glyceraldehyde-3-phosphate, whereas galactose is metabolized to glucose and enters in the form of glucose-6-phosphate.

The Regulation of Glycolysis

The glycolysis pathway, like all metabolic pathways, is controlled constantly. The precise regulation of the concentrations of pathway intermediates is efficient and makes possible the rapid adjustment of the output level of pathway products as the need arises.

DR. MELINA B. JAMPOLIS, M.D.

© Michael Roud Photography

Dr. Melina B. Jampolis, M.D. is a Los Angeles, California, Physician Nutrition Specialist—a specialty practiced by only a few hundred physicians in the United States. She focuses exclusively on nutrition for weight loss and disease prevention and treatment.

Ask an Expert 23.1

Q: How can we avoid energy crashes?

A: An "energy crash" typically occurs one to three hours after a meal, usually late morning, after breakfast, and early afternoon, after lunch. The term *energy crash* is not scientific, but is generally used to indicate a rapid drop in blood sugar that is accompanied by symptoms including headaches, hunger, decreased ability to concentrate, and even mood changes. The reason for the rapid decline in blood sugar is usually related to the nutrient content of the previous meal. For example, meals containing large amounts of rapidly digested carbohydrates can cause a rapid increase in blood sugar. The blood sugar increase leads to a surge in the release of insulin, a hormone that transfers sugar from the blood to cells of the brain or muscles for use as energy, or to fat cells for storage. Thus, a quick spike in blood sugar, leading to an exaggerated release of insulin, can cause a fairly rapid drop in blood sugar, which in turn causes symptoms of an energy crash.

The measure of how quickly and significantly a specific food increases blood sugar levels is known as the glycemic index (GI) of the food. The GI is obtained by comparing the total increase in blood sugar during the two hours following the consumption of a sample of the food that contains 50 grams of carbohydrate. This increase is compared to the increase caused by a control that generally consists of the consumption of 50 grams of glucose, which has a GI of 100. Foods with generally high GI values include refined grains, white potatoes, white rice, white bread, sugary cereals, candy, baked goods, crackers, pretzels, fruit drinks, and sodas. The GI indicates the ability of carbohydrates to increase blood sugar levels, but in order to understand the true effect of a food on blood sugar, the amount of carbohydrates present in the food is equally important. The glycemic load of a food includes both the ability of carbohydrates in the food to increase blood sugar levels and the amount of carbohydrate present in the food. It is calculated by multiplying together the glycemic index and the amount of carbohydrates in a typical serving of the food.

The glycemic index of a meal can be decreased in several ways. Consuming lower GI carbohydrates like whole grains, oats, whole grain cereals and breads, brown rice, and beans instead of refined grains, sugary cereals, white rice, and white potatoes is key. Opting for fiber-rich whole fruit instead of juice is helpful, and limiting the intake of sugary beverages, snacks, baked goods, and candy is important. Finally, combining healthy fat or lean protein with carbohydrates at each meal also helps lower the GI of the meal. By lowering the GI of meals, blood sugar levels remain more constant throughout the day, helping you avoid energy crashes. Lowering the GI of your diet may also decrease your risk of type 2 diabetes, heart disease, and age-related macular degeneration, the leading cause of blindness in older Americans.

One final thought: If you consume a high-GI breakfast, like a bagel with fat-free cream cheese and orange juice *with* a large amount of coffee, energy crashes can be particularly significant one to two hours after breakfast. Caffeine reaches peak levels in the body approximately 30–45 minutes after consumption. The drop in blood sugar following a high-GI meal combined with the drop in the stimulant effects of caffeine can enhance symptoms of lethargy and decreased concentration. By limiting yourself to moderate amounts of caffeine and lowering the GI of your diet, you can stay alert and energized throughout the day and improve your health.

Sugary foods have high GI values.

The glycolysis pathway is regulated by three enzymes: hexokinase, phosphofructokinase, and pyruvate kinase. The regulation of the pathway is shown in ▶ Figure 23.3.

Glucose

Feedback inhibition ---→ hexokinase (inhibited by glucose-6-phosphate)

glucose-6-phosphate

fructose-6-phosphate

phosphofructokinase (inhibited by ATP and citrate; activated by ADP and AMP)

fructose-1,6-bisphosphate

3-phosphoenolpyruvate

pyruvate kinase (inhibited by ATP)

Pyruvate

Figure 23.3 The regulation of the glycolysis pathway. Glucose-6-phosphate is a noncompetitive inhibitor of hexokinase. Phosphofructokinase and pyruvate kinase are also allosteric enzymes subject to control.

Hexokinase catalyzes the conversion of glucose to glucose-6-phosphate and thus initiates the glycolysis pathway. The enzyme is inhibited by a high concentration of glucose-6-phosphate, the product of the reaction it catalyzes. Thus, the phosphorylation of glucose is controlled by feedback inhibition (Section 20.8).

A second and very important control point for glycolysis shown in Figure 23.3 is the step catalyzed by phosphofructokinase. Once glucose is converted to fructose-1,6-bisphosphate, its carbon skeleton must continue through the glycolytic pathway. The phosphorylation of fructose-6-phosphate is a committed step that will occur as long as the enzyme is active. As an allosteric enzyme (Section 20.8), phosphofructokinase is inhibited by high concentrations of ATP and citrate, and it is activated by high concentrations of ADP and AMP.

The third control point is the last step of glycolysis, the conversion of phosphoenolpyruvate to pyruvate catalyzed by pyruvate kinase. This enzyme, too, is an allosteric enzyme that is inhibited by higher concentrations of ATP.

To understand how these controls interact, remember that when the glycolysis pathway is operating at a maximum rate, so also are the citric acid cycle and the electron transport chain. As a result of their activity, large quantities of ATP are produced. The entire pathway continues to operate at a high rate, as long as the produced ATP is used up by processes within the cell. However, if ATP use decreases, the concentration of ATP increases, and more diffuses to the binding sites of the allosteric enzymes sensitive to ATP. Thus, the activity of these enzymes decreases. When phosphofructokinase is inhibited in this way, the entire glycolysis pathway slows or stops. As a result, the concentration of glucose-6-phosphate increases, thus inhibiting hexokinase and the initial step of the glycolysis pathway.

Conversely, when ATP concentrations are low, the concentrations of AMP and ADP are high. The AMP and ADP function as activators (Section 20.8) that influence phosphofructokinase and thereby speed up the entire glycolysis pathway.

▶ **LEARNING CHECK 23.1** Explain how each of the following enzymes helps regulate the glycolysis pathway:

a. hexokinase
b. phosphofructokinase
c. pyruvate kinase

23.4 The Fates of Pyruvate

Learning Objective

5. Name the three fates of pyruvate.

The sequence of reactions that converts glucose to pyruvate is very similar in all organisms and in all kinds of cells. However, the fate of the pyruvate as it is used to generate energy is variable. Three different fates of pyruvate are considered here.

As glucose is oxidized to pyruvate in glycolysis, NAD^+ is reduced to NADH. The need for a continuous supply of NAD^+ for glycolysis is a key to understanding the fates of pyruvate.

$$\text{glucose} + 2NAD^+ \longrightarrow 2 \text{ pyruvate} + 2NADH + 2H^+ \quad (23.6)$$
$$2ADP + 2P_i \quad 2ATP$$

In each case, pyruvate is metabolized in ways that regenerate NAD^+ so that glycolysis can continue.

Oxidation to Acetyl CoA

aerobic In the presence of oxygen.

The mitochondrial membrane is permeable to pyruvate formed by glycolysis in the cytoplasm, and under **aerobic** conditions (a plentiful oxygen supply), pyruvate is converted inside the mitochondria to acetyl CoA.

$$\underset{\text{pyruvate}}{CH_3-\overset{O}{\overset{\|}{C}}-COO^-} + CoA-S-H + NAD^+ \xrightarrow[\text{complex}]{\text{pyruvate}\atop\text{dehydrogenase}} \underset{\text{acetyl CoA}}{CH_3-\overset{O}{\overset{\|}{C}}-S-CoA} + NADH + CO_2 \quad (23.7)$$

Acetyl CoA formed in this reaction can enter the citric acid cycle on its way to complete oxidation to CO_2. The NAD^+ needed for the conversion of pyruvate to acetyl CoA (Reaction 23.7) and for the operation of the glycolysis pathway (Step 6) is regenerated when NADH transfers its electrons to O_2 in the electron transport chain.

Not all acetyl CoA generated metabolically enters the citric acid cycle. Some also serve as a starting material for fatty acid biosynthesis (Section 24.7). The fatty acid components of triglycerides, for example, are synthesized using acetyl CoA. Thus, as most people are aware, the intake of excess dietary carbohydrates can lead to an increase in body fat storage.

Reduction to Lactate

anaerobic In the absence of oxygen.

Under **anaerobic** conditions, such as those that accompany strenuous or long-term muscle activity, the cellular supply of oxygen is not adequate for the reoxidation of NADH to NAD^+. Under such conditions, the cells begin reducing pyruvate to lactate as a means of regenerating NAD^+:

$$\underset{\text{pyruvate}}{CH_3-\overset{O}{\overset{\|}{C}}-COO^-} + NADH + H^+ \underset{\text{dehydrogenase}}{\overset{\text{lactate}}{\rightleftharpoons}} \underset{\text{lactate}}{CH_3-\overset{OH}{\overset{|}{CH}}-COO^-} + NAD^+ \quad (23.8)$$

lactate fermentation The production of lactate from glucose.

When Reaction 23.8 is added to the net reaction of glycolysis, an overall reaction for **lactate fermentation** results:

$$\underset{\text{glucose}}{C_6H_{12}O_6} + 2ADP + 2P_i \xrightarrow[\text{fermentation}]{\text{lactate}} \underset{\text{lactate}}{2CH_3-\overset{OH}{\overset{|}{CH}}-COO^-} + 2ATP + 2H_2O \quad (23.9)$$

Notice that the NAD$^+$ produced when pyruvate is reduced (Reaction 23.8) is used up and does not appear in lactate fermentation (Reaction 23.9). Although much more energy is available from the complete oxidation of pyruvate under aerobic conditions, the two ATPs produced from lactate fermentation are sufficient to sustain the life of anaerobic microorganisms. In human metabolism, those two molecules of ATP also play a critical role by furnishing energy when cellular supplies of oxygen are insufficient for ATP production through the complete oxidation of pyruvate.

Reduction to Ethanol

Several organisms, including yeast, have developed an alternative pathway for the regeneration of NAD$^+$ under anaerobic conditions. The process, called **alcoholic fermentation,** involves the decarboxylation of pyruvate to form acetaldehyde:

$$CH_3 - \overset{\overset{\displaystyle O}{\|}}{C} - COO^- + H^+ \xrightarrow[\text{decarboxylase}]{\text{pyruvate}} CH_3 - \overset{\overset{\displaystyle O}{\|}}{C} - H + CO_2 \qquad (23.10)$$

pyruvate acetaldehyde

alcoholic fermentation The conversion of glucose to ethanol.

The carbon dioxide produced in this reaction causes beer to foam and provides carbonation for naturally fermented wines and champagnes (see ▶ Figure 23.4).

The second step in alcoholic fermentation is the reduction of acetaldehyde to ethanol by NADH:

$$CH_3 - \overset{\overset{\displaystyle O}{\|}}{C} - H + NADH + H^+ \underset{}{\overset{\text{alcohol}}{\underset{\text{dehydrogenase}}{\rightleftharpoons}}} CH_3 - \overset{\overset{\displaystyle OH}{|}}{\underset{\underset{\displaystyle H}{|}}{C}} - H + NAD^+ \qquad (23.11)$$

acetaldehyde ethanol

© Sherri Woods/Photo Researchers Inc.

Figure 23.4 Bread, wine, and cheese are all produced through fermentation processes.

The NAD$^+$ regenerated by this reaction may then be used in the glycolysis pathway.

An overall reaction for alcoholic fermentation is obtained by combining the reaction for the conversion of pyruvate to ethanol and the reactions of glycolysis. Notice that because NAD$^+$ is used up in glycolysis but regenerated in ethanol formation, it does not appear in the overall equation:

$$C_6H_{12}O_6 + 2ADP + 2P_i \xrightarrow[\text{fermentation}]{\text{alcoholic}} 2CH_3CH_2-OH + 2CO_2 + 2ATP \qquad (23.12)$$

glucose ethanol

▶ Figure 23.5 summarizes the various pathways pyruvate can follow as it is used to regenerate NAD$^+$.

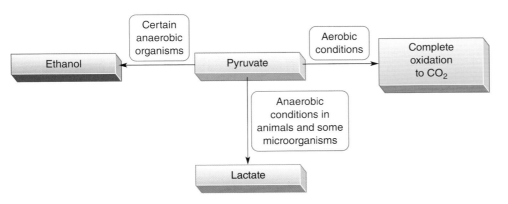

Figure 23.5 The fates of pyruvate.

▶ **LEARNING CHECK 23.2** Why is it important that each biochemical fate of pyruvate involve the production of NAD$^+$?

23.5 The Citric Acid Cycle

citric acid cycle A series of reactions in which acetyl CoA is oxidized to carbon dioxide and reduced forms of coenzymes FAD and NAD$^+$ are produced.

Learning Objectives

6. Identify the two major functions of the citric acid cycle.
7. Describe how the citric acid cycle is regulated in response to cellular energy needs.

Stage III in the oxidation of fuel molecules (Section 22.6) begins when the two-carbon acetyl units (of acetyl CoA) enter the **citric acid cycle.** This process is called the citric acid cycle because one of the key intermediates is citric acid. However, it is also called the tricarboxylic acid cycle (TCA) in reference to the three carboxylic acid groups in citric acid, and the Krebs cycle in honor of Sir Hans A. Krebs, who deduced its reaction sequence in 1937 (see ▶ Figure 23.6).

The citric acid cycle is the principal process for generating the reduced coenzymes NADH and FADH$_2$, which are necessary for the reduction of oxygen and ATP synthesis in the electron transport chain. Another important function of the citric acid cycle as a source of intermediates for biosynthesis is discussed in Section 24.11.

Figure 23.6 Sir Hans Adolf Krebs (1900–1981), German-born British biochemist, received the 1953 Nobel Prize in physiology or medicine.

Reactions of the Citric Acid Cycle

The reactions of the citric acid cycle occur within the matrix of the mitochondrion. ▶ Figure 23.7 summarizes the details of the eight reactions that make up the citric acid cycle. Of particular importance are those reactions in which molecules of NADH and FADH$_2$ are produced. Notice that a two-carbon unit (the acetyl group) enters the cycle and that two carbon atoms are liberated in the form of two CO$_2$ molecules, one each in Reactions 3 and 4. Thus, this series of reactions both begins and ends with a C$_4$ compound, oxaloacetate. This is why the pathway is called a cycle. In each trip around the cycle, the starting material is regenerated and the reactions can proceed again as long as more acetyl CoA is available as fuel.

A Summary of the Citric Acid Cycle

The individual reactions of the cycle can be added to give an overall net equation:

$$\text{acetyl CoA} + 3\text{NAD}^+ + \text{FAD} + \text{GDP} + \text{P}_i + 2\text{H}_2\text{O} \rightarrow$$
$$2\text{CO}_2 + \text{CoA—S—H} + 3\text{NADH} + 2\text{H}^+ + \text{FADH}_2 + \text{GTP} \qquad (23.13)$$

Some important features of the citric acid cycle are the following:

1. Acetyl CoA, available from the breakdown of carbohydrates, lipids, and amino acids, is the fuel of the citric acid cycle.
2. The operation of the cycle requires a supply of the oxidizing agents NAD$^+$ and FAD. The cycle is dependent on reactions of the electron transport chain to supply the necessary NAD$^+$ and FAD (Section 23.6). Because oxygen is the final acceptor of electrons in the electron transport chain, the continued operation of the citric acid cycle depends ultimately on an adequate supply of oxygen.
3. Two carbon atoms enter the cycle as an acetyl unit, and two carbon atoms leave the cycle as two molecules of CO$_2$. However, the carbon atoms leaving the cycle correspond to carbon atoms that entered in the previous cycle; there is a one-cycle delay between the entry of two carbon atoms as an acetyl unit and their release as CO$_2$.
4. In each complete cycle, four oxidation–reduction reactions produce three molecules of NADH and one molecule of FADH$_2$.
5. One molecule of the high-energy phosphate compound guanosine triphosphate (GTP, Section 22.7) is generated.

Regulation of the Citric Acid Cycle

The rate at which the citric acid cycle operates is precisely adjusted to meet cellular needs for ATP. One important control point is the very first step in the cycle, the synthesis of citrate. The catalyst for this reaction, citrate synthetase, is an allosteric enzyme that is

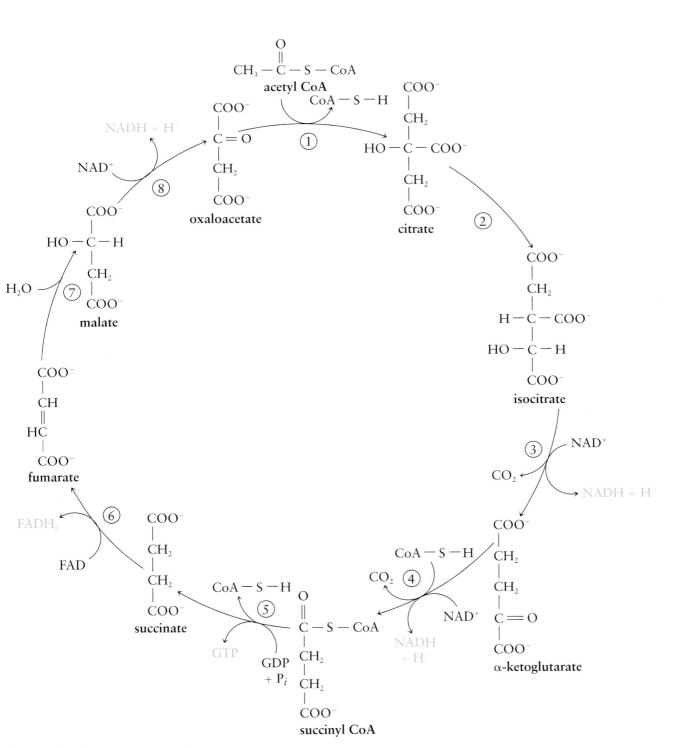

Figure 23.7 The citric acid cycle.

inhibited by ATP and NADH and activated by ADP. When cellular needs for ATP are met, ATP interacts with citrate synthetase and reduces its affinity for acetyl CoA. Thus, ATP acts as a modulator (inhibitor) of citrate synthetase and inhibits the entry of acetyl CoA into the citric acid cycle. Similarly, NADH acts as an inhibitor and signals the citric acid cycle to slow the production of NADH and $FADH_2$. On the other hand, when ATP levels are low, ADP levels are usually high. ADP, an activator of citrate synthetase, stimulates the entry of acetyl CoA into the citric acid cycle and thus boosts the production of NADH and $FADH_2$.

Lactate Accumulation

During vigorous exercise, the oxygen supply to muscles can become too low to support increased aerobic conversion of pyruvate to acetyl CoA. Under such conditions, a shift occurs from aerobic pyruvate oxidation to anaerobic production of lactate as the means for producing ATP. The resulting accumulation of lactate causes the muscle pain and cramps that accompany physical exhaustion. The buildup of lactate also causes a slight decrease in blood pH, which triggers an increase in the rate and depth of breathing, a response that provides more oxygen to the cells. The combination of pain from lactate accumulation and the maximum rate of breathing represents a limit to physical activities. Regular training and exercise increase this limit by improving the efficiency with which oxygen is delivered to the cells. The muscle cells of a well-conditioned athlete can maintain the aerobic oxidation of pyruvate for a much longer period of activity than can those of a nonathlete.

The shift to anaerobic lactate formation also occurs in the heart muscle during an episode of cardiac arrest, in which the oxygen-carrying blood supply to the heart is cut off by the blockage of an artery leading to the heart muscles. Aerobic oxidation of pyruvate and its ATP production are stopped. Glycolysis proceeds at an accelerated rate to meet the energy needs,

and lactate accumulates. The heart muscle contracts, producing a cramp, and stops beating. Massaging the heart muscle relieves such cramps, just as it does for skeletal muscles. Thus, it is sometimes possible to start the heart beating by massaging it.

Premature infants, whose lungs are not fully developed, are given pure oxygen to breathe in order to prevent a shift to anaerobic lactate production. In addition, they are given bicarbonate solutions intravenously to combat the increasing acidity of the blood due to lactate buildup.

Vigorous exercise causes a buildup of lactate in tissues.

Isocitrate dehydrogenase (Reaction 3), a second controlling enzyme, is an allosteric enzyme that is activated by ADP and inhibited by NADH in very much the same way as is citrate synthetase. The third control point (Reaction 4) is catalyzed by the α-ketoglutarate dehydrogenase complex. This group of enzymes is inhibited by succinyl CoA and NADH, products of the reaction it catalyzes, and also by ATP. These control points are indicated in ❯ Figure 23.8. In short, the entry of acetyl CoA into the citric acid cycle and the rate at which the cycle operates are reduced when cellular ATP levels are high. When ATP supplies are low (and ADP levels are high), the cycle is stimulated.

Figure 23.8 Control points in the citric acid cycle.

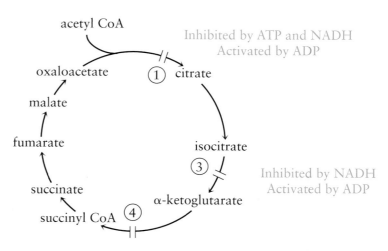

Unless otherwise noted all art on this page © Cengage Learning 2014

23.6 The Electron Transport Chain

Learning Objective

8. Explain the function of the electron transport chain and describe how electrons move down the chain.

The reduced coenzymes NADH and $FADH_2$ are end products of the citric acid cycle. In the final stage of food oxidation, the hydrogen ions and electrons carried by these coenzymes combine with oxygen and form water.

$$4H^+ + 4e^- + O_2 \rightarrow 2H_2O \qquad (23.14)$$

This simple energy-releasing process does not take place in a single step. Instead, it occurs as a series of steps that involve a number of enzymes and cofactors located within the inner membrane of the mitochondria. Electrons from the reduced coenzymes are passed from one electron carrier to another within the membrane in assembly-line fashion and are finally combined with molecular oxygen, the final electron acceptor. The series of reactions involved in the process is called the **electron transport chain.** As illustrated in ▶ Figure 23.9, there are several intermediate electron carriers between NADH and molecular oxygen. The electron carriers are lined up in order of increasing affinity for electrons.

electron transport chain A series of reactions in which protons and electrons from the oxidation of foods are used to reduce molecular oxygen to water.

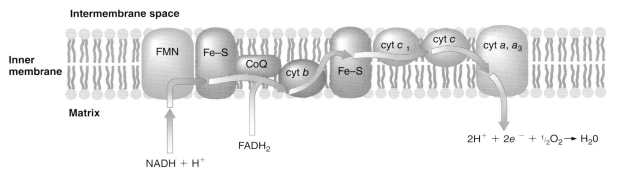

Figure 23.9 The electron transport chain. The heavy arrows show the path of the electrons as they pass from one carrier to the next.

The first electron carrier in the electron transport chain is an enzyme that contains a tightly bound coenzyme. The coenzyme has a structure similar to FAD. The enzyme formed by the combination of this coenzyme with a protein is called flavin mononucleotide (FMN). Two electrons and one H^+ ion from NADH plus another H^+ ion from a mitochondrion pass to FMN, then to an iron–sulfur (Fe—S) protein, and then to coenzyme Q (CoQ). CoQ is also the entry point into the electron transport chain for the two electrons and two H^+ ions from $FADH_2$. As NADH and $FADH_2$ release their hydrogen atoms and electrons, NAD^+ and FAD are regenerated for reuse in the citric acid cycle.

Four of the five remaining electron carriers are **cytochromes** (abbreviated cyt), which are structurally related proteins that contain an iron group. CoQ passes along the two electrons to two molecules of cytochrome b, and the two H^+ ions are given up to the mitochondrion. The electrons are passed along the chain, and in the final step, an oxygen atom accepts the electrons and combines with two H^+ ions to form water.

cytochrome An iron-containing enzyme located in the electron transport chain.

23.7 Oxidative Phosphorylation

Learning Objective

9. List the major features of the chemiosmotic hypothesis.

As electrons are transported along the electron transport chain, a significant amount of free energy is released (52.6 kcal/mol). Some of this energy is conserved by the

oxidative phosphorylation
A process coupled with the electron transport chain whereby ADP is converted to ATP.

Figure 23.10 ATP is synthesized at three sites within the electron transport chain. Energy decreases at other locations result in the release of heat energy.

synthesis of ATP from ADP and P$_i$. Because this synthesis of ATP (a phosphorylation reaction) is linked to the oxidation of NADH and FADH$_2$, it is termed **oxidative phosphorylation.** It takes place at three different locations of the electron transport chain (see ▶ Figure 23.10).

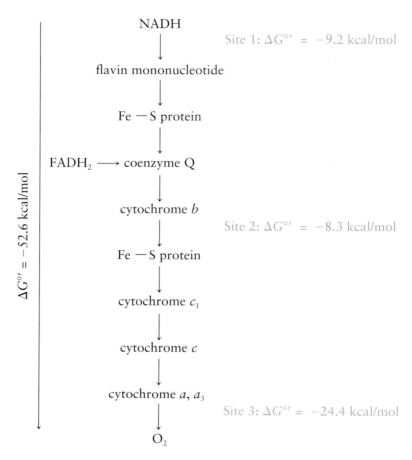

For each mole of NADH oxidized in the electron transport chain, 2.5 mol of ATP is formed. The free energy required for the phosphorylation of ADP is 7.3 kcal/mol, or 18 kcal for 2.5 mol of ATP. Because the oxidation of NADH liberates 52.6 kcal/mol, coupling the oxidation and phosphorylation reactions conserves 18 kcal/52.6 kcal, or approximately 34% of the energy released.

The electron donor FADH$_2$ enters the electron transport chain later than does NADH. Thus, for every FADH$_2$ oxidized to FAD, only 1.5 ATP molecules are formed during oxidative phosphorylation, and approximately 25% of the released free energy is conserved as ATP.

Now we can calculate the energy yield for the entire catabolic pathway (citric acid cycle, electron transport chain, and oxidative phosphorylation combined). According to Section 23.5, every acetyl CoA entering the citric acid cycle produces 3 NADH and 1 FADH$_2$ plus 1 GTP, which is equivalent in energy to 1 ATP. Thus, 10 ATP molecules are formed per molecule of acetyl CoA catabolized.

3 NADH ultimately produce	7.5 ATP
1 FADH$_2$ ultimately produces	1.5 ATP
1 GTP is equivalent to	1 ATP
	10 ATP total produced

chemiosmotic hypothesis The postulate that a proton flow across the inner mitochondrial membrane during operation of the electron transport chain provides energy for ATP synthesis.

The complex mechanism by which the cell couples the oxidations of the electron transport chain and the synthesis of ATP is believed to involve a flow of protons. This explanation, called the **chemiosmotic hypothesis,** proposes that the flow of electrons through

the electron transport chain causes protons to be "pumped" from the matrix across the inner membrane and into the space between the inner and outer mitochondrial membranes (see ▶ Figure 23.11). This creates a difference in proton concentration across the inner

Figure 23.11 The chemiosmotic hypothesis. Electron transport pumps protons (H^+) out of the matrix. The formation of ATP accompanies the flow of protons through F_1-ATPase back into the matrix.

mitochondrial membrane, along with an electrical potential difference. As a result of the concentration and potential differences, protons flow back through the membrane using a channel formed by the enzyme F_1-ATPase. The flow of protons through this enzyme is believed to drive the phosphorylation reaction.

$$\text{ADP+ P}_i \xrightarrow[\text{F_1-ATPase}]{H^+ \text{ flow through}} \text{ATP} \qquad (23.15)$$

▶ **LEARNING CHECK 23.3** How many molecules of ATP are produced from the complete catabolism of the following?

a. Two molecules of $FADH_2$
b. Two molecules of NADH
c. Two molecules of acetyl CoA

23.8 The Complete Oxidation of Glucose

Learning Objective

10. Calculate the amount of ATP produced by the complete oxidation of a mole of glucose.

The information given to this point about glycolysis, the citric acid cycle, and the electron transport chain almost makes it possible to calculate the ATP yield from the total oxidation of 1 mol of glucose. However, one more factor must be considered. NADH produced in the cytoplasm during glycolysis does not pass through the mitochondrial membrane to the site of the electron transport chain. Brain and muscle cells employ a transport mechanism

that passes electrons from the cytoplasmic NADH through the membrane to FAD molecules inside the mitochondria, forming $FADH_2$. In Section 23.7, we pointed out that one molecule of $FADH_2$ gives 1.5 molecules of ATP using the electron transport chain. Thus, with this transport mechanism, one molecule of cytoplasmic NADH generates only 1.5 molecules of ATP, whereas 2.5 molecules of ATP come from each molecule of mitochondrial NADH. A more efficient shuttle mechanism is found in liver, heart, and kidney cells, where one cytoplasmic NADH results in one mitochondrial NADH. Thus, 2.5 molecules of ATP are formed in this case.

This production of ATP from the complete aerobic catabolism of 1 mol of glucose in the liver is summarized in ▶ Table 23.1. Notice from the table that of the 32 mol of ATP generated, the great majority (28 mol) is formed as a result of oxidative phosphorylation (last category in Table 23.1). In Section 23.4, we learned that only 2 mol of ATP is produced per mole of glucose by lactate fermentation and by alcoholic fermentation. Thus, in terms of ATP production from fuels, the complete aerobic oxidation of glucose is 16 times more efficient than either lactate or alcoholic fermentation.

TABLE 23.1 The ATP Yield from the Complete Oxidation of One mol of Glucose

Reaction	Comments	Yield of ATP (moles)
Cytoplasmic reactions		
Glycolysis		
glucose → glucose-6-phosphate	1 mol consumes 1 ATP	−1
glucose-6-phosphate → fructose-1,6-bisphosphate	1 mol consumes 1 ATP	−1
glyceraldehyde-3-phosphate → 1,3-bisphosphoglycerate	2 mol produces 2 mol of cytoplasmic NADH	
1,3-bisphosphoglycerate → 3-phosphoglycerate	2 mol produces 2 ATP	+2
phosphoenolpyruvate → pyruvate	2 mol produces 2 ATP	+2
Mitochondrial reactions		
Oxidation of pyruvate		
pyruvate → acetyl CoA + CO_2	2 mol produces 2 NADH	
Citric acid cycle		
isocitrate → α-ketoglutarate + CO_2	2 mol produces 2 NADH	
α-ketoglutarate → succinyl CoA + CO_2	2 mol produces 2 NADH	
succinyl CoA → succinate	2 mol produces 2 GTP	+2
succinate → fumarate	2 mol produces 2 $FADH_2$	
malate → oxaloacetate	2 mol produces 2 NADH	
Electron transport chain and oxidative phosphorylation		
2 cytoplasmic NADH formed in glycolysis	each yields 2.5 ATP	+5[a]
2 NADH formed in the oxidation of pyruvate	each yields 2.5 ATP	+5
2 $FADH_2$ formed in the citric acid cycle	each yields 1.5 ATP	+3
6 NADH formed in the citric acid cycle	each yields 2.5 ATP	+15
	Net yield of ATP	+32

[a]In muscle and brain cells, 3 ATP are produced in this step and only 30 ATP overall.

Another useful way to look at the efficiency of the complete oxidation of glucose is to compare the amount of free energy available in glucose and the amount of free energy stored in synthesized ATP.

Glucose oxidation:

$$C_6H_{12}O_6 + 6O_2 \rightarrow 6CO_2 + H_2O \qquad \Delta G°' = -686 \text{ kcal/mol} \qquad (23.16)$$

ATP synthesis:

$$32ADP + 32P_i \rightarrow 32ATP + 32H_2O \qquad \Delta G°' = +234 \text{ kcal/mol} \qquad (23.17)$$

Overall reaction:

$$C_6H_{12}O_6 + 6O_2 + 32ADP + 32P_i \rightarrow 6CO_2 + 32ATP + 38H_2O \qquad (23.18)$$

$$\text{Total: } \Delta G^{\circ\prime} = -452 \text{ kcal/mol}$$

Thus, glucose oxidation liberates 686 kcal/mol, whereas the synthesis of 32 mol of ATP stores 234 kcal/mol. The efficiency of energy stored is

$$\frac{\text{energy stored}}{\text{energy available}} \times 100 = \frac{234 \text{ kcal/mol}}{686 \text{ kcal/mol}} \times 100 = 34.1\%$$

It is remarkable that living cells can capture 34% of the released free energy and make it available to do biochemical work. By contrast, an automobile engine makes available only about 20–30% of the energy actually released by burning gasoline.

23.9 Glycogen Metabolism

Learning Objective

11. Explain the importance of the processes of glycogenesis and glycogenolysis.

Glycogen Synthesis

Glucose consumed in excess of immediate body requirements is converted to glycogen (Section 17.8), which is stored primarily in the liver and muscle tissue. The liver of an average adult can store about 110 g of glycogen, and the muscles can store about 245 g. The process by which glucose is converted to glycogen is called **glycogenesis.** Glycogenesis can occur in all cells, but it is an especially important function of liver and muscle cells. The net result of this anabolic process is the bonding of glucose units to a growing glycogen chain, with the hydrolysis of a high-energy nucleotide, UTP (uridine triphosphate, Section 22.7), providing the energy. The enzyme glycogen synthase forms the new $\alpha(1 \rightarrow 4)$ linkages between each glucose unit and lengthens the chain. The $\alpha(1 \rightarrow 6)$ branch points on the chain are inserted by a "branching enzyme called amylo (1,4-1,6)-trans-glycosylase."

glycogenesis The synthesis of glycogen from glucose.

The overall process of glycogenesis is summarized by Reaction 23.19:

$$(\text{glucose})_n \xrightarrow{\hspace{3cm}} (\text{glucose})_{n+1} = \text{glycogen} \qquad (23.19)$$
$$\text{UTP} \qquad \text{UDP} + P_i$$

Glycogen Breakdown

The breakdown of glycogen back to glucose is called **glycogenolysis.** Although major amounts of glycogen are stored in both muscle tissue and the liver, glycogenolysis can occur in the liver (and kidney and intestinal cells) but not in muscle tissue because one essential enzyme (glucose-6-phosphatase) is lacking. The first step in glycogen breakdown is the cleavage of $\alpha(1 \rightarrow 4)$ linkages, catalyzed by glycogen phosphorylase. In this reaction, glucose units are released from the glycogen chain as glucose-1-phosphate:

glycogenolysis The breakdown of glycogen to glucose.

$$(\text{glucose})_n + P_i \rightarrow (\text{glucose})_{n-1} + \text{glucose-1-phosphate} \qquad (23.20)$$
glycogen glycogen with one
 fewer glucose unit

The second step in glycogen breakdown is the cleavage of the $\alpha(1 \rightarrow 6)$ linkages by hydrolysis, which is carried out by the debranching enzyme. When the branch points are eliminated, the phosphorylase can then continue to act on the rest of the chain.

It is important to be able to determine the energy yield in terms of the number of ATP molecules produced by the stepwise catabolism of glucose. Some of the relationships used in this determination will be used in the next chapter to calculate the energy yield from fatty acid catabolism. The three key substances to focus on are acetyl CoA, NADH, and FADH$_2$. Every mitochondrial NADH produces 2.5 ATP molecules, and every FADH$_2$ produces 1.5 ATP molecules. Every acetyl CoA that passes through the citric acid cycle gives 3 NADH, 1 FADH$_2$, and 1 GTP, which in turn produce a total of 10 ATP molecules. These reactions are outlined here.

Catabolic step		Energy production
Glycolysis (1 glucose ⟶ 2 pyruvate)	produces	2 NADH (cytoplasmic) + 2 ATP
		liver, heart, kidneys → 5 ATP
		brain, muscle → (3 ATP)
Oxidation of 2 pyruvates to 2 acetyl CoA	produces	2 NADH (mitochondrial) → 5 ATP
Citric acid cycle, one turn	produces	3 NADH → 7.5 ATP
		1 FADH$_2$ → 1.5 ATP
		1 GTP → 1 ATP
		10 ATP
Citric acid cycle, two turns	produce	2 × 10 = 20 ATP
		Total/glucose molecule = 32 ATP (30 ATP)

In the debranching reaction, phosphoglucomutase catalyzes the isomerization of glucose-1-phosphate to glucose-6-phosphate:

$$\text{glucose-1-phosphate} \rightleftharpoons \text{glucose-6-phosphate} \tag{23.21}$$

The final step in glycogen breakdown is the hydrolysis of glucose-6-phosphate to produce free glucose. The enzyme for this reaction, glucose-6-phosphatase, is the one found only in liver, kidney, and intestinal cells:

$$\text{glucose-6-phosphate} + H_2O \rightarrow \text{glucose} + P_i \tag{23.22}$$

Without glucose-6-phosphatase, muscle cells cannot form free glucose from glycogen. However, they can carry out the first two steps of glycogenolysis to produce glucose-6-phosphate. This form of glucose is the first intermediate in the glycolysis pathway and can still be used to produce energy even if the reaction does not proceed to the formation of D-glucose. In this way, muscle cells utilize glycogen only for energy production. An important function of the liver is to maintain a relatively constant level of blood glucose, necessitating that this organ have a broader biochemical function than muscle. Thus, it has the capacity to degrade glycogen all the way to glucose, which is released into the blood during muscular activity and between meals.

▶ **LEARNING CHECK 23.10** What enzyme enables the liver to form glucose from glycogen? Why can't muscles carry out the same conversion?

23.10 Gluconeogenesis

Learning Objective

12. Describe gluconeogenesis and the operation of the Cori cycle.

The supply of glucose in the form of liver and muscle glycogen can be depleted by about 12–18 hours of fasting. These stores of glucose are also depleted in a short time as a result

of heavy work or strenuous exercise (see ◗ Figure 23.12). Nerve tissue, including the brain, would be deprived of glucose under such conditions if the only source was glycogen. Fortunately, a metabolic pathway exists that overcomes this problem.

Glucose can be synthesized from noncarbohydrate materials in a process called **gluconeogenesis.** When carbohydrate intake is low and when glycogen stores are depleted, the carbon skeletons of lactate, glycerol (derived from the hydrolysis of fats), and certain amino acids are used to synthesize pyruvate, which is then converted to glucose:

$$\text{(lactate, certain amino acids, glycerol)} \rightarrow \text{pyruvate} \rightarrow \text{glucose} \qquad (23.23)$$

About 90% of gluconeogenesis takes place in the liver. Very little occurs in the kidneys, brain, skeletal muscle, or heart, even though these organs have a high demand for glucose. Thus, gluconeogenesis taking place in the liver helps maintain the blood glucose level so that tissues needing glucose can extract it from the blood.

Gluconeogenesis involving lactate is especially important. As might be expected, this process follows a separate and different pathway from glycolysis. During active exercise, lactate levels increase in muscle tissue, and the compound diffuses out of the tissue into the blood. It is transported to the liver, where lactate dehydrogenase, the enzyme that catalyzes lactate formation in muscle, converts it back to pyruvate:

$$\underset{\text{lactate}}{CH_3-\overset{\overset{\displaystyle OH}{|}}{C}H-COO^-} + NAD^+ \rightleftharpoons \underset{\text{pyruvate}}{CH_3-\overset{\overset{\displaystyle O}{\|}}{C}-COO^-} + NADH + H^- \qquad (23.24)$$

The pyruvate is then converted to glucose by the gluconeogenesis pathway, and the glucose enters the blood. In this way, the liver increases a low blood glucose level and makes glucose available to muscle. This cyclic process, involving the transport of lactate from muscle to the liver, the resynthesis of glucose by gluconeogenesis, and the return of glucose to muscle tissue, is called the **Cori cycle** (see ◗ Figure 23.13).

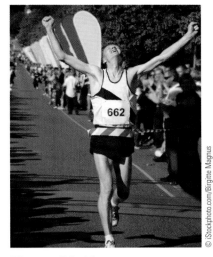

Figure 23.12 Gluconeogenesis provides a source of glucose when glycogen supplies are exhausted after vigorous exercise.

© iStockphoto.com/Birgitte Magnus

gluconeogenesis The synthesis of glucose from noncarbohydrate molecules.

Cori cycle The process in which glucose is converted to lactate in muscle tissue, lactate is reconverted to glucose in the liver, and glucose is returned to the muscle.

Figure 23.13 The Cori cycle, showing the relationship between glycolysis (in the muscle) and gluconeogenesis (in the liver).

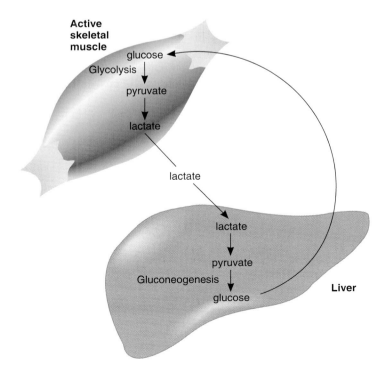

What Is the Best Weight-Loss Strategy?

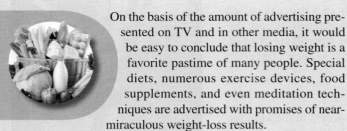

On the basis of the amount of advertising presented on TV and in other media, it would be easy to conclude that losing weight is a favorite pastime of many people. Special diets, numerous exercise devices, food supplements, and even meditation techniques are advertised with promises of near-miraculous weight-loss results.

The correct approach to weight loss is relatively easy to understand, but often quite challenging to put into practice. The human body must have a source of energy in order to function properly. The normal source of energy is digested food that is converted into chemical energy through a variety of biochemical processes. The produced energy is used to do work such as the movement of body parts and the synthesis of new tissue used for growth and the repair of damaged tissue. In the event that enough food is ingested to provide more energy than the body needs at that time, the energy is not wasted. It is converted into adipose tissue (fat) and stored in the body for later use as needed. Thus, the easily understood but challenging-to-use approach to weight loss can be represented by the following three conditions:

1. **Constant body weight:** Energy into body (food) = Energy used by body
2. **Weight gain:** Energy into body is greater than energy used by body
3. **Weight loss:** Energy into body is less than energy used by body

The challenge for those trying to lose weight is to achieve condition number three.

Once again, numerous approaches are widely advertised. We hear of the grapefruit diet, the high-protein diet, the low-carbohydrate diet, the twist-and-turn exercise device, and the portable doorway gym. In addition, each of the diets and devices is accompanied by testimonials from individuals in great physical condition. It can be hard to resist these well-designed "miracle" approaches, but the real truth about weight loss was given earlier in condition three. This condition can be achieved in several ways: decrease energy intake (food) into the body, increase energy used by the body (exercise), or both.

Nutritional studies indicate that for most people it is easier to decrease energy intake (food calories) than it is to use up the equivalent number of calories by exercising. For example, one pound (0.45 kg) of body fat represents 3500 calories of energy. If an individual reduced their total food calorie intake by 500 calories per day and did not change their exercise habits, the result would be the loss of 1 pound of body fat per week (52 pounds per year!). In order to use an extra 500 calories per day by exercising, a 140-pound person would have to walk 6.5 miles in about 1.5 hours each day in addition to their normal daily physical activities.

It is not surprising that studies indicate it is more difficult for most people to lose weight by increased exercising than by dieting. The exercising usually requires a significant change in habits, not to mention the requirement to set aside the needed time on a regular basis. Calorie-counting, on the other hand, is relatively easy to do because of such things as the information given on most packaged food labels about the serving sizes and the number of calories per serving. With such available information, it is not too hard to keep a record of current daily caloric intake for a couple of weeks, then plan on how to reduce it by the desired amount. The same studies show that calorie counting and reduced caloric intake coupled with increased physical activity results in the greatest long-term (permanent) weight loss. This is consistent with condition number 3 because both the energy into the body and the energy used by the body are each being changed in the direction that will lead to weight loss.

Exercise

+

Good nutrition

= Weight Loss

Figure 23.14 shows the relationship of gluconeogenesis to the other major pathways of glucose metabolism.

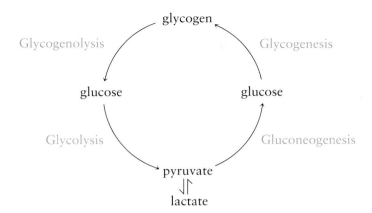

23.11 The Hormonal Control of Carbohydrate Metabolism

Learning Objective

13. Describe how hormones regulate carbohydrate metabolism.

It is important that metabolic pathways be responsive to cellular conditions so that energy is not wasted in producing unneeded materials. Besides the regulation of enzymes at key control points (Section 23.3), the body also uses three important regulatory hormones: epinephrine, glucagon, and insulin.

In Section 23.2, we pointed out that when carbohydrates are consumed, the blood glucose level increases. This increase signals the β-cells of the pancreas to release a small amount of the hormone insulin into the bloodstream. The hormone enhances the absorption of glucose from the blood into cells of active tissue such as skeletal and heart muscles (Section 19.6). In addition, insulin increases the rate of synthesis of glycogen, fatty acids, and proteins and stimulates glycolysis. Each of these activities uses up glucose. As a result of insulin released into the bloodstream, the blood glucose level begins to decrease within 1 hour after carbohydrates have been ingested and returns to normal within about 3 hours.

Glucagon, a second polypeptide hormone, is synthesized and secreted by the α-cells of the pancreas. Glucagon activates the breakdown of glycogen (glycogenolysis) in the liver and thus counteracts the effect of insulin by raising blood glucose levels. ▶ Figure 23.15 emphasizes the fact that insulin and glucagon work in opposition to each other and that the blood sugar level at any given time depends, in part, on the biochemical balance between these two hormones. Blood levels of glucose are also influenced to some degree by growth hormone and adrenal cortex steroids.

Reactive Hypoglycemia: What Causes It?

The word hypoglycemia comes from two parts: hypo, which means "low" and glycemia, which refers to the presence of glucose in the blood. Thus, hypoglycemia literally means low blood glucose (sugar). Glucose is obtained by our bodies from the food in our diets. The main dietary sources of glucose are foods high in carbohydrates such as breads, rice, fruits, and sweets. Glucose within the body is carried by the bloodstream to the cells. With the aid of insulin, glucose enters through the cell membrane and is converted to useable energy inside the cells. Any glucose not immediately needed to provide energy is stored as glycogen. When the body lacks enough glucose to maintain normal blood sugar levels, the hormone glucagon is used to convert stored glycogen back to the usable form of glucose.

Traditional hypoglycemia usually occurs as a result of fasting, where the blood glucose level drops below normal because of deficient intake of food sources of glucose. However, reactive hypoglycemia occurs without fasting. In fact, symptoms of reactive hypoglycemia can manifest within 1 to 3 hours of eating. As with traditional hypoglycemia, symptoms of reactive hypoglycemia include: shakiness, clumsiness, dizziness, weakness, sweating, hunger, anxiety, pounding heartbeat, and confusion. It should be noted that these symptoms are not exclusive of hypoglycemia and could, in fact, be indicators of a more serious condition. It any of the above-mentioned symptoms are experienced, an appointment with a health care provider should be made to figure out the cause.

The exact cause of reactive hypoglycemia is difficult to determine, but most researchers believe that the main cause is a shortage of glucagon, resulting in an inability to raise blood glucose levels when necessary. Others speculate that the cause is a hypersensitive response to the release of the normal physiological hormone called epinephrine, a reaction that is the opposite of epinephrine's normal effect on blood sugar, which is to raise it. Still others consider excessive insulin production to be the culprit.

Regardless of the origin, reactive hypoglycemia is easily managed through diet and an active lifestyle. Dietary modifications such as eating smaller, more frequent meals with a high-fiber and low-sugar content can significantly reduce the incidence of reactive hypoglycemia.

The discomfort of reactive hypoglycemia can appear within 1 to 3 hours of eating

© iStockphoto.com/Suprijono Suharjoto

The third hormone affecting glucose metabolism is epinephrine, synthesized by the adrenal gland (Section 16.6). Epinephrine stimulates glycogen breakdown in muscles and, to a smaller extent, in the liver. This glycogenolysis reaction—usually a response to pain, anger, or fear—provides energy for a sudden burst of muscular activity. ▶ Table 23.2 summarizes the hormonal control of glycogen.

TABLE 23.2 The Hormonal Control of Glycogen

Hormone	Source	Effect on Glycogen	Impact on Blood Glucose
Insulin	β-cells of pancreas	Increases formation	Lowers blood glucose levels
Glucagon	α-cells of pancreas	Activates breakdown of liver glycogen	Raises blood glucose levels
Epinephrine	Adrenal medulla	Stimulates breakdown	Raises blood glucose levels

Case Study Follow-up

The Juvenile Diabetes Research Foundation (JDRF) is an excellent resource for the newly diagnosed adult with type I diabetes. The JDRF has extensive information available online and free publications such as the "Adult Type 1 Toolkit (Newly Diagnosed)." It covers the procedures to manage the diabetes and the common emotional reactions that accompany the diagnosis. The Toolkit outlines steps to educate friends and family concerning diabetes and suggests conducting a "fire drill," or rehearsal, for dealing with the possibility of discovering a person with diabetes in a hypoglycemic coma. The American Diabetes Association (ADA) also has excellent resources for people with diabetes. Support groups meeting locally or online are also available.

The steps for treating diabetes are complex and can be frustrating. Diabetes can affect a person's ability to fight infection; have an adverse effect on vision; and, for women, complicate pregnancy. Diabetes is considered a coronary heart disease (CHD) risk factor equal to smoking (NHLBI, 2001). For couples, all of these complications may have a negative impact on their relationship. Adequate emotional support for both partners is important to managing the disease and maintaining a positive relationship.

Concept Summary

The Digestion of Carbohydrates

Glucose is the key food molecule for most organisms, and it is the central substance in carbohydrate metabolism. During digestion, carbohydrates are hydrolyzed to the monosaccharides glucose, fructose, and galactose, which are absorbed into the bloodstream through the lining of the small intestine. **Objective 1 (Section 23.1), Exercise 23.2**

Blood Glucose

Glucose is the most abundant carbohydrate in the blood. The liver regulates blood glucose levels so that a sufficient concentration is always available to meet the body's energy needs. **Objective 2 (Section 23.2), Exercise 23.6.** A lower-than-normal blood glucose level is referred to as hypoglycemia; a higher-than-normal blood glucose level is termed hyperglycemia.

Glycolysis

Glycolysis, a series of ten reactions that occurs in the cytoplasm, is a process in which one glucose molecule is converted into two molecules of pyruvate. Two molecules of ATP and two molecules of NADH are produced in the process. **Objective 3 (Section 23.3), Exercise 23.10.** Both galactose and fructose are converted into intermediates that enter the glycolysis pathway. The glycolysis pathway is controlled by the regulation of three key enzymes in the reaction sequence. **Objective 4 (Section 23.3), Exercise 23.14**

The Fates of Pyruvate

Pyruvate, the product of glycolysis, has three different fates. Under aerobic conditions, pyruvate enters mitochondria and is converted to acetyl CoA. The acetyl CoA enters the citric acid cycle. Products of the citric acid cycle enter the electron transport chain, where oxidation is completed and ATP is synthesized. A second fate of pyruvate is conversion to lactate. This takes place in anaerobic microorganisms and in humans when glycolysis occurs faster than the oxygen-dependent citric acid cycle and the electron transport chain can operate. Some microorganisms convert pyruvate to ethanol, the third fate of pyruvate. In each of these three processes, NAD^+ is regenerated so that glycolysis can continue. **Objective 5 (Section 23.4), Exercise 23.20**

The Citric Acid Cycle

The citric acid cycle generates NADH and FADH$_2$, which are necessary for ATP synthesis. It also produces intermediates used for biosynthesis. **Objective 6 (Section 23.5), Exercise 23.24.** This pathway consists of eight reactions that process incoming molecules of acetyl CoA. The carbon atoms leave the cycle in the form of molecules of CO$_2$. The hydrogen atoms and electrons leave the cycle in the form of reduced coenzymes NADH and FADH$_2$. The cycle is regulated by three allosteric enzymes in response to cellular levels of ATP. **Objective 7 (Section 23.5), Exercise 23.32.** One acetyl CoA molecule entering the citric acid cycle produces three molecules of NADH, one of FADH$_2$, and one of GTP.

The Electron Transport Chain

This pathway involves a series of reactions that pass electrons from NADH and FADH$_2$ to molecular oxygen. Each carrier in the series has an increasing affinity for electrons. Four of the carriers, which are referred to as cytochromes, contain iron, which accepts and then transfers the electrons. As NADH and FADH$_2$ release their hydrogen atoms and electrons, NAD$^+$ and FAD are regenerated for return to the citric acid cycle. **Objective 8 (Section 23.6), Exercises 23.34 and 23.36**

Oxidative Phosphorylation

At three sites within the electron transport chain, the decrease in free energy is sufficient to convert ADP to ATP. One molecule of NADH produces 2.5 molecules of ATP. FADH$_2$, which enters the chain one step later, produces 1.5 molecules of ATP. According to the chemiosmotic hypothesis, the synthesis of ATP takes place because of a flow of protons across the inner mitochondrial membrane. **Objective 9 (Section 23.7), Exercise 23.46**

The Complete Oxidation of Glucose

The complete oxidation of 1 mol of glucose produces 32 (or 30) mol of ATP. **Objective 10 (Section 23.8), Exercise 23.48.** In contrast, lactate and alcoholic fermentation produce only 2 mol of ATP.

Glycogen Metabolism

When blood glucose levels are high, excess glucose is converted into glycogen by the process of glycogenesis. The glycogen is stored within the liver and muscle tissue. Glycogenolysis, the breakdown of glycogen into glucose, occurs when muscles need energy and when the liver is restoring a low blood sugar level to normal. **Objective 11 (Section 23.9), Exercise 23.50**

Gluconeogenesis

Lactate, certain amino acids, and glycerol can be converted into glucose. This process, called gluconeogenesis, takes place in the liver when glycogen supplies are being depleted and when carbohydrate intake is low. Gluconeogenesis from lactate is especially important during periods of high muscle activity; the liver converts excess lactate from the muscles into glucose, which is then cycled back to the muscles. This process is called the Cori cycle. **Objective 12 (Section 23.10), Exercise 23.58**

The Hormonal Control of Carbohydrate Metabolism

Three hormones exert major interactive effects on carbohydrate metabolism: insulin, glucagon, and epinephrine. Insulin promotes the uptake and utilization of glucose by the cells. Thus, insulin lowers blood sugar levels. Glucagon stimulates the conversion of glycogen to glucose and thus raises blood glucose levels. Epinephrine is released in response to anger, fear, and excitement. It also stimulates the release of glucose from glycogen and raises blood glucose levels. **Objective 13 (Section 23.11), Exercise 23.62**

Key Terms and Concepts

Aerobic (23.4)
Alcoholic fermentation (23.4)
Anaerobic (23.4)
Blood sugar level (23.2)
Chemiosmotic hypothesis (23.7)
Citric acid cycle (23.5)
Cori cycle (23.10)

Cytochrome (23.6)
Electron transport chain (23.6)
Gluconeogenesis (23.10)
Glucosuria (23.2)
Glycogenesis (23.9)
Glycogenolysis (23.9)

Glycolysis (23.3)
Hyperglycemia (23.2)
Hypoglycemia (23.2)
Lactate fermentation (23.4)
Oxidative phosphorylation (23.7)
Renal threshold (23.2)

Key Reactions

1. Glycolysis (Section 23.3):

$$glucose + 2P_i + 2ADP + 2NAD^+ \longrightarrow 2\ pyruvate + 2ATP + 2NADH + 4H^+ + 2H_2O$$

Reaction 23.5

2. Oxidation of pyruvate to acetyl CoA (Section 23.4):

$$CH_3-\overset{\overset{O}{\|}}{C}-COO^- + CoA-S-H + NAD^+ \longrightarrow CH_3-\overset{\overset{O}{\|}}{C}-S-CoA + NADH + CO_2$$

Reaction 23.7

3. Reduction of pyruvate to lactate (Section 23.4):

$$CH_3-\overset{\overset{O}{\|}}{C}-COO^- + NADH + H^+ \rightleftharpoons CH_3-\overset{\overset{OH}{|}}{CH}-COO^- + NAD^+$$

Reaction 23.8

4. Net reaction of lactate fermentation (Section 23.4):

$$C_6H_{12}O_6 + 2ADP + 2P_i \longrightarrow 2CH_3-\overset{\overset{OH}{|}}{CH}-COO^- + 2ATP$$

Reaction 23.9

5. Reduction of pyruvate to ethanol (Section 23.4):

$$CH_3-\overset{\overset{O}{\|}}{C}-COO^- + 2H^+ + NADH \longrightarrow CH_3CH_2-OH + NAD^+ + CO_2$$

Reactions 23.10 and 23.11

6. Net reaction of alcoholic fermentation (Section 23.4):

$$C_6H_{12}O_6 + 2ADP + 2P_i \longrightarrow 2CH_3CH_2-OH + 2CO_2 + 2ATP$$

Reaction 23.12

7. The citric acid cycle (Section 23.5):

$$acetyl\ CoA + 3NAD^+ + FAD + GDP + P_i + 2H_2O \longrightarrow 2CO_2 + CoA-S-H + 3NADH + 2H^+ + FADH_2 + GTP$$

Reaction 23.13

8. The electron transport chain (Section 23.6):

$$4H^+ + 4e^- + O_2 \rightarrow 2H_2O$$

Reaction 23.14

9. Oxidative phosphorylation (Section 23.7):

$$ADP + P_i \rightarrow ATP$$

Reaction 23.15

10. Complete oxidation of glucose (Section 23.8):

$$C_6H_{12}O_6 + 6O_2 + 32ADP + 32P_i \rightarrow 6CO_2 + 32ATP + 38H_2O$$

Reaction 23.18

11. Glycogenesis (Section 23.9):

$$glucose \rightarrow glycogen$$

Reaction 23.19

12. Glycogenolysis (Section 23.9):

 glycogen → glucose Reactions 23.20, 23.21, and 23.22

13. Gluconeogenesis (Section 23.10):

 lactate, certain amino acids, glycerol ⟶ pyruvate ⟶ glucose Reaction 23.23

Exercises

Even-numbered exercises are answered in Appendix B.

Blue-numbered exercises are more challenging.

The Digestion of Carbohydrates (Section 23.1)

23.1 Why is glucose considered the pivotal compound in carbohydrate metabolism?

23.2 Name the products produced by the digestion of

 a. starch

 b. lactose

 c. sucrose

 d. maltose

23.3 What type of reaction is involved as carbohydrates undergo digestion?

Blood Glucose (Section 23.2)

23.4 Describe what is meant by the terms *blood sugar level* and *normal fasting level.*

23.5 What range of concentrations for glucose in blood is considered a normal fasting level?

23.6 How do each of the following terms relate to blood sugar level?

 a. Hypoglycemia

 b. Hyperglycemia

 c. Renal threshold

 d. Glucosuria

23.7 Explain how the synthesis and degradation of glycogen in the liver help regulate blood sugar levels.

23.8 Explain why severe hypoglycemia can be very serious.

Glycolysis (Section 23.3)

23.9 What is the main purpose of glycolysis?

23.10 What is the starting material for glycolysis? The product?

23.11 In what part of the cell does glycolysis take place?

23.12 How many steps in glycolysis require ATP? How many steps produce ATP? What is the net production of ATP from one glucose molecule undergoing glycolysis?

23.13 Which coenzyme serves as an oxidizing agent in glycolysis?

23.14 What is the third control point in glycolysis? How is it responsive to cellular needs?

23.15 Number the carbon atoms of glucose 1 through 6, and show the location of each carbon in the two molecules of pyruvate produced by glycolysis.

23.16 Explain how a high concentration of glucose-6-phosphate causes a decrease in the rate of glycolysis.

23.17 Why is the conversion of fructose-6-phosphate to fructose-1,6-bisphosphate sometimes called the "committed step" of glycolysis?

The Fates of Pyruvate (Section 23.4)

23.18 Distinguish between the terms *aerobic* and *anaerobic.*

23.19 Explain how lactate formation allows glycolysis to continue under anaerobic conditions.

23.20 Compare the fate of pyruvate in the body under (a) aerobic conditions and (b) anaerobic conditions.

23.21 Write a summary equation for the conversion of glucose to:

 a. lactate

 b. pyruvate

 c. ethanol

23.22 What is the fate of the pyruvate molecule's carboxylate group during alcoholic fermentation? Explain how ethanol formation from pyruvate allows yeast to survive with limited oxygen supplies.

The Citric Acid Cycle (Section 23.5)

23.23 What are two other names for the citric acid cycle?

23.24 What is the primary function of the citric acid cycle in ATP production? What other vital role is served by the citric acid cycle?

23.25 Why is it appropriate to refer to the sequence of reactions in the citric acid cycle as a cycle?

23.26 Describe the citric acid cycle by identifying the following:

 a. The fuel needed by the cycle

 b. The form in which carbon atoms leave the cycle

 c. The form in which hydrogen atoms and electrons leave the cycle

23.27 The citric acid cycle is located in close cellular proximity to the electron transport chain. Why?

23.28 How many molecules of each of the following are produced by one run through the citric acid cycle?

 a. NADH

 b. $FADH_2$

 c. GTP

 d. CO_2

23.29 Write reactions for the steps in the citric acid cycle that involve oxidation by NAD^+.

23.30 Write a reaction for the step in the citric acid cycle that involves oxidation by FAD.

23.31 Write a reaction for the step in the citric acid that involves the phosphorylation of GDP. What is the structural difference between ATP and GTP? Explain why GTP can function as a high-energy compound.

23.32 The reactions in the citric acid cycle involve enzymes.

 a. Identify the enzymes at the three control points.

 b. Each control-point enzyme is inhibited by NADH and ATP. Explain how this enables the cell to be responsive to energy needs.

 c. Two of the control-point enzymes are activated by ADP. Explain the benefit of this regulation to the cell.

The Electron Transport Chain (Section 23.6)

23.33 What is the primary function of the electron transport chain?

23.34 Which coenzymes bring electrons to the electron transport chain?

23.35 List the participants of the electron transport chain in the order in which they accept electrons.

23.36 What is the role of the cytochromes in the electron transport chain?

23.37 What is the role of oxygen in the functioning of the electron transport chain? Write a reaction that summarizes the fate of the oxygen.

Oxidative Phosphorylation (Section 23.7)

23.38 The third stage in the oxidation of foods to provide energy involves oxidative phosphorylation. What is oxidized? What is phosphorylated?

23.39 How many ATP molecules are synthesized when NADH passes electrons to molecular oxygen?

23.40 How many ATP molecules are synthesized when $FADH_2$ passes electrons to molecular oxygen?

23.41 Explain what is meant by the statement: "Oxidation of NADH in the electron transport chain results in 34% energy conservation."

23.42 How many ATP molecules can be formed by the oxidation of ten acetyl CoA molecules in the common catabolic pathway?

23.43 Identify the steps in the electron transport chain where ATP is synthesized.

23.44 The change in free energy for the complete oxidation of glucose to CO_2 and H_2O is -686 kcal per mole of glucose. If all this free energy could be used to drive the synthesis of ATP, how many moles of ATP could be formed from 1 mol of glucose?

23.45 What is the function of the protein F_1-ATPase?

23.46 According to the chemiosmotic theory, ATP synthesis results from the flow of what particles? Across what membrane does this flow occur?

The Complete Oxidation Of Glucose (Section 23.8)

23.47 Explain why NADH produced in muscles during glycolysis ultimately gives rise to just 1.5 molecules of ATP.

23.48 A total of 32 mol of ATP can be produced by the complete oxidation of 1 mol of glucose in the liver. Indicate the number of these moles of ATP produced by:

 a. glycolysis

 b. the citric acid cycle

 c. the electron transport chain and oxidative phosphorylation

23.49 The complete biochemical oxidation of glucose to ATP is only 34% efficient in capturing the total amount of energy released. The remaining 66% is released as what form of energy?

Glycogen Metabolism (Section 23.9)

23.50 Compare the terms *glycogenesis* and *glycogenolysis*.

23.51 Fructose and galactose from digested food enter the glycolysis pathway. Name the intermediates of the pathway which serve as entry points for these substances.

23.52 What high-energy compound is involved in the conversion of glucose to glycogen?

23.53 Why is it important that the liver store glycogen? How does this aid the controlling of blood sugar levels?

23.54 Why can liver glycogen, but not muscle glycogen, be used to raise blood sugar levels?

23.55 Summarize the reactions for glycogenolysis.

Gluconeogenesis (Section 23.10)

23.56 What organ serves as the principal site for gluconeogenesis?

23.57 A friend has been fasting for three days. Where does the energy come from to keep his brain functioning?

23.58 What are the sources of compounds that undergo gluconeogenesis?

23.59 Explain the operation of the Cori cycle and its importance to muscles.

23.60 Would the Cori cycle operate if the body's muscles were completely oxidizing the glucose supplied? Why or why not?

The Hormonal Control of Carbohydrate Metabolism (Section 23.11)

23.61 What cells produce insulin and glucagon in the body?

23.62 Describe the influence of glucagon and insulin on the following:

 a. Blood sugar level

 b. Glycogen formation

23.63 Why is it more important that epinephrine stimulate the breakdown of glycogen in the muscles rather than elevating blood sugar levels?

Additional Exercises

23.64 You eat a dextrose tablet that contains 10.0 g of glucose for an energy boost. How many molecules of ATP can be produced with the complete oxidation of this glucose by muscle cells?

23.65 As an athlete's cells begin to go anaerobic, what happens to the rate of pyruvate oxidation by the citric acid cycle? What happens to the rate of glycolysis? Explain how each of these rate changes occurs and which enzymes are affected.

23.66 Lactate dehydrogenase catalyzes the following equilibrium reaction in both liver and muscle cells:

$$\text{pyruvate} + \text{NADH} + \text{H}^+ \rightleftharpoons \text{lactate} + \text{NAD}^+$$

In terms of equilibrium, explain why lactate must be removed from muscle cells under anaerobic conditions and why lactate does not accumulate in the liver under these conditions. (HINT: Think of the Cori cycle.)

23.67 Identify all chiral carbon atoms in citrate and isocitrate.

citrate isocitrate

23.68 The pyruvate dehydrogenase enzyme complex becomes inactive when a specific serine residue in the enzyme complex is phosphorylated by ATP. Phosphorylation is the covalent addition of a phosphate group. Show how this reaction occurs and name the type of bond formed.

Allied Health Exam Connection

The following questions are from these sources:

1. *Nursing School Entrance Exam* © 2005, Learning Express, LLC.

2. *McGraw-Hill's Nursing School Entrance Exams* by Thomas A. Evangelist, Tamara B. Orr and Judy Unrein © 2009, The McGraw-Hill Companies, Inc.

3. *NSEE Nursing School Entrance Exams*, 3rd Edition © 2009, Kaplan Publishing.

4. *Cliffs Test Prep: Nursing School Entrance Exams* by Fred N. Grayson © 2004, Wiley Publishing, Inc.

5. *Peterson's Master the Nursing School and Allied Health Entrance Exams*, 18th Edition by Marion F. Gooding © 2008, Peterson's, a Nelnet Company.

23.69 In order to be absorbed into the blood, complex carbohydrates must first be hydrolyzed into _____ units, primarily _____.

23.70 Which of the following are true statements about glycolysis?

 a. It requires 1 ATP molecule to activate a molecule of glucose.

 b. It occurs in the mitochondria.

 c. It does not require oxygen.

23.71 Compare the fate of pyruvate (a) in the body under aerobic conditions, (b) in the body under anaerobic conditions, and (c) in alcoholic fermentative microbes under anaerobic conditions.

23.72 Which of the following are true statements about the citric acid cycle?

 a. It produces H_2O, CO_2, and NADH.

 b. It occurs in the mitochondria.

 c. It is the first stage of aerobic cellular respiration.

 d. It is also called the Krebs cycle.

23.73 What is the final electron acceptor of the electron transport system? Write the reaction for the last step of the electron transport chain.

23.74 Most soluble food substances enter the bloodstream through the:

 a. small intestine

 b. duodenum

 c. capillaries in the stomach

 d. hepatic vein

23.75 Glycogenesis occurs primarily in the:

 a. blood cells and spleen

 b. pancreas and gallbladder

 c. small intestines and stomach

 d. liver and muscles

23.76. Insulin is produced in the:

 a. pituitary gland

 b. thymus

 c. pancreas

 d. pineal gland

23.77 Which of the following describes the function of insulin in the body?

 a. It decreases glucose uptake by cells.

 b. It stimulates the release of glucagon.

 c. It increases serum levels of glucose.

 d. It increases glucose conversion to glycogen.

23.78 For the aerobic resperation pathway, electron transport systems are located in the:

 a. cytoplasm

 b. golgi bodies

 c. lysosomes

 d. mitochondrion

23.79 During strenuous exercise, a build-up of what substance may cause muscle cramps?

 a. lactic acid

 b. lactose

 c. adrenaline

 d. serotonin

Chemistry for Thought

23.80 The citric acid cycle does not utilize oxygen, yet it cannot function without oxygen. Why?

23.81 Malonate ($^-$OOC—CH_2—COO$^-$) is an extremely effective competitive inhibitor of the citric acid cycle. Which enzyme do you think malonate inhibits? Explain.

23.82 A friend started to make wine by adding yeast to fresh grape juice and placing the mixture in a sealed bottle. Several days later the bottle exploded. Explain.

23.83 Two students are debating whether 30 or 32 molecules of ATP can be formed by the catabolism of one molecule of glucose. Who is correct?

23.84 Explain why monitoring blood lactate levels might be a useful technique to gauge the amount of conditioning in an Olympic runner.

23.85 You may have experienced a rush of epinephrine during a recent exam or athletic event. Are there other physiological responses to epinephrine in addition to a higher blood sugar level?

23.86 In Figure 23.4, it is noted that making bread involves a fermentation process. Why, then, is the alcohol content of bread zero?

23.87 A friend has the habit of eating four or five candy bars per day as snacks. What might be the metabolic consequences of such a practice?

23.88 List some pros and cons of a low-carbohydrate diet.

23.89 Cyanide is believed to act as an inhibitor of the electron transport chain. Why is such an inhibitor so toxic?

23.90 Drinking milk always seems to make you slightly nauseous. What might be an explanation for this?

Case Study

Debbie was a fast-food addict who lost her mother to a heart attack when Debbie was 22. Now that Debbie was nearing the age at which her mother passed away, she was frightened. However, Debbie believed that knowledge is power, so she decided to research heart disease. Diet was one of the foremost subjects found in her search, and Debbie learned that there is a difference in types of fat. Not only should a heart-conscious person eat a low-fat diet, but healthy fats should be included as well. She learned about the difference between saturated, monounsaturated, and polyunsaturated fats; essential fatty acids; and trans-fats. She even learned that cholesterol is a fat-like substance called a lipoprotein and that the blood level should be below 200mg/dL. Debbie decided to change her diet and get her cholesterol checked. She wanted, for the sake of her own children, to live beyond her mother's age.

What might help Debbie give up her fast-food habit? What role does fiber play in a cardiac-friendly diet? What is the difference between soluble and insoluble dietary fiber?

Follow-up to this Case Study appears at the end the chapter before the Concept Summary.

© Brian Hagiwara/Getty Images

Learning Objectives

When you have completed your study of this chapter, you should be able to:

1 Describe the digestion, absorption, and distribution of lipids in the body. **(Section 24.1)**

2 Explain what happens during fat mobilization. **(Section 24.2)**

3 Identify the metabolic pathway by which glycerol is catabolized. **(Section 24.3)**

4 Outline the steps of β-oxidation for fatty acids. **(Section 24.4)**

5 Determine the amount of ATP produced by the complete catabolism of a fatty acid. **(Section 24.5)**

6 Name the three ketone bodies and list the conditions that cause their overproduction. **(Section 24.6)**

7 Describe the pathway for fatty acid synthesis. **(Section 24.7)**

8 Describe the source and function of the body's amino acid pool. **(Section 24.8)**

9 Write equations for transamination and deamination reactions. **(Section 24.9)**

10 Explain the overall results of the urea cycle. **(Section 24.9)**

11 Describe how amino acids can be used for energy production, the synthesis of triglycerides, and gluconeogenesis. **(Section 24.10)**

12 State the relationship between intermediates of carbohydrate metabolism and the synthesis of nonessential amino acids. **(Section 24.11)**

Triglycerides (fats and oils) are important dietary sources of energy. Fat also functions as the major form of energy storage in humans. Fat, with a caloric value of 9 calories/g, contains more than twice the energy per gram of glycogen or starch. Thus, fat is a more concentrated and efficient storage form of energy than carbohydrates. Because it is water insoluble, fat can be stored in much larger quantities in our bodies. For example, the limited carbohydrate reserves in the body are depleted after about 1 day without food, but stored fat can provide needed calories (but not other nutrients) in an individual for 30–40 days.

Amino acids perform three vital functions in the human body: They are the building blocks for the synthesis of proteins, they provide carbon and nitrogen atoms for the synthesis of other biomolecules, and they can be sources of energy.

In this chapter, we discuss the storage, degradation, and synthesis of lipids. We also study the degradation and synthesis of amino acids and the relationships between amino acid metabolism and the metabolism of carbohydrates and lipids.

24.1 Blood Lipids

Learning Objective

1. Describe the digestion, absorption, and distribution of lipids in the body.

During digestion, triglycerides are hydrolyzed to glycerol, fatty acids, and monoglycerides (one fatty acid attached to glycerol). Phosphoglycerides are also hydrolyzed to their component substances. These smaller molecules, along with cholesterol, are absorbed into cells of the intestinal mucosa, where resynthesis of the triglycerides and phosphoglycerides occurs. For transport within the aqueous environment of the lymph and blood, these insoluble lipids are complexed with proteins to form lipoprotein aggregates called **chylomicrons.** The chylomicrons (which contain triglycerides, phosphoglycerides, and cholesterol) pass into the lymph system and then into the bloodstream. Chylomicrons are modified by the liver into smaller lipoprotein particles, the form in which most lipids are transported to various parts of the body by the bloodstream (see ❱ Figure 24.1).

chylomicron A lipoprotein aggregate found in the lymph and the bloodstream.

Figure 24.1 The digestion and absorption of triglycerides.

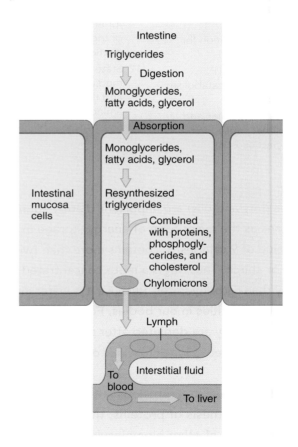

Figure 24.2 The rise in blood lipids following a meal containing fat.

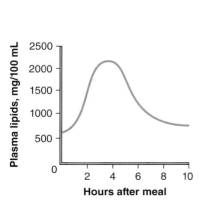

To some extent, the behavior of blood lipids parallels that of blood sugar. The concentration of both substances increases following a meal and returns to normal as a result of storage in fat depots and of oxidation to provide energy. As shown in ❱ Figure 24.2, the concentration of plasma lipids usually begins to rise within 2 hours after a meal, reaches a peak in 4–6 hours, and then drops rather rapidly to a normal level.

One general method of classifying lipoproteins is by density. Because lipids are less dense than proteins, lipoprotein particles with a higher proportion of lipids are less dense than those with a lower proportion. Chylomicrons are the least dense because they have the highest ratio of lipid to protein. ❱ Figure 24.3 is a schematic model of a low-density lipoprotein (LDL). The compositions of the four classes of lipoprotein are compared in ❱ Figure 24.4. We see from Figure 24.4 that the protein content of chylomicrons is

Figure 24.3 A schematic model of low-density lipoprotein (LDL).

Triglyceride and cholesterol esters

Phosphoglyceride

Protein

CHYLOMICRON

1%–2% protein

2%–7% cholesterol

3%–6% phosphoglyceride

80%–90% triglyceride

5%–10% protein

10%–15% cholesterol

15%–20% phosphoglyceride

55%–65% triglyceride

VLDL

10% triglyceride

22% phosphoglyceride

25% protein

45% cholesterol

LDL

5% triglyceride

20% cholesterol

30% phosphoglyceride

45%–50% protein

HDL

Figure 24.4 Relative amounts of cholesterol, protein, triglyceride, and phosphoglyceride in the four classes of lipoproteins.

significantly lower than that of other plasma lipoproteins, and that this low percentage results in a density of the particle that is less than 0.95 g/mL. Notice that the so-called high-density lipoproteins (HDL) have a protein mass that is 45–50% of the total mass of the particles. The densities of HDL particles have correspondingly high values, ranging from 1.06–1.21 g/mL.

DR. MELINA JAMPOLIS

© Michael Roud Photography

Dr. Melina Jampolis is a San Francisco, California, physician nutrition specialist—a specialty practiced by only about 200 physicians in the United States. She focuses exclusively on nutrition for weight loss and disease prevention and treatment.

Ask an Expert 24.1

Q: Are certain foods better for the brain?

A: When it comes to eating better for your brain, there are several foods and nutrients that may improve mood and memory and prevent age-related declines in cognitive function. Most research points to the so-called Mediterranean diet—one that is high in healthy fats, legumes, nuts, cereal, fish, fruits, and vegetables—as being the best for the brain. This dietary pattern, which is also lower in saturated fat and meat and contains moderate amounts of alcohol and dairy products, has several benefits when it comes to memory, cognitive function, and mood.

Research shows that higher levels of HDL cholesterol, commonly referred to as "good" cholesterol, may play a role in the preservation of memory. Many of the key components of the Mediterranean diet, including replacing saturated fat with unsaturated fat, eating plenty of soluble fiber found in legumes and cereal, and moderate alcohol consumption, may also help support healthy HDL levels.

Nuts and seeds may also be particularly beneficial for the brain. Almonds and sunflower seeds are good sources of monounsaturated fat and vitamin E, an antioxidant that helps protect neuronal (brain cell) membranes. Neuronal membranes are lined with fat. Healthy dietary fats like monounsaturated fat may improve the binding of neurotransmitters to these membranes. Neurotransmitters allow brain cells to communicate with each other, and their improved binding might improve mood. Animal studies indicate that walnuts, rich in polyphenols, polyunsaturated fatty acids, and antioxidants, provide a potent brain boost.

Almonds are a good source of vitamin E.

The omega-3 fatty acid DHA (docosahexaenoic) is also an important component of neuronal membranes. DHA plays a key role in brain structure and function and may offer protection against age-related cognitive decline. Since our bodies do not produce DHA, it is considered an essential fatty acid and must be obtained from our diet. Fatty fish including salmon, tuna, mackerel, herring, and sardines are excellent sources of DHA and should be consumed at least twice per week. Research also suggests that higher intakes of fish may be linked to lower levels of depression.

Berries, rich in fiber, vitamin C, antioxidants, and polyphenols, also appear to play an important role in brain health by improving brain

DHA is present in salmon.

signaling and protecting the brain from oxidative stress. Blueberries seem to be especially useful in terms of memory. Curcumin, another potent polyphenol and the active ingredient in the spice turmeric, also plays an active role in brain health. This might partially explain the lower incidence of Alzheimer's disease in Northern India, where turmeric, as a curry ingredient, is widely consumed.

© iStockphoto.com/Daniel Loiselle

The spice turmeric contains a polyphenol.

It is also important to eat adequate amounts of healthy carbohydrates for optimal brain function. The brain does not store glucose, and studies suggest that low-carbohydrate diets might impair cognitive function. Low-carbohydrate diets might also negatively affect mood over time. Try to consume mainly healthy carbs, such as whole grains, fruits, and vegetables, to prevent large fluctuations in blood sugar, which can cause fatigue and thereby impair brain function.

Foods with whole grains are important.

Finally, staying well hydrated plays a part in optimal brain function. A study of college students found that even a mild 1–2% dehydration led to fatigue and confusion. Exercise is also key. Moderate aerobic activity, such as walking 20 to 30 minutes per day, helps to significantly improve cognitive function and performance.

So, while food may not necessarily be able to boost your IQ, eating a healthy, nutrient-rich Mediterranean-type of diet, staying well hydrated, and getting regular exercise can help keep your brain fit and healthy.

Staying hydrated is essential.

Aerobic activity helps keep your brain fit.

24.2 Fat Mobilization

Learning Objective

2. Explain what happens during fat mobilization.

Carbohydrates from dietary sources and glycogen catabolism are the compounds utilized preferentially for energy production by some tissues. The brain and active skeletal muscles are examples of such tissues. But as we have seen, the body's stores of glycogen are depleted after only a few hours of fasting. When this happens, fatty acids stored in triglycerides are called on as energy sources. Even when glycogen supplies are adequate, many body cells, such as those of resting muscle and liver, utilize energy derived from the breakdown of fatty acids. This helps conserve the body's glycogen stores and glucose for use by brain cells and red blood cells. Red blood cells cannot oxidize fatty acids because red blood cells have no mitochondria, the site of fatty acid oxidation. Brain cells are bathed in cerebrospinal fluid and do not obtain nutrients directly from the blood because of the blood-brain barrier. Glucose and many other substances can cross the barrier into the cerebrospinal fluid, but fatty acids cannot.

When body cells need fatty acids for energy, the endocrine system is stimulated to produce several hormones, including epinephrine, which interact with **adipose tissue.** Earlier we saw that epinephrine stimulates the conversion of glycogen to glucose. In the fat cells of adipose tissue, epinephrine stimulates the hydrolysis of triglycerides to fatty acids and

adipose tissue A kind of connective tissue where triglycerides are stored.

glycerol, which enter the bloodstream. This process is called **fat mobilization.** In the blood, mobilized fatty acids form a lipoprotein with the plasma protein called serum albumin. In this form, the fatty acids are transported to the tissue cells that need them. The glycerol produced by the hydrolysis of the triglyceride is water soluble, so it dissolves in the blood and is also transported to cells that need it.

24.3 Glycerol Metabolism

Learning Objective

3. Identify the metabolic pathway by which glycerol is catabolized.

The glycerol hydrolyzed from fats can provide energy to cells. Glycerol is converted in the cytoplasm of the cell to dihydroxyacetone phosphate in two steps:

$$
\begin{array}{ccccc}
\text{H}_2\text{C}-\text{OH} & & \text{H}_2\text{C}-\text{OH} & & \text{H}_2\text{C}-\text{OH} \\
| & & | & & | \\
\text{HC}-\text{OH} & \longrightarrow & \text{HC}-\text{OH} & \longrightarrow & \text{C}=\text{O} \longrightarrow \text{Glycolysis} \\
| & & | & & | \\
\text{H}_2\text{C}-\text{OH} & & \text{H}_2\text{C}-\text{OPO}_3^{2-} & & \text{H}_2\text{C}-\text{OPO}_3^{2-} \\
\quad \text{ATP} \quad \text{ADP} & & \text{NAD}^+ \quad \text{NADH}+\text{H}^+ & & \\
\text{glycerol} & & \text{glycerol-} & & \text{dihydroxyacetone} \\
& & \text{3-phosphate} & & \text{phosphate}
\end{array}
$$

(24.1)

Dihydroxyacetone phosphate is one of the chemical intermediates of glycolysis (Section 23.3). Thus, glycerol, by entering glycolysis, can be converted to pyruvate and contribute to cellular energy production. The pyruvate formed from glycerol can also be converted to glucose through gluconeogenesis (Section 23.10).

24.4 The Oxidation of Fatty Acids

Learning Objective

4. Outline the steps of β-oxidation for fatty acids.

Fatty acids that enter tissue cells cannot be oxidized to produce energy until they pass through the mitochondrial membrane. This cannot occur until the fatty acid is converted into fatty acyl CoA by reaction with coenzyme A. Fatty acyl refers to the

$$
\begin{array}{c}
\text{O} \\
\| \\
\text{R}-\text{C}-\text{ portion of the molecule.}
\end{array}
$$

$$
\begin{array}{ccc}
\text{O} & & \text{O} \\
\| & & \| \\
\text{R}-\text{C}-\text{OH}+\text{HS}-\text{CoA} & \longrightarrow & \text{R}-\text{C}-\text{S}-\text{CoA}+\text{H}_2\text{O} \\
\text{fatty acid} & & \text{fatty acyl CoA} \\
& \text{ATP} \quad \text{AMP}+\text{PP}_i &
\end{array}
$$

(24.2)

This reaction, which is catalyzed by acyl CoA synthetase, is referred to as activation of the fatty acid because the fatty acyl CoA is a high-energy compound. The energy needed

for its synthesis is provided by the hydrolysis of ATP to AMP and PP_i and the subsequent hydrolysis of PP_i to $2P_i$. The process of forming fatty acyl CoA molecules demonstrates how the energy stored in the phosphate bonds of ATP can be used to drive chemical processes that normally could not occur. The cost to the cell of activating one molecule of fatty acid is the loss of two high-energy bonds in an ATP molecule.

The fatty acyl CoA molecules that enter mitochondria are then degraded in a catabolic process called **β-oxidation.** During β-oxidation, the second (or beta) carbon down the chain from the carbonyl of the fatty acyl CoA molecule is oxidized to a ketone:

β-oxidation process A pathway in which fatty acids are broken down into molecules of acetyl CoA.

$$\underset{\text{fatty acyl CoA}}{R - \underset{\underset{H}{\overset{\beta}{|}}}{\overset{\overset{H}{|}}{C}} - \underset{1}{\overset{\alpha}{CH_2}} - \overset{\overset{O}{\|}}{C} - S - CoA} \xrightarrow{\text{Oxidation}} R - \overset{\overset{O}{\|}}{C} - CH_2 - \overset{\overset{O}{\|}}{C} - S - CoA \qquad (24.3)$$

Four reactions are involved in oxidizing the β-carbon to a ketone. We will use the fatty acyl CoA formed from one 18-carbon acid, stearic acid, as an example of the reactions. We will also keep track of any NADH or $FADH_2$ produced in the reactions because these molecules can enter the respiration process (electron transport chain). The reactions involved in β-oxidation are shown in ▶ Figure 24.5.

In the final step of β-oxidation (Step 4), the chain is broken between the α- and β-carbons by reaction with coenzyme A. As a result, a new fatty acyl CoA is formed with a chain shortened by two carbon atoms, and a unit of acetyl CoA is released:

$$\underset{\substack{\beta\text{-carbon} \\ 18 \text{ carbons}}}{CH_3(CH_2)_{14} - \overset{\overset{O}{\|}}{\underset{\uparrow}{C}} - \overset{\alpha\text{-carbon}}{\underset{\downarrow}{CH_2}} - \overset{\overset{O}{\|}}{C} - S - CoA} + H - S - CoA \rightarrow \underset{\substack{\text{new fatty acyl CoA} \\ 16 \text{ carbons}}}{CH_3(CH_2)_{14} - \overset{\overset{O}{\|}}{C} - S - CoA} + \underset{\substack{\text{acetyl CoA} \\ 2 \text{ carbons}}}{CH_3 - \overset{\overset{O}{\|}}{C} - S - CoA} \qquad (24.4)$$

The new fatty acyl compound enters the β-oxidation process at Step 1, and the sequence is repeated until the fatty acyl CoA is completely degraded to acetyl CoA (Figure 24.5). The fatty acyl CoA molecule that starts each run through the β-oxidation process is two carbons shorter than the one going through the previous run. For this reason, the β-oxidation pathway for fatty acid degradation to acetyl CoA is often called the fatty acid spiral (rather than cycle).

Every run through the spiral produces one molecule each of acetyl CoA, NADH, and $FADH_2$ until the fatty acyl CoA is only four carbons long:

$$\underset{\substack{\text{fatty acyl CoA} \\ \text{entering the spiral}}}{R - CH_2CH_2 - \overset{\overset{O}{\|}}{C} - S - CoA} + NAD^+ + FAD + H_2O + CoA - SH \longrightarrow$$

$$\underset{\substack{\text{fatty acyl CoA} \\ 2 \text{ carbons shorter}}}{R - \overset{\overset{O}{\|}}{C} - S - CoA} + \underset{\text{acetyl CoA}}{CH_3\overset{\overset{O}{\|}}{C} - S - CoA} + NADH + H^+ + FADH_2 \qquad (24.5)$$

Lipid and Amino Acid Metabolism **781**

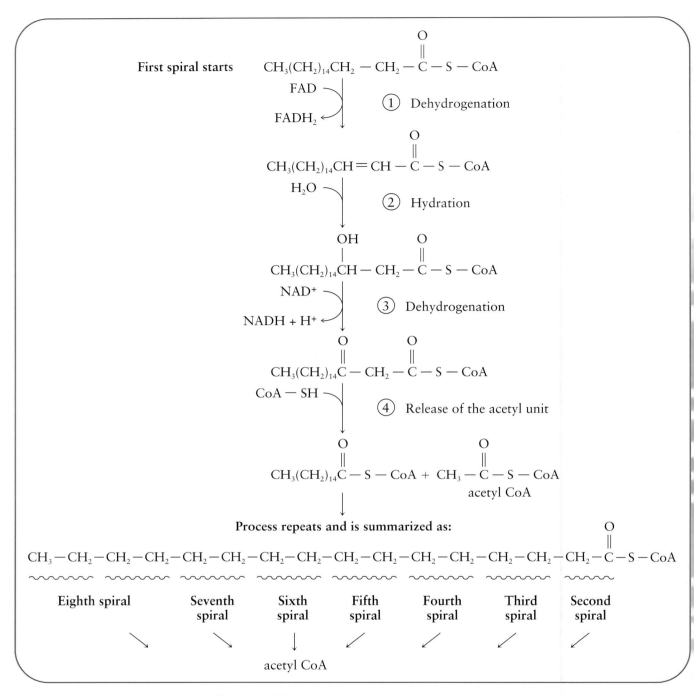

Figure 24.5 The fatty acid spiral: β-oxidation of stearic acid.

In the last spiral, the four-carbon chain of butyryl CoA passes through the β-oxidation sequence, and it produces one molecule of $FADH_2$, one molecule of NADH, and two molecules of acetyl CoA:

$$CH_3-CH_2-CH_2-\overset{\overset{\displaystyle O}{\|}}{C}-S-CoA + NAD^+ + H_2O + FAD + CoA-SH \longrightarrow$$
butyryl CoA

$$2CH_3-\overset{\overset{\displaystyle O}{\|}}{C}-S-CoA + NADH + H^+ + FADH_2 \qquad (24.6)$$
2 acetyl CoA molecules

In other words, the complete conversion of a fatty acyl CoA to two-carbon fragments of acetyl CoA always produces one more molecule of acetyl CoA than of FADH$_2$ or NADH. Thus, the breakdown of stearic acid requires eight passes through the β-oxidation sequence and produces nine molecules of acetyl CoA, but only eight molecules of FADH$_2$ and eight molecules of NADH.

Net reaction:

$$CH_3(CH_2)_{16}\overset{\overset{\displaystyle O}{\|}}{C}-S-CoA + 8FAD + 8NAD^+ + 8H_2O + 8CoA-SH \longrightarrow$$

$$9CH_3\overset{\overset{\displaystyle O}{\|}}{C}-S-CoA + 8FADH_2 + 8NADH + 8H^+ \qquad (24.7)$$

> ▶ **LEARNING CHECK 24.1** Capric acid (ten carbon atoms) is converted to acetyl CoA through β-oxidation. What are the yields of the following?
>
> **a.** acetyl CoA **b.** FADH$_2$ **c.** NADH

24.5 The Energy from Fatty Acids

Learning Objective

5. Determine the amount of ATP produced by the complete catabolism of a fatty acid.

To compare the energy yield from fatty acids with that from glucose, let's continue our discussion with stearic acid, a typical and abundant fatty acid.

We start with the activation of stearic acid by reacting it with coenzyme A to form stearoyl CoA. The energy needed to cause this reaction to occur comes from the hydrolysis of ATP to AMP and PP$_i$ and the subsequent hydrolysis of PP$_i$ to 2P$_i$. This is equivalent to hydrolyzing two molecules of ATP to ADP.

As a stearoyl CoA molecule (18 carbons) passes through the β-oxidation spiral, 9 acetyl CoA, 8 FADH$_2$, and 8 NADH molecules are produced. Acetyl CoA produced in the fatty acid spiral can enter the citric acid cycle (followed by the electron transport chain), where each molecule of acetyl CoA results in the production of 10 ATP molecules. In addition, when the FADH$_2$ and NADH molecules enter the electron transport chain, each FADH$_2$ yields 1.5 ATP molecules, and each NADH yields 2.5 molecules. The calculations are summarized in ▶ Table 24.1, which shows a total of 120 molecules of ATP formed from the 18-carbon fatty acid.

TABLE 24.1 Energy Produced by the Oxidation of Stearic Acid

Oxidation Product or Step	ATP/Unit	Total ATP
Activation step		−2
9 acetyl CoA	10	90
8 FADH$_2$	1.5	12
8 (NADH + H$^+$)	2.5	20
Total ATP from the 18-carbon fatty acid		120

It is instructive to compare the energy yield from the complete oxidation of fatty acids with that obtained from an equivalent amount of glucose because both are important constituents of the diet. In Section 23.8, we saw that the oxidation of a single glucose molecule produces 32 ATP molecules. The complete oxidation of three 6-carbon glucose molecules

(18 carbons) yields 3×32, or 96, ATP molecules. Thus, on the basis of equal numbers of carbons, lipids are nearly 25% more efficient than carbohydrates as energy-storage systems.

On a mass basis, the difference is even more striking. One mole of stearic acid weighs 284 g, and, as we have seen, it yields 120 mol of ATP on complete degradation. Three moles of glucose weigh 540 g and yield 96 mol of ATP. On this basis, 284 g of glucose would generate 50 mol of ATP. On an equal-mass basis, lipids contain more than twice the energy of carbohydrates. The reason for this difference is that fatty acids are a more reduced form of fuel, with a number of —CH_2— groups as plentiful sources of H atoms for the energy-yielding oxidation process. Glucose, in contrast, is already partially oxidized, with an oxygen atom located on each carbon atom.

> ▶ **LEARNING CHECK 24.2** Calculate the number of molecules of ATP produced by the complete oxidation of palmitic acid (16 carbon atoms) to carbon dioxide and water.

24.6 Ketone Bodies

Learning Objective

6. Name the three ketone bodies and list the conditions that cause their overproduction.

It is generally agreed by nutrition scientists that a diet balanced in carbohydrates and fats as energy sources is best for good health. When such a balanced diet is followed, most of the acetyl CoA produced by fatty acid metabolism is processed through the citric acid cycle.

Under certain conditions, the balance between carbohydrate and fatty acid metabolism is lost. During a fast, for example, fatty acids from stored fats become the body's primary energy source. With a minimum amount of cellular glucose available, the level of glycolysis decreases, and a reduced amount of oxaloacetate is synthesized. In addition, oxaloacetate is used for gluconeogenesis to a greater-than-normal extent as the cells react to make their own glucose. The lack of oxaloacetate reduces the activity of the citric acid cycle. As a result of these events, more acetyl CoA is produced by fatty acid oxidation than can be processed through the citric acid cycle. As the concentration of acetyl CoA builds up, the excess is converted within the liver to three substances called **ketone bodies**— acetoacetate, β-hydroxybutyrate, and acetone.

ketone bodies Three compounds—acetoacetate, β-hydroxybutyrate, and acetone—formed from acetyl CoA.

$$
\underset{\text{acetoacetate}}{CH_3 - \overset{\displaystyle O}{\overset{\|}{C}} - CH_2 - \overset{\displaystyle O}{\overset{\|}{C}} - O^-}
\quad
\underset{\substack{\text{β-hydroxybutyrate}\\ \text{(not a ketone)}}}{CH_3 - \overset{\displaystyle OH}{\overset{|}{C}}H - CH_2 - \overset{\displaystyle O}{\overset{\|}{C}} - O^-}
\quad
\underset{\text{acetone}}{CH_3 - \overset{\displaystyle O}{\overset{\|}{C}} - CH_3}
$$

The ketone bodies are carried by the blood to body tissues, mainly the brain, heart, and skeletal muscle, where they may be oxidized to meet energy needs (see ▶ Figure 24.6). You can see from their structural formulas that β-hydroxybutyrate does not actually contain a ketone group, but it is nevertheless included in the designation because it is always produced along with the other two. Under normal conditions, the concentration of ketone bodies in the blood averages a very low 0.5 mg/100 mL.

Diabetes mellitus, like a long fast or starvation, also produces an imbalance in carbohydrate and lipid metabolism. Even though blood glucose reaches hyperglycemic levels, a deficiency of insulin prevents the glucose from entering tissue cells in sufficient amounts to meet cellular energy needs. The resulting increase in fatty acid metabolism leads to excessive production of acetyl CoA and a substantial increase in the level of ketone bodies in the blood of poorly controlled diabetes. A concentration higher than about 20 mg/100 mL of blood is called **ketonemia** ("ketones in the blood"). At a level of about 70 mg/100 mL of blood, the renal threshold for ketone bodies is exceeded, and ketone bodies are excreted in the urine. This condition is called **ketonuria** ("ketones in the urine"). A routine check

ketonemia An elevated level of ketone bodies in the blood.

ketonuria The presence of ketone bodies in the urine.

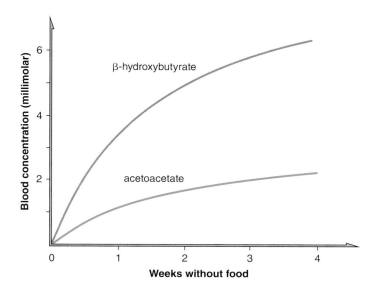

Figure 24.6 The effect of starvation on blood levels of β-hydroxybutyrate and acetoacetate.

of urine for ketone bodies is useful in the diagnosis of diabetes. Occasionally, the concentration of acetone in the blood reaches levels that cause it to be expelled through the lungs, and the odor of acetone can be detected on the breath. When ketonemia, ketonuria, and **acetone breath** exist simultaneously, the condition is called **ketosis**.

Two of the ketone bodies are acids, and their accumulation in the blood as ketosis worsens results in a condition of **acidosis** called **ketoacidosis** because it is caused by ketone bodies in the blood. If ketoacidosis is not controlled, the person becomes severely dehydrated because the kidneys excrete excessive amounts of water in response to low blood pH. Prolonged ketoacidosis leads to general debilitation, coma, and even death.

Patients suffering from diabetes-related ketosis are usually given insulin as a first step in their treatment. The insulin restores normal glucose metabolism and reduces the rate of formation of ketone bodies. If the patient is also suffering severe dehydration, the return to fluid and acid–base balance is sped up by the intravenous administration of solutions containing sodium bicarbonate. Excessive alcohol consumption can also cause ketone bodies to be produced with acetone on the breath.

acetone breath A condition in which acetone can be detected in the breath.

ketosis A condition in which ketonemia, ketonuria, and acetone breath exist together.

acidosis A low blood pH.

ketoacidosis A low blood pH due to elevated levels of ketone bodies.

Study Skills 24.1

Key Numbers for ATP Calculations

The calculation of the energy yield in terms of ATP molecules from the metabolism of a fatty acid is a useful exercise because it may help you better understand this metabolic process. The three key substances to account for in such calculations are acetyl CoA, NADH, and FADH$_2$. Two carbon atoms must be transported by coenzyme A in order to synthesize acetyl CoA; thus, the number of acetyl CoA molecules formed is determined by the following equation:

$$\text{acetyl CoA} = \frac{\text{number of fatty acid carbons}}{2}$$

For example, a 10-carbon fatty acid would produce 10/2, or 5, acetyl CoA molecules.

Every trip through the fatty acid spiral produces one NADH + H$^+$ molecule and one FADH$_2$ molecule. Thus,

number of trips = molecules NADH = molecules FADH$_2$

Furthermore, the number of trips equals one less than the number of acetyl CoA molecules produced (because the last trip of the spiral produces two molecules of acetyl CoA). Thus, for the 10-carbon fatty acid above, 5 acetyl CoA molecules are produced during four trips through the spiral. Also, the four trips produce four NADH + H$^+$ molecules and four FADH$_2$ molecules.

Finally, remember the multipliers: Every acetyl CoA gives rise to 10 ATPs, every NADH produces 2.5 ATPs, and every FADH$_2$ gives 1.5 ATPs. The summary for the 10-carbon fatty acid is:

(5 acetyl CoA) × 10	= 50 ATP
(4 NADH + H$^+$) × 2.5	= 10 ATP
(4 FADH$_2$) × 1.5	= 6 ATP
Activation step	= −2 ATP
Total ATP	= 64 ATP

24.7 Fatty Acid Synthesis

Learning Objective

7. Describe the pathway for fatty acid synthesis.

When organisms (including humans) take in more nutrients than are needed for energy requirements, the excesses are not excreted; they are converted first to fatty acids and then to body fat. Most of the conversion reactions take place in the liver, adipose tissue, and mammary glands. The mammary glands become especially active in the process during lactation.

As is true in the opposing processes of glycolysis and gluconeogenesis, the pathways for the opposing processes of fatty acid degradation and fatty acid synthesis are not simply the reverse of each other. The processes are separate from each other, utilize different enzyme systems, and are even located in different cellular compartments. Degradation by the β-oxidation pathway takes place in cellular mitochondria, whereas biosynthesis of fatty acids occurs in the cytoplasm.

However, one aspect of fatty acid synthesis and fatty acid degradation is the same. Both processes require units of two carbon atoms as a result of involving acetyl CoA. Thus, fatty acid chains are built up two carbons at a time during synthesis and broken down two carbons at a time during β-oxidation.

Acetyl CoA is generated inside mitochondria and so must be transported into the cytoplasm if it is to be used to synthesize fatty acids. This transport is done by first reacting acetyl CoA with oxaloacetate (the first step of the citric acid cycle). The product is citrate:

$$\text{acetyl CoA} + \text{oxaloacetate} + H_2O \longrightarrow \text{citrate} + \text{CoA}—\text{SH} \qquad (24.8)$$

Mitochondrial membranes contain a citrate transport system that enables excess citrate to move out of the mitochondria into the cytoplasm. Once in the cytoplasm, the citrate reacts to regenerate acetyl CoA and oxaloacetate.

Fatty acid synthesis occurs by way of a rather complex series of reactions catalyzed by a multienzyme complex called the *fatty acid synthetase system*. This system is made up of six enzymes and an additional protein, acyl carrier protein (ACP), to which all intermediates are attached.

The summary equation for the synthesis of palmitic acid from acetyl CoA demonstrates that a great deal of energy, 7 ATP + 14 NADPH (a phosphate derivative of NADH), is required:

$$8CH_3 - \overset{\displaystyle O}{\overset{\displaystyle \|}{C}} - S - CoA + 14NADPH + 13H^+ + 7ATP \longrightarrow$$
$$\text{acetyl CoA}$$

(24.9)

$$CH_3(CH_2)_{14}COO^- + 8CoA - SH + 6H_2O + 14NADP^+ + 7ADP + 7P_i$$
$$\text{palmitate}$$

This large input of energy is stored in the synthesized fatty acids and is one of the reasons it is so difficult to lose excess weight due to fat. After synthesis, the fatty acids are incorporated into triglycerides and stored in the form of fat in adipose tissues.

The liver is the most important organ involved in fatty acid and triglyceride synthesis. It is able to modify body fats by lengthening or shortening and saturating or unsaturating the fatty acid chains. The only fatty acids that cannot be synthesized by the body are those that are polyunsaturated. However, linoleic acid (two double bonds) and linolenic acid (three double bonds) from the diet can be converted to other polyunsaturated fatty acids. This utilization of linoleic and linolenic acids as sources of other polyunsaturated fatty acids is the basis for classifying them as essential fatty acids for humans (Section 18.2).

The human body can convert glucose to fatty acids, but it cannot convert fatty acids to glucose. Our cells contain no enzyme that can catalyze the conversion of acetyl CoA to pyruvate, a compound required for gluconeogenesis (Figure 23.13). However, plants and some bacteria do possess such enzymes and convert fats to carbohydrates as part of their normal metabolism.

24.8 Amino Acid Metabolism

Learning Objective

8. Describe the source and function of the body's amino acid pool.

In terms of amount used, the most important function of amino acids is to provide building blocks for the synthesis of proteins in the body. It is estimated that about 75% of amino acid utilization in a normal, healthy adult is for this function. The maintenance of body proteins must occur constantly in the body because tissue proteins break down regularly from normal wear and tear, as well as from diseases and injuries. The amino acids used in this maintenance come from proteins that are eaten and hydrolyzed during digestion, from the body's own degraded tissue, and from the synthesis in the liver of certain amino acids. The amino acids from these three sources constitute what is called the **amino acid pool** of the body. This cellular supply of amino acids is constantly being restocked to allow the synthesis of new proteins and other necessary metabolic processes to take place as needed.

amino acid pool The total supply of amino acids in the body.

The dynamic process in which body proteins are continuously hydrolyzed and resynthesized is called **protein turnover.** The turnover rate, or life expectancy, of body proteins is a measure of how fast the proteins are broken down and resynthesized. The turnover rate is usually expressed as a half-life. The use of radioactive amino acids has enabled researchers to estimate half-lives by measuring the exchange rate between body proteins and the amino acid pool. For example, the half-life of liver proteins is about 10 days. This means that over a 10-day period, half the proteins in the liver are hydrolyzed to amino acids and replaced by equivalent proteins. Plasma proteins also have a half-life of about 10 days, hemoglobin about 120 days, and muscle protein about 180 days. The half-life of collagen, a protein of connective tissue, is considerably longer—some estimates are as high as 1000 days. Other proteins, particularly enzyme and polypeptide hormones, have much shorter half-lives of only a few minutes. Once it is released from the pancreas, insulin has a half-life estimated to be only 7–10 minutes.

protein turnover The continuing process in which body proteins are hydrolyzed and resynthesized.

Because of the high turnover rate of proteins in the body, manufactured proteins do not have enough time to become a permanent part of the body structure or function. The frequent turnover of proteins is advantageous, for it allows the body to continually renew important molecules and to respond quickly to its own changing needs.

In addition to tissue protein synthesis, there is a constant draw on the amino acid pool for the synthesis of other nitrogen-containing biomolecules. These molecules include the purine and pyrimidine bases of nucleic acids; heme structures for hemoglobin and myoglobin; choline and ethanolamine, which are the building blocks of phospholipids; and neurotransmitters such as acetylcholine and dopamine. Like proteins, these compounds are also constantly being degraded and replaced. ❱ Table 24.2 lists some of the important nitrogen-containing compounds that are synthesized from amino acids.

TABLE 24.2 Compounds Derived from Amino Acids

Amino Acid	Product	Function
Tyrosine	dopamine	Neurotransmitter
	norepinephrine	Neurotransmitter, hormone
	epinephrine	Hormone
	thyroxine (T3 & T4)	Hormone
	melanin	Skin pigmentation
Tryptophan	serotonin	Neurotransmitter
Histidine	histamine	Involved in allergic reactions
Serine	ethanolamine	Required in cephalin synthesis
Cysteine	taurine	A compound of bile salts

Unlike carbohydrates and fatty acids, amino acids in excess of immediate body requirements cannot be stored for later use. They are degraded and, depending on the organism, their nitrogen atoms are converted to either ammonium ions, urea, or uric acid and excreted. Their carbon skeletons are converted to pyruvate, acetyl CoA, or one of the intermediates of the citric acid cycle and used for energy production, the synthesis of glucose through gluconeogenesis (Section 23.10), or conversion to triglycerides. The various pathways involved in amino acid metabolism are summarized in ❱ Figure 24.7.

Figure 24.7 The major metabolic pathways of amino acids.

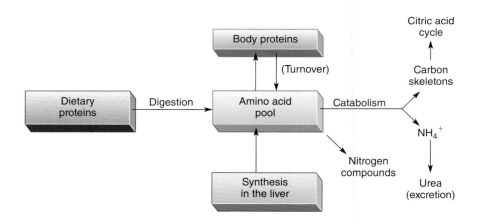

24.9 Amino Acid Catabolism: The Fate of the Nitrogen Atoms

Learning Objectives

9. Write equations for transamination and deamination reactions.

10. Explain the overall results of the urea cycle.

As previously noted, excess amino acids cannot be stored in the body but are catabolized for energy production, and the nitrogen is either excreted or used to synthesize other nitrogen-containing compounds. In this section, we will study the chemical pathways involved with the nitrogen. The chemical fate of the carbon skeleton of the amino acids is discussed in Section 24.10.

In essence, there are three stages in nitrogen catabolism (see ❱ Figure 24.8). These processes (which occur in the liver) are transamination, deamination, and urea formation.

Figure 24.8 An overview of the catabolic fate of nitrogen atoms in amino acids.

transaminase An enzyme that catalyzes the transfer of an amino group.

transamination The enzyme-catalyzed transfer of an amino group to a keto acid.

Stage 1: Transamination

In the tissues, amino groups freely move from one amino acid to another under the catalytic influence of enzymes called aminotransferases, or more commonly, **transaminases.** A key reaction for amino acids undergoing catabolism is a **transamination** involving the

transfer of amino groups to α-ketoglutarate. The carbon skeleton of the amino acid re-mains behind and is transformed into a new α-keto acid:

General reaction:

$$R-\underset{\underset{\text{a donor}}{\underset{\alpha\text{-amino acid}}{}}{\overset{\overset{NH_3^+}{|}}{CH}}-COO^- + {}^-OOC-CH_2CH_2-\underset{\underset{\alpha\text{-keto acid}}{\underset{\text{an }\alpha\text{-keto acid}}{}}{\overset{\overset{O}{\parallel}}{C}}-COO^- \overset{\text{transaminase}}{\rightleftharpoons}$$

(24.10)

$$R-\underset{\underset{\text{a new}}{\underset{\alpha\text{-keto acid}}{}}{\overset{\overset{O}{\parallel}}{C}}-COO^- + {}^-OOC-CH_2CH_2-\underset{\underset{\text{glutamate}}{\underset{\text{the new amino acid}}{}}{\overset{\overset{NH_3^+}{|}}{CH}}-COO^-$$

Specific example:

$$CH_3-\underset{\underset{\text{alanine}}{}}{\overset{\overset{NH_3^+}{|}}{CH}}-COO^- + {}^-OOC-CH_2CH_2-\underset{\underset{\alpha\text{-ketoglutarate}}{}}{\overset{\overset{O}{\parallel}}{C}}-COO^- \overset{\underset{\text{transaminase}}{\text{alanine}}}{\rightleftharpoons}$$

(24.11)

$$CH_3-\underset{\underset{\text{pyruvate}}{}}{\overset{\overset{O}{\parallel}}{C}}-COO^- + {}^-OOC-CH_2CH_2-\underset{\underset{\text{glutamate}}{}}{\overset{\overset{NH_3^+}{|}}{CH}}-COO^-$$

Notice that in the reaction, the $-NH_3^+$ group trades places with a carbonyl oxygen.

A second important example of transamination is the production of aspartate, which is used in Stage 3, urea formation. In this case, the amino group is transferred to oxaloacetate:

Specific example:

$$CH_3-\overset{\overset{NH_3^+}{|}}{CH}-\underset{\underset{\underset{\text{valine}}{CH_3}}{|}}{CH}-COO^- + {}^-OOC-CH_2-\underset{\underset{\text{oxaloacetate}}{}}{\overset{\overset{O}{\parallel}}{C}}-COO^- \rightleftharpoons$$

(24.12)

$$CH_3-\underset{\underset{CH_3}{|}}{CH}-\overset{\overset{O}{\parallel}}{C}-COO^- + {}^-OOC-CH_2-\underset{\underset{\text{aspartate}}{}}{\overset{\overset{NH_3^+}{|}}{CH}}-COO^-$$

The net effect of the transamination reactions in the catabolism of amino acids is to use nitrogen from a variety of amino acids to form glutamate and aspartate. In Section 24.11, we'll see that transamination is also an important method in the biosynthesis of amino acids.

▶ **LEARNING CHECK 24.3** Complete the following transamination reaction:

$$HO-\text{⬡}-CH_2-\underset{\underset{\text{tyrosine}}{}}{\overset{\overset{NH_3^+}{|}}{CH}}-COO^- + {}^-OOC-CH_2CH_2-\overset{\overset{O}{\parallel}}{C}-COO^- \rightleftharpoons$$

Omega-3 Fatty Acids: Will They Improve Heart Health?

Omega-3 fatty acids are an essential form of polyunsaturated fat, meaning they are required for a healthy body but are not produced by the body. As a result, we must obtain omega-3 fatty acids from foods such as flaxseed, pumpkin seeds, soybeans, purslane, walnuts, algae, and fish—particularly fatty fish (salmon, albacore tuna, mackerel, sardines, herring, halibut, and lake trout). Alpha-linolenic acid (ALA), eicosapentaenoic acid (EPA), and docosahexaenoic acid (DHA) are the three main types of omega-3 fatty acids consumed in foods. Of the three, EPA and DHA are easier for the body to use, therefore ALA is converted to either EPA or DHA by the body.

In the body, omega-3 fatty acids are essential to growth, development, and brain function. In fact, omega-3 fatty acids are believed to improve brain performance and memory. Additionally, studies have found evidence that omega-3 fatty acids are successful at reducing the risk of heart disease. This is accomplished by the reduction of cholesterol blood pressure and the intake of fewer trans and saturated fats from foods such as beef, pork sausage, and added hydrogenated oils and consumption of more omega-3 fatty acids. Furthermore, omega-3 fatty acids may reduce the risk of stroke by preventing blood clots and plaque build-up if low-risk fish or omega-3 fatty acid supplements are incorporated into the diet twice weekly. If your body is not receiving enough omega-3 fatty acids, you may experience memory problems, dry skin, fatigue, mood swings, depression, heart problems, and poor circulation.

Studies also suggest that omega-3 fatty acids can help alleviate or prevent a wide range of other health issues such as: diabetes, arthritis, osteoporosis, depression, bipolar disorder, schizophrenia, attention deficit/hyperactivity disorder, eating disorders, skin disorders, inflammatory bowel disease, asthma, macular degeneration, menstrual pain, colon cancer, breast cancer, and prostate cancer. Further studies are needed, but preliminary indications are that omega-3 fatty acids might also be useful in treating autism, ulcers, migraine headaches, pre-term labor, emphysema, psoriasis, glaucoma, Lyme disease, systemic lupus erythmatosus, irregular heartbeat, multiple sclerosis, panic attacks, and stress.

However, as with most good things, moderation is key. With such a long list of potential benefits you might want to start consuming as much omega-3 fatty acids as possible. More is better, right? Wrong! If the omega-3 fatty acids are from fish or fish products, they might contain heavy metals, dioxins, and polychlorinated biphenyls (reduced by consuming low-risk fish or mercury-free supplements). These contaminants could cause bleeding and hemorrhagic strokes, as well as negative interactions with medications taken for the treatment of diabetes, psoriasis, high cholesterol, high blood pressure, and blood clotting. Talk with your doctor about your health and diet to see if a supplement of omega-3 fatty acids would benefit you.

Capsules of fatty acid supplement.

© iStockphoto.com/Donna Franklin

Stage 2: Deamination

This phase of amino acid catabolism uses the glutamate produced in Stage 1. The enzyme glutamate dehydrogenase catalyzes the removal of the amino group as an ammonium ion and regenerates α-ketoglutarate, which can again participate in the first stage (transamination). This reaction is the principal source of NH_4^+ in humans. Because the deamination results in the oxidation of glutamate, it is called **oxidative deamination:**

oxidative deamination An oxidation process resulting in the removal of an amino group.

$$^-OOC-CH_2CH_2-\underset{\substack{| \\ \text{glutamate}}}{\overset{\overset{NH_3^+}{|}}{CH}}-COO^- + NAD^+ + H_2O \rightleftharpoons$$

$$NH_4^+ + {}^-OOC-CH_2CH_2-\overset{\overset{O}{\|}}{C}-COO^- + NADH + H^+$$
$$\text{α-ketoglutarate}$$

(24.13)

The NADH produced in this second stage enters the electron transport chain and eventually produces 2.5 ATP molecules. Other amino acids in addition to glutamate may also be catabolized by oxidative deamination. The reactions are catalyzed by enzymes in the liver called amino acid oxidases. In each case, an α-keto acid and NH_4^+ are the products.

Stage 3: Urea Formation

The ammonium ions released by the glutamate dehydrogenase reaction are toxic to the body and must be prevented from accumulating. In the **urea cycle,** which occurs only in the liver, ammonium ions are converted to urea (see ▶ Figure 24.9). This compound is less toxic than ammonium ions and can be allowed to concentrate until it is convenient to excrete it in urine.

urea cycle A metabolic pathway in which ammonium ions are converted to urea.

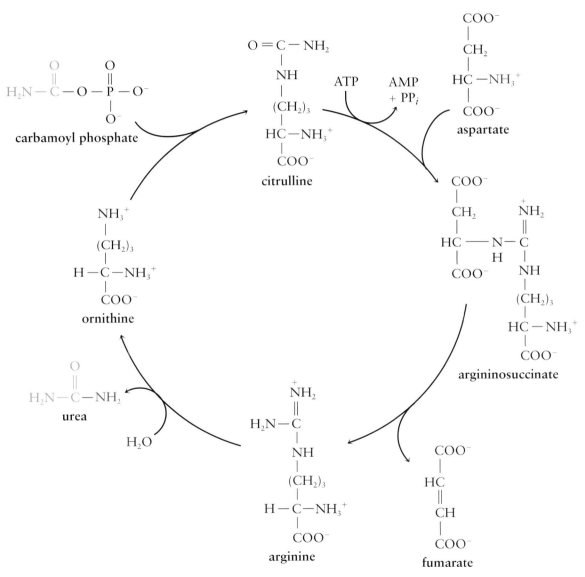

Figure 24.9 The urea cycle. Nitrogen atoms enter the cycle from carbamoyl phosphate and aspartate.

The urea cycle processes the ammonium ions in the form of carbamoyl phosphate, the fuel for the urea cycle. This compound is synthesized in the mitochondria from ammonium ions and bicarbonate ions.

$$NH_4^+ + HCO_3^- + 2ATP + H_2O \xrightarrow{\text{carbamoyl phosphate synthetase}} H_2N-\overset{\displaystyle O}{\overset{\|}{C}}-O-\overset{\displaystyle O}{\underset{\displaystyle O^-}{\overset{\|}{P}}}-O^- + 2ADP + P_i + 3H^+ \quad (24.14)$$

carbamoyl phosphate

As we see, the energy for the synthesis of one molecule of carbamoyl phosphate is derived from two molecules of ATP. Figure 24.9 summarizes the reactions of the urea cycle. The net reaction for carbamoyl phosphate formation and the urea cycle is

$$NH_4^+ + HCO_3^- + 3ATP + 2H_2O + \begin{array}{c} COO^- \\ | \\ CH_2 \\ | \\ CH-NH_3^+ \\ | \\ COO^- \end{array} \longrightarrow$$

aspartate $\qquad\qquad\qquad\qquad\qquad\qquad\qquad\qquad\qquad$ (24.15)

$$H_2N-\overset{\displaystyle O}{\overset{\|}{C}}-NH_2 + \overset{H}{\underset{^-OOC}{\diagdown}}C=C\overset{COO^-}{\underset{H}{\diagup}} + 2ADP + 2P_i + AMP + PP_i$$

urea $\qquad\qquad\qquad$ fumarate

After urea is formed, it diffuses out of liver cells into the blood, the kidneys filter it out, and it is excreted in the urine. Normal urine from an adult usually contains about 25–30 g of urea daily, although the exact amount varies with the protein content of the diet. The direct excretion of NH_4^+ accounts for a small but important amount of total urinary nitrogen. Ammonium ions can be excreted along with acidic ions, a mechanism that helps the kidneys control the acid–base balance of body fluids.

▶ LEARNING CHECK 24.4

a. What is the primary function of the urea cycle?
b. What is the fuel for the urea cycle?

24.10 Amino Acid Catabolism: The Fate of the Carbon Skeleton

Learning Objective

11. Describe how amino acids can be used for energy production, the synthesis of triglycerides, and gluconeogenesis.

After removal of the amino group of an amino acid is accomplished by transamination or oxidative deamination (Section 24.9), the remaining carbon skeleton undergoes catabolism and is converted into one of several products. We will not study the various pathways followed, but we will focus on the final forms the skeleton assumes and the metabolic fate of these forms.

Phenylketonuria (PKU)

At least 35 different hereditary changes in amino acid metabolism have been identified. One of the more well known is an inherited disease associated with abnormal aromatic amino acid metabolism. In *phenylketonuria (PKU)*, there is a lack of the enzyme phenylalanine hydroxylase. As a result, phenylalanine cannot be converted to tyrosine, leading to the accumulation of phenylalanine and its metabolites (phenylpyruvate and phenylacetate) in the tissues and blood:

$$
\text{phenylpyruvate}
$$

phenylpyruvate

phenylacetate

Abnormally high levels of phenylpyruvate and phenylacetate damage developing brain cells, causing severe mental retardation. It is estimated that 1 out of every 20,000 newborns is afflicted with PKU. A federal regulation requires that all infants be tested for this disease, which can be detected very easily by analyzing blood or urine samples for phenylalanine or phenylpyruvic acid.

The disease is treated by restricting the amount of phenylalanine in the diet of the infant starting 2–3 weeks after birth. The diet is also supplemented with tyrosine because it is not being formed in the PKU patient. Strict dietary management is not as critical after the age of 6 because the brain has matured by this time and is not as susceptible to the toxic effects of phenylalanine metabolites.

Infants with PKU have an excellent chance for a normal healthy life, if the disease is detected and treated early. Here a nurse is taking blood samples from an infant's foot to be used in a simple chemical test for PKU.

Science Photo Lib./Custom Medical Stock Photo

After the amino group is gone, the skeletons of all 20 amino acids are degraded into either pyruvate, acetyl CoA, acetoacetyl CoA (which is degraded to acetyl CoA), or various substances that are intermediates in the citric acid cycle. As shown in ▶ Figure 24.10, all

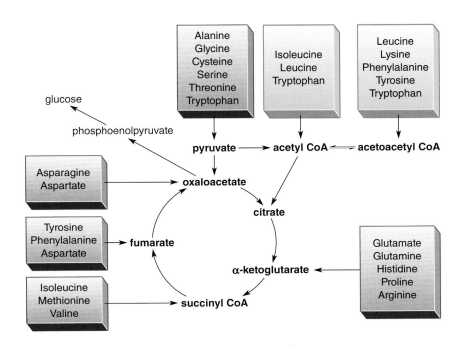

Figure 24.10 Fates of the carbon atoms of amino acids. Glucogenic amino acids are shaded purple, and ketogenic amino acids are shaded green.

Phenylalanine and Diet Foods

In human society, we often want to indulge ourselves but we don't want to suffer any negative consequences of the indulgence. A good example of this is the desire to satisfy our craving for a sweet taste in foods, but not wanting to suffer the results of excessive caloric intake. As a result, a large industry has developed based on the production and distribution of low-calorie or no-calorie food sweeteners (see Chemistry Around Us 17.1). One popular product of this industry is a dipeptide of the two amino acids aspartic acid and phenylalanine. The product, called *aspartame,* has a sweet taste about 180 times that of ordinary table sugar (sucrose). When aspartame is hydrolyzed during digestion, the two amino acids are released.

Most foods that contain aspartame carry a warning on the label stating that they contain phenylalanine, although the phenylalanine is only released during the digestion of the food. The label warning is, for the most part, a protection for the food manufacturer against the somewhat remote possibility that the user of the food product suffers from a genetic metabolic disorder called phenylketonuria, or PKU (see Chemistry Around Us 24.1). The label warning also complies with federal regulations that require any food product containing aspartame to carry the warning.

People who have PKU suffer serious complications from ingesting phenylalanine, such as mental retardation, brain damage, seizures, and other problems. People who don't have PKU do not have to worry about ingesting phenylalanine or aspartame, with a certain few exceptions. It is known that aspartame or phenylalanine-rich foods can cause a rapid increase in brain levels of phenylalanine. So, aspartame and other products containing phenylalanine should be used cautiously by individuals with the following characteristics:

- Those who are taking medications such as monoamine oxidase inhibitors, neuroleptics, or medications containing levodopa
- Those who have a sleep disorder
- Those who have an anxiety disorder or other mental health disorder

Aspartame is present in many low-calorie drinks.

these degraded forms of the carbon skeletons are a part of or can enter the citric acid cycle, and thus may be very important in the production of energy.

Even though the degraded carbon skeletons can be used to produce energy via the citric acid cycle, not all are used this way because cellular needs might dictate other uses. For example, once a carbon skeleton is catabolized to pyruvate, there are two possible uses for it: the production of energy or the synthesis of glucose through gluconeogenesis (Section 23.10). The skeleton of an amino acid that is degraded into pyruvate or intermediates of the citric acid cycle can be used to make glucose and is classified as a **glucogenic amino acid.** Amino acids with skeletons that are degraded into acetyl CoA or acetoacetyl CoA cannot be converted into glucose but can, in addition to energy production, be used to make ketone bodies and fatty acids. Such amino acids are classified as **ketogenic.** Figure 24.10 shows this catabolic classification of the 20 amino acids. Notice that some amino acids appear in more than one location in the diagram.

Glucogenic amino acids play a special role in the metabolic changes that occur during starvation. To maintain the blood glucose level, the body first uses the glycogen stored in the liver. After 12–18 hours without food, the glycogen supplies are exhausted. Glucose is then synthesized from glucogenic amino acids through the process of gluconeogenesis. Hydrolysis of proteins from body tissues, particularly from muscle, supplies the amino acids for gluconeogenesis. Because each protein in the body has an important function, the body can meet its energy needs for only a limited time by sacrificing proteins.

glucogenic amino acid An amino acid whose carbon skeleton can be converted metabolically to an intermediate used in the synthesis of glucose.

ketogenic amino acid An amino acid whose carbon skeleton can be converted metabolically to acetyl CoA or acetoacetyl CoA.

24.11 Amino Acid Biosynthesis

Learning Objective

12. State the relationship between intermediates of carbohydrate metabolism and the synthesis of nonessential amino acids.

As we have already seen, the liver is highly active biochemically. In biosynthesis, it is responsible for producing most of the amino acids the body can synthesize. Amino acids that can be synthesized in the amounts needed by the body are called **nonessential amino acids** (see ▶ Table 24.3). As explained in Chapter 22, essential amino acids either cannot be made or cannot be made in large enough amounts to meet bodily needs and must be included in the diet.

nonessential amino acid An amino acid that can be synthesized within the body in adequate amounts.

TABLE 24.3 Essential and Nonessential Amino Acids

Essential	Nonessential	Essential	Nonessential
Histidine	Alanine	Threonine	Glutamine
Isoleucine	Arginine	Tryptophan	Glycine
Leucine	Asparagine	Valine	Proline
Lysine	Aspartate		Serine
Methionine	Cysteine		Tyrosine
Phenylalanine	Glutamate		

The key starting materials for the synthesis of 10 nonessential amino acids are intermediates of the glycolysis pathway and the citric acid cycle (see ▶ Figure 24.11). Tyrosine, the only nonessential amino acid with an aromatic side chain, is produced from the essential amino acid phenylalanine in a conversion that requires a single oxidation step catalyzed by the enzyme phenylalanine hydroxylase:

$$\text{phenylalanine} + O_2 + NADPH + H^+ \xrightarrow{\text{phenylalanine hydroxylase}} \text{tyrosine} + NADP^+ + H_2O \qquad (24.16)$$

Figure 24.11 A summary of amino acid biosynthesis.

Three nonessential amino acids (glutamate, alanine, and aspartate) are synthesized from α-keto acids via reactions catalyzed by transaminases. For example, alanine is produced from pyruvate and glutamate (which furnishes the amino group):

$$\underset{\text{pyruvate}}{CH_3-\overset{O}{\overset{||}{C}}-COO^-} + \text{glutamate} \xrightleftharpoons[\text{transaminase}]{\text{glutamic pyruvic}} \underset{\text{alanine}}{CH_3-\overset{NH_3^+}{\overset{|}{CH}}-COO^-} + \alpha\text{-ketoglutarate} \qquad (24.17)$$

Thus, we see that transaminases perform two vital functions in amino acid metabolism. By taking part in the biosynthesis of nonessential amino acids, they provide a means to help readjust the relative proportions of amino acids to meet the particular needs of the body. This is a vital function because most of our diets do not contain amino acids in the exact proportions the body requires. Also, as we noted in Section 24.9, transamination reactions allow the nitrogen atoms of all amino acids to be transferred to α-keto acids to form glutamate and aspartate when disposal of nitrogen is necessary.

Two other nonessential amino acids, asparagine and glutamine, are formed from aspartate and glutamate by reaction of the side-chain carboxylate groups with ammonium ions:

$$
\underset{\text{aspartate}}{{}^-\text{O}-\overset{\overset{\text{O}}{\|}}{\text{C}}-\text{CH}_2-\underset{\overset{|}{\text{NH}_3^+}}{\text{CH}}-\text{COO}^-} + \text{NH}_4^+ \quad \xrightarrow{\ \ \text{ATP}\quad\text{ADP} + \text{P}_i\ \ } \quad \underset{\text{asparagine}}{\text{H}_2\text{N}-\overset{\overset{\text{O}}{\|}}{\text{C}}-\text{CH}_2-\underset{\overset{|}{\text{NH}_3^+}}{\text{CH}}-\text{COO}^-} \qquad (24.18)
$$

$$
\underset{\text{glutamate}}{{}^-\text{O}-\overset{\overset{\text{O}}{\|}}{\text{C}}-\text{CH}_2-\text{CH}_2-\underset{\overset{|}{\text{NH}_3^+}}{\text{CH}}-\text{COO}^-} + \text{NH}_4^+ \quad \xrightarrow{\ \ \text{ATP}\quad\text{ADP} + \text{P}_i\ \ } \quad \underset{\text{glutamine}}{\text{H}_2\text{N}-\overset{\overset{\text{O}}{\|}}{\text{C}}-\text{CH}_2\text{CH}_2-\underset{\overset{|}{\text{NH}_3^+}}{\text{CH}}-\text{COO}^-} \qquad (24.19)
$$

So far, we have shown how 6 of the 11 nonessential amino acids are synthesized. The syntheses of the remaining 5 are more complex, and we will not consider them here.

Case Study Follow-up

Changing unhealthy habits is difficult. Research has shown that making small changes is more likely to help a person succeed than a complete overhaul. The acronym SMART is useful in setting goals to change habitual behavior: specific, measurable, attainable, relevant, and time limited. An example is setting a goal of walking for 30 minutes a day, five days a week. People who keep track of changes, as in keeping a daily food journal, lose twice as much weight as those who don't. Adequate sleep is particularly important to successful dietary change, as is a supportive environment (Mayo Clinic, 2011). Poor eating habits are a normal cultural behavior in the United States, and going against the norm requires a significant commitment to healthy behavior. Substitution is more effective than self-denial. Choosing baked potato chips, rather than French fries, while not as healthy as choosing carrot sticks or apples, is still a step in the right direction. Small sustainable change is the key to success.

Fiber plays an important role in maintaining health. In addition to preventing and relieving constipation, fiber can reduce the risk of heart disease and type 2 diabetes. Insoluble fiber, or roughage, is mainly associated with bowel health. Soluble fiber is the type of fiber that is responsible for lowering low-density lipoprotein levels (LDL cholesterol) and slows the absorption of sugar, decreasing the chance of developing type 2 diabetes, which is also a cardiac risk factor. A diet high in soluble fiber can also lower high blood pressure and inflammation, both of which contribute to heart disease. Soluble fiber is found in oats, peas, beans, apples, citrus fruits, carrots, barley, and psyllium.

Concept Summary

Blood Lipids

Fatty acids, glycerol, and monoglycerides that result from lipid digestion are absorbed into the lymph, recombined into triglycerides, and deposited into the bloodstream as lipoprotein aggregates.
Objective 1 (Section 24.1), Exercises 24.2 and 24.4

Fat Mobilization

When stored fats are needed for energy, hydrolysis reactions liberate the fatty acids and glycerol. These component substances of fat then enter the bloodstream and travel to tissues, where they are utilized.
Objective 2 (Section 24.2), Exercise 24.8

Glycerol Metabolism

The glycerol available from fat mobilization is first phosphorylated and then oxidized to dihydroxyacetone phosphate, an intermediate of glycosis. By having an entry point into the glycolysis pathway, glycerol can ultimately be converted into glucose or oxidized to CO_2 and H_2O.
Objective 3 (Section 24.3), Exercise 24.12

The Oxidation of Fatty Acids

The catabolism of fatty acids begins in the cytoplasm, where they are activated by combining with CoA—SH. After being transported into mitochondria, the degradation of fatty acids occurs by the β-oxidation pathway. The β-oxidation pathway produces reduced coenzymes ($FADH_2$ and NADH) and cleaves the fatty acid chain into two-carbon fragments bound to coenzyme A (acetyl CoA).
Objective 4 (Section 24.4), Exercise 24.22

The Energy from Fatty Acids

The energy available from a fatty acid for ATP synthesis can be calculated by determining the amount of acetyl CoA, $FADH_2$, and NADH produced. **Objective 5 (Section 24.5), Exercise 24.26.** On an equal-mass basis, fatty acids contain more than twice the energy of glucose.

Ketone Bodies

Acetoacetate, β-hydroxybutyrate, and acetone are known as ketone bodies. They are synthesized in the liver from acetyl CoA. During starvation, in unchecked diabetes, and after excessive alcohol consumption, the level of ketone bodies becomes very high, leading to several conditions: ketonemia, ketonuria, acetone breath, and ketosis.
Objective 6 (Section 24.6), Exercise 24.28

Fatty Acid Synthesis

This process occurs in the cytoplasm and uses acetyl CoA as a starting material. Two-carbon fragments are added to growing fatty acid molecules as energy is supplied by ATP and NADPH.
Objective 7 (Section 24.7), Exercise 24.34

Amino Acid Metabolism

Amino acids and proteins are not stored within the body. Amino acids absorbed from digested food or synthesized in the body become a part of a temporary supply or pool that may be used in metabolic processes. **Objective 8 (Section 24.8), Exercise 24.38.** The turnover, or life expectancy, of proteins is usually expressed in half-lives. Protein half-lives range from several minutes to hundreds of days. Some amino acids in the body are converted into relatively simple but vital nitrogen-containing compounds. The catabolism of amino acids produces intermediates used for energy production, synthesis of glucose, or formation of triglycerides.

Amino Acid Catabolism: The Fate of the Nitrogen Atoms

As an amino acid undergoes catabolism, the amino group may be transferred to an α-keto acid through a process called transamination. In the process of deamination, an amino acid is converted into a keto acid and ammonia. **Objective 9 (Section 24.9), Exercise 24.44.** The urea cycle converts toxic ammonium ions into urea for excretion.
Objective 10 (Section 24.9), Exercise 24.54

Amino Acid Catabolism: The Fate of the Carbon Skeleton

Amino acids are classified as glucogenic or ketogenic based on their catabolic products. Glucogenic amino acids are degraded into pyruvate or intermediates of the citric acid cycle and can be used for glucose synthesis. Ketogenic amino acids are degraded into acetoacetyl CoA and acetyl CoA for energy production and triglyceride synthesis.

Objective 11 (Section 24.10), Exercise 24.58

Amino Acid Biosynthesis

The body can synthesize amino acids, known as non-essential amino acids. The key starting materials are intermediates of the glycolysis pathway and the citric acid cycle, and phenylalanine in the case of tyrosine.

Objective 12 (Section 24.11), Exercise 24.64

Key Terms and Concepts

Acetone breath (24.6)
Acidosis (24.6)
Adipose tissue (24.2)
Amino acid pool (24.8)
β-oxidation process (24.4)
Chylomicron (24.1)
Fat mobilization (24.2)

Glucogenic amino acid (24.10)
Ketoacidosis (24.6)
Ketogenic amino acid (24.10)
Ketone bodies (24.6)
Ketonemia (24.6)
Ketonuria (24.6)
Ketosis (24.6)

Nonessential amino acid (24.11)
Oxidative deamination (24.9)
Protein turnover (24.8)
Transaminase (24.9)
Transamination (24.9)
Urea cycle (24.9)

Key Reactions

1. Digestion of triglycerides (Section 24.1):

$$\text{triglyceride} + H_2O \xrightarrow{\text{lipase}} \text{fatty acids} + \text{glycerol} + \text{monoglycerides}$$

2. Fat mobilization (Section 24.2):

$$\text{triglyceride} + 3H_2O \xrightarrow{\text{lipase}} 3 \text{ fatty acids} + \text{glycerol}$$

3. Activation of fatty acids (Section 24.4):

Reaction 24.2

$$\underset{\text{fatty acid}}{R - \overset{\overset{\textstyle O}{\|}}{C} - OH} + HS - CoA \longrightarrow \underset{\text{fatty acyl CoA}}{R - \overset{\overset{\textstyle O}{\|}}{C} - S - CoA} + H_2O$$

$$\text{ATP} \qquad \text{AMP} + PP_i$$

4. Oxidation of fatty acids (Section 24.4):

Reaction 24.5

$$R - CH_2CH_2 - \overset{\overset{\textstyle O}{\|}}{C} - S - CoA + NAD^+ + FAD + H_2O + CoA - SH \longrightarrow$$

$$R - \overset{\overset{\textstyle O}{\|}}{C} - S - CoA + CH_3\overset{\overset{\textstyle O}{\|}}{C} - S - CoA + NADH + H^+ + FADH_2$$

5. Fatty acid synthesis (Section 24.7):

Reaction 24.9

$$8CH_3-\overset{\displaystyle O}{\overset{\|}{C}}-S-CoA + 14NADPH + 13H^+ + 7ATP \longrightarrow$$

$$CH_3(CH_2)_{14}COO^- + 8CoA-SH + 6H_2O + 14NADP^+ + 7ADP + 7P_i$$

6. Transamination (Section 24.9):

Reaction 24.10

$$R-\overset{\displaystyle NH_3^+}{\overset{|}{CH}}-COO^- + {}^-OOC-CH_2CH_2-\overset{\displaystyle O}{\overset{\|}{C}}-COO^- \rightleftharpoons R-\overset{\displaystyle O}{\overset{\|}{C}}-COO^- + {}^-OOC-CH_2CH_2-\overset{\displaystyle NH_3^+}{\overset{|}{CH}}-COO^-$$

7. Oxidative deamination (Section 24.9):

Reaction 24.13

$${}^-OOC-CH_2CH_2-\overset{\displaystyle NH_3^+}{\overset{|}{CH}}-COO^- + NAD^+ + H_2O \rightleftharpoons NH_4^+ + {}^-OOC-CH_2CH_2-\overset{\displaystyle O}{\overset{\|}{C}}-COO^- + NADH + H^+$$

8. Urea formation (Section 24.9):

Reaction 24.15

$$NH_4^+ + HCO_3^- + 3ATP + 2H_2O + \begin{matrix} COO^- \\ | \\ CH_2 \\ | \\ CH-NH_3^+ \\ | \\ COO^- \end{matrix} \longrightarrow \underset{\text{urea}}{H_2N-\overset{\displaystyle O}{\overset{\|}{C}}-NH_2} + \underset{\text{fumarate}}{\overset{\displaystyle H \qquad COO^-}{\underset{\displaystyle {}^-OOC \qquad H}{C=C}}} + 2ADP + 2P_i + AMP + PP_i$$

aspartate

Exercises

Even-numbered exercises are answered in Appendix B.

Blue-numbered exercises are more challenging.

Blood Lipids (Section 24.1)

24.1 How does the caloric value of fat compare with the caloric value of glycogen and starch?

24.2 What are the products of triglyceride digestion?

24.3 What happens to the products of triglyceride digestion as they pass into the cells of the intestinal mucosa?

24.4 What mechanism exists in the body for transporting insoluble lipids?

24.5 Describe what happens to the level of blood lipids after a meal rich in fat.

24.6 List the major types of lipoproteins.

Fat Mobilization (Section 24.2)

24.7 What signals the need for mobilization of triglycerides from adipose tissue?

24.8 Describe what is meant by the term *fat mobilization*.

24.9 Explain why fatty acids cannot serve as fuel for the brain.

24.10 Which cells utilize fatty acids over glucose to satisfy their energy needs?

Glycerol Metabolism (Section 24.3)

24.11 At what point does glycerol enter the glycolysis pathway?

24.12 Describe the two fates of glycerol after it has been converted to an intermediate of glycolysis.

The Oxidation of Fatty Acids (Section 24.4)

24.13 Where in the cell does fatty acid catabolism take place?

24.14 How is the fatty acid prepared for catabolism? Where in the cell does fatty acid activation take place?

24.15 Why is the oxidation of fatty acids referred to as β-oxidation?

24.16 What hydrogen-transporting coenzymes play important roles in the oxidation of fatty acids?

24.17 Label the α- and β-positions in the following acids:

a. $CH_3CH_2CH_2CH_2CH_2-\overset{\displaystyle O}{\overset{\|}{C}}-OH$

b. $CH_3(CH_2)_6\overset{\displaystyle OH}{\overset{|}{CH}}-CH_2-\overset{\displaystyle O}{\overset{\|}{C}}-OH$

24.18 Write an equation for the activation of palmitic acid (16 carbons).

24.19 Write formulas for the products that result when activated palmitic acid is taken through the following:

a. One turn of the fatty acid spiral

b. Two turns of the fatty acid spiral

24.20 Why is the oxidation of fatty acids referred to as the fatty acid spiral rather than the fatty acid cycle?

24.21 How many molecules of acetyl CoA are produced in the catabolism of a molecule of stearic acid, an 18-carbon carboxylic acid? How many times does the spiral reaction sequence occur?

24.22 Complete the following equations for one turn of the fatty acid spiral:

a. $CH_3CH_2CH_2CH_2CH_2-\overset{\overset{O}{\|}}{C}-S-CoA + FAD \longrightarrow$ ____ + ____

b. ____ + $H_2O \rightarrow$ ____

c. ____ + $NAD^+ \rightarrow$ ___ + ___ + ___

d. ____ + $CoA-SH \rightarrow$ ___ + ___

24.23 Outline the four reactions that occur in the fatty acid spiral.

The Energy from Fatty Acids (Section 24.5)

24.24 Determine the ATP yield per molecule of acetyl CoA that enters the citric acid cycle.

24.25 What is the energy cost in ATP molecules to activate a fatty acid?

24.26 Calculate the number of ATP molecules that can be produced from the complete oxidation of a ten-carbon fatty acid to carbon dioxide and water.

24.27 Compare the energy available (in ATP molecules) from a 6-carbon fatty acid to the energy available from a molecule of glucose.

Ketone Bodies (Section 24.6)

24.28 What are ketone bodies?

24.29 Explain how excessive ketone bodies may form in the following:

a. During starvation

b. In patients with diabetes mellitus

24.30 Where are ketone bodies formed? What tissues utilize ketone bodies to meet energy needs?

24.31 Differentiate between (a) ketonemia, (b) ketonuria, (c) acetone breath, and (d) ketosis.

24.32 Why is ketosis frequently accompanied by acidosis?

Fatty Acid Synthesis (Section 24.7)

24.33 Where within a liver cell does fatty acid synthesis occur?

24.34 What substance supplies the carbons for fatty acid synthesis?

24.35 What substances furnish the energy for fatty acid synthesis?

24.36 Why can the liver convert glucose to fatty acids but cannot convert fatty acids to glucose?

Amino Acid Metabolism (Section 24.8)

24.37 List three vital functions served by amino acids in the body.

24.38 What is the amino acid pool?

24.39 What are the sources of amino acids in the pool?

24.40 What term is used to denote the breakdown and resynthesis of body proteins?

24.41 What percentage of amino acids is used to synthesize proteins?

24.42 Name four important biomolecules other than proteins that are synthesized from amino acids.

24.43 Compare the half-life of plasma proteins with the half-life of enzymes.

Amino Acid Catabolism: The Fate of the Nitrogen Atoms (Section 24.9)

24.44 Match the terms *transamination* and *deamination* to the following:

a. An amino group is removed from an amino acid and donated to a keto acid.

b. An ammonium ion is produced.

c. New amino acids are synthesized from other amino acids.

d. A keto acid is produced from an amino acid.

24.45 Complete the following transamination reaction and name the amino acid that is produced:

$$\text{C}_6\text{H}_5-CH_2-\overset{\overset{O}{\|}}{C}-COO^- + \overset{+}{H_3N}-\underset{\underset{\underset{\underset{COO^-}{|}}{CH_2}}{|}}{\underset{|}{CH}}-COO^- \xrightarrow{\text{transaminase}}$$

24.46 Write an equation to illustrate transamination between leucine and pyruvate.

24.47 Complete the following oxidative deamination reaction:

$$\overset{+}{H_3N}-\underset{\underset{\underset{\underset{NH_2}{|}}{C=O}}{|}}{\underset{|}{CH}}-COO^- + NAD^+ + H_2O \xrightarrow{\substack{\text{amino acid} \\ \text{oxidase}}}$$

24.48 Write an equation to illustrate the oxidative deamination of glycine.

24.49 By writing two reactions, the first a transamination and the second an oxidative deamination, show how the amino group of alanine can be removed as NH_4^+.

24.50 In what organ of the body is urea synthesized?

24.51 What are the sources of the carbon atom and two nitrogen atoms in urea?

24.52 Name the compound that enters the urea cycle by combining with ornithine.

24.53 How much energy (in number of ATP molecules) is expended to synthesize a molecule of urea?

24.54 Write a summary equation of the formation of urea.

Amino Acid Catabolism: The Fate of the Carbon Skeleton (Section 24.10)

24.55 Differentiate between glucogenic and ketogenic amino acids.

24.56 Is any amino acid both glucogenic and ketogenic?

24.57 Identify the five locations at which the carbon skeletons of amino acids enter the citric acid cycle.

24.58 Based on the following conversions, classify each amino acid as glucogenic or ketogenic.

 a. aspartate $\rightarrow$ oxaloacetate

 b. leucine $\rightarrow$ acetyl CoA

 c. tyrosine $\rightarrow$ acetoacetyl CoA

24.59 What special role is played by glucogenic amino acids during fasting or starvation?

Amino Acid Biosynthesis (Section 24.11)

24.60 Differentiate between essential and nonessential amino acids.

24.61 What essential amino acid makes tyrosine nonessential?

24.62 List two vital functions performed by transaminases.

24.63 What amino acids are synthesized from glutamate?

24.64 List two general sources of intermediates for the biosynthesis of amino acids.

Additional Exercises

24.65 Trace glycerol metabolism after it enters the glycolytic pathway as dihydroxyacetone phosphate and give an overall net reaction (including ATP, NAD^+, etc.) for the conversion of glycerol to pyruvate.

24.66 A change in the concentration of enzymes that catalyze fatty acid synthesis has been shown to be a major mechanism for controlling synthesis rate. Give two regulatory means of changing enzyme concentrations.

24.67 A ketone body has a molecular weight of 58.1 g/mol and a concentration of 0.050 mg/100 mL in a patient's blood. Which ketone body is it, and how many molecules of it would be found in 1.0 mL of the patient's blood?

24.68 A 7.48-mg sample of a blood lipid was found to contain 1.87 mg of protein. Use Figure 24.4 to classify this lipid.

24.69 The following reaction proceeded in an aqueous solution as the pH was monitored. After a while, the pH quit changing even though there was excess urea present in the solution.

$$NH_2-\overset{\overset{\displaystyle O}{\displaystyle \|}}{C}-NH_2 + H_2O \xrightarrow{\text{urease}} 2NH_{3(aq)} + CO_{2(g)}$$

urea

Was the initial pH when the reaction began acidic, neutral, or basic? How did the pH change over time? Why did the pH quit changing?

Allied Health Exam Connection

The following questions are from these sources:

1. *Nursing School Entrance Exam* © 2005, Learning Express, LLC.

2. *McGraw-Hill's Nursing School Entrance Exams* by Thomas A. Evangelist, Tamara B. Orr and Judy Unrein © 2009, The McGraw-Hill Companies, Inc.

3. *NSEE Nursing School Entrance Exams,* 3rd Edition © 2009, Kaplan Publishing.

4. *Cliffs Test Prep: Nursing School Entrance Exams* by Fred N. Grayson © 2004, Wiley Publishing, Inc.

5. *Peterson's Master the Nursing School and Allied Health Entrance Exams,* 18th Edition by Marion F. Gooding © 2008, Peterson's, a Nelnet Company.

24.70 Which of the following processes must occur before amino acids can be metabolized to release energy?

 a. Fermentation

 b. Deamination

 c. Dehydrogenation

24.71 When in excess, which element is eliminated from the human body through the formation of urea? In what organ of the body is urea synthesized?

24.72 What substances are produced by the digestion of proteins?

24.73 What is the name for amino acids that cannot be manufactured by the body?

24.74 The clinic nurse is evaluating a man wearing a diabetic medic alert band, who appears confused, with hot, dry, flushed skin. His respirations are deep and fast, and he says he is nauseated. His breath smells fruity. What diabetes-related medical condition is this man exhibiting?

Chemistry for Thought

24.75 Cellular reactions for the biosynthesis and catabolism of amino acids are not simply the reversals of the same metabolic pathways. Why is this an advantage for the cell?

24.76 Why do you think the half-lives of enzymes are comparatively short?

24.77 Why do you think the half-life of collagen is comparatively long?

24.78 How might HDL levels suggest a partial explanation for the observation that women as a group have fewer heart attacks than do men as a group?

24.79 A student calculates the net yield of ATP molecules from a 12-carbon fatty acid to be 80. What did the student probably overlook?

24.80 If researchers discovered a method of reducing blood cholesterol to extremely low levels, why might it be undesirable to do so?

24.81 Could there be a connection between high sugar intake and high blood levels of triglycerides? Explain.

25 Body Fluids

© Timothey Kosachev/Shutterstock.com

Case Study

Wesley had studied blood types in biology class. He understood that he had O negative blood and was a universal donor. Recently, his cousin Trina had been in an auto accident involving a drunk-driver, and Wesley was astounded to find that she had received 50 units of blood. For the first time, the need for donated blood became a personal issue, but Wesley was ashamed to say he had never donated blood. There were blood drives at his work twice a year, but he hadn't participated and, to be honest, he was a little scared. He didn't like doctor appointments or medical procedures of any kind, but now he realized his cousin was alive only because of the generosity of other people. He felt that if he donated, it would be fighting back against the drunk-driver who hurt Trina. He was determined to make the effort to donate before the week was over.

How many units of blood are required each year in the United States? Why do cancer patients require transfusions? To what extent can artificial blood substitutes be used?

Follow-up to this Case Study appears at the end the chapter before the Concept Summary.

Learning Objectives

When you have completed your study of this chapter, you should be able to:

1 Compare the chemical compositions of plasma, interstitial fluid, and intracellular fluid. **(Section 25.1)**

2 Explain how oxygen and carbon dioxide are transported within the bloodstream. **(Section 25.2)**

3 Explain how materials move from the blood into the body cells and from the body cells into the blood. **(Section 25.3)**

4 List the normal and abnormal constituents of urine. **(Section 25.4)**

5 Discuss how proper fluid and electrolyte balance is maintained in the body. **(Section 25.5)**

6 Explain how acid–base balance is maintained in the body. **(Section 25.6)**

7 Explain how buffers work to control blood pH. **(Section 25.7)**

8 Describe respiratory control of blood pH. **(Section 25.8)**

9 Describe urinary control of blood pH. **(Section 25.9)**

10 List the causes of acidosis and alkalosis. **(Section 25.10)**

To carry out its complex function, a living cell requires a steady supply of reactants, such as nutrients and oxygen. A cell also requires a reliable system for removing the resulting waste products—carbon dioxide and water, for example. Both of these conditions are met by the simple process of diffusion. Reactants can diffuse into the cell through the thin cell membrane, and the products of cell function can diffuse out of the cell and be absorbed by the surrounding liquid.

However, a complex organism, which consists of many closely packed cells, cannot depend solely on diffusion. Some circulating system must bring necessary materials to the cells and carry away the wastes. Otherwise, the liquid surrounding the cells would soon be depleted of reactants and saturated with wastes.

25.1 A Comparison of Body Fluids

Learning Objective

1. Compare the chemical compositions of plasma, interstitial fluid, and intracellular fluid.

The average adult body contains about 42 L of fluids, which accounts for two-thirds of the total body weight. Most of these fluids are compartmentalized in three regions of the body: the interior of cells, tissue spaces between cells (including the lymph vessels), and the blood vessels. The majority, about 28 L, is located inside the cells and is called **intracellular fluid.** All body fluids not located inside the cells are collectively known as **extracellular fluids.** Thus, fluids in two of the fluid compartments are extracellular: the **interstitial fluid,** which fills the space between tissue cells and moves in lymph vessels, and the fluid of the bloodstream—**plasma.** Interstitial fluid constitutes about 25% (10.5 L) of the total body fluid, and the plasma (nearly 3.5 L) makes up about 8% of the total.

intracellular fluid Body fluid located inside cells.

extracellular fluid Body fluid located outside cells.

interstitial fluid The fluid surrounding individual tissue cells.

plasma The liquid portion of whole blood.

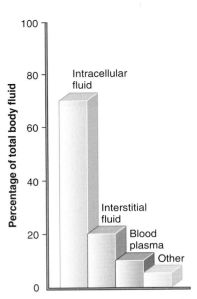

Figure 25.1 The distribution of body fluids.

Other body fluids that occur in lesser amounts are urine, digestive juices, and cerebrospinal fluid. The distribution of the various body fluids is illustrated in ▶ Figure 25.1. Extracellular fluid provides a relatively constant environment for the cells and transports substances to and from the cells. Intracellular fluid, on the other hand, is the medium in which the vital life-maintaining reactions take place.

Chemically, the two extracellular fluids, plasma and interstitial fluid, are nearly identical. The only difference is that plasma contains an appreciable amount of protein not found in interstitial fluid. Intracellular fluid is chemically different from extracellular fluid. Intracellular fluid contains larger amounts of protein and a much different ionic population (see ▶ Figure 25.2). From Figure 25.2, we can see that:

1. The principal cation of plasma and interstitial fluid is Na^+. The principal cation of intracellular fluid is K^+ (actually, about 98% of the body's potassium is found inside cells).
2. The principal anion of extracellular fluid is chloride, Cl^-, whereas phosphate (mainly HPO_4^{2-}) is the main anion inside cells.
3. Intracellular fluid contains more than four times as much protein as plasma, and there is remarkably little protein in interstitial fluid.

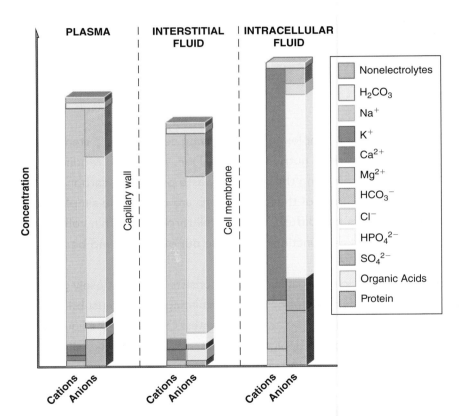

Figure 25.2 The relative chemical composition of the major body fluids.

25.2 Oxygen and Carbon Dioxide Transport

Learning Objective

2. Explain how oxygen and carbon dioxide are transported within the bloodstream.

One of the most important functions of blood is to carry oxygen from the lungs to the tissues. An average adult at rest requires about 350 mL of oxygen per minute. The limited solubility of oxygen in plasma allows only about 2% of this total to be dissolved

and transported in solution. About 98% of the needed oxygen is carried by red blood cells (see ▶ Figure 25.3) in the form of an oxygen-hemoglobin combination called **oxyhemoglobin.** The nonoxygenated hemoglobin is called **deoxyhemoglobin,** or simply **hemoglobin.** Normal human blood contains about 15 g of hemoglobin per 100 mL.

Because of its physiological importance, hemoglobin has been studied extensively. It is known to be a conjugated protein containing four chains (the globin portion of the molecule) and four heme groups. Each heme group consists of an Fe^{2+} ion in the center of a nitrogenous heterocyclic structure (see ▶ Figure 25.4). The iron in oxyhemoglobin is bonded at six positions, as shown in Figure 25.4. The four nitrogens are part of the heme group, and the iron is directly attached to the histidine, which is a part of the globin molecule. The sixth bond is between iron and oxygen. Because each hemoglobin molecule contains four heme groups, it can bind a total of four O_2 molecules. When one of the four heme groups binds an oxygen molecule, the affinity of the other heme groups for oxygen is increased.

Figure 25.3 Red blood cells passing through a narrow capillary.

© Professors P. M. Motta and S. Correr/Science Photo Library/Photo Researchers Inc.

oxyhemoglobin Hemoglobin combined with oxygen.

deoxyhemoglobin (hemoglobin) Nonoxygenated hemoglobin.

Figure 25.4 The iron in oxyhemoglobin.

The reversible binding that takes place between hemoglobin (HHb) and molecular oxygen is represented like this:

$$HHb + O_2 \rightleftharpoons HbO_2^- + H^+ \qquad (25.1)$$
$$\text{hemoglobin} \quad \text{oxyhemoglobin}$$

When CO_2 is present, hemoglobin can combine with it to form **carbaminohemoglobin.** This reversible reaction is favored by conditions found in body tissues:

$$HHb + CO_2 \rightleftharpoons HHbCO_2 \qquad (25.2)$$
$$\text{carbaminohemoglobin}$$

carbaminohemoglobin Hemoglobin combined with carbon dioxide.

About 25% of the total CO_2 in the body is carried from body tissues to the lungs in the form of carbaminohemoglobin. Another 5% dissolves in the plasma and travels in solution; the remaining 70% is transported in the form of bicarbonate ions (HCO_3^-).

The transport of oxygen to tissues begins when inhaled air fills the alveoli of the lungs. These clusters of small sacs are surrounded by many tiny blood capillaries, and it is here

Erythropoietin: A Performance-enhancing Drug

Erythropoietin (EPO) is a hormone produced by the kidneys for the regulation of red blood cell production. Synthesized forms of EPO, referred to as ESAs (erythropoietin stimulating agents), are also available as a prescription drug. In the medical profession, ESAs are used to reduce the need for red blood cell transfusions in patients with low red blood cell counts resulting from cancer treatment, liver failure and elective surgery. However, there is current debate over whether ESAs encourage tumor growth rates. For this reason, the National Cancer Institute is offering research funds to scientists to study the effects of ESAs on tumor growth. Furthermore, the FDA reported that certain levels of ESAs increase the risk of heart problems which may result in death.

A black market of ESAs has developed because they are used by some athletes who participate in endurance events, such a long-distance running and cross-country skiing. Although their use in athletic events is prohibited, ESAs are virtually undetectable in drug tests performed on the athletes. The difficulty in detecting ESA use is because of the way they function in the body. They stimulate the body to overproduce red blood cells. The red blood cells contain hemoglobin, which transports oxygen to the cells. An increased number of red blood cells translates into more oxygen being transported to muscle cells, and an increased ability of the muscles to continue doing what would otherwise be anaerobic work.

The drug is usually taken 2–4 weeks before a competition to allow the body to build up the level of red blood cells. The use of the drug accomplishes through chemical means the same thing that was accomplished by the former practice of blood packing. When this practice was allegedly used, an athlete would, over time, have blood removed and stored. The athlete's body would replace the blood that was removed. Then, a few days before the athletic competition, the red blood cells would be removed from the stored blood and injected back into the athlete's bloodstream. The increased number of red blood cells would in turn increase the oxygen-carrying capacity of the blood, thereby giving the athlete an endurance edge.

Suspicions and allegations of blood packing by athletes reached their high point just before and during the 1968 summer Olympic Games, held in Mexico City. The high altitude and thin air of the host city was thought to give an advantage to athletes who normally lived and trained at higher altitudes. It was suggested that blood packing was used by some athletes to compensate.

Natural EPO is secreted from the kidneys and is transported to the marrow of the bones where it stimulates red blood cell production. Artificial EPO (ESA) is injected into a vein or just under the skin. The excessive stimulation of the red blood cell production causes the blood to become thicker than normal, a condition that can lead to some serious side effects. There is an increased chance for blood clots to form, which can lead to strokes or heart attacks. A large infusion of red blood cells from blood packing would also increase blood viscosity and bring about a decrease in cardiac output and a decrease in blood flow velocity. Intravascular clotting, air, clot embolisms and heart failure could result from a homologous blood transfusion. Any athlete considering the use of ESAs or the old technique of blood packing would be well advised to carefully weigh the value of winning a medal against the potential of having a debilitating stroke or heart attack.

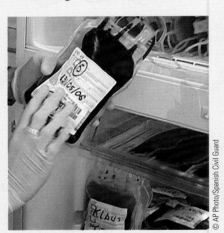

A frozen bag of blood obtained during a doping investigation.

that oxygen is absorbed into the blood. ▶ Figure 25.5 represents the processes that take place as oxygen is absorbed and carbon dioxide is released. The main steps (circled numbers in the figure) are:

1. Oxygen partial pressure is higher in the alveoli than in the red blood cells. As a result, oxygen diffuses from the alveoli through the capillary wall and into the red blood cells.
2. Inside the red blood cells, oxygen reacts with hemoglobin to form oxyhemoglobin and H^+ ions. Oxyhemoglobin formation is favored (according to Le Châtelier's principle) by a high partial pressure of oxygen, a slight cooling of the blood, and an increase in pH (decrease in H^+ ions)—conditions encountered by the blood as it passes through the capillaries of the lungs.

Exercise Beats Angioplasty

Exercise is not just about looking good and fitting into that new pair of jeans; it is about maintaining a level of health with benefits ranging from a decrease in the chances of having a heart attack or stroke to reducing stress and symptoms of depression. That 20-minute jog around the block is one of the best medicines you can give your body to promote long-term health. Exercise has been identified as providing a surprising number of specific benefits including muscular endurance, increased energy, reduced risk of coronary artery disease, lower blood pressure and cholesterol levels, weight control, increased bone strength, higher metabolism rates, and improved reaction times. After a good workout, the body and mind both experience a state of relaxation that promotes elevated thinking, contributing to a more balanced life. In this fast-paced world driven by work and deadlines, every person should be exercising regularly to promote their mental health as well as their physical health.

Well-rounded physical fitness includes four basic elements that can be improved with regular exercise: cardiovascular endurance, muscular strength, muscular endurance, and flexibility. To be truly fit, each element should be developed, but the most vital is cardiovascular endurance. Physiologically, cardiovascular endurance is the sustained ability of the heart, blood vessels, and blood to carry oxygen to the cells, coupled with the ability of the cells to use oxygen, and the ability of the blood to carry away waste products. Since every cell in the body requires oxygen to function, there is no more basic element of fitness than this—to see that the heart, lungs, and circulatory system function properly.

Cardiovascular endurance is improved through exercises that require the body's systems to deliver even larger amounts of oxygen to working muscles. To achieve this, the exercise should utilize the large muscle groups (such as those in the legs), but,

most importantly, it must be sustained. With regular aerobic exercise, your heart will develop the ability to pump more blood and thus deliver more oxygen with greater efficiency. Your muscles will develop a correspondingly greater capacity to use this oxygen. These improvements are part of what is called the aerobic "training effect." Because your heart is stronger, it can pump more blood per beat, and, as a result, your heart rate, both at rest and during exertions, will decrease. Your heart will also acquire the ability to recover from the stress of exercise more quickly.

The next time you are tempted to miss that daily dose of exercise, remember the benefits of getting up and moving. Your body, mind, and heart will thank you.

Exercise is one of the best things you can do to promote long-term health.

Figure 25.5 At the lungs, the carbon dioxide of red blood cells is exchanged for oxygen.

3. Bicarbonate ions (HCO_3^-) diffuse from the plasma into the red blood cells.
4. The bicarbonate ions are replaced in the plasma by chloride ions that diffuse out of the blood cells. This step, called the **chloride shift**, maintains charge balance and osmotic pressure relationships between the plasma and red blood cells.
5. Protons released by hemoglobin as it is oxygenated (Step 2) react with bicarbonate ions to form carbonic acid.
6. An enzyme in the red blood cells, carbonic anhydrase, promotes the breakdown of carbonic acid to water and carbon dioxide. The reaction is reversible, but the low pressure of carbon dioxide in the lungs favors the formation of carbon dioxide and water (Le Châtelier's principle, again).
7. Carbaminohemoglobin ($HHbCO_2$), formed from hemoglobin and CO_2 at the cellular level, breaks apart to yield hemoglobin and carbon dioxide.
8. Because the carbon dioxide pressure is high in the red blood cells but low in the alveoli, carbon dioxide molecules diffuse out of the red blood cells and into the lung. The carbon dioxide and some of the water formed in Step 6 are expelled in the exhaled air.

chloride shift The movement of chloride ions from one fluid to another to maintain charge neutrality.

Oxygenated red blood cells are carried by the bloodstream into the capillaries surrounding the cells of active tissues. ❱ Figure 25.6 shows the steps involved in delivering oxygen to the tissues and accepting carbon dioxide for transport to the lungs. These steps are essentially the reverse of those at the lungs:

1. Tissue cells use oxygen to produce energy; carbon dioxide and water are formed as byproducts. The concentration of carbon dioxide is higher in the tissue cells than in the red blood cells, so carbon dioxide diffuses from the tissue cells into the interstitial fluid and then into the red blood cells.
2. Inside the red blood cells, carbon dioxide rapidly reacts with water in the presence of carbonic anhydrase to produce carbonic acid.
3. Carbonic acid dissociates to give hydrogen ions and bicarbonate ions.
4. The bicarbonate ions diffuse into the plasma. Most carbon dioxide in the plasma is transported in the bicarbonate ion form, moving from tissue cells to the lungs.
5. The chloride shift again takes place (this time in the opposite direction) to maintain electrolyte balance.
6. A smaller amount (25%) of carbon dioxide from Step 1 reacts with hemoglobin to form carbaminohemoglobin ($HHbCO_2$) for transport to the lungs.

Figure 25.6 At the tissue cells, oxygen of red blood cells is exchanged for carbon dioxide.

7. The increase in concentration of hydrogen ions inside the red blood cells promotes a reaction with oxyhemoglobin, which releases oxygen.

8. The free oxygen diffuses out of the red blood cells through the plasma, capillary membrane, interstitial fluid, and into the tissue cells.

> ▶ **LEARNING CHECK 25.1** Decide whether each of the following red blood cell reactions occurs at the lungs or at the site of the tissue cells:
>
> **a.** $HHbCO_2 \rightleftarrows HHb + CO_2$
> **b.** $H_2O + CO_2 \rightleftarrows H_2CO_3$
> **c.** $H^+ + HCO_3^- \rightleftarrows H_2CO_3$
> **d.** $HbO_2^- + H^+ \rightleftarrows HHb + O_2$

25.3 Chemical Transport to the Cells

Learning Objective

3. Explain how materials move from the blood into the body cells and from the body cells into the blood.

For substances to be chemically transported in the body, they must become part of the moving bloodstream. They may dissolve in the water-based plasma (as do sugars, amino acids, ions, and gases to some extent), they may become chemically bonded to cellular components (as do oxygen and carbon dioxide with the hemoglobin of blood cells), or they may form a suspension in the plasma of the blood (as do lipids).

Materials transported by the bloodstream to the cells must move through the capillary wall into the interstitial fluid and through the cell membrane into the cell. The reverse must take place when waste products move from inside tissue cells into the bloodstream. During these processes, capillary walls behave as selectively permeable membranes or filters, allowing water containing dissolved nutrients—including oxygen—to pass in one direction and water containing dissolved wastes to pass in the other direction.

The movement of water and dissolved materials through the capillary walls is governed by two factors—by the pressure of blood against the capillary walls and by the differences in protein concentration on each side of the capillary walls.

The concentration of protein in plasma is much higher than the protein concentration of the interstitial fluid outside the blood vessels. This concentration difference results in an osmotic pressure of about 18 torr, which tends to move fluid into the bloodstream. However, the pumping action of the heart puts the blood under pressure (blood pressure) that is greater at the arterial end of a capillary (about 32 torr) than at the venous end (about 12 torr). Because the blood pressure at the arterial end is higher than the osmotic pressure, the tendency is for a net flow to occur from the capillary into the interstitial fluid (see ▶ Figure 25.7). The fluid that leaves the capillary contains the dissolved nutrients, oxygen, hormones, and vitamins needed by the tissue cells.

Figure 25.7 The flow of fluid between capillaries and interstitial spaces.

TABLE 25.1 Major Dissolved Solids in Normal Urine

Constituent[a]	Grams per 24 Hours[b]
Amino acids	0.80
Urea	25.0
Creatinine	1.5
Uric acid	0.7
H^+	pH 4.5–8.0
Na^+	3.0
K^+	1.7
NH_4^+	0.8
Ca^{2+}	0.2
Mg^{2+}	0.15
Cl^-	6.3
SO_4^{2-}	1.4
$H_2PO_4^-$	1.2
HCO_3^-	0–3
Other compounds	2–3

[a]The 24-hour volume and composition of urine vary widely, depending on the fluid intake and diet.

[b]These data are for an average 24-hour specimen with a total volume of 1400 mL.

Figure 25.8 Urinalysis test strips. A urine sample is tested for several components simultaneously by dipping a test strip into a sample and comparing the reagent areas to a color chart.

As the blood moves through the capillary, its pressure decreases, until at the venous end, it becomes lower than the osmotic pressure, and a net flow of fluid takes place from the interstitial fluid into the capillary. The incoming fluid contains the metabolic waste products, such as carbon dioxide and excess water. This mechanism allows the exchange of nutrients and wastes and maintains fluid balance between the blood and interstitial space.

25.4 The Constituents of Urine

Learning Objective

4. List the normal and abnormal constituents of urine.

Urine contains about 96% water and 4% dissolved organic and inorganic waste products. Approximately 40–50 g of dissolved solids are contained in the daily urine output of an adult (see ▶ Table 25.1). The urine of a healthy person has a pH of 4.5–8.0, with 6.6 being a reasonable average for a person on an ordinary diet. Fruits and vegetables tend to make the urine alkaline, whereas high-protein foods tend to make the urine acidic.

The composition of urine is an excellent indicator of the state of health. This accounts for the importance of urinalysis as part of a physical checkup or a diagnosis. Normal constituents are considered abnormal when they are eliminated in excess amounts. ▶ Table 25.2 lists some conditions that lead to abnormally high urinary levels of normal constituents; some other substances (such as pus or blood), which are considered abnormal in *any* measurable amount, are also listed.

TABLE 25.2 Some Abnormal Urine Constituents

Abnormal Constituent	Condition	Causes
Glucose (in large amounts)	Glucosuria	Diabetes mellitus, renal diabetes, alimentary glycosuria
Protein	Proteinuria or albuminuria	Kidney damage, nephritis, bladder infection
Ketone bodies	Ketonuria	Diabetes mellitus, starvation, high-fat diets
Pus (leukocytes)		Kidney or bladder infection
Hemoglobin	Hemoglobinuria	Excessive hemolysis of red blood cells
Red blood cells	Hematuria	Hemorrhage in the urinary tract
Bile pigments (in large amounts)	Jaundice	Blockage of bile duct, hepatitis, cirrhosis

A urine specimen is often collected from a patient entering a hospital and is checked with a paper test strip that contains bands of different reagents that will react with the different abnormal constituents (see ▶ Figure 25.8). This one simple test quickly checks for indications of pathological conditions.

25.5 Fluid and Electrolyte Balance

Learning Objective

5. Discuss how proper fluid and electrolyte balance is maintained in the body.

The body is 45–75% water (by weight), the percentage depending on a number of factors, including age, sex, and especially the amount of body fat. In general, the percentage of water increases as fat content decreases.

Fluid balance within the body is maintained not only by a balance in the total amount but by a normal and stable distribution of fluid in the body's three fluid-containing areas. Thus, the amounts of fluid inside the cells, in the interstitial spaces, and in the blood vessels must remain relatively constant if a fluid balance is to exist.

Fluid and electrolyte balance are interdependent. If one deviates from normal, so does the other. In modern medical practice, a great deal of attention is given to these matters. Many of today's hospital patients receive some form of fluid and electrolyte balance therapy.

An important and obvious principle of fluid balance is that fluid output and intake must be equal. Water from food and drink is absorbed into the body from the digestive tract. Besides this well-known source, water is also derived within the cells from food metabolism. This byproduct water enters the bloodstream along with the water that is absorbed from the digestive tract.

Water intake is regulated in part by the thirst mechanism (see ❯ Figure 25.9). When the body loses large amounts of water, salivary secretions decrease, and a dry feeling develops in the mouth. This and other sensations are recognized as thirst, and water is drunk to relieve the condition. The fluid intake compensates for the fluid lost, and balance is reestablished.

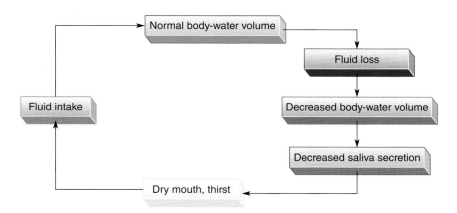

Figure 25.9 The thirst mechanism.

Water normally leaves the body through the kidneys (urine), lungs (water vapor in expired air), skin (by diffusion and perspiration), and intestines (feces) (see ❯ Table 25.3). Abnormally high fluid losses, and possibly dehydration, can be caused by hyperventilation, excessive sweating, vomiting, or diarrhea.

Fluid balance in the body is maintained or restored primarily by variations in urine output. Normally, this amounts to about 1400 mL/day, but the total excretion fluctuates according to water intake. The primary factor that controls urine production is the rate of water reabsorption from the renal tubules in the kidneys. This rate is regulated chiefly by the pituitary hormone vasopressin and by the adrenal cortex hormone aldosterone.

Vasopressin, also called antidiuretic hormone (ADH), exerts its action by affecting the permeability of the renal tubules to water. In the absence of vasopressin, less water is reabsorbed into the bloodstream, and a large volume of light yellow, dilute urine results. Patients with the rare disease diabetes insipidus do not produce vasopressin; their urine is extremely voluminous and dilute. In the presence of vasopressin, the tubules become more permeable to water that is drawn into the capillaries, thus increasing blood volume. The reabsorption of water from the tubules produces a low volume of dark yellow, concentrated urine. (Diabetes insipidus is very different from diabetes mellitus, mentioned elsewhere in the text.)

With the help of vasopressin, a healthy person can vary the intake of water widely and yet preserve a stable overall concentration of substances in the blood. But sometimes the water level of the body gets dangerously low, from not drinking enough water or excessive water loss caused by diarrhea or excessive perspiration. Under such circumstances, the adrenal gland secretes the steroid hormone aldosterone. At the kidneys, aldosterone

TABLE 25.3 Typical Normal Values for Water Entry and Exit

Intake (mL)	
Ingested liquids	1500
Water in foods	700
Water formed by catabolism	200
Total	2400
Output (mL)	
Kidneys (urine)	1400
Lungs (water in expired air)	350
Skin	
By diffusion	350
By perspiration	100
Intestines (in feces)	200
Total	2400

Pulse Oximetry

Often when we think of a hospital, we think of rooms full of people lying in high-tech beds with tubes leading into their veins carrying antibiotics or other fluids, and debilitated people wearing oxygen masks to assist with their breathing. To complete the picture, we might imagine a small clamp-like device attached to the finger of all the patients. This device glows with a subdued red light and has wires leading to an important-looking monitor. But, what exactly is this device? What is its purpose? How does it work? Is it safe?

The object in question is called a pulse oximeter. It measures both the pulse rate and the oxygen saturation level of the blood. This information is used to monitor the breathing of a patient. Monitoring breathing is one method used to determine if a patient's condition is stable, improving, or worsening. Generally, a young healthy individual will have an oxygen saturation level of 95–99%. Naturally, this percentage of oxygen saturation varies with age, aerobic fitness, and the altitude at which the person lives and at which the measurement is being made. Because of these characteristics, a single pulse oximetry reading is not very informative. It is much better to make multiple readings over time as a means of monitoring change over that time.

A pulse oximeter determines the quality of breathing by measuring the level of oxygen saturation of the blood. The color of blood changes depending on the amount of oxygen that is attached to each molecule of hemoglobin, i.e., the oxygen saturation of the blood. Highly oxygenated blood is bright red in color, while deoxygenated blood is a deep red color. These changes in color are detected by passing a beam of red light and a beam of infrared light through an extremity such as a finger, toe, or an ear lobe. The amount of light absorbed by the blood changes as the color of the blood changes. Thus, the readings of the pulse oximeter give an indication of the extent of oxygen saturation of the blood, which gives an indication of how well a patient is breathing.

A pulse oximeter alone poses few dangers for the patient to whom it is attached. In some cases, particularly older models, a pulse oximeter can cause burns or pressure ulcers. However, greater hazards involving the use of a pulse oximeter come when it is the only means of monitoring the health of a patient. If the readings from the pulse oximeter look good, a healthcare provider might have a false sense of security and overlook other indicators of the patient's overall condition. Furthermore, a pulse oximeter requires a strong signal to operate correctly. Once again, a false sense of security might be obtained if the instrument appears to have a strong signal, but is in fact displaying inaccurate values.

Technology can aid the medical profession, but there is no substitute for personal care from an attentive, knowledgeable medical professional.

A pulse oximeter measures the pulse rate and oxygen concentration of the blood.

alkalosis An abnormally high blood pH.

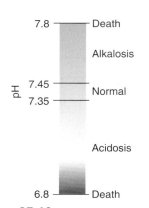

Figure 25.10 Human circulatory and respiratory processes operate only within a very narrow range of blood pH.

stimulates the reabsorption of sodium ions (electrolytes) from the renal tubes into the blood. Chloride ions follow the sodium ions to maintain electrical neutrality, and water follows the sodium chloride. Thus, aldosterone secretion conserves both salt and water in the body. When the fluid level of the body returns to normal, the amount of aldosterone secreted decreases.

25.6 Acid–Base Balance

Learning Objective

6. Explain how acid–base balance is maintained in the body.

Blood pH normally remains within the rather narrow range of 7.35–7.45. A decrease in pH, called acidosis, or an increase, called **alkalosis,** is serious and requires prompt attention. Death can result when the pH value falls below 6.8 or rises above 7.8 (see ▶ Figure 25.10). Acidosis, an abnormally low blood pH, was introduced in Section 24.6.

Large amounts of acids and smaller amounts of bases normally enter the blood. Some mechanisms must neutralize or eliminate these substances if the blood pH is to remain constant. In practice, a constant pH is maintained by the interactive operation of three systems: buffer, respiratory, and urinary. Only when all three parts of this complex mechanism function properly can the acid–base balance be maintained.

25.7 Buffer Control of Blood pH

Learning Objective

7. Explain how buffers work to control blood pH.

A buffer system prevents marked changes in the pH of a solution when an acid or base is added. Three major buffer systems of the blood are the bicarbonate buffer, the phosphate buffer, and the plasma proteins. The most important of these is the bicarbonate buffer system, consisting of a mixture of bicarbonate ions (HCO_3^-) and carbonic acid (H_2CO_3).

Buffer systems work by neutralizing H^+ or OH^- ions that come from the dissociation of acids or bases added to a system. As an example of buffers in action, consider the fate of lactic acid (HLac) entering the bloodstream. When lactic acid dissolves in the blood, it dissociates to produce H^+ and lactate ions (Lac^-). The liberated H^+ ions drive the pH of the blood down. The bicarbonate ions of the bicarbonate buffer system react with the excess H^+ and return the pH to the normal range:

$$HLac \rightleftharpoons H^+ + Lac^- \qquad (25.3)$$

$$H^+ + HCO_3^- \rightleftharpoons H_2CO_3 \qquad (25.4)$$

Reaction 25.4 is a net ionic reaction for the buffering process. When a total reaction is written, we see that the effect of the buffering is to replace lactic acid in the blood by carbonic acid, which is a weaker acid and so releases fewer H^+ ions to the blood than does lactic acid:

$$\underset{\substack{\text{stronger} \\ \text{acid}}}{HLac} + HCO_3^- \longrightarrow \underset{\substack{\text{weaker} \\ \text{acid}}}{H_2CO_3} + Lac^- \qquad (25.5)$$

This replacement of a stronger acid with a weaker acid is how biochemists often describe buffering reactions.

Although the bicarbonate system is not the strongest buffer system in the body (the most powerful and plentiful one utilizes the proteins of plasma and cells), it is very important because the concentrations of both bicarbonate and carbonic acid are regulated by the kidneys and by the respiratory system. Without the respiratory and urinary processes, the capacity of buffers would eventually be exceeded.

25.8 Respiratory Control of Blood pH

Learning Objective

8. Describe respiratory control of blood pH.

The respiratory system helps control the acidity of blood by regulating the elimination of carbon dioxide and water molecules. These molecules, exhaled in every breath, come from carbonic acid as follows (see Figure 25.5):

$$\underset{\text{carbonic acid}}{H_2CO_3} \rightleftharpoons H_2O + CO_2 \qquad (25.6)$$

The more CO_2 and H_2O that are exhaled, the more carbonic acid is removed from the blood, thus elevating the blood pH to a more alkaline level.

The respiratory mechanism for controlling blood pH begins in the brain with respiratory center neurons that are sensitive to blood CO_2 levels and pH. A significant increase in the CO_2 of arterial blood, or a decrease below about 7.38 of arterial blood pH, causes the breathing to increase both in rate and depth, resulting in **hyperventilation.** This increased ventilation eliminates more carbon dioxide, reduces carbonic acid and hydrogen-ion concentrations, and increases the blood pH back toward the normal level (see ▶ Figure 25.11).

hyperventilation Rapid, deep breathing.

Figure 25.11 Respiratory control of blood pH.

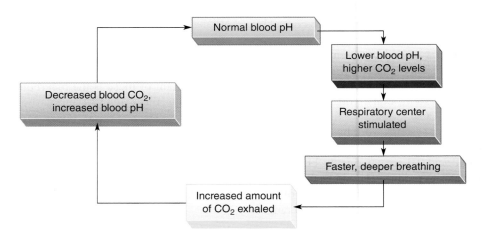

hypoventilation Slow, shallow breathing.

In the opposite situation, an increase in blood pH above normal causes **hypoventilation,** a reduced rate of respiration. Less CO_2 is exhaled, and the higher concentration of carbonic acid remaining in the blood lowers the pH back to normal.

25.9 Urinary Control of Blood pH

Learning Objective

9. Describe urinary control of blood pH.

Because they can excrete varying amounts of acid and base, the kidneys, like the lungs, play a vital role in pH control. For example, with acidic blood, the excretion of hydrogen ions by the kidneys decreases the urine pH and simultaneously increases the blood pH back toward normal.

▶ Figure 25.12 traces the reactions involved in the excretion of hydrogen ions by the kidneys:

1. Carbon dioxide diffuses from the blood capillaries into the kidney distal tubule cells.
2. Catalyzed by carbonic anhydrase, water and carbon dioxide react to give carbonic acid.
3. The carbonic acid ionizes to give hydrogen ions and bicarbonate ions. The hydrogen ions diffuse into the developing urine.
4. For every hydrogen ion entering the urine, a sodium ion passes into the tubule cells.
5. The sodium ions and bicarbonate ions enter the bloodstream capillaries.

The net result of these reactions is the conversion of CO_2 to HCO_3^- within the blood. Both the decrease in CO_2 and the increase in HCO_3^- tend to increase blood pH levels back to normal. The developing urine has picked up the hydrogen ions, which now react with buffering ions such as phosphate that are present in urine:

$$H^+ + HPO_4^{2-} \rightarrow H_2PO_4^- \tag{25.7}$$

The presence of the phosphate buffer system $H_2PO_4^{2-}/HPO_4^{2-}$ usually keeps urine from going much below pH 6, but too great an excess of protons from carbonic acid can exceed the buffer capacity of the system and result in quite acidic urine.

Figure 25.12 Urinary control of blood pH in the kidney.

25.10 **Acidosis and Alkalosis**

Learning Objective

10. List the causes of acidosis and alkalosis.

When blood pH is normal and a state of acid–base balance exists, components of the bicarbonate buffer are present in plasma in a ratio of 20 parts of bicarbonate (HCO_3^-) to 1 part of carbonic acid (H_2CO_3).

When respiratory and urinary systems work together to maintain the blood at pH 7.4, they do so primarily by maintaining the HCO_3^-/H_2CO_3 ratio at 20:1. Any change in the ratio produces a change in pH. An increase in the ratio of bicarbonate to carbonic acid causes the pH to increase (alkalosis); and a decrease, which is much more common, causes the pH to decrease (acidosis) (see ▶ Figure 25.13).

Figure 25.13 Blood pH depends on the relative concentrations of carbonic acid and bicarbonate ion.

Two adjectives describe the general cause or origin of pH imbalances in body fluids: metabolic and respiratory. Respiratory acid–base imbalances (respiratory acidosis and respiratory alkalosis) result from abnormal breathing patterns. Metabolic acidosis and metabolic alkalosis are caused by factors other than abnormal breathing.

Respiratory Alkalosis

Respiratory alkalosis is caused by hyperventilating—breathing rapidly and deeply. Hysteria, anxiety, or prolonged crying may result in hyperventilation in which too much carbon dioxide is exhaled, which disturbs the blood's normal carbon dioxide/carbonic acid ratio. According to Le Châtelier's principle, Reaction 25.6 (written again below) shifts to the right as it attempts to restore the equilibrium:

$$\underset{\substack{\text{direction of shift to} \\ \text{restore equilibrium}}}{\xrightarrow{\hspace{3cm}}} \quad H_2CO_3 \rightleftharpoons H_2O + CO_2 \uparrow \quad \overset{loss\ of\ CO_2}{} \tag{25.8}$$

The equilibrium shift reduces the amount of carbonic acid present and rapidly increases the HCO_3^-/H_2CO_3 ratio to a value greater than 20:1. As a result, blood pH rises to 7.54 or higher within a few minutes. A corresponding loss of HCO_3^- also occurs, but it is not large enough to maintain the HCO_3^-/H_2CO_3 ratio at 20:1.

The treatment of respiratory alkalosis involves rebreathing one's own exhaled air by breathing into a paper bag (*not* a plastic bag), administering carbon dioxide, and treating the underlying causes of the hyperventilation.

Respiratory Acidosis

Respiratory acidosis is sometimes the result of slow or shallow breathing (hypoventilation) caused by an overdose of narcotics or barbiturates. Anesthetists need to be particularly aware of respiratory acidosis, because most inhaled anesthetics depress respiration rates. Lung diseases, such as emphysema and pneumonia, or an object lodged in the windpipe can also result in hypoventilation. In respiratory acidosis, too little carbon dioxide is exhaled, and its concentration within the blood increases. The carbon dioxide/carbonic acid equilibrium shifts to the left to restore the equilibrium:

$$\underset{\substack{\text{direction of shift} \\ \text{of equilibrium}}}{\xleftarrow{\hspace{3cm}}} \quad H_2CO_3 \rightleftharpoons H_2O + CO_2 \quad \overset{increased\ CO_2}{} \tag{25.9}$$

As a result of the shift, the concentration of carbonic acid in the blood increases, the HCO_3^-/H_2CO_3 ratio decreases to less than 20:1, and respiratory acidosis sets in. The treatment of respiratory acidosis involves identifying the underlying causes and possibly the intravenous administration of isotonic sodium bicarbonate solution or hemodialysis.

Metabolic Acidosis

Various body processes—collectively called metabolism—produce acidic substances that liberate H^+ in solution. The diffusion of these substances into the bloodstream causes a shift in the carbonic acid–bicarbonate equilibrium:

$$\underset{\substack{\text{direction of shift to} \\ \text{restore equilibrium}}}{\xleftarrow{\hspace{3cm}}} \quad H_2CO_3 \rightleftharpoons H^+ + HCO_3^- \quad \overset{increased\ H^+}{} \tag{25.10}$$

The shift decreases the concentration of bicarbonate ions and increases the concentration of carbonic acid. As a result, the HCO_3^-/H_2CO_3 ratio decreases, as does the blood pH. **Metabolic acidosis** is often a serious problem in uncontrolled diabetes mellitus, and it also occurs temporarily after heavy exercise. Other causes include severe diarrhea and aspirin overdose.

Symptoms of metabolic acidosis, besides low blood pH and high levels of H_2CO_3, include the following: hyperventilation as the respiratory center tries to get excess CO_2 out of the lungs, increased urine formation as the kidneys try to remove excess acids, thirst (to replace urination water loss), drowsiness, headache, and disorientation. The treatment again

depends on the cause; it may involve insulin therapy, intravenous bicarbonate, or hemodialysis. Note carefully that hyperventilation can be a symptom of metabolic acidosis and a cause of respiratory alkalosis, two different conditions requiring very different treatments.

Metabolic Alkalosis

In **metabolic alkalosis**, the body has lost acid in some form, perhaps from prolonged vomiting of the acidic stomach contents, or there has been an ingestion of alkaline substances. Excessive use of sodium bicarbonate (baking soda), for example, a common home remedy for upset stomach, increases the concentration of bicarbonate ions in the blood.

A decrease in acid concentration within the body (from vomiting) or an increase in HCO_3^- levels (from excessive $NaHCO_3$) causes the HCO_3^-/H_2CO_3 ratio to rise above 20:1, and measurable alkalosis is observed. The respiratory center responds to the higher blood pH by slowing the breathing (hypoventilation). Other symptoms may include numbness, tingling, and headache. ▶ Table 25.4 is a summary of causes of acidosis and alkalosis.

metabolic alkalosis A condition of alkalosis resulting from causes other than hyperventilation.

TABLE 25.4 Some Causes of Blood Acid–Base Imbalance

Condition	Causes
Respiratory	
Acidosis: $CO_2 \uparrow pH \downarrow$	Hypoventilation, blockage of diffusion within lungs, respiratory center depressants
Alkalosis: $CO_2 \downarrow pH \uparrow$	Hyperventilation, excitement, trauma
Metabolic	
Acidosis: $H^+ \uparrow pH \downarrow$	Kidney failure, prolonged diarrhea, ketone bodies from diabetes mellitus
Alkalosis: $H^+ \downarrow pH \uparrow$	Kidney disease, prolonged vomiting, excessive intake of baking soda

Case Study Follow-up

A total of 30 million blood components are transfused each year in the United States (2006). The average red blood cell transfusion is approximately 3 pints, resulting in a need of 38,000 blood donations a day. Blood cannot be manufactured and therefore must come from donors. Keeping up with the demand for acceptable (disease-free) blood donations is not guaranteed and the practice of donating is declining among young people. As a result, the cost of blood is steadily rising (American Red Cross, 2011).

Blood is a complex tissue, and making a synthetic substitute that performs all of its functions is not currently possible. The U.S. FDA approves no blood substitute; however, some are used in South Africa and Russia. "Pharming" blood from stem cells gathered from discarded umbilical cord blood is showing some potential. Perfluorocarbon (PFC) or hemoglobin-based oxygen carriers (HBOC) blood substitutes are promising, but still experimental. Many require human donated blood as a starting material, and others use bovine hemoglobin (Lowe 2008).

Cancer patients may require blood transfusions for several reasons, one of which is the cancer itself, if it affects the ability of the body to manufacture blood, or if it causes internal bleeding, as in the case of digestive system cancers. Cancer surgeries are often major operations requiring transfusion. Most chemotherapy and radiation treatments negatively impact the patient's ability to produce blood (ACS, 2010).

Concept Summary

A Comparison of Body Fluids

Most fluids of the body are located in three regions of the body: inside tissue cells (intracellular fluid), outside tissue cells (extracellular fluid), and in blood vessels. Volumetrically, most of the extracellular fluids are of two types—blood and interstitial fluid, the fluid that occupies spaces between cells and moves in the lymph vessels. Other extracellular body fluids that occur in smaller amounts are urine, digestive juices, and cerebrospinal fluid. Chemically, blood (plasma) and interstitial fluid (including lymph) are similar. Intracellular fluid is chemically different from the extracellular fluids.

Objective 1 (Section 25.1), Exercise 25.2

Oxygen and Carbon Dioxide Transport

Nearly all oxygen that is transported from the lungs to tissue cells is transported by the blood in the form of oxyhemoglobin. Most carbon dioxide transported from the cells to the lungs is transported by the blood in the form of bicarbonate ions dissolved in the plasma. Smaller amounts also travel as carbaminohemoglobin and as CO_2 gas dissolved in plasma. The formation of the two hemoglobin compounds and the dissolving of various materials in the plasma are influenced by equilibria related to concentration differences of materials in the blood as it passes through capillaries in the lungs or near tissue cells.

Objective 2 (Section 25.2), Exercise 25.10

Chemical Transport to the Cells

Substances transported by the blood to tissue cells move from the blood, through capillary walls, into the interstitial fluid, then through cell membranes, and finally into the cytoplasm of the cells. Waste products of the cells move in the opposite direction. The movement of fluid through capillary walls is governed by the blood pressure against the capillary walls and by osmotic pressure differences that arise from protein concentration differences between blood and interstitial fluid.

Objective 3 (Section 25.3), Exercise 25.14

The Constituents of Urine

Normal urine is about 96% water and 4% dissolved organic and inorganic wastes. Because urine composition is an excellent indicator of a person's health, urinalysis is a routine procedure in physical checkups.

Objective 4 (Section 25.4), Exercise 25.18

Fluid and Electrolyte Balance

Fluid balance in the body involves a balance between fluid intake and output, and a proper distribution of fluid between the three fluid areas. Fluid and electrolyte balance are interdependent. Water enters the body through food and drink and leaves in the form of urine, water vapor in exhaled air, perspiration, and feces. The amount of fluid in the body is maintained or restored primarily by variations in urine output, which is regulated chiefly by the hormones vasopressin and aldosterone.

Objective 5 (Section 25.5), Exercise 25.22

Acid-Base Balance

Blood pH is normally in the range of 7.35–7.45. Three systems cooperate to maintain the pH in this narrow range. Objective 6 (Section 25.6), Exercise 25.26. Acidosis and alkalosis exist when the blood pH becomes lower or higher, respectively, than these values.

Buffer Control of Blood pH

The blood contains three major buffer systems: the bicarbonate system, the phosphate system, and the plasma protein system. The most important is the bicarbonate system, which consists of a mixture of bicarbonate ions and carbonic acid.

Objective 7 (Section 25.7), Exercise 25.28

Respiratory Control of Blood pH

The respiratory system influences blood pH by regulating the elimination of carbon dioxide and water. Because carbon dioxide and water are produced during the decomposition of carbonic acid, the greater the elimination of carbon dioxide and water from the body, the greater is the elimination of carbonic acid from the blood.

Objective 8 (Section 25.8), Exercise 25.30

Concept Summary (continued)

Urinary Control of Blood pH

The kidneys influence blood pH by varying the amount of hydrogen ions excreted in the urine. When the blood is too acidic, carbonic acid is converted to bicarbonate ions and hydrogen ions. The hydrogen ions are excreted, and the bicarbonate ions enter the blood.

Objective 9 (Section 25.9), Exercise 25.34

Acidosis and Alkalosis

Acidosis and alkalosis can result from metabolic or respiratory causes. Respiratory acidosis and alkalosis are the result of abnormal breathing patterns. Alkalosis is caused by hyperventilation that accompanies hysteria, anxiety, or prolonged crying. Acidosis can result from hypoventilation brought on by such factors as an overdose of depressant narcotics or anesthesia. Metabolic acidosis can result from the metabolic production of acids in the body or the elimination of alkaline materials, as during severe diarrhea. Metabolic alkalosis results from the loss of acid in some form such as the prolonged vomiting of acidic stomach contents or the ingestion of alkaline materials.

Objective 10 (Section 25.10), Exercise 25.38

Key Terms and Concepts

Alkalosis (25.6)
Carbaminohemoglobin (25.2)
Chloride shift (25.2)
Deoxyhemoglobin (hemoglobin) (25.2)
Extracellular fluid (25.1)

Hyperventilation (25.8)
Hypoventilation (25.8)
Interstitial fluid (25.1)
Intracellular fluid (25.1)
Metabolic acidosis (25.10)

Metabolic alkalosis (25.10)
Oxyhemoglobin (25.2)
Plasma (25.1)
Respiratory acidosis (25.10)
Respiratory alkalosis (25.10)

Key Reactions

1.	Formation of oxyhemoglobin (Section 25.2):	$HHb + O_2 \rightleftarrows HbO_2^- + H^+$	Reaction 25.1
2.	Formation of carbaminohemoglobin (Section 25.2):	$HHb + CO_2 \rightleftarrows HHbCO_2$	Reaction 25.2
3.	Decomposition of carbonic acid (Section 25.8):	$H_2CO_3 \rightleftarrows H_2O + CO_2$	Reaction 25.6

Exercises

Even-numbered exercises are answered in Appendix B.

Blue-numbered exercises are more challenging.

A Comparison of Body Fluids (Section 25.1)

25.1 Where is most fluid in the body located? What is it called?

25.2 Which two of the following have nearly the same chemical composition: plasma, intracellular fluid, interstitial fluid?

25.3 In what way does the composition of the two similar fluids in Exercise 25.2 differ?

25.4 Which of the fluids of Exercise 25.2 contains the highest concentration of the following?

 a. protein

 b. K^+

 c. Na^+

 d. HPO_4^{2-}

 e. HCO_3^-

 f. Mg^{2+}

 g. Cl^-

Even-numbered exercises answered in Appendix B.

Blue-numbered exercises are more challenging.

25.5 What is the principal cation found in the following?

 a. blood plasma

 b. interstitial fluid

 c. intracellular fluid

25.6 What is the principal anion in the following?

 a. blood plasma

 b. interstitial fluid

 c. intracellular fluid

25.7 What is the principal type of organic compound found in intracellular fluid?

Oxygen and Carbon Dioxide Transport (Section 25.2)

25.8 Write a reversible chemical equation that shows the reaction of hemoglobin (Hb) with:

 a. oxygen

 b. carbon dioxide

25.9 Hemoglobin exists in several forms—oxyhemoglobin, deoxyhemoglobin, and carbaminohemoglobin. Match each of the following to the type of hemoglobin involved:

 a. Formed when CO_2 combines with hemoglobin

 b. The oxygen-transporting form of hemoglobin

 c. The form of hemoglobin designated as HHb

25.10 What percentages of the total O_2 and CO_2 transported by the blood are in the following forms?

 a. O_2 as dissolved gas in plasma

 b. O_2 as oxyhemoglobin

 c. CO_2 as carbaminohemoglobin

 d. CO_2 as dissolved gas in plasma

 e. CO_2 as bicarbonate ions

25.11 What term is given to the reversible flow of chloride ions across the red blood cell membrane during the oxygen and carbon dioxide transport process?

25.12 Why are large capillary surface areas critical to O_2 and CO_2 transport processes? What driving force causes O_2 to move from lung alveoli into the bloodstream and CO_2 to move from the bloodstream into lung alveoli?

25.13 Write the equilibrium equation representing the reaction between oxygen and hemoglobin. In which direction will the equilibrium shift when the following occurs?

 a. The pH is increased.

 b. The concentration (pressure) of O_2 is increased.

 c. The concentration of CO_2 is increased (see Figure 25.5).

 d. The blood is in a capillary near actively metabolizing tissue cells.

Chemical Transport to the Cells (Section 25.3)

25.14 Which factor, blood pressure or osmotic pressure, has the greater influence on the direction of fluid movement through capillary walls at (a) the venous end of a capillary and (b) the arterial end of a capillary?

25.15 What types of compounds leave the capillaries and enter the interstitial fluid? What types of compounds leave the interstitial fluid and enter the capillaries to be transported away?

The Constituents of Urine (Section 25.4)

25.16 What organic material is normally excreted in the largest amount in urine?

25.17 What cation and anion are normally excreted in the largest amounts in urine?

25.18 List the abnormal constituents of urine.

25.19 Under what circumstances would the presence of a normal constituent of urine be considered abnormal?

Fluid and Electrolyte Balance (Section 25.5)

25.20 List four routes by which water leaves the body.

25.21 What are three sources of water that contribute to the fluid intake of a human body?

25.22 What is the primary way fluid balance is maintained in the body?

25.23 Describe how vasopressin and aldosterone function to maintain fluid levels in the blood.

25.24 Trace the events of the regulation of fluid balance by the thirst mechanism.

Acid–Base Balance (Section 25.6)

25.25 What is the normal pH range of human blood? Outside what pH range will death occur?

25.26 List three systems that cooperate to maintain blood pH in an appropriate narrow range. Which one of these provides the most rapid response to changes in blood pH?

25.27 What is meant by the terms *acidosis* and *alkalosis*?

Buffer Control of Blood pH (Section 25.7)

25.28 List three major buffer systems of the blood.

25.29 Hemoglobin (HHb) is a weak acid that forms the Hb^- anion. Write equations to show how the HHb/Hb^- buffer would react to added H^+ and added OH^-.

Respiratory Control of Blood pH (Section 25.8)

25.30 Describe the respiratory mechanism for controlling blood pH.

25.31 Hyperventilation is a symptom of what type of acid–base imbalance in the body?

25.32 Hypoventilation is a symptom of what type of acid–base imbalance in the body?

Urinary Control of Blood pH (Section 25.9)

25.33 Write a short summary description of the role of the kidneys and urine in the control of blood pH.

25.34 What happens to CO_2 in the blood when the kidneys function to control blood pH?

25.35 What buffer system in the urine usually keeps the urine pH from dropping lower than 6?

25.36 What ionic shift maintains electron charge balance when the kidneys function to increase the pH of blood?

Acidosis and Alkalosis (Section 25.10)

25.37 What is the normal ratio of bicarbonate to carbonic acid in the blood?

25.38 What is the difference between the causes of respiratory acid–base imbalances and metabolic acid–base imbalances in the body?

Even-numbered exercises answered in Appendix B.

Unless otherwise noted all art on this page © Cengage Learning 2014

25.39 What type of acid–base imbalance in the blood is caused by hypoventilation? By hyperventilation?

25.40 What type of acid–base imbalance might develop in an individual who has taken an overdose of a depressant narcotic? In an individual with uncontrolled diabetes mellitus?

25.41 Explain how prolonged vomiting can lead to alkalosis.

Additional Exercises

25.42 An average adult excretes about 25.0 g of urea in his or her urine daily. Assuming both nitrogen atoms of the urea molecule come from the deamination of amino acids (one N atom/amino acid), how many amino acid molecules were deaminated to produce this amount of urea?

$$\underset{\text{urea}}{H_2N-\overset{\overset{\displaystyle O}{\|}}{C}-NH_2}$$

25.43 A person inhales O_2 and exhales CO_2. What is the ultimate use for the O_2 in the cell? Is the O_2 that we inhale incorporated into the CO_2 we exhale? What is the source of the CO_2 we exhale?

25.44 When the body is dehydrated, aldosterone causes the active readsorption of Na^+ ions from the renal tubules into the blood, which causes water to "follow" the Na^+ ions into the blood. Explain what causes this flow of water to occur.

25.45 The body uses the phosphate buffer system shown in the following reaction (a).

$$H^+ + HPO_4^{2-} \rightleftharpoons H_2PO_4^- \text{ (a)}$$

$$H^+ + H_2PO_4^- \rightleftharpoons H_3PO_4 \text{ (b)}$$

Explain why reaction (b) is not used in the human body as a buffer system. (HINT: What are the pKa values for the dissociations of the individual hydrogen ions?)

25.46 Explain how heavy exercise can cause metabolic acidosis.

Allied Health Exam Connection

The following questions are from these sources:

1. *Nursing School Entrance Exam* © 2005, Learning Express, LLC.

2. *McGraw-Hill's Nursing School Entrance Exams* by Thomas A. Evangelist, Tamara B. Orr and Judy Unrein © 2009, The McGraw-Hill Companies, Inc.

3. *NSEE Nursing School Entrance Exams,* 3rd Edition © 2009, Kaplan Publishing.

4. *Cliffs Test Prep: Nursing School Entrance Exams* by Fred N. Grayson © 2004, Wiley Publishing, Inc.

5. *Peterson's Master the Nursing School and Allied Health Entrance Exams,* 18th Edition by Marion F. Gooding © 2008, Peterson's, a Nelnet Company.

25.47 Rank the following in order from least important to most important in removing CO_2 from the body: carbaminohemoglobin, dissolving it in plasma, bicarbonate.

25.48 Movement of respiratory gases into and out of blood is primarily dependent upon the presence of a _____ gradient.

25.49 The most rapid method of pH regulation involves the blood's _____ system.

25.50 Which of the following are normal constituents of urine?

 a. creatinine **e.** sugar

 b. urea **f.** hormones

 c. water **g.** blood

 d. ammonia

25.51 Uncontrolled diabetes mellitus results in _____ acidosis.

25.52 The liquid portion of the blood is called:

 a. serum **c.** plasma

 b. gamma globulin **d.** lymph

25.53 The cation in the highest concentration within extracellular fluid that plays a major role in water distribution is:

 a. sodium **c.** calcium

 b. potassium **d.** magnesium

25.54 Water reabsorption in the collecting duct of the kidneys is controlled by _____ from the posterior pituitary.

 a. oxytocin **c.** epinephrine

 b. ADH **d.** aldosterone

25.55 The hormone most responsible for the renal regulation of sodium is:

 a. thyroxine **c.** glucagon

 b. insulin **d.** aldosterone

25.56 The presence of protein in the urine is called:

 a. polyuria **c.** albuminuria

 b. anuria **c.** hematuria

25.57 Hyperventilation resulting from hysteria may cause:

 a. respiratory acidosis **c.** metabolic acidosis

 b. respiratory alkalosis **d.** metabolic alkalosis

Chemistry for Thought

25.58 Explain why an hysterical individual might develop alkalosis.

25.59 Explain why a person suffering from metabolic acidosis might develop a thirst.

25.60 Ordinary water may be the most effective "sports drink." Explain why this might be true.

25.61 How does the concentration of hemoglobin of someone living in the Himalayas compare with that of someone living at a lower altitude?

25.62 What happens if the amount of H^+ ions in the urine exceeds urine's buffering capacity?

25.63 Aerobic exercise causes your cells to produce CO_2 and H_2O. Why can you dehydrate during aerobic exercise even if you don't perspire?

25.64 What types of food can make urine acidic? What types of food will make it basic?

25.65 Explain how uncontrolled diarrhea can lead to acidosis.

The International System of Measurements

The International System of Units (SI units) was established in 1960 by the International Bureau of Weights and Measures. The system was established in an attempt to streamline the metric system, which included certain traditional units that had historical origins but that were not logically related to other metric units. The International System established fundamental units to represent seven basic physical quantities. These quantities and the fundamental units used to express them are given in Table A.1.

TABLE A.1 Fundamental SI Units

Physical Quantity	SI Unit	Abbreviation
Length	meter	m
Mass	kilogram	kg
Temperature	kelvin	K
Amount of substance	mole	mol
Electrical current	ampere	A
Time	second	s
Luminous intensity	candela	cd

All other SI units are derived from the seven fundamental units. Prefixes are used to indicate multiples or fractions of the fundamental units (Table 1.2). In some cases, it has been found convenient to give derived units specific names. For example, the derived unit for force is kg m/s^2, which has been given the name newton (abbreviated N) in honor of Sir Isaac Newton (1642–1726). Some examples of derived units are given in Table A.2.

TABLE A.2 Examples of Derived SI Units

Physical Quantity	Definition in Fundamental Units	Specific Name	Abbreviation
Volume	m^3 (see NOTE below)	—	—
Force	kg m/s^2	newton	N
Energy	kg m^2/s^2 = N m	joule	J
Power	kg m^2/s^3 = J/s	watt	W
Pressure	kg/m s^2 = N/m^2	pascal	Pa
Electrical charge	A s	coulomb	C
Electrical potential	kg m^2/A s^3 = W/A	volt	V
Electrical resistance	kg m^2/A^2 s^3 = V/A	Ohm	Ω
Frequency	1/s	hertz	Hz

NOTE: The liter (L), a popular volume unit of the metric system, has been redefined in terms of SI units as 1 dm^3 or 1/1000 m^3. It and its fractions (mL, μL, etc.) are still widely used to express volume.

Answers to
Even-Numbered End-of-Chapter Exercises

CHAPTER 1

1.2 Mass is a measurement of the amount of matter in an object. Weight is a measurement of the gravitational force acting on an object.

1.4
a. The distance the ball could be thrown on the moon would be greater. Although the throwing force would be the same, the smaller gravitational force pulling the ball downward would allow the ball to travel farther before hitting the surface of the moon.

b. The rolling distance would be the same in both locations because gravity does not influence rolling motion on a smooth surface.

1.6 The gravitational force is greater the closer an object is to the center of Earth. Thus, a person would weigh more at the poles (closer to the center) and less at the equator.

1.8
a. Physical: Both pieces of the stick are still made of the same substance.

b. Chemical: The smoke is a new substance.

c. Physical: Each smaller piece is still the substance salt.

d. Chemical: The change in color indicates a change in the substances present.

1.10
a. Physical: The state of a substance (solid, liquid, or gas) can be changed without changing the identity of the substance.

b. Chemical: The word *reacts* indicates a chemical change.

c. Physical: Freezing is a physical change, so the temperature at which it occurs is a physical property.

d. Chemical: Because rusting is a chemical change (rust is a different substance from the metal), the ability to rust or not to rust is a chemical property.

e. Physical: Color is a physical property because it can be observed without trying to change the substance into another substance.

1.12
a. Yes: The change in melting point indicates a different substance has been formed. Also, the evolved gas is a different substance.

b. No: It must be different because its melting point is different from that of succinic acid.

c. The succinic acid molecules must be larger because the atoms of the succinic acid were divided between the molecules of the new solid and the molecules of the evolved gas.

d. Heteroatomic: Because the succinic acid changed into two different substances, molecules of succinic acid must contain at least two different kinds of atoms.

1.14 Heteroatomic: Because only a single substance is formed, its molecules must contain at least one atom from each of the two reacting substances.

1.16 Heteroatomic: The molecules of the products hydrogen and oxygen contain hydrogen atoms and oxygen atoms, respectively. The two different kinds of atoms must have come from the water.

1.18
a. A is a compound because compounds are made up of heteroatomic molecules.

b. D is an element because elements are made up of homoatomic molecules.

c. E is a compound because it can be changed into the simpler substances G and J. The simpler substances G and J cannot be classified without conducting further tests on them to see if they can be changed into still other simpler substances.

1.20
a. R cannot be classified as an element or a compound. Even though none of the tests changed it into a simpler substance, all possible tests were not done on it, and some test might exist that would change it.

b. T can be classified as a compound because it was changed into simpler substances.

c. The remaining solid cannot be classified because no tests were done to see if it could be changed into simpler substances.

1.22
a. homogeneous
b. homogeneous
c. heterogeneous
d. heterogeneous
e. homogeneous
f. heterogeneous
g. homogeneous

1.24
a. pure substance
b. solution
e. solution
g. solution

1.26 In a modern society, quantities must be expressed with precision. Goods, services, time, and so on must be clearly expressed as quantities in order for trade, purchases, salaries, and the like to be carried out or determined.

1.28 The units are given in parentheses following the measuring device: clock (hours, minutes, and seconds), bathroom scale (pounds and ounces), ruler (inches or centimeters), kitchen measuring cup (cups, ounces, or milliliters), cooking thermometer

(Fahrenheit or Celsius degrees), fever thermometer (Fahrenheit or Celsius degrees), kitchen measuring spoons (tablespoons, or teaspoons), automobile speedometer (miles per hour or kilometers per hour), directional compass (degrees), tire pressure gauge (pounds per square inch), protractor (degrees).

1.30 **a.** metric

b. metric

c. nonmetric

d. metric

e. nonmetric

f. metric

1.32 **c.** meters

e. liters

1.34 **a.** 1 million microliters

b. 75 thousand watts

c. 15 million hertz

d. 200×10^{-12} meters

1.36 0.240 L, 240 cm^3

1.38 8.8 lb

1.40 **a.** About 3 in.

b. 65 K

c. About 2 kg

1.42 **a.** 0.001 kg, or 1 g

b. About 68 fl oz

c. 333 mg, or about 300 mg

1.44 $97.0°$F in the morning and $99.0°$F at bedtime

1.46 **a.** Incorrect: No zero should precede the first number in the nonexponential number. 2.7×10^{-3} is correct.

b. Correct

c. Incorrect: The decimal is not in the standard position in the nonexponential number. 7.19×10^{-5} is correct.

d. Incorrect: No nonexponential number is given. 1×10^3 is correct.

e. Incorrect: The decimal is not in the standard position in the nonexponential number. 4.05×10^{-4} is correct.

f. Incorrect: No exponent is used, and the decimal is not in the standard position in the nonexponential number. 1.19×10^{-1} is correct.

1.48 **a.** 1.4×10^4

b. 3.65×10^2

c. 2.04×10^{-3}

d. 4.618×10^2

e. 1.00×10^{-3}

f. 9.11×10^2

1.50 1.86×10^5 mi/s; 1.100×10^9 km/h

1.52 $0.000\ 000\ 000\ 000\ 000\ 000\ 000\ 105$

1.54 **a.** 9.0×10^{-5}

b. 1.4×10^7

c. 7.6×10^{-2}

d. 1.9×10^1

e. 2.6×10^{12}

1.56 **a.** $(1.44 \times 10^2)(8.76 \times 10^{-2}) = 1.26 \times 10^1$

b. $(7.51 \times 10^2)(1.06 \times 10^2) = 7.96 \times 10^4$

c. $(4.22 \times 10^{-2})(1.19 \times 10^{-3}) = 5.02 \times 10^{-5}$

d. $(1.28000 \times 10^5)(3.16 \times 10^{-5}) = 4.04 \times 10^0$

1.58 **a.** 2.6×10^{-5}

b. 2.2×10^2

c. 6.4×10^{-4}

d. 7.25×10^{-4}

e. 3.1×10^{-2}

1.60 **a.** 1.7×10^{-1}

b. 1.0×10^{-9}

c. 2.6×10^6

d. 2.3×10^0

e. 1.5×10^7

1.62 **a.** 0.01 cm

b. 0.01 mm

c. $0.1°$

d. 0.1 lb/in.2

1.64 **a.** 6.00 mL

b. $37.0°$C

c. 9.00 s

d. $15.5°$

1.66 **a.** Measured: 5.06 lb; exact: 16 potatoes; 0.316 lb/potato

b. Measured: the individual percentages; exact: the 5 players; 71.34%/player. Note that the sum of the five percentages has four significant figures, so the calculated average must have four.

1.68 **a.** 3

b. 3

c. 4

d. 2

e. 4

f. 5

1.70 **a.** 5.2

b. 0.104

c. 0.518

d. 1.0×10^2

e. 2.52×10^{-18}

1.72 **a.** 6.2

b. 230

c. 0.589

d. 0.58

e. 27.75

f. 21.64

1.74 a. 4.60×10^{-3}

 b. 2.208

 c. 2.65

 d. -13

 e. 3

 f. 0.81

1.76 a. Black rectangle: Area = 124.8 cm^2; perimeter = 44.80 cm

 Red rectangle: Area = 48.9 cm^2; perimeter = 45.24 cm

 Green rectangle: Area = 8.11 cm^2; perimeter = 11.46 cm

 Orange rectangle: Area = 9.0 cm^2; perimeter = 27.80 cm

 b. Black rectangle: Area = 0.01248 m^2; perimeter = 0.4480 m

 Red rectangle: Area = 0.00489 m^2; perimeter = 0.4524 m

 Green rectangle: Area = 0.000811 m^2; perimeter = 0.1146 m

 Orange rectangle: Area = 0.00090 m^2; perimeter = 0.2780 m

 c. No

1.78 a. $\dfrac{0.015 \text{ grain}}{1 \text{ mg}}$

 b. $\dfrac{0.0338 \text{ fl oz}}{1 \text{ mL}}$

 c. $\dfrac{1 \text{ L}}{1.057 \text{ qt}}$

 d. $\dfrac{1 \text{ m}}{1.094 \text{ yd}}$

1.80 The factor is $\dfrac{1 \text{ km}}{0.621 \text{ mi}}$. The race is about 42 km long.

1.82 1.06 cups or 1 cup

1.84 39.6 lb; your baggage is not overweight.

1.86 1.31 g/L

1.88 $25.73/$467.80 $\times$ 100 = 5.500%

1.90 71%

1.92 IgG = 75.09%; IgA = 16.23%; IgM = 7.58%; IgD = 1.10%; IgE = 0.008%

1.94 a. 0.792 g/mL

 b. 1.03 g/mL

 c. 1.98 g/L

 d. 8.90 g/cm^3

1.96 Volume = 63.0 cm^3; density = 11.4 g/cm^3

1.98 380 mL

1.100 a. 4.5×10^6 mm

 b. 6.0×10^3 g

 c. 9.86×10^{12} km

 d. 1.91×10^2 mg

 e. 5.0×10^{-6} mg

1.102 54 days

1.104 9.5×10^2 mg

1.106 b and d

1.108 b

1.110 d

1.112 d

1.114 b

1.116 d

1.118 c

1.120 b

1.122 d

1.124 c

1.126 d

CHAPTER 2

2.2 a.

 b.

 c.

 d.

2.4 a. H_2O

 b. H_2O_2

 c. H_2SO_4

 d. C_2H_6O

2.6 a. One carbon (C), four hydrogen (H)

 b. One hydrogen (H), one chlorine (Cl), four oxygen (O)

 c. One carbon (C), five hydrogen (H), one nitrogen (N)

 d. Three carbon (C), eight hydrogen (H)

2.8 a. The two hydrogen atoms should be denoted by a subscript: H_2S

 b. The letter L of chlorine should be lowercase: $HClO_2$

 c. The coefficient 2 should not be used to indicate the number of atoms in the molecule. Subscripts should be used instead: H_2N_4

 d. The numbers in the formula should be written as subscripts: C_2H_6

2.10 a. Charge = 4+; mass = 9 u

 b. Charge = 9+; mass = 19 u

 c. Charge = 20+; mass = 43 u

 d. Charge = 47+; mass = 107 u

2.12 a. 4

 b. 9

 c. 20

 d. 47

2.14 a. 19 electrons, 19 protons

 b. 48 electrons, 48 protons

 c. 51 electrons, 51 protons

2.16 **a.** 16 protons, 18 neutrons, 16 electrons

 b. 40 protons, 51 neutrons, 40 electrons

 c. 54 protons, 77 neutrons, 54 electrons

2.18 **a.** $^{28}_{14}Si$

 b. $^{40}_{18}Ar$

 c. $^{88}_{38}Sr$

2.20 **a.** Atomic number = 4; mass number = 9; 9_4Be

 b. Atomic number = 9; mass number = 19; $^{19}_9F$

 c. Atomic number = 20; mass number = 43; $^{43}_{20}Ca$

 d. Atomic number = 47; mass number = 107; $^{107}_{47}Ag$

2.22 **a.** $^{37}_{17}Cl$

 b. $^{65}_{29}Cu$

 c. $^{66}_{30}Zn$

2.24 Atomic weights rounded to nearest whole number give He = 4.0 u and C = 12 u. Three He total 12 u, which will balance one C, which also totals 12 u.

2.26 Ca, calcium

2.28 N, nitrogen

2.30 **a.** 80.06 u

 b. 92.03 u

 c. 98.06 u

 d. 28.02 u

 e. 44.03 u

2.32 Ethylene, C_2H_4

2.34 $y = 3$

2.36 **a.** 14 neutrons

 b. 27.0 u

2.38 Calculated value = 10.81 u

 Periodic table value = 10.81 u

2.40 Calculated value = 63.55 u

 Periodic table value = 63.55 u

2.42 1.90 g F

2.44 **a.** 1 mol Si atoms = 6.02×10^{23} Si atoms

 6.02×10^{23} Si atoms = 28.1 g Si

 1 mol Si atoms = 28.1 g Si

 b. 1 mol Ca atoms = 6.02×10^{23} Ca atoms

 6.02×10^{23} Ca atoms = 40.1 g Ca

 1 mol Ca atoms = 40.1 g Ca

 c. 1 mol Ar atoms = 6.02×10^{23} Ar atoms

 6.02×10^{23} Ar atoms = 40.0 g Ar

 1 mol Ar atoms = 40.0 g Ar

2.46 **a.** 35.1 g Si

 b. 6.66×10^{-23} g Ca

 c. 3.09×10^{23} Ar atoms

2.48 Molecular weight BF_3 = 67.8 u

 Molecular weight H_2S = 34.1 u

 0.68 g BF_3

2.50 **a.** 1. 2 C_6H_6 molecules contain 12 C atoms and 12 H atoms.

 2. 10 C_6H_6 molecules contain 60 C atoms and 60 H atoms.

 3. 100 C_6H_6 molecules contain 600 C atoms and 600 H atoms.

 4. 6.02×10^{23} C_6H_6 molecules contain 36.12×10^{23} C atoms and 36.12×10^{23} H atoms.

 5. 1 mol of C_6H_6 molecules contains 6 mol of C atoms and 6 mol of H atoms.

 6. 78.1 g of C_6H_6 contains 72.0 g of C and 6.1 g of H.

 b. 1. 2 NO_2 molecules contain 2 N atoms and 4 O atoms.

 2. 10 NO_2 molecules contain 10 N atoms and 20 O atoms.

 3. 100 NO_2 molecules contain 100 N atoms and 200 O atoms.

 4. 6.02×10^{23} NO_2 molecules contain 6.02×10^{23} N atoms and 12.04×10^{23} O atoms.

 5. 1 mol of NO_2 molecules contains 1 mol of N atoms and 2 mol of O atoms.

 6. 46.0 g of NO_2 contains 14.0 g of N and 32.0 g of O.

 c. 1. 2 HCl molecules contain 2 H atoms and 2 Cl atoms.

 2. 10 HCl molecules contain 10 H atoms and 10 Cl atoms.

 3. 100 HCl molecules contain 100 H atoms and 100 Cl atoms.

 4. 6.02×10^{23} HCl molecules contain 6.02×10^{23} H atoms and 6.02×10^{23} Cl atoms.

 5. 1 mol of HCl molecules contains 1 mol of H atoms and 1 mol of Cl atoms.

 6. 36.5 g of HCl contains 1.01 g of H and 35.5 g of Cl.

2.52 **a.** 4.5 mol H atoms

 b. 6.00×10^{23} O atoms

 c. 97.3% Cl

2.54 34.6 g C_2H_6O

2.56 In CH_4, mass % H = 25.3%.

 In C_2H_6, mass % H = 20.1%.

2.58 Statements 4–6 are:

 4. 6.02×10^{23} H_3PO_4 molecules contain 18.06×10^{23} H atoms, 6.02×10^{23} P atoms, and 24.08×10^{23} O atoms.

 5. 1 mol of H_3PO_4 molecules contains 3 mol of H atoms, 1 mol of P atoms, and 4 mol of O atoms.

 6. 98.0 g of H_3PO_4 contains 3.03 g of H, 31.0 g of P, and 64.0 g of O.

 a. 1.45 g of H

 b. 5.00 mol of O atoms

 c. 8.42×10^{21} P atoms

2.60 Magnetite = 72.36% Fe; hematite = 69.94% Fe. Magnetite has the higher % Fe by mass.

2.62 U-238 would have a greater density because each U-238 nucleus would contain 3 more neutrons than a U-235 nucleus and thus have a greater mass. However, the size (volume) of each atom (measured from the nucleus to the outer electrons) would be the same, so one cm^3 of each isotope would contain the same number of atoms.

2.64 2.32×10^{-23} g

2.66 The density would increase tremendously because many more of the smaller atoms (measured from the nucleus to the outer electrons) would fit into a cm^3. Each of the smaller atoms would have the same mass as the larger atoms, so the density (mass/volume) would be much greater.

2.68 b

2.70 a

2.72 b

2.74 b

2.76 a

2.78 d

2.80 b

2.82 c

2.84 a

2.86 b

CHAPTER 3

3.2 **a.** Group VA (15), period 5

 b. Group IIB (12), period 5

 c. Group IIIA (13), period 4

 d. Group IVB (4), period 5

3.4 **a.** Kr, krypton

 b. Sn, tin

 c. Mo, molybdenum

 d. Nd, neodymium

3.6 **a.** 4

 b. 10

 c. 18

3.8 **a.** period

 b. period

 c. group

 d. group

3.10 protons

3.12 **a.** 2

 b. 6

 c. 8

3.14 Four orbitals; one $2s$, and three $2p$.

3.16 Seven orbitals in the subshell can contain a maximum of 14 electrons.

3.18 **a.** 8

 b. 5

 c. 4

 d. 4

3.20 Cesium, Cs, has chemical properties most like sodium, Na. Both elements have one valence-shell electron.

3.22 An ore deposit that contained copper might also be expected to contain gold and silver because all three elements belong to group IB (11) of the periodic table and thus have similar chemical properties.

3.24 **a.** $1s^22s^22p^63s^23p^64s^23d^{10}4p^65s^1$; one electron is unpaired.

 b. $1s^22s^22p^63s^23p^2$; two electrons are unpaired.

 c. $1s^22s^22p^63s^23p^64s^23d^2$; two electrons are unpaired.

 d. $1s^22s^22p^63s^23p^6$; no electrons are unpaired.

3.26 **a.** $1s^22s^22p^63s^23p^64s^1$; 7 s electrons.

 b. $1s^22s^22p^63s^23p^1$; 1 unpaired electron.

 c. $1s^22s^22p^63s^2$; 4 subshells are filled.

3.28 **a.** C, carbon

 b. Na, sodium

 c. Si, silicon, and S, sulfur

 d. Nb, niobium

 e. V, vanadium, and Co, cobalt

3.30 **a.** $[Ar]4s^23d^{10}4p^3$

 b. $[Ar]4s^23d^5$

 c. $[Ne]3s^23p^2$

 d. $[Kr]5s^24d^{10}5p^5$

3.32 Na: $[Ne]3s^1$

 Mg: $[Ne]3s^2$

 Al: $[Ne]3s^23p^1$

 Si: $[Ne]3s^23p^2$

 P: $[Ne]3s^23p^3$

 S: $[Ne]3s^23p^4$

 Cl: $[Ne]3s^23p^5$

 Ar: $[Ne]3s^23p^6$

3.34 **a.** p area

 b. d area

 c. f area

 d. s area

3.36 **a.** transition

 b. representative

 c. inner-transition

 d. noble gas

 e. representative

3.38 **a.** nonmetal

 b. metal

 c. metalloid

 d. metalloid

 e. metal

3.40 **a.** K

 b. Bi

 c. Sr

 d. Sn

3.42 **a.** Ga

 b. Sb

c. C

d. Te

3.44 a. Si

b. Ba

c. Br

d. Ca

3.46 The chemical properties would be the same because chemical properties depend on the number of valence electrons in the atom. The number of valence electrons in isotopes of the same element is identical.

3.48 8.0 mg

3.50 The element has an atomic weight of 40.0, and so is calcium (Ca). It is a representative element and will conduct electricity because it is a metal.

3.52 d

3.54 d

3.56 a

3.58 b

3.60 b

3.62 b

3.64 d

3.66 d

3.68 a

3.70 b

CHAPTER 4

4.2 a. $:\ddot{\underset{.}{I}}\cdot$

b. $Sr\cdot$

c. $\cdot\dot{Sn}\cdot$

d. $:\ddot{\underset{.}{S}}\cdot$

4.4 a. $[Kr]\,5s^2 4d^{10}5p^2$

b. $[Xe]\,6s^1$

c. $[Kr]\,5s^2 4d^{10}5p^1$

d. $[Kr]\,5s^2$

4.6 a. $\cdot\dot{Sn}\cdot$

b. $Cs\cdot$

c. $\dot{In}\cdot$

d. $Sr\cdot$

4.8 a. $\dot{E}\cdot$

b. $\cdot\dot{\underset{.}{E}}:$

4.10 a. Add 4 or lose 14

b. Add 31 or lose 1

c. Add 5 or lose 13

d. Add 16 or lose 2

4.12 a. Lose 1: $Cs \rightarrow Cs^+ + e^-$

b. Add 2: $O + 2e^- \rightarrow O^{2-}$

c. Add 3: $N + 3e^- \rightarrow N^{3-}$

d. Add 1: $I + e^- \rightarrow I^-$

4.14 a. P^{3-}

b. Sr^{2+}

c. I^-

4.16 a. sulfur, S

b. aluminum, Al

c. sodium, Na

d. chlorine, Cl

4.18 a. argon, Ar

b. argon, Ar

c. krypton, Kr

d. xenon, Xe

4.20 a. $Ca \rightarrow Ca^{2+} + 2e^-$; $Cl + e^- \rightarrow Cl^-$
Formula is $CaCl_2$.

b. $Li \rightarrow Li^+ + e^-$; $Br + e^- \rightarrow Br^-$
Formula is LiBr.

c. $Mg \rightarrow Mg^{2+} + 2e^-$; $S + 2e^- \rightarrow S^{2-}$
Formula is MgS.

4.22 a. BaSe

b. Ba_3P_2

c. BaI_2

d. Ba_3As_2

4.24 a. binary

b. binary

c. not binary

d. not binary

e. binary

4.26 a. lithium ion

b. magnesium ion

c. barium ion

d. cesium ion

4.28 a. bromide ion

b. oxide ion

c. phosphide ion

d. telluride ion

4.30 a. strontium sulfide

b. calcium fluoride

c. barium chloride

d. lithium oxide

e. magnesium oxide

4.32 a. lead (II) oxide and lead (IV) oxide

b. copper (I) chloride and copper (II) chloride

c. gold (I) sulfide and gold (III) sulfide

d. cobalt (II) oxide and cobalt (III) oxide

4.34 a. plumbous oxide and plumbic oxide

b. cuprous chloride and cupric chloride

c. aurous sulfide and auric sulfide

d. cobaltous oxide and cobaltic oxide

4.36 a. PbO_2

b. $CoCl_2$

c. CuS

d. NiN

e. Pt_3P_2

4.38 a. 102.9 u

b. 78.1 u

c. 159.2 u

d. 34.8 u

4.40 a. Na^+ and Br^-

b. Ca^{2+} and F^-

c. Cu^+ and S^{2-}

d. Li^+ and N^{3-}

4.42 a. 22.99 g of Na^+ and 79.90 g of Br^-

b. 40.08 g of Ca^{2+} and 38.00 g of F^-

c. 127.10 g of Cu^+ and 32.06 g of S^{2-}

d. 20.82 g of Li^+ and 14.01 g of N^{3-}

4.44 a. 6.02×10^{23} Na^+ ions and 6.02×10^{23} Br^- ions

b. 6.02×10^{23} Ca^{2+} ions and 12.04×10^{23} F^- ions

c. 12.04×10^{23} Cu^+ ions and 6.02×10^{23} S^{2-} ions

d. 18.06×10^{23} Li^+ ions and 6.02×10^{23} N^{3-} ions

4.46

4.48

a. $H:\!\ddot{C}\!:\!H$ or $H\!-\!\overset{\displaystyle H}{\underset{\displaystyle H}{C}}\!-\!H$

b. $:\!\ddot{O}\!::\!C\!::\!\ddot{O}\!:$ or $O\!=\!C\!=\!O$

c. $H:\!\ddot{S}\!e\!:\!H$ or $H\!-\!Se\!-\!H$

d. $H:\!\ddot{N}\!:\!H$ or $H\!-\!\underset{\displaystyle H}{N}\!-\!H$

4.50 a. $\left[\, H:\!\overset{\displaystyle H}{\underset{\displaystyle \ddot{H}}{N}}\!:\!H \,\right]^{+}$

b. $\left[\, :\!\ddot{O}\!:\!\overset{\displaystyle :\ddot{O}:}{\underset{\displaystyle :\ddot{O}:}{P}}\!:\!\ddot{O}\!: \,\right]^{3-}$

c. $\left[\, :\!\ddot{O}\!:\!\overset{\displaystyle :\ddot{O}:}{S}\!:\!\ddot{O}\!: \,\right]^{2-}$

4.52 a. $H:\!\ddot{S}\!:\!H$ Bent

b. $:\!\ddot{C}\!l\!:\!\overset{\displaystyle }{\underset{\displaystyle :\ddot{C}l:}{P}}\!:\!\ddot{C}\!l\!:$ Triangular pyramid with P at the top

c. $:\!\ddot{F}\!:\!\ddot{O}\!:\!\ddot{F}\!:$ Bent

d. $:\!\ddot{F}\!:\!\overset{\displaystyle :\ddot{F}:}{\underset{\displaystyle :\ddot{F}:}{S}}\!n\!:\!\ddot{F}\!:$ Tetrahedral with Sn in center

4.54 a. $\left[:\!\ddot{O}\!:\!N\!::\!\ddot{O}\!: \right]^{-}$ Bent

b. $\left[:\!\ddot{O}\!:\!\overset{\displaystyle }{\underset{\displaystyle :\ddot{O}:}{C}}\!l\!:\!\ddot{O}\!: \right]^{-}$ Triangular pyramid with Cl at the top

c. $\left[:\!\ddot{O}\!:\!\overset{\displaystyle }{\underset{\displaystyle :\ddot{O}:}{C}}\!::\!\ddot{O}\!: \right]^{2-}$ Flat triangle with C in the center

d. $\left[H:\!\overset{\displaystyle }{\underset{\displaystyle H}{\ddot{O}}}\!:\!H \right]^{+}$ Triangular pyramid with O at the top

4.56 a. $\overset{\delta^+}{H}\!-\!\overset{\delta^-}{I}$

b. $\overset{\delta^{2+}}{S}\!=\!\overset{\delta^-}{O}$, $\overset{\delta^-}{O}$

c. Nonpolarized $O\!-\!O\!\!\diagdown\!\!_O$

4.58 a. polar covalent

b. polar covalent

c. nonpolar covalent

d. polar covalent

e. ionic

4.60 a. polar

b. polar

c. nonpolar

4.62 a. polar covalent

b. polar covalent

c. nonpolar covalent

4.64 a. Polar $\overset{\delta^+}{C}\!\equiv\!\overset{\delta^-}{O}$

b. Polar $\overset{\delta^+}{H}\!-\!\overset{\delta^{2-}}{S}\!e\!\diagdown\!\!_{H^{\delta^+}}$

c. Nonpolar $\overset{I^{\delta^-}}{\underset{\delta^-}{\diagup}}\!Al^{\delta^{3+}}\!\!\diagdown\!\!_{I^{\delta^-}}$, $\overset{}{I}$

4.66 a. phosphorus trichloride

b. dinitrogen pentoxide

c. carbon tetrachloride

d. boron trifluoride

e. carbon disulfide

4.68 a. ClO_2

b. N_2O

c. SO_2

d. CCl_4

4.70 a. $Ca(NO_2)_2$, calcium nitrite

b. $Mg(ClO)_2$, magnesium hypochlorite

c. $Cs_2Cr_2O_7$, cesium dichromate

d. K_2SO_3, potassium sulfite

4.72 a. $Ba(OH)_2$

b. $MgSO_3$

c. $CaCO_3$

d. $(NH_4)_2SO_4$

e. $LiHCO_3$

4.74 a. M_2SO_3

b. $MC_2H_3O_2$

c. MCr_2O_7

d. MPO_4

e. $M(NO_3)_3$

4.76 The stronger the attractive forces between molecules, the higher the melting and boiling points. Thus, we can conclude that the forces attracting dimethyl ether molecules to one another are weaker than the forces attracting ethyl alcohol molecules to one another. Because both compounds are covalently bonded, it is likely that the attractive forces are polar forces, and we might conclude that ethyl alcohol is more polar than dimethyl ether.

4.78 The predominant forces that exist between molecules of noble gases are dispersion forces because noble gas molecules are nonpolar. Dispersion forces increase with increasing mass of the particles involved, so the boiling points of the noble gases would increase in the order of He, Ne, Ar, Kr, Xe, and Rn.

4.80 The relatively high melting point indicates that it is unlikely that weak dispersion forces are the predominant forces present. Dipolar forces are also quite weak and therefore are also un-likely to be the forces present.

4.82 NH_3

$$H-\overset{\overset{\displaystyle H}{|}}{N}-H\cdots\overset{}{N}-H$$

with H below each N

4.84 8.06 g

4.86 N_2O, covalent, dinitrogen monoxide

4.88 a

4.90 a

4.92 c

4.94 b

4.96 b

4.98 c

4.100 c

4.102 a

4.104 a

4.106 b

CHAPTER 5

5.2

	Reactants	Products
a.	H_2, Cl_2	HCl
b.	$KClO_3$	KCl, O_2
c.	magnesium oxide, carbon	magnesium, carbon monoxide
d.	ethane, oxygen	carbon dioxide, water

5.4 a. Not consistent: The number of O atoms is not the same on both sides.

b. Consistent

c. Not consistent: The masses of reactants and products are not equal.

d. Consistent

5.6

	Left side	Right side	Classification
a.	1Ag, 1Cu, 2N, 6O	1Ag, 1Cu, 1N, 3O	Unbalanced
b.	4N, 8O	4N, 8O	Balanced
c.	1Mg, 2O	2Mg, 2O	Unbalanced
d.	4H, 1S, 6O, 1Ca	4H, 1S, 6O, 1Ca	Balanced

5.8 a. $2KClO_3(s) \rightarrow 2KCl(s) + 3O_2(g)$

b. $2C_2H_6(g) + 7O_2(g) \rightarrow 4CO_2(g) + 6H_2O(\ell)$

c. $2N_2(g) + 5O_2(g) \rightarrow 2N_2O_5(g)$

d. $MgCl_2(s) + H_2O(g) \rightarrow MgO(s) + 2HCl(g)$

e. $CaH_2(s) + 2H_2O(\ell) \rightarrow Ca(OH)_2(s) + 2H_2(g)$

f. $2Al(s) + Fe_2O_3(s) \rightarrow Al_2O_3(s) + 2Fe(s)$

g. $2Al(s) + 3Br_2(g) \rightarrow 2AlBr_3(s)$

h. $Hg_2(NO_3)_2(aq) + 2NaCl(aq) \rightarrow$
$$Hg_2Cl_2(s) + 2NaNO_3(aq)$$

5.10 a. $+1$

b. $+3$

c. 0

d. $+1$

e. $+3$

f. $+5$

5.12 a. Cr ($+6$)

b. S ($+2$)

c. N ($+5$)

d. P ($+5$)

e. Cl ($+7$)

f. Cl ($+3$)

5.14 **a.** oxidized

b. neither

c. reduced

d. oxidized

e. oxidized

5.16 **a.** $2Cu(s) + O_2(g) \rightarrow 2CuO(s)$
$\qquad\quad 0 \qquad\; 0 \qquad\qquad +2\; -2$

Oxidizing agent: O_2

Reducing agent: Cu

b. $Cl_2(g) + 2KI(aq) \rightarrow 2KCl(aq) + I_2(aq)$
$\quad\;\; 0 \qquad\;\; +1\; -1 \qquad\;\; +1\; -1 \qquad\;\; 0$

Oxidizing agent: Cl_2

Reducing agent: KI (I)

c. $3MnO_2(s) + 4Al(s) \rightarrow 2Al_2O_3(s) + 3Mn(s)$
$\quad\;\; +4\; -2 \qquad\;\; 0 \qquad\qquad +3\; -2 \qquad\;\; 0$

Oxidizing agent: MnO_2 (Mn)

Reducing agent: Al

d. $2H^+(aq) + 3SO_3^{2-}(aq) + 2NO_3^-(aq) \rightarrow$
$\quad\;\; +1 \qquad\qquad +4\; -2 \qquad\;\; +5\; -2$
$\qquad\qquad\qquad 2NO(g) + H_2O(\ell) + 3SO_4^{2-}(aq)$
$\qquad\qquad\qquad\;\; +2\; -2 \qquad +1\; -2 \qquad\;\; +6\; -2$

Oxidizing agent: NO_3^- (N)

Reducing agent: SO_3^{2-} (S)

e. $Mg(s) + 2HCl(aq) \rightarrow MgCl_2(aq) + H_2(g)$
$\quad\;\; 0 \qquad\;\; +1\; -1 \qquad\;\; +2\; -1 \qquad\;\; 0$

Oxidizing agent: HCl (H^+)

Reducing agent: Mg

f. $4NO_2(g) + O_2(g) \rightarrow 2N_2O_5(g)$
$\quad\;\; +4\; -2 \qquad\; 0 \qquad\;\; +5\; -2$

Oxidizing agent: O_2

Reducing agent: NO_2 (N)

5.18 Oxidizing agent: NaOH (H)

Reducing agent: Al

5.20 **a.** Nonredox, decomposition

b. Redox, single replacement

c. Nonredox, double replacement

d. Nonredox, combination

e. Redox, combination

f. Redox, combination

5.22 Nonredox, decomposition

5.24 Redox

5.26 Redox

5.28 **a.** Li^+, NO_3^-

b. Na^+, HPO_4^{2-}

c. Ca^{2+}, ClO_3^-

d. K^+, OH^-

e. Mg^{2+}, Br^-

f. NH_4^+, SO_4^{2-}

5.30 **a.** Total ionic: $SO_2(aq) + H_2O(\ell) \rightarrow 2H^+(aq) + SO_3^{2-}(aq)$

Spectator ions: none

Net ionic: $SO_2(aq) + H_2O(\ell) \rightarrow 2H^+(aq) + SO_3^{2-}(aq)$

b. Total ionic: $Cu^{2+}(aq) + SO_4^{2-}(aq) + Zn(s) \rightarrow$
$\qquad\qquad\qquad Cu(s) + Zn^{2+}(aq) + SO_4^{2-}(aq)$

Spectator ions: SO_4^{2-}

Net ionic: $Cu^{2+}(aq) + Zn(s) \rightarrow Cu(s) + Zn^{2+}(aq)$

c. Total ionic:
$2K^+(aq) + 2Br^-(aq) + 4H^+(aq) + 2SO_4^{2-}(aq) \rightarrow$
$Br_2(aq) + SO_2(aq) + 2K^+(aq) + SO_4^{2-}(aq) + 2H_2O(\ell)$

Spectator ions: K^+, one SO_4^{2-}

Net ionic: $2Br^-(aq) + 4H^+(aq) + SO_4^{2-}(aq) \rightarrow$
$\qquad\qquad\qquad Br_2(aq) + SO_2(aq) + 2H_2O(\ell)$

d. Total ionic:
$Ag^+(aq) + NO_3^-(aq) + Na^+(aq) + OH^-(aq) \rightarrow$
$\qquad\qquad\qquad AgOH(s) + Na^+(aq) + NO_3^-(aq)$

Spectator ions: Na^+, NO_3^-

Net ionic: $Ag^+(aq) + OH^-(aq) \rightarrow AgOH(s)$

e. Total ionic: $BaCO_3(s) + 2H^+(aq) + 2NO_3^-(aq) \rightarrow$
$\qquad\qquad Ba^{2+}(aq) + 2NO_3^-(aq) + CO_2(g) + H_2O(\ell)$

Spectator ions: NO_3^-

Net ionic:
$BaCO_3(s) + 2H^+(aq) \rightarrow Ba^{2+}(aq) + CO_2(g) + H_2O(\ell)$

f. Total ionic:
$N_2O_5(aq) + H_2O(\ell) \rightarrow 2H^+(aq) + 2NO_3^-(aq)$

Spectator ions: none

Net ionic: $N_2O_5(aq) + H_2O(\ell) \rightarrow 2H^+(aq) + 2NO_3^-(aq)$

5.32 **a.** $H^+(aq) + NO_3^-(aq) + K^+(aq) + OH^-(aq) \rightarrow$
$\qquad\qquad\qquad K^+(aq) + NO_3^-(aq) + H_2O(\ell)$

Spectator ions: K^+, NO_3^-

Net ionic: $H^+(aq) + OH^-(aq) \rightarrow H_2O(\ell)$

b. $3H^+(aq) + PO_4^{3-}(aq) + 3NH_4^+(aq) + 3OH^-(aq) \rightarrow$
$\qquad\qquad\qquad 3NH_4^+(aq) + PO_4^{3-}(aq) + 3H_2O(\ell)$

Spectator ions: NH_4^+, PO_4^{3-}

Net ionic: $3H^+(aq) + 3OH^-(aq) \rightarrow 3H_2O(\ell)$

c. $H^+(aq) + I^-(aq) + Na^+(aq) + OH^-(aq) \rightarrow$
$\qquad\qquad\qquad Na^+(aq) + I^-(aq) + H_2O(\ell)$

Spectator ions: Na^+, I^-

Net ionic: $H^+(aq) + OH^-(aq) \rightarrow H_2O(\ell)$
In every net ionic reaction, H^+ reacts with OH^- to form H_2O

5.34 Exothermic: Heat is a product of the reaction.

5.36 The insulation around the ice slows its rate of melting by preventing it from absorbing heat. However, this prevents the ice from performing its cooling function in the cooler. For the cooler to work properly, heat must move from the warmer food to the cooler ice, where it is absorbed as the ice melts.

5.38 **a.** $S(s) + O_2(g) \rightarrow SO_2(g)$

 2. $1\text{ mol S} + 1\text{ mol } O_2 \rightarrow 1\text{ mol } SO_2$

 3. 6.02×10^{23} S atoms $+ 6.02 \times 10^{23}$ O_2 molecules $\rightarrow$ 6.02×10^{23} SO_2 molecules

 4. $32.06\text{ g S} + 32.00\text{ g } O_2 \rightarrow 64.06\text{ g } SO_2$

 b. $Sr(s) + 2H_2O(\ell) \rightarrow Sr(OH)_2(s) + H_2(g)$

 2. $1\text{ mol Sr} + 2\text{ mol } H_2O \rightarrow 1\text{ mol Sr(OH)}_2 + 1\text{ mol } H_2$

 3. 6.02×10^{23} Sr atoms $+ 12.04 \times 10^{23}$ H_2O molecules $\rightarrow 6.02 \times 10^{23}$ $Sr(OH)_2$ molecules $+ 6.02 \times 10^{23}$ H_2 molecules

 4. $87.62\text{ g Sr} + 36.03\text{ g } H_2O \rightarrow 121.64\text{ g Sr(OH)}_2 + 2.02\text{ g } H_2$

 c. $2H_2S(g) + 3O_2(g) \rightarrow 2H_2O(g) + 2SO_2(g)$

 2. $2\text{ mol } H_2S + 3\text{ mol } O_2 \rightarrow 2\text{ mol } H_2O + 2\text{ mol SO2}$

 3. 12.04×10^{23} H_2S molecules $+ 18.06 \times 10^{23}$ O_2 molecules $\rightarrow 12.04 \times 10^{23}$ H_2O molecules $+ 12.04 \times 10^{23}$ SO_2 molecules

 4. $68.15\text{ g } H_2S + 96.00\text{ g } O_2 \rightarrow 36.03\text{ g } H_2O + 128.12\text{ g } SO_2$

 d. $4NH_3(g) + 5O_2(g) \rightarrow 4NO(g) + 6H_2O(g)$

 2. $4\text{ mol } NH_3 + 5\text{ mol } O_2 \rightarrow 4\text{ mol NO} + 6\text{ mol } H_2O$

 3. 24.08×10^{23} NH_3 molecules $+ 30.10 \times 10^{23}$ O_2 molecules $\rightarrow 24.08 \times 10^{23}$ NO molecules $+ 36.12 \times 10^{23}$ H_2O molecules

 4. $68.14\text{ g } NH_3 + 160.00\text{ g } O_2 \rightarrow 120.04\text{ g NO} + 108.10\text{ g } H_2O$

 e. $CaO(s) + 3C(s) \rightarrow CaC_2(s) + CO(g)$

 2. $1\text{ mol CaO} + 3\text{ mol C} \rightarrow 1\text{ mol } CaC_2 + 1\text{ mol CO}$

 3. 6.02×10^{23} CaO molecules $+ 18.06 \times 10^{23}$ C atoms $\rightarrow 6.02 \times 10^{23}$ CaC_2 molecules $+ 6.02 \times 10^{23}$ CO molecules

 4. $56.08\text{ g CaO} + 36.03\text{ g C} \rightarrow 64.10\text{ g } CaC_2 + 28.01\text{ g CO}$

5.40 $2SO_2(g) + O_2(g) \rightarrow 2SO_3(g)$

 2. $2\text{ mol } SO_2 + 1\text{ mol } O_2 \rightarrow 2\text{ mol } SO_3$

 3. 12.0×10^{23} SO_2 molecules $+ 6.02 \times 10^{23}$ O_2 molecules $\rightarrow 12.0 \times 10^{23}$ SO_3 molecules

 4. $128\text{ g } SO_2 + 32.0\text{ g } O_2 \rightarrow 160\text{ g } SO_3$

Factors:

$$\frac{12.0 \times 10^{23}\text{ } SO_2\text{ molecules}}{6.02 \times 10^{23}\text{ } O_2\text{ molecules}}, \quad \frac{12.0 \times 10^{23}\text{ } SO_3\text{ molecules}}{12.0 \times 10^{23}\text{ } SO_2\text{ molecules}},$$

$$\frac{32.0\text{ g } O_2}{128\text{ g } SO_2}, \frac{128\text{ g } SO_2}{160\text{ g } SO_3}, \frac{32.0\text{ g } O_2}{160\text{ g } SO_3}, \frac{128\text{ g } SO_2}{32.0\text{ g } O_2},$$

$$\frac{2\text{ mol } SO_2}{1\text{ mol } O_2}, \frac{2\text{ mol } SO_3}{2\text{ mol } SO_2}, \frac{1\text{ mol } O_2}{2\text{ mol } SO_3}, \frac{1\text{ mol } O_2}{2\text{ mol } SO_2}, \frac{2\text{ mol } SO_3}{32.0\text{ g } O_2},$$

$$\frac{128\text{ g } SO_2}{2\text{ mol } SO_2}, \frac{2\text{ mol } SO_2}{32.0\text{ g } O_2}, \frac{2\text{ mol } SO_3}{1\text{ mol } O_2}, \frac{160\text{ g } SO_3}{32.0\text{ g } O_2}, \frac{32.0\text{ g } O_2}{1\text{ mol } O_2}$$

This list does not include all possible factors.

5.42 892 g

5.44 445 g

5.46 495 g

5.48 1.02×10^3 g

5.50 256 g

5.52 **a.** O_2 is the limiting reactant.

 b. 71.9 g NO_2

5.54 144 g

5.56 72.96%

5.58 72.5%

5.60 89.0%

5.62 $BaCl_2(aq) + Na_2SO_4(aq) \rightarrow 2NaCl(aq) + BaSO_4(s)$

 Net ionic: $Ba^{2+}(aq) + SO_4^{2-}(aq) \rightarrow BaSO_4(s)$

5.64 7.502 g

5.66 c

5.68 c

5.70 b

5.72 b

5.74 c

5.76 a

5.78 b

5.80 a

5.82 d

5.84 b

5.86 c

5.88 d

CHAPTER 6

6.2 **a.** 121 mL

 b. 158 mL

 c. 67.9 mL

6.4 2 mL

6.6 **a.** The density will decrease because density is equal to mass/volume, and the volume of carbon dioxide will increase on heating while the mass remains unchanged.

 b. 1.67 g/L

6.8 As the ball travels upward and slows, more and more of its kinetic energy is converted into potential energy. At the maximum height, when the ball stops before starting to fall, all the energy is in the form of potential energy. As the ball falls faster and faster, more and more of the potential energy is converted back into kinetic energy. If there were no energy losses from air

resistance, the ball would gain back as much kinetic energy as it had when it was initially thrown.

6.10 Each type of molecule has the same kinetic energy of 3.18×10^{10} u cm^2/s^2.

6.12 **a.** Particles (molecules) in a liquid move freely and therefore assume the container shape, but the cohesive forces between the particles prevent them from separating completely from each other and filling the container.

b. There is very little space between the particles (molecules) of liquids and solids. As a result, increased pressure cannot push the particles closer together and will have little influence on their volumes.

c. Gas molecules move around essentially unrestricted, and on average, equal numbers collide with each of the walls of a container in a given amount of time. The collisions cause the pressure on the walls, so the pressure on all the walls is the same.

6.14 Heat must be added to a substance to convert it from the solid to the liquid state, and then from the liquid to the gaseous state. If the added heat causes no temperature difference between the two states, as when a solid melts to a liquid at the melting point, then the added heat increases the potential energy of the particles of the substance. Thus, at the melting point, the particles of both solid and liquid forms of a substance will have the same kinetic energy because they are at the same temperature. However, particles of the liquid will have more potential energy, corresponding to the energy that had to be added to change the solid to a liquid. Similar arguments apply for a comparison of the liquid and gaseous states of a substance.

6.16 **a.** gaseous

b. solid

c. gaseous

d. gaseous

6.18 **a.** 0.957 atm

b. 727 torr

c. 14.1 psi

d. 0.966 bar

6.20 **a.** 14.3 atm

b. 14.4 bar

c. 1.09×10^4 mmHg

d. 427 in. Hg

6.22 **a.** 337 K

b. $-259°C$

c. 4 K

6.24 Column A: $P_f = 1.50$ atm; Column B: $V_f = 4.49$ L; Column C: $T_f = 221$ K

6.26 147 mL

6.28 2.73 atm

6.30 28.1 L

6.32 684 mL

6.34 4.6 L

6.36 2.5 L

6.38 100 atm

6.40 1.4×10^4 ft^3

6.42 842 mL

6.44 5.00 g/L

6.46 **a.** 0.0130 mol

b. 7.65 atm

c. 8.35 L

6.48 3.19 atm

6.50 26.3 g

6.52 2.7 mol

6.54 46.0 g/mol

6.56 44.1 g/mol; the gas is most likely CO_2

6.58 370 torr

6.60 O_2 mass/H_2 mass = 16 according to Graham's law. From the periodic table, O_2 mass/H_2 mass = 32 u/2 u = 16. The agreement is very good.

6.62 The helium-filled balloon would appear to go flat first because helium molecules diffuse through the rubber balloon faster than do nitrogen molecules. The rates of diffusion according to Graham's law would be He rate/N_2 rate = $\sqrt{28.0 \text{ u}/4.00 \text{ u}}$ = 2.6. Thus, He would be expected to escape through the balloon 2.6 times as fast as nitrogen.

6.64 **a.** exothermic

b. exothermic

c. endothermic

6.66 A change in state refers to a process in which a substance changes from one of the three states of matter—solid, liquid, or gas—to another of the three states.

6.68 Liquid methylene chloride evaporates very rapidly, and when it evaporates, it absorbs heat. Thus, the liquid acted to cool and temporarily anesthetize any tissue on which it was sprayed.

6.70 The boiling points of the two liquids are different. Thus, a measurement of the temperature of each boiling liquid would differentiate between them. The ethylene glycol would have the higher boiling point of the two.

6.72 The temperature of boiling water is influenced by the atmospheric pressure on the water. On top of Mount Everest the atmospheric pressure is quite low, so water boils at a temperature significantly lower than the normal boiling point of 100°C. The temperature of the burning campfire would not be influenced by the altitude. Thus, the potato would cook faster if it were put into the campfire.

6.74 Since sand does not sublime, heat the mixture and lead the hot iodine vapor out of the hot chamber and to a cool surface. The pure iodine vapor will condense to a solid on the cool surface, and can be scraped off and collected.

6.76 **a.** 3.6×10^2 cal

 b. 7×10^3 cal

 c. 2.4×10^3 cal

6.78 **a.** 4.07×10^7 cal

 b. 7.07×10^7 cal

 c. 5.71×10^7 cal

6.80 7.72×10^4 cal

6.82 1.78×10^{-3} g/mL

6.84 1.16 L The reaction is a redox combination reaction.

6.86 The air of the atmosphere contains about 21 volume percent oxygen at any altitude. However, the pressure of the atmosphere at high altitudes is less than the pressure at lower altitudes. If the air at a higher altitude is at the same temperature as at a lower altitude, and since $P = nRT/V$, the same volume (V) of a lung full of air at a higher altitude and lower pressure (P) contains fewer moles of gas (n), and so fewer moles of oxygen. So, from the point of view of the number of molecules of oxygen, the higher altitude air has less oxygen, but from a percentage point of view it still contains 21% oxygen.

6.88 a

6.90 c

6.92 d

6.94 d

6.96 a

6.98 c

6.100 a

6.102 c

6.104 a

6.106 a

6.108 d

6.110 a

6.112 d

6.114 d

6.116 b

CHAPTER 7

7.2 **a.** Solvent: water; solute: sodium hypochlorite

 b. Solvent: isopropyl alcohol; solute: water

 c. Solvent: water; solute: hydrogen peroxide

 d. Solvent: SD alcohol; solutes: water, glycerin, fragrance, menthol, benzophenone, coloring

7.4 **a.** Not a solution because it is not homogeneous. It is cloudy rather than clear.

 b. Solution; solvent: water; solutes: all dissolved components.

 c. Not a solution because it is not homogeneous. Bits of pulp can be seen.

 d. Solution if prepared carefully with a tea bag or good strainer; solvent: water; solutes: all dissolved components.

 e. Not a solution because it is not homogeneous.

7.6 **a.** The oil and vinegar are immiscible.

 b. The alcohol is soluble in the water.

 c. The tar is soluble in the chloroform.

7.8 **a.** unsaturated

 b. supersaturated

 c. saturated

7.10 The solution could be carefully cooled to a temperature lower than room temperature. Another method would be to allow some of the solvent to evaporate.

7.12 **a.** soluble

 b. insoluble

 c. slightly soluble

 d. very soluble

 e. slightly soluble

7.14 Add pure water to the mixture. The $CaCl_2$ is soluble and will dissolve in the water. The liquid that contains the dissolved $CaCl_2$ can then be poured off carefully, leaving behind the insoluble solid $CaCO_3$.

7.16 **a.** Soluble in benzene

 b. Soluble in benzene

 c. Soluble in water

 d. Soluble in benzene

7.18 The structure indicates that Freon-114 is a nonpolar material. Grease is also nonpolar, as indicated by its insolubility in water. Thus, grease would dissolve readily in Freon-114.

7.20 **a.** 0.364 M

 b. 0.860 M

 c. 1.75 M

7.22 **a.** 0.500 M

 b. 0.200 M

 c. 0.26 M

7.24 **a.** 0.376 mol

 b. 0.0750 mol

 c. 571 mL

7.26 **a.** 0.584 g

 b. 0.157 L

 c. 1.18×10^3 mL

7.28 **a.** 5.0%

 b. 5.0%

 c. 5.0%

7.30 **a.** 6.98%

 b. 5.08%

 c. 13.0%

 d. 51.3%

7.32 **a.** 12.5%

 b. 13.4%

 c. 6.24%

7.34 **a.** 8.00%

 b. 8.00%

 c. 2.3%

 d. 34.2%

7.36 0.025 L or 25 mL

7.38 **a.** 5.00%

 b. 5.00%

 c. 8.77%

7.40 About 40%

7.42 **a.** Put 0.0300 mol (4.26 g) of solid Na_2SO_4 into a 200 mL volumetric flask and add enough pure water to fill the flask to the mark after the solid dissolves.

 b. Put 0.0625 mol (11.8 g) of solid $Zn(NO_3)_2$ into a 250 mL volumetric flask and add enough pure water to fill the flask to the mark after the solid dissolves.

 c. Mix together 3.38 g of solid NaCl and 147 g (147 mL) of pure water. Allow the NaCl to dissolve.

 d. Put 0.94 g of solid KCl into a 125 mL volumetric flask and add enough pure water to fill the flask to the mark after the solid dissolves.

7.44 %(w/w) = 25.0; %(w/v) = 23.8

7.46 **a.** 32.3 g

 b. 0.700 mol

 c. 31.3 mL

 d. 2.10 g

7.48 **a.** Add 1.67 L of 18.0 M H_2SO_4 solution to enough water to give 5.00 L of solution. The 18.0 M acid should be added to water, and not the water to the acid. One way to make the desired solution is to add the 1.67 L of 18.0 M acid to about 3 L of pure water. Stir the resulting solution, then add enough additional water to bring the total volume to 5.00 L.

 b. Put 41.7 mL of 3.00 M $CaCl_2$ solution into a 250 mL volumetric flask and add enough pure water to fill the flask to the mark when the contents are well mixed.

 c. Put 30.0 mL of a 10.0% solution into a calibrated volumetric container (such as a volumetric flask or large volumetric cylinder) and add enough pure water to bring the total volume of well-mixed solution to 200 mL.

 d. Put 100 mL of a 50.0% solution into a calibrated volumetric container and add enough pure water to bring the total volume of well-mixed solution to 500 mL.

7.50 **a.** 0.0113 M

 b. 0.100 M

 c. 0.0375 M

 d. 0.0265 M

7.52 16.6 g

7.54 20.0 mL

7.56 50.7 mL

7.58 27.8 mL

7.60 1.3 g

7.62 Because ice cream is essentially a solution of substances dissolved in water, the freezing point of the solution is lower than that of pure water. The temperature of a mixture of ice and pure water is the same as the freezing point of pure water. Thus, a mixture of ice and water has a temperature higher than the freezing point of the ice cream solution. A mixture of ice, salt, and water has a temperature (freezing point) lower than that of pure water. If enough salt is added to the ice and water mixture, the temperature can be made lower than the freezing point of the ice cream solution, and it will freeze.

7.64 **a.** Boiling point = 101.6°C; freezing point = −5.58°C

 b. Boiling point = 100.78°C; freezing point = −2.79°C

 c. Boiling point = 102.3°C; freezing point = −8.37°C

 d. Boiling point = 103.1°C; freezing point = −11.2°C

7.66 **a.** Boiling point = 100.39°C; freezing point = −1.40°C

 b. Boiling point = 100.23°C; freezing point = −0.837°C

 c. Boiling point = 102.51°C; freezing point = −8.98°C

7.68 **a.** Osmolarity = 0.20

 b. Osmolarity = 0.60

 c. Osmolarity = 3.18

7.70 $\pi = 4.65 \times 10^3$ torr $= 4.65 \times 10^3$ mmHg = 6.12 atm

7.72 $\pi = 1.12 \times 10^4$ torr $= 1.12 \times 10^4$ mmHg = 14.7 atm

7.74 $\pi = 5.88 \times 10^4$ torr $= 5.88 \times 10^4$ mmHg = 77.4 atm

7.76 $\pi = 3.5 \times 10^3$ torr $= 3.5 \times 10^3$ mmHg = 4.6 atm

7.78 $\pi = 9.95 \times 10^3$ torr $= 9.95 \times 10^3$ mmHg = 13.1 atm

7.80 Water will flow from the 5.00% solution into the 10.0% solution. The 10.0% solution will become diluted as osmosis takes place.

7.82 Much of the soiling material to be removed by washing consists of fats and oils, which are nonpolar and will not dissolve in water. The soaps or detergents act as emulsifying agents, which allow the nonpolar materials to be suspended in water and removed from the material being washed.

7.84 **a.** Na^+ and Cl^-

 b. urea molecules

 c. K^+, Cl^- and glucose molecules

7.86 1.07 g/mL

7.88 10.2 mL

7.90 a

7.92 c

7.94 b

7.96 c

7.98 b

7.100 b

7.102 b

7.104 b

7.106 a

7.108 d

7.110 a

7.112 d

7.114 c

CHAPTER 8

8.2 **a.** Nonspontaneous: The rocket engines of the shuttle must operate continuously to push the shuttle into an orbit.

 b. Spontaneous: Once ignited, the fuel continues to burn without additional input of energy.

 c. Nonspontaneous: Heat must be supplied continuously to keep the water boiling.

 d. Nonspontaneous: The only way to raise the temperature of a substance is to supply heat.

 e. Nonspontaneous: To make your room orderly, someone must provide some work to move the clothing, etc., around. The work done represents an input of energy to the room.

8.4 **a.** Exergonic: The person doing the pushing is giving up energy to the automobile.

 b. Endergonic: The ice must gain energy in the form of heat in order to melt.

 c. Exergonic: The surroundings lose heat to the ice in order for the ice to melt.

 d. Exergonic: In order to condense, the steam must give up some energy in the form of heat.

 e. Endergonic: The heat given up by the steam as it condenses is accepted by the surroundings.

8.6 **a.** Both the energy and the entropy of the water decrease when water freezes. The process is spontaneous if the temperature of the surroundings is lower than 0°C.

 b. The energy of the water decreases while the entropy stays essentially constant. The process is spontaneous.

 c. The energy of the perfume increases slightly as energy is absorbed during evaporation. The entropy of the perfume increases a great deal as the molecules evaporate from the liquid and disperse throughout the room. The process is spontaneous.

8.8 **a.** Entropy is highest at the end of the play because the players are in a more mixed-up state as compared to just before the play began.

 b. The answer is the 10% copper/gold alloy or the 2% alloy, depending on the atoms discussed. A lower concentration of copper atoms allows more disorder among the copper atoms, but more order among the gold atoms. A higher concentration of copper allows less disorder for the copper atoms, but increases the disorder of the gold atoms.

 c. Entropy is highest with the purse on the ground and the contents scattered.

 d. The mixture characteristic of coins in a piggy bank would have the highest entropy of the choices.

 e. The mixture of loose pearls in a box would have the highest entropy of the choices.

8.10 The answers are subjective and depend on the meaning given to the terms *very slow, slow,* and *fast.*

 a. slow

 b. very slow

 c. slow

 d. fast

 e. very slow

8.12 **a.** Any of the following could be measured at different times: the weight of the block, the weight or volume of the water produced by the melting block, and the physical dimensions of the melting block.

 b. Either of the following could be measured at different times: the distance a weighted object penetrates into a sample, and the force required to break a specific-sized piece.

 c. Either of the following could be measured at different times: the length of the unburned candle and the weight of the candle.

8.14 **a.** Rate = 0.0330 M/min

 b. Rate = 0.0194 M/min

8.16 Rate = 3.96×10^{-3} M/min

8.18 Rate = 1.51×10^{-6} M/sec

8.20 **a.** Assumption #1 is being violated. According to assumption #1, decreasing the concentrations of reactants would decrease the number of collisions and so decrease the rate at which the molecules would react.

 b. Assumption #2 is being violated. According to assumption #2, molecules must collide with a certain minimum energy in order to react. At a lower temperature, fewer molecules would have the necessary minimum energy, so the reaction should go slower, not faster.

 c. Assumption #1 is being violated. According to assumption #1, increasing the concentration of either of the reactants should increase the number of collisions and so increase the rate of the reaction.

8.22 An increase in temperature increases the speeds of the molecules involved in a reaction. The increased speed acts to increase the reaction rate in two ways. First, it causes more collisions to occur between molecules in a given amount of time. Second, it causes the energy of the colliding molecules to be greater so that more of the collisions will involve molecules that have at least the minimum energy needed for a reaction to take place.

8.24 **a.**

b.

8.26 **a.**

AT ROOM TEMP.

b.

AT 150° C

Both reactions are exothermic and the products have 500 kJ/mol less energy than the reactants, so both reactions give up 500 kJ/mol. The reaction that takes place at room temperature has a smaller activation energy than the reaction that must be heated to 150°C.

8.28 **a.** Rapid. The oppositely charged ions in solution will be attracted to each other and undergo many collisions per second.

b. Won't react. The reactant particles in solution both have a negative electrical charge and will repel each other. Collisions are highly unlikely.

c. Rapid. The reacting particles are in the gaseous state where they move about freely, making effective collisions likely.

d. Slow to rapid, depending on the state of division of the solid. If large lumps of CaO were exposed to gaseous CO_2 the reaction would be slow, since only the CaO on the surface of the lumps would be available. If the CaO were divided into dust-size articles and blown into gaseous CO_2 the reaction would proceed more rapidly.

8.30 Heat the reaction mixture, add a catalyst, or increase the concentration of one or more of the reactants.

8.32 About 7.5 minutes

8.34 Catalysts provide reaction pathways with lower activation energy. They may do this by reacting to form an intermediate structure that yields products when it breaks up or by providing a surface on which the reactants react.

8.36 **a.** Equilibrium would be indicated when the intensity of the violet color of the reaction mixture remained constant with time.

b. Equilibrium would be indicated when the amount of undissolved sugar remained constant with time.

c. Equilibrium would be indicated when either the intensity of the red-brown color of the reaction mixture remained constant with time or the total pressure of the reaction mixture remained constant with time.

8.38 The concentrations of H_2 and Br_2 would decrease, and the concentration of HBr would increase. The intensity of the red-brown color of the mixture would stop decreasing and would become constant when equilibrium was established.

8.40 **a.** $K = \dfrac{[CO_2]^2}{[CO]^2[O_2]}$

b. $K = \dfrac{[NO_2]^2}{[N_2O_4]}$

c. $K = \dfrac{[CO_2]^4[H_2O]^6}{[C_2H_6]^2[O_2]^7}$

d. $K = \dfrac{[NO]^2[Cl_2]}{[NOCl]^2}$

e. $K = \dfrac{[O_2][ClO_2]^4}{[Cl_2O_5]^2}$

8.42 **a.** $K = \dfrac{[Fe(CN)_6^{3-}]}{[Fe^{3+}][CN^-]^6}$

b. $K = \dfrac{[Ag(NH_3)_2^+]}{[Ag^+][NH_3]^2}$

c. $K = \dfrac{[AuCl_4^-]}{[Au^{3+}][Cl^-]^4}$

8.44 **a.** $CH_4 + 2O_2 \rightleftarrows CO_2 + 2H_2O$

b. $3H_2 + CO \rightleftarrows CH_4 + H_2O$

c. $2O_3 \rightleftarrows 3O_2$

d. $4NO_2 + 6H_2O \rightleftarrows 4NH_3 + 7O_2$

8.46 $K = 0.47$

8.48 $K = 0.099$

8.50 **a.** The concentration of products will be larger than the concentration of reactants.

b. The concentration of products will be larger than the concentration of reactants.

c. The concentration of products will be smaller than the concentration of reactants.

d. The concentration of products will be smaller than the concentration of reactants.

8.52 **a.** Shift left

b. Shift right

c. Shift left

8.54 **a.** Shift right: The color will become less blue and more purple.

b. Shift right: The amount of solid $PbCl_2$ will increase.

c. Shift right: The intensity of the violet color of the mixture will decrease.

d. Shift right: The intensity of the violet color of the mixture will decrease.

e. Shift left: The intensity of the brown color of the mixture will increase.

8.56 a. The concentrations of NO_2 and O_2 will increase and the concentration of N_2O will decrease.

b. The concentrations of SO_2 and O_2 will increase and the concentration of SO_3 will decrease.

c. The concentration of CO_2 will increase and the concentrations of CO and O_2 will decrease.

8.58 a. Shift right

b. Shift left

c. Shift right

d. Shift left

e. No shift will occur

f. Shift left

8.60 Apply pressure to the balloon and decrease its volume. This would increase the concentrations of the gaseous reactants A and B inside the balloon and speed up the reaction.

8.62 a. Criterion 2

b. Criterion 3

c. Criterion 2

d. Criterion 3

e. Criterion 3

8.64 a

8.66 a

8.68 c

8.70 b

8.72 a

8.74 a

8.76 a

8.78 a

8.80 a

8.82 c

8.84 d

CHAPTER 9

9.2 a. $HBrO_2(aq) \rightarrow H^+(aq) + BrO_2^-(aq)$

b. $HS^-(aq) \rightarrow H^+(aq) + S^{2-}(aq)$

c. $HBr(aq) \rightarrow H^+(aq) + Br^-(aq)$

d. $HC_2H_3O_2(aq) \rightarrow H^+(aq) + C_2H_3O_2^-(aq)$

9.4 a. Arrhenius base: $LiOH(aq) \rightarrow Li^+(aq) + OH^-(aq)$

b. Not an Arrhenius base

c. Arrhenius base: $Sr(OH)_2(aq) \rightarrow Sr^{2+}(aq) + 2OH^-(aq)$

d. Not an Arrhenius base

9.6 a. Acids: $HC_2O_4^-$ and H_3O^+
Bases: H_2O and $C_2O_4^{2-}$

b. Acids: HNO_2 and H_3O^+
Bases: H_2O and NO_2^-

c. Acids: H_2O and HPO_4^{2-}
Bases: PO_4^{3-} and OH^-

d. Acids: H_2SO_3 and H_3O^+
Bases: H_2O and HSO_3^-

e. Acids: H_2O and HF
Bases: F^- and OH^-

9.8

	Acid	Conjugate base	Base	Conjugate acid
a.	$HC_2O_4^-$	$C_2O_4^{2-}$	H_2O	H_3O^+
b.	HNO_2	NO_2^-	H_2O	H_3O^+
c.	H_2O	OH^-	PO_4^{3-}	HPO_4^{2-}
d.	H_2SO_3	HSO_3^-	H_2O	H_3O^+
e.	H_2O	OH^-	F^-	HF

9.10 a. $HF + H_2O \rightleftarrows H_3O^+ + F^-$

b. $HClO_3 + H_2O \rightleftarrows H_3O^+ + ClO_3^-$

c. $HClO + H_2O \rightleftarrows H_3O^+ + ClO^-$

d. $HS^- + H_2O \rightleftarrows H_3O^+ + S^{2-}$

9.12 a. SO_4^{2-}

b. CH_3NH_2

c. ClO_4^-

d. NH_3

e. Cl^-

9.14 a. H_2CO_3

b. HS^-

c. H_2S

d. $H_2C_2O_4$

e. $H_2N_2O_2$

9.16 The substance added to complete each equation appears in blue.

a. $H_2AsO_4^-(aq) + NH_3(aq) \rightarrow NH_4^+(aq) + HAsO_4^{2-}(aq)$

b. $C_6H_5NH_2(aq) + H_2O(\ell) \rightarrow C_6H_5NH_3^+(aq) + OH^-(aq)$

c. $S^{2-}(aq) + H_2O(\ell) \rightarrow HS^-(aq) + OH^-(aq)$

d. $(CH_3)_2NH(aq) + HBr(aq) \rightarrow (CH_3)_2NH_2^+(aq) + Br^-(aq)$

e. $H_2PO_4^-(aq) + CH_3NH_2(aq) \rightarrow$
$\qquad HPO_4^{2-}(aq) + CH_3NH_3^+(aq)$

9.18 a. $HS^-(aq) + NH_3(aq) \rightarrow S^{2-}(aq) + NH_4^+(aq)$

b. $H_2O(\ell) + ClO_3^-(aq) \rightarrow OH^-(aq) + HClO_3(aq)$

c. $H_2O(\ell) + NH_2^-(aq) \rightarrow OH^-(aq) + NH_3(aq)$

d. $HBO_3^{2-}(aq) + H_2O(\ell) \rightarrow BO_3^{3-}(aq) + H_3O^+(aq)$

e. $HNO_2(aq) + NH_3(aq) \rightarrow NO_2^-(aq) + NH_4^+(aq)$

9.20 hydrocyanic acid

9.22 a. hydrotelluric acid

b. hypochlorous acid

c. sulfurous acid

d. nitrous acid

9.24 succinic acid

9.26 H_2CO_3

9.28
 a. 2.3×10^{-13} M
 b. 7.7×10^{-11} M
 c. 1.1×10^{-12} M
 d. 1.3×10^{-5} M
 e. 3.0×10^{-13} M

9.30
 a. 1.4×10^{-10} M
 b. 1.4×10^{-13} M
 c. 2.0×10^{-15} M
 d. 5.9×10^{-12} M
 e. 1.1×10^{-6} M

9.32 In Exercise 9.28: (a) acidic, (b) acidic, (c) acidic, (d) basic, (e) acidic

In Exercise 9.30: (a) basic, (b) basic, (c) basic, (d) basic, (e) acidic

9.34
 a. acidic
 b. basic
 c. acidic
 d. basic
 e. acidic

9.36
 a. 8.39, basic
 b. 10.97, basic
 c. 7.50, basic
 d. 1.64, acidic
 e. 4.71, acidic

9.38
 a. 2.66, acidic
 b. 11.41, basic
 c. 5.12, acidic
 d. 10.40, basic
 e. 4.94, acidic

9.40
 a. 5.4×10^{-10} M
 b. 2.8×10^{-3} M
 c. 3.8×10^{-6} M

9.42
 a. $[H^+] = 1.1 \times 10^{-4}$ M; $[OH^-] = 8.9 \times 10^{-11}$ M
 b. $[H^+] = 1.0 \times 10^{-4}$ M; $[OH^-] = 1.0 \times 10^{-10}$ M
 c. $[H^+] = 1.4 \times 10^{-12}$ M; $[OH^-] = 7.2 \times 10^{-3}$ M

9.44
 a. 8.9×10^{-9} M, basic
 b. 1.2×10^{-4} M, acidic
 c. 4.2×10^{-8} M, basic
 d. 4.0×10^{-8} M, basic
 e. 5.9×10^{-7} M, acidic

9.46
 a. 1.2×10^{-3} M, acidic
 b. 7.8×10^{-5} M, acidic
 c. 4.8×10^{-3} M, acidic
 d. 8.5×10^{-4} M, acidic

9.48
 a. Add 1.0 L of dilute (6 M) HNO_3 to 1.0 L of pure water and mix well.
 b. Add 50 mL of concentrated (15 M) NH_3 to 450 mL of pure water and mix well.
 c. Add 83 mL of concentrated (12 M) HCl to 4.9 L of pure water and mix well.

9.50
 a. $H_2SO_4(aq) + 2H_2O(\ell) \rightarrow 2H_3O^+(aq) + SO_4^{2-}(aq)$
 b. $H_2SO_4(aq) + CaO(s) \rightarrow CaSO_4(aq) + H_2O(\ell)$
 c. $H_2SO_4(aq) + Mg(OH)_2(s) \rightarrow MgSO_4(aq) + 2H_2O(\ell)$
 d. $H_2SO_4(aq) + CuCO_3(s) \rightarrow CuSO_4(aq) + CO_2(g) + H_2O(\ell)$
 e. $H_2SO_4(aq) + 2KHCO_3(s) \rightarrow K_2SO_4(aq) + 2CO_2(g) + 2H_2O(\ell)$
 f. $H_2SO_4(aq) + Mg(s) \rightarrow MgSO_4(aq) + H_2(g)$

9.52
 a. Total ionic: $2H^+(aq) + SO_4^{2-}(aq) + 2H_2O(\ell) \rightarrow 2H_3O^+(aq) + SO_4^{2-}(aq)$

 Net ionic: $2H^+(aq) + 2H_2O(\ell) \rightarrow 2H_3O^+(aq)$

 Simplified net ionic: $H^+(aq) + H_2O(\ell) \rightarrow H_3O^+(aq)$

 b. Total ionic: $2H^+(aq) + SO_4^{2-}(aq) + CaO(s) \rightarrow Ca^{2+}(aq) + SO_4^{2-}(aq) + H_2O(\ell)$

 Net ionic: $2H^+(aq) + CaO(s) \rightarrow Ca^{2+}(aq) + H_2O(\ell)$

 c. Total ionic: $2H^+(aq) + SO_4^{2-}(aq) + Mg(OH)_2(s) \rightarrow Mg^{2+}(aq) + SO_4^{2-}(aq) + 2H_2O(\ell)$

 Net ionic: $2H^+(aq) + Mg(OH)_2(s) \rightarrow Mg^{2+}(aq) + 2H_2O(\ell)$

 d. Total ionic: $2H^+(aq) + SO_4^{2-}(aq) + CuCO_3(s) \rightarrow Cu^{2+}(aq) + SO_4^{2-}(aq) + CO_2(g) + H_2O(\ell)$

 Net ionic: $2H^+(aq) + CuCO_3(s) \rightarrow Cu^{2+}(aq) + CO_2(g) + H_2O(\ell)$

 e. Total ionic: $2H^+(aq) + SO_4^{2-}(aq) + 2KHCO_3(s) \rightarrow 2K^+(aq) + SO_4^{2-}(aq) + 2CO_2(g) + 2H_2O(\ell)$

 Net ionic: $2H^+(aq) + 2KHCO_3(s) \rightarrow 2K^+(aq) + 2CO_2(g) + 2H_2O(\ell)$

 Simplified net ionic: $H^+(aq) + KHCO_3(s) \rightarrow K^+(aq) + CO_2(g) + H_2O(\ell)$

 f. Total ionic: $2H^+(aq) + SO_4^{2-}(aq) + Mg(s) \rightarrow Mg^{2+}(aq) + SO_4^{2-}(aq) + H_2(g)$

 Net ionic: $2H^+(aq) + Mg(s) \rightarrow Mg^{2+}(aq) + H_2(g)$

9.54 $2HCl(aq) + MgO(s) \rightarrow MgCl_2(aq) + H_2O(\ell)$

 $2HCl(aq) + Mg(OH)_2(s) \rightarrow MgCl_2(aq) + 2H_2O(\ell)$

 $2HCl(aq) + MgCO_3(s) \rightarrow MgCl_2(aq) + H_2O(\ell) + CO_2(g)$

 $2HCl(aq) + Mg(HCO_3)_2(s) \rightarrow MgCl_2(aq) + 2H_2O(\ell) + 2CO_2(g)$

 $2HCl(aq) + Mg(s) \rightarrow MgCl_2(aq) + H_2(g)$

9.56
 a. Molecular: $Sn(s) + H_2SO_3(aq) \rightarrow SnSO_3(aq) + H_2(g)$

 Total ionic: $Sn(s) + 2H^+(aq) + SO_3^{2-}(aq) \rightarrow Sn^{2+}(aq) + SO_3^{2-}(aq) + H_2(g)$

 Net ionic: $Sn(s) + 2H^+(aq) \rightarrow Sn^{2+}(aq) + H_2(g)$

b. Molecular: $3Mg(s) + 2H_3PO_4(aq) \rightarrow Mg_3(PO_4)_2(s) + 3H_2(g)$

Total ionic: $3Mg(s) + 6H^+(aq) + 2PO_4^{3-}(aq) \rightarrow Mg_3(PO_4)_2(s) + 3H_2(g)$

Net ionic: $3Mg(s) + 6H^+(aq) + 2PO_4^{3-}(aq) \rightarrow Mg_3(PO_4)_2(s) + 3H_2(g)$

c. Molecular: $Ca(s) + 2HBr(aq) \rightarrow CaBr_2(aq) + H_2(g)$

Total ionic: $Ca(s) + 2H^+(aq) + 2Br^-(aq) \rightarrow Ca^{2+}(aq) + 2Br^-(aq) + H_2(g)$

Net ionic: $Ca(s) + 2H^+(aq) \rightarrow Ca^{2+}(aq) + H_2(g)$

9.58 a. Molecular: $RbOH(aq) + HBr(aq) \rightarrow RbBr(aq) + H_2O(\ell)$

Total ionic:

$Rb^+(aq) + OH^-(aq) + H^+(aq) + Br^-(aq) \rightarrow Rb^+(aq) + Br^-(aq) + H_2O(\ell)$

Net ionic: $OH^-(aq) + H^+(aq) \rightarrow H_2O(\ell)$

b. Molecular: $2RbOH(aq) + H_2SO_3(aq) \rightarrow Rb_2SO_3(aq) + 2H_2O(\ell)$

Total ionic:

$2Rb^+(aq) + 2OH^-(aq) + 2H^+(aq) + SO_3^{2-}(aq) \rightarrow 2Rb^+(aq) + SO_3^{2-}(aq) + 2H_2O(\ell)$

Net ionic: $2OH^-(aq) + 2H^+(aq) \rightarrow 2H_2O(\ell)$

Simplified net ionic: $OH^-(aq) + H^+(aq) \rightarrow H_2O(\ell)$

c. Molecular:

$2RbOH(aq) + H_3PO_3(aq) \rightarrow Rb_2HPO_3(aq) + 2H_2O(\ell)$

Total ionic:

$2Rb^+(aq) + 2OH^-(aq) + 2H^+(aq) + HPO_3^{2-}(aq) \rightarrow 2Rb^+(aq) + HPO_3^{2-}(aq) + 2H_2O(\ell)$

Net ionic: $2OH^-(aq) + 2H^+(aq) \rightarrow 2H_2O(\ell)$

Simplified net ionic: $OH^-(aq) + H^+(aq) \rightarrow H_2O(\ell)$

9.60 a. Molecular: $2KOH(aq) + H_3PO_4(aq) \rightarrow K_2HPO_4(aq) + 2H_2O(\ell)$

Total ionic:

$2K^+(aq) + 2OH^-(aq) + 2H^+(aq) + HPO_4^{2-}(aq) \rightarrow 2K^+(aq) + HPO_4^{2-}(aq) + 2H_2O(\ell)$

Net ionic: $2OH^-(aq) + 2H^+(aq) \rightarrow 2H_2O(\ell)$

Simplified net ionic: $OH^-(aq) + H^+(aq) \rightarrow H_2O(\ell)$

b. Molecular: $3KOH(aq) + H_3PO_4 \rightarrow K_3PO_4(aq) + 3H_2O(\ell)$

Total ionic:

$3K^+(aq) + 3OH^-(aq) + 3H^+(aq) + PO_4^{3-}(aq) \rightarrow 3K^+(aq) + PO_4^{3-}(aq) + 3H_2O(\ell)$

Net ionic: $3OH^-(aq) + 3H^+(aq) \rightarrow 3H_2O(\ell)$

Simplified net ionic: $OH^-(aq) + H^+(aq) \rightarrow H_2O(\ell)$

c. Molecular: $KOH(aq) + H_2C_2O_4(aq) \rightarrow KHC_2O_4(aq) + H_2O(\ell)$

Total ionic:

$K^+(aq) + OH^-(aq) + H^+(aq) + HC_2O_4^-(aq) \rightarrow K^+(aq) + HC_2O_4^-(aq) + H_2O(\ell)$

Net ionic: $OH^-(aq) + H^+(aq) \rightarrow H_2O(\ell)$

9.62 a. Cation: Cu^{2+}; anion: Cl^-

b. Cation: NH_4^+; anion: SO_4^{2-}

c. Cation: Li^+; anion: PO_4^{3-}

d. Cation: Mg^{2+}; anion: CO_3^{2-}

e. Cation: Ca^{2+}; anion: $C_2H_3O_2^-$

f. Cation: K^+; anion: NO_3^-

9.64 a. Acid: HCl; base: $Cu(OH)_2$

b. Acid: H_2SO_4; base: NH_3 or NH_4OH

c. Acid: H_3PO_4; base: LiOH

d. Acid: H_2CO_3; base: $Mg(OH)_2$

e. Acid: $HC_2H_3O_2$; base: $Ca(OH)_2$

f. Acid: HNO_3; base: KOH

9.66 a. 1.3×10^2 g; the product would be $MgSO_4$

b. 1.8×10^2 g; the product would be $Na_2B_4O_7$

9.68 a. Acid: HNO_3; solid: $MgCO_3$

b. Acid: HCl; solid: CaO

c. Acid: H_2SO_4; solid $RbHCO_3$

9.70 a. $2HNO_3(aq) + MgCO_3(s) \rightarrow Mg(NO_3)_2(aq) + H_2O(\ell) + CO_2(g)$

b. $2HCl(aq) + CaO(s) \rightarrow CaCl_2(aq) + H_2O(\ell)$

c. $H_2SO_4(aq) + 2RbHCO_3(s) \rightarrow Rb_2SO_4(aq) + 2H_2O(\ell) + 2CO_2(g)$

9.72 a. 1/2 mol

b. 1/2 mol

c. 1/3 mol

9.74 a. 0.44 eq; 4.4×10^2 meq

b. 0.45 eq; 4.5×10^2 meq

c. 6.24×10^{-2} eq; 62.4 meq

9.76 a. 3.50×10^{-2} eq; 35.0 meq

b. 4.01×10^{-2} eq; 40.1 meq

c. 1.35×10^{-1} eq; 135 meq

d. 4.17×10^{-2} eq; 41.7 meq

9.78 9.98×10^{-3} mol, 1.74 g

9.80 B, A, C, D

9.82 a. Acid order is B, A, C, D.

b. Conjugate base order is D, C, A, B.

9.84 a. $HNO_2(aq) \rightleftharpoons H^+(aq) + NO_2^-(aq)$

$K_a = \dfrac{[H^+][NO_2^-]}{[HNO_2]}$

b. $HCO_3^-(aq) \rightleftarrows H^+(aq) + CO_3^{2-}(aq)$

$$K_a = \frac{[H^+][CO_3^{2-}]}{[HCO_3^{2-}]}$$

c. $H_2PO_4^-(aq) \rightleftarrows H^+(aq) + HPO_4^{2-}(aq)$

$$K_a = \frac{[H^+][HPO_4^{2-}]}{[H_2PO_4^-]}$$

d. $HS^-(aq) \rightleftarrows H^+(aq) + S^{2-}(aq)$

$$K_a = \frac{[H^+][S^{2-}]}{[HS^-]}$$

e. $HBrO(aq) \rightleftarrows H^+(aq) + BrO^-(aq)$

$$K_a = \frac{[H^+][BrO^-]}{[HBrO]}$$

9.86 According to the definitions given in the chapter, the person should be given the 20% acetic acid solution. If the other solution were the one desired, the term *dilute* should have been used rather than *weak*.

9.88 Titrations are done in order to analyze acids or bases. The amount of acid or base contained in a titrated sample can be determined from the volume of titrant added and the concentration of the titrant.

9.90 a. The endpoint and equivalence point will be the same if the chosen indicator changes color at the same pH as the pH of the salt solution produced by the reaction of the acid and base involved in the titration.

b. The endpoint and equivalence point will not be the same if the chosen indicator changes color at a pH that is different from the pH of the salt solution produced by the reaction of the acid and base involved in the titration.

9.92 a. 0.100 mol

b. 0.225 mol

9.94 a. $2NaOH(aq) + H_2CrO_4(aq) \rightarrow Na_2CrO_4(aq) + 2H_2O(\ell)$

b. $NaOH(aq) + HClO_3(aq) \rightarrow NaClO_3(aq) + H_2O(\ell)$

c. $3NaOH(aq) + H_3AsO_3(aq) \rightarrow Na_3AsO_3(aq) + 3H_2O(\ell)$

9.96 a. $2HCl(aq) + Sr(OH)_2(aq) \rightarrow SrCl_2(aq) + 2H_2O(\ell)$

b. $3HCl(aq) + Ni(OH)_3(aq) \rightarrow NiCl_3(aq) + 3H_2O(\ell)$

c. $2HCl(aq) + Zn(OH)_2(aq) \rightarrow ZnCl_2(aq) + 2H_2O(\ell)$

9.98 0.1660 M

9.100 a. 33.3 mL

b. 41.7 mL

c. 100 mL

d. 120 mL

e. 85.0 mL

f. 83.3 mL

9.102 a. 3.50 M

b. 0.891 M

c. 12.4 M

9.104 122.0 g/mol

9.106 The ions produced when Na_2CO_3 dissolves in water are Na^+ and CO_3^{2-}. The Na^+ ion is the conjugate acid of the strong base

NaOH and therefore is a very weak Brønsted acid. The CO_3^{2-} ion is the conjugate base of the weak acid HCO_3^- and therefore will act as a base in a hydrolysis reaction with water and will contribute to the pH of the solution. The reaction is

$$CO_3^{2-}(aq) + H_2O(\ell) \rightarrow HCO_3^-(aq) + OH^-(aq)$$

Thus, we see that the hydrolysis reaction contributes OH^- ions to the solution, causing it to have a pH greater than 7.

9.108 a. pH greater than 7. The ions produced when the salt dissolves in water are Na^+ and OCl^-. The Na^+ is the conjugate acid of a strong base (NaOH). It will be a weak acid and will not undergo a significant hydrolysis reaction. The OCl^- ion is the conjugate base of a weak acid (HOCl) and will therefore undergo a significant hydrolysis reaction that will contribute to the pH of the solution. The reaction is:

$$OCl^-(aq) + H_2O(\ell) \rightarrow HOCl(aq) + OH^-$$

The OH^- ions produced by this reaction will cause the pH of the solution to be greater than 7.

b. pH greater than 7. The explanation is the same as in part a. The hydrolysis reaction of the CHO_2^- ion is:

$$CHO_2^-(aq) + H_2O(\ell) \rightarrow HCHO_2(aq) + OH^-(aq)$$

c. pH equal to 7. The ions produced when the salt dissolves in water are K^+ and NO_3^-. The K^+ is the conjugate acid of the strong base KOH, and the NO_3^- is the conjugate base of the strong acid HNO_3. Since both ions come from strong sources, they are both weak in their respective behaviors as a conjugate acid or base. As a result, neither of them will undergo a significant hydrolysis reaction that will influence the solution pH.

d. pH greater than 7. The explanation is the same as in part a. The hydrolysis reaction of the PO_4^{3-} ion is:

$$PO_4^{3-}(aq) + H_2O(\ell) \rightarrow HPO_4^{2-}(aq) + OH^-(aq)$$

9.110 Different salts will hydrolyze to different extents in water solution and produce solutions of different pH. In titrations, the pH at the equivalence point is the pH characteristic of a solution of the salt produced by the reaction of the acid and base involved in the titration. Different acids and bases will produce different salts and possibly different solution pH values at the equivalence point. Thus, an indicator must be chosen that will change color at a pH as near as possible to the pH of the salt solution resulting from the titration.

9.112 The buffering anions present in the solution of the two salts are HPO_4^{2-} and $H_2PO_4^-$. When acid is added to the solution, the buffering reaction (like Equation 9.48) is:

$$HPO_4^{2-}(aq) + H^+(aq) \rightleftarrows H_2PO_4^-(aq)$$

When base is added, the buffering reaction (like Equation 9.49) is:

$$H_2PO_4^-(aq) + OH^-(aq) \rightleftarrows HPO_4^{2-}(aq) + H_2O(\ell)$$

9.114 $HCO_3^-(aq) + H^+(aq) \rightleftarrows H_2CO_3(aq)$

9.116 a. pH = 3.85

b. pH = 3.85

c. The difference is that the buffer of part b would have a greater buffer capacity; that is, it could buffer against larger added amounts of acid or base.

9.118 a. pH = 4.54

b. pH = 7.81

c. pH = 6.12

9.120 $[HPO_4^{2-}]/[H_2PO_4^-] = 2.8$

9.122 $Cl^-(aq) + H_3O^+(aq) \rightarrow HCl(aq) + H_2O(\ell)$

$$\left[:\overset{..}{\underset{..}{Cl}}:\right]^- + \left[H:\overset{..}{\underset{H}{O}}:H\right]^+ \rightarrow H:\overset{..}{\underset{..}{Cl}}: + H:\overset{..}{\underset{H}{O}}:$$

$\quad\quad$ base $\quad\quad\quad$ acid $\quad\quad\quad$ acid $\quad\quad\quad$ base

A base donates a pair of electrons to form a covalent bond, while an acid accepts a pair.

9.124 pH = 6.63

9.126 a

9.128 c

9.130 c

9.132 c

9.134 c

9.136 a

9.138 d

9.140 d

9.142 b

9.144 c

9.146 c

CHAPTER 10

10.2 **a.** Beta, gamma, and positron

$\quad$ **b.** Alpha and positron

$\quad$ **c.** Gamma and neutron

10.4 **a.** A beta particle is identical with an electron.

$\quad$ **b.** An alpha particle is made up of two protons and two neutrons.

$\quad$ **c.** A positron is a positively charged electron.

10.6 **a.** The mass number is reduced by 4, and the atomic number is reduced by 2.

$\quad$ **b.** The mass number is unchanged, and the atomic number is increased by 1.

$\quad$ **c.** The mass number is unchanged, and the atomic number is reduced by 1.

$\quad$ **d.** The mass number and atomic number are both unchanged.

$\quad$ **e.** The mass number is unchanged, and the atomic number is reduced by 1.

10.8 **a.** $^{27}_{13}Al$

$\quad$ **b.** $^{90}_{38}Sr$

$\quad$ **c.** $^{76}_{36}Kr$

10.10 The quantity added to complete each equation appears in blue.

$\quad$ **a.** $^{234}_{90}Th \rightarrow {}^{0}_{-1}\beta + {}^{234}_{91}Pa$

$\quad$ **b.** $^{35}_{16}S \rightarrow {}^{35}_{17}Cl + {}^{0}_{-1}\beta$

$\quad$ **c.** $^{248}_{100}Fm \rightarrow {}^{4}_{2}\alpha + {}^{244}_{98}Cf$

$\quad$ **d.** $^{226}_{88}Ra \rightarrow {}^{222}_{86}Rn + {}^{4}_{2}\alpha$

$\quad$ **e.** $^{113}_{47}Ag \rightarrow {}^{113}_{48}Cd + {}^{0}_{-1}\beta$

$\quad$ **f.** $^{41}_{18}Ar + {}^{0}_{-1}e \rightarrow {}^{41}_{17}Cl$

10.12 **a.** $^{157}_{63}Eu \rightarrow {}^{0}_{-1}\beta + {}^{157}_{64}Gd$

$\quad$ **b.** $^{190}_{78}Pt \rightarrow {}^{4}_{2}\alpha + {}^{186}_{76}Os$

$\quad$ **c.** $^{138}_{62}Sm + {}^{0}_{-1}e \rightarrow {}^{138}_{61}Pm$

$\quad$ **d.** $^{188}_{80}Hg \rightarrow {}^{188}_{79}Au + {}^{0}_{1}\beta$

$\quad$ **e.** $^{234}_{90}Th \rightarrow {}^{0}_{-1}\beta + {}^{234}_{91}Pa$

$\quad$ **f.** $^{218}_{85}At \rightarrow {}^{4}_{2}\alpha + {}^{214}_{83}Bi$

10.14 The half-life of a dozen cookies would be the time it takes for the number to be reduced to 6. The half-life of a $500 checking account would be the time it takes to reduce the amount in the account to $250.

10.16 0.56 ng remains

10.18 1.68×10^4 years old

10.20 2.24×10^4 years old

10.22 Long-term exposure to low-level radiation is more likely to cause changes to genetic material in cells. Such changes might result in genetic mutations, cancer, or other serious consequences. Short-term exposure to intense radiation destroys tissue rapidly and causes radiation sickness, which can lead to death, depending on the dose of radiation received.

10.24 A physical unit of radiation, such as a curie, indicates the activity of a source of radiation in terms of the number of nuclear decays that occur per minute. A biological unit of radiation, such as a rem, indicates the damage caused by radiation in living tissue.

10.26 3.2 R of X-rays

10.28 1.7×10^5 disintegrations/s

10.30 Hot spots are concentrations of radioisotope in tissue. Cold spots are areas of tissue that reject or keep out radioactive tracers.

10.32 $^{51}_{24}Cr + {}^{0}_{-1}e \rightarrow {}^{51}_{23}V$. The daughter is vanadium-51.

10.34 Use a radioactive isotope of oxygen to make water by burning hydrogen in it. Mix the radioactive water with hydrogen peroxide. Add the catalyst and collect the oxygen gas given off. If the gas is radioactive, it came from the water; if it is not radioactive, it came from the hydrogen peroxide.

10.36 Use a Geiger-Müller tube to measure the radioactivity of a gallon of water that contains the radioisotope. Pour that water into the pool and allow time for it to become completely and uniformly mixed with the water in the pool. Then, remove a gallon of the pool water and measure its radioactivity. For example, if the pool water has a radioactivity one ten-thousandth that of the original tracer-containing water, it means the original gallon of water has been diluted by a factor of 10,000, and therefore the pool contains 10,000 gal of water. Thus, the pool's volume is equal to the factor by which the radioactivity has been reduced.

10.38 $^{24}_{12}Mg + {}^{4}_{2}\alpha \rightarrow {}^{1}_{0}n + {}^{27}_{14}Si$

10.40 $^{238}_{92}U + {}^{1}_{0}n \rightarrow {}^{239}_{94}Pu + 2\ {}^{0}_{-1}\beta$

10.42 A moderator slows neutrons so that their chances of being captured and interacting with a target nucleus are greater.

10.44 $^{66}_{30}Zn + {}^{1}_{1}p \rightarrow {}^{67}_{31}Ga$

10.46 $2{}^{1}_{1}H \rightarrow {}^{2}_{1}H + {}^{0}_{1}\beta$

10.48 Nuclear fission is a process in which heavy nuclei split into smaller nuclei when they are hit by a neutron. Energy is released by the process. An example is:

$$_{92}^{235}\text{U} + _{0}^{1}\text{n} \rightarrow {}_{54}^{139}\text{Xe} + {}_{38}^{95}\text{Sr} + 2{}_{0}^{1}\text{n}$$

When nuclear fusion occurs, small nuclei fuse together and form heavier nuclei. Energy is released by the process. An example is: $\quad _{1}^{1}\text{H} + _{1}^{2}\text{H} \rightarrow {}_{2}^{3}\text{He} + \gamma$

10.50 $_{94}^{238}\text{Pu} \rightarrow {}_{2}^{4}\alpha + {}_{92}^{234}\text{U}$

10.52 The positive nuclei of the reacting hydrogen atoms naturally repel each other. In order to overcome this repulsion and get close enough together to fuse, the nuclei must have very high speeds (kinetic energy). The necessary high kinetic energy can only be obtained by the nuclei at very high temperatures. Remember, temperature is a measurement of the average kinetic energy of particles in matter.

10.54 3.5×10^{20} counts/minute $= 1.6 \times 10^{8}$ Ci

10.56 a

10.58 a

10.60 a

10.62 d

10.64 d

10.66 a

10.68 d

10.70 a

10.72 b

10.74 b

10.76 a

10.78 c

CHAPTER 11

11.2 Hair, skin, clothing, paper, plastic, carpet

11.4 They all contain carbon.

11.6 Covalent

11.8
 a. Organic; most organic compounds are flammable.
 b. Inorganic; a high-melting solid is typical of ionic compounds.
 c. Organic; many organic compounds are insoluble in water.
 d. Organic; most organic compounds can undergo combustion.
 e. Organic; a low-melting solid is characteristic of covalent materials, which are usually organic.

11.10 Organic compounds do not readily accept electrons to transport them, thus making the flow of electrical current impossible.

11.12 The ability of carbon to bond to itself repeatedly; isomerism.

11.14 The s orbital of the hydrogen overlaps with the sp^3 orbital of carbon.

11.16 A p orbital and an sp^3 orbital both have a two-lobed shape. A p orbital has equal-sized lobes, whereas an sp^3 orbital has different-sized lobes.

11.18 a.

b.

c.

d.

11.20 b, d, e

11.22 a. Incorrect; H cannot have two bonds.
 b. Correct
 c. Incorrect; the carbon with the $C=O$ bond has five bonds.
 d. Incorrect; both carbons of the $C=C$ double bond have three bonds.
 e. Correct

11.24
 a. $CH_3CH_2CH_2CH{=}CH{-}\overset{\displaystyle O}{\overset{\|}{C}}{-}CH_2CH_3$
 b. $CH_3CH_2{-}\overset{\displaystyle O}{\overset{\|}{C}}{-}NH_2$

11.26 a.

 b.

11.28 a. branched
 b. normal
 c. normal
 d. normal
 e. branched
 f. branched

11.30 a. same
 b. same
 c. isomers
 d. same

11.32 a. six
 b. six
 c. eight

11.34 a. 3-methylpentane
 b. 2-methylpropane
 c. 3,6-diethyl-4-methylnonane
 d. 4,7-diethyl-5-methyldecane
 e. 3-ethyl-5-methylnonane

11.36 a. CH₃—CH₂—CH—CH₂—CH₃
　　　　　　　　　|
　　　　　　　CH₂CH₃

b.
　　　　　CH₃
　　　　　|
CH₃—C—CH₂—CH₃
　　　　　|
　　　　　CH₃

c.
　　　　　　　　CH₃　　CH₂CH₂CH₃
　　　　　　　　|　　　|
CH₃—CH₂—C—CH—CH—CH₂—CH₂—CH₂—CH₂—CH₃
　　　　　　　　|　　　|
　　　　　　　CH₃　CH₂CH₃

d. CH₃—CH₂—CH₂—CH₂—CH—CH₂—CH₂—CH₂—CH₂—CH₃
　　　　　　　　　　　　　　　　|
　　　　　　　　　　　　　CH₃CHCH₂CH₃

11.38
　　　　　　　　　　　　　　　CH₃
　　　　　　　　　　　　　　　|
CH₃CH₂CH₂CH₂CH₃　　CH₃CHCH₂CH₃
　　pentane　　　　　　2-methylbutane

　　　　　　　CH₃
　　　　　　　|
　　　CH₃CCH₃
　　　　　　　|
　　　　　　　CH₃
　　2,2-dimethylpropane

11.40 CH₃CH₂CH₂CH₂CH₂CH₃　　　　　hexane

　　　CH₃　　　　　　　　　　2-methylpentane
　　　|
CH₃CHCH₂CH₂CH₃

　　　　　　CH₃
　　　　　　|
CH₃CH₂CHCH₂CH₃　　　　3-methylpentane

　　　CH₃
　　　|
CH₃CCH₂CH₃　　　　　2,2-dimethylbutane
　　　|
　　　CH₃

　　　CH₃
　　　|
CH₃CHCHCH₃　　　　2,3-dimethylbutane
　　　　|
　　　　CH₃

11.42 a.
　　　　CH₃
　　　　|
CH₂CHCH₃
　　|
　　CH₃

The longest carbon chain is four carbon atoms rather than three. The correct name is 2-methylbutane.

b.
　　　　　　　　CH₃
　　　　　　　　|
CH₃CH₂CHCHCH₃
　　　　　　　|
　　　　　　CH₃

The chain should be numbered from the right to give 2,3-dimethylpentane.

c.
　　CH₂CH₃
　　|
CH₃CHCH₂CHCH₃
　　　　　　　|
　　　　　　CH₃

The longest carbon chain is six carbon atoms and should be numbered from the right to give 2,4-dimethylhexane.

d.
　　Br
　　|
CH₃CHCHCH₃
　　　　|
　　　CH₂CH₃

The longest carbon chain is five carbon atoms rather than four. The correct name is 2-bromo-3-methylpentane.

11.44 a. cyclopentane

b. 1,2-dimethylcyclobutane

c. 1,1-dimethylcyclohexane

d. 1,2,3-trimethylcyclobutane

11.46 a.
□—CH₂CH₃

b.

c.

11.48 b, c, and d

11.50 So that the carbon atoms with attached hydrogens can assume a tetrahedral shape.

11.52 a. none

b. none

c. *trans*-1,2-dimethylcyclobutane　　*cis*-1,2-dimethylcyclob

d. *trans*-1-isopropyl-2-methylcyclopropane　　*cis*-1-isopropyl-2-methylcyclopropane

11.54 a. *trans*-1-ethyl-2-methylcyclopropane

 b. *cis*-1-bromo-2-chlorocyclopentane

 c. *trans*-1-methyl-2-propylcyclobutane

 d. *trans*-1,3-dimethylcyclohexane

11.56 a. liquid

 b. no

 c. yes

 d. less dense

11.58 2-methylheptane

11.60 a. $2C_4H_{10}+13O_2 \rightarrow 8CO_2+10H_2O$

 b. $C_5H_{12}+8O_2 \rightarrow 5CO_2+6H_2O$

 c. $C_4H_8+6O_2 \rightarrow 4CO_2+4H_2O$

11.62 $2C_6H_{14}+13O_2 \rightarrow 12CO+14H_2O$

11.64 Because of the rigid structure of cycloalkanes, stronger dispersion forces can develop between molecules. This increase of intermolecular attraction causes an increase in boiling point.

11.66 pentane: 414.5 torr; hexane: 113.9 torr; heptane: 37.2 torr

11.68 13 L of air

11.70 a. C_3H_8 $CH_3-CH_2-CH_3$

 b. C_8H_{18}
 $CH_3-CH_2-CH_2-CH_2-CH_2-CH_2-CH_2-CH_3$

 c. C_4H_{10} $CH_3-CH_2-CH_2-CH_3$

11.72 a. C_2H_6

11.74 d. CO_2 and H_2O

11.76 c. high affinity for hemoglobin

CHAPTER 12

12.2 An alkene contains one or more C=C bonds.

 An alkyne contains one or more C≡C bonds.

 An aromatic hydrocarbon contains the characteristic benzene ring or similar feature.

12.4 a. 2-butene

 b. 3-ethyl-2-pentene

 c. 4,4-dimethyl-2-hexyne

 d. 4-methylcyclopentene

 e. 6-bromo-2-methyl-3-heptyne

 f. 1-ethyl-2,3-dimethylcyclopropene

 g. 6-methyl-1,4-heptadiene

12.6

 a. $CH_3-CH=\overset{\overset{\displaystyle CH_2CH_3}{|}}{C}-CH_2-CH_2-CH_3$

 b. $CH_2=CH-\overset{\overset{\displaystyle CH_3}{|}}{CH}-\overset{\overset{\displaystyle CH_3}{|}}{CH}-CH_3$

12.8 Several possibilities exist including these:

 $CH\equiv CCH_2CH_2CH_3$ 1-pentyne

 $CH_2=CHCH=CHCH_3$ 1,3-pentadiene

 cyclopentene

12.10 3,7,11-trimethyl-1,3,6,10-dodecatetraene

12.12

 a. $CH_3\overset{\overset{\displaystyle CH_3}{|}}{CH}-CH_2CH=CHCH_3$
 5-methyl-2-hexene

 b. $CH_3CH_2CH=CHCH=CHCH_3$
 2,4-heptadiene

 c.
 3-methylcyclobutene

12.14 The overlap of two p orbitals forms a π (pi) bond containing two electrons.

12.16 Structural isomers have a different order of linkage of atoms. Geometric isomers have the same order of linkage of atoms but different three-dimensional arrangements of their atoms in space.

12.18 a. and **c.** cannot have cis- and trans-isomers.

 b. *cis*-3-hexene

 trans-3-hexene

12.20 a.

 b.

12.6 c. (top right)

12.6 d. **e.**

12.22 Both alkanes and alkenes are nonpolar compounds that are insoluble in water, less dense than water, and soluble in nonpolar solvents.

12.24 When H—X adds to an alkene, the hydrogen becomes attached to the carbon atom that is already bonded to more hydrogens.

$$CH_2 = CH - CH_3 + HCl \longrightarrow CH_3\overset{\overset{\displaystyle Cl}{|}}{C}HCH_3$$

12.26

a.
Br Br
| |
CH—CHCH$_3$ (on cyclohexane ring)

b. OH (on cyclohexane ring)

c.
CH$_3$
|
CH$_3$CHCH$_2$CH$_3$

d. (cyclopentane ring with) CH$_3$ / Cl

12.28 a. Br$_2$

b. H$_2$ with Pt catalyst

c. HCl

d. H$_2$O with H$_2$SO$_4$ catalyst

12.30 The addition of Br$_2$ to these samples will cause the cyclohexane solution to become light orange with unreacted Br$_2$, whereas the 2-hexene will react with the Br$_2$ and remain colorless.

12.32 A monomer is a starting material used in the preparation of polymers, long-chain molecules made up of many repeating units. Addition polymers are long-chain molecules prepared from alkene monomers through numerous addition reactions. A copolymer is prepared from two monomer starting materials.

12.34 A carbon–carbon double bond

12.36
$$nCH_2 = \underset{\underset{\displaystyle Cl}{|}}{C}H \xrightarrow{\text{catalyst}} (CH_2 - \underset{\underset{\displaystyle Cl}{|}}{C}H)_n$$

12.38 *sp*; two

12.40 Linear

12.42 Acetylene is a fuel used by welding torches and in the synthesis of monomers for plastics and fibers.

12.44 H—C≡C—CH$_2$CH$_2$CH$_3$
1-pentyne

CH$_3$—C≡C—CH$_2$CH$_3$
2-pentyne

CH$_3$
|
CH$_3$CH—C≡C—H
3-methyl-1-butyne

12.46 Unhydridized *p* orbitals

12.48 Aromatic refers to compounds containing the benzene ring. Aliphatic substances do not contain a benzene ring.

12.50 In cyclopentane, attached groups are located above and below the plane of the ring. In benzene, attached groups are located in the same plane as the ring.

12.52 a. 1,3,5-trimethylbenzene

b. 1,4-diethylbenzene

12.54 a. 3-phenyl-1-pentene

b. 2,5-diphenylhexane

12.56 a. *m*-ethylphenol

b. *o*-chlorophenol

12.58 a. 2-ethyl-3-propyltoluene

b. 3-bromo-5-chlorobenzoic acid

12.60

a.
OH
CH$_2$CH$_3$
(on benzene ring)

b.
HO—C=O
(benzene ring with) Cl

c.
CH$_3$
|
CH$_3$CH$_2$CCH$_2$CH$_3$
(attached to phenyl)

12.62 Nonpolar and insoluble in water

12.64 Cyclohexene readily undergoes addition reactions. Benzene resists addition reactions and favors substitution reactions. Both undergo combustion.

12.66 a. phenol

b. styrene

c. aniline

d. phenol

12.68 Heat increases the kinetic energy of the ethylene molecules and increases the number of molecules having the required activation energy.

Pressure on a gas increases the temperature and concentration of the gas.

Catalysts lower the activation energy requirements.

12.70

12.72 a and d

12.74 c, an alkene

12.76 b, melanin

CHAPTER 13

13.2 R—O—R

13.4 **a.** 1-butanol

b. 3,4-dibromo-2-butanol

c. 3-ethyl-3-pentanol

d. 2-phenyl-1-ethanol

e. 2-bromo-6-methylcyclohexanol

f. 2, 4-pentanediol

13.6 **a.** methanol

b. 2-propanol

c. ethanol

d. 1,2-ethanediol

e. 1,2,3-propanetriol

13.8

a. $CH_3CCH_2CH_2CH_3$ with OH and CH$_3$ substituents

b. $CH_2CH_2CHCH_3$ with two OH groups

c.

13.10 **a.** 2-ethylphenol or *o*-ethylphenol

b. 2-ethyl-4,6-dimethylphenol

13.12

a.

b.

13.14 **a.** secondary

b. primary

c. primary

13.16 $CH_3CH_2CH_2CH_2 — OH$ 1-butanol primary

$CH_3CHCH_2CH_3$ (OH) 2-butanol secondary

$CH_3CHCH_2 — OH$ (CH$_3$) 2-methyl-1-propanol primary

CH_3CCH_3 (OH, CH$_3$) 2-methyl-2-propanol tertiary

13.18 **a.** methanol, ethanol, 1-propanol

b. butane, 1-propanol, ethylene glycol

13.20 **a.** $CH_3CH_2CH_2CH_2 — O$ ⋯ H—O—CH$_2$CH$_3$

b.

13.22 **a.** $CH_3CH{=}CHCH_3$

b. $CH_3CH{=}CCH_3$ with CH$_3$

13.24 **a.** $CH_3CH_2CH_2 — O — CH_2CH_2CH_3$

b.

c.

13.26 **a.**

b. $CH_3CH_2CHCHCH_3$ with OH and CH$_3$

c. $CH_3CH_2CH_2CH_2$ with OH

13.28 **a.** $CH_3CCH_2CH_3 + (O) \longrightarrow$ no reaction, with CH$_3$

b. $2CH_3CH_2CH_2 — OH \xrightarrow[140°C]{H_2SO_4}$
$CH_3CH_2CH_2 — O — CH_2CH_2CH_3 + H_2O$

c. $CH_3CH_2CHCH_2CH_3 + (O) \longrightarrow$ with OH
$$CH_3CH_2CCH_2CH_3 + H_2O$$
(ketone with $C{=}O$)

d. $CH_3CH_2\overset{\overset{\displaystyle OH}{|}}{CH}CH_2CH_3 \xrightarrow[180°C]{H_2SO_4}$
$CH_3CH=CHCH_2CH_3 + H_2O$

e. $CH_3CH_2CH_2CH_2CH_2CH_2-OH + 2(O) \longrightarrow$

$CH_3CH_2CH_2CH_2CH_2-\overset{\overset{\displaystyle O}{\|}}{C}-OH + H_2O$

13.30

a. $CH_3CH_2CH=CH_2 + H_2O \xrightarrow{H_2SO_4} CH_3CH_2\overset{\overset{\displaystyle OH}{|}}{C}HCH_3$

$CH_3CH_2\overset{\overset{\displaystyle OH}{|}}{C}HCH_3 + (O) \rightarrow CH_3CH_2\overset{\overset{\displaystyle O}{\|}}{C}CH_3 + H_2O$

b.
$\xrightarrow[180°C]{H_2SO_4}$
$+\ H_2O$

$+\ H_2O \xrightarrow{H_2SO_4}$

c. $CH_3CH_2CH_2\overset{\overset{\displaystyle OH}{|}}{C}H_2 \xrightarrow[180°C]{H_2SO_4} CH_3CH_2CH=CH_2 + H_2O$

$CH_3CH_2CH=CH_2 + H_2O \xrightarrow{H_2SO_4} CH_3CH_2\overset{\overset{\displaystyle OH}{|}}{C}HCH_3$

$CH_3CH_2\overset{\overset{\displaystyle OH}{|}}{C}HCH_3 + (O) \rightarrow CH_3CH_2\overset{\overset{\displaystyle O}{\|}}{C}CH_3 + H_2O$

13.32 $CH_3\overset{\overset{\displaystyle O}{\|}}{C}-\overset{\overset{\displaystyle O}{\|}}{C}-OH$

13.34 Methanol is used as an automobile fuel and in the preparation of formaldehyde, a starting material for certain plastics.

13.36 a. glycerol

b. ethanol

c. ethylene glycol

d. isopropyl alcohol

e. menthol

f. ethanol

13.38 a. *o*-phenylphenol or 2-benzyl-4-chlorophenol

b. 4-hexylresorcinol or phenol

c. BHA or BHT

13.40 a. ethyl isopropyl ether

b. butyl methyl ether

c. diphenyl ether

13.42 a. 1-ethoxypropane

b. 2-ethoxypropane

c. ethoxybenzene

d. 1,2-dimethoxycyclopentane

13.44 a. $CH_3-O-CH_2CH_2CH_3$

b. $CH_3\overset{\overset{\displaystyle CH_3}{|}}{C}HCH_2-O-$

c. $CH_3-O-\overset{\overset{\displaystyle CH_3}{|}}{C}HCH_2CH_3$

d.

e. $CH_3-\overset{\overset{\displaystyle CH_3}{|}}{\underset{\underset{\displaystyle O}{|}}{C}}-CH_3$
$\quad CH_3-\overset{\overset{\displaystyle}{}}{C}=CHCH_2CH_3$

13.46 Inertness

13.48 $CH_3CH_2CH_2-OH$, $CH_3CH_2-O-CH_3$, $CH_3CH_2CH_2CH_3$

This order is based on the decreasing ability to form hydrogen bonds with water.

13.50

13.52 a. $CH_3CH_2CH_2-S-Hg-S-CH_2CH_2CH_3 + 2H^+$

b. $CH_3CH_2CH_2-S-S-CH_2CH_2CH_3 + H_2O$

c. $+\ CH_3-SH$

13.54 Alcohols are oxidized to aldehydes and ketones, whereas thiols are oxidized to disulfides.

13.56 aromatic, alkene, aldehyde

13.58 The electronegativity difference between S and H is less than between O and H. This means the S—H bond is less polar, leading to a decreased ability to hydrogen bond. The decrease in hydrogen bonding ability would decrease a thiol's boiling point and water solubility in comparison to the alcohol.

13.60 The negative charge that forms on the oxygen atom when phenol acts as an acid can be delocalized around the ring structure of benzene.

13.62 d, C_3H_7OH

13.64 d, ethyl alcohol

13.66 b, CH_3-O-CH_3

CHAPTER 14

14.2

Simplest aldehyde:

$$H-\underset{\underset{O}{\|}}{C}-H$$

Simplest ketone:

$$H_3C-\underset{\underset{O}{\|}}{C}-CH_3$$

14.4 **a.** aldehyde

b. neither

c. ketone

d. neither

e. ketone

f. neither

14.6 **a.** butanal

b. 2, 4-dibromobutanal

c. 4-methyl-2-pentanone

d. 2, 5-dichlorocyclopentanone

e. 3-methyl-1-phenyl-2-butanone

14.8

a. $CH_3CH_2-\underset{\underset{O}{\|}}{C}-H$

b. $CH_3-\underset{\underset{O}{\|}}{C}-\underset{\underset{CH_3}{|}}{CH}-CH_3$

c.

d. $CH_2\underset{\underset{}{|}}{CH}CH_2-\underset{\underset{O}{\|}}{C}-H$ with Br and phenyl

14.10

$$CH_3CH_2\underset{\underset{O}{\|}}{C}-H \quad \text{and} \quad CH_3-\underset{\underset{O}{\|}}{C}-CH_3$$

14.12

a. $H-\underset{\underset{O}{\|}}{C}-\underset{\underset{CH_3}{|}}{\overset{\overset{CH_2CH_3}{|}}{CH}}CHCH_3$

The longest chain contains five carbon atoms. The correct name is 2,3-dimethylpentanal.

b. The compound is an aldehyde. Number from the carbonyl group.

$$CH_3\underset{\underset{CH_3}{|}}{CH}CH_2-\underset{\underset{O}{\|}}{C}-H$$

The correct name is 3-methylbutanal.

c.

Number the ring so that the bromines have lower numbers. The correct name is 2,3-dibromocyclopentanone.

14.14 Acetone dissolves remaining traces of water, and together they are discarded. The remaining small amounts of acetone evaporate.

14.16 Propane is nonpolar. Ethanal is a polar molecule and exhibits greater interparticle forces.

14.18 **a.**

b. $CH_3CH_2-\underset{\underset{O}{\|}}{C}-H$

14.20 The alcohol will have the higher melting point because of hydrogen bonding. Menthol is a solid, and menthone is a liquid.

14.22

a. $CH_3\underset{\underset{OH}{|}}{CH}CH_2\underset{\underset{CH_3}{|}}{CH}CH_3 + (O) \longrightarrow$

$$CH_3-\underset{\underset{O}{\|}}{C}-CH_2\underset{\underset{CH_3}{|}}{CH}CH_3 + H_2O$$

b.

c.

14.24 **a.** hemiacetal

b. hemiketal

c. neither

d. hemiketal

14.26 **a.** neither

b. ketal

c. acetal

14.28 **a.** ketal

b. none of these

c. hemiacetal

14.30 They are unstable, splitting into an alcohol and aldehyde.

14.32 The formation of a silver precipitate or mirror.

14.34

b.

d. $CH_3CH_2-\overset{\displaystyle O}{\overset{\|}{C}}-O^-NH_4^+$

14.36 a. no

b. no

c. yes

d. yes

e. no

14.38

$\underset{\overset{|}{CH_2}}{\overset{OH}{|}}-\underset{\overset{|}{CH}}{\overset{OH}{|}}-\underset{\overset{|}{CH}}{\overset{OH}{|}}-\underset{\overset{|}{CH}}{\overset{OH}{|}}-\boxed{\underset{\overset{|}{CH}}{\overset{OH}{|}}-\overset{\displaystyle O}{\overset{\|}{C}}-H}$

14.40

$\underset{\overset{|}{CH_2}}{\overset{OH}{|}}-\underset{\overset{|}{CH}}{\boxed{\overset{OH}{}}}-\underset{\overset{|}{CH}}{\overset{OH}{|}}-\underset{\overset{|}{CH}}{\overset{OH}{|}}-\underset{\overset{|}{CH}}{\overset{OH}{|}}-\overset{\displaystyle O}{\overset{\|}{C}}-H \quad \Longrightarrow$

14.42

a.

b. $CH_3CH_2-\underset{\overset{|}{CH_3}}{\overset{\overset{\displaystyle OCH_2CH_2CH_3}{|}}{C}}-OCH_3 \quad + H_2O$

c. $CH_3CH_2-\underset{\overset{|}{O-CHCH_3}}{\overset{\overset{\displaystyle O-\overset{\displaystyle CH_3}{\overset{|}{CHCH_3}}}{|}}{\overset{|}{C}}}-H \quad + H_2O$
(with $\overset{|}{CH_3}$ below)

d.

e. $CH_3CH_2\underset{\overset{|}{CH_3}}{CHCH_2}-OH$

14.44 Alkenes give alkanes.

Alkynes give alkenes and alkanes.

Aldehydes give primary alcohols.

Ketones give secondary alcohols.

14.46 a.

$+ 2CH_3CH_2OH$

b. $CH_3CH_2-\overset{\displaystyle O}{\overset{\|}{C}}-CH_2CH_3 + 2CH_3OH$

c. $H-\overset{\displaystyle O}{\overset{\|}{C}}-H + 2CH_3CH_2CH_2OH$

d. $CH_3CH_2\overset{\displaystyle O}{\overset{\|}{C}}-H + 2CH_3OH$

14.48 a.

$\overset{\displaystyle O}{\overset{\|}{C}}-CH_3 + HO-CH_2CH_3$

b.

$\underset{\overset{|}{H}}{C}=O + HO-CH_2CH_2CH_3$

14.50 a. $CH_3CH_2\underset{\overset{|}{CH_2}}{\overset{\overset{\displaystyle OH}{|}}{}} + (O) \longrightarrow CH_3CH_2-\overset{\displaystyle O}{\overset{\|}{C}}-H$

$CH_3CH_2-\overset{\displaystyle O}{\overset{\|}{C}}-H + 2CH_3CH_2-OH \overset{H^+}{\rightleftharpoons}$

$CH_3CH_2-\underset{\overset{|}{OCH_2CH_3}}{\overset{\overset{\displaystyle OCH_2CH_3}{|}}{CH}} \quad + H_2O$

b. $CH_3\underset{\overset{|}{CH_3}}{CH}-\overset{\displaystyle O}{\overset{\|}{C}}-CH_3 + H_2 \overset{Pt}{\longrightarrow} CH_3\underset{\overset{|}{CH_3}}{CH}-\underset{\overset{|}{OH}}{CH}-CH_3$

$CH_3\underset{\overset{|}{CH_3}}{CH}-\underset{\overset{|}{OH}}{CH}-CH_3 \overset{H_2SO_4}{\underset{180°}{\longrightarrow}} CH_3\underset{\overset{|}{CH_3}}{C}=CH-CH_3 + H_2$

14.52 a. menthone

b. biacetyl

c. cinnamaldehyde

d. vanillin

14.54 461 g

14.56

$CH_3CH_2\overset{\displaystyle O}{\overset{\|}{C}}CH_2CH_3 + 2CH_3CH_2CH_2-OH \overset{H^+}{\longrightarrow}$

$CH_3CH_2\underset{\overset{|}{O-CH_2CH_2CH_3}}{\overset{\overset{\displaystyle O-CH_2CH_2CH_3}{|}}{C}}CH_2CH_3 \quad + H_2O$

14.58 a. aldehyde

b. alcohol

c. ketone

CHAPTER 15

15.2 Carboxylic acids with more than ten carbon atoms are called fatty acids. They were originally produced by the saponification of fats.

15.4 lactic acid

15.6 a. 2-methylpropanoic acid

b. 4-bromobutanoic acid

c. 3-isopropylbenzoic acid or *m*-isopropylbenzoic acid

d. 3-methoxypentanoic acid

e. 4-phenylbutanoic acid

15.8

a. $CH_3CH_2CH_2CH_2 - \overset{\overset{\displaystyle O}{\|}}{C} - OH$

b. $CH_3CH_2CH_2\overset{\overset{\displaystyle Br}{|}}{C}H\overset{}{C}H - \overset{\overset{\displaystyle O}{\|}}{C} - OH$ with CH_3 below

c. structure: benzene ring with $\overset{\overset{\displaystyle O}{\|}}{C} - OH$ on top and $CH_2CH_2CH_3$ on bottom

15.10 a. Acetic acid because it forms dimers

b. Propanoic acid because it forms dimers

c. Butyric acid because it has a higher molecular weight

15.12 $CH_3CH_2 - \overset{\overset{\displaystyle O \cdots \cdots HO}{\|}}{C} - OH \cdots \cdots O$... $\overset{}{C} - CH_2CH_3$

15.14 The carboxyl group is hydrophilic; the carbon chain is hydrophobic.

15.16 pentane < ethoxyethane < 1-butanol < propanoic acid

15.18 $CH_3CH_2 - \overset{\overset{\displaystyle O}{\|}}{C} - O^-$

15.20 Under cellular pH conditions, lactic acid ionizes to produce the anion lactate.

15.22 $CH_3CH_2CH_2\overset{\overset{\displaystyle O}{\|}}{C} - OH$

15.24

a. $CH_3CH_2 - \overset{\overset{\displaystyle O}{\|}}{C} - O^-Na^+ + H_2O$

b. $CH_3\overset{\overset{\displaystyle OH}{|}}{C}H - \overset{\overset{\displaystyle O}{\|}}{C} - O^-K^+ + H_2O$

15.26

a. $CH_3 - \overset{\overset{\displaystyle O}{\|}}{C} - OH + NaOH \longrightarrow$

$CH_3 - \overset{\overset{\displaystyle O}{\|}}{C} - O^-Na^+ + H_2O$

b. $CH_3 - \overset{\overset{\displaystyle O}{\|}}{C} - OH + KOH \longrightarrow$

$CH_3 - \overset{\overset{\displaystyle O}{\|}}{C} - O^-K^+ + H_2O$

c. $2CH_3 - \overset{\overset{\displaystyle O}{\|}}{C} - OH + Ca(OH)_2 \longrightarrow$

$(CH_3 - \overset{\overset{\displaystyle O}{\|}}{C} - O^-)_2Ca^{2+} + 2H_2O$

15.28 a. sodium 3-bromobutanoate

b. calcium methanoate

c. potassium 3-phenoxypropanoate

15.30

a. $CH_3 - \overset{\overset{\displaystyle O}{\|}}{C} - O^-K^+$

b. benzene ring with $\overset{\overset{\displaystyle O}{\|}}{C} - O^-Na^+$ and CH_3

c. $CH_3CH_2\overset{\overset{\displaystyle CH_3}{|}}{C}H - \overset{\overset{\displaystyle O}{\|}}{C} - O^-Na^+$

15.32 a. sodium stearate

b. acetic acid

c. sodium benzoate

d. zinc 10-undecylenate

e. sodium propanoate or calcium propanoate

f. citric acid/sodium citrate

15.34 b. $CH_3 - \overset{\overset{\displaystyle O}{\|}}{C}$ ⟧ $- O - CH_2CH_3$

d. benzene-O ⟧ $\overset{\overset{\displaystyle O}{\|}}{C} - CH_3$

f.

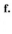

$$\text{C}=\text{O} \quad \text{C}-\text{O}-\text{CH}_2\text{CH}_3 \uparrow$$

15.36

a. $\text{CH}_3-\overset{\text{O}}{\underset{\|}{\text{C}}}-\text{O}-\text{CH}_3 + \text{CH}_3-\overset{\text{O}}{\underset{\|}{\text{C}}}-\text{OH}$

b. $\text{CH}_3\text{CH}-\overset{\text{O}}{\underset{\|}{\text{C}}}-\text{O}-\text{CH}_2-\langle\bigcirc\rangle \quad + \text{ H}_2\text{O}$, with CH_3 substituent

c. $\text{CH}_3\text{CH}-\overset{\text{O}}{\underset{\|}{\text{C}}}-\text{O}-\langle\bigcirc\rangle \quad + \text{ HCl}$, with CH_3 substituent

15.38

a. $\text{CH}_3\text{CH}_2-\overset{\text{O}}{\underset{\|}{\text{C}}}-\text{O}-\text{CH}_3$

b. $\text{CH}_3\text{CH}_2-\overset{\text{O}}{\underset{\|}{\text{C}}}-\text{O}-\langle\bigcirc\rangle$

c. $\text{CH}_3\text{CH}_2-\overset{\text{O}}{\underset{\|}{\text{C}}}-\text{O}-\text{CH}_2\text{CHCH}_3$, with CH_3 substituent

15.40

(structure with N–CH₃ and $\text{CH}_3-\overset{\text{O}}{\underset{\|}{\text{C}}}-\text{O}$ and $\text{O}-\overset{\text{O}}{\underset{\|}{\text{C}}}-\text{CH}_3$)

15.42

$-(\text{O}-\overset{\text{O}}{\underset{\|}{\text{C}}}-\overset{\text{O}}{\underset{\|}{\text{C}}}-\text{O}-\text{CH}_2\text{CH}_2\text{CH}_2)_n-$

15.44 a. ethyl lactate

 b. propyl butyrate

15.46 a. methyl 2-methylpropanoate

 b. ethyl 3,5-dichlorobenzoate

15.48 a. methyl propionate

 b. methyl butyrate

 c. methyl lactate

15.50

a. $\text{H}-\overset{\text{O}}{\underset{\|}{\text{C}}}-\text{O}-\langle\bigcirc\rangle$

b. $\overset{\text{O}}{\underset{\|}{\text{C}}}-\text{O}-\text{CH}_3$ (benzene ring with NO_2 para)

c. $\text{CH}_3\text{CH}-\overset{\text{O}}{\underset{\|}{\text{C}}}-\text{O}-\text{CH}_2\text{CH}_3$, with Cl substituent

15.52

$\text{CH}_3-\overset{\text{O}}{\underset{\|}{\text{C}}}-\text{OCH}_2\text{CH}_3 + \text{H}_2\text{O} \xrightarrow{\text{H}^+}$

$\text{CH}_3-\overset{\text{O}}{\underset{\|}{\text{C}}}-\text{OH} + \text{CH}_3\text{CH}_2-\text{OH}$

$\text{CH}_3-\overset{\text{O}}{\underset{\|}{\text{C}}}-\text{OCH}_2\text{CH}_3 + \text{NaOH} \longrightarrow$

$\text{CH}_3-\overset{\text{O}}{\underset{\|}{\text{C}}}-\text{O}^-\text{Na}^+ + \text{CH}_3\text{CH}_2-\text{O}$

15.54

a. $\text{CH}_3(\text{CH}_2)_{16}-\overset{\text{O}}{\underset{\|}{\text{C}}}-\text{O}^-\text{Na}^+ + \text{CH}_3\text{CH}_2-\text{OH}$

b. $\text{CH}_3\text{CH}-\overset{\text{O}}{\underset{\|}{\text{C}}}-\text{OH} + \text{HO}-\langle\bigcirc\rangle$, with CH_3 substituent

15.56

$\text{CH}_2-\overset{\text{O}}{\underset{\|}{\text{C}}}-\text{CH}_2-\text{O}-\overset{\text{O}}{\underset{\|}{\text{P}}}-\text{OH} + \text{H}_2\text{O}$, with OH and OH substituents

15.58 When NaHCO_3 reacts with an acid, it forms CO_2 gas, water, and a salt:

$$\text{RCO}_2\text{H} + \text{NaHCO}_3 \rightarrow \text{RCO}_2^-\text{Na}^+ + \text{CO}_2 + \text{H}_2\text{O}$$

There would be no reaction with an alcohol. Therefore, the presence of effervescence ("bubbling") indicates an acid.

15.60

$\text{CH}_3\text{CH}_2\text{CH}_2\text{CHCH}_2\overset{\text{O}}{\underset{\|}{\text{C}}}-\text{O}-\langle\bigcirc\rangle$, with CH_3CH_2 substituent

phenyl 3-ethylhexanoate

15.62 1. Use an excessive quantity of ethanol.

2. Remove the water as it is being formed.

15.64 Polarity: d > a > b > c

Boiling Points: c < b < a < d

CHAPTER 16

16.2 R—NH_2 (primary), R_2NH (secondary), and R_3N (tertiary).

16.4 **a.** secondary

b. tertiary

c. primary

d. secondary

16.6

(1) $CH_3-CH_2-CH_2-NH_2$ primary

(2) $CH_3-CH-NH_2$ primary
 |
 CH_3

(3) $CH_3-CH_2-NH-CH_3$ secondary

(4) CH_3-N-CH_3 tertiary
 |
 CH_3

16.8 **a.** isopropylmethylamine

b. ethylmethylphenylamine

c. butylamine

16.10 **a.** 2-methyl-1-butanamine

b. cyclobutanamine

c. *N*-methylcyclobutanamine

16.12 **a.** *N*-propylaniline

b. *N,N*-dimethylaniline

16.14

a. $CH_3CHCHCH_2CH_3$ with NH_2 and CH_2CH_3 substituents

b.

c.

16.16 Amines form hydrogen bonds with water.

16.18 Tertiary amines do not form hydrogen bonds among themselves.

16.20

a.

b.

16.22 b < c < a

16.24 $CH_3CH_2-NH-CH_2CH_3 + H_2O \rightleftharpoons$

$$CH_3CH_2-\overset{\overset{\displaystyle H}{|}}{\underset{\underset{\displaystyle H}{|}}{N^+}}-CH_2CH_3 + OH^-$$

16.26 **a.** $CH_3CH_2CH_2CH_2-NH_3{}^+Cl^-$

b.
$NH_3{}^+ + OH^-$

c.
$NH_3{}^+ \quad CH_3\overset{\overset{\displaystyle O}{||}}{C}-O^-$

d. $CH_3\overset{\overset{\displaystyle NH_2}{|}}{C}HCH_3 + NaCl + H_2O$

e. $CH_3\overset{\overset{\displaystyle O}{||}}{C}H-\overset{}{C}-NH-CH_3 + HCl$ with CH_3 below

f.

16.28 The amine salts are much more soluble in water (or the aqueous fluids in the body).

16.30

(1) $CH_3-\overset{\overset{\displaystyle O}{||}}{C}-Cl + CH_3-NH-CH_3 \longrightarrow$

$$CH_3-\overset{\overset{\displaystyle O}{||}}{C}-\overset{\underset{\underset{\displaystyle CH_3}{|}}{}}{N}-CH_3 + HCl$$

(2) $CH_3-\overset{\overset{\displaystyle O}{||}}{C}-O-\overset{\overset{\displaystyle O}{||}}{C}-CH_3 + CH_3-NH-CH_3 \longrightarrow$

$$CH_3-\overset{\overset{\displaystyle O}{||}}{C}-\overset{\underset{\underset{\displaystyle CH_3}{|}}{}}{N}-CH_3 + HO-\overset{\overset{\displaystyle O}{||}}{C}-CH_3$$

16.32 a. NaOH

b. NH_3

c. HCl

16.34 Synapse

16.36 Norepinephrine and serotonin

16.38 Norepinephrine, serotonin, acetylcholine, and dopamine

16.40 Epinephrine is used clinically in local anesthetics to constrict blood vessels in the area of injection.

16.42 Plants

16.44 a. caffeine

b. atropine

c. nicotine

d. codeine

e. quinine

f. morphine

16.46 a. N-methylbutanamide

b. N,N-dimethylethanamide

c. 2-methylbenzamide or o-methylbenzamide

d. 2-methylbutanamide

16.48

a. $CH_3CH_2-\overset{\overset{O}{\|}}{C}-NH_2$

b. $CH_3CH_2CH_2CH_2-\overset{\overset{O}{\|}}{C}-NH-CH_2CH_3$

c. $H-\overset{\overset{O}{\|}}{C}-\underset{\underset{CH_3}{|}}{N}-CH_3$

16.50

a.

b. $CH_3\underset{\underset{CH_3}{|}}{CH}-\overset{\overset{O}{\|}}{C}-\underset{\underset{H}{|}}{N}-H\cdots O=\overset{\overset{NH_2}{|}}{C}-\underset{\underset{CH_3}{|}}{CHCH_3}$

16.52

a. $CH_3-\overset{\overset{O}{\|}}{C}-O^-Na^+ + CH_3CH_2-NH_2$

b. $CH_3CH_2-\overset{\overset{O}{\|}}{C}-OH + NH_4^+Cl^-$

16.54

16.56 a. saturated

b. one C=C bond

c. two C=C bonds

16.58 $Na^{+\,-}O_2C(CH_2)_4CO_2^-\,Na^+$ and $NH_2(CH_2)_6NH_2$

16.60

$CH_3\overset{\overset{O}{\|}}{C}-OH$ and $\left[HO-CH_2CH_2-\underset{\underset{CH_3}{|}}{\overset{\overset{CH_3}{|}}{N}}-CH_3\right]^+$

acetic acid choline

16.62 Primary: $R-NH_2$

Secondary: R_2-NH

Tertiary: R_3N

16.64 a

CHAPTER 17

17.2 a. A structural material in plants

b. An energy source in our diet

c. A stored form of energy in animals

d. A stored form of energy in plants

17.4 a. carbohydrate, disaccharide

b. carbohydrate, monosaccharide

c. carbohydrate, polysaccharide

d. carbohydrate, monosaccharide

e. carbohydrate, polysaccharide

f. carbohydrate, disaccharide

g. carbohydrate, polysaccharide

h. carbohydrate, polysaccharide

17.6 They don't have four different groups attached; C number 1 has only three groups; C number 3 has four groups, but two are hydrogens.

17.8 a. No chiral carbon atoms

b. $CH_3CH_2-\underset{\underset{OH}{|}}{\overset{*}{C}H}-\overset{\overset{O}{\|}}{C}-CH_3$ Yes, can have enantiomers.
* denotes the chiral carbon

c. Yes, can have enantiomers.
* denotes the chiral carbon

17.10 The chiral carbon is at the intersection of the lines. The H and OH are above the plane of the paper, and the CHO and CH_2CH_3 are below the plane.

17.12 a. The D form is given; the L enantiomer is:

b. The L form is given; the D enantiomer is:

$$
\begin{array}{c}
CH_2OH \\
| \\
C=O \\
HO \!-\!\!|\!-\! H \\
H \!-\!\!|\!-\! OH \\
H \!-\!\!|\!-\! OH \\
CH_2OH
\end{array}
$$

17.14 a.

L-alanine D-alanine

b.

L-leucine D-leucine

17.16 a. Two chiral carbon atoms; four stereoisomers

 b. Three chiral carbon atoms; eight stereoisomers

17.18 8 aldopentoses; 4 are in the D form, and 4 are in the L form.

17.20 Optically active molecules rotate the plane of polarized light.

17.22 a. ketopentose

 b. aldopentose

17.24 Some carbohydrates have a sweet taste; these are sugars.

17.26 * denotes sites where the hydrogens of a water molecule can hydrogen-bond.

17.28 a. The α form is given in the text; the β form is:

 b. The β form is given in the text; the α form is:

17.30

α-mannose β-mannose

17.32 Nonreducing sugar

17.34 a.

$$
\begin{array}{c}
COOH \\
H \!-\!\!|\!-\! OH \\
H \!-\!\!|\!-\! OH + Cu_2O \\
H \!-\!\!|\!-\! OH \\
CH_2OH
\end{array}
$$

b.

c.

17.36 Ribose is found is RNA and deoxyribose is found in DNA.

17.38 Dextrose; blood sugar

17.40 The hexoses glucose and galactose differ in the positions of H and OH on carbon number 4.

17.42 Fructose can be used as a low-calorie sweetener because the caloric content per gram is about the same as for sucrose. However, since fructose is so much sweeter, less is needed to provide the same degree of sweetness.

17.44 a. sucrose

 b. maltose

 c. lactose

 d. maltose

 e. sucrose

 f. sucrose

17.46 The glucose ring opens at the hemiacetal group, exposing an aldehyde group which then reacts with the Cu^{2+} of the Benedict's reagent.

17.48 Perform a Benedict's test. Sucrose is not a reducing sugar, but honey contains reducing sugars.

17.50 The right ring in lactose has a hemiacetal group that can open to form the aldehyde and alcohol; hence, it is a reducing sugar. Sucrose has no hemiacetal bonds, so it can't reduce Cu^{2+}.

17.52 a. Galactose and glucose

 b. Yes; there is a hemiacetal on the glucose ring.

 c. $\alpha(1 \rightarrow 6)$

17.54 a. amylose

 b. cellulose

 c. amylopectin

 d. cellulose

 e. glycogen

17.56 The boiling point of the glucose solution will be higher because the molarity of the solution is higher.

17.58 Glucose and fructose are formed in equal amounts (52.6 g). The extra mass comes from the water needed for hydrolysis.

17.60 As hydrolysis occurred, the molarity of the solution would increase, causing an increase in osmotic pressure, and the solution level in the tube would rise.

17.62 a, b, and d

17.64 hydrolysis

17.66 c

CHAPTER 18

18.2 Energy storage, structural components, some hormones

18.4 a. nonsaponifiable

 b. saponifiable

 c. saponifiable

 d. saponifiable

 e. saponifiable

 f. nonsaponifiable

18.6 1. They have a straight-chain carbon segment with a carboxylic acid group.

 2. The straight-chain carbon segment is 10-20 carbons long.

 3. There is an even number of total C atoms.

 4. The carbon chain may be saturated or unsaturated.

18.8 Linoleic acid and linolenic acid are essential fatty acids because they are needed by the body but are not synthesized within the body.

18.10 Unsaturated fatty acids have a bent structure that prevents the molecules from packing as tightly as saturated fatty acids.

18.12 Fats and oils are both triglycerides (esters). Fats are solid at room temperature; oils are liquid at room temperature. Fats tend to have more saturated fatty acids, whereas oils tend to have more unsaturated fatty acids.

18.14

18.16 Triglyceride B

18.18 Hydrogenation

18.20 A number of commercially useful margarines and cooking shortenings are prepared by the hydrogenation of vegetable oils.

18.22 a.

 b. Same reaction as in part a.

 c.

d.

$$CH_2-O-\overset{\overset{\displaystyle O}{\|}}{C}-(CH_2)_{16}CH_3$$

$$CH-O-\overset{\overset{\displaystyle O}{\|}}{C}-(CH_2)_{16}CH_3 + 3NaOH \longrightarrow$$

$$CH_2-O-\overset{\overset{\displaystyle O}{\|}}{C}-(CH_2)_{16}CH_3$$

$$CH_2-OH$$
$$CH-OH + 3Na^{+\,-}O-\overset{\overset{\displaystyle O}{\|}}{C}-(CH_2)_{16}CH_3$$
$$CH_2-OH \qquad\qquad\qquad \text{soap}$$
$$\text{glycerol}$$

18.24 Fats are a triester between glycerol and fatty acids. Waxes are a monoester between a long-chain alcohol and a fatty acid.

18.26 In nature, waxes often occur as protective coatings.

18.28
g
l
y
c — fatty acid
e
r
o — phosphoric acid
l |
 alcohol

— fatty acid (under g l y c e r)

18.30 Lecithins serve as components in cell membranes and aid in lipid transport.

18.32 They differ in the identity of the amino alcohol portion. Lecithins contain choline, and cephalins contain ethanolamine or serine.

18.34
s
p
h
i
n — fatty acid
g
o
s
i — phosphoric acid
n |
e choline

18.36 Tay-Sachs, Gaucher's, and Niemann-Pick

18.38 Cerebrosides, brain tissue

18.40 Phosphoglycerides, sphingomyelin, and cholesterol

18.42 The model is composed of a flexible bilayer structure with protein molecules floating in the bilayer. The lipid molecules are free to move in a lateral direction.

18.44 The fused ring system:

18.46 Bile salts, sex hormones, and adrenocorticoid hormones. Cell membranes.

18.48 Cholesterol

18.50 The two groups are glucocorticoids and mineralocorticoids. Cortisol, a glucocorticoid, acts to increase the glucose and glycogen concentrations in the body. Aldosterone, a mineralocorticoid, regulates the retention of Na^+ and Cl^- during urine formation.

18.52 Testosterone; estradiol, estrone, and progesterone

18.54 Estrogens are involved in egg development; progesterone causes changes in the wall of the uterus to prepare it to accept a fertilized egg and maintain the resulting pregnancy.

18.56 Arachidonic acid

18.58 Induction of labor, treatment of asthma, treatment of peptic ulcers

18.60 The lipid is unsaturated (see Figure 12.5).

18.62 The phosphate and amino alcohol groups found in complex lipids are much more hydrophilic and capable of interacting with water than simple lipids.

18.64 Ester, ester

18.66 **a.** estrogens and progesterone

 b. testosterone

18.68 c: The gallbladder stores bile from the liver, which is used to emulsify fats to aid in their digestion in the intestines.

18.70 c

18.72 b

18.74 d

18.76 d

CHAPTER 19

19.2 The amine group ($-NH_2$) and the carboxylic acid group ($-COOH$), or the corresponding protonated $-NH_3^+$ group and unprotonated $-COO^-$ group.

19.4 **a.**

$$H_3N^+ - \underset{\underset{\displaystyle CH-CH_3}{\underset{\displaystyle OH}{|}}}{\overset{\overset{\displaystyle H}{|}}{C}} - COO^-$$

b.

$$H_3N^+ - \underset{\underset{\displaystyle CH_2}{\underset{\displaystyle COO^-}{|}}}{\overset{\overset{\displaystyle H}{|}}{C}} - COO^-$$

c.

$$H_3N^+ - \underset{\underset{\displaystyle CH_2}{\underset{\displaystyle OH}{|}}}{\overset{\overset{\displaystyle H}{|}}{C}} - COO^-$$

d. $H_3\overset{+}{N} - C - COO^-$

(with H on top, and CH₂ connected to a benzene ring below)

19.6

$^+H_3N - \overset{*}{C} - COO^-$ and $^+H_3N - CH - COO^-$

(left structure with side chain CH—CH₃, CH₂, CH₃; right structure with H—$\overset{*}{C}$—CH₃, then CH₂, CH₃)

19.8 a.

COO⁻	COO⁻
$H_3\overset{+}{N}$——H	H——$\overset{+}{N}H_3$
CH₂—SH	CH₂—SH
L-cysteine	D-cysteine

b.

COO⁻	COO⁻
$H_3\overset{+}{N}$——H	H——$\overset{+}{N}H_3$
CH₂	CH₂
CH₂	CH₂
COO⁻	COO⁻
L-glutamate	D-glutamate

19.10 They are crystalline solids with relatively high melting points and high water solubilities.

19.12

a. $H_2N - CH - COO^-$
(side chain: CH₂, SH)

b. $H_2N - CH - COO^-$
(side chain: CH₃)

19.14 a.

$H_3\overset{+}{N} - CH - COO^- + OH^- \longrightarrow H_2N - CH - COO^- + H_2O$
(both side chains: CH₂, OH)

b.

$H_3\overset{+}{N} - CH - COO^- + H_3O^+ \longrightarrow H_3\overset{+}{N} - CH - COOH + H_2O$
(both side chains: CH₂, OH)

19.16

$H_3\overset{+}{N} - CH - \overset{\overset{O}{\|}}{C} - NH - CH - \overset{\overset{O}{\|}}{C} - NH - CH - \overset{\overset{O}{\|}}{C} - ($

(side chains: CHCH₃ / CH₃; CH₂ / COO⁻; CH₂ / SH)

Val-Asp-Cys

19.18 Ala-Phe-Arg, Phe-Arg-Ala, Arg-Ala-Phe

Ala-Arg-Phe, Phe-Ala-Arg, Arg-Phe-Ala

19.20 Six

19.22 Each peptide contains a disulfide bridge in which two cysteines have been linked.

19.24 Normally, proteins do not pass through membranes, and the appearance of an abnormal protein in blood or urine indicates cellular damage, which has released those substances.

19.26 When a protein is at a pH corresponding to the isoelectric point, the net charge on the protein is 0. The protein is not as soluble with a 0 charge as when it possesses a net negative or positive charge.

19.28 Catalysis, structural, storage, protection, regulatory, nerve impulse transmission, motion, transport

19.30 a. Fibrous; collagen is a structural protein.

b. Globular; lactate dehydrogenase is an enzyme and needs to be water soluble.

19.32 Simple proteins contain only amino acid residues, whereas conjugated proteins contain additional components.

19.34 The sequence of the amino acid residues in the protein.

19.36

$- NH - CH - \overset{\overset{O}{\|}}{C} - NH - CH - \overset{\overset{O}{\|}}{C} - NH - CH - \overset{\overset{O}{\|}}{C} - NH -$

(side chains: R; R′; R″)

19.38 Hydrogen bonding between the amide hydrogen and the carboxyl oxygen along the backbone.

19.40 In secondary structures, the hydrogen bonding is between the atoms in the backbone; in tertiary structures, the hydrogen bonding is between atoms in the side chains.

19.42 a. Hydrogen bonding

b. Salt bridges

c. Hydrophobic interactions

d. Hydrophobic interactions

19.44 The nonpolar R groups in phenylalanine, alanine, and methionine will point inward; the polar R groups in glutamate and lysine will point toward the water.

19.46 Ionic attractions, disulfide bridges, hydrogen bonds, and hydrophobic forces.

19.48 A subunit is a polypeptide chain that is part of a larger protein.

19.50 The products of hydrolysis are the separate, individual amino acid molecules. The product of denaturation has the same primary protein backbone with different secondary, tertiary, and quaternary structures.

19.52 The primary structure of the protein is the same.

19.54 Cooking egg white is an irreversible denaturation. Whipping air into them is a reversible denaturation.

19.56 The heavy metal ions denature the protein in the egg white by interacting with the —SH groups and the carboxylate (—COO$^-$) groups. Vomiting should then be induced to remove the denatured proteins so they are not digested, releasing the metal ions.

19.58 valine, methionine, and threonine

19.60

Conjugate acid:
$$\overset{\displaystyle H}{\underset{\displaystyle R}{H_3\overset{+}{N} - C - COOH}}$$

Conjugate base:
$$\overset{\displaystyle H}{\underset{\displaystyle R}{H_2N - C - COO^-}}$$

19.62 Oxytocin

19.64 a and c

19.66 Hemoglobin is nearly spherical with four chains (subunits) and four heme groups held together.

19.68 a

CHAPTER 20

20.2 Enzymes are highly specific in the reactions they catalyze, and their activity as catalysts can be regulated.

20.4 Each one is specific for a single type of reaction and often is specific for a single substrate.

20.6 Enzymes that are specific for a single reactant exhibit absolute specificity.

20.8 -ase

20.10 a. sucrose

 b. amylose

 c. lactose

 d. maltose

 e. arginine

20.12 a. catalyzes the dehydrogenation (oxidation) of succinate

 b. catalyzes the reduction of L-amino acids

 c. catalyzes the oxidation of cytochrome

 d. catalyzes the isomerization of glucose-6-phosphate

20.14 An enzyme is a catalytically active structure made up of a protein portion called an apoenzyme and a nonprotein portion called a cofactor.

20.16 Mg^{2+}, Zn^{2+}, Fe^{2+}, Ca^{2+}

20.18 E = enzymes, S = substrate, ES = enzyme–substrate complex, and P = product of reaction. Thus E + S $\rightleftarrows$ ES $\rightarrow$ E + P represents the reaction of an enzyme with a substrate molecule to form an enzyme–substrate complex, which then gives the reaction product and regenerates the enzyme.

20.20 The shape of the enzyme active site allows only specific substrates having the correct shape to bind and be acted upon.

20.22 Induced-fit theory, because the enzyme catalyzes reactions of several related compounds.

20.24 Any observation that allows the rate of product formation or reactant depletion to be measured will allow enzyme activity to be determined.

20.26 One international unit (IU) is the amount of enzyme that will convert 1 micromol (μmol) of substrate to product in 1 minute. The international unit is useful in medical diagnosis because it represents a standard quantity of enzyme (or enzyme activity level) against which the level present in a patient can be compared.

20.28 a. The enzyme activity (rate of reaction) increases with increased substrate concentration until all the enzyme is utilized, at which point no further increase in rate occurs.

 b. The activity (rate) increases with an increase in enzyme concentration.

 c. There is an optimum pH for the reaction, so at a pH above or below the optimum value, the rate will decrease.

 d. The activity (rate) increases up to a maximum as the temperature increases, and then decreases with further temperature increase.

20.30 Prepare a series of reactions with constant enzyme amount and increasing substrate amounts. Plot reaction rate versus substrate concentration. A constant rate at higher substrate concentrations is V_{max}.

20.32 Enzymes could be denatured at pH values far from the optimum pH.

20.34 In competitive inhibition another substance, an inhibitor, competes with the substrate in binding to the active site of the enzyme. In noncompetitive inhibition the inhibitor binds to another site on the enzyme, and in doing so alters the shape of the enzyme so that it can no longer bind to the substrate, essentially prohibiting a reaction.

20.36 a. Cyanide poisoning is treated with $Na_2S_2O_3$ (sodium thiosulfate), which oxidizes CN^- to SCN^-. The thiocyanate does not bind to the iron in the enzyme.

 b. Heavy metal poisoning is treated by administering chelating agents such as EDTA. The chelating agents bond to the metal ions to form water-soluble complexes that are excreted from the body in the urine.

20.38 1. Zymogens or proenzymes

 2. Allosteric regulation

 3. Genetic control over the synthesis of enzymes

20.40 So the blood doesn't clot as it circulates, but only when clotting is needed to stop bleeding.

20.42 Modulators may increase activity (activators) or decrease the activity (inhibitors).

20.44 Genetic control of enzyme activity means that a cell synthesizes an enzyme when conditions temporarily require it. Such a controlled synthesis is called enzyme induction.

20.46 a. CK assays are used in diagnosing a heart attack.

 b. ALP assays are useful in diagnosing liver or bone disease.

 c. Amylase assays are useful in diagnosing diseases of the pancreas.

20.48 An LDH assay is a good initial diagnostic test because the iso-enzyme forms of LDH are so widespread in the human system. Thus, the locations of diseases can be pinpointed.

20.50 An ionic bond is formed:

sample substrate arginine side chain

20.52 A covalent ester linkage is formed between the acid chloride and the —OH of the serine:

$$CH_3CH_2\overset{\overset{\displaystyle O}{\|}}{C}-Cl + HO-CH_2-\boxed{Enzyme} \longrightarrow CH_3CH_2\overset{\overset{\displaystyle O}{\|}}{C}-O-CH_2-\boxed{Enzyme}$$
$$+ HCl$$

20.54 There will be no shift in the equilibrium. Enzymes are catalysts and cannot change the position of equilibrium, only the speed of which an equilibrium is reached.

20.56 a.

b.

c.

d.

20.58 b

20.60 d

20.62 c

CHAPTER 21

21.2 Deoxyribose in DNA, ribose in RNA

21.4 **a.** purine
 b. pyrimidine
 c. pyrimidine
 d. pyrimidine
 e. purine

21.6

21.8 By convention, in the DNA segment AGTCAT, the 5′ end is the A and the 3′ end is the T.

21.10 Each DNA has two complementary nucleic acid strands arranged in a double helix with the bases protruding into the interior of the helix and the 5′ end of one strand next to the 3′ end of the other. The bases on one strand form hydrogen bonds with the bases on the other.

21.12 a. 15
 b. 14

21.14 GATGCAT

21.16 A chromosome is a tightly packed bundle of DNA and protein that is involved in cell division. A human cell normally contains 46 chromosomes with about 25,000 genes.

21.18 The point in the double helix where "unwinding" begins.

21.20 1. The double helix unwinds.
 2. The new DNA segments are synthesized.
 3. The "nicks" in the new strand are closed.

21.22 The daughter strand forms from its 5′ end toward the 3′ end.

21.24 a. ACGTCT
 TGCAGA

 b.
Old strand	5′ ACGTCT 3′	daughter
New strand	3′ TGCAGA 5′	DNA molecule
New strand	5′ ACGTCT 3′	daughter
Old strand	3′ TGCAGA 5′	DNA molecule

21.26 The sugar in the RNA backbone is ribose, and that in the DNA backbone is deoxyribose.

21.28 1. mRNA functions as a messenger. It consists of a base sequence that is complementary to a DNA strand. It is formed in the nucleus and then moves into the cytoplasm where

protein synthesis occurs. It carries the genetic code to control protein synthesis.

2. Ribosomal RNA functions as the site of protein synthesis in the ribosome.

3. tRNA delivers an amino acid to the site of protein synthesis.

21.30 The two important regions of a tRNA molecule are the anticodon, which binds the tRNA to mRNA during protein synthesis, and the 3′ end, which binds to an amino acid by an ester linkage.

21.32 Transcription is the transferring of genetic DNA information to messenger RNA. Translation is the expression of messenger RNA information in the form of an amino acid sequence in a protein.

21.34 5′ CAAUAUGGC 3′

21.36 In the DNA of eukaryotic cells, segments called introns carry no amino acid coding, whereas exons are coded segments. Both introns and exons are copied (transcribed) and produce hnRNA. A series of enzyme-catalyzed reactions cut out the introns and splice the remaining segments to produce mRNA.

21.38 a. 5′ AUA 3′, tyrosine

b. 5′ AUG 3′, histidine

c. 5′ UGA 3′, serine

d. 5′ AGA 3′, serine

21.40 a. False; should be three bases.

b. True

c. False; 61 of 64 codons represent amino acids.

d. False; each living species is thought to use the same genetic code.

e. True

f. False; stop signals for protein synthesis are represented by three codons: UAA, UAG, and UGA.

21.42 A complex of mRNA and several ribosomes; also called polysome.

21.44 Initiation, elongation, termination

21.46 The A site (aminoacyl site) is where an incoming tRNA carrying the next amino acid will bond. The P site (peptidyl site) is where the tRNA carrying the peptide chain is located.

21.48 A change in the DNA of a cell wherein a wrong base sequence is produced on the DNA.

21.50 The protein synthesized would contain a proline rather than an alanine residue at that site in the protein.

21.52 Recombinant DNA is DNA of one organism that contains segments of DNA from another organism.

21.54 Human insulin will become widely available for treating diabetes. Human growth hormone will be used for treating pituitary disorders. Recombivax Hb, a vaccine for hepatitis B, will be marketed.

21.56 Hydrolysis of the phosphodiester linkage would break the nucleic acid backbone and allow the removal of intron segments. Esterification (ester formation) of the $5′ — PO_4^{2-}$ group of one exon segment to the $3′ — OH$ group of another exon segment would be used to join exons.

21.58 a. Glucose and fructose

b. Enzyme induction

c. Somehow the presence of sucrose activates the bacterial cell's DNA to produce more copies of mRNA that codes for enzyme Q.

21.60 DNA → RNA → protein

21.62 a. Small circular self-replicating DNA molecules found in bacterial cells that are used as vectors to incorporate recombinant DNA.

b. Enzymes used to fragment chromosomes to be incorporated into a plasmid; also used to open plasmids.

c. Enzyme used to join together DNA strands.

21.64 a

21.66 a

CHAPTER 22

22.2 Macronutrients are needed in large quantities per day (1 gram or more). Micronutrients are needed in small quantities (milligrams or less).

22.4

Carbohydrates	Energy source
	Provide materials for cell and tissue synthesis
Proteins	Provide amino acids for cell repair and maintenance
	Provide ingredients for the synthesis of enzymes and hormones
Lipids	Energy source; solvent for fat-soluble vitamins
	Source of essential fatty acids

22.6 a. Carbohydrates, lipids, proteins

b. Carbohydrates, lipids, proteins

c. Carbohydrates, proteins

d. Carbohydrates, lipids, proteins

e. Proteins, lipids

f. Lipids, proteins, carbohydrates

22.8 Fat, 65 g; saturated fat, 20 g; total carbohydrate, 300 g; fiber, 25 g

22.10 a. fat soluble

b. water soluble

c. water soluble

d. fat soluble

22.12 Water-soluble vitamins can be excreted in water-based fluids much more readily than fat-soluble vitamins. Thus, large doses of fat-soluble vitamins accumulate in the body.

22.14 a. vitamin C

b. vitamin B_1

c. vitamin B_{12}

d. niacin

22.16 Ca: component of bones and teeth; regulation of muscle activity

P: component of bones and teeth, nucleic acids, phospholipids, and enzymes

K: charge balance in cells; regulates heartbeat

S: component of the amino acid cysteine; charge balance in cells (as SO_4^{2-})

Na: charge balance in cells

Cl: charge balance in cells

Mg: component of enzymes; regulation of muscle activity

22.18 The general functions of trace minerals in the body are to serve as components of vitamins (Co), enzymes (Zn, Se), hormones (I), or specialized proteins (Fe, Cu).

22.20 Hydrogen

22.22 $6 CO_2 + 6 H_2O + energy \rightarrow C_6H_{12}O_6 + 6 O_2$

22.24 Energy from the sun powers the process of photosynthesis in plants. As the carbohydrates of plants are converted to CO_2 and H_2O, the released energy is trapped in molecules of ATP.

22.26 Catabolism includes all of the breakdown processes. Anabolism includes all of the synthesis processes.

22.28 a. Stage III

b. Stage I

c. Stage III

d. Stage II

22.30 The production of ATP.

22.32 ATP is involved in both.

22.34 ATP molecules store the energy released during the oxidation of food and deliver the energy to the parts of the cell where energy is needed.

22.36 P_i is the symbol for the phosphate ion. PP_i represents the pyrophosphate ion.

22.38 The hydrolysis of phosphoenolpyruvate liberates 14.8 kcal/mol, while the hydrolysis of glycerol-3-phosphate liberates only 2.2 kcal/mol.

22.40 The triphosphate portion.

22.42 Mitochondria are the sites for most ATP synthesis in the cells.

22.44 Mitochondria are cigar-shaped organelles with both an outer and an inner membrane. The inner membrane has many folds and contains the enzymes for the electron transport chain and oxidative phosphorylation. The enzymes for the citric acid cycle are attached to or near to the surface of the inner membrane.

22.46 a. Coenzyme A is part of acetyl coenzyme A, which is formed from all foods as they pass through the common metabolic pathway. Acetyl coenzyme A is the fuel for the citric acid cycle.

b. and c. FAD and NAD^+ carry hydrogen atoms from the citric acid cycle to the electron transport chain.

22.48 $^-OOC - CH_2CH_2 - COO^-$ is oxidized. FAD is reduced.

22.50 a. $HO{-}CH_2{-}COOH + NAD^+ \rightarrow$
$$O{=}CH{-}COOH + NADH + H^+$$

b. $HO{-}CH_2CH_2{-}OH + FAD \rightarrow$
$$HO{-}CH{=}CH{-}OH + FADH_2$$

22.52

a. FAD b. FADH$_2$

22.54 $CH_4 + O_2 + 2 NAD^+ \rightarrow CO_2 + 2 NADH + 2 H^+$

A total of four electrons are transferred to the 2NADH molecules.

22.56 Protein synthesis, translation

22.58 a. A, D, E, and K

b. B$_1$

c. D

d. K

e. B$_{12}$

22.60 a

22.62 Lipids or fats

22.64 a

22.66 b

22.68 c

CHAPTER 23

23.2 a. glucose

b. glucose and galactose

c. glucose and fructose

d. glucose

23.4 Blood sugar level is the concentration of glucose in the blood. The normal fasting level is the blood glucose concentration after a fast of 8–12 hours.

23.6 a. A blood sugar level below the normal range.

b. A blood sugar level above the normal fasting level.

c. A blood sugar level at which glucose is not reabsorbed by the kidneys.

d. An elevated blood sugar level resulting in the excretion of glucose in the urine.

23.8 If the blood sugar is too low, severe hypoglycemia can cause convulsions and coma.

23.10 Glucose gives pyruvate.

23.12 Steps 1 and 3 require ATP, Steps 7 and 10 produce ATP. A net of 2 ATP molecules are produced for each glucose molecule.

23.14 The third control point is in the last step of glycolysis. The enzyme for this step, pyruvate kinase, is inhibited by a high ATP concentration. If the cell does not need ATP, the ATP concentration will inhibit glycolysis and slow the production of ATP. As the need for ATP increases, the inhibition of the enzyme no longer occurs and glycolysis proceeds to make more ATP.

23.16 Glucose-6-phosphate is a feedback inhibitor of the enzyme hexokinase and causes a decrease in the enzymatic turnover rate (activity) of that enzyme.

23.18 Aerobic denotes the presence of oxygen, whereas anaerobic means without oxygen.

23.20 Under aerobic conditions, the pyruvate is converted to acetyl CoA. Under anaerobic conditions, the pyruvate is converted to lactate.

23.22 It is released as CO_2. Ethanol formation allows the yeast to regenerate NAD^+ in the absence of oxygen and still generate sufficient ATP to sustain life.

23.24 The citric acid cycle is the principal process for generating NADH and $FADH_2$, which are necessary for ATP synthesis. The citric acid cycle is also important as a source of intermediates in the biosynthesis of amino acids.

23.26 a. acetyl CoA

 b. CO_2

 c. NADH and $FADH_2$

23.28 a. three

 b. one

 c. one

 d. two

23.30

$$\begin{array}{c} COO^- \\ | \\ CH_2 \\ | \\ CH_2 \\ | \\ COO^- \end{array} + FAD \longrightarrow \begin{array}{c} H \quad COO^- \\ \diagdown \diagup \\ C \\ \| \\ C \\ \diagup \diagdown \\ {}^-OOC \quad H \end{array} + FADH_2$$

23.32 a. Step 1, citrate synthetase

 Step 3, isocitrate dehydrogenase

 Step 4, α-ketoglutarate dehydrogenase

 b. When supplies of NADH and ATP are abundant, the cell has sufficient energy for its needs, so the operation of the citric acid cycle is inhibited.

 c. As the cell uses ATP and makes ADP, the enzymes controlling the cycle are activated to make more ATP.

23.34 NADH and $FADH_2$

23.36 Cytochromes pass electrons along the electron transport chain to oxygen, which combines with H^+ ions to form water.

23.38 NADH and $FADH_2$ are oxidized to NAD^+ and FAD, respectively. ADP is phosphorylated to ATP.

23.40 1.5 molecules of ATP are formed during a sequence of reactions.

23.42 100 ATP molecules

23.44 94 mol of ATP

23.46 ATP synthesis results from the flow of protons (H^+) across the inner mitochondrial membranes.

23.48 a. 2 **b.** 2 **c.** 28

23.50 Glycogenesis is the synthesis of glycogen, while glycogenolysis is the breakdown of glycogen.

23.52 UTP

23.54 Liver cells have the essential enzyme glucose-6-phosphatase, which is lacking in muscle tissue.

23.56 The liver

23.58 Lactate (formed from pyruvate generated in the muscles), glycerol (derived from the hydrolysis of fats), and certain amino acids (from the amino acid pool).

23.60 There would be no lactate produced, so the Cori cycle wouldn't operate.

23.62 a. Insulin promotes the utilization of blood glucose, causing the level to decrease. Glucagon activates the breakdown of glycogen, thereby raising blood glucose levels.

 b. Insulin promotes glycogen formation, while glucagon stimulates the breakdown.

23.64 1.00×10^{24} ATP molecules

23.66 The removal of lactate from muscle cells shifts the equilibrium to the right, ensuring the regeneration of NAD^+ and the production of pyruvate by glycolysis. In the liver, pyruvate is used to make glucose, thus decreasing the pyruvate concentration, which shifts the equilibrium to the left and prevents the accumulation of lactate.

23.68

$$\boxed{\text{enzyme}} - CH_2 - OH \xrightarrow[\text{ATP} \quad \text{ADP}]{} \boxed{\text{enzyme}} - CH_2 - O - \overset{\displaystyle O}{\underset{\displaystyle O^-}{\overset{\|}{P}}} - O^-$$

An ester linkage is formed.

23.70 a and c

23.72 b, c, and d

23.74 a

23.76 c

23.78 d

CHAPTER 24

24.2 Glycerol, fatty acids, and monoglycerides

24.4 Chylomicrons are lipoprotein aggregates found in the lymph and the bloodstream.

24.6 Chylomicrons, very low-density lipoproteins, low-density lipoproteins, high-density lipoproteins

24.8 Fat mobilization is the process of hydrolyzing triglycerides to produce fatty acids and glycerol, both of which can be used for energy in muscle cells.

24.10 Resting muscle and liver cells

24.12 Glycerol can be converted to pyruvate and contribute to cellular energy production or be converted to glucose.

24.14 A fatty acid is first converted to a fatty acyl CoA, a high-energy compound. This occurs in the cytoplasm of the cell.

24.16 FAD and NAD^+

24.18

$$CH_3(CH_2)_{14} - \overset{\displaystyle O}{\overset{\|}{C}} - OH + HS - CoA \longrightarrow$$

$$\xrightarrow[\text{ATP} \quad \text{AMP} + 2P_i]{}$$

$$CH_3(CH_2)_{14} - \overset{\displaystyle O}{\overset{\|}{C}} - SCoA + H_2O$$

24.20 The word *cycle* implies that the product is identical to the starting material, which is not the case. The fatty acyl product of a trip through the sequence has two fewer carbon atoms than the starting material.

24.22 a.

$$CH_3CH_2CH_2CH=CH-\overset{\overset{O}{\|}}{C}-S-CoA + FADH_2$$

b.

$$CH_3CH_2CH_2CH=CH-\overset{\overset{O}{\|}}{C}-S-CoA + H_2O \longrightarrow$$

$$CH_3CH_2CH_2\overset{\overset{OH}{|}}{C}HCH_2-\overset{\overset{O}{\|}}{C}-S-CoA$$

c.

$$CH_3CH_2CH_2\overset{\overset{OH}{|}}{C}HCH_2-\overset{\overset{O}{\|}}{C}-S-CoA + NAD^+ \longrightarrow$$

$$CH_3CH_2CH_2\overset{\overset{O}{\|}}{C}CH_2-\overset{\overset{O}{\|}}{C}-S-CoA + NADH + H^+$$

d.

$$CH_3CH_2CH_2\overset{\overset{O}{\|}}{C}CH_2-\overset{\overset{O}{\|}}{C}-S-CoA + CoA-SH \longrightarrow$$

$$CH_3CH_2CH_2-\overset{\overset{O}{\|}}{C}-S-CoA + CH_3-\overset{\overset{O}{\|}}{C}-S-CoA$$

24.24 10 ATP

24.26 64 ATP molecules

24.28 Ketone bodies are three compounds formed from acetyl CoA: acetoacetate, β-hydroxybutyrate, and acetone.

24.30 The liver; the brain, heart, and skeletal muscles

24.32 Two of the ketone bodies are carboxylic acids, which lower blood pH.

24.34 Fatty acids are built two carbons at a time and broken down two carbons at a time.

24.36 The required enzymes are missing.

24.38 The amino acid pool is a supply of amino acids located within the blood and cellular spaces.

24.40 Protein turnover

24.42 Purines and pyrimidines, heme, choline, ethanolamine

24.44 a. transamination

b. deamination

c. transamination

d. transamination and deamination

24.46

$$CH_3-\overset{\overset{O}{\|}}{C}-COO^- + \overset{+}{H_3N}-CH-COO^- \longrightarrow$$

with side chain:
$$\begin{array}{c} CH_2 \\ | \\ CH-CH_3 \\ | \\ CH_3 \end{array}$$

pyruvate leucine

$$CH_3-\overset{\overset{NH_3^+}{|}}{C}H-COO^- + \overset{\overset{O}{\|}}{C}-COO^-$$

with side chain:
$$\begin{array}{c} CH_2 \\ | \\ CH-CH_3 \\ | \\ CH_3 \end{array}$$

24.48

$$\overset{+}{H_3N}-CH_2-\overset{\overset{O}{\|}}{C}-O^- + NAD^+ + H_2O \longrightarrow$$

$$H-\overset{\overset{O}{\|}}{C}-\overset{\overset{O}{\|}}{C}-O^- + NADH + NH_4^+ + H^+$$

24.50 The liver

24.52 Carbamoyl phosphate

24.54 $NH_4^+ + HCO_3^- + 3ATP + 2H_2O + COO^- \longrightarrow$

$$\begin{array}{c} CH_2 \\ | \\ CH-NH_3^+ \\ | \\ COO^- \end{array}$$
aspartate

$$H_2N-\overset{\overset{O}{\|}}{C}-NH_2 + {}^-OOC-CH=CH-COO^-$$
urea fumarate

$$+ 2ADP + 2P_i + AMP + PP_i$$

24.56 Yes; isoleucine, tryptophan, phenylalanine, and tyrosine

24.58 a. glucogenic

b. ketogenic

c. ketogenic

24.60 Amino acids that can be synthesized by the body are called nonessential. Those amino acids that must be obtained from the diet because the body cannot produce them are called essential amino acids.

24.62 Transaminases are used in the biosynthesis of amino acids and in the transfer of nitrogen atoms from amino acids when the disposal of nitrogen is necessary.

24.64 The glycolysis pathway and the citric acid cycle

24.66 Activation of zymogens and the production of new enzymes through induction

24.68 It is an LDL.

24.70 b

24.72 Amino acids

24.74 ketoacidosis

CHAPTER 25

25.2 Plasma and interstitial fluid

25.4 **a.** Intracellular fluid

 b. Intracellular fluid

 c. Plasma and interstitial fluid

 d. Intracellular fluid

 e. Plasma and interstitial fluid

 f. Intracellular fluid

 g. Plasma and interstitial fluid

25.6 **a.** Cl^-

 b. Cl^-

 c. HPO_4^{2-}

25.8 **a.** $HHb + O_2 \rightleftarrows HbO_2^- + H^+$

 b. $HHb + CO_2 \rightleftarrows HHbCO_2$

25.10 **a.** 2% **b.** 98% **c.** 25% **d.** 5% **e.** 70%

25.12 A larger surface area increases the amount of O_2 and CO_2 that can diffuse through the surface. The partial pressure gradient is the force that causes O_2 and CO_2 movement.

25.14 **a.** Osmotic pressure

 b. Blood pressure

25.16 Urea

25.18 Glucose (in large amounts), protein, ketone bodies, pus, hemoglobin, red blood cells, bile pigments (in large amounts)

25.20 Kidneys (urine), lungs (water vapor), skin (perspiration), and intestines (feces)

25.22 Variations in urine output

25.24 As fluid level decreases, saliva output decreases, giving the "thirst" feeling. Drinking water raises fluid level.

25.26 Blood buffers, urinary system, and respiratory system. The blood buffer system is the fastest to react.

25.28 Bicarbonate, phosphate, and protein

25.30 Exhaled H_2O and CO_2 are derived from H_2CO_3. The more CO_2 and H_2O that are exhaled, the more carbonic acid is removed from the blood, thus elevating the blood pH.

25.32 Respiratory alkalosis

25.34 CO_2 diffuses into the distal tubule cells to form carbonic acid, which then ionizes to H^+ and HCO_3^-. Thus, CO_2 concentration is lowered in the blood.

25.36 As H^+ enters the urine, Na^+ is reabsorbed into the blood from the urine.

25.38 Respiratory acid-base imbalances are the result of abnormal breathing patterns. Acid-base imbalances caused by any other factor are metabolic acid-base imbalances.

25.40 The depressant narcotic often causes a lower breathing rate, causing respiratory acidosis. Diabetes mellitus can cause metabolic acidosis.

25.42 5.01×10^{23} amino acid molecules

25.44 The increased concentration of Na^+ (and Cl^-) ions in the blood increases the osmotic pressure gradient and water flows from the region of low solute concentration to the region of high solute concentration.

25.46 Heavy exercise would cause anaerobic conditions to occur in some cells, which would then release lactate from glycolysis into the bloodstream.

25.48 Partial pressure

25.50 a, b, c, and d

25.52 c

25.54 b

25.56 c

Solutions to Learning Checks

CHAPTER 1

1.1 A change is chemical if new substances are formed and physical if no new substances are formed.

 a. Chemical: The changes in taste and odor indicate that new substances form.

 b. Physical: The handkerchief doesn't change, and the evaporated water is still water.

 c. Chemical: The changes in color and taste indicate that new substances form.

 d. Chemical: The gases and smoke released indicate that new substances form.

 e. Physical: The air is still air, as indicated by appearance, odor, and so on.

 f. Physical: On being condensed, the steam forms water, which is the same substance present before the change.

1.2 **a.** Triatomic and heteroatomic: The three atoms of two kinds (oxygen and hydrogen) make it both triatomic (three atoms) and heteroatomic (two or more kinds of atoms).

 b. Triatomic and homoatomic: The three atoms make it triatomic, but all three atoms are the same (oxygen).

 c. Polyatomic and heteroatomic: The total of five atoms makes it polyatomic, and the two different kinds of atoms (carbon and hydrogen) make it heteroatomic.

1.3 Molecules of elements can be diatomic, triatomic, or polyatomic, but all atoms will be identical and will be represented by the same color. Molecules of compounds must be diatomic, triatomic, or polyatomic (more than one atom), and the atoms will not all be identical.

 a. Compound: polyatomic and heteroatomic

 b. Element: diatomic and homoatomic

 c. Element: polyatomic and homoatomic

 d. Compound: polyatomic and heteroatomic

1.4 The product would have to be a compound because it would be polyatomic (more than one atom because two substances were used) and heteroatomic (different atoms from the two different substances).

1.5 Substitute the given radius and π values into the equation:

$A = \pi r^2 = (3.14)(3.5 \text{ cm})^2 = (3.14)(12.25 \text{ cm}^2) = 38 \text{ cm}^2$

1.6 The volume of a rectangular object is equal to the product of the three sides.

$V = (30.0 \text{ cm})(20.0 \text{ cm})(15.0 \text{ cm})$

$= 9000 \text{ cm}^3, \text{ or } (9.00 \times 10^3 \text{ cm}^3)$

$1 \text{ cm}^3 = 1 \text{ mL}$, so the volume is 9.00×10^3 mL. A liter is equal to 1000 mL, so 9000 mL = 9 L. The correct answers are 9.00×10^3 mL and 9.00 L.

1.7 Because 1 kg = 1000 g,

$$0.819 \text{ kg} \times \frac{1000 \text{ g}}{1 \text{ kg}} = 819 \text{ g}$$

1.8 Use Equation 1.4 and the fact that 77°F = 25°C, as shown in Example 1.7.

$$\text{K} = °\text{C} + 273 = 25°\text{C} + 273 = 298 \text{ K}$$

1.9 **a.** Scientific notation is used. In nonscientific notation, the number is written 588.

 b. Scientific notation is not used. In scientific notation, the number is written 4.39×10^{-4}.

 c. Scientific notation is used. In nonscientific notation, the number is written 0.0003915.

 d. Scientific notation is not used. In scientific notation, the number is written 9.870×10^3.

 e. Scientific notation is not used. In scientific notation, the number is written 3.677×10^1.

 f. Scientific notation is not used. In scientific notation, the number is written 1.02×10^{-1}.

1.10 The two important things to note are the placement of the decimal in the standard position and the correct value of the exponent.

 a. Written incorrectly: The decimal is not in standard position. Move the decimal 1 place to the left and increase the exponent by 1 to account for moving the decimal: 6.25×10^5.

 b. Written incorrectly: The decimal is not in the standard position, and no exponent is used. Move the decimal 3 places to the right and use −3 for the exponent to account for moving the decimal: 9.8×10^{-3}.

 c. Written incorrectly: The decimal is not in the standard position. Move the decimal 3 places to the right and reduce the exponent by 3 to account for moving the decimal: 4.1×10^{-6}.

 d. Written correctly.

1.11 Perform multiplications and divisions separately for the nonexponential and exponential terms, then combine the results into the final answer.

 a. $(2.4 \times 10^3)(1.5 \times 10^4) = (2.4 \times 1.5)(10^3 \times 10^4) = (3.6)(10^{3+4}) = 3.6 \times 10^7$

 b. $(3.5 \times 10^2)(2.0 \times 10^{-3}) = (3.5 \times 2.0)(10^2 \times 10^{-3}) = (7.0)(10^{2+(-3)}) = 7.0 \times 10^{-1}$

c. $\dfrac{6.3 \times 10^5}{2.1 \times 10^3} = \left(\dfrac{6.3}{2.1}\right)\left(\dfrac{10^5}{10^3}\right) = (3.0)(10^{5-3})$

$$= 3.0 \times 10^2$$

d. $\dfrac{4.4 \times 10^{-2}}{8.8 \times 10^{-3}} = \left(\dfrac{4.4}{8.8}\right)\left(\dfrac{10^{-2}}{10^{-3}}\right) = (.50)(10^{-2-(-3)})$

$$= .50 \times 10^1 = 5.0 \times 10^0, \text{ or } 5.0$$

1.12 The primary challenge is to interpret correctly the significance of zeros. Leading zeros to the left of nonzero numbers are not significant; all other zeros, including trailing zeros, are significant.

 a. 3, trailing zero is significant.

 b. 4

 c. 3, leading zeros are not significant.

 d. 2

 e. 1, leading zeros are not significant.

 f. 4, trailing zero is significant.

1.13 **a.** 3 significant figures; original decimal position is 2 places to the right of standard position, so exponent is +2.
1.01×10^2 m.

 b. 4 significant figures; original decimal position is 3 places to the right of standard position, so exponent is +3.
1.200×10^3 g.

 c. 3 significant figures; original decimal position is 3 places to the left of standard position, so exponent is −3.
2.30×10^{-3} kg.

 d. 4 significant figures; original decimal position is 3 places to the right of standard position, so exponent is +3.
1.296×10^{3}°C.

 e. 4 significant figures; original decimal position is 1 place to the right of standard position, so exponent is +1.
2.165×10^1 mL.

 f. 2 significant figures; original decimal position is 2 places to the left of standard position, so exponent is −2.
1.5×10^{-2} km.

1.14 **a.** Answer will be rounded to 2 significant figures to match 0.0019.

$$(0.0019)(21.39) = 0.04064 = 4.1 \times 10^{-2}$$

 b. Answer will be rounded to 2 significant figures to match 4.1.

$$\dfrac{8.321}{4.1} = 2.0295 = 2.0$$

 c. Answer will be rounded to 3 significant figures to match 0.0911 and 3.22.

$$\dfrac{(0.0911)(3.22)}{(1.379)} = 0.21272 = 0.213, \text{ or } 2.13 \times 10^{-1}$$

1.15 In each case, the sum or difference is rounded to have the same number of places to the right of the decimal as the least number of places in the terms added or subtracted.

 a. Answer will be rounded to have one place to the right of the decimal to match 3.2.

$$8.01 + 3.2 = 11.21 = 11.2$$

b. Answer will be rounded to have no places to the right of the decimal to match 3000.

$$3000 + 20.3 + 0.009 = 3020.309 = 3020$$

c. Answer will be rounded to have two places to the right of the decimal to match both 4.33 and 3.12.

$$4.33 - 3.12 = 1.21$$

d. Answer will be rounded to have two places to the right of the decimal to match 2.42.

$$6.023 - 2.42 = 3.603 = 3.60$$

1.16 Two factors result from the relationship 1 g = 1000 mg. The factors are:

$$\dfrac{1 \text{ g}}{1000 \text{ mg}} \quad \text{and} \quad \dfrac{1000 \text{ mg}}{1 \text{ g}}$$

The first factor is used because it cancels the mg unit and generates the g unit:

Step 1. 1.1 mg

Step 2. 1.1 mg $\qquad\qquad\qquad = \qquad\qquad$ g

Step 3. $1.1 \text{ m\cancel{g}} \times \dfrac{1 \text{ g}}{1000 \text{ m\cancel{g}}} \quad = \qquad$ g

Step 4. $\dfrac{(1.1)(1 \text{ g})}{(1000)} = 0.0011 \text{ g} = 1.1 \times 10^{-3} \text{ g}$

The number of significant figures matches the number in 1.1 because the 1 and 1000 are exact numbers.

1.17 Two factors, 1 km/1000 m and 0.621 mi/1 km, are used to convert meters to miles, and two factors, 60 s/1 min and 60 min/1 h, are used to convert seconds in the denominator to hours.

$$10.0\, \dfrac{\cancel{m}}{\cancel{s}} \times \dfrac{1 \text{ k\cancel{m}}}{1000\, \cancel{m}} \times \dfrac{0.621 \text{ mi}}{1 \text{ k\cancel{m}}} \times \dfrac{60\, \cancel{s}}{1\, \cancel{min}}$$

$$\times \dfrac{60\, \cancel{min}}{1 \text{ h}} = 22.356 \text{ mi/h}$$

Rounding to 3 significant figures gives 22.4 mi/h.

1.18 **a.** $\% = \dfrac{\text{part}}{\text{total}} \times 100; \% = \dfrac{\$988}{\$1200} \times 100 = 82.3\%$

 b. $\% = \dfrac{\text{part}}{\text{total}} \times 100$

$$90.4\% = \dfrac{\text{part}}{83} \times 100$$

$$\dfrac{(90.4\%)(83)}{100} = \text{part}$$

$$= \text{no. voting to not take final}$$

$$= 75.0$$

Number voting to take exam = 83 − 75 = 8.

1.19 The value of the density gives two factors that may be used to solve problems of this type:

$$\dfrac{2.7 \text{ g}}{1.0 \text{ cm}^3} \quad \text{and} \quad \dfrac{1.0 \text{ cm}^3}{2.7 \text{ g}}$$

 a. The sample volume is 60.0 cm³, and we wish to use a factor that will convert this to grams. The first factor given above will work.

$$60.0 \text{ c\cancel{m}}^3 \times \dfrac{2.7 \text{ g}}{1.0 \text{ c\cancel{m}}^3} = 162 \text{ g (calculator answer)}$$

$$= 1.6 \times 10^2 \text{ g (properly rounded answer)}$$

b. The sample mass is 98.5 g, and we wish to convert this to cm^3. The second factor given above will work.

$$98.5 \text{ g} \times \frac{1.0 \text{ cm}^3}{2.7 \text{ g}} = 36.48 \text{ cm}^3 \text{ (calculator answer)}$$

$$= 3.6 \times 10^1 \text{ cm}^3 \text{ (properly rounded answer)}$$

1.20 a. The sample mass is equal to the difference between the mass of the container with the sample inside and the mass of the empty container:

$$m = 64.93 \text{ g} - 51.22 \text{ g} = 13.71 \text{ g}$$

The density of the sample is equal to the sample mass divided by the sample volume:

$$d = \frac{m}{V} = \frac{13.71 \text{ g}}{10.00 \text{ mL}}$$

$$= 1.371 \text{ g/mL (properly rounded answer)}$$

b. The identity can be determined by calculating the density of the sample from the data and comparing the density with the known densities of the two possible metals. The volume of the sample is equal to the difference between the cylinder readings with the sample present and with the sample absent:

$$V = 25.2 \text{ mL} - 21.2 \text{ mL} = 4.0 \text{ mL}$$

According to Table 1.3, 1 mL = 1 cm^3, so the sample volume is equal to 4.0 cm^3. The density of the sample is equal to the sample mass divided by the sample volume:

$$d = \frac{m}{V} = \frac{35.66 \text{ g}}{4.0 \text{ cm}^3}$$

$$= 8.9 \text{ g/cm}^3 \text{ (properly rounded answer)}$$

A comparison with the known densities of nickel and chromium allows the metal to be identified as nickel.

CHAPTER 2

2.1 The number of atoms in each molecule is represented by a subscript in the formula.

a. H_3PO_4 **b.** SO_3 **c.** $C_6H_{12}O_6$

2.2 a. The atomic number, Z, equals the number of protons: $Z = 4$. The mass number, A, equals the sum of the number of protons and the number of neutrons: $A = 4 + 5 = 9$. According to the periodic table, the element with an atomic number of 4 is beryllium, with the symbol Be. The isotope symbol is ^{9_4}Be.

b. According to the periodic table, chlorine has the symbol Cl and an atomic number, Z, of 17. The mass number, 37, is equal to the sum of the number of protons and neutrons: $A = \#p + \#n$. Therefore, the number of neutrons is equal to the mass number, A, minus the number of protons: $\#n = A - 17 = 37 - 17 = 20$.

c. According to the periodic table, the element with the symbol Si is silicon, which has an atomic number of 14. Therefore, the atom contains 14 protons. Since $A = \#p + \#n$, we see that $\#n = A - \#p = 28 - 14 = 14$.

2.3 a. Nitrogen atoms have a periodic table weight of 14.01 u, which rounds to 14 u. Iron atoms have a periodic table weight of 55.85 u, which rounds to 56 u. Thus, four nitrogen atoms (4×14 u = 56 u) will balance one iron atom.

b. Carbon atoms have a periodic table weight of 12.01 u, which rounds to 12 u. Helium atoms have a periodic table weight of 4.00 u, which rounds to 4 u. Thus, two carbon atoms (2×12 u = 24 u) will balance six helium atoms (6×4 u = 24 u).

c. Calcium atoms have a periodic table weight of 40.08 u, which rounds to 40 u. Argon atoms have a periodic table weight of 39.95 u, which rounds to 40 u. Thus, two calcium atoms (2×40 u = 80 u) will balance two argon atoms (2×40 u = 80 u).

2.4 Molecular weights are obtained by adding the atomic weights of the atoms in molecules. We have used four significant figures in atomic weights.

a. H_2SO_4; molecular weight = 2(at. wt. H) + (at. wt. S) + 4(at. wt. O)

$$MW = 2(1.008 \text{ u}) + 32.06 \text{ u} + 4(16.00 \text{ u})$$

$$= 2.016 \text{ u} + 32.06 \text{ u} + 64.00 \text{ u}$$

$$= 98.08 \text{ u}$$

b. C_3H_8O; molecular weight = 3(at. wt. C) + 8(at. wt. H) + (at. wt. O)

$$MW = 3(12.01 \text{ u}) + 8(1.008 \text{ u}) + 16.00 \text{ u}$$

$$= 36.03 \text{ u} + 8.064 \text{ u} + 16.00 \text{ u}$$

$$= 60.09 \text{ u}$$

2.5 a. Because naturally occuring fluorine consists of only a single isotope, the equation for calculating atomic weight becomes:

$$\text{At. wt.} = \frac{(\% \text{ fluorine-19})(\text{mass fluorine-19})}{100}$$

$$= \frac{(100)(19.00 \text{ u})}{100} = 19.00 \text{ u}$$

The calculated value is the same as the periodic table value.

b.

$$\text{At. wt.} = \frac{(\% \text{ Mg-24})(\text{mass Mg-24})}{100}$$

$$+ \frac{(\% \text{ Mg-25})(\text{mass Mg-25}) + (\% \text{ Mg-26})(\text{mass Mg-26})}{100}$$

$$= \frac{(78.70)(23.99 \text{ u}) + (10.13)(24.99 \text{ u})}{100}$$

$$+ \frac{(11.17)(25.98 \text{ u})}{100}$$

$$= 24.31 \text{ u}$$

Once again, the calculated value is the same as the periodic table value.

2.6 The mass ratio is obtained by dividing the mass of the magnesium sample by the mass of the carbon sample:

$$\frac{\text{Mg mass}}{\text{C mass}} = \frac{13.66 \text{ g}}{6.748 \text{ g}} = 2.024$$

The number of atoms in each sample is calculated using the factors obtained earlier from the mass of one atom of each element:

$$13.66 \text{ g Mg} \times \frac{1 \text{ Mg atom}}{4.037 \times 10^{-23} \text{ g Mg}}$$

$$= 3.384 \times 10^{23} \text{ Mg atoms}$$

$$6.748 \text{ g } \cancel{C} \times \frac{1 \text{ C atom}}{1.994 \times 10^{-23} \text{ g } \cancel{C}} = 3.384 \times 10^{23} \text{ C atoms}$$

2.7 The known quantity is one O atom, and the unit of the unknown is grams of O. The factor comes from the relationship 6.02×10^{23} O atoms = 16.00 g O. This relationship provides two factors:

$$\frac{6.02 \times 10^{23} \text{ O atoms}}{16.00 \text{ g O}} \quad \text{and} \quad \frac{16.00 \text{ g O}}{6.02 \times 10^{23} \text{ O atoms}}$$

The second factor is the one used:

$$(1 \cancel{\text{O atom}})\left(\frac{16.00 \text{ g O}}{6.02 \times 10^{23} \cancel{\text{O atoms}}}\right) = 2.66 \times 10^{-23} \text{ g O}$$

The ratio of this mass to the mass of a carbon atom is:

$$\frac{2.66 \times 10^{-23} \text{ g O}}{1.994 \times 10^{-23} \text{ g C}} = 1.33 \text{ (properly rounded answer)}$$

The ratio of the atomic weights of oxygen and carbon is:

$$\frac{16.00 \cancel{u}}{12.01 \cancel{u}} = 1.33 \text{ (rounded to 3 significant figures)}$$

The two ratios are the same to 3 significant figures.

2.8 MW = 1(At. wt. C) + 1(At. wt. O) = 1(12.0 u) + 1(16.0 u) = 28.0 u

Application of the mole concept to CO molecules gives the following relationships:

$$1 \text{ mol CO molecules} = 6.02 \times 10^{23} \text{ CO molecules}$$
$$= 28.0 \text{ g CO}$$

The calculation of the mass of one CO molecule is done as follows: The known quantity is 1 CO molecule, and the unit of the unknown is g CO. The factor comes from the relationship 6.02×10^{23} CO molecules = 28.0 g CO.

$$(1 \cancel{\text{CO molecule}})\left(\frac{28.0 \text{ g CO}}{6.02 \times 10^{23} \cancel{\text{CO molecules}}}\right)$$
$$= 4.65 \times 10^{-23} \text{ g CO}$$

Comparing the mass of a CO molecule to the mass of a CO_2 molecule gives:

$$\frac{\text{mass of 1 CO molecule}}{\text{mass of 1 } CO_2 \text{ molecule}} = \frac{4.65 \times 10^{-23} \text{ g}}{7.31 \times 10^{-23} \text{ g}} = 0.636$$

Comparing the molecular weight of CO to the molecular weight of CO_2 gives:

$$\frac{\text{MW CO}}{\text{MW } CO_2} = \frac{28.0 \text{ u}}{44.0 \text{ u}} = 0.636$$

It is seen that the ratio of the actual masses of the molecules is identical to the ratio of their relative masses (their molecular weights).

2.9 The relationships between moles of atoms in 1 mol of molecules is given by the subscripts of the atoms. Thus, 1 mol of glucose molecules would contain 6 mol of C atoms, 12 mol of H atoms, and 6 mol of O atoms. One-half mol of glucose molecules would contain half as many moles of each atom, or 3 mol of C atoms, 6 mol of H atoms, and 3 mol of O atoms.

2.10 $\% = \dfrac{\text{part}}{\text{total}} \times 100$

In each compound, the part will be the mass of carbon associated with some mass of compound (the total). The mass relationships

are easily obtained by assuming a sample size equal to 1.00 mol of each compound.

CO_2: 1.00 mol CO_2 molecules = 1.00 mol C atoms + 2.00 mol O atoms or, using atomic weights,

$$44.01 \text{ g } CO_2 = 12.01 \text{ g C} + 32.00 \text{ g O}$$

$$\% \text{ C} = \frac{(12.01 \text{ g C}) \times 100}{(44.01 \text{ g } CO_2)} = 27.29\% \text{ C}$$

CO: 1.00 mol CO molecules = 1.00 mol C atoms + 1.00 mol O atoms

$$28.01 \text{ g CO} = 12.01 \text{ g C} + 16.00 \text{ g O}$$

$$\% \text{ C} = \frac{(12.01 \text{ g C})}{(28.01 \text{ g CO})} \times 100 = 42.88\% \text{ C}$$

CHAPTER 3

3.1 Each element is found at the intersection of the given group (vertical columns) and period (horizontal rows).

 a. Ge **b.** Re

3.2 **a.** Period 1 has 2 elements, H and He.

 b. Group IIB(12) has 4 elements, Zn, Cd, Hg, and element 112.

3.3 **a.** The maximum number of electrons that can be found in any orbital, including a $4p$ orbital, is 2.

 b. All d subshells, including the $5d$, contain 5 orbitals with a capacity of 2 electrons each. Thus, the $5d$ subshell can contain a maximum of 10 electrons.

 c. Shell number 1 contains only a single s orbital, the $1s$ orbital, and so can contain a maximum of 2 electrons.

3.4 The valence shell is the last shell with electrons. According to Table 3.2, group VA(15) elements all have 5 electrons in the valence shell. Group VIA(16) elements have 6, group VIIA(17) have 7, and the noble gases VIIIA(18) have 8.

3.5 **a.** Strontium (Sr) is in group IIA(2) and so contains 2 electrons in its valence shell.

 b. Once again, the roman numeral of the group heading gives the number of valence-shell electrons. The element is Ge, and because it is in group IVA(14), it has 4 electrons in the valence shell.

 c. The fifteenth element in period 4 is As, which is in group VA(15) and therefore has 5 electrons in the valence shell.

3.6 The subshell filling order is obtained from Figure 3.7 or Figure 3.8. All subshells except the last one are filled to their capacities as follows: s subshells—filled with 2, p subshells—filled with 6, d subshells—filled with 10, and f subshells—filled with 14. The last subshell has only enough electrons added to bring the total number of electrons to the desired value.

 a. Element 9 requires 9 electrons: $1s^2 2s^2 2p^5$; 1 unpaired

 b. Mg is element 12 and so needs 12 electrons:

$$1s^2 2s^2 2p^6 3s^2; \text{ 0 unpaired}$$

 c. The element in group VIA(16) and period 3 is S, which is element 16. Therefore, it needs 16 electrons:

$$1s^2 2s^2 2p^6 3s^2 3p^4; \text{ 2 unpaired}$$

 d. An atom with 23 protons needs 23 electrons:

$$1s^2 2s^2 2p^6 3s^2 3p^6 4s^2 3d^3; \text{ 3 unpaired}$$

3.7 **a.** From Learning Check 3.6, the electronic configuration of element number 9 is $1s^2 2s^2 2p^5$. The $1s^2$ electrons represent the configuration of helium. So, we can write the configuration as $[He]2s^2 2p^5$.

b. The configuration of Mg is $1s^2 2s^2 2p^6 3s^2$. The first 10 electrons represent the configuration of neon: $[Ne]3s^2$.

c. The configuration of S is $1s^2 2s^2 2p^6 3s^2 3p^4$. Once again, the first 10 electrons represent the configuration of neon: $[Ne]3s^2 3p^4$.

d. The 23 electrons are represented by $1s^2 2s^2 2p^6 3s^2 3p^6 4s^2 3d^3$. The first 18 electrons represent the configuration of argon: $[Ar]4s^2 3d^3$.

3.8 **a.** On the basis of the location of each element in Figure 3.9, the distinguishing electrons are of the following types: element 38(Sr): s; element 47(Ag): d; element 50(Sn): p; element 86(Rn): p.

b. Their classifications based on Figure 3.10 are element 38(Sr): representative element; element 47(Ag): transition element; element 50(Sn): representative element; element 86(Rn): noble gas.

3.9 The periodic table and Figure 3.12 are used.

a. Xe: nonmetal

b. As: metalloid

c. Hg: metal

d. Ba: metal

e. Th: metal

3.10 **a.** The slowest reaction involves Li, and the fastest involves K.

Li
Na
K

b. The rate of the reaction increases coming down the group, and according to Table 3.3, the ionization energy decreases coming down the group.

c. The decrease in ionization energy coming down the group means less energy is required to remove electrons from atoms of the elements located farther down the group. The reactions in Figure 3.17 involve the removal of an electron from atoms of the metals, so the easier it is to remove electrons (less energy required), the faster the reaction should go. This trend in speed is what is observed.

CHAPTER 4

4.1 The subshell filling order is obtained from Figure 3.7 or Figure 3.8.

F; 9 electrons: $1s^2 2s^2 2p^5$

K; 19 electrons: $1s^2 2s^2 2p^6 3s^2 3p^6 4s^1$

The configuration of F can be changed to that of He ($1s^2$) by giving up 7 electrons or to that of Ne ($1s^2 2s^2 2p^6$) by accepting 1 electron. The configuration of K can be changed to that of Ar ($1s^2 2s^2 2p^6 3s^2 3p^6$) by giving up 1 electron or to that of Kr ($1s^2 2s^2 2p^6 3s^2 3p^6 4s^2 3d^{10} 4p^6$) by accepting 17 electrons.

4.2 **a.** Element number 9 is fluorine, which is in group VIIA(17) and so has 7 valence-shell electrons. The Lewis structure is $:\overset{\cdot\cdot}{\underset{\cdot\cdot}{F}}\cdot$.

b. Magnesium is in group IIA(2) and so has 2 valence-shell electrons. The Lewis structure is $\overset{\cdot}{Mg}\cdot$.

c. Sulfur is in group VIA(16) and so has 6 valence-shell electrons. The Lewis structure is $:\overset{\cdot\cdot}{\underset{\cdot}{S}}\cdot$.

d. Krypton is a noble gas and so has 8 valence-shell electrons. The Lewis structure is $:\overset{\cdot\cdot}{\underset{\cdot\cdot}{Kr}}:$.

4.3 **a.** Lithium contains 3 electrons, with one of them classified as a valence-shell electron: $[He]2s^1$ and Li·.

b. Bromine contains 35 electrons, with 7 of them classified as valence-shell electrons: $[Ar]4s^2 3d^{10} 4p^5$ and $:\overset{\cdot\cdot}{\underset{\cdot}{Br}}\cdot$.

c. Strontium contains 38 electrons, with 2 classified as valence-shell electrons: $[Kr]5s^2$ and $\overset{\cdot}{Sr}\cdot$.

d. Sulfur contains 16 electrons, with 6 classified as valence-shell electrons: $[Ne]3s^2 3p^4$ and $:\overset{\cdot\cdot}{\underset{\cdot}{S}}\cdot$.

4.4 The change that will actually take place is the one that involves the fewest electrons. Thus, F will gain 1 electron rather than give up 7, and K will give up 1 electron rather than gain 17:

$$F + 1e^- \rightarrow F^-$$

$$K \rightarrow K^+ + 1e^-$$

4.5 **a.** Element number 34 is a nonmetal. It is in group VIA(16) and will, when treated using the rules for nonmetals, accept $8 - 6$ or 2 electrons during ionic bond formation:

$$Se + 2e^- \rightarrow Se^{2-}$$

b. Rb, a metal in group IA(1), will lose 1 electron during ionic bond formation:

$$Rb \rightarrow Rb^+ + 1e^-$$

c. Element 18 is a nonmetallic noble gas. It will not react to form ionic bonds.

d. In, a metal in group IIIA(13), will lose 3 electrons during ionic bond formation:

$$In \rightarrow In^{3+} + 3e^-$$

4.6 **a.** Mg, a metal in group IIA(2), will lose 2 electrons:

$$Mg \rightarrow Mg^{2+} + 2e^-$$

O, a nonmetal in group VIA(16), will gain 2 electrons:

$$O + 2e^- \rightarrow O^{2-}$$

The positive and negative ions are combined in the lowest numbers possible to give the compound formula. The combining requirement is that the total number of positive charges from the positive ion must equal the total number of negative charges from the negative ion. In the case of Mg^{2+} and O^{2-}, one of each ion satisfies the requirement, and the formula is MgO.

b. K, a group IA(1) metal, will lose 1 electron:

$$K \rightarrow K^+ + 1e^-$$

S, a group VIA(16) nonmetal, will gain 2 electrons:

$$S + 2e^- \rightarrow S^{2-}$$

In the formula, $2K^+$ will be needed for each S^{2-}. Thus, the compound formula is K_2S.

c. Ca, a group IIA(2) metal, will lose 2 electrons:

$$Ca \rightarrow Ca^{2+} + 2e^-$$

Br, a group VIIA(17) nonmetal, will gain 1 electron:

$$Br + 1e^- \rightarrow Br^-$$

In the formula, $2Br^-$ will combine with each Ca^{2+}: $CaBr_2$

4.7 **a.** magnesium oxide

 b. potassium sulfide

 c. calcium bromide

4.8 **a.** Charge balance requires that $2Br^-$ combine with each Co^{2+}: $CoBr_2$. Names are cobalt(II) bromide and cobaltous bromide.

 b. Charge balance requires that $3Br^-$ combine with each Co^{3+}: $CoBr_3$. Names are cobalt(III) bromide and cobaltic bromide.

4.9 **a.** For H_2S, the molecular weight is the sum of the atomic weights of the atoms in the formula:

$$MW = (2)(\text{at. wt. H}) + (1)(\text{at. wt. S})$$
$$= (2)(1.01\ u) + (1)(32.1\ u)$$
$$MW = 34.1\ u$$

For CaO, the formula weight is also equal to the sum of the atomic weights of the atoms in the formula:

$$FW = (1)(\text{at. wt. Ca}) + (1)(\text{at. wt. O})$$
$$= (1)(40.1\ u) + (1)(16.0\ u)$$
$$FW = 56.1\ u$$

 b. According to Section 2.6, 1.00 mol of a molecular compound has a mass in grams equal to the molecular weight of the compound. Thus, 1.00 mol H_2S = 34.1 g H_2S. For ionic compounds, 1.00 mol of compound has a mass in grams equal to the formula weight of the compound. Thus, 1.00 mol CaO = 56.1 g CaO.

 c. In Section 2.6, we learned that 1.00 mol of a molecular compound contains Avogadro's number of molecules. Thus, 1.00 mol H_2S = 6.02×10^{23} molecules of H_2S. In the case of ionic compounds, 1.00 mol of compound contains Avogadro's number of formula units. That is, 1.00 mol of calcium oxide contains Avogadro's number of CaO units, where each unit represents one Ca^{2+} ion and one O^{2-} ion. Thus:

1.00 mol CaO = 6.02×10^{23} CaO units or

1.00 mol CaO = 6.02×10^{23} Ca^{2+} ions

 + 6.02×10^{23} O^{2-} ions

4.10 **a.** N is in group VA(15) and therefore has 5 valence-shell electrons. Two N atoms will provide 10 total electrons to satisfy the octets. At least 2 electrons are needed to bond the atoms. This leaves only 8 electrons to satisfy the remaining octet requirements of both atoms. This deficiency of electrons means some multiple bonds will be needed between the atoms:

$$:\!\overset{\cdot}{N}\!\cdot + \cdot\overset{\cdot}{N}\!: \longrightarrow :N:::N: \quad \text{or} \quad N\equiv N$$

 b. Br is in group VIIA(17) and therefore has 7 valence-shell electrons. Two atoms will provide 14 electrons, and the bonding is readily shown:

$$:\!\overset{\cdot\cdot}{\underset{\cdot\cdot}{Br}}\!\cdot + \cdot\overset{\cdot\cdot}{\underset{\cdot\cdot}{Br}}\!: \longrightarrow :\!\overset{\cdot\cdot}{\underset{\cdot\cdot}{Br}}\!:\!\overset{\cdot\cdot}{\underset{\cdot\cdot}{Br}}\!: \quad \text{or} \quad Br - Br$$

4.11 **a.** Each C contributes 4 valence-shell electrons, and each H contributes 1. The total available is 8:

$$H\!:\!\overset{\cdot\cdot}{\underset{\cdot\cdot}{C}}\!:\!H \quad \text{or} \quad H - \underset{\displaystyle H}{\overset{\displaystyle H}{C}} - H$$

 b. Each H contributes 1 electron, the C contributes 4, and the O contributes 6. The total of 12 electrons cannot satisfy all octets unless two pair are shared between the C and O atoms:

$$H\!:\!\underset{\displaystyle H}{C}\!:\!:\!\overset{\cdot\cdot}{\underset{\cdot\cdot}{O}}\!: \quad \text{or} \quad H - \underset{\displaystyle H}{C} = O$$

 c. Each H contributes 1 electron, each O contributes 6, and the N contributes 5. The 24 total electrons can satisfy all octets only if two pair are shared between the N and one of the O atoms:

$$H\!:\!\overset{\cdot\cdot}{\underset{\cdot\cdot}{O}}\!:\!\underset{\displaystyle :\overset{\cdot\cdot}{\underset{\cdot\cdot}{O}}:}{N}\!:\!:\!\overset{\cdot\cdot}{\underset{\cdot\cdot}{O}}\!: \quad \text{or} \quad H - O - \underset{\displaystyle O}{N} = O$$

4.12 **a.** The P provides 5 electrons, each O provides 6, and the 3− charge indicates an additional 3 electrons. The total number of electrons is therefore 32, which is enough to satisfy all octets without any multiple bonds:

$$\left[\ :\!\overset{\cdot\cdot}{\underset{\cdot\cdot}{O}}\!:\!\underset{\displaystyle :\overset{\cdot\cdot}{\underset{\cdot\cdot}{O}}:}{\overset{\displaystyle :\overset{\cdot\cdot}{O}:}{P}}\!:\!\overset{\cdot\cdot}{\underset{\cdot\cdot}{O}}\!:\ \right]^{3-}$$

 b. The S provides 6 electrons, each O provides 6, and the 2− charge indicates an additional 2 electrons. The total number of electrons is therefore 26, which is enough to satisfy all octets without any multiple bonds:

$$\left[\ :\!\overset{\cdot\cdot}{\underset{\cdot\cdot}{O}}\!:\!\underset{\displaystyle \cdot\cdot}{\overset{\displaystyle :\overset{\cdot\cdot}{O}:}{S}}\!:\!\overset{\cdot\cdot}{\underset{\cdot\cdot}{O}}\!:\ \right]^{2-}$$

 c. The N provides 5 electrons, each H provides 1, and the + charge indicates that 1 must be subtracted. The total number of electrons is therefore 8, which is enough to satisfy the octet of N, and each H requirement of 2 electrons without any multiple bonds:

$$\left[\ H\!:\!\underset{\displaystyle H}{\overset{\displaystyle H}{N}}\!:\!H\ \right]^{+}$$

4.13 **a.** The 3 electron pairs around the B atom will arrange themselves in a flat triangle around the B. Therefore, the molecule will be flat (planar) with the F atoms forming a triangle around the B.

 b. The Lewis structure is:

$$:\!\overset{\cdot\cdot}{\underset{\cdot\cdot}{Cl}}\!:\!\underset{\displaystyle :\overset{\cdot\cdot}{\underset{\cdot\cdot}{Cl}}:}{\overset{\displaystyle :\overset{\cdot\cdot}{Cl}:}{C}}\!:\!\overset{\cdot\cdot}{\underset{\cdot\cdot}{Cl}}\!:$$

The 4 electron pairs around the C atom will arrange themselves in a tetrahedral orientation. Thus, the molecule will be tetrahedral with C in the center and a Cl atom at each of the corners of the tetrahedron around the C.

 c. The Lewis structure is:

$$:\!\overset{\cdot\cdot}{\underset{\cdot\cdot}{O}}\!:\!\underset{\cdot\cdot}{S}\!:\!:\!\overset{\cdot\cdot}{\underset{\cdot\cdot}{O}}\!:$$

The 3 electron pairs around the S will occupy the corners of a triangle around the S. This will give rise to a bent molecule

$$O - \overset{\cdot\cdot}{S} \diagdown_{O}$$

d. The Lewis structure is:

$$:\!\overset{\cdot\cdot}{S}\!::\!C\!::\!\overset{\cdot\cdot}{S}\!:$$

Each double bond on the central C atom is treated like a single pair of electrons when VSEPR theory is used. Thus, the double bonds are treated like 2 pairs and will arrange themselves to be on opposite sides of the C atom. A linear molecule results: S=C=S.

4.14 a. The Lewis structure from Learning Check 4.12 is:

$$\left[\begin{array}{c} :\!\overset{\cdot\cdot}{O}\!: \\ :\!\overset{\cdot\cdot}{O}\!:\!\overset{}{P}\!:\!\overset{\cdot\cdot}{O}\!: \\ :\!\overset{\cdot\cdot}{O}\!: \end{array} \right]^{3-}$$

We see that phosphorus is the central atom, and it has four electron pairs around it. The four pairs will be located at the corners of a tetrahedron with the P in the middle. The four O atoms will occupy the corners of the tetrahedron, giving the same shape as that of the SO_4^{2-} ion of Example 4.14a.

b. The Lewis structure from Learning Check 4.12 is:

$$\left[\begin{array}{c} :\!\overset{\cdot\cdot}{O}\!: \\ :\!\overset{\cdot\cdot}{O}\!:\!\overset{}{S}\!:\!\overset{\cdot\cdot}{O}\!: \end{array} \right]^{2-}$$

We see that sulfur is the central atom, and it has four electron pairs around it. The four pairs will be located at the corners of a tetrahedron with the S in the middle. The shape of the ion is determined by the location of the oxygen atoms and the S atom. The O atoms will occupy three of the corners of the tetrahedron, and one pair of electrons will occupy the fourth. Thus, the shape of the ion will be a triangular-based pyramid with the O atoms at the three corners of the base and the S atom at the top.

c. The Lewis structure from Learning Check 4.12 is:

$$\left[\begin{array}{c} H \\ H\!:\!\overset{\cdot\cdot}{N}\!:\!H \\ H \end{array} \right]^{+}$$

We see that nitrogen is the central atom, and it has four electron pairs around it. The four pairs will be located at the corners of a tetrahedron with the N in the middle. The four H atoms will thus be located at the corners of the tetrahedron with the N in the middle, giving a tetrahedral-shaped ion like the SO_4^{2-} ion of Example 4.14a.

4.15 a. No polarization because bound atoms are identical.

b. Br is located higher in the group and so is more electronegative than I:

$$\overset{\delta^+ \quad \delta^-}{I - Br}$$
$$\longrightarrow$$

c. Br is farther toward the right in the periodic table and so is more electronegative than H:

$$\overset{\delta^+ \quad \delta^-}{H - Br}$$
$$\longrightarrow$$

4.16 The values of ΔEN are used.

a. ΔEN = 4.0 − 0.8 = 3.2. Bond is classified as ionic.

b. ΔEN = 3.5 − 3.0 = 0.5. Bond is classified as polar covalent.

c. ΔEN = 3.0 − 1.5 = 1.5. Bond is classified as polar covalent.

d. ΔEN = 3.5 − 0.8 = 2.7. Bond is classified as ionic.

4.17 a. sulfur trioxide

b. boron trifluoride

c. disulfur heptoxide

d. carbon tetrachloride

4.18 a. Ca is a group IIA(2) metal and so forms Ca^{2+} ions. Formula: $CaHPO_4$; name: calcium hydrogen phosphate.

b. Mg is a group IIA(2) metal and so forms Mg^{2+} ions. Formula: $Mg_3(PO_4)_2$; name: magnesium phosphate.

c. K is a group IA(1) metal and so forms K^+ ions. Formula: $KMnO_4$; name: potassium permanganate.

d. The ammonium ion, NH_4^+, acts as the positive ion in this compound. Formula: $(NH_4)_2Cr_2O_7$; name: ammonium dichromate.

4.19 Assuming that dispersion forces are significant in establishing the melting and boiling points of these elements leads to the conclusion that, in each pair, the element with the higher atomic weight would have the higher melting and boiling points.

a. Se **b.** Sb **c.** Ne

CHAPTER 5

5.1 Both subscripts and coefficients are used.

N_2 : 2 atoms—on the basis of subscript.

$3H_2$: 6 atoms—on the basis of subscript and coefficient.

$2NH_3$: 2 N atoms (on the basis of coefficient) and 6 H atoms (on the basis of subscript and coefficient).

5.2 $2SO_2 + O_2 \rightarrow 2SO_3$

5.3 a. Oxygen is −2 (Rule 5).

Sulfur is +6 (Rule 6).

b. Calcium is +2 (Rule 3).

Oxygen is −2 (Rule 5).

Chlorine is +5 (Rule 6).

c. Oxygen is −2 (Rule 5).

Chlorine is +7 (Rule 7).

5.4 a. Zn = 0 (Rule 1), H^+ = +1 (Rule 2), Zn^{2+} = +2 (Rule 2), H_2 = 0 (Rule 1).

Zn is oxidized, so it is the reducing agent.

H^+ is reduced, so it is the oxidizing agent.

b. In KI: K = +1 (Rule 3), I = −1 (Rule 6).

Cl_2 = 0 (Rule 1).

In KCl: K = +1 (Rule 3), Cl = −1 (Rule 6).

$I_2 = 0$ (Rule 1).

v. I in KI is oxidized, so KI is the reducing agent.

Cl$_2$ is reduced, so Cl$_2$ is the oxidizing agent.

c. In IO_3^-: $O = -2$ (Rule 5), $I = +5$ (Rule 7).

In HSO_3^-: $H = +1$ (Rule 4), $O = -2$ (Rule 5), $S = +4$ (Rule 7).

$I^- = -1$ (Rule 2).

In HSO_4^-: $H = +1$ (Rule 4), $O = -2$ (Rule 5), $S = +6$ (Rule 7).

S in HSO_3^- is oxidized, so HSO_3^- is the reducing agent.

I in IO_3^- is reduced, so IO_3^- is the oxidizing agent.

5.5 **a.** The O.N. of H changes from $+1$ to 0, and the O.N. of I changes from -1 to 0. Reaction is redox. Because one substance changes into two substances, the reaction is a decomposition.

b. The O.N. of H does not change. The O.N. of O changes from -1 (in a peroxide) to -2 (in water) and 0 (in O_2). This is an example in which the same element is both oxidized and reduced. The reaction is redox. Because one substance changes into two substances, the reaction is a decomposition.

c. No oxidation numbers change. The reaction is nonredox. This is a double-replacement (metathesis) reaction.

d. The O.N. of P changes from 0 to $+5$, and the O.N. of O changes from 0 to -2. The reaction is redox. Because two substances combine to form a single substance, the reaction is a combination.

e. The O.N. of Na does not change. The O.N. of I changes from -1 to 0, and the O.N. of Cl changes from 0 to -1. The reaction is redox. Because the Cl simply replaces the I in the compound, this is a single-replacement reaction.

5.6 **a.** Total ionic: $2Na^+(aq) + 2I^-(aq) + Cl_2(aq) \rightarrow 2Na^+(aq)$
$+ 2Cl^-(aq) + I_2(aq)$

Na^+ is a spectator ion.

Net ionic: $2I^-(aq) + Cl_2(aq) \rightarrow 2Cl^-(aq) + I_2(aq)$

b. Total ionic: $Ca^{2+}(aq) + 2Cl^-(aq) + 2Na^+(aq) +$
$CO_3^{2-}(aq) \rightarrow 2Na^+(aq) + 2Cl^-(aq) + CaCO_3(s)$

Na^+ and Cl^- are spectator ions.

Net ionic: $Ca^{2+}(aq) + CO_3^{2-}(aq) \rightarrow CaCO_3(s)$

c. Total ionic: $Ba^{2+}(aq) + 2OH^-(aq) + 2H^+(aq) +$
$SO_4^{2-}(aq) \rightarrow 2H_2O(\ell) + BaSO_4(s)$

There are no spectator ions, so the net ionic reaction is the same as the total ionic reaction.

5.7 **a.** 2. $1\ mol\ N_2(g) + 3\ mol\ H_2(g) \longrightarrow 2\ mol\ NH_3(g)$

3. $6.02 \times 10^{23}\ N_2$ molecules $+ 3(6.02 \times 10^{23})\ H_2$ molecules
$\longrightarrow 2(6.02 \times 10^{23})\ NH_3$ molecules

4. $28.0\ g\ N_2 + 3(2.00)g\ H_2 \longrightarrow 2(17.0)g\ NH_3$

b. **Step 1.** 2.11 mol H$_2$

Step 2. 2.11 mol H$_2$ $\qquad = $ mol NH$_3$

Step 3. $2.11\ \text{mol H}_2 \times \dfrac{2\ mol\ NH_3}{3\ \text{mol H}_2} = $ mol NH$_3$

Step 4. $2.11 \times \dfrac{2\ mol\ NH_3}{3} = 1.406\ mol\ NH_3 = 1.41\ mol\ NH_3$

The answer was rounded to 3 significant figures to match the three in 2.11. The 2 and 3 are exact counting numbers.

c. **Step 1.** 9.47 g H$_2$

Step 2. 9.47 g H$_2$ $\qquad\qquad = $ g N$_2$

Step 3. $9.47\ \text{g H}_2 \times \dfrac{28.0\ g\ N_2}{6.00\ \text{g H}_2} = $ g N$_2$

Step 4. $9.47 \times \dfrac{28.0\ g\ N_2}{6.00} = 44.19\ g\ N_2 = 44.2\ g\ N_2$

The answer was rounded to 3 significant figures to match the three in 9.47, 28.0 g N$_2$ and 6.00.

5.8 The mass of NH$_3$ possible from each reactant is calculated. The reactant giving the smallest mass of NH$_3$ is the limiting reactant, and the mass of NH$_3$ calculated for the limiting reactant is the amount that will be produced:

$$2.00\ \text{mol H}_2 \times \dfrac{34.0\ g\ NH_3}{3\ \text{mol H}_2} = 22.7\ g\ NH_3$$

$$15.5\ \text{g N}_2 \times \dfrac{34.0\ g\ NH_3}{28.0\ \text{g N}_2} = 18.8\ g\ NH_3$$

The results show the limiting reactant to be the 15.5 g of N$_2$, and the amount of NH$_3$ produced will be 18.8 g.

5.9 **a.** $\%\ \text{yield} = \dfrac{\text{actual yield}}{\text{theoretical yield}} \times 100$

$= \dfrac{17.43\ g}{21.34\ g} \times 100 = 81.68\%$

b. The theoretical yield must be calculated.

$$510\ \text{g CaCO}_3 \times \dfrac{56.08\ g\ CaO}{100.1\ \text{g CaCO}_3} = 285.722\ g\ CaO = 286\ g\ CaO$$

The % yield is then calculated using this theoretical yield:

$$\%\ \text{yield} = \dfrac{\text{actual yield}}{\text{theoretical yield}} \times 100$$

$$= \dfrac{235\ g}{286\ g} \times 100 = 82.2\%$$

CHAPTER 6

6.1 **a.** $d = \dfrac{\text{mass}}{\text{volume}}$

copper: $d = \dfrac{114.2\ g}{12.8\ mL} = 8.92\ g/mL$

glycerin: $d = \dfrac{63.0\ g}{50.0\ mL} = 1.26\ g/mL$

helium: $d = \dfrac{0.286\ g}{1500\ mL} = 1.91 \times 10^{-4}\ g/mL$

b. Copper: Doubling the pressure will not influence the volume, mass, or density of a solid.

Glycerin: Doubling the pressure will not significantly influence the volume and will not influence the mass or density of a liquid.

Helium: The increased pressure will cause the volume to decrease. The mass will not be changed, so the density will increase.

6.2 $d = \dfrac{m}{V}$, so $m = Vd$

$m = (1200 \text{ mL})(1.18 \times 10^{-3} \text{ g/mL})$

$= 1.42 \text{ g}$

6.3 $KE = \frac{1}{2}mv^2 = \frac{1}{2}(3.00 \text{ g})(10.0 \text{ cm/s})^2 = 1.50 \times 10^2 \text{ g cm}^2/\text{s}^2$

$KE = \frac{1}{2}mv^2 = \frac{1}{2}(3.00 \text{ g})(20.0 \text{ cm/s})^2 = 6.00 \times 10^2 \text{ g cm}^2/\text{s}^2$

6.4 The factors used come from the information in Table 6.3.

a. $670 \text{ torr} \times \dfrac{1 \text{ atm}}{760 \text{ torr}} = 0.882 \text{ atm}$

b. $670 \text{ torr} \times \dfrac{14.7 \text{ psi}}{760 \text{ torr}} = 13.0 \text{ psi}$

6.5 **a.** $K = °C + 273 = 27 + 273 = 300 \text{ K}$

b. $K = °C + 273 = 0 + 273 = 273 \text{ K}$

c. $°C = K - 273 = 0 - 273 = -273°C$

d. $°C = K - 273 = 100 - 273 = -173°C$

6.6 **a.** Equation 6.8 is used. Temperatures must be converted to kelvins:

$P_i = 1.90 \text{ atm} \qquad P_f = 1.00 \text{ atm}$

$V_i = 10.0 \text{ L} \qquad V_f = ?$

$T_i = 30°C = 303 \text{ K} \quad T_f = -10.2°C = 262.8 \text{ K}$

$$\frac{P_i V_i}{T_i} = \frac{P_f V_f}{T_f}$$

$$\frac{(1.90 \text{ atm})(10.0 \text{ L})}{303 \text{ K}} = \frac{(1.00 \text{ atm})(V_f)}{262.8 \text{ K}}$$

Solve for V_f:

$$V_f = \frac{(1.90 \text{ atm})(10.0 \text{ L})(262.8 \text{ K})}{(1.00 \text{ atm})(303 \text{ K})} = 16.5 \text{ L}$$

b. $P_i = 800 \text{ torr} \qquad P_f = 900 \text{ torr}$

$V_i = 500 \text{ mL} \qquad V_f = 250 \text{ mL}$

$T_i = 300 \text{ K} \qquad T_f = ?$

$$\frac{P_i V_i}{T_i} = \frac{P_f V_f}{T_f}$$

$$\frac{(800 \text{ torr})(500 \text{ mL})}{300 \text{ K}} = \frac{(900 \text{ torr})(250 \text{ mL})}{T_f}$$

Invert both sides and solve for T_f:

$$T_f = \frac{(300 \text{ K})(900 \text{ torr})(250 \text{ mL})}{(800 \text{ torr})(500 \text{ mL})} = 169 \text{ K}$$

$$°C = K - 273 = 169 \text{ K} - 273 = -104°C$$

6.7 To use the ideal gas law, all quantities must have units to match those of R. The only unit that needs to be changed is the temperature:

$$K = °C + 273 = 30°C + 273 = 303 \text{ K}$$

$$PV = nRT$$

Solve for P:

$$P = \frac{nRT}{V}$$

$$= \frac{(2.15 \text{ mol})\left(0.0821 \dfrac{\text{L atm}}{\text{mol K}}\right)(303 \text{ K})}{(12.6 \text{ L})}$$

$$= 4.24 \text{ atm}$$

6.8 The ideal gas law in the form $PV = mRT/MW$ is solved for MW:

$$MW = \frac{mRT}{PV}$$

The temperature must be converted to kelvins:

$$K = 27°C + 273 = 300 \text{ K}$$

$$MW = \frac{(3.35 \text{ g})\left(0.0821 \dfrac{\text{L atm}}{\text{mol K}}\right)(300 \text{ K})}{(1.21 \text{ atm})(2.00 \text{ L})}$$

$$= 34.1 \text{ g/mol}$$

This matches the molecular weight of H_2S.

6.9 $P_{\text{total}} = P_{\text{He}} + P_{N_2} + P_{O_2}$

The partial pressures of N_2 and O_2 are changed to torr before adding. The factors used come from information in Table 6.3.

P_{N_2}: $0.200 \text{ atm} \times \dfrac{760 \text{ torr}}{1 \text{ atm}} = 152 \text{ torr}$

P_{O_2}: $7.35 \text{ psi} \times \dfrac{760 \text{ torr}}{14.7 \text{ psi}} = 380 \text{ torr}$

$P_{\text{total}} = P_{\text{He}} + P_{N_2} + P_{O_2} = 310 \text{ torr} + 152 \text{ torr} + 380 \text{ torr}$
$= 842 \text{ torr}$

6.10 The lighter (least massive) helium molecules will diffuse faster than the neon molecules. The relationship between the diffusion rates is given by Graham's law.

$$\frac{\text{Rate of He}}{\text{Rate of Ne}} = \sqrt{\frac{\text{mass of Ne}}{\text{mass of He}}} = \sqrt{\frac{20.18}{4.003}}$$

$$= \sqrt{5.041} = 2.25$$

Thus, rate of He $= (2.25)$ rate of Ne. So, helium is seen to diffuse at a rate more than twice that of neon.

6.11 **a.** Evaporation is endothermic.

b. Freezing is exothermic.

c. Melting is endothermic.

6.12 The lower the forces between particles, the higher will be the vapor pressure.

a. Both substances form hydrogen bonds, but dispersion forces are stronger in propyl alcohol. Thus, methyl alcohol has the higher vapor pressure.

b. The only forces acting between the molecules in each case are dispersion forces. These are stronger between the heavier nitrogen molecules, so helium has the higher vapor pressure.

c. Molecules of HF form strong hydrogen bonds with one another, whereas the only forces between neon molecules are weak dispersion forces. Thus, neon has the higher vapor pressure.

6.13 Heat absorbed = (mass)(specific heat)(temp. change). The specific heat of helium is obtained from Table 6.8.

$$\text{Heat absorbed} = (1000 \text{ g})(1.25 \text{ cal/g } °C)(700°C - 25°C)$$
$$= 8.44 \times 10^5 \text{ cal}$$

6.14 Heat absorbed = (mass)(heat of vaporization). The heat of vaporization for water was given in the text.

$$\text{Heat absorbed} = (5000 \text{ g})(540 \text{ cal/g}) = 2.70 \times 10^6 \text{ cal}$$

CHAPTER 7

7.1 **a.** Solvent is gold; solutes are copper, zinc, and nickel.

b. Solvent is nitrogen; solutes are oxygen, argon, and the other gases.

7.2 At 80°C, a saturated solution of KNO_3 contains about 181 g of solute/100 g of H_2O, and a saturated solution of NaBr contains about 118 g of solute per 100 g H_2O. At 50°C both solutions are still saturated, but the KNO_3 solution contains only about 102 g of solute per 100 g H_2O, while the NaBr solution contains about 117 g of solute per 100 g H_2O. Thus, the solubility of KNO_3 is seen to be much more temperature dependent than the solubility of NaBr.

7.3 **a.** The solubility of nitrates and lack of solubility of sulfates and carbonates of barium makes barium nitrate, $Ba(NO_3)_2$, the salt to use. More of it would dissolve and would release more Ba^{2+} ions.

b. Like dissolves like, so oil will dissolve best in oily solvents such as light mineral oil or gasoline. Light mineral oil is the solvent used because it leaves a residue that is similar to the natural oily secretions found on the bird feathers. Gasoline would be hazardous to use (flammable) and leaves no such useful residue.

7.4 **a.** The data may be substituted directly into Equation 7.5:

$$M = \frac{1.25 \text{ mol solute}}{2.50 \text{ L solution}} = 0.500 \frac{\text{mol solute}}{\text{L solution}}$$

The solution is 0.500 molar, or 0.500 M.

b. In this problem, the volume of solution must be converted to liters before the data are substituted into Equation 7.5:

$$(225 \text{ mL solution})\left(\frac{1 \text{ L}}{1000 \text{ mL}}\right) = 0.225 \text{ L solution}$$

$$M = \frac{0.486 \text{ mol solute}}{0.225 \text{ L solution}} = 2.16 \frac{\text{mol solute}}{\text{L solution}}$$

The solution is 2.16 molar, or 2.16 M.

c. In this problem, the volume of solution must be converted to liters and the mass of solute must be converted to moles before the data can be substituted into Equation 7.5:

$$(100 \text{ mL solution})\left(\frac{1 \text{ L}}{1000 \text{ mL}}\right) = 0.100 \text{ L solution}$$

$$(2.60 \text{ g NaCl})\left(\frac{1 \text{ mol NaCl}}{58.44 \text{ g NaCl}}\right) = 0.0445 \text{ mol NaCl}$$

In the last calculation, the factor $\frac{1 \text{ mol NaCl}}{58.44 \text{ g NaCl}}$ comes from the calculated formula weight of 58.44 u for NaCl. The data are now substituted into Equation 7.5:

$$M = \frac{0.0445 \text{ mol NaCl}}{0.100 \text{ L solution}} = 0.445 \frac{\text{mol NaCl}}{\text{L solution}}$$

The solution is 0.445 molar, or 0.445 M.

7.5 **a.** To calculate %(w/w), the mass of solute contained in a specific mass of solution is needed. The mass of solute is 0.900 g, and the mass of solution is equal to the solvent mass (100 g) plus the solute mass (0.900 g):

$$\%(w/w) = \frac{\text{solute mass}}{\text{solution mass}} \times 100 = \frac{0.900 \text{ g}}{100.9 \text{ g}} \times 100$$
$$= 0.892 \%(w/w)$$

To calculate %(w/v), the number of grams of solute must be known along with the number of milliliters of solution. The mass of solute is 0.900 g, and the solution volume is 100 mL:

$$\%(w/v) = \frac{\text{g of solute}}{\text{mL of solution}} \times 100 = \frac{0.900 \text{ g}}{100 \text{ mL}} \times 100$$
$$= 0.900 \%(w/v)$$

b. The given quantity is 30 mL of beverage, and the desired quantity is milliliters of pure alcohol. The %(v/v) provides the necessary factor:

$$30 \text{ mL beverage} \times \frac{45 \text{ mL alcohol}}{100 \text{ mL beverage}} = 14 \text{ mL alcohol}$$

7.6 **a.** $M = \dfrac{\text{mol of solute}}{\text{liters of solution}}$

$$\text{mol of solute} = (M)(\text{liters of solution})$$
$$= (1.00 \text{ M})(0.500 \text{ L})$$
$$= 0.500 \text{ mol of solute}$$

The solute is $MgCl_2$, which has a formula weight of 95.2 u. The formula weight provides the factor in the following calculation:

$$0.500 \text{ mol MgCl}_2 \times \frac{95.2 \text{ g MgCl}_2}{1 \text{ mol MgCl}_2} = 47.6 \text{ g MgCl}_2$$

The solution is prepared by putting 47.6 g of $MgCl_2$ into a 500-mL flask and adding pure water to the mark, making certain all the solid solute dissolves and the resulting solution is well mixed.

b. $\%(w/v) = \dfrac{\text{g of solute}}{\text{mL of solution}} \times 100$

$$\text{g of solute} = \frac{\%(w/v)(\text{mL of solution})}{100}$$
$$= \frac{(12.0\%)(100 \text{ mL})}{100} = 12.0 \text{ g}$$

The solution is prepared by putting 12.0 g of $MgCl_2$ into a 100-mL flask and adding pure water to the mark, making certain all the solid solute dissolves and the resulting solution is well mixed.

c. $\%(v/v) = \dfrac{\text{solute volume}}{\text{solution volume}} \times 100$

$$\text{solute volume} = \frac{\%(v/v)(\text{solution volume})}{100}$$
$$= \frac{(20.0\%)(1.00 \text{ L})}{100} = 0.200 \text{ L}$$
$$= 200 \text{ mL}$$

The solution is prepared by putting 200 mL of ethylene glycol into a 1.00-L flask and adding pure water to the mark, making certain the two liquids are completely mixed to form the final solution.

7.7 Equation 7.9 is used to calculate the volume of 6.00 M NaOH solution needed.

$$(C_c)(V_c) = (C_d)(V_d)$$

$$(6.00 \text{ M})(V_c) = (0.250 \text{ M})(500 \text{ mL})$$

$$V_c = \frac{(0.250 \text{ M})(500 \text{ mL})}{(6.00 \text{ M})} = 20.8 \text{ mL}$$

The solution is prepared by putting 20.8 mL of 6.00 M NaOH solution into a 500-mL flask, adding pure water to the mark, and making certain the resulting solution is well mixed.

7.8 **a.** Because $CaCl_2$ is a strong electrolyte, it dissociates completely:

$$CaCl_2 \rightarrow Ca^{2+} + 2Cl^-. \text{ Thus, } n = 3.$$

$$\Delta T_b = nK_b\text{M} = (3)(0.52°\text{C/M})(0.100 \text{ M}) = 0.16°\text{C}$$

Because the boiling point of a solution is higher than the boiling point of the pure solvent, ΔT_b is added to the boiling point of the pure solvent.

Solution B.P. = 100.00°C + 0.16°C = 100.16°C

$$\Delta T_f = nK_f\text{M} = (3)(1.86°\text{C/M})(0.100 \text{ M}) = 0.558°\text{C}$$

Because the freezing point of a solution is lower than the freezing point of the pure solvent, ΔT_f is subtracted from the freezing point of the solvent.

Solution F.P. = 0.00°C − 0.558°C = −0.558°C = −0.56°C

$$\pi = nMRT$$

$$= (3)(0.100 \text{ mol/L})(62.4 \text{ L torr/K mol})(300 \text{ K})$$

$$= 5.62 \times 10^3 \text{ torr} = 7.39 \text{ atm}$$

b. Because ethylene glycol does not dissociate in solution, $n = 1$.

$$\Delta T_b = nK_b\text{M} = (1)(0.52°\text{C/M})(0.100 \text{ M}) = 0.052°\text{C}$$

Solution B.P. = 100.00°C + 0.052°C = 100.05°C

$$\Delta T_f = nK_f\text{M} = (1)(1.86°\text{C/M})(0.100 \text{ M}) = 0.186°\text{C}$$

Solution F.P. = 0.00°C − 0.186°C = −0.186°C

$$= -0.19°\text{C}$$

$$\pi = nMRT$$

$$= (1)(0.100 \text{ mol/L})(62.4 \text{ L torr/K mol})(300 \text{ K})$$

$$= 1.87 \times 10^3 \text{ torr} = 2.46 \text{ atm}$$

CHAPTER 8

8.1 Because only Ce^{4+} and Fe^{2+} are mixed, the initial concentration of Ce^{3+} is 0.

$$\text{Rate} = \frac{C_t - C_0}{\Delta t} = \frac{1.50 \times 10^{-5} \text{ mol/L} - 0 \text{ mol/L}}{75.0 \text{ s}}$$

$$= 2.00 \times 10^{-7} \frac{\text{mol/L}}{\text{s}}$$

8.2 **a.** $K = \dfrac{[NO_2]^2}{[N_2O_4]}$

b. $K = \dfrac{[N_2O][NO_2]}{[NO]^3}$

8.3 **a.** $K = \dfrac{[IBr]^2}{[Br_2][I_2]}$

$$= \frac{(1.96 \times 10^{-2})^2}{(1.50 \times 10^{-1})(5.00 \times 10^{-2})}$$

$$= 5.12 \times 10^{-2}$$

The small value of K indicates the equilibrium position is toward the left.

b. $K = \dfrac{[NH_3]^2}{[N_2][H_2]^3}$

$$= \frac{(9.00)^2}{(9.23 \times 10^{-3})(2.77 \times 10^{-2})^3}$$

$$= 4.13 \times 10^8$$

The large K value indicates the equilibrium position is toward the right.

8.4 **a.** Heat + $NH_4NO_3(s) \rightleftarrows NH_4^+(aq) + NO_3^-(aq)$

The equilibrium will shift to the right when heat is added in an attempt to use up the added heat. This shift corresponds to dissolving more of the solid at the higher temperature. The solubility is higher at a higher temperature.

b. $2SO_2(g) + O_2(g) \rightleftarrows 2SO_3(g)$

If O_2 were removed from an equilibrium mixture, the equilibrium would shift left in an attempt to replenish the removed O_2. This shift would reduce the amount of SO_3 present at equilibrium, which means the concentration of SO_3 would be lower than it was in the initial equilibrium.

CHAPTER 9

9.1 **a.** $HC_2H_3O_2 + H_2O \rightleftarrows H_3O^+ + C_2H_3O_2^-$
 acid base acid base
 conjugate pair
 conjugate pair

b. $NO_2^- + H_2O \rightleftarrows OH^- + HNO_2$
 base acid base acid
 conjugate pair
 conjugate pair

c. $HS^- + H_2O \rightleftarrows H_3O^+ + S^{2-}$
 acid base acid base
 conjugate pair
 conjugate pair

9.2 **a.** The anhydrous compound is called hydrogen iodide. The name of the water solution is obtained by dropping *hydrogen* from the anhydrous compound name and adding the prefix *hydro-* to the stem *iod*. The *-ide* suffix on the *iod* stem is replaced by the suffix *-ic* to give the name *hydroiodic*. The word *acid* is added, giving the final name *hydroiodic acid* for the water solution.

b. The anhydrous compound is called hydrogen bromide. The name of the water solution is obtained the same way it was for HI(aq) in part a, using the stem *brom* in place of *iod*. The resulting name for the water solution is *hydrobromic acid*.

9.3 The removal of the two H^+ ions leaves behind the CO_3^{2-} polyatomic ion. From Table 4.6, this ion is the carbonate ion. According to rules 1-4, the *-ate* suffix is replaced by the *-ic* suffix to give the name *carbonic acid*.

9.4 **a.** Solution is basic because $[OH^-]$ is greater than 1.0×10^{-7} mol/L:

$$[H_3O^+] = \frac{1.0 \times 10^{-14}(mol/L)^2}{[OH^-]} = \frac{1.0 \times 10^{-14}(mol/L)^2}{1.0 \times 10^{-5} \, mol/L}$$

$$= 1.0 \times 10^{-9} \, mol/L$$

b. Solution is basic because $[H_3O^+]$ is less than 1.0×10^{-7} mol/L:

$$[OH^-] = \frac{1.0 \times 10^{-14}(mol/L)^2}{[H_3O^+]} = \frac{1.0 \times 10^{-14}(mol/L)^2}{1.0 \times 10^{-9} \, mol/L}$$

$$= 1.0 \times 10^{-5} \, mol/L$$

This solution has the same $[H_3O^+]$ and $[OH^-]$ as the solution in part a.

c. Solution is acidic because $[H_3O^+]$ is greater than 1.0×10^{-7} mol/L:

$$[OH^-] = \frac{1.0 \times 10^{-14}(mol/L)^2}{[H_3O^+]} = \frac{1.0 \times 10^{-14}(mol/L)^2}{1.0 \times 10^{-2} \, mol/L}$$

$$= 1.0 \times 10^{-12} \, mol/L$$

9.5 **a.** $[H^+] = 1 \times 10^{-14}$ mol/L. pH is the negative of the exponent used to express $[H^+]$, so pH $= -(-14) = 14.0$.

b. $[OH^-] = 1.0$ mol/L. The value of $[H^+]$ is calculated:

$$[H^+] = \frac{1 \times 10^{-14}(mol/L)^2}{[OH^-]} = \frac{1 \times 10^{-14}(mol/L)^2}{1.0 \, mol/L}$$

$$= 1 \times 10^{-14} \, mol/L$$

pH is the negative of the exponent used to express $[H^+]$, so pH $= -(-14) = 14.0$.

c. $[OH^-] = 1 \times 10^{-8}$ mol/L. The value of $[H^+]$ is calculated:

$$[H^+] = \frac{1 \times 10^{-14}(mol/L)^2}{[OH^-]} = \frac{1 \times 10^{-14}(mol/L)^2}{1 \times 10^{-8} \, mol/L}$$

$$= 1 \times 10^{-6} \, mol/L$$

pH is the negative of the exponent used to express $[H^+]$, so pH $= -(-6) = 6.0$.

9.6 **a.** pH $= 10.0$, and

$$[H^+] = 1 \times 10^{-pH} = 1 \times 10^{-10} \, mol/L$$

$$[OH^-] = \frac{K_w}{[H^+]} = \frac{1 \times 10^{-14} \, (mol/L)^2}{1 \times 10^{-10} \, mol/L} = 1 \times 10^{-4} \, mol/L$$

b. pH $= 4.0$, and $[H^+] = 1 \times 10^{-pH} = 1 \times 10^{-4}$

$$[OH^-] = \frac{K_w}{[H^+]} = \frac{1 \times 10^{-14} \, (mol/L)^2}{1 \times 10^{-4} \, mol/L} = 1 \times 10^{-10} \, mol/L$$

c. pH $= 5.0$, and $[H^+] = 1 \times 10^{-pH} = 1 \times 10^{-5}$

$$[OH^-] = \frac{K_w}{[H^+]} = \frac{1 \times 10^{-14} \, (mol/L)^2}{1 \times 10^{-5} \, mol/L} = 1 \times 10^{-9} \, mol/L$$

9.7 **a.** The calculator answer is 4.3768. The correctly rounded value is 4.38.

b. The calculator answer is 8.0915. The correctly rounded value is 8.09.

9.8 **a.** The calculator answer is 0.0017783, or 1.7783×10^{-3}. The correctly rounded value should have two significant figures to match the two figures to the right of the decimal in the pH value. The answer is 1.8×10^{-3} mol/L.

b. The calculator answer is 4.6774×10^{-9}. The correctly rounded answer is 4.7×10^{-9} mol/L.

9.9 According to Table 9.4, concentrated NH_3 stock solution is 15 M. Equation 7.9 is used to determine the amount of this solution needed.

$$C_c V_c = C_d V_d$$

$$(15 \, M)(V_c) = (3.0 \, M)(500 \, mL)$$

$$V_c = \frac{(3.0 \, M)(500 \, mL)}{(15 \, M)}$$

$$= 100 \, mL$$

Because the resulting solution molarity is given using only two significant figures, the volumes can be measured using graduated cylinders. Measure 100 mL of stock (15 M) aqueous ammonia, put it into a container and add 400 mL of distilled water. Mix the resulting solution well.

9.10 $2HCl(aq) + Sr(HCO_3)_2(s) \rightarrow$
$$SrCl_2(aq) + 2CO_2(g) + 2H_2O(\ell)$$

Total Ionic: $2H^+(aq) + 2Cl^-(aq) + Sr(HCO_3)_2(s) \rightarrow$
$$Sr^{2+}(aq) + 2Cl^-(aq) + 2CO_2(g) + 2H_2O(\ell)$$
Cl^- is a spectator ion.

Net Ionic: $2H^+(aq) + Sr(HCO_3)_2(s) \rightarrow$
$$Sr^{2+}(aq) + 2CO_2(g) + 2H_2O(\ell)$$

9.11 **a.** Molecular: $Ca(s) + 2H_2O(\ell) \rightarrow H_2(g) + Ca(OH)_2(s)$

Total Ionic: $Ca(s) + 2H_2O(\ell) \rightarrow H_2(g) + Ca(OH)_2(s)$

Net Ionic: $Ca(s) + 2H_2O(\ell) \rightarrow H_2(g) + Ca(OH)_2(s)$

All three equations are the same because none of the reactants or products form ions in solution.

b. Molecular: $Mg(s) + H_2SO_4(aq) \rightarrow H_2(g) + MgSO_4(aq)$

Total Ionic: $Mg(s) + 2H^+(aq) + SO_4^{2-}(aq) \rightarrow$
$$H_2(g) + Mg^{2+}(aq) + SO_4^{2-}(aq)$$
The SO_4^{2-} is a spectator ion.

Net Ionic: $Mg(s) + 2H^+(aq) \rightarrow H_2(g) + Mg^{2+}(aq)$

9.12 **a.** Molecular: $HNO_3(aq) + NaOH(aq) \rightarrow$
$$H_2O(\ell) + NaNO_3(aq)$$

Total Ionic: $H^+(aq) + NO_3^-(aq) + Na^+(aq) + OH^-(aq) \rightarrow$
$$H_2O(\ell) + Na^+(aq) + NO_3^-(aq)$$
Na^+ and NO_3^- are spectator ions.

Net Ionic: $H^+(aq) + OH^-(aq) \rightarrow H_2O(\ell)$

b. Molecular: $H_2SO_4(aq) + 2KOH(aq) \rightarrow$
$$2H_2O(\ell) + K_2SO_4(aq)$$

Total Ionic:
$2H^+(aq) + SO_4^{2-}(aq) + 2K^+(aq) + 2OH^-(aq) \rightarrow$
$$2H_2O(\ell) + 2K^+(aq) + SO_4^{2-}(aq)$$

K^+ and SO_4^{2-} are spectator ions.

Net Ionic: $2H^+(aq) + 2OH^-(aq) \rightarrow 2H_2O(\ell)$

9.13 $6HCl(aq) + 2Al(s) \rightarrow 2AlCl_3(aq) + 3H_2(g)$

$6HCl(aq) + Al_2O_3(s) \rightarrow 2AlCl_3(aq) + 3H_2O(\ell)$

$3HCl(aq) + Al(OH)_3(s) \rightarrow AlCl_3(aq) + 3H_2O(\ell)$

$6HCl(aq) + Al_2(CO_3)_3(s) \rightarrow$
$$2AlCl_3(aq) + 3H_2O(\ell) + 3CO_2(g)$$

$3HCl(aq) + Al(HCO_3)_3(s) \rightarrow$
$$AlCl_3(aq) + 3H_2O(\ell) + 3CO_2(g)$$

9.14 a. The dissociation reaction is $NaCl(aq) \rightarrow Na^+(aq) + Cl^-(aq)$. Thus, 1 mol of NaCl produces 1 mol of Na^+ or 1 mol of positive charges. Thus, 1 mol NaCl = 1 eq NaCl. Therefore,

$$0.10 \text{ mol NaCl} \times \frac{1 \text{ eq NaCl}}{1 \text{ mol NaCl}} = 0.10 \text{ eq NaCl}$$

Also, because 1 eq = 1000 meq,

$$0.10 \text{ eq} \times \frac{1000 \text{ meq}}{1 \text{ eq}} = 1.0 \times 10^2 \text{ meq}$$

b. The dissociation reaction is $Mg(NO_3)_2(aq) \rightarrow Mg^{2+}(aq) + 2NO_3^-(aq)$. Thus, 1 mol of $Mg(NO_3)_2$ produces 1 mol of Mg^{2+} or 2 mol of positive charges. Thus, 1 mol $Mg(NO_3)_2$ = 2 eq $Mg(NO_3)_2$. Therefore,

$$0.10 \text{ mol Mg(NO}_3)_2 \times \frac{2 \text{ eq Mg(NO}_3)_2}{1 \text{ mol Mg(NO}_3)_2}$$
$$= 0.20 \text{ eq Mg(NO}_3)_2$$

Also, because 1 eq = 1000 meq,

$$0.20 \text{ eq} \times \frac{1000 \text{ meq}}{1 \text{ eq}} = 2.0 \times 10^2 \text{ meq}$$

9.15 The Cl^- ion has a single charge, so we may write:

$$1.00 \text{ mol NaCl} = 1.00 \text{ mol Cl}^- = 1.00 \text{ eq Cl}^- = 1.00 \text{ eq NaCl}$$

As in Example 9.11, the pattern for the calculation is liters solution $A \rightarrow$ eq A, and the pathway is liters Cl^- solution $\rightarrow$ eq Cl^-. The conversion factor comes from the concentration of 0.103 eq/L given in the problem:

$$(0.250 \text{ L Cl}^- \text{ solution})\left(\frac{0.103 \text{ eq Cl}^-}{1.00 \text{ L solution}}\right) = 0.0258 \text{ eq Cl}^-$$

The equivalents of Cl^- are converted to the quantities asked for by using factors from the relationships given above and the formula weight for NaCl, 58.44 u:

$$(0.0258 \text{ eq Cl}^-)\left(\frac{1.00 \text{ eq NaCl}}{1.00 \text{ eq Cl}^-}\right) = 0.0258 \text{ eq NaCl}$$

$$(0.0258 \text{ eq NaCl})\left(\frac{1.00 \text{ mol NaCl}}{1.00 \text{ eq NaCl}}\right) = 0.0258 \text{ mol NaCl}$$

$$(0.0258 \text{ mol NaCl})\left(\frac{58.44 \text{ g NaCl}}{1.00 \text{ mol NaCl}}\right) = 1.51 \text{ g NaCl}$$

9.16 a. $HPO_4^{2-} \rightleftarrows H^+ + PO_4^{3-}$

$$K_a = \frac{[H^+][PO_4^{3-}]}{[HPO_4^{2-}]}$$

b. $HNO_2 \rightleftarrows H^+ + NO_2^-$

$$K_a = \frac{[H^+][NO_2^-]}{[HNO_2]}$$

c. $HF \rightleftarrows H^+ + F^-$

$$K_a = \frac{[H^+][F^-]}{[HF]}$$

9.17 a. In a series of similar oxyacids, acid strength increases with increases in the number of oxygens: $HClO_3, HClO_2, HClO$.

b. The anion from the weakest acid will be the strongest base. HNO_3 is a stronger acid than HNO_2, so NO_2^- is a stronger base than NO_3^-.

c. The anion of an acid behaves as a weaker acid than the acid from which it came. The anion actually behaves as a base in this case, so $HC_2H_3O_2$ is a stronger acid than $C_2H_3O_2^-$.

9.18 The pattern is liters solution $A \rightarrow$ mol B, and the pathway is liters NaOH solution $\rightarrow$ mol NaOH $\rightarrow$ mol H_3PO_4. In combined form, the steps in the factor-unit method are:

Step 1. 0.0141 L NaOH solution

Step 2. 0.0141 L NaOH solution = mol H_3PO_4

Step 3. $0.0141 \text{ L NaOH solution} \times \dfrac{0.250 \text{ mol NaOH}}{1 \text{ L NaOH solution}}$

$$\times \frac{1 \text{ mol H}_3\text{PO}_4}{3 \text{ mol NaOH}} = \text{mol H}_3\text{PO}_4$$

Step 4. $(0.0141)\left(\dfrac{0.250}{1}\right)\left(\dfrac{1 \text{ mol H}_3\text{PO}_4}{3}\right)$
$$= 0.00118 \text{ mol H}_3\text{PO}_4$$

The molarity of the H_3PO_4 solution is calculated:

$$M = \frac{\text{mol H}_3\text{PO}_4}{\text{L H}_3\text{PO}_4 \text{ solution}}$$
$$= \frac{0.00118 \text{ mol H}_3\text{PO}_4}{0.0250 \text{ L H}_3\text{PO}_4 \text{ solution}}$$
$$= \frac{0.0472 \text{ mol H}_3\text{PO}_4}{\text{L H}_3\text{PO}_4 \text{ solution}} = 0.0472 \text{ M}$$

9.19 a. The ions resulting from dissociation are Na^+ and NO_3^-. Na^+ is the cation of a strong base, and NO_3^- is the anion of a strong acid. Neither ion will hydrolyze significantly in water, so the solution pH will be about 7.

b. The ions resulting from dissociation are Na^+ and NO_2^-. Na^+ is the cation of a strong base and will not hydrolyze significantly. NO_2^- is the anion of a weak acid and will behave as a base in the hydrolysis reaction. The solution will therefore be basic, and the pH will be higher than 7.

c. The ions resulting from dissociation are K^+ and BO_3^{3-}. K^+ is the cation of a strong base and will not hydrolyze significantly. BO_3^{3-} is the anion of a weak acid and will behave as a base in the hydrolysis reaction. The solution will therefore be basic, and the pH will be higher than 7.

9.20 a. Because the acid (HCOOH) and conjugate base ($HCOO^-$) concentrations are the same, the pH will equal pK_a for the acid. This is shown by the following calculation:

$$pH = pK_a + \log\frac{[B^-]}{[HB]}$$
$$= 3.74 + \log\frac{[HCOO^-]}{[HCOOH]}$$
$$= 3.74 + \log\frac{0.22 \text{ mol/L}}{0.22 \text{ mol/L}}$$
$$= 3.74 + \log 1$$
$$= 3.74 + 0 = 3.74$$

b. The acid is H_2SO_3, and the conjugate base is HSO_3^- (produced when the $NaHSO_3$ salt dissociates).

$$pH = pK_a + \log\frac{[B^-]}{[HB]}$$
$$= 1.82 + \log\frac{(0.10 \text{ mol/L})}{(0.25 \text{ mol/L})}$$
$$= 1.82 + \log 0.40$$
$$= 1.82 - 0.40$$
$$= 1.42$$

c. The acid is H_2CO_3 and the conjugate base is HCO_3^-. The desired pH is 7.40. Substitution into Equation 9.54 gives:

$$pH = pK_a + \log \frac{[HCO_3^-]}{[H_2CO_3]}$$

$$7.40 = 6.37 + \log \frac{[HCO_3^-]}{[H_2CO_3]}$$

$$7.40 - 6.37 = \log \frac{[HCO_3^-]}{[H_2CO_3]}$$

$$1.03 = \log \frac{[HCO_3^-]}{[H_2CO_3]}$$

We now know the log of the desired ratio. Use Step 3 in Table 9.3 to get the antilog of 1.03. The correctly rounded value is 11. Thus, the concentration of HCO_3^- must be 11 times the concentration of H_2CO_3 in the blood to maintain the desired pH.

CHAPTER 10

10.1 **a.** $^{131}_{53}I$ **b.** $^{0}_{-1}\beta$ **c.** $^{4}_{4}X$ **d.** $^{0}_{-4}X$

10.2 $^{234}_{90}Th \rightarrow \, ^{0}_{-1}\beta + \, ^{234}_{91}Pa$

In general: $^{A}_{Z}X \rightarrow \, ^{0}_{-1}\beta + \, ^{A}_{Z+1}Y$

When a β particle is emitted, the daughter has the same mass number and an atomic number higher by 1 than that of the decaying nucleus.

10.3 $^{A}_{Z}X \rightarrow \, ^{0}_{1}\beta + \, ^{A}_{Z-1}Y$

The atomic number of the daughter is 1 less than that of the decaying nucleus.

10.4 $^{A}_{Z}X + \, ^{0}_{-1}e \rightarrow \, ^{A}_{Z-1}Y$

The atomic number of the daughter is 1 less than that of the decaying nucleus.

10.5 **a.** $^{50}_{25}Mn \rightarrow \, ^{0}_{1}\beta + \, ^{50}_{24}Cr$

 b. $^{54}_{25}Mn + \, ^{0}_{-1}e \rightarrow \, ^{54}_{24}Cr$

 c. $^{56}_{25}Mn \rightarrow \, ^{0}_{-1}\beta + \, ^{56}_{26}Fe$

 d. $^{224}_{88}Ra \rightarrow \, ^{4}_{2}\alpha + \, ^{220}_{86}Rn$

10.6 During the first half-life, the original 200.00 mg will be reduced to 100.00 mg. This will be reduced to 50.00 mg during the second half-life and to 25.00 mg during the third. Thus, 3 half-lives or 3(7.7 min) = 23.1 min will be required.

10.7 The elapsed time of 79.8 hours is 6 half-lives (79.8/13.3 = 6). The fraction remaining is $1/2 \times 1/2 \times 1/2 \times 1/2 \times 1/2 \times 1/2 = 1/64$ of the original diagnostic dose.

10.8 Equation 10.2 is used: $\dfrac{I_x}{I_y} = \dfrac{d_y^2}{d_x^2}$

$$\frac{10.0 \text{ units}}{I_5} = \frac{(5 \text{ ft})^2}{(25 \text{ ft})^2}$$

$$I_5 = \frac{(10.0 \text{ units})(25 \text{ ft})^2}{(5 \text{ ft})^2} = 250 \text{ units}$$

10.9 $^{55}_{25}Mn + \, ^{1}_{1}p \rightarrow \, ^{1}_{0}n + \, ^{55}_{26}Fe$

The product is iron-55.

CHAPTER 11

11.1 Look for the presence of carbon atoms.

 a. inorganic **d.** inorganic

 b. organic **e.** organic

 c. organic **f.** inorganic

11.2 Refer to Table 11.1 for help.

 a. organic

 b. organic

 c. inorganic

11.3 Compound (a) is a structural isomer because it has the same molecular formula but a different structural formula.

11.4 **a.** $CH_3 - \overset{\overset{\displaystyle OH}{|}}{CH} - CH_2 - CH_2 - CH_3$

 b. $CH_3 - \underset{\underset{\displaystyle CH_3}{|}}{CH} - CH_2 - \overset{\overset{\displaystyle O}{\|}}{C} - OH$

11.5 **a.** The number of hydrogen atoms is twice the carbon atoms plus two: C_8H_{18}.

 b. $CH_3 - CH_2 - CH_2 - CH_2 - CH_2 - CH_2 - CH_2 - CH_3$

11.6 **a.** Same molecule: In both molecules, the five carbons are bonded in a continuous chain.

 b. Same molecule: In both molecules, there is a continuous chain of four carbons with a branch at position 2.

$$\underset{1}{CH_3} - \underset{2}{\overset{\overset{\displaystyle CH_3}{|}}{CH}} - \underset{3}{CH_2} - \underset{4}{CH_3} \qquad \underset{1}{CH_3} - \underset{2}{\overset{\overset{\displaystyle 3}{\overset{\displaystyle CH_2 - CH_3}{|}}}{CH}} - CH_3$$

 c. Structural isomers: Both molecules have a continuous chain of five carbons, but the branch is located at different positions.

11.7 **a.** $\underset{2}{CH_2} - \underset{3}{CH_2} - \underset{4}{CH_3}$ a butane

 b. $\underset{2}{CH_2} - \underset{3}{CH} - \underset{4}{CH_2}$ with $\underset{1}{CH_3}$, $\underset{5}{CH_3}$ above and CH_3 below a pentane

 c. $\underset{1}{CH_3} - \underset{2}{CH} - CH_3$ / $CH_3 - \underset{3}{CH} - \underset{4}{CH_3}$; $\underset{3}{CH_3} - CH - CH_3$; $CH_3 - \underset{1}{CH} - \underset{2}{CH_3}$ a butane **or**

11.8 **a.** $\underset{}{CH_3} - \overset{3}{CH} - \overset{4}{CH_2} - \overset{5}{CH_2} - \overset{6}{CH_3}$ with $\underset{2}{CH_2}$ and $\underset{1}{CH_3}$ below

A CH₃ group is located at position 3. If the chain had been numbered beginning at the right, the CH₃ group would have been at position 4.

b. Numbering from the left, groups are located at positions 5, 5, 7. From the right, the groups are at positions 2, 4, 4. The first difference occurs with the first number, so numbering from the right (2, 4, 4) is correct.

11.9 Proceeding from the left, the groups are methyl, propyl, isopropyl, *sec*-butyl, and ethyl.

11.10 a. The chain is numbered from the right to give 2-methylhexane.

b.
$$CH_3 - CH_2 - CH_2 - \overset{\overset{\displaystyle CH_2 - CH_3}{|}}{\underset{\underset{\displaystyle CH_2 - CH_3}{|}}{CH}} - CH_2 - CH - CH_3$$

The chain is numbered from the right to give 5-ethyl-3-methyloctane.

c. The chain is numbered from the right to give 4-isopropyl-2,3-dimethylheptane.

11.11

a.
$$CH_3 - \overset{\overset{\displaystyle CH_3}{|}}{\underset{\underset{\displaystyle CH_3}{|}}{C}} - CH_2 - \overset{\overset{\displaystyle CH_3}{|}}{CH} - CH_3$$

b.
$$CH_3 - CH_2 - \overset{\overset{\displaystyle CH - CH_3}{\overset{|}{\overset{\displaystyle CH_3}{|}}}}{CH} - CH_2 - CH_2 - CH_3$$

c.
$$CH_3 - \overset{}{CH} - \overset{\overset{\displaystyle CH_2 - CH_3}{|}}{CH} - CH - CH_2 - CH_2 - CH_3$$
(with CH₃ below first CH and CH₃ below fourth CH)

11.12 a. 1,4-dimethylcyclohexane

b. The correct name is ethylcyclopropane. When only one group is attached to a ring, the position is not designated.

c. The name 1-ethyl-2-methylcyclopentane is correct, whereas 2-ethyl-1-methylcyclopentane is incorrect because the ring numbering begins with the carbon attached to the first group alphabetically.

11.13 a. (1) *Trans* because the two Br's are on opposite sides of the ring.

(2) *Cis*; both Cl's are on the same side.

(3) *Cis*; the two groups are on the same side.

b. In showing geometric isomers of ring compounds, it helps to draw the ring in perspective:

CHAPTER 12

12.1 In each of these alkenes, the double-bonded carbons occur at positions 1 and 2.

a. 3-bromo-1-propene

b. 2-ethyl-1-pentene

c. 3,4-dimethylcyclohexene

12.2 a. The chain is correctly numbered from the right to give 2-methyl-1,3-butadiene.

b. The chain is correctly numbered from the left to give 2-methyl-1,3,6-octatriene.

c. 7-bromo-1,3,5-cycloheptatriene

12.3 a. This structure does not exhibit geometric isomerism because there are two H's attached to the carbon at position 1.

b.

cis trans

c. This structure does not exhibit geometric isomerism because there are two methyl groups attached to the left double-bonded carbon.

12.4

a.
$$CH_3 - \overset{\overset{\displaystyle Br}{|}}{\underset{\underset{\displaystyle CH_3}{|}}{C}} - CH_2$$
(with Br on top of C and CH₃ below, Br Br at top)

b. (cyclopentane with Cl at top right and Cl at bottom)

12.5 a.
$$CH_3 - \overset{\overset{}{}}{\underset{\underset{\displaystyle CH_3}{|}}{CH}} - CH_2 - CH_3$$

b. (cyclopentane with CH₃ and H) = (cyclopentane with CH₃)

12.6 a. The major product will be the one where H attaches to the CH carbon:

$$CH_3 - CH_2 - \overset{\overset{\displaystyle CH_3}{|}}{\underset{\underset{\displaystyle Br}{|}}{C}} - CH_2 - CH_3$$

b. Position 1 on the ring has an attached hydrogen, whereas position 2 does not have any attached hydrogens:

(cyclohexene ring with CH₃, CH₂CH₃ at position 2, and H at position 1)

Thus, H attaches at position 1 to give:

12.7 a. Markovnikov's rule predicts that H will attach at position 1 to give:

$$\underset{\text{OH}}{\underset{|}{\text{CH}_3\text{CH}_2\text{CH}_2\text{CH}}} \underset{\text{H}}{\underset{|}{-\text{CH}_2}} = \text{CH}_3\text{CH}_2\text{CH}_2\overset{\text{OH}}{\overset{|}{\text{CHCH}_3}}$$

b.

12.8 The double bond becomes a single bond:

12.9 Each chain is correctly numbered from the right.

a. 2-pentyne **b.** 5-methyl-2-hexyne

12.10 a. Numbers or the term *meta* may be used:

1,3-diethylbenzene or *m*-diethylbenzene

b. The compound must be named as a derivative of cyclopentane. The correct name is 1-chloro-3-phenylcyclopentane.

c. Numbers must be used when there are three groups: 1,2, 3-tribromobenzene.

d. If the compound is named as a derivative of benzoic acid, then the methyl group is at position 2. The name is 2-methylbenzoic acid.

CHAPTER 13

13.1

a. 2-methyl-1-propanol

b. 2,5-dimethyl-4-heptanol

c. 2-methylcyclopentanol

13.2 a. 1,4-butanediol **b.** 1,2-cyclohexanediol

13.3 Because the compound is named as a phenol, the OH group is at position 1. The name is 2-ethylphenol or *o*-ethylphenol.

13.4 In each case, count the number of carbon atoms attached to the hydroxy-bearing carbon.

a. primary **b.** secondary **c.** secondary

13.5 b, c, a

13.6 Methanol molecules form hydrogen bonds, whereas molecules of propane do not.

13.7 a. There are two ways of removing water from this structure, but they both produce the same product:

$$\text{CH}_3\text{CH}=\text{CHCH}_2\text{CH}_3$$

b. Dehydration will occur in the direction that gives the highest number of carbon groups attached to the double-bonded carbons:

13.8 a. Ether formation is favored by H_2SO_4 at 140°C.

b. Alkene formation predominates when H_2SO_4 is used at 180°C.

13.9

first product **second product**

13.10

$+ H_2O$

13.11 The alcohols in a and c react because they are secondary and primary, respectively. Alcohol b is tertiary and does not react.

13.12 Working backward, you could prepare an ether product from an alcohol. Thus, the starting alkene must first be converted to an alcohol.

$$\text{CH}_2=\text{CH}_2 + H_2O \xrightarrow{\text{H}_2\text{SO}_4} \text{CH}_3\text{CH}_2-\text{OH}$$

$$2\text{CH}_3\text{CH}_2-\text{OH} \xrightarrow[140°\text{C}]{\text{H}_2\text{SO}_4} \text{CH}_3\text{CH}_2-\text{O}-\text{CH}_2\text{CH}_3 + H_2O$$

13.13 Use Table 13.2 to answer these questions:

a. solvent

b. alcoholic beverages

c. rubbing alcohol

d. antifreeze

e. food moisturizer

f. cough drops

13.14 a. antioxidant in gasoline

b. throat lozenges

13.15 a. ethyl phenyl ether

b. diisopropyl ether

13.16 a. 1,2-dimethoxycyclopentane

b. 3-isopropoxypentane

13.17 a. Ether molecules do not form hydrogen bonds, whereas alcohol molecules do form hydrogen bonds.

b. They are quite unreactive.

13.18 Oxidation of a thiol produces a disulfide:

$$CH_3CH-S-S-CHCH_3 + H_2O$$
$$\quad\ |\qquad\qquad\ |$$
$$\quad CH_3\qquad\quad CH_3$$

13.19 a. 2CH_3CH—SH
$$\qquad\qquad |$$
$$\qquad\quad CH_3$$

b. 2 [cyclopentane ring with SH group]

13.20 $CH_3CH-S-Pb-S-CHCH_3 + 2H^+$
$$\quad\ \ |\qquad\qquad\qquad\ |$$
$$\quad\ CH_3\qquad\qquad\quad CH_3$$

13.21 Ether, phenolic OH, and benzene ring

CHAPTER 14

14.1 a. The aldehyde contains five carbon atoms, and the name is pentanal.

b. The aldehyde carbon is position 1. The name is 3, 4-dimethylpentanal.

14.2 a. The chain is numbered from the right. The name is 4, 6-dibromo-2-heptanone.

b. The carbonyl carbon atom is position 1. The name is 2, 5-dimethylcyclopentanone.

14.3 a.
$$\qquad\ CH_3\qquad\quad O$$
$$\qquad\ \ |\qquad\qquad\ ||$$
$$CH_3CHCH_2 - C - OH$$

b. This is a ketone, and it does not undergo oxidation.

14.4 a.
$$\qquad\qquad OH$$
$$\qquad\qquad |$$
$$CH_3CH_2CHCH_2CH_3$$

b. [benzene ring] CH_2 — OH

14.5 a.

[benzene ring] C—H with OH and OCH_2CH_3 groups (hemiacetal) $\xrightarrow{H^+,\ CH_3CH_2-OH}$ [benzene ring] C—H with OCH_2CH_3 and OCH_2CH_3 groups (acetal) + H_2O

hemiacetal → acetal

b.

[benzene ring] C—CH_3 with OH and OCH_3 groups (hemiketal) $\xrightarrow{H^+,\ CH_3-OH}$ [benzene ring] C—CH_3 with OCH_3 and OCH_3 groups (ketal) + H_2O

hemiketal → ketal

14.6 a.
$$\qquad\qquad\qquad\qquad\ O$$
$$\qquad\qquad\qquad\qquad\ ||$$
$$CH_3CH_2CH_2 - C - H + 2CH_3CH_2 - OH$$

b. [cyclopentane ring]=O + 2CH_3 — OH

14.7 a. This compound is not a hemiacetal or hemiketal because there is no OH group. The presence of the ring hydrogen makes it an acetal.

Hydrolysis breaks these bonds

[ring structure with O, OCH_3, H] + H_2O $\xrightarrow{H^+}$ [ring with OH, C=O, H] + CH_3 — OH

b. An OH group is missing, so this compound is an acetal or ketal. Because the carbon with two attached oxygens does not have a hydrogen present, the compound is a ketal.

[ring structure with O, CH_3, OCH_3] + H_2O $\xrightarrow{H^+}$ [ring with OH, C=O, CH_3] + CH_3 — OH

Hydrolysis breaks these bonds

CHAPTER 15

15.1 a. The longest chain beginning with the carboxyl group has four carbon atoms. The name is 2-methylbutanoic acid.

b. The carboxyl group is at position 1. The name is 3, 4-dibromobenzoic acid.

15.2
$$\qquad\quad O\quad\ O$$
$$\qquad\quad ||\quad\ ||$$
$$CH_3 - C - C - O^-$$

15.3
$$\qquad\qquad\qquad\qquad\ O$$
$$\qquad\qquad\qquad\qquad\ ||$$
$$CH_3CH_2CH_2 - C - O^-Na^+ + H_2O$$

15.4 a. This is the lithium salt of 2-methylbenzoic acid. The name is lithium 2-methylbenzoate.

b. This is the sodium salt of butanoic acid. The name is sodium butanoate.

15.5 Each of these reactions requires H^+ as a catalyst. The products are as follows:

a.
$$\qquad\qquad\qquad\ O$$
$$\qquad\qquad\qquad\ ||$$
$$CH_3CH_2 - C - OCH_3 + H_2O$$

b.
$$\qquad\quad O$$
$$\qquad\quad ||$$
$$CH_3 - C - O - [benzene ring] + H_2O$$

c.
[benzene ring]—$\overset{\overset{\displaystyle O}{||}}{C}$—O—CHCH_3 + H_2O
$$\qquad\qquad\qquad\qquad\ |$$
$$\qquad\qquad\qquad\qquad CH_3$$

15.6 a.

[benzene ring]$-\overset{\overset{\displaystyle O}{||}}{C}-O-\overset{\overset{\displaystyle O}{||}}{C}-$[benzene ring] + CH_3 — OH $\longrightarrow$

[benzene ring]$-\overset{\overset{\displaystyle O}{||}}{C}-O-CH_3$ + [benzene ring]$-\overset{\overset{\displaystyle O}{||}}{C}-OH$

b.

$$CH_3CH_2 - \overset{\overset{\displaystyle O}{\|}}{C} - Cl + CH_3CH - OH \longrightarrow$$
$$\qquad\qquad\qquad\qquad\qquad |$$
$$\qquad\qquad\qquad\qquad\quad CH_3$$

$$CH_3CH_2 - \overset{\overset{\displaystyle O}{\|}}{C} - O - CHCH_3 + HCl$$
$$\qquad\qquad\qquad\qquad\qquad\qquad |$$
$$\qquad\qquad\qquad\qquad\qquad CH_3$$

15.7 a. The common name for the acid used to prepare this ester is formic acid. The alkyl group attached to oxygen is isopropyl. Thus, the common name is isopropyl formate. The IUPAC name for formic acid is methanoic acid. Thus, the IUPAC name for the ester is isopropyl methanoate.

b. The common and IUPAC names are identical when the carboxylic acid is benzoic acid. The name of the ester is methyl benzoate.

15.8

C — OH with benzene ring, $+ \; HO - CH_2CH_2CH_3$

15.9 a. $CH_3CH_2 - \overset{\overset{\displaystyle O}{\|}}{C} - O^-Na^+ + HO - CHCH_3$
$$\qquad\qquad\qquad\qquad\qquad\qquad\qquad |$$
$$\qquad\qquad\qquad\qquad\qquad\qquad CH_3$$

b. benzene ring $- \overset{\overset{\displaystyle O}{\|}}{C} - O^-K^+ + HO - CH_2CH_3$

CHAPTER 16

16.1 In each case, count the number of carbon atoms directly attached to the nitrogen.

a. secondary **b.** secondary **c.** tertiary

16.2 Identify the groups attached to the nitrogen.

a. propylamine

b. methylphenylamine

c. trimethylamine

16.3 a. 1-butanamine

b. N-methyl-1-butanamine

16.4 a. N-ethylaniline

b. N-ethyl-N-methylaniline

c. 3-ethyl-2-methylaniline

16.5 a.

$$CH_3 - \underset{\underset{\displaystyle H}{|}}{N} - H \cdots O \quad \text{or} \quad CH_3 - \underset{\underset{\displaystyle H}{|}}{N} - H$$

b.

$$CH_3CH_2 - \underset{\underset{\displaystyle CH_3}{|}}{N} - CH_3$$ (with O, H, H above)

16.6 a.

$$CH_3 - \overset{\overset{\displaystyle H}{|}}{\underset{\underset{\displaystyle CH_3}{|}}{N^+}} - CH_2CH_3 + OH^-$$

b. benzene ring $- NH_3^+ + OH^-$

16.7 a. benzene ring $- \underset{\underset{\displaystyle CH_3}{|}}{NH_2^+} Cl^-$

b. cyclopentane $NH_3^+ CH_3CH_2COO^-$

16.8

a. $CH_3 - \overset{\overset{\displaystyle O}{\|}}{C} - NH - CH_2CH_2CH_3 + CH_3 - \overset{\overset{\displaystyle O}{\|}}{C} - OH$

b. $CH_3CH_2 - \overset{\overset{\displaystyle O}{\|}}{C} - NH_2 + HCl$

16.9 a. This amide is derived from butanoic acid. The name is butanamide.

b. hexanamide

16.10 a. This amide is a derivative of the two-carbon acid acetic acid (common name) or ethanoic acid (IUPAC name). The amide is named N,N-diethylacetamide (common name) or N,N-diethylethanamide (IUPAC name).

b. This amide is a derivative of butyric acid (common name) or butanoic acid (IUPAC name). The amide is named N-isobutylbutyramide (common name) or N-isobutylbutanamide (IUPAC name).

c. The acid portion of this amide came from benzoic acid. The amide is named N-ethyl-N-phenylbenzamide.

d. The acid portion of this amide came from 2-methylbenzoic acid. The amide is named 2,N-dimethylbenzamide.

16.11 a.

$$CH_3 - \overset{\overset{\displaystyle O}{\|}}{C} - \underset{\underset{\displaystyle H}{|}}{N} - CH_3$$

(with O below, dotted)

$$CH_3 - \overset{\overset{\displaystyle O}{\|}}{C} - \underset{\underset{\displaystyle H}{|}}{N} - CH_3$$

b.

16.12 a. Under acidic conditions, amide hydrolysis produces a carboxylic acid and the salt of an amine.

C — OH + CH$_3$CH$_2$ — NH$_3^+$Cl$^-$

b. Under basic conditions, amide hydrolysis produces an amine and the salt of a carboxylic acid.

C — O$^-$Na$^+$ + CH$_3$CH$_2$ — NH$_2$

CHAPTER 17

17.1 In each case, look for the presence of four different groups attached to the colored atom.

a. The carbon is not chiral because of the two attached CH$_2$OH groups.

b. Yes

c. The carbon is not chiral because it is attached to two H's.

d. Yes

17.2 Each of the atoms marked with an asterisk has four different attached groups and is chiral.

a.
CH$_2$OH
|
C=O
|
HO — C*— H
|
H — C*— OH
|
CH$_2$OH

b.
CHO
|
*CH — OH
|
*CH — OH
|
*CH — OH
|
CH$_2$OH

c.
HOCH$_2$ O OH
* H H *
H * * H
OH OH

17.3 The chiral carbon atoms (three of them) are marked with an asterisk. Thus, there are 2^3, or 8, possible stereoisomers:

OH OH OH OH
| | | |
CH$_2$ — CH — CH — CH — CHO
 * * *

17.4 The chiral carbon atom is the one with the attached nitrogen. The chiral carbon atom is placed at the intersection of the two lines, and the COOH is placed at the top:

COOH COOH
| |
H ———— NH$_2$ H$_2$N ———— H
| |
CHCH$_3$ CHCH$_3$
| |
CH$_3$ CH$_3$
D form L form

17.5 In each case, look at the direction of the OH group on the bottom chiral carbon.

 a. L **b.** D **c.** L

17.6 a. aldopentose

 b. ketotetrose

 c. aldotetrose

17.7

17.8 a.

b.

CHAPTER 18

18.1 One of several possibilities is the following structure:

O
||
CH$_2$ — O — C — (CH$_2$)$_{16}$CH$_3$ (stearic acid component)
|
 O
 ||
CH — O — C — (CH$_2$)$_7$CH=CH(CH$_2$)$_7$CH$_3$ (oleic acid component)
|
 O
 ||
CH$_2$ — O — C — (CH$_2$)$_{14}$CH$_3$ (palmitic acid component)

18.2

CH$_2$ — OH HOOC — (CH$_2$)$_7$CH=CH(CH$_2$)$_7$CH$_3$
|
CH — OH + HOOC — (CH$_2$)$_{14}$CH$_3$
|
CH$_2$ — OH HOOC — (CH$_2$)$_{16}$CH$_3$

18.3

$$CH_2-OH \quad Na^{+-}OOC-(CH_2)_{16}CH_3$$
$$CH-OH + 2Na^{+-}OOC-(CH_2)_7CH=CH(CH_2)_7CH_3$$
$$CH_2-OH$$

18.4 During complete hydrogenation, all CH=CH groups become CH₂—CH₂ groups:

$$CH_2-O-\overset{\overset{\displaystyle O}{\|}}{C}-(CH_2)_7CH_2CH_2(CH_2)_7CH_3$$
$$CH-O-\overset{\overset{\displaystyle O}{\|}}{C}-(CH_2)_7CH_2CH_2CH_2CH_2CH_2CH_2CH_2CH_2CH_3$$
$$CH_2-O-\overset{\overset{\displaystyle O}{\|}}{C}-(CH_2)_7CH_2CH_2CH_2CH_2CH_2(CH_2)_4CH_3$$

Combining all the CH₂ groups gives:

$$CH_2-O-\overset{\overset{\displaystyle O}{\|}}{C}-(CH_2)_{16}CH_3$$
$$CH-O-\overset{\overset{\displaystyle O}{\|}}{C}-(CH_2)_{16}CH_3$$
$$CH_2-O-\overset{\overset{\displaystyle O}{\|}}{C}-(CH_2)_{16}CH_3$$

18.5

$$CH_2-O-\overset{\overset{\displaystyle O}{\|}}{C}-(CH_2)_{14}CH_3$$
$$CH-O-\overset{\overset{\displaystyle O}{\|}}{C}-(CH_2)_7CH=CH(CH_2)_7CH_3$$
$$CH_2-O-\overset{\overset{\displaystyle O}{\|}}{\underset{\underset{\displaystyle O^-}{|}}{P}}-OCH_2CH_2-NH_3^+$$

CHAPTER 19

19.1

a. $H_3\overset{+}{N}-CH-\overset{\overset{\displaystyle O}{\|}}{C}-OH$
$\qquad CH_2-OH$

b. $H_2N-CH-\overset{\overset{\displaystyle O}{\|}}{C}-O^-$
$\qquad CH_2-OH$

19.2

$$H_3\overset{+}{N}-CH-\overset{\overset{\displaystyle O}{\|}}{C}-NH-CH-\overset{\overset{\displaystyle O}{\|}}{C}-NH-$$
$$CH_2 \qquad\qquad CH_2$$
$$\bigcirc \qquad\qquad SH$$

N-terminal
residue

$$-CH-\overset{\overset{\displaystyle O}{\|}}{C}-NH-CH-\overset{\overset{\displaystyle O}{\|}}{C}-O$$
$$CH_2 \qquad\qquad CHCH_3$$
$$OH \qquad\qquad CH_2CH_3$$

C-terminal
residue

19.3 a. Hydrophobic attractions between nonpolar groups

b. Hydrogen bonding

c. Salt bridges between the ionic groups

CHAPTER 20

20.1 a. maltose

b. peptides

c. glucose-6-phosphate

20.2 Turnover number is the number of substrate molecules acted on per minute by one molecule of enzyme. One enzyme international unit is the amount of enzyme that catalyzes 1 μmol of substrate to react per minute.

20.3 a. An increase in enzyme concentration increases the rate of an enzyme-catalyzed reaction.

b. An increase in substrate concentration increases the rate until the enzyme is saturated. Above the saturation point, the rate of reaction is constant.

c. An increase in temperature increases the rate of the enzyme-catalyzed reaction until the optimum temperature is reached. Above the optimum temperature, the rate decreases.

d. An increase in pH increases the reaction rate until the optimum pH is reached. Above the optimum pH, the rate decreases.

20.4 a. The structure of a competitive inhibitor resembles that of the substrate. The structure of a noncompetitive inhibitor bears no resemblance to that of the substrate.

b. A competitive inhibitor binds at the active site. A non-competitive inhibitor binds at some other region of the enzyme.

c. Increasing substrate concentration reverses the effect of a competitive inhibitor, but has no effect on a noncompetitive inhibitor.

20.5 **a.** Several enzymes are synthesized in inactive forms called zymogens. Under the proper reaction conditions, zymogens are activated to carry out their catalytic role.

b. The catalytic ability of allosteric enzymes may be either increased or decreased by the binding of modulators.

c. Certain enzymes are synthesized in greater amounts when needed and in smaller amounts when not needed.

CHAPTER 21

21.1

5' end

phosphodiester linkages

OH
3' end

21.2 5' T-T-A-C-G 3' original strand

3' A-A-T-G-C 5' complementary strand

The complementary strand written in the 5' to 3' direction is C-G-T-A-A.

21.3 5' A-T-T-A-G-C-C-G 3' DNA template

3' U-A-A-U-C-G-G-C 5' mRNA

The mRNA written in the 5' to 3' direction is C-G-G-C-U-A-A-U.

21.4 f Met-His-His-Val-Leu-Cys

CHAPTER 22

22.1

$$\underset{\underset{CH_2-COO^-}{|}}{\overset{\overset{OH}{|}}{CH}}-COO^- + NAD^+ \longrightarrow \underset{\underset{CH_2-COO^-}{|}}{\overset{\overset{O}{\|}}{C}}-COO^- + NADH + H^+$$

22.2 **a.** $^-OOC-CH=CH-COO^- + FADH_2$

b. $CH_3-\overset{\overset{O}{\|}}{C}-COO^- + NADH + H^+$

CHAPTER 23

23.1 **a.** Hexokinase regulates the first step of the glycolysis pathway. The enzyme is controlled by concentrations of glucose-6-phosphate through feedback inhibition.

b. Phosphofructokinase is an allosteric enzyme which regulates the production of fructose-1,6-bisphosphate. The enzyme is inhibited by high concentrations of ATP and citrate, and it is activated by high concentrations of ADP and AMP.

c. Pyruvate kinase controls the last step of glycolysis. It is inhibited by higher concentrations of ATP.

23.2 NAD^+ produced from the various fates of pyruvate can be used in the glycolysis pathway, enabling further glycolysis to take place.

23.3 **a.** Three: Each $FADH_2$ produces 1.5 molecules of ATP.

b. Five: Each NADH produces 2.5 molecules of ATP.

c. 20: Each acetyl CoA produces 10 molecules of ATP.

23.4 Glucose-6-phosphatase is present in the liver but not in the muscles.

CHAPTER 24

24.1 **a.** Each acetyl CoA contains two carbon atoms from capric acid. Thus, five acetyl CoA molecules are formed.

b. Ten carbon atoms require four trips through the fatty acid spiral. Thus, four molecules of $FADH_2$ are formed.

c. Four trips through the spiral also produce four NADH molecules and four H^+ ions.

24.2 A 16-carbon fatty acid would yield eight molecules of acetyl CoA. Seven trips through the spiral are necessary and would produce 7 $FADH_2$ and 7 NADH +7 H^+.

8 acetyl CoA × 10 ATP/acetyl CoA	=	80 ATP
7 $FADH_2$ × 1.5 ATP/$FADH_2$	=	10.5 ATP
7 NADH × 2.5 ATP/NADH	=	17.5 ATP
		108 ATP

Two high-energy bonds in ATP are consumed in the activation step.

−2
106 ATP

24.3

$$HO-\langle\!\!\langle\bigcirc\rangle\!\!\rangle-CH_2-\overset{\overset{O}{\|}}{C}-COO^-$$

$$+\ ^-OOC-CH_2-CH_2-\underset{\underset{NH_3^+}{|}}{CH}-COO^-$$

24.4 **a.** The urea cycle converts toxic ammonia into less toxic urea for excretion from the body.

b. carbamoyl phosphate

CHAPTER 25

25.1 **a.** lungs

b. tissue cells

c. lungs

d. tissue cells

absolute specificity The characteristic of an enzyme that it acts on one and only one substrate.

absolute zero The temperature at which all motion stops; a value of 0 on the Kelvin scale.

acetal A compound that contains the $-\overset{\displaystyle OR}{\underset{\displaystyle OR}{\overset{|}{\underset{|}{C}}}}-H$ arrangement of atoms.

acetone breath A condition in which acetone can be detected in the breath.

acid dissociation constant The ratio of product molarities (H^+ and acid anion) multiplied together and divided by the molarity of undissociated acid. All molarities are measured at equilibrium.

acidic solution A solution in which the concentration of H_3O^+ is greater than the concentration of OH^-; also, a solution in which pH is less than 7.

acidosis A low blood pH.

activation energy Energy needed to start some spontaneous processes. Once started, the processes continue without further stimulus or energy from an outside source.

activator A substance that binds to an allosteric enzyme and increases its activity.

active site The location on an enzyme where a substrate is bound and catalysis occurs.

activity series A tabular representation of the tendencies of metals to react with H^+.

acute radiation syndrome A condition following short-term exposure to intense radiation.

addition polymer A polymer formed by the linking together of many alkene molecules through addition reactions.

addition reaction A reaction in which a compound adds to a multiple bond.

adipose tissue A kind of connective tissue where triglycerides are stored.

aerobic In the presence of oxygen.

alcohol A compound in which an —OH group is connected to an aliphatic carbon atom.

alcoholic fermentation The conversion of glucose to ethanol.

aldehyde A compound that contains the $-\overset{\displaystyle O}{\overset{||}{C}}-H$ group; the general formula is $R-\overset{\displaystyle O}{\overset{||}{C}}-H$.

aliphatic compound Any organic compound that is not aromatic.

alkaline solution See **basic solution**.

alkaloids A class of nitrogen-containing organic compounds obtained from plants.

alkalosis An abnormally high blood pH.

alkane A hydrocarbon that contains only single bonds.

alkene A hydrocarbon that contains one or more double bonds.

alkoxy group The —O—R functional group.

alkyl group A group differing by one hydrogen from an alkane.

alkyl halide See **haloalkane**.

alkyne A hydrocarbon that contains one or more triple bonds.

allosteric enzyme An enzyme with quaternary structure whose activity is changed by the binding of modulators.

alpha-amino acid An organic compound containing both an amino group and a carboxylate group, with the amino group attached to the carbon next to the carboxylate group.

α-helix The helical structure in proteins that is maintained by hydrogen bonds.

alpha particle The particle that makes up alpha rays; identical to the helium nucleus and composed of two protons and two neutrons.

amide An organic compound having the functional group $-\overset{\displaystyle O}{\overset{||}{\underset{|}{C}}}-N-$.

amide linkage The carbonyl carbon-nitrogen single bond of the amide group.

amine An organic compound derived by replacing one or more of the hydrogen atoms of ammonia with alkyl or aromatic groups, as in RNH_2, R_2NH, and R_3N.

amino acid pool The total supply of amino acids in the body.

amino acid residue An amino acid that is a part of a peptide, polypeptide, or protein chain.

amphetamines A class of drugs structurally similar to epinephrine, used to stimulate the central nervous system.

anabolism All reactions involved in the synthesis of biomolecules.

anaerobic In the absence of oxygen.

anion A negatively charged ion.

anomeric carbon An acetal, ketal, hemiacetal, or hemiketal carbon atom giving rise to two stereoisomers.

anomers Stereoisomers that differ in the three-dimensional arrangement of groups at the carbon of an acetal, ketal, hemiacetal, or hemiketal group.

antibiotic A substance produced by one microorganism that kills or inhibits the growth of other microorganisms.

antibody A substance that helps protect the body from invasion by foreign materials known as antigens.

anticodon A three-base sequence in tRNA that is complementary to one of the codons in mRNA.

antioxidant A substance that prevents another substance from being oxidized.

apoenzyme A catalytically inactive protein formed by removal of the cofactor from an active enzyme.

aromatic hydrocarbon Any organic compound that contains the characteristic benzene ring or similar feature.

Arrhenius acid Any substance that provides H^+ ions when dissolved in water.

Arrhenius base Any substance that provides OH^- ions when dissolved in water.

atom The limit of chemical subdivision for matter.

atomic mass unit (u) A unit used to express the relative masses of atoms. One u is equal to $\frac{1}{12}$ the mass of an atom of carbon-12.

atomic number of an atom A number equal to the number of protons in the nucleus of an atom. Symbolically it is represented by Z.

atomic orbital A volume of space around atomic nuclei in which electrons of the same energy move. Groups of orbitals with the same n values form subshells.

atomic weight The mass of an average atom of an element expressed in atomic mass units.

Avogadro's law Equal volumes of gases measured at the same temperature and pressure contain equal numbers of molecules.

balanced equation An equation in which the number of atoms of each element in the reactants is the same as the number of atoms of that same element in the products.

basic solution A solution in which the concentration of OH^- is greater than the concentration of H_3O^+; also, a solution in which pH is greater than 7; also called alkaline solution.

basic unit of measurement A specific unit from which other units for the same quantity are obtained by multiplication or division.

becquerel A physical unit of radiation measurement corresponding to one nuclear disintegration per second.

Benedict's reagent A mild oxidizing solution containing Cu^{2+} ions used to test for the presence of aldehydes.

β-oxidation process A pathway in which fatty acids are broken down into molecules of acetyl CoA.

beta particle The particle that makes up beta rays; identical to an electron but produced in the nucleus when a neutron is changed into a proton and an electron.

β-pleated sheet A secondary protein structure in which protein chains are aligned side by side in a sheetlike array held together by hydrogen bonds.

binary compound A compound made up of two different elements.

biochemistry A study of the compounds and processes associated with living organisms.

biological unit of radiation A radiation measurement unit that indicates the damage caused by radiation in living tissue.

biomolecule A general term referring to an organic compound essential to life.

blood sugar level The amount of glucose present in blood, normally expressed as milligrams per 100 mL of blood.

boiling point The temperature at which the vapor pressure of a liquid is equal to the prevailing atmospheric pressure.

bond polarization A result of the attraction of shared electrons to the more electronegative atom of a bonded pair of atoms.

Boyle's law A gas law that describes the pressure and volume behavior of a gas sample kept at constant temperature. Mathematically, it is $PV = k$.

branched alkane An alkane in which at least one carbon atom is not part of a continuous chain.

branching chain reaction See **expanding chain reaction**.

breeder reaction A nuclear reaction in which isotopes that will not undergo spontaneous fission are changed into isotopes that will.

Brønsted acid Any hydrogen-containing substance that is capable of donating a proton (H^+) to another substance.

Brønsted base Any substance capable of accepting a proton from another substance.

buffer A solution with the ability to resist changing pH when acids (H^+) or bases (OH^-) are added.

buffer capacity The amount of acid (H^+) or base (OH^-) that can be absorbed by a buffer without causing a significant change in pH.

carbaminohemoglobin Hemoglobin combined with carbon dioxide.

carbocation An ion of the form $-\overset{+}{\underset{|}{C}}-$.

carbohydrate A polyhydroxy aldehyde, ketone, or substance that yields such compounds on hydrolysis.

carbonyl group The $-\overset{\overset{\displaystyle O}{\|}}{C}-$ group.

carboxyl group The $-\overset{\overset{\displaystyle O}{\|}}{C}-OH$ group.

carboxylate ion The $R-\overset{\overset{\displaystyle O}{\|}}{C}-O^-$ ion that results from the dissociation of a carboxylic acid.

carboxylic acid An organic compound that contains the $-\overset{\overset{\displaystyle O}{\|}}{C}-OH$ functional group.

carboxylic acid anhydride An organic compound that contains the $-\overset{\overset{\displaystyle O}{\|}}{C}-O-\overset{\overset{\displaystyle O}{\|}}{C}-$ functional group.

carboxylic acid chloride An organic compound that contains the $-\overset{\overset{\displaystyle O}{\|}}{C}-Cl$ functional group.

carboxylic ester A compound with the $-\overset{\overset{\displaystyle O}{\|}}{C}-OR$ functional group.

catabolism All reactions involved in the breakdown of biomolecules.

catalyst A substance that changes (usually increases) reaction rates without being used up in the reaction.

cation A positively charged ion.

cellular respiration The entire process involved in the use of oxygen by cells.

central dogma of molecular biology The well-established process by which genetic information stored in DNA molecules is expressed in the structure of synthesized proteins.

cephalin A phosphoglyceride containing ethanolamine or serine.

chain reaction A nuclear reaction in which the products of one reaction cause a repeat of the reaction to take place.

Charles's law A gas law that describes the temperature and volume behavior of a gas sample kept at constant pressure. Mathematically, it is $V/T = k'$.

chemical change A change matter undergoes that involves changes in composition.

chemical property A property matter demonstrates when attempts are made to change it into new substances.

chemiosmotic hypothesis The postulate that a proton flow across the inner mitochondrial membrane during operation of the electron transport chain provides energy for ATP synthesis.

chiral A descriptive term for compounds or objects that cannot be superimposed on their mirror image.

chiral carbon A carbon atom with four different groups attached.

chloride shift The movement of chloride ions from one fluid to another to maintain charge neutrality.

chromosome A tightly packaged bundle of DNA and protein that is involved in cell division.

chylomicron A lipoprotein aggregate found in the lymph and the bloodstream.

cis- On the same side (as applied to geometric isomers).

citric acid cycle A series of reactions in which acetyl CoA is oxidized to carbon dioxide and reduced forms of coenzymes FAD and NAD^+ are produced.

codon A sequence of three nucleotide bases that represents a code word on mRNA molecules.

coenzyme An organic molecule required by an enzyme for catalytic activity.

cofactor A nonprotein molecule or ion required by an enzyme for catalytic activity.

cohesive force The attractive force between particles; it is associated with potential energy.

cold spot Tissue from which a radioactive tracer is excluded or rejected.

colligative property A solution property that depends only on the concentration of solute particles in solution.

colloid A homogeneous mixture of two or more substances in which the dispersed substances are present as larger particles than are found in solutions.

combination reaction A chemical reaction in which two or more substances react to form a single substance.

combined gas law A gas law that describes the pressure, volume, and temperature behavior of a gas sample. Mathematically, it is $PV/T = k''$.

common catabolic pathway The reactions of the citric acid cycle plus those of the electron transport chain and oxidative phosphorylation.

competitive inhibitor An inhibitor that competes with substrate for binding at the active site of an enzyme.

complementary DNA strands Two strands of DNA in a double-helical form such that adenine and guanine of one strand are matched and hydrogen bonded to thymine and cytosine, respectively, of the second strand.

complete protein Protein in food that contains all essential amino acids in the proportions needed by the body.

complex carbohydrates The polysaccharides amylose and amylopectin, collectively called starch.

complex lipid An ester-containing lipid with more than two types of components: an alcohol, fatty acids, plus other components.

compound A pure substance consisting of two or more kinds of atoms in the form of heteroatomic molecules or individual atoms.

compound formula A symbol for the molecule of a compound, consisting of the symbols of the atoms found in the molecule. Atoms present in numbers higher than 1 have the number indicated by a subscript.

compressibility The change in volume of a sample resulting from a pressure change acting on the sample.

concentration The amount of solute contained in a specific amount of solution.

condensation An exothermic process in which a gas or vapor is changed to a liquid or solid.

condensation polymerization The process by which monomers combine with the simultaneous elimination of a small molecule.

condensed structural formula A structural molecular formula showing the general arrangement of atoms but without showing all the covalent bonds.

conformations The different arrangements of atoms in space achieved by rotation about single bonds.

conjugate acid–base pair A Brønsted acid and its conjugate base.

conjugate base The species remaining when a Brønsted acid donates a proton.

conjugated protein A protein made up of amino acid residues and other organic or inorganic components.

copolymer An addition polymer formed by the reaction of two different monomers.

Cori cycle The process in which glucose is converted to lactate in muscle tissue, lactate is reconverted to glucose in the liver, and glucose is returned to the muscle.

covalent bond The attractive force that results between two atoms that are both attracted to a shared pair of electrons.

critical mass The minimum amount of fissionable material needed to sustain a critical chain reaction at a constant rate.

critical reaction A constant-rate chain reaction.

crystal lattice A rigid three-dimensional arrangement of particles.

C-terminal residue An amino acid on the end of a chain that has an unreacted or free carboxylate group.

curie A physical unit of radiation measurement corresponding to 3.7×10^{10} nuclear disintegrations per second.

cycloalkane An alkane in which carbon atoms form a ring.

cyclotron A cyclic particle accelerator that works by changing electrical polarities as charged particles cross a gap. The particles are kept in a spiral path by a strong magnetic field.

cytochrome An iron-containing enzyme located in the electron transport chain.

daily reference values (DRV) A set of standards for nutrients and food components (such as fat and fiber) that have important relationships with health; used on food labels as part of the Daily Values.

daily values (DV) Reference values developed by the FDA specifically for use on food labels. The Daily Values represent two sets of standards: Reference Daily Intakes (RDI) and Daily Reference Values (DRV).

Dalton's law of partial pressures The total pressure exerted by a mixture of gases is equal to the sum of the partial pressures of the gases in the mixture.

daughter nuclei The new nuclei produced when unstable nuclei undergo radioactive decay.

decomposition A change in chemical composition that can result from heating.

decomposition reaction A chemical reaction in which a single substance reacts to form two or more simpler substances.

dehydration reaction A reaction in which water is chemically removed from a compound.

denaturation The process by which a protein loses its characteristic native structure and function.

density The number given when the mass of a sample of a substance is divided by the volume of the same sample.

deoxyhemoglobin (hemoglobin) Nonoxygenated hemoglobin.

deoxyribonucleic acid (DNA) A nucleic acid found primarily in the nuclei of cells.

derived unit of measurement A unit obtained by multiplication or division of one or more basic units.

dextrorotatory Describes substances that rotate plane-polarized light to the right.

dialysis A process in which solvent molecules, other small molecules, and hydrated ions pass from a solution through a membrane.

dialyzing membrane A semipermeable membrane with pores large enough to allow solvent molecules, other small molecules, and hydrated ions to pass through.

diatomic molecule A molecule that contains two atoms.

diffusion A process that causes substances to spontaneously intermingle when they are brought together.

dimer Two identical molecules bonded together.

dipeptide A compound formed when two amino acids are bonded by an amide linkage.

dipolar force The attractive force that exists between the positive end of one polar molecule and the negative end of another.

diprotic acid An acid that gives up two protons (H^+) per molecule when dissolved.

disaccharide A carbohydrate formed by the combination of two monosaccharides.

dispersed phase The substance present in a colloidal dispersion in amounts less than the amount of dispersing medium.

dispersing medium The substance present in a collodial dispersion in the largest amount.

dispersion force A very weak attraction force acting between the particles of all matter; results from momentary nonsymmetric electron distributions in molecules or atoms.

disruptive force The force resulting from particle motion; associated with kinetic energy.

dissolving A term used to describe the process of solution formation when the solvent and solutes form a homogeneous mixture.

distinguishing electron The last or highest-energy electron found in an element.

disulfide A compound containing an —S—S— group.

disulfide bridge A bond produced by the oxidation of —SH groups on two cysteine residues. The bond loops or holds two peptide chains together.

double bond The bond resulting from the sharing of two pairs of electrons.

double-replacement reaction A chemical reaction in which two compounds react and exchange partners to form two new compounds.

effective collision A collision that causes a reaction to occur between colliding molecules.

effusion A process in which a gas escapes from a container through a small hole.

electrolyte A solute that when dissolved in water forms a solution that conducts electricity.

electron capture A mode of radioactive decay for some unstable nuclei in which an electron from outside the nucleus is drawn into the nucleus, where it combines with a proton to form a neutron.

electron transport chain A series of reactions in which protons and electrons from the oxidation of foods are used to reduce molecular oxygen to water.

electronegativity The tendency of an atom to attract shared electrons of a covalent bond.

electronic configurations The detailed arrangements of electrons indicated by a specific notation, $1s^2 2s^2 2p^4$, and so on.

element A pure substance consisting of only one kind of atom in the form of homoatomic molecules or individual atoms.

elemental symbol A symbol assigned to an element that is based on the name of the element and consists of one capital letter or a capital letter followed by a lowercase letter.

elimination reaction A reaction in which two or more covalent bonds are broken and a new multiple bond is formed.

emulsifying agent (stabilizing agent) A substance that when added to colloids prevents them from coalescing and settling.

enantiomers Stereoisomers that are mirror images.

endergonic process A process that gains or accepts energy as it takes place.

endothermic reaction A reaction that absorbs heat.

endpoint of a titration The point at which the titration is stopped on the basis of an indicator color change or pH meter reading.

entropy A measurement or indication of the disorder or randomness of a system; the more disorderly a system, the higher its entropy.

enzyme A protein molecule that catalyzes chemical reactions.

enzyme activity The rate at which an enzyme catalyzes a reaction.

enzyme induction The synthesis of an enzyme in response to a cellular need.

enzyme inhibitor A substance that decreases the activity of an enzyme.

enzyme international unit (IU) A quantity of enzyme that catalyzes the conversion of 1 μmol of substrate per minute under specified conditions.

equilibrium concentration The unchanging concentration of reactants and products in a reaction system that is in a state of equilibrium.

equilibrium constant A constant that relates the equilibrium concentrations of products to those of reactants, each being raised to exponents obtained from stoichiometric coefficients.

equilibrium expression An equation relating the equilibrium constant and reactant and product concentrations.

equivalence point of a titration The point at which the unknown solution has exactly reacted with the known solution. Neither is in excess.

equivalent of salt The amount that will produce 1 mol of positive charges on dissolving and dissociating into ions.

essential amino acid An amino acid that cannot be synthesized within the body at a rate adequate to meet metabolic needs.

essential fatty acid A fatty acid needed by the body that cannot be synthesized within the body.

ester A compound in which the —OH of an acid is replaced by an —OR.

ester linkage The carbonyl carbon–oxygen single bond of the ester group.

esterification The process of forming an ester.

ether A compound that contains a $-\overset{|}{\underset{|}{C}}-O-\overset{|}{\underset{|}{C}}-$ functional group.

eukaryotic cell A cell containing membrane-enclosed organelles, particularly a nucleus.

evaporation An endothermic process in which a liquid is changed to a gas; also called vaporization.

exact numbers Numbers that have no uncertainty; numbers from defined relationships, counting numbers, and numbers that are part of reduced simple fractions.

exergonic process A process that gives up energy as it takes place.

exon A segment of a eukaryotic DNA molecule that is coded for amino acids.

exothermic reaction A reaction that liberates heat.

expanded structural formula A structural molecular formula showing all the covalent bonds.

expanding chain reaction A reaction in which the products of one reaction cause more than one more reaction to occur; also called branching chain reaction.

extracellular fluid Body fluid located outside cells.

extremozyme A nickname for certain enzymes isolated from microorganisms that thrive in extreme environments.

factors used in the factor-unit method Fractions obtained from fixed relationships between quantities.

family of the periodic table See **Group of the periodic table**.

fat A triglyceride that is a solid at room temperature.

fat mobilization The hydrolysis of stored triglycerides followed by the entry of fatty acids and glycerol into the bloodstream.

fatty acid A long-chain carboxylic acid found in fats.

feedback inhibition A process in which the end product of a sequence of enzyme-catalyzed reactions inhibits an earlier step in the process.

fermentation A reaction of sugars, starch, or cellulose to produce ethanol and carbon dioxide.

fibrous protein A protein made up of long rod-shaped or stringlike molecules that intertwine to form fibers.

first ionization energy The energy required to remove the first electron from a neutral atom.

Fischer projection A method of depicting three-dimensional shapes for chiral molecules.

fluid-mosaic model A model of membrane structure in which proteins are embedded in a flexible lipid bilayer.

formula weight The sum of the atomic weights of the atoms shown in the formula of an ionic compound.

functional group A unique reactive combination of atoms that differentiates molecules of organic compounds of one class from those of another.

furanose ring A five-membered sugar ring system containing an oxygen atom.

gamma ray A high-energy ray that is like an X ray but with a higher energy.

gas law A mathematical relationship that describes the behavior of gases as they are mixed, subjected to pressure or temperature changes, or allowed to diffuse.

Geiger-Müller tube A radiation-detection device operating on the principle that ions form when radiation passes through a tube filled with low-pressure gas.

gene An individual section of a chromosomal DNA molecule that is the fundamental unit of heredity.

genome A summation of all the genetic material (chromosomes) of a cell; a person's genetic blueprint.

geometric isomers Molecules that differ in the three-dimensional arrangements of their atoms in space and not in the order of linkage of atoms.

globular protein A spherical protein that usually forms stable suspensions in water or dissolves in water.

glucogenic amino acid An amino acid whose carbon skeleton can be converted metabolically to an intermediate used in the synthesis of glucose.

gluconeogenesis The synthesis of glucose from noncarbohydrate molecules.

glucosuria A condition in which elevated blood sugar levels result in the excretion of glucose in the urine.

glycogenesis The synthesis of glycogen from glucose.

glycogenolysis The breakdown of glycogen to glucose.

glycolipid A complex lipid containing sphingosine, a fatty acid, and a carbohydrate.

glycolysis A series of reactions by which glucose is oxidized to pyruvate.

glycoside Another name for a carbohydrate containing an acetal or ketal group.

glycosidic linkage The carbon-oxygen-carbon linkage that joins the components of a glycoside to the ring.

Graham's law A mathematical expression that relates rates of effusion or diffusion of two gases to the masses of the molecules of the two gases.

gray A biological unit of radiation measurement that corresponds to the transfer of 1 J of energy to 1 kg of tissue.

group of the periodic table A vertical column of elements that have similar chemical properties; also called family of the periodic table.

half-life The time required for one-half the unstable nuclei in a sample to undergo radioactive decay.

haloalkane A derivative of an alkane in which one or more hydrogens are replaced by halogens; also called alkyl halide.

Haworth structure A method of depicting three-dimensional carbohydrate structures.

heat of fusion The amount of heat energy required to melt exactly 1 g of a solid substance at constant temperature.

heat of vaporization The amount of heat energy required to vaporize exactly 1 g of a liquid substance at constant temperature.

hemiacetal A compound that contains the functional group

$$-\overset{\displaystyle OH}{\underset{\displaystyle OR}{C}}-H.$$

hemiketal A compound that contains the $-\overset{\displaystyle OH}{\underset{\displaystyle OR}{C}}-\overset{\displaystyle OH}{C}-\overset{\displaystyle OH}{\underset{\displaystyle OR}{C}}-$ group.

Henderson-Hasselbalch equation A relationship between the pH of a buffer, pK_a, and the concentrations of acid and salt in the buffer.

heteroatomic molecule A molecule that contains two or more kinds of atoms.

heterocyclic ring A ring in which one or more atoms is an atom other than carbon.

heterogeneous matter Matter with properties that are not the same throughout the sample.

heterogeneous nuclear RNA (hnRNA) RNA produced when both introns and exons of eukaryotic cellular DNA are transcribed.

heterogeneous catalyst A catalytic substance normally used in the form of a solid with a large surface area on which reactions take place; also called surface catalyst.

high-energy compound A substance that on hydrolysis liberates a great amount of free energy.

homeostasis A condition of chemical balance in the body.

homoatomic molecule A molecule that contains only one kind of atom.

homogeneous catalyst A catalytic substance that is distributed uniformly throughout the reaction mixture.

homogeneous matter Matter that has the same properties throughout the sample.

homologous series Compounds of the same functional class that differ by a —CH_2— group.

hormone A chemical messenger secreted by specific glands and carried by the blood to a target tissue, where it triggers a particular response.

hot spot Tissue in which a radioactive tracer concentrates.

Hund's rule A statement of the behavior of electrons when they occupy orbitals: Electrons will not join other electrons in an orbital if an empty orbital of the same energy is available for occupancy.

hybrid orbital An orbital produced from the combination of two or more nonequivalent orbitals of an atom.

hydrate A salt that contains specific numbers of water molecules as part of the solid crystalline structure.

hydrated ion An ion in solution that is surrounded by water molecules.

hydration The addition of water to a multiple bond.

hydrocarbon An organic compound that contains only carbon and hydrogen.

hydrogen bonding The result of attractive dipolar forces between molecules in which hydrogen atoms are covalently bonded to very electronegative elements (O, N, or F).

hydrogenation A reaction in which the addition of hydrogen takes place.

hydrolysis Bond breakage by reaction with water.

hydrolysis reaction Any reaction with water; for salts, a reaction of the acidic cation and/or basic anion of the salt with water.

hydrophobic Characterizing molecules or parts of molecules that repel (are insoluble in) water.

hydroxy group The —OH functional group.

hyperglycemia A higher-than-normal blood sugar level.

hyperventilation Rapid, deep breathing.

hypoglycemia A lower-than-normal blood sugar level.

hypoventilation Slow, shallow breathing.

ideal gas law A gas law that relates the pressure, volume, temperature, and number of moles in a gas sample. The equation is $PV = nRT$.

immiscible A term used to describe liquids that are insoluble in each other.

inborn error of metabolism A disease in which a genetic change causes a deficiency of a particular protein, often an enzyme.

induced-fit theory The theory of enzyme action proposing that the conformation of an enzyme changes to accommodate an incoming substrate.

inhibitor A substance that decreases reaction rates.

inner-transition element An element in which the distinguishing electron is found in an *f* subshell.

inorganic chemistry The study of the elements and all noncarbon compounds.

insoluble substance A substance that does not dissolve to a significant extent in the solvent.

internal energy The energy associated with vibrations within molecules.

International Unit (IU) A measure of vitamin activity, determined by biological methods.

interstitial fluid The fluid surrounding individual tissue cells.

intracellular fluid Body fluid located inside cells.

intron A segment of a eukaryotic DNA molecule that carries no codes for amino acids.

inverse square law of radiation A mathematical way of saying that the intensity of radiation is inversely proportional to the square of the distance from the source of the radiation.

invert sugar A mixture of equal amounts of glucose and fructose.

ionic bond The attractive force that holds together ions of opposite charge.

ion product of water The equilibrium constant for the dissociation of pure water into H_3O^+ and OH^-.

isoelectric point The characteristic solution pH at which an amino acid has a net charge of zero.

isoelectric A term meaning "same electronic," used to describe atoms or ions that have identical electronic configurations.

isoenzyme A slightly different form of the same enzyme produced by different tissues.

isomerism A property in which two or more compounds have the same molecular formula but different arrangements of atoms.

isotopes Atoms having the same atomic number but different mass numbers; that is, they are atoms of the same element that contain different numbers of neutrons in their nuclei.

ketal A compound that contains the
$$\begin{array}{c} \text{OR} \\ | \quad | \quad | \\ -C-C-C- \\ | \quad | \quad | \\ \text{OR} \end{array}$$
group.

ketoacidosis A low blood pH due to elevated levels of ketone bodies.

ketogenic amino acid An amino acid whose carbon skeleton can be converted metabolically to acetyl CoA or acetoacetyl CoA.

ketone A compound that contains the
$$\begin{array}{c} \text{O} \\ | \quad || \quad | \\ -C-C-C- \\ | \qquad | \end{array}$$
group;

the general formula is
$$\begin{array}{c} \text{O} \\ || \\ R-C-R'. \end{array}$$

ketone bodies Three compounds—acetoacetate, β-hydroxybutyrate, and acetone—formed from acetyl CoA.

ketonemia An elevated level of ketone bodies in the blood.

ketonuria The presence of ketone bodies in the urine.

ketosis A condition in which ketonemia, ketonuria, and acetone breath exist together.

kinetic energy The energy a particle has as a result of its motion. Mathematically, it is $KE = \frac{1}{2}mv^2$.

lactate fermentation The production of lactate from glucose.

lattice site The individual location occupied by a particle in a crystal lattice.

law of conservation of matter Atoms are neither created nor destroyed in chemical reactions.

Le Châtelier's principle The position of equilibrium will shift to compensate for changes made that upset a system at equilibrium.

lecithin A phosphoglyceride containing choline.

levorotatory Describes substances that rotate plane-polarized light to the left.

Lewis structure A representation of an atom or ion in which the elemental symbol represents the atomic nucleus and all but the valence-shell electrons. The valence-shell electrons are represented by dots arranged around the elemental symbol.

limiting reactant The reactant present in a reaction in the least amount based on its reaction coefficients and molecular weight. The limiting reactant determines the maximum amount of product that can be formed.

limiting-reactant principle The maximum amount of product possible from a reaction is determined by the amount of reactant present in the least amount, based on its reaction coefficient and molecular weight.

linear accelerator A particle accelerator that works by changing electrical polarities as charged particles cross gaps between segments of a long tube.

lipid A biological compound that is soluble only in nonpolar solvents.

lipid bilayer A structure found in membranes, consisting of two sheets of lipid molecules arranged so that the hydrophobic portions are facing each other.

lock-and-key theory The theory of enzyme specificity proposing that a substrate has a shape fitting that of the enzyme's active site, as a key fits a lock.

macronutrient A substance needed by the body in relatively large amounts.

major mineral A mineral found in the body in quantities greater than 5 g.

Markovnikov's rule In the addition of H—X to an alkene, the hydrogen becomes attached to the carbon atom that is already bonded to more hydrogens.

mass A measurement of the amount of matter in an object.

mass number of an atom A number equal to the sum of the number of protons and neutrons in the nucleus of an atom. Symbolically, it is represented by A.

matter Anything that has mass and occupies space.

melting point The temperature at which a solid changes to a liquid; the solid and liquid have the same vapor pressure.

messenger RNA (mRNA) RNA that carries genetic information from the DNA in the cell nucleus to the site of protein synthesis in the cytoplasm.

metabolic acidosis A condition of acidosis resulting from causes other than hypoventilation.

metabolic alkalosis A condition of alkalosis resulting from causes other than hyperventilation.

metabolic pathway A sequence of reactions used to produce one product or accomplish one process.

metabolism The sum of all reactions occurring in an organism.

metal An element found in the left two-thirds of the periodic table. Most have the following properties: high thermal and electrical conductivities, high malleability and ductility, and a metallic luster.

metallic bond An attractive force responsible for holding solid metals together, originating from the attraction between positively charged atomic kernels that occupy the lattice sites and mobile electrons that move freely through the lattice.

metalloids Elements that form a narrow diagonal band in the periodic table between the metals and nonmetals; they have properties somewhat between those of metals and nonmetals.

micelle A spherical cluster of molecules in which the polar portions of the molecules are on the surface and the nonpolar portions are located in the interior.

micronutrient A substance needed by the body only in small amounts.

mineral A metal or nonmetal used in the body in the form of ions or compounds.

mitochondrion A cellular organelle where reactions of the common catabolic pathway occur.

mixture A physical blend of matter that can be physically separated into two or more components.

moderator A material capable of slowing down neutrons that pass through it.

modulator A substance that binds to an enzyme at a location other than the active site and alters the catalytic activity.

molarity A solution concentration that is expressed in terms of the number of moles of solute contained in 1 L of solution.

mole The number of particles (atoms or molecules) contained in a sample of element or compound with a mass in grams equal to the atomic or molecular weight, respectively.

molecular equation An equation written with each compound represented by its un-ionized formula.

molecular weight The relative mass of a molecule expressed in atomic mass units and calculated by adding the atomic weights of the atoms in the molecule.

molecule The smallest particle of a pure substance that has the properties of that substance.

monomer The starting material that becomes the repeating unit of polymers.

monoprotic acid An acid that gives up only one proton (H^+) per molecule when dissolved.

monosaccharide A simple carbohydrate most commonly consisting of three to six carbon atoms.

mutagen A chemical that induces mutations by reacting with DNA.

mutation Any change resulting in an incorrect base sequence on DNA.

native state The natural three-dimensional conformation of a functional protein.

net ionic equation An equation that contains only un-ionized or insoluble materials and ions that undergo changes as the reaction proceeds. All spectator ions are eliminated.

network solid A solid in which the lattice sites are occupied by atoms that are covalently bonded to each other.

neurotransmitter A substance that acts as a chemical bridge in nerve impulse transmission between nerve cells.

neutral A term used to describe any water solution in which the concentrations of H_3O^+ and OH^- are equal; also, a water solution with pH = 7.

neutralization reaction A reaction in which an acid and base react completely, leaving a solution that contains only a salt and water.

noble gas configuration An electronic configuration in which the last eight electrons occupy and fill the s and p subshells of the highest-occupied shell.

noncompetitive inhibitor An inhibitor that binds to the enzyme at a location other than the active site.

nonelectrolyte A solute that when dissolved in water forms a solution that does not conduct electricity.

nonessential amino acid An amino acid that can be synthesized within the body in adequate amounts.

nonmetal An element found in the right one-third of the periodic table. Most occur as brittle, powdery solids or gases and have properties generally opposite those of metals.

nonpolar covalent bond A covalent bond in which the bonding pair of electrons is shared equally by the bonded atoms.

nonpolar molecule A molecule that contains no polarized bonds, or a molecule containing polarized bonds in which the resulting charges are distributed symmetrically throughout the molecule.

normal alkane Any alkane in which all the carbon atoms are aligned in a continuous chain.

normal boiling point The temperature at which the vapor pressure of a liquid is equal to one standard atmosphere (760 torr); also called standard boiling point.

N-terminal residue An amino acid on the end of a chain that has an unreacted or free amino group.

nuclear fission A process in which large nuclei split into smaller, approximately equal-sized nuclei when bombarded by neutrons.

nuclear fusion A process in which small nuclei combine or fuse to form larger nuclei.

nucleic acid A biomolecule involved in the transfer of genetic information from existing cells to new cells.

nucleic acid backbone The sugar-phosphate chain that is common to all nucleic acids.

nucleotide The repeating structural unit or monomer of polymeric nucleic acids.

nucleus The central core of atoms that contains protons, neutrons, and most of the mass of atoms.

nutrition An applied science that studies food, water, and other nutrients and the ways living organisms use them.

octet rule A rule for predicting electron behavior in reacting atoms: Atoms will gain or lose sufficient electrons to achieve an outer electron arrangement identical to that of a noble gas. This arrangement usually consists of eight electrons in the valence shell.

oil A triglyceride that is a liquid at room temperature.

Okazaki fragment A DNA fragment produced during replication as a result of strand growth in a direction away from the replication fork.

optically active molecule A molecule that rotates the plane of polarized light.

optimum pH The pH at which enzyme activity is highest.

optimum temperature The temperature at which enzyme activity is highest.

organelle A membrane-enclosed structure in the interior of a cell.

organic chemistry The study of carbon-containing compounds.

organic compound A compound that contains the element carbon.

osmolarity The product of n and M in the equation $\pi = nMRT$.

osmosis The process in which solvent flows through a semipermeable membrane into a solution.

osmotic pressure The hydrostatic pressure required to prevent the net flow of solvent through a semipermeable membrane into a solution.

oxidation Originally, a process involving a reaction with oxygen. Today it means a number of things, including a process in which electrons are given up, hydrogen is lost, or an oxidation number increases.

oxidation number A positive or negative number assigned to the elements in chemical formulas according to a specific set of rules; also called oxidation state.

oxidation state See **oxidation number**.

oxidative deamination An oxidation process resulting in the removal of an amino group.

oxidative phosphorylation A process coupled with the electron transport chain whereby ADP is converted to ATP.

oxidizing agent The substance that contains an element that is reduced during a chemical reaction.

oxyhemoglobin Hemoglobin combined with oxygen.

partial pressure The pressure an individual gas of a mixture would exert if it were in the container alone at the same temperature as the mixture.

Pauli exclusion principle A statement of the behavior of electrons when they occupy orbitals: Only electrons spinning in opposite directions can simultaneously occupy the same orbital.

peptide An amino acid polymer of short chain length.

peptide linkage (peptide bond) The amide linkage between amino acids that results when the amino group of one acid reacts with the carboxylate group of another.

percent A solution concentration that expresses the amount of solute in 100 parts of solution.

percentage yield The percentage of the theoretical amount of product actually produced by a reaction.

periodic law A statement about the behavior of the elements when they are arranged in a specific order. In its present form, it is stated as follows: Elements with similar chemical properties occur at regular (periodic) intervals when the elements are arranged in order of increasing atomic numbers.

period of the periodic table A horizontal row of elements.

pH The negative logarithm of the molar concentration of H^+ (H_3O^+) in a solution.

phenol A compound in which an —OH group is connected to a benzene ring. The parent compound is also called phenol.

phenyl group A benzene ring with one hydrogen absent, C_6H_5—.

phosphoglyceride A complex lipid containing glycerol, fatty acids, phosphoric acid, and an alcohol component.

phospholipid A phosphorus-containing lipid.

phosphoric anhydride A compound that contains the

$$-O-\overset{\overset{\textstyle O}{\|}}{\underset{\underset{\textstyle O^-}{|}}{P}}-O-\overset{\overset{\textstyle O}{\|}}{\underset{\underset{\textstyle O^-}{|}}{P}}-O-\text{ group.}$$

physical change A change matter undergoes without changing composition.

physical property A property of matter that can be observed or measured without trying to change the composition of the matter being studied.

physical unit of radiation A radiation measurement unit that indicates the activity of the source of the radiation; for example, the number of nuclear decays per minute.

pK_a The negative logarithm of K_a.

plasma The liquid portion of whole blood.

plasmid Circular, double-stranded DNA found in the cytoplasm of bacterial cells.

polar covalent bond A covalent bond that shows bond polarization; that is, the bonding electrons are shared unequally.

polar molecule A molecule that contains polarized bonds and in which the resulting charges are distributed asymmetrically throughout the molecule.

polyatomic ion A covalently bonded group of atoms that carries a net electrical charge.

polyatomic molecule A molecule that contains three or more atoms.

polycyclic aromatic compound A derivative of benzene in which carbon atoms are shared between two or more benzene rings.

polyfunctional compound A compound with two or more functional groups.

polymer A very large molecule made up of repeating units.

polymerization A reaction that produces a polymer.

polypeptide An amino acid polymer of intermediate chain length containing up to 50 amino acid residues.

polyribosome A complex of mRNA and several ribosomes; also called polysome.

polysaccharide A carbohydrate formed by the combination of many monosaccharide units.

polysome See **polyribosome**.

polyunsaturated A term usually applied to molecules with several double bonds.

position of equilibrium An indication of the relative amounts of reactants and products present at equilibrium.

positron A positively charged electron.

potential energy The energy a particle has as a result of attractive or repulsive forces acting on it.

pressure A force per unit area of surface on which the force acts. In measurements and calculations involving gases, it is often expressed in units related to measurements of atmospheric pressure.

primary alcohol An alcohol in which the carbon bearing the —OH group is attached to one other carbon atom.

primary amine An amine having one alkyl or aromatic group bonded to nitrogen, as in R—NH_2.

primary protein structure The linear sequence of amino acid residues in a protein chain.

product of a reaction A substance produced as a result of a chemical reaction; written on the right side of the equation representing the reaction.

prokaryotic cell A simple unicellular organism that contains no nucleus and no membrane-enclosed organelles.

prostaglandin A substance derived from unsaturated fatty acids, with hormonelike effects on a number of body tissues.

prosthetic group The non–amino acid parts of conjugated proteins.

protein An amino acid polymer made up of more than 50 amino acids.

protein turnover The continuing process in which body proteins are hydrolyzed and resynthesized.

pure substance Matter that has a constant composition and fixed properties.

pyranose ring A six-membered sugar ring system containing an oxygen atom.

quaternary ammonium salt An ionic compound containing a positively charged ion in which four alkyl or aromatic groups are bonded to nitrogen, as in R_4N^+.

quaternary protein structure The arrangement of subunits that form a larger protein.

rad A biological unit of radiation measurement that corresponds to the transfer of 1×10^{-2} J or 2.4×10^{-3} cal of energy to 1 kg of tissue.

radical An electron-deficient particle that is very reactive; also called free radical.

radioactive dating A process for determining the age of artifacts and rocks, based on the amount and half-life of radioisotopes contained in the object.

radioactive decay A process in which an unstable nucleus changes energy states and in the process emits radiation.

radioactive nuclei Nuclei that undergo spontaneous changes and emit energy in the form of radiation.

radioisotope An isotope of an element that emits nuclear radiation.

reactant of a reaction A substance that undergoes chemical change during a reaction; written on the left side of the equation representing the reaction.

reaction mechanism A detailed explanation of how a reaction actually takes place.

reaction rate The speed at which a chemical reaction takes place.

recombinant DNA DNA of an organism that contains genetic material from another organism.

reducing agent The substance that contains an element that is oxidized during a chemical reaction.

reducing sugar A sugar that can be oxidized by Cu^{2+} in solution.

reduction Originally, a process in which oxygen was lost. Today it means a number of things, including a process in which electrons are gained, hydrogen is accepted, or an oxidation number decreases.

reference daily intakes (RDI) A set of standards for protein, vitamins, and minerals used on food labels as part of the Daily Values.

relative specificity The characteristic of an enzyme that it acts on several structurally related substances.

rem A biological unit of radiation measurement that corresponds to the health effect produced by one roentgen of gamma rays or X rays regardless of the type of radiation involved.

renal threshold The blood glucose level at which glucose begins to be excreted in the urine.

replication The process by which an exact copy of a DNA molecule is produced.

replication fork A point where the double helix of a DNA molecule unwinds during replication.

representative element An element in which the distinguishing electron is found in an *s* or a *p* subshell.

respiratory acidosis A condition of acidosis caused by hypoventilation.

respiratory alkalosis A condition of alkalosis caused by hyperventilation.

restriction enzyme A protective enzyme found in some bacteria that catalyzes the cleaving of all but a few specific types of DNA.

retrovirus A virus in which RNA directs the synthesis of DNA.

ribonucleic acid (RNA) A nucleic acid found mainly in the cytoplasm of cells.

ribosomal RNA (rRNA) RNA that constitutes about 65% of the material in ribosomes, the sites of protein synthesis.

ribosome A subcellular particle that serves as the site of protein synthesis in all organisms.

roentgen A biological unit of radiation measurement used with X rays and gamma rays; the quantity of radiation that generates 2.1×10^9 ion pairs per cubic centimeter of dry air or 1.8×10^{12} ion pairs per gram of tissue.

salt A solid crystalline ionic compound at room temperature that contains the cation of a base and the anion of an acid.

saponification The basic cleavage of an ester linkage.

satiety A state of satisfaction or fullness.

saturated hydrocarbon Another name for an alkane.

saturated solution A solution that contains the maximum amount possible of dissolved solute in a stable situation under the prevailing conditions of temperature and pressure.

scientific models Explanations for observed behavior in nature.

scientific notation A way of representing numbers consisting of a product between a nonexponential number and 10 raised to a whole-number exponent that may be positive or negative.

scintillation counter A radiation-detection device that works on the principle that phosphors give off light when struck by radiation.

secondary alcohol An alcohol in which the carbon bearing the —OH group is attached to two other carbon atoms.

secondary amine An amine having two alkyl or aromatic groups bonded to nitrogen, as in R_2NH.

secondary protein structure The arrangement of protein chains into patterns as a result of hydrogen bonds between amide groups of amino acid residues in the chain. The common secondary structures are the α-helix and the β-pleated sheet.

semiconservative replication A replication process that produces DNA molecules containing one strand from the parent and a new strand that is complementary to the strand from the parent.

shape Shape depends on the physical state of matter.

shell A location and energy of electrons around a nucleus that is designated by a value for n, where $n = 1, 2, 3$, etc.

side reaction A reaction that does not give the desired product of a reaction.

significant figures The numbers in a measurement that represent the certainty of the measurement, plus one number representing an estimate.

simple carbohydrates Monosaccharides and disaccharides, commonly called sugars.

simple ion An atom that has acquired a net positive or negative charge by losing or gaining electrons.

simple lipid An ester-containing lipid with just two types of components: an alcohol and one or more fatty acids.

simple protein A protein made up entirely of amino acid residues.

single-replacement reaction A chemical reaction in which an element reacts with a compound and displaces another element from the compound.

soap A salt of a fatty acid often used as a cleaning agent.

solubility The maximum amount of solute that can be dissolved in a specific amount of solvent under specific conditions of temperature and pressure.

soluble substance A substance that dissolves to a significant extent in the solvent.

solute One or more substances present in a solution in amounts less than that of the solvent.

solution A homogeneous mixture of two or more pure substances.

solvent The substance present in a solution in the largest amount.

specific heat The amount of heat energy required to raise the temperature of exactly 1 g of a substance by exactly 1°C.

spectator ion An ion in a total ionic reaction that is not changed as the reaction proceeds. It appears in identical forms on the left and right sides of the equation.

sphingolipid A complex lipid containing the aminoalcohol sphingosine.

spontaneous process A process that takes place naturally with no apparent cause or stimulus.

stable substance A substance that does not undergo spontaneous changes under the surrounding conditions.

standard atmosphere The pressure needed to support a 760-mm column of mercury in a barometer tube.

standard boiling point See **normal boiling point**.

standard conditions A set of specific temperature and pressure values used for gas measurements.

standard position for a decimal In scientific notation, the position to the right of the first nonzero digit in the nonexponential number.

state of equilibrium A condition in a reaction system in which the rates of the forward and reverse reactions are equal.

stem cell A cell with the ability to divide for indefinite periods in culture and to give rise to specialized cells.

stereochemical specificity An enzyme's ability to distinguish between stereoisomers.

stereoisomers Compounds with the same structural formula but different spatial arrangements of atoms.

steroid A compound containing four rings fused in a particular pattern.

stoichiometry The study of mass relationships in chemical reactions.

strong acid or base An acid or base that dissociates (ionizes) essentially completely when dissolved to form a solution.

structural isomers Compounds that have the same molecular formula but in which the atoms bond in different patterns.

sublimation The endothermic process in which a solid is changed directly to a gas without first becoming a liquid.

subshell A component of a shell that is designated by a letter from the group s, p, d, and f.

substrate The substance that undergoes a chemical change catalyzed by an enzyme.

subunit A polypeptide chain having primary, secondary, and tertiary structural features that is a part of a larger protein.

sulfhydryl group The —SH functional group.

supercritical mass The minimum amount of fissionable material that must be present to cause a branching chain reaction to occur.

supercritical reaction A branching chain reaction.

supersaturated solution An unstable solution that contains an amount of solute greater than the solute solubility under the prevailing conditions of temperature and pressure.

surface catalyst See **heterogeneous catalyst**.

tertiary alcohol An alcohol in which the carbon bearing the —OH group is attached to three other carbon atoms.

tertiary amine An amine having three alkyl or aromatic groups bonded to nitrogen, as in R_3N.

tertiary protein structure A specific three-dimensional shape of a protein resulting from interactions between R groups of the amino acid residues in the protein.

thermal expansion A change in volume of a sample resulting from a change in temperature of the sample.

thermonuclear reaction A nuclear fusion reaction that requires a very high temperature to start.

thioester bond The carbon–sulfur bond of the

$$-\overset{\overset{\displaystyle O}{\|}}{C}-S- \text{ functional group.}$$

thiol A compound containing an —SH group.

titration An analytical procedure in which one solution (often a base) of known concentration is slowly added to a measured volume of an unknown solution (often an acid). The volume of the added solution is measured with a buret.

Tollens' reagent A mild oxidizing solution containing silver ions used to test for aldehydes.

torr The pressure needed to support a 1-mm column of mercury in a barometer tube.

total ionic equation An equation written with all soluble ionic substances represented by the ions they form in solution.

trace mineral A mineral found in the body in quantities smaller than 5 g.

tracer A radioisotope used medically because its progress through the body or localization in specific organs can be followed.

trans- On opposite sides (as applied to geometric isomers).

transaminase An enzyme that catalyzes the transfer of an amino group.

transamination The enzyme-catalyzed transfer of an amino group to a keto acid.

transcription The transfer of genetic information from a DNA molecule to a molecule of messenger RNA.

transfer RNA (tRNA) RNA that delivers individual amino acid molecules to the site of protein synthesis.

transition element An element in which the distinguishing electron is found in a *d* subshell.

translation The conversion of the code carried by messenger RNA into an amino acid sequence of a protein.

transuranium element A synthetic element with atomic number greater than that of uranium.

triatomic molecule A molecule that contains three atoms.

triglyceride (triacylglycerol) A triester of glycerol in which all three alcohol groups are esterified.

triple bond The bond resulting from the sharing of three pairs of electrons.

triprotic acid An acid that gives up three protons (H^+) per molecule when dissolved.

turnover number The number of molecules of substrate acted on by one molecule of enzyme per minute.

Tyndall effect A property of colloids in which the path of a beam of light through the colloid is visible because the light is scattered.

universal gas constant The constant that relates pressure, volume, temperature, and the number of moles of gas in the ideal gas law.

unsaturated hydrocarbon A hydrocarbon containing one or more multiple bonds.

urea cycle A metabolic pathway in which ammonium ions are converted to urea.

valence shell The outermost (highest-energy) shell that contains electrons.

vaporization See **evaporation**.

vapor pressure The pressure exerted by vapor that is in equilibrium with its liquid.

vector A carrier of foreign DNA into a cell.

virus An infectious particle composed of only proteins and DNA or RNA.

vitamin An organic nutrient that the body cannot produce in the small amounts needed for good health.

vitamin international unit A measure of vitamin activity, determined by biological methods.

volume/volume percent A concentration that expresses the volume of liquid solute contained in 100 volumes of solution.

VSEPR theory A theory based on the mutual repulsion of electron pairs; used to predict molecular shapes.

water of hydration Water retained as a part of the solid crystalline structure of some salts.

wax An ester of a long-chain fatty acid and a long-chain alcohol.

weak (or moderately weak) acid or base An acid or base that dissociates (ionizes) less than completely when dissolved to form a solution.

weight A measurement of the gravitational force acting on an object.

weight/volume percent A concentration that expresses the grams of solute contained in 100 mL of solution.

weight/weight percent A concentration that expresses the mass of solute contained in 100 mass units of solution.

zwitterion A dipolar ion that carries both a positive and a negative charge as a result of an internal acid-base reaction in an amino acid molecule.

zymogen or proenzyme The inactive precursor of an enzyme.

Chiral carbon, 562
Chlorides
 carboxylic acid, 508
 usage, 628
Chloride shift, 808
Chlorine
 deficiency of, 727
 dietary sources of, 727
 functions of, 727
 as group VIIA(17), 91
 isotopes contrast, 56
 molecules of, 124–125
 reaction of, 110
Cholesterol
 description of, 608–609
 dietary effects on, 610–611
 emulsification, 611–612
 high-density lipoprotein, 778
 hypercholesterolemia, 675
 lipoprotein levels of, 777
 low-density lipoprotein, 615
 structural formula of, 433, 608
Choline, 534, 604–605
Cholinesterase, 662
ChooseMyPlate, 719
Chromium, 442, 727
Chromosomes, 688–689
Chylomicrons, 776
Chymotrypsin, 657, 662
Chymotrypsinogen, 670
Cigarette smoke, 423
Cinnamaldehyde, 487
Cis double bond, 404
Cis fatty acids, 601
Cis-trans isomerism, 405
Cis-trans isomers, 385
Cis-trans stereoisomerism, 405
Citral, 487
Citrate, 440
Citric acid, 497, 505
Citric acid cycle
 control points, 756
 definition of, 754
 description of, 751
 reactions, 754
 regulation of, 754–756
 schematic diagram of, 755
 summary of, 754
Clear liquid diet, 586
Closed container, liquid evaporation in, 196
Clostridium botulinum, 646
Coal tar, 423
Cobalt, 727
Cobalt-60, 341–342
Codeine, 545
Codons, 700, 703
Coenzyme A, 735–736
Coenzyme A sulfhydryl group (CoA-SH), 735
Coenzymes, 659, 736–738
Cofactor, 659
Cohesive force, 181
Coil molecular structure, 640
Cold spot, 341
Collagen, 634
Colligative property, 234, 237
Collisions
 effective, 263
 factors, 259
 molecular orientations, 260

Colloidal silver, 244
Colloid particles, 240
Colloids, 215, 239–240
Combination reactions, 155
Combined gas law, 188
Combustion, 152, 389
Combustion reaction, 163
Common catabolic pathway, 730, 736–738
Competitive inhibition, 668–670
Complementary base pairs, 687
Complementary DNA strands, 687
Complete protein, 722
Complex carbohydrates, 719
Complex lipid, 594
Compound(s). See also specific compound
 aliphatic, 417, 501
 aromatic. See Aromatic compounds
 atom molecules, 12
 binary, 110–112
 boiling points, 499–500
 definition of, 9, 12
 formation of, 127, 150–151
 heterocyclic, 682
 inorganic, 363
 ionic. See Ionic compounds
 molecular weight comparisons of, 500
 naming of, 128–131
 organic. See Organic compounds
 polyatomic ions, 129
 polyfunctional, 455–456
 types of, 285
Compound formula
 definition of, 48
 example of, 49
 oxidation number, algebraic sum, 151
Compressibility, 179, 182–183
Concentrations, 224, 268
Condensation, 196, 507
Condensation polymers, 581
Condensed structural formula, 367
Confined zeros, 23
Conformations, 373
Conjugate acid–base pair, 284
Conjugate base, 284, 304
Conjugated protein, 637
Copolymer, 413
Copper
 crystals, 156
 deficiency of, 727
 dietary sources of, 727
 functions of, 727
 ionic forms, 111
 ions, 476
Corey, Robert, 638–639
Cori cycle, 763
Coronary heart disease, 767
Cortisol, 612
Cortisone, 612
Cosmetics
 alpha-hydroxy acids in, 501
 FD&C definition, 6
 mixtures/regulations, 6
Cottrel precipitator, 241
Coughing, 203
Covalent bond/bonding, 114–118
 definition of, 115
 example of, 116
 formation of, 129
 involvement of, 262

 orbital overlap, 114–115
 representation, 134
Covalent molecules, 124–128
C-reactive protein, 632
Creatine kinase, 673
Crick, Francis H. C., 684–685
Criminal investigations, DNA's role in, 707
Critical mass, 349
Critical reaction, 348
CRP. See C-reactive protein
Crystal
 interionic attractions, 220
 three-dimensional arrangement, 112
Crystal lattice, 112, 131
Crystallization, 219
C-terminal residue, 630–631
Curie, 338
Cyanide, 362, 664–665
Cyanosis, 203
Cyclic Haworth structures, 572
Cyclic hemiacetal, 480, 572
Cyclic hemiketal, 480
Cyclic structure, 3
Cycloalkanes. See also Alkanes
 definition of, 381
 IUPAC naming rules for, 381
 shape of, 383–385
 structural formulas and symbols for, 381
1,3-Cyclohexadiene, 401
Cyclohexanone, 469
Cyclopropane, 260, 381
Cyclotron, 345
Cysteine
 oxidation, 628
 products derived from, 787
 residues, 641
 structural formula of, 624–625
Cytochrome, 757
Cytochrome c, 634
Cytochrome oxidase, 664–665
Cytosine, 682

D

Dacron, 507
Daily reference values, 718
Daily values, 718
D aldoses, 570
Dalton, John, 8–9, 193
Dalton's law, 193–194
Daughter nucleus, 332, 341
D-deoxyribose, 682
Deactivated toxin, 646
Deamination, 790–791
Decane, 387
Decimals, 19–21
Decomposition, 199
Decomposition reactions, 154
Decompression sickness, 220
Degeneracy, 701
Dehydration, 227
Dehydration reaction, 439
Dehydration synthesis, 441
Delocalized pi lobes, 418
Denaturation, 645–646
Denatured toxin, 646
Dendrites, 539
Density, 30–33, 178
 calculation of, 180
 definition of, 31

Unless otherwise noted all art on this page © Cengage Learning 2014

in oxidation reactions, 740
 oxidizing agents, 754
 structure of, 738
Flavin mononucleotide, 757
Fleming, Alexander, 666
Fluid balance, 810–812
Fluid-mosaic model, 607–608
Fluorine, 109, 727
FMN. See Flavin mononucleotide
Folacin, 659
Folic acid, 668–669
Food. See also Diet
 brain health, for 778–779
 catabolism, 729–730
 color of, 158
 density of, 34
 digestion of, 730
 eating of, while driving, 624
 energy extraction from, 729
 fats in, 721
 fiber-fortified, 739
 genetically modified, 709
 glycemic index of, 750
 heartburn affected by, 316
 high-fiber, 34
 irradiation of, 350
 polyphenol levels in, 449
 protein content of, 722
 soy-protein, 610
 sugar-free, 574
 unhealthy habits, 796
Food, Drug, and Cosmetic Act, 6
Food label, 718
Formaldehyde
 ball-and-stick model of, 468
 description of, 485–486
 structure of, 116
Formalin, 485
Formamide, 546
Formic acid, 304, 498, 500
Formulas, 47–49
Formula weight, 113
Fortrel, 507
Forward activation energies, 271
Free energy changes, 732
Free glucose, 762
Free metal, 150
Free radicals, 336
Free rotation, 383–384
Freezing point, 17, 235
French Système International d'Units, 14
Fructose, 467, 571, 577, 580, 661, 749
Fructose-6-phosphate, 575
Fuel molecules, 754
Fumaric acid, 411
Functional groups, 367–369, 455–456
Furan, 452
Furanose rings, 572
Fusion
 heat, 201
 nuclear, 351

G

Galactose, 571, 577, 749
Galactosemia, 658
Gallstones, 612
Gamma globulin, 634, 638
Gamma radiation, 337

Gamma rays
 characteristics, 332
 definition of, 331
 ionization effects, 338
 penetrating abilities, 337
Gas(es). See also specific gas
 behavior of, 8
 compression of, 183
 filling of, 179
 hospital use of, 260
 ideal law, 191–193
 kinetic molecular view, 182
 mass of, 191
 partial pressure of, 193
 physical properties of, 179
 solubility of, 220
 volume of, 187–188, 191
Gaseous state, 183
Gas laws, 183–187, 202
 combined, 188
 definition of, 184
 ideal, 191
Gasoline, 389
Gas-phase reactions, 263
Gastroenteritis, 586
Gastroesophageal reflux disease, 306
Gaucher's disease, 606, 658
Geiger-Müller counter
 detection tube, 340
 use of, 335
Gels, 240
Gene, 688
General anesthetics, 454
Generic medications, 190
Genetically modified foods, 709
Genetic code
 characteristics of, 701
 discovery of, 699–700
 mRNA codons, 700
Genetic control, 671–673
Genetic engineering, 706–707
Genetic information, 696–697
Geometric isomers, 385, 405
GERD. See Gastroesophageal reflux disease
Global warming, 243
Globular proteins, 636–637, 642
Glucagon, 765
Glucocorticoids, 612
Glucogenic amino acid, 794
Gluconeogenesis
 definition, 763
 description of, 762–764, 788
 lactate in, 763
Glucose
 aldohexose, 569
 anomeric position, 580
 characteristics of, 576–577, 661
 cyclization, 571
 functional group of, 456
 metabolism pathways of, 765
 molecular weight of, 633
 oxidation of, 759–761
 solution containing, 476
 structure of, 467
 sweetness of, 571
 utilization, 444
Glucose-1-phosphate, 761
Glucose-6-phosphate

as noncompetitive inhibitor of hexokinase, 751
 isomerization, 761
 structural formula of, 516, 575
ß-Glucosidase, 664
Glucosuria, 748
Glutamate, 625, 634
Glutamate dehydrogenase, 790
Glutamine
 description of, 624–625
 formation of, 796
Glycemic index, 750
Glyceraldehyde
 chiral carbon, 562
 enantiomers
 ball-and-stick model of, 561, 565
 definition of, 561
 Fischer projections of, 565
Glycerol
 alcohol derivation, 597
 bonding of, 720
 esterification of, 597
 metabolism of, 780
 -OH groups, 602–603
 structural formula of, 599
 use of, 446
Glycine, 625, 630
Glycogen
 breakdown of, 761–762
 definition of, 583
 hormonal control of, 765
 metabolism of, 761–762
Glycogenesis, 761
Glycolic acid, 501
Glycolipids, 606
Glycolysis, 748–749, 751
Glycoproteins, 637
Glycosides, 575–576
Glycosidic linkage, 576–577
Glycylalanine, 628
Gold, 269
Gore-Tex, 412
Graham, Thomas, 194
Graham's law, 194–195
Gray, 338
Greek numerical prefixes, 129
Green tea catechins, 530
Group(s). See also specific group
 number, 104
 periodic table of elements, 74
Group IA(1) elements, 150
Group IIA(2) elements, 150
Group IIA(2) metals, 305
Group VIIA(17) elements, 136
Growth hormone, 634, 638
Growth-promoting steroids, 613
Guanine, 682, 687

H

Hahn, Otto, 347
Half-life, 334–336
Haloalkane, 408
Halogens, 409
Halothane, 454
Haworth structure, 571–572
HCl. See Hydrochloric acid
HDL. See High-density lipoproteins
Health information on web sites, 32
Heart attack, 654, 675

Mass
 as basic unit (metric system), 16
 definition of, 4
 density and, relationship between, 31
Mass number, 51
Mass spectrometers, 53
Matter
 classification of, 10–13, 36
 composition, 180
 concept summary, 36
 definition of, 4
 density, 31
 destruction, 165
 kinetic molecular theory,
 180–181
 law of conservation of, 148
 model of, 8–10, 35
 properties, observation, 178–180
 shape of, 178
 states of
 characteristics, 178
 description of, 177
 energy and, relationship between,
 199–203
Measurement
 basic unit, 14
 basis of, 14
 uncertainty associated with, 22
 units of, 13–14, 36
Medical imaging, 339
Mediterranean diet, 778
Meitner, Lise, 347
Melanin, 420
Melting
 description of, 198–199
 heat of fusion, 201
 heat requirements for, 135
Melting point, 132, 199
Membranes
 cellular, 606–608
 lipid, 608
Mendeleev, Dmitri, 74
Mental illness, 540
Menthol, 433
Menthone, 487
Mercury, 666–667
Mercury barometer, 184
Messenger RNA
 alignment of, 702
 codons, 700
 definition of, 694
 molecules, 696
 ribosomes, 703
 synthesis of, 697
 translation of, 696–697
Metabolic acidosis, 816–817
Metabolic alkalosis, 817
Metabolic pathway, 729
Metabolism
 ATP hydrolysis, 732
 definition of, 161
 diseases caused by abnormalities in, 606
 energy production from, 729–730
 inborn errors of, 658
 protein effects on, 629–630
Metal(s)
 activity series of, 295
 burning of, 155

hydrogen ion reduction ability, 295
 loss of electrons, 107
 in periodic table, 89
 properties of, 89
Metal atoms, 108
Metal ions
 characteristics of, 108
 inorganic ions, 659
 sulfhydryl groups, 455
Metallic bond, 133
Metallic luster, 89
Metalloids, 89
Metalloproteins, 637
Metal-nonmetal reaction, 127
Metathesis reactions. See Double-replacement
 reaction
Methanal, 469
Methandrostenolone, 613
Methane. See also Natural gas
 carbon-hydrogen bond, 365
 description of, 49, 371, 387
 structural representation of, 371
Methanol, 444–445
Methedrine, 542
Methemoglobinemia, 658
Methicillin, 666
Methionine, 625, 701
Methoxymethane, 452
Methyl alcohol, 434, 444
Methylamine, 531, 536
5-methylcytosine, 706
Methyl ether. See Dimethyl ether
Methyl group, 377
Methyl red, 308
Metric system, 14–18, 36
Metric units, 18
Meyer, Julius Lothar, 74
Micelle, 595
Microalgae, 609
Micronutrients
 definition, 717
 minerals, 725–726
 vitamins, 722–723
Milk sugar. See Lactose
Millimeters of mercury, 185
Mineralocorticoids, 612
Mineral oil, 387, 389
Minerals, 725–727
Mirror-image isomers, 561
Mitochondria, 734, 779
Mitochondrial membranes space, 759
Mixture, 10, 242
Moderately weak acids, 300
Moderately weak bases, 300
Moderators, 346
Modulator, 671
Moisturizers, skin, 386
Molarity
 calculations, 238, 292
 definition of, 225
 formula for, 238
 use of, 292
Mole, 57–61
 calculations, assistance, 63
 chemical equations, 160–163
 chemical formulas and, relationship between,
 62–64
 definition of, 59

expression of, 225
Molecular biology, central dogma of, 696
Molecular collisions, 258–260
Molecular equation, 157
Molecular formula, 115
Molecular orbital, 114
Molecular orientations, 260
Molecular shapes
 determination of, 127
 prediction of, 120–121
Molecular weight, 55, 59, 192
Molecules
 definition of, 8
 evaporation, 196
 internal energy, 260
 optically active, 568
 polar bonds, 130
 polarity of, 128, 130
 relative masses, 52–55, 59
 shapes of, 120–124
 types of, 130
 use of, 263
Molybdenum, 727
Monoesters, 515–516
Monomer, 412, 507
Monoprotic acid, 303–304
Monosaccharides. See also specific monosaccharide
 aldoses, 569
 chemical properties, 570–573
 classification of, 569
 conversion of, 730
 cyclic forms of, 570–573
 cyclic Haworth structures, 572
 cyclic hemiacetals/hemiketals, 570–571
 definition of, 560
 important types of, 576–577
 open-chain form, 573
 overview of, 569–570
 oxidation of, 573, 575
 phosphate esters, 575
 physical properties of, 570
 properties of, 570–576, 581
Monosubstituted amides, 546
Monounsaturated fatty acids, 614
Morphine, 545
mRNA. See Messenger RNA
Mullis, Kary, 691
Multi-coiled DNA, 689
Multipotent adult stem cells, 703
Muscle development, 613
Muscular dystrophy, 705
Mutagenesis, 665
Mutagens, 705
Mutations, 705
MW. See Molecular weight
Mylar, 508
Myocardial infarction, 654, 675
Myoglobin, 638
Myosin, 634, 639
MyPlate, 719
Myristic acid, 500, 596

N

NAD. See Nicotinamide adenine dinucleotide
Nagasaki atomic attack, 349
Nanotechnology, 84
Naphthalene, 423
Naproxen, 538

Native state, 645
Natural amino acids, 623
Natural gas. *See also* Methane
 components, 389
 odor, absence, 454
n-butane, 373
Negative polyatomic ion, 130
Nerve impulse transmission, 635
Nerve signal transmission, 539–540
Net ionic equation, 159
Network solid, 133
Neuron, 539
Neurotransmitters, 539–540
Neutral, 287
Neutralization reaction, 296
Neutrons
 bombardment reaction usage, 345
 conversion of, 333
 description of, 50–51
 number combinations, 51
 release of, 347
N-formylmethionine, 702–703
Niacin, 659
Nicotinamide adenine dinucleotide
 alcohol substrate, 737
 cellular reaction of, 737
 characteristics of, 736–738
 oxidizing agents, 754
 reduction of, 738
 structure of, 736
 use of, 659
Nicotine, 422, 543
Niemann-Pick disease, 606, 658
Nirenberg, Marshall, 700
Nitric acid, 302, 304, 515
Nitrogen
 in amino acid catabolism, 788–792
 atoms of, 789
 nonmetals, 91
Nitroglycerin, 517
Nitrous acid, 302
Nitrous oxide, 454
N-methylbenzamide, 536
N-methyl group, 542
N,N-methylbenzamide, 536
Noble gases
 atoms, metal atom/metal ion (comparison), 108
 chemical stability, 103
 configuration, 85, 103–105
No-Doz™, 543
Nomenclature system, 111
Nonalkyl groups, 377
Nonane, 387
Nonbonding pairs, 121
Noncompetitive inhibitor, 669
Nonelectrolytes, 234
Nonessential amino acids, 795
Nonionic solutes, 221–222
Nonmetallic elements
 burning of, 261
 ion formulas for, 110–111
 stem names for, 110–111
Nonmetals
 description of, 89
 electron gain, 107
 hydrogen covalent bond, 286
 nonpolar/polar covalent bond, 127

periodic table location of, 89
 stem name of, 110
Nonpolar, 127, 130
Nonpolar carbon tetrachloride molecules, 128
Nonpolar covalent bond, 125, 130
Nonpolar groups, 642
Nonpolar molecule, 127–128, 130
Nonpolar side chains, 625
Nonpolar solutes, 222
Nonprescription medicines, 53
Nonredox combination reaction, 155
Nonsaponifiable lipids, 594
Nonspontaneous process, 256–257
Nonzero numbers, 23
Norepinephrine, 540
Norethynodrel, 475
Normal alkanes, 372, 386–387
Normal boiling point, 198
Norplant, 475
N-terminal amino acid, 702
N-terminal residue, 630
Nuclear bomb, 349
Nuclear chain reaction, 348
Nuclear electricity power plant, 351
Nuclear energy, 347–352
Nuclear fission, 347
Nuclear fusion, 351
Nuclear magnetic resonance, 339
Nuclear radiation, 330–334
Nuclear reactions
 equations, 331–334
 induction, 344–347
Nucleic acid(s). *See also* Deoxyribonucleic acid;
 Ribonucleic acid
 bases of, 682
 components of, 682–684
 composition of, 682
 definition of, 681–682
 formation of, 682
Nucleic acid backbone, 684
Nucleic acid supplements, 688
Nucleoproteins, 637
Nucleotide, 682–683
Nucleus, 50
Numbers, arrangement methods for, 27–28
NutraSweet™, 574
Nutrition, 717. *See also* Diet; Food
Nutritional calorie, 18
Nutritional requirements, 717–719
Nylon, 536–537

O
Obesity, 733
Ocean, 301
Octane, 387
Octet rule, 103, 106
Octets, 116
Oil (petroleum), 384, 609
Oils
 chemical properties of, 599–602
 definition of, 598
 hydrogenation of, 601–602
 hydrolysis of, 599, 730
 saponification of, 600
 structure of, 597–598
 triglycerides as, 720
Okazaki fragments, 691
Oleic acid, 595–596

Oligosaccharides, 560
Olive oil, 614
Omega-3 fatty acids, 597, 706, 778, 790
Open-chain alkanes, 404
Open-chain compounds, 480
Open-chain polyhydroxyl aldehydes, 570
Open-chain structure, 381
Open three-dimensional lattice, 135
Opium, 543
Optical activity, 568
Optically active molecule, 568
Optimum pH, 664–665
Optimum temperature, 663
Oral rehydration therapy, 225
Orbitals
 creation of, 114–115
 overlap of, 114–115
 shapes of, 77–78
Organelle, 606
Organic chemistry
 definition of, 362
 learning about, 364
 organization of, 367–369
Organic compounds
 arrangement of, 502
 carbon as component of, 361–362
 classes of, 368
 definition of, 362
 functional groups of, 368
 inorganic compounds and, comparison
 between, 363
 properties of, 363
Organic foods, 370
Organic micronutrients, 722–723
Orientation effects, 260
ORT. *See* Oral rehydration therapy
Osmolarity, 239
Osmosis, 237–238
Osmotic pressure, 237–239
Osteoporosis, 54, 76
OTC medications. *See* Over-the-counter medications
Ovalbumin, 634
Ovaries, 613
Over-the-counter medications, 53, 316, 550
Oxalic acid, 497–498
Oxaloacetate, 786, 789
Oxidation
 definition of, 150
 description of, 150, 442–443
 reaction, 442
 representation of, 152
 resistance, 443
 states of, 150
 susceptibility to, 473
Oxidation number
 algebraic sum, 151
 assignment rules for, 150, 152
 assistance with, 166
 change in, 150
 definition of, 150
Oxidative deamination, 790–792
Oxidative phosphorylation, 757–759
Oxidizing agent, 152
Oxygen
 burning of, 260
 carbonyl. *See* Carbonyl oxygen
 molecules, 135
 oxidation number, 150, 152

Unless otherwise noted all art on this page © Cengage Learning 2014

oxygenation, 808
oxygen in
combination, 641
exchange, 808
hemoglobin reaction, 806
transfusion of, 817
Redox reactions, 161
Reducing agent, 152, 628
Reducing sugars, 573
Reduction, 150
Reduction-oxidation reactions, 149–154
Reference daily intake, 718
Relative masses, 54
Relative specificity, 656
Rem, 338–339
Renal threshold, 748
Replacement reactions, 155–157
Replication, 689–691
Replication fork, 690
Representative elements, 87
Reproductive rights, 710
Repulsion, 181
Resiniferatoxin, 483
Respiratory acidosis, 816
Respiratory alkalosis, 816
Restriction enzymes, 706
Reverse activation energies, 271
Reversible inhibition, of enzymes,
668–670
R groups
extension of, 639
interactions of, 641–643
polarity of, 624
tertiary protein structure, 642
Rheumatoid arthritis, 612
Rhubarb, 497
Riboflavin, 424, 659
Ribonucleic acid, 576, 692–696
cellular distribution of, 694
characteristics of, 692
definition of, 682
distribution, 694
messenger. See Messenger RNA
polymerase, 697
ribosomal, 694
structure of, 692–693
sugar component, 682
synthesis of, 697–698
Ribose, 560, 576, 682
Ribosomal RNA, 694
Ribosomal subunit, 702
Ribosome, 694
Ribosome shift, 704
Ribulose, 569
Ring structure, 381
RNA. See Ribonucleic acid
Roentgen, 338
Roentgen, Wilhelm, 339
rRNA. See Ribosomal RNA
R side chains, 624
RTX. See Resiniferatoxin
Rubbing alcohol, 446
Rubidium, 104
Rutherford, Ernest, 75, 347

S

Saccharin, 574
Salt bridges, 642

Salts
amine, 532–535
carboxylic acid, 504–505
definition of, 297
description of, 283, 297–300
equivalent of, 299
hydrolysis reactions of, 310–312
ions, 299
potassium, 600
preparation, 297–298
quaternary ammonium, 534
sodium, 600
table. See Sodium chloride
Saltwater solution, 220
Saponifiable lipids, 594
Saponification, 511, 513–514, 600
Satiety, 721
Saturated fatty acids, 598, 720
Saturated hydrocarbons, 369
Saturated solution, 218
Scanning tunneling microscope, 51
Schrödinger, Ernest, 77
Scientific measurements, 14
Scientific models, 8
Scientific notation, 19–21
Scintillation counter, 340
Scintillations, 340
Sebum, 602
Secondary alcohol, 437, 443
Secondary amine
cation, 534
definition of, 527
hydrogen bonding of, 531
usage, 535
Secondary protein structures, 638–639
Selenium, 727
Self-ionization, 287–289
Semiconservative replication, 689
Semipermeable membrane, 238
Serine
phosphate group attachment, 604
products derived from, 787
structural formula of, 625
Serotonin, 540–541
Serum albumin, 780
Sex hormones, 613–614
Shared electron pairs, 114
Shells, 77–78
electron-filling order, 81–82
electron occupancy, 79
model, 79–81
relative energies, 81
valence, 80
Short-term intense radiation, 336
Short-term whole-body radiation exposure, 337
Sickle-cell anemia, 641
Sickle-cell disease, 638, 641, 705
Sickle-cell trait, 641
Side reactions, 165
Sigma bond, 415
Significant figures, 22–27, 36
Silicon, 727
Silicon dioxide, 133
Silk, 539
Silver chloride, 262
Simple carbohydrates, 719
Simple ion, 106, 150
Simple lipid, 594

Simple protein, 637
Simplified carbon cycle, 728
Single-replacement reaction, 155
SI units, 14
Skin moisturizers, 386
Skunks, 453
Sleep, 796
Small numbers, 19–22, 36
Smoking
cessation of, 422, 517
peptic ulcer disease and, 316
"Sniffing," 186
Soaps
bile salts and, comparison between, 611
cleaning action, 242
creation of, 600
products, usage, 505
triglycerides in, 600
Soddy, Frederick, 347
Sodium, 727
Sodium acetate, 311
Sodium benzoate, 505
Sodium carbonate decahydrate, 298
Sodium chloride (table salt)
crystal lattice, 112
dissolving, 238, 311
solution, 159
Sodium glycocholate, 611
Sodium hydroxide, 296, 312
Sodium phosphate dodecahydrate, 298
Sodium salts, 600
Sodium stearate, 505
Sodium sulfate decahydrate, 298
Sodium tetraborate decahydrate, 298
Sodium thiosulfate pentahydrate, 298
Solid oxygen, 135
Solids
heating of, 199–200
kinetic molecular view of, 182
melting of, 135
properties of, 179, 182
shape of, 178–179
vapor pressures, 199
volume of, 178–179
Solid state, 181–182
Solid water, 135
Solubility, 217–220
Soluble substance, 217
Solute
definition of, 216, 239
dispersed phase, 239
dissociation effects, 237
dissolution rate for, 223
excess of, 219
moles, 225
solubilities, 218–219, 223
Solute ions, 221
Solution-forming process, 221
Solutions, 215, 220–224
analysis, 307
boiling points of, 235
colligative properties of, 235
concentrations of, 224–228
definition of, 11
dilution of, 231
dissolved solute, 239
electrolyte, 234
freezing points of, 235

Features within the Text

Chemistry Around Us

1.1 A Central Science
1.2 Cosmetics: Complex Mixtures and Complex Regulations
1.3 Effects of Temperature on Body Function
2.1 Looking at Atoms
3.1 Nano World
4.1 Water: One of Earth's Special Compounds
4.2 Redox Reactions and Energy for Life
5.1 Ozone: The Good and The Bad
5.2 Air Bag Chemistry
6.1 Blood Pressure: A Barometer of Health
6.2 Therapeutic Uses of Oxygen Gas
7.1 Tears: Solutions for Many Eye Problems
7.2 Global Warming and a Cooler Europe
8.1 The True Value of Platinum and Gold
9.1 Carbon Dioxide in the Oceans
10.1 Radiation Exposure in Modern Life
10.2 Radon: A Chemically Inert Health Risk
11.1 Oil Production from Wells and Sands
11.2 Ice Storms and Deadly Carbon Monoxide
12.1 Watermelon: A Source of Lycopene
12.2 Seeing the Light
13.1 Alcohol and Antidepressants Don't Mix
13.2 General Anesthetics
14.1 Faking a Tan
14.2 Vanilloids: Hot Relief from Pain
15.1 Nitroglycerin in Dynamite and in Medicine
16.1 Aspirin Substitutes
17.1 Sugar-Free Foods and Diabetes
18.1 Algae in Your Fuel Tank
18.2 Olive Oil: A Heart Healthy Lipid
19.1 Alzheimer's Disease
19.2 Sickle-Cell Disease
20.1 Enzyme Discovery Heats Up
20.2 Avoiding Mercury in Fish
21.1 The Clone Wars
21.2 Is There a DNA Checkup in Your Future?
21.3 Stem Cell Research
21.4 DNA and the Crime Scene
22.1 The Ten Most Dangerous Foods to Eat While Driving
22.2 Calorie Language
23.1 Lactate Accumulation
23.2 What Is the Best Weight-Loss Strategy?
24.1 Phenylketonuria (PKU)
24.2 Penylalanine and Diet Foods
25.1 Pulse Oximetry

Chemistry and Your Health

1.1 Health Information on the Web
2.1 Are You at Risk for Osteoporosis?
3.1 Iron: Too Much of a Good Thing
4.1 Fight Hypertension With Potassium
5.1 The Importance of Color in Your Diet
6.1 Huffing: A Potential Introduction of Children to Drug Abuse
7.1 The Risk of Dehydration During Vigorous Youth Activities
8.1 Hypothermia: Surviving the Big Chill
9.1 Do You Have Acid Reflux Disease?
10.1 Is Irradiated Food Safe?
11.1 Skin Moisturizers: Choosing One That Works
12.1 Beautiful, Brown ... and Overdone
13.1 Why Do Teens Drink?
14.1 Vitamin A and Birth Defects
15.1 Aspirin: Should You Take a Daily Dose?
16.1 Energy Drinks: Are They Really Harmless as a Source of Energy?
17.1 Potato Comeback: The Healthy Side of Spuds
18.1 Performance Enhancing Steroids
19.1 C-Reactive Protein: A Message from the Heart
20.1 Enzymes and Disease

21.1 Genetically Modified Foods
22.1 Vitamin Water: Beneficial or Not?
23.1 Reactive Hypoglycemia: What Causes It?
24.1 Omega-3 Fatty Acids: Will They Improve Heart Health?
25.1 Exercise Beats Angioplasty

Ask an Expert

1.1 Does food density matter when you're trying to lose weight?
3.1 Are calcium supplements necessary?
9.1 Does diet play a role in peptic ulcer disease?
11.1 Is organic food worth the price?
13.1 What are polyphenols?
16.1 Does caffeine help with weight loss?
17.1 Is high-fructose corn syrup worse for your health than table sugar?
18.1 How significantly can diet really lower cholesterol?
19.1 Can a higher protein diet help me lose weight?
22.1 Is it best to take a fiber supplement or to eat fiber-fortified foods?
23.1 How can we avoid energy crashes?
24.1 Are certain foods better for the brain?

At the Counter

2.1 Nonprescription Medicines
4.1 Versatile Zinc Oxide
5.1 Antiseptics and Disinfectants
6.1 Cutting Drug Costs with Generics
7.1 Oral Rehydration Therapy
8.1 Timed-Release Medications
10.1 The Do's and Don'ts of Buying Prescription Drugs Online
12.1 Smoking: It's Quitting Time
14.1 Birth Control: Progesterone Substitutes
15.1 Alpha Hydroxy Acids in Cosmetics
20.1 ACE Inhibitors (Angiotensin-Converting Enzyme Inhibitors)
21.1 Nucleic Acid Supplements
25.1 Erythropoietin: A Performance-Enhancing Drug

Study Skills

1.1 Help with Calculations
2.1 Help with Mole Calculations
3.1 The Convention Hotels Analogy
4.1 Help with Polar and Nonpolar Molecules
5.1 Help with Oxidation Numbers
6.1 Which Gas Law to Use
7.1 Getting Started with Molarity Calculations
8.1 Le Châtelier's Principle in Everyday Life
9.1 Writing Reactions of Acids
11.1 Changing Gears for Organic Chemistry
12.1 Keeping a Reaction Card File
12.2 A Reaction Map for Alkenes
13.1 A Reaction Map for Alcohols
14.1 A Reaction Map for Aldehydes and Ketones
15.1 A Reaction Map for Carboxylic Acids
16.1 A Reaction Map for Amines
17.1 Biomolecules: A New Focus
18.1 A Reaction Map for Triglycerides
19.1 Visualizing Protein Structure
20.1 A Summary Chart of Enzyme Inhibitors
21.1 Remembering Key Words
22.1 Bioprocesses
23.1 Key Numbers for ATP Calculations
24.1 Key Numbers for ATP Calculations

How Reactions Occur

12.1 The Hydration of Alkenes: An Addition Reaction
13.1 The Dehydration of an Alcohol
14.1 Hemiacetal Formation
15.1 Ester Saponification